More Than Just a Textbook

Internet Resources

Step 1   Connect to **Math Online** glencoe.com

Step 2   Connect to online resources by using **QuickPass** codes. You can connect directly to the chapter you want.

IM7031c1

Enter this code with the appropriate chapter number.

For Students

Connect to *StudentWorks Plus Online* which contains all of the following online assets. You don't need to take your textbook home every night.

- Personal Tutor
- Chapter Readiness Quizzes
- Multilingual eGlossary
- Concepts in Motion
- Chapter Test Practice
- Test Practice

For Teachers

Connect to professional development content at glencoe.com and *Advance Tracker* at AdvanceTracker.com

For Parents

Connect to glencoe.com for access to *StudentWorks Plus Online* and all the resources for students and teachers that are listed above.

Glencoe McGraw-Hill

IMPACT
Mathematics

Glencoe

New York, New York   Columbus, Ohio   Chicago, Illinois   Woodland Hills, California

Teacher Guide

COURSE 1

About the Cover

Artifacts of a bowling-like sport can be traced to 3200 B.C. Today, 100 million, or 10^8, people in over 90 countries enjoy bowling, or ten pins, as a recreational activity.

Bowling is played by rolling a ball, or bowl, down a narrow track. The goal is to knock down ten pins, which are placed in a triangular arrangement. A game consists of ten frames. A bowler is allowed two balls per frame, with an opportunity for two bonus balls at the end of the game. Applying the sport's rules, a perfect score of 300 is achieved when a player knocks down all ten pins with each roll.

Typically, three games are played in competitive situations. Suppose a player's average, or mean, score is 240. If the player rolled games of 230 and 235, the player would need to roll a game of 255 to achieve the mean score.

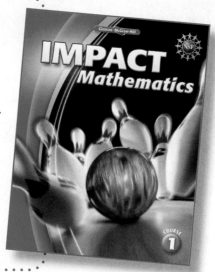

These materials include work supported in part by the National Science Foundation under Grant No. ESI-9726403 to MARS (Mathematics Assessment Resource Service). Any opinions, findings, and conclusions or recommendations expressed in this material are those of the authors and do not necessarily reflect the views of the funding agencies. For more information on MARS, visit http://www.nottingham.ac.uk/education/MARS.

The *McGraw-Hill* Companies

 Macmillan/McGraw-Hill
Glencoe

The algebra content for *IMPACT Mathematics* was adapted from the series *Access to Algebra,* by Neville Grace, Jayne Johnston, Barry Kissane, Ian Lowe, and Sue Willis. Permission to adapt this material was obtained from the publisher, Curriculum Corporation of Level 5, 2 Lonsdale Street, Melbourne, Australia.

Send all inquiries to:
Glencoe/McGraw-Hill
8787 Orion Place
Columbus, OH 43240-4027

ISBN: 978-0-07-888706-2
MHID: 0-07-888706-2

Printed in the United States of America.

3 4 5 6 7 8 9 10 QDB 17 16 15 14 13 12 11 10

Contents in Brief

Focal Points and Connections
See pages vi and vii for key.

Principal Investigator

Faye Nisonoff Ruopp
Brandeis University
Waltham, Massachusetts

Consultants and Developers

Consultants

Frances Basich Whitney
Project Director, Mathematics K–12
Santa Cruz County Office of Education
Santa Cruz, California

Robyn Silbey
Mathematics Content Coach
Montgomery County Public Schools
Gaithersburg, Maryland

Dr. Selina Vásquez Mireles
Associate Professor of Mathematics
Texas State University—San Marcos
San Marcos, Texas

Teri Willard
Assistant Professor
Central Washington University
Ellensburg, Washington

Special thanks to:

Peter Braunfeld
Professor of Mathematics Emeritus
University of Illinois

Sherry L. Meier
Assistant Professor of Mathematics
Illinois State University

Judith Roitman
Professor of Mathematics
University of Kansas

Developers

Senior Project Director
Cynthia J. Orrell

Senior Curriculum Developers
Michele Manes, Sydney Foster, Daniel Lynn Watt, Ricky Carter, Joan Lukas, Kristen Herbert

Curriculum Developers
Haim Eshach, Phil Lewis, Melanie Palma, Peter Braunfeld, Amy Gluckman, Paula Pace

Special Contributors
Elizabeth D. Bjork, E. Paul Goldenberg

Project Reviewers

Glencoe and Education Development Center would like to thank the curriculum specialists, teachers, and schools who participated in the review and testing of the first edition of *IMPACT Mathematics*. The results of their efforts were the foundation for this second edition. In addition, we appreciate all of the feedback from the curriculum specialists and teachers who participated in review and testing of this edition.

Debra Allred
Math Teacher
Wiley Middle School
Leander, Texas

Tricia S. Biesmann
Retired Teacher
Sisters Middle School
Sisters, Oregon

Kathryn Blizzard Ballin
Secondary Math Supervisor
Newark Public Schools
Newark, New Jersey

Linda A. Bohny
District Supervisor of Mathematics
Mahwah Township School District
Mahwah, New Jersey

Julia A. Butler
Teacher of Mathematics
Richfield Public School Academy
Flint, Michigan

April Chauvette
Secondary Mathematics Facilitator
Leander ISD
Leander, Texas

Amy L. Chazaretta
Math Teacher/Math Department Chair
Wayside Middle School, EM-S ISD
Fort Worth, Texas

Franco A. DiPasqua
Director of K–12 Mathematics
West Seneca Central
West Seneca, New York

Mark J. Forzley
Junior High School Math Teacher
Westmont Junior High School
Westmont, Illinois

Virginia G. Harrell
Education Consultant
Brandon, Florida

Lynn Hurt
Director
Wayne County Schools
Wayne, West Virginia

Andrea D. Kent
7th Grade Math & Pre-Algebra
Dodge Middle School, TUSD
Tucson, Arizona

Russ Lush
6th Grade Teacher & Math Dept. Chair
New Augusta—North
Indianapolis, Indiana

Katherine V. Martinez De Marchena
Director of Education 7–12
Bloomfield Public Schools
Bloomfield, New Jersey

Marcy Myers
Math Facilitator
Southwest Middle School
Charlotte, North Carolina

Joyce B. McClain
Middle School Mathematics Consultant
Hillsborough County Schools
Tampa, Florida

Suzanne D. Obuchowski
Math Teacher
Proctor School
Topsfield, Massachusetts

Michele K. Older
Mathematics Instructor
Edward A. Fulton Jr. High
O'Fallon, Illinois

Jill Plattner
Math Program Developer (Retired)
Bend La Pine School District
Bend, Oregon

E. Elaine Rafferty
Retired Math Coordinator
Summerville, South Carolina

Karen L. Reed
Math Teacher—Pre-AP
Chisholm Trail Intermediate
Fort Worth, Texas

Robyn L. Rice
Math Department Chair
Maricopa Wells Middle School
Maricopa, Arizona

Brian Stiles
Math Teacher
Glen Crest Middle School
Glen Ellyn, Illinois

Nimisha Tejani, M.Ed.
Mathematics Teacher
Kino Jr. High
Mesa, Arizona

Stefanie Turnage
Middle School Mathematics
Grand Blanc Academy
Grand Blanc, Michigan

Kimberly Walters
Math Teacher
Collinsville Middle School
Collinsville, Illinois

Susan Wesson
Math Teacher/Consultant
Pilot Butte Middle School
Bend, Oregon

Tonya Lynnae Williams
Teacher
Edison Preparatory School
Tulsa, Oklahoma

Kim C. Wrightenberry
Math Teacher
Cane Creek Middle School
Asheville, North Carolina

Focal Points

The Curriculum Focal Points identify key mathematical ideas for this grade. They are not discrete topics or a checklist to be mastered; rather, they provide a framework for the majority of instruction at a particular grade level and the foundation for future mathematics study. The complete document may be viewed at www.nctm.org/focalpoints.

KEY

G6-FP1
Grade 6 Focal Point 1

G6-FP2
Grade 6 Focal Point 2

G6-FP3
Grade 6 Focal Point 3

G6-FP4C
Grade 6 Focal Point 4
Connection

G6-FP5C
Grade 6 Focal Point 5
Connection

G6-FP6C
Grade 6 Focal Point 6
Connection

G6-FP1 Number and Operations: **Developing an understanding of and fluency with multiplication and division of fractions and decimals**

Students use the meanings of fractions, multiplication and division, and the inverse relationship between multiplication and division to make sense of procedures for multiplying and dividing fractions and explain why they work. They use the relationship between decimals and fractions, as well as the relationship between finite decimals and whole numbers (i.e., a finite decimal multiplied by an appropriate power of 10 is a whole number), to understand and explain the procedures for multiplying and dividing decimals. Students use common procedures to multiply and divide fractions and decimals efficiently and accurately. They multiply and divide fractions and decimals to solve problems, including multistep problems and problems involving measurement.

G6-FP2 Number and Operations: **Connecting ratio and rate to multiplication and division**

Students use simple reasoning about multiplication and division to solve ratio and rate problems (e.g., "If 5 items cost $3.75 and all items are the same price, then I can find the cost of 12 items by first dividing $3.75 by 5 to find out how much one item costs and then multiplying the cost of a single item by 12"). By viewing equivalent ratios and rates as deriving from, and extending, pairs of rows (or columns) in the multiplication table, and by analyzing simple drawings that indicate the relative sizes of quantities, students extend whole number multiplication and division to ratios and rates. Thus, they expand the repertoire of problems that they can solve by using multiplication and division, and they build on their understanding of fractions to understand ratios. Students solve a wide variety of problems involving ratios and rates.

G6-FP3 Algebra: **Writing, interpreting, and using mathematical expressions and equations**

Students write mathematical expressions and equations that correspond to given situations, they evaluate expressions, and they use expressions and formulas to solve problems. They understand that variables represent numbers whose exact values are not yet specified, and they use variables appropriately. Students understand that expressions in different forms can be equivalent, and they can rewrite an expression to represent a quantity in a different way (e.g., to make it more compact or to feature different information). Students know that the solutions of an equation are the values of the variables that make the equation true. They solve simple one-step equations by using number sense, properties of operations, and the idea of maintaining equality on both sides of an equation. They construct and analyze tables (e.g., to show quantities that are in equivalent ratios), and they use equations to describe simple relationships (such as $3x = y$) shown in a table.

G6-FP4C **Number and Operations:** Students' work in dividing fractions shows them that they can express the result of dividing two whole numbers as a fraction (viewed as parts of a whole). Students then extend their work in grade 5 with division of whole numbers to give mixed number and decimal solutions to division problems with whole numbers. They recognize that ratio tables not only derive from rows in the multiplication table but also connect with equivalent fractions. Students distinguish multiplicative comparisons from additive comparisons.

G6-FP5C **Algebra:** Students use the commutative, associative, and distributive properties to show that two expressions are equivalent. They also illustrate properties of operations by showing that two expressions are equivalent in a given context (e.g., determining the area in two different ways for a rectangle whose dimensions are $x + 3$ by 5). Sequences, including those that arise in the context of finding possible rules for patterns of figures or stacks of objects, provide opportunities for students to develop formulas.

G6-FP6C **Measurement and Geometry:** Problems that involve areas and volumes, calling on students to find areas or volumes from lengths or to find lengths from volumes or areas and lengths, are especially appropriate. These problems extend the students' work in grade 5 on area and volume and provide a context for applying new work with equations.

Program Philosophy

In developing *IMPACT Mathematics* we have relied on our collective experiences as teachers, parents, and former students. Our main goal is to offer a curriculum that respects the background and knowledge of middle school teachers, recognizes the competence and energy of middle school students, and addresses the need for intellectually challenging and inclusive mathematics materials. With *IMPACT Mathematics,* we have combined the best of what is known as "reform" curricula with the best of "traditional" curricula, incorporating more active involvement on the part of students in making sense of important mathematical ideas.

With middle grades teachers and students in mind, we have created a comprehensive curriculum for Grades 6 through 8 that completes a full year of algebra by the end of Grade 8. While the number and operations, geometry, and data and probability strands were created especially for this program, the algebra strand is based on the highly successful Australian program, *Access to Algebra,* developed by Curriculum Corporation.

The rewarding and interesting introduction to algebra offered by this program can help develop and maintain students' ongoing interest in all areas of mathematics. The materials created for *IMPACT Mathematics* follow the *Access to Algebra* material in style: use of narrative and realistic contexts, personalization in the form of cartoons in which middle grades students explain how they approach problems, and opportunities for students to choose or create their own problems.

Conceptual Understanding and Basic Skills

Discussions regarding mathematics learning in both professional circles and the popular media might lead you to believe that teaching for conceptual understanding and teaching basic skills are mutually exclusive. But, in fact, the opposite is true. Conceptual understanding and basic skills are not opposing interests; they go hand in hand and support each other.

IMPACT Mathematics makes the big ideas as well as the important skills of mathematics accessible to middle school students. It presents mathematical ideas intact, not broken down into bite-sized bits that lack the big idea. *IMPACT Mathematics* helps students both build new mathematical ideas and see how these new ideas relate to ideas they have already developed. In this way, *IMPACT Mathematics* takes a conceptual approach.

At the same time, *IMPACT Mathematics* recognizes that for students to be able to use the new ideas and procedures effectively, they need practice. Practice need not be the enemy of learning; the enemy of learning is mindless drill. Instead, practice can encourage students to stay interested in the mathematical concepts. *IMPACT Mathematics* provides plenty of opportunity for practice, but with variety and contrast to keep students' attention focused.

Algebraic Focus in a Comprehensive Program

IMPACT Mathematics is a comprehensive program including number and operations, proportional reasoning, geometry, probability, and data, with a focus on the development of algebraic thinking. The program takes a developmental approach to algebra. Student understanding of the algebra strand—interwoven with and related to the other mathematical strands—evolves over a three-year period, allowing the ideas and skills to develop and become familiar over time.

Most students develop strong algebraic ideas in the early years of elementary school, but they do not acquire ways of expressing and manipulating them in algebraic terms until later, when algebra is formally taught. For example, young children know how to share $36 among three people by first distributing the ten dollar bills and then distributing the ones. Later, if children learn a standard method for dividing $3 \overline{)36}$ they may see again that the process is like dividing $3 \overline{)30}$, then dividing $3 \overline{)6}$, and finally adding the results. If this process is written out as $\frac{36}{3} = \frac{30}{3} + \frac{6}{3}$, that concise statement contains an important idea about adding fractions and an even more general algebraic idea. Students who understand *why* $\frac{36}{3} = \frac{30}{3} + \frac{6}{3}$ know that the sum of $\frac{30}{3}$ and $\frac{6}{3}$ must be $\frac{36}{3}$, and not $\frac{36}{6}$. The idea, expressed more generally, is $\frac{a}{3} + \frac{b}{3} = \frac{a+b}{3}$, and even more generally, is $\frac{a}{c} + \frac{b}{c} = \frac{a+b}{c}$, and so leads to the distributive law of division over addition.

Our approach in *IMPACT Mathematics* is to start with algebra as a notation for "generic" arithmetic, a description of processes that students understand. Later, algebra also becomes a handy language for "unlocking secrets" (equation solving) and building mathematical models. By the end of Course 3, students will have learned both to express functions using variables and to graph these functions. They will have also learned how to use variables to set up and solve equations, as well as how to factor some familiar polynomials, and to understand the origin and use of the quadratic formula.

Use of Manipulatives and Calculators

Manipulatives and calculators can be powerful tools for teaching and learning mathematics. There is, however, much discussion and controversy about the appropriateness of their use. As the authors of *IMPACT Mathematics*, we believe that when manipulatives and calculators are used, they must be used to support the content learning. More specifically, we consider the important mathematical ideas first and then determine whether manipulatives or calculators can be used in learning those ideas more completely.

We believe it is critical that students develop good number sense and calculation skills before they work extensively with calculators. For example, we incorporate graphing calculators in Course 3 to explore families of functions, but only *after* students have a firm idea of how to graph "parent" functions by hand. Graphing technology can then be used to allow students to graph more complex functions, analyze their behavior, and compare representations. Similar to our philosophy of integrating skills with understanding, we believe that students need experiences with pencil and paper along with graphing technology.

Organization by Content

IMPACT Mathematics often uses applications to help develop a particular mathematical concept or place it in context. However, *IMPACT Mathematics* remains organized by mathematical content, not by contexts. This organization helps both teacher and student keep the mathematical ideas at the fore, easily recognizable and never buried or lost in the settings. While the mathematical focus shifts with each chapter, the *IMPACT Mathematics* approach offers opportunities to connect topics to one another so that earlier learning is not abandoned as new ideas are introduced.

Developing Concepts in Varied Contexts

The contexts used for developing concepts and practicing skills include real-world applications, as well as mathematical settings such as number puzzles, and the world of the imagination such as a factory that uniformly resizes objects using stretching machines. Sometimes, *IMPACT Mathematics* provides exercises that are *not* set in contexts or integrated into word problems precisely so that students can focus on the mathematical ideas, undistracted by surrounding material.

A Final Note

The unique power of mathematics stems from the world of the imagination in which one envisions triangles with perfectly straight sides, or two-dimensional objects embedded in perfectly smooth planes. In the real world, all objects are three dimensional (even a line drawn on paper has thickness, or it wouldn't be visible!), all lines are irregular, and all surfaces are pitted. Likewise, all measurements are only approximations, and no physical object can have an irrational length. Our minds reason well precisely because we can ignore irregularities and focus instead on the essential features. We can reason about quantities that no physical ruler can measure but that we can "measure" with our mental rulers. In sum, we reason well because we can abstract reality.

We, the authors of *IMPACT Mathematics*, recognize that all people, from early childhood on, do reason abstractly, and that what grows over time is both their ability to recognize the abstractions, and the formality with which they are able to express abstractions. We also recognize that mathematics, while not simply common sense, is rooted in common sense. Mathematics is a human product that has developed as an extension and a codification of ways of thinking that are natural to us all. Students must not think of mathematics as a departure from natural, logical thinking. To that aim *IMPACT Mathematics* is written to help students use and sharpen their own logical thinking, learn to be comfortable with the abstractions that give mathematics its power, develop their ideas and mathematical imagination, and acquire the skills that support all that good thinking and the ability to express it clearly to others.

We hope you will enjoy teaching and learning with these materials.

Expectations

Entrance Expectations for Course

What students should know as they begin Course 1

Algebra

- Are familiar with some relationships in tabular form such as input/output boxes
- Have some limited experience with variables

Geometry

- Know the names of common geometric figures
- Identify figures with line symmetry
- Measure lengths and are familiar with both customary and metric measures of length
- Find the perimeter of figures with straight-line sides
- Find the areas of rectangles

Number and Operation

- Are proficient with whole number arithmetic
- Are proficient with decimal addition and subtraction
- Have multiplied decimals but are not proficient
- Know the algorithm for finding equivalent fractions but may not understand why it works
- Are proficient with writing decimals as fractions
- Know decimal equivalents for $\frac{1}{4}$, $\frac{1}{2}$, and $\frac{3}{4}$ and for fractions with denominators that are powers of 10
- Add and subtract fractions with the same denominator
- Have been exposed to addition and subtraction of fractions with unlike denominators but may not be proficient
- Have been exposed to multiplication of fractions but are not proficient
- Have seen percents but know only simple things about them

Data and Probability

- Interpret and create bar graphs and pictographs

Exit Expectations for Course

Entrance Expectations for Course 2

What students should know as they finish Course 1;
*   What students should know as they begin Course 2*

Algebra

- Understand the concept of a variable
- Solve simple one- and two-step equations with the variable on one side only

Geometry

- Understand area and perimeter and have committed important formulas to memory
- Calculate volume of a rectangular prism and understand capacity
- Give reasonable estimates for angle measures and measure angles with a protractor
- Plot points in the first quadrant

Number and Operation

- Are proficient with fraction and decimal operations
- Move efficiently among fraction, decimal, and percent representations

Data and Probability

- Conduct simple experiments to determine experimental probabilities
- Calculate theoretical probabilities in simple situations with a small number of equally likely outcomes
- Calculate measures of central tendency
- Interpret bar graphs, line graphs, Venn Diagrams, line plots, and stem-and-leaf plots

The Instructional Cycle

IMPACT Mathematics is designed to actively engage students in their own learning. To facilitate the learning and teaching process, *IMPACT Mathematics* is designed around a three-step instructional cycle.

Introduce

Each multiday lesson begins with a class discussion, activity, or problem designed to introduce the mathematics and help set a context for learning. To help guide the introduction, **Explore** activities and **Think & Discuss** questions are provided in the student materials.

Develop

Each lesson in *IMPACT Mathematics* is composed of in-class **Investigations** that provide a mix of worked-out examples, direct modeling through cartoons, and interactive problem sets. During Investigations, the mathematics, not an artificial format, determines the approach and the day's activity. Most Investigations are designed to last about 45 minutes or one class period.

The **Share & Summarize** questions signal the end of each Investigation. These questions offer students an opportunity to share what they did and what was learned. For teachers they offer an important assessment opportunity.

Assign & Assess

Independent assignments and opportunities to assess what students have learned are a regular part of the curriculum. The **On Your Own Exercises** at the end of each lesson are an integral part of program instruction and are intended for individual work done primarily outside of class. You will find three types of problems in each set of On Your Own Exercises.

- *Practice & Apply* problems provide opportunities for students to reinforce and directly apply the skills and concepts they have learned in each of the Investigations.

- *Connect & Extend* problems relate student learning in the lesson to other mathematical topics and strands, and sometimes require students to stretch their thinking.

- *Mixed Review* problems are an important part of the instructional and assignment structure. Frequent review of previously learned skills helps students maintain mastery and replaces the need to reteach topics.

Steps in the Instructional Cycle

INTRODUCE

The multiday lesson begins with a full-class discussion, activity, or problem. The teacher poses questions, orchestrates an activity, or monitors strategies students use to solve problems. **Explore** activities and **Think & Discuss** questions can be used to guide discussion.

DEVELOP

In-class **Investigations** provide a mix of worked out examples, direct modeling through cartoons, and interactive problem sets. Students may work independently or in small, collaborative groups. Investigations can be completed in one class period. The mathematical content of

Assessment

The assessment tools in *IMPACT Mathematics* are broader than those in traditional mathematics programs. They encompass the processes of problem solving, reasoning, communication, connections, concepts, applications, representational strategies, and procedures.

In the Student Edition

- **Share & Summarize** questions provide a forum for students to summarize and share their learning with the class.
- **On Your Own Exercises,** an integral part of daily instruction, are independent assignments intended for individual work outside of class.
- **Review & Self-Assessment** provides students with an opportunity to reflect on the important topics within the chapter and to prepare for formal assessment.

In the Teacher's Guide

- **Problem Set Wrap-Ups** ensure students are making appropriate progress through an Investigation.
- **Troubleshooting** notes provide remedial work students might need in order to move on to the next Investigation successfully.
- **Additional Examples** can be used as on-the-run assessment tools.
- **Quick Checks** provide checklists of what students should be able to do at the end of each lesson.
- **Quick Quizzes** provide brief end-of-lesson assessment opportunities.

In the Chapter Resource Masters

- A **Pretest** determines whether students have the prerequisite skills for the course.
- **Chapter Tests** provide a comprehensive evaluation of chapter content.
- **Performance Assessments** provide open-ended opportunities to measure student achievement. They can be used to supplement or replace items on chapter and semester tests, as take-home assignments, as group assessments, or as challenge or extra-credit problems.
- **Semester Tests** provide cumulative midyear and end-of-year evaluations.

ASSIGN & ASSESS

the Investigations determines the approach and the day's activity. Homework or assignment guides are available for each Investigation, and each Investigation wraps up with **Share & Summarize** questions.

Independent assignments and assessment opportunities provide rich opportunities for students to demonstrate their learning. Each lesson concludes with **On Your Own Exercises**. The types of problems included in each set of On Your Own Exercises are

- **Practice & Apply,** which are similar to the Investigations.
- **Connect & Extend,** which relate the lesson topics to other mathematical topics and strands.
- **Mixed Review,** which provides review of previously learned skills to maintain mastery.

About MARS

Mathematics Assessment Resource Service

MARS, the Mathematics Assessment Resource Service, is a U.S.-based international team that created the performance-based assessments in the *IMPACT Mathematics* program. MARS is under the direction of a Mathematics Board that includes teachers and recognized United States and international experts in the mathematics education and assessment fields.

Background

An NSF grant (National Science Foundation grant #ESI-9726403) has supported the many years of research, development, and evaluation that form the basis of the high-quality, performance-based assessments that comprise the assessment section of *IMPACT Mathematics*.

Development Process

Each assessment task is carefully constructed to assess the broad domain of mathematical performance that national and local standards specify. Tasks go through a development and review process to ensure validity and usability for student evaluation and continued improvement in instruction.

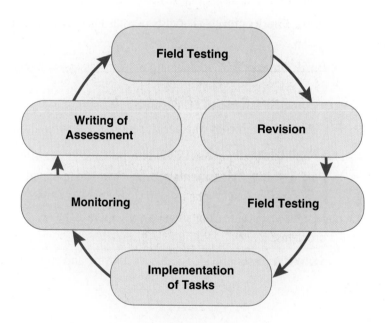

During the writing and revision process, the scoring rubric is refined and student work is collected. Rubrics, along with scored student work, accompany the MARS assessments, allowing teachers to evaluate student knowledge and progress and better inform instruction.

Evaluative Evidence

Over the years, MARS performance-based assessments have been used both throughout the United States and internationally. Evidence shows that the MARS assessments test a broader range of skills and knowledge than many state tests and are comparably challenging overall.

Figure 1. In one particular study, teachers used MARS assessments as part of a formative-assessment piece prior to taking the SAT-9 standardized test. The data show that students in classrooms receiving the MARS treatment outperformed control classrooms without MARS.

Figure 1
Average Gain in Math Percentile Rank Between 1999 SAT-9 and 2000 SAT-9

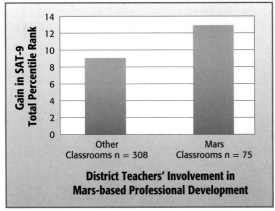

Source: Noyce Foundation Annual Report 2000

Figure 2
Student Achievement By Performance Levels on Mars Exam
Comparison Between First Year and 2005

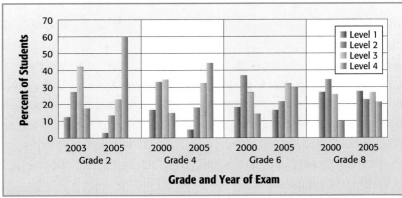

Source: Noyce Foundation Annual Report 2005

Figure 2. Over time, the evidence for MARS follows similar trends. The number of students performing at the highest levels (Level 4) of the MARS assessments climbs each year and at every grade level, while the number performing at the lower levels (Level 1) declines.

Research Support

The Research Used to Develop IMPACT Mathematics

To attain excellence in mathematics learning, there is a need for high-quality curricula that allow students to think deeply about mathematics, require them to explain their ideas, and connect their understanding to other contexts both within and outside of mathematics. *IMPACT Mathematics* relied heavily on key research about mathematics education during its development. Some of these are discussed below.

Principles and Standards for School Mathematics (National Council of Teachers of Mathematics, 1989)

Curriculum Focal Points for Prekindergarten through Grade 8 Mathematics (NCTM, 2006)

The National Council of Teachers of Mathematics produced a set of national math standards in 1989 and reshaped those standards in 2006 with the intent of improving mathematics education on a national level. These publications emphasize the belief that all students can and should learn and understand important mathematical ideas. *IMPACT Mathematics* is both a comprehensive program, including the strands of number and operations, proportional reasoning, geometry, probability, and data, as well as a program focused on the development of algebraic thinking.

Algebra for Everyone (NCTM, 1990)

Algebra for Everyone put forth the view of algebra as the gateway course, a course that must be part of the basic knowledge of all. Therefore, algebra must be taught on a broadened scale, where students come into it with the appropriate mathematical background and disposition.

Algebra in the K–12 curriculum: Dilemmas and possibilities (NCTM Algebra Working Group, 1995)

This report examined the research evidence pointing to the inaccessibility of the traditional algebra curriculum, generally taught as a stand-alone course in the 9th grade. In *IMPACT Mathematics*, student understanding of the algebra strand—interwoven with and related to the other mathematical strands—evolves over a three-year period, allowing such important ideas as patterns, functions, proportional reasoning, and algebraic structure and skills to develop and become familiar over time. The algebra strand is based on the highly successful Australian program, *Access to Algebra*, developed by Curriculum Corporation. This program provided an algebra curriculum relevant to students' lives, more inclusive of the interests and experiences of middle school students.

The National Forum to Accelerate Middle-Grades Reform

The Forum identified three components of academically excellent curricula: academic rigor, equity, and developmental appropriateness. The main goal of *IMPACT Mathematics* is to offer a curriculum that respects the background and knowledge of middle school teachers, recognizes the competence and energy of middle school students, and addresses the need for intellectually challenging and inclusive materials.

IMPACT Mathematics has combined the best of research on "reform" curricula with the best of "traditional" curricula, incorporating more active involvement on the part of students in making sense of important mathematical ideas.

Evidence of Effectiveness:
New York City Mathematics Results

Since the adoption of *IMPACT Mathematics* in grades 6–8, New York City students have seen their test scores improve dramatically. When compared against other students in the state, the positive trend is immediately apparent.

The graph in Figure 1 shows the performance on New York mathematics tests of students who used *IMPACT Mathematics*.

- In **Grade 6** in 2007, **10.5% more** students performed at Levels 3 and 4 on the state test than in the previous year.

- In **Grade 7**, **11.6% more** students performed at the highest levels.

- In **Grade 8**, **6.7% more** students performed at higher levels than their 2006 peers.

Figure 1
Students' Performance in Levels 3 and 4
Percent Increase in Grades 6–8

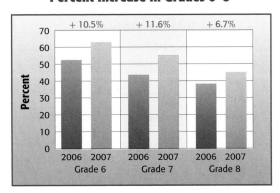

Figure 2
New York State Mathematics
Achievement Comparisons
(Grades 3–8 at Levels 3 and 4)

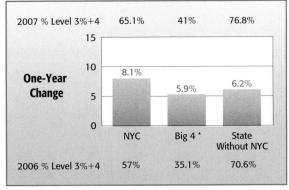

*Buffalo, Rochester, Syracuse, and Yonkers

The graph Figure 2 shows the comparison of students in New York City (where *IMPACT Mathematics* is the core mathematics curriculum) to their peers in other large cities within the state of New York and to New York State on the whole.

In 2007, the number of students using *IMPACT Mathematics* in New York City who performed at the top levels on state tests increased by 8.1% from 2006. The rest of the state (where other math programs are used) did not see such gains.

Scope & Sequence
Algebra

| | Course 1 | | | | | | | | | | Course 2 | | | | | | | | | | Course 3 | | | | | | | | | | | |
TOPICS	1	2	3	4	5	6	7	8	9	10	1	2	3	4	5	6	7	8	9	10	1	2	3	4	5	6	7	8	9	10	11	12
Algebraic Representations					Develop										Develop										Develop							
Coordinate Graphs																																
Plotting and reading points								F		F							C		C		C	C				C	C	C		C		
Make predictions								F		F		C							F		F	F						C	C		C	
Modeling situations				F				F		C		C							F		F	F						F	F		F	
Relate to tables and written descriptions			F			C	F	C											F		F	F						F	F			
Relate to equations and expressions						C	C		C										F		F	F						F	F		F	
Solve equations, approximate solutions							C	F											F		F	F						F	F		F	
Graphing equations							C	C											F		F	F						F	F		F	
Direct, indirect, and inverse variation																			F		C	F	C					C				
Slope and rates of change							C												F		C	F	F					C		C		
Distance formula																	F															
Coordinate models of transformations																					C					F				F		
Tables and Graphs																																
Analyze change vs. time data							F		F							C		F			F	C							C		F	
Making predictions and generalizations	F	C			C			F		F	C	C	C	C	C	C	F		F	F	F	F					C	F		C		
Modeling data patterns		C	C		F			F	C	F	F	C			C	C	F		F	C	C	F					C	C				
Relate to written descriptions			F			F		F		F	F								F	F	C	F					F	C				
Relate to equations and expressions							C	C	C	F			C		C				F	F	F					C		F	F	C	F	
Solve equations, approximate solutions		C							F		F								F	F	F	F						F	C	C	F	
"What's My Rule?"		C	F						C		F								F	F												
Algebraic Reasoning					Develop										Develop										Develop							
Patterns and Numeric Forms																																
Find and describe patterns		F	F			C	F	C		C	C	F	C	C	F	F		F		C	F	F		C				F		F		C
Extend and generalize patterns		F	F			C	F	C			C	F	C	C	F	F		F		C	F	F		C				F		F		C
Create and verify patterns	F	F	F			C	F				C	F	C	C	F	F		F			F			C				F				
Express patterns as algebraic rules		C	C							C	F	F			F			F	F		F							F		C		
"What's My Rule?"			F					C			F							F	F													
Equivalent expressions			F		C					C	F	C	C	C	C			C	F		F	F		F	F		C			C	C	C
Factoring, expanding, simplifying											F							C	F		F	F		C	F		C	C	F			
Signed numbers and operations															F							F										
Absolute value and opposites							F								F										C							
Exponents, roots, and radicals			F			C						C			F	C						F								C		
Scientific notation			C												F							F										
Evaluating expressions			C							C	F	F	C	C				F	F		C				C	F		C	C	C		F
Flowcharts and backtracking									F		F								F		C							C		F		
Verify solutions by substitution									F		F									F	F	F		F	C			F	F			

KEY

F = This topic is a Focus of Instruction in this chapter.

C = This topic is Connected to the content of the chapter and is either reviewed in this chapter or informally introduced.

Expose: Ideas are introduced at an informal concrete level and will be fullydeveloped later in the program.

Develop: Ideas are formalized and fully developed.

Apply: Ideas are reviewed and used to extend understanding of related ideas.

Scope and Sequence

TOPICS	C1 1	2	3	4	5	6	7	8	9	10	C2 1	2	3	4	5	6	7	8	9	10	C3 1	2	3	4	5	6	7	8	9	10	11	12
Algebraic Reasoning — *Develop (C1), Develop (C2), Develop (C3)*																																
Properties and Rules																																
Order of operations	C		F						C	C	F	C		C							C											C
Combining like terms			F						F	C	F						C	C			C	C			C		C					C
Formulas	F		F				C		C	C	F	C				F													C			
Distributive property			F								F							F			C	C		C	F				F			C
Laws of exponents			F											F		F					F	C			C							
Additive and multiplicative inverse			F	C					C	C	C						C								C		C					
Additive and multiplicative identities			C						C	C	C														C		C					
Zero product rule										C																		C	F	C		
Pythagorean Theorem																	F															
Operations with Radicals																								F					C			
Functions and Relations — *Expose (C1), Develop (C2), Develop (C3)*																																
Linear Expressions/Equations																																
Recognize as equations, graphs, tables			C						C									F	F		F	F					F			C		
Relate equations, graphs, and tables							C	C	C	C	C							F	F		F	F					F			C		
Modeling situations								C	C	C								F	C		F	F					F			C		
Direct and indirect variation																		F	C	C	F	F					C					
Slope and rates of change																		F	C	C	F	F					C			C		
Slopes of parallel and perpendicular lines																		C			F	F										
Intercepts			C				C	C	C									F			F	F					C					
Symbolic forms and effects of parameters									C									F			F	F					C			C		
Solve equations using backtracking									F		F								C		C						C					
Solve using guess-check-improve									F		C								F		C						C					
Solve equations symbolically									F										F		C	F					F		F			
Solve, approximate graphically									F												F	F										
Solve inequalities																					C	C					F					
Solve systems of equations/inequalities																			F								F					
Quadratic Expressions/Equations — *Develop (C3)*																																
Recognize as equations, graphs, tables																							F				F	F				
Relate equations, graphs, and tables												C											F				F	F				
Modeling situations																							F				F	F	C			
Intercepts																							F				F	F	F			
Symbolic forms and effects of parameters																							F				F	F	F			
Zero product rule																											F	F	C			
Solve equations using backtracking								F															C				C	F				
Solve using guess-check-improve								F															C				C	C				
Solve, approximate graphically																							C				C	C	C			
Solve factored equations																												F	C			
Solve by factoring																												F	C			
Solve by completing the square																												F				
Solve using the quadratic formula																												F				
Number of solutions																											C	F	F			
Exponential Expressions/Equations																																
Recognize as equations, graphs, tables																														C		
Relate equations, graphs, and tables																														C		
Modeling situations																														C		
Rates of change and asymptotes																														C		
Symbolic forms and effects of parameters																														C		
Solve, approximate graphically																														F		
Rational Expressions/Equations																																
Symbolic forms and effects of parameters										C																		F		F		F
Graphs, intercepts, and asymptotes																												F		F		C
Modeling situations										C									F									F		C		F
Solving equations										C									F									C		C		F

Geometry

TOPICS	Course 1										Course 2										Course 3												
	1	2	3	4	5	6	7	8	9	10	1	2	3	4	5	6	7	8	9	10	1	2	3	4	5	6	7	8	9	10	11	12
Two-Dimensional Shapes					Develop										Apply											Apply						
Polygons — Definitions and properties	F				C		C								C							C				C						
Classification and naming	F				C		C								C																	
Reflectional symmetry	C																									F						
Rotational symmetry																										F						
Angle sums of polygons	F																															
Area and perimeter	F	C	C				C								C		C			C						C						
On the coordinate plane								C																		C						
Quadrilaterals — Definitions and properties	F				C										C											C						
Determining uniqueness	C				F																											
Interior angle sum	F											C										C										
Triangles — Acute, right, obtuse	F																									C						
Equilateral, isosceles, scalene	F														C											C						
Properties of special triangles	F														C																	
Triangle inequality	F																															
Triangle Sum Theorem	C																							C								
Pythagorean Theorem																		F														
Angles — Estimate and measure	F					C	C																									
Classify acute, right, obtuse	F																									C						
Geometric Relationships					Expose										Develop											Apply						
Congruence — Definition and properties					F		C															C				C						
Identifies, determines congruence					F															C		F				C						
Identify corresponding parts					F															C		F				C						
As special case of similarity																				C						C						
Represented by transformation							C															F				F						
Similarity — Definition and properties					F															C		C				C						
Identifies, determines similarity					F															C						C						
Properties of similar figures					F															C						C						
Scale factors					F															F	C					F						C
Congruence as scale factor of 1					F																					C						
Relation to area and perimeter					C		C													C						C						
Relation to surface area and volume							C									C				C												
Relation to ratio and rates					F															F	C					C						
Proportional reasoning		C			C	C				C										F	C					F						
AA Similarity Property					F																					C						
Indirect measurement					C																											
Scale drawings and maps					C													C		C						F						

T16   **Scope and Sequence**

	Course 1										Course 2										Course 3											
TOPICS	1	2	3	4	5	6	7	8	9	10	1	2	3	4	5	6	7	8	9	10	1	2	3	4	5	6	7	8	9	10	11	12
Three-Dimensional Figures (Course 1: Expose, Course 2: Develop, Course 3: Apply)																																
Spatial Visualization — Visualizing structures							F								F											C						
Creating and drawing structures							C								F											C						
Types of 3-D drawings															C																	
Determining unique structures															F																	
3-D Solids — Definitions and properties						C								F																		
Prisms and pyramids						F								F																		
Cones and cylinders														F																		
Nets					C									F																		
Volume and surface area						F								F																		
Measurement (Course 1: Develop, Course 2: Develop, Course 3: Apply)																																
Perimeter and Area — Approximation and estimation	F	C	C				F									C		C														
Formulas for squares and rectangles	F						F							C																		
Areas of parallelograms							F							C																		
Areas of triangles							F							C																		
Areas of circles and circumference	F						F							C																		
Relating perimeter and area	F						C																									
Changes due to scale factor				C															F							C						
Maximizing and minimizing	F																															
Pythagorean Theorem																	F															
Surface Area and Volume — Approximation and estimation							F																									
Formulas for prisms and cylinders							F								F																	
Formulas for pyramids and cones															F																	
Relating surface area and volume							F								F																	
Changes due to scale factor															F																	
Maximizing and minimizing															F																	
Capacity							F								F																	
Coordinate Geometry (Course 1: Develop, Course 2: Develop, Course 3: Develop)																																
Coordinate Representations — Plotting and reading points							F									C		C			C			C	C		C	C		C		
Graphing equations							C				C							F			F			F			F	F		F		
Relating graphs, tables, equations							C	C			C							F			F			F			F	F		F		
Written descriptions of graphs							F											C			F			F			C	F				
Approximating and finding solutions							C				C							F			C			F			F	F		F		
Direct and indirect variation																		F		C	F						C					
Slope of a line and rates of change							C											F		C	F						C			C		
Equations of lines							C											F		C	F						C			F		
Slopes of parallel lines																		C			F									F		
Slopes of perpendicular lines																		C			F											
Distance formula																	F															
Transformations — Reflectional symmetry																										F						
Rotational symmetry																										F						
Translations																					C	C				F				C		
Changes of magnitude (dilations)																										F				C		
Rotations																										F						
Compound transformations																										F				C		
Congruence and similarity																										F						
Relating to equations																					F					C				F		

Number and Operations

Numbers and Number Sense — Course 1: Develop | Course 2: Develop | Course 3: Apply

TOPICS	C1·1	C1·2	C1·3	C1·4	C1·5	C1·6	C1·7	C1·8	C1·9	C1·10	C2·1	C2·2	C2·3	C2·4	C2·5	C2·6	C2·7	C2·8	C2·9	C2·10	C3·1	C3·2	C3·3	C3·4	C3·5	C3·6	C3·7	C3·8	C3·9	C3·10	C3·11	C3·12
Whole Numbers																																
Magnitude of large, small numbers			F										C		F									C								
Operations on odd and even numbers											C	C																				
Factors and multiples	C		F	C									F							C		C			C							C
Common factors and multiples				C									F							C		C										C
Factor pairs and area models				C							C		F												C							C
Greatest common factor				C									F												C							C
Least common multiple				C									F							C					C							C
Prime and composite													F																			
Relatively prime													F												C							
Prime factorization													F																			
Fundamental Theorem of Arithmetic													F																			
Factor trees													F																			
Signed Numbers																																
Meaning and basic concepts							C						F	C																		
Concrete and number line models							F						F				F	C								C						
Four quadrant coordinate model							F						C																			
Comparison							F						F	C																		
Order							F						F																			
Absolute value and opposites							F						F																			
Addition and subtraction													F																			
Multiplication and division													F				C															
Meaning in exponential notation														F										F								
Negative slope																		F			F	C										
Exponents and Roots																																
Meaning and basic concepts			F										F											C								
Positive and negative exponents			F										F	F										F								
Scientific notation			F											F										F								
Laws of exponents			F										F	F										F								
Used in expressions and equations			F										F	F										F	C				C	C		
Geometric interpretation of square			F																													
Geometric interpretation of cube			F																													

Rationals and Irrationals — Course 1: Develop | Course 2: Apply | Course 3: Apply

TOPICS	C1·1	C1·2	C1·3	C1·4	C1·5	C1·6	C1·7	C1·8	C1·9	C1·10	C2·1	C2·2	C2·3	C2·4	C2·5	C2·6	C2·7	C2·8	C2·9	C2·10	C3·1	C3·2	C3·3	C3·4	C3·5	C3·6	C3·7	C3·8	C3·9	C3·10	C3·11	C3·12
Fraction and Decimal Concepts																																
Rational and irrational numbers		F															F							F								C
Geometric and number line models		F		C		C							F				F															
Fractional relationships to a whole		F		F	C	F														C						C						C
Comparison		F		F		F		C							C		F			C			C									
Benchmarks for comparison		F		F		F											F															
Order		F		F		F		C						C	C		F															
Naming equivalent fractions		F		C	C	C				C					C		F			C				C							C	F
Naming equivalent decimals		F		F		F											F															
Fraction and decimal equivalencies		F		C		C											C			C				C								
Fraction and decimal approximations		F		C		C									C		C			C												
Fractions as indicated division		F		C		C														F				C								C
Repeating decimals		F		C		C																		F								
Relating fractions and decimals		F		C		C														F			C	C								
Converting fractions to decimals		F		C		C														C			C	C								
Converting decimals to fractions		F		C		C														C			C	C								

TOPICS	C1-1	C1-2	C1-3	C1-4	C1-5	C1-6	C1-7	C1-8	C1-9	C1-10	C2-1	C2-2	C2-3	C2-4	C2-5	C2-6	C2-7	C2-8	C2-9	C2-10	C3-1	C3-2	C3-3	C3-4	C3-5	C3-6	C3-7	C3-8	C3-9	C3-10	C3-11	C3-12
Percents — Develop / Develop / Apply																																
Definition and basic concepts						F														C			F									
Greater than 100 or less than 1						F														C			F									
Common scale comparisons						F														F												
Relating to fractions and decimals						F														C			F									
Relating to ratios and proportions						C														F			F									
Converting to a decimal						F														C												
Converting to a fraction						F														C												
Estimate percent using benchmarks						F														C			C									
Calculate percent						F														F			F									
Solve percent problems (all cases)						C														F			F									
Relating to proportional reasoning						F														F			F									
Percent increase and decrease						F														F			F	C								
Ratios and Rates — Expose / Develop / Apply																																
Basic concepts	C		C	F	C			C										F		F												
Comparison statements				F	C															F												
Part-to-part comparisons				F																F					C							
Part-to-whole comparisons	C			F	F								C							F					C				C			
Relating unlike quantities or units				F	C													F		F												
Types and uses of ratio notation				F																F												
Equivalent ratios and ratio tables				F														F		F												
Comparing ratios	C		C	F	C								C					F		F												
Equivalent rates				F														F		F	F											
Rate tables and rate graphs				F													F	F	F	F	F											
Slope and rates of change																		F	F	C	F											
Definition and basic concepts					C														C	F	F					C						
Proportions as equations								C												F	F		F									C
Checking if a proportion exists																		F		F	C		F									
Methods of solving proportions																				F			F									C
Proportional relationships																		F		F	F		F			C						
Proportional reasoning	C				C				C										C	F			F	C		C	C		C			
Algorithms and Operations — Develop / Apply / Apply																																
Generating equivalent fractions	F	C	C		C															C			C									C
Fraction, mixed number conversions	F		C																													C
Percent, decimal conversion	F		C		F																		F									
Addition and subtraction				F		C								C																		C
Multiplication and division				F		C								C																		C
Fraction, percent conversions	F		F		F																		F									
Addition and subtraction			C			C						C	C																			
Multiplication and division			C			C						C	C																			
Addition and subtraction (Signed Numbers)													F																			
Multiplication and division (Signed Numbers)													F																			

Probability and Statistics

TOPICS	Course 1 1	2	3	4	5	6	7	8	9	10	Course 2 1	2	3	4	5	6	7	8	9	10	Course 3 1	2	3	4	5	6	7	8	9	10	11	12
Data Analysis						Develop										Develop									Develop							
Graphs and Displays																																
Line plots				F		C				F						F																
Stem-and-leaf plots										F						F																
Box plots																															F	
Venn Diagrams	C									F					C																	
Circle graphs						C				C						F																
Frequency tables						C				F						C																
Histograms										F																						
Scatter plots								C		F																						
Choose appropriate displays										F						F																
Skewness and symmetry										F																						
Modeling and Analysis																																
Identify patterns and trends		C	F					C		F						F		C			C	C		C				C				
Identify clusters, gaps, and outliers										F																						
Describe shape and scatter										F							C					F		C			C					
Compare data sets										F						F							C									
Fit a line by "eyeballing"										C							C					F										
Make predictions and generalizations		C	C							F						F		C				C		C			C					
Misleading graphs										C						F					C											
Law of large numbers										F																						C
Outlier affect on measurers of center																							C									
Compare measures of center																F																
Choose appropriate measure of center																C																
Statistical Measures																																
Frequency				F						C																						
Range				F																												
Mode				F																												
Median				F																												
Mean				F																												
Quartiles																															F	
Surveys and Sampling																																
Sample survey vs. census																F																
Randomization										C						F																
Simple random sample																F																
Sample size										C						F																
Law of large numbers										F						C																
Bias in survey methods										C						C																
Population and sample identification																F																

		Course 1										Course 2										Course 3											
TOPICS		1	2	3	4	5	6	7	8	9	10	1	2	3	4	5	6	7	8	9	10	1	2	3	4	5	6	7	8	9	10	11	12
Probability						Develop											Develop										Develop							
Basic Concepts and Rules	Measure between 0 and 1										F						F															F	
	Empirical and theoretical probabilities										F						F															F	
	Equally likely										F						C															F	
	Compound events										C																					F	
	Mutually exclusive events										C																					F	
	Independent events										F						F															C	
	Dependent events										F						F															C	
	Confidence										C																						
	Expected value										C																						
Counting Methods	Counting trees										F						F															F	
	Combinations																F															F	
	Permutations																															F	
Experiments and Simulations	Estimate likelihood										C						C															C	
	Relate to theoretical probabilities										F																					C	
	Analyze fairness										C						F															C	

Pacing

IMPACT Mathematics and the accompanying support materials allow you to create a mathematics course that meets the needs of your students. The chart shown on these two pages offers general suggestions for pacing your students through the book.

Chapter	Lesson (Investigation)	Day(s)
1	Lesson 1.1(1)	1–2
	Lesson 1.1(2)	3
	Lesson 1.1(3)	4
	Lesson 1.1(4) Inquiry	5
	Lesson 1.2(1)	6–7
	Lesson 1.2(2)	8
	Quiz, Lessons 1.1–1.2	9
	Lesson 1.3(1)	10–11
	Lesson 1.3(2)	12
	Quiz, Lesson 1.3	13
	Chapter 1 Review	14
	Chapter 1 Test	15
2	Lesson 2.1(1)	16
	Lesson 2.1(2)	17
	Lesson 2.1(3)	18
	Lesson 2.1(4)	19
	Lesson 2.2(1)	20–21
	Lesson 2.2(2)	22
	Lesson 2.2(3) Inquiry Quiz, Lesson 2.1–2.2	23
	Lesson 2.3(1)	24
	Lesson 2.3(2)	25
	Lesson 2.3(3)	26
	Lesson 2.3(4)	27
	Quiz, Lesson 2.3	28
	Chapter 2 Review	29
	Chapter 2 Test	30

Chapter	Lesson (Investigation)	Day(s)
3	Lesson 3.1(1)	31
	Lesson 3.1(2)	32
	Lesson 3.2(1)	33–34
	Lesson 3.2(2)	35
	Lesson 3.2(3)	36
	Lesson 3.2(4)	37
	Quiz, Lesson 3.1–3.2	38
	Lesson 3.3(1)	39–40
	Lesson 3.3(2)	41
	Lesson 3.3(3)	42
	Lesson 3.3(4) Inquiry	43
	Lesson 3.3(5)	44
	Lesson 3.3(6)	45
	Lesson 3.4(1)	46–47
	Lesson 3.4(2)	48
	Lesson 3.4(3)	49
	Quiz, Lesson 3.3–3.4	50
	Chapter 3 Review	51
	Chapter 3 Test	52
4	Lesson 4.1(1)	53–54
	Lesson 4.1(2)	55
	Lesson 4.1(3)	56
	Lesson 4.1(4) Inquiry	57
	Lesson 4.2(1)	58–59
	Lesson 4.2(2)	60
	Lesson 4.2(3)	61
	Lesson 4.2(4)	62
	Lesson 4.2(5)	63
	Quiz, Lessons 4.1–4.2	64
	Lesson 4.3(1)	65–66
	Lesson 4.3(2)	67
	Lesson 4.3(3)	68
	Lesson 4.3(4)	69
	Lesson 4.3(5)	70
	Lesson 4.4(1)	71–72
	Lesson 4.4(2)	73
	Lesson 4.4(3)	74
	Quiz, Lessons 4.3–4.4	75
	Chapter 4 Review	76
	Chapter 4 Test	77

Chapter	Lesson (Investigation)	Day(s)
5	Lesson 5.1(1)	78
	Lesson 5.1(2)	79
	Lesson 5.1(3)	80
	Lesson 5.1(4)	81
	Lesson 5.2(1)	82
	Lesson 5.2(2)	83
	Lesson 5.2(3) Inquiry Quiz, Lessons 5.1–5.2	84
	Lesson 5.3(1)	85
	Lesson 5.3(2)	86
	Lesson 5.3(3)	87
	Lesson 5.3(4)	88
	Quiz, Lesson 5.3	89
	Chapter 5 Review	90
	Chapter 5 Test	91
6	Lesson 6.1(1)	92–93
	Lesson 6.1(2)	94
	Lesson 6.1(3)	95
	Lesson 6.1(4)	96
	Lesson 6.2(1)	97–98
	Lesson 6.2(2)	99
	Quiz, Lesson 6.1–6.2	100
	Lesson 6.3(1)	101–102
	Lesson 6.3(2)	103
	Lesson 6.3(3) Inquiry Quiz, Lesson 6.3	104
	Chapter 6 Review	105
	Chapter 6 Test	106
7	Lesson 7.1(1)	107–108
	Lesson 7.1(2)	109
	Lesson 7.2(1)	110–111
	Lesson 7.2(2)	112
	Lesson 7.2(3)	113
	Lesson 7.2(4)	114
	Lesson 7.2(5)	115
	Quiz, Lesson 7.1–7.2	116
	Lesson 7.3(1)	117–118
	Lesson 7.3(2)	119
	Lesson 7.3(3) Inquiry	120
	Lesson 7.4(1)	121
	Lesson 7.4(2)	122
	Quiz, Lessons 7.3–7.4	123
	Chapter 7 Review	124
	Chapter 7 Test	125

Chapter	Lesson (Investigation)	Day(s)
8	Lesson 8.1(1)	126–127
	Lesson 8.1(2)	128
	Lesson 8.1(3)	129
	Lesson 8.2(1)	130
	Lesson 8.2(2)	131
	Lesson 8.2(3)	132
	Lesson 8.2(4)	133
	Quiz, Lesson 8.1–8.2	134
	Lesson 8.3(1)	135–136
	Lesson 8.3(2)	137
	Lesson 8.3(3)	138
	Lesson 8.3(4)	139
	Lesson 8.3(5) Inquiry Quiz, Lesson 8.3	140
	Chapter 8 Review	141
	Chapter 8 Test	142
9	Lesson 9.1(1)	143–144
	Lesson 9.1(2)	145
	Lesson 9.1(3) Inquiry	146
	Lesson 9.2(1)	147–148
	Lesson 9.2(2)	149
	Lesson 9.2(3)	150
	Quiz, Lesson 9.1–9.2	151
	Lesson 9.3(1)	152–153
	Lesson 9.3(2)	154
	Lesson 9.3(3)	155
	Quiz, Lesson 9.3	156
	Chapter 9 Review	157
	Chapter 9 Test	158
10	Lesson 10.1(1)	159–160
	Lesson 10.1(2)	161
	Lesson 10.1(3)	162
	Lesson 10.1(4)	163
	Lesson 10.2(1)	164–165
	Lesson 10.2(2)	166
	Lesson 10.2(3)	167
	Lesson 10.2(4)	168
	Quiz, Lesson 10.1–10.2	169
	Lesson 10.3(1)	170–171
	Lesson 10.3(2)	172
	Lesson 10.3(3) Inquiry	173
	Lesson 10.3(4)	174
	Lesson 10.4(1)	175
	Lesson 10.4(2)	176
	Lesson 10.4(3)	177
	Quiz, Lesson 10.3–10.4	178
	Chapter 10 Review	179
	Chapter 10 Test	180

Table of Contents

Focal Points and Connections
See pages vi and vii for key.

G6-FP1

G6-FP6C

Focal Points
and Connections
See pages vi and vii
for key.

G6-FP1

G6-FP4C

Focal Points and Connections
See pages vi and vii for key.

G6-FP3

G6-FP5C

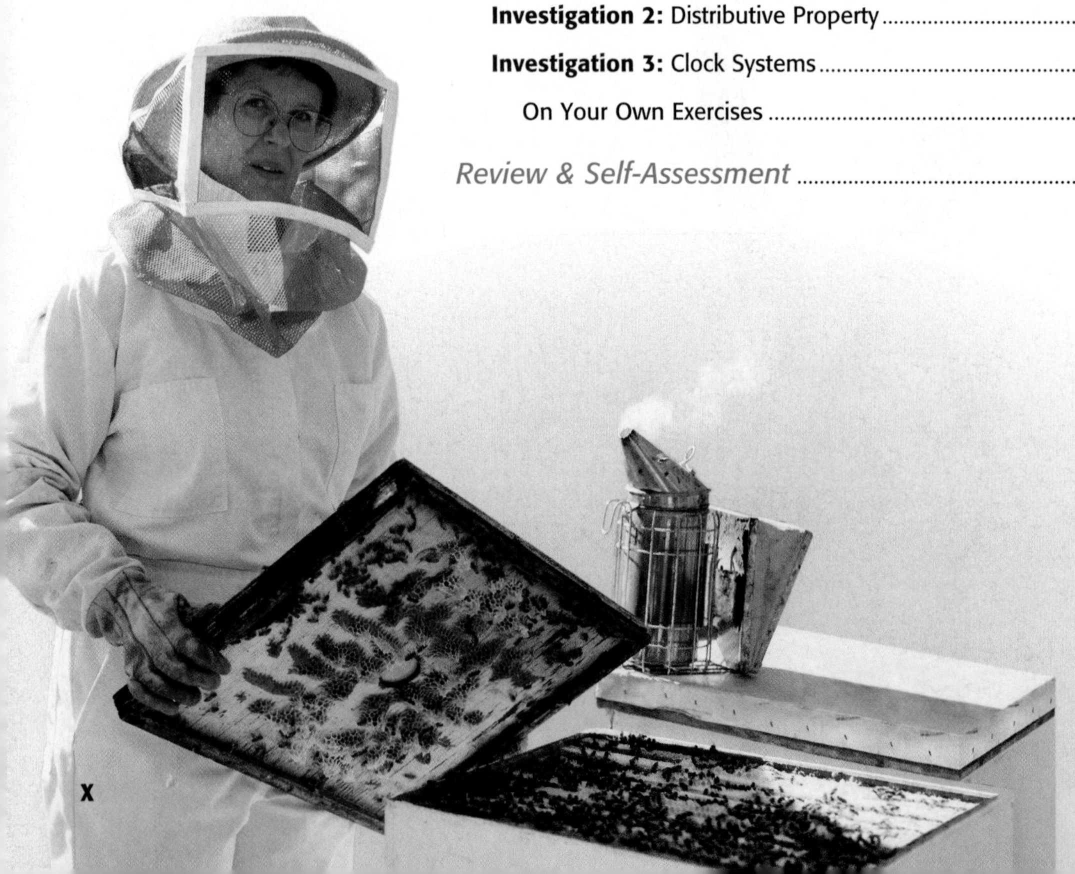

Focal Points and Connections
See pages vi and vii for key.

G6-FP1

G6-FP4C

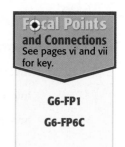

Focal Points and Connections
See pages vi and vii for key.

G6-FP1

G6-FP6C

Focal Points
and Connections
See pages vi and vii
for key.

G6-FP3

1

CHAPTER 1

Polygons, Angles, and Circles

Chapter Overview

In the first lesson, students estimate the measures of angles using benchmark angles and comparisons. They use Venn diagrams to classify polygons, and they discover the triangle inequality. Next, students learn how to measure, draw, and classify angles. They will find the sum of the measures of the interior angles of any polygon, and in the final lesson, they will find the perimeter of a polygon and the circumference of a circle.

The Big Picture

Links to past and future content found in The Big Picture illustrate vertical alignment throughout the program.

Links to the Past	Chapter 1	Links to the Future
Grade 5 Naming and classifying common geometric shapes.	**Lesson 1.1** (p. 4) Patterns in Geometry	**Course 1, Chapter 7** Area, Volume, and Capacity (pp. 396–465) **Course 2, Chapter 5** Geometry in Three Dimensions (pp. 210–259)
Grade 5 Classifying, estimating, and measuring angles. Naming different types of triangles.	**Lesson 1.2** (p. 24) Angles	**Course 1, Chapter 5** Rate, Ratio, and Proportion (pp. 288–345) **Course 2, Chapter 6** Data and Probability (pp. 260–317) **Course 3, Chapter 6** Transformational Geometry (pp. 258–309)
Grade 5 Finding perimeter of a rectangle. Using formulas to find perimeter. Reviewing circumference and radius. Adding decimals. Reading rulers (fractional parts of inches).	**Lesson 1.3** (p. 40) Measure Around	**Course 1, Chapter 7** Area, Volume, and Capacity (pp. 396–465) **Course 2, Chapter 6** Data and Probability (pp. 260–317)

Mathematical Background

Chapter 1 introduces students to polygons and angles. Students look for patterns in the polygons they can recognize. Patterns in geometry include the triangle sum rule, which states that the sum of the angles of a triangle is 180 degrees. To be mathematically accurate, this rule applies only to triangles in a plane or, in a language students will understand, to *flat* triangles. Although students will most likely not realize the importance of this added data, they may encounter triangles on curved surfaces that have angle sums that are more or less than 180 degrees.

Students will draw the diagonals in a polygon and use the triangle sum rule to find the sum of the interior angles of the polygon.

Sum of the Angles of a Triangle The sum of the angles of any triangle is 180 degrees. To show this, students can be asked to draw a triangle and then tear off the three vertices. They then rearrange the vertices so they form a straight line. Prior to this, students have learned how to measure angles and have learned that the measure of a straight angle is 180 degrees, so this establishes a rule to find the sum of the angles of any triangle. They can then use this rule to find similar rules about the sums of the interior angles of other polygons.

Mathematical Background gives additional information on mathematics content and research, and suggestions for further reading.

Sum of the Interior Angles of a Polygon The sum of the interior angles of a polygon is found by redrawing the polygon with diagonals either from one vertex or so that the polygon is broken up into the least number of triangles possible. The number of triangles will be two less than the number of sides. Then the sum of the interior angles of a polygon is the number of triangles times 180.

The ideas in this chapter lay the groundwork for more extensive work on geometry in Courses 2 and 3. In particular, students will find the area and volume of geometric figures and will find transformations.

Additional Reading

According to Miller and Mercer in *Educational Aspects of Mathematical Disabilities,* activities-based, hands-on learning, as well as reasoning and problem-solving experiences benefit students with disabilities. Students will be introduced to angle relationships and polygons in this chapter.

Planning Guide
Lesson Resources

The **Planning Guide** presents important planning information for the entire chapter, including lesson objectives, suggested pacing, materials, and extra resources.

	Lesson 1.1 Pacing: 5 days	**Lesson 1.2** Pacing: 3 days	**Lesson 1.3** Pacing: 3 days
Lesson Title	**Patterns in Geometry** (p. 4)	**Angles** (p. 24)	**Measure Around** (p. 40)
Lesson Objectives	• To name polygons and classify them by concavity and line symmetry • To use Venn diagrams to classify objects • To find the measures of identical angles summing to 90°, 180°, or 360° • To estimate angle measures • To determine whether three segments could form a triangle	• To measure angles by using a protractor • To classify angles whose measures are greater than 0° and less than 180° as acute, right, or obtuse • To find the sum of the angles of any polygon given the number of sides of the polygon	• To use the side lengths of a polygon to calculate the perimeter of the polygon • To use polygons to approximate the perimeter of a shape with curved sides • To understand and use formulas for the circumference of a circle
Materials	rulers, Chapter 1 Master 1, *linkage strips and fasteners, pattern blocks, set of polygons, Lesson 1.1 Masters 1–7, scissors	copies of the angles, protractor, ruler, Lesson 1.2 Master 1	Lesson 1.3 Master 1, scissors, ruler, string, 5 objects with circular faces
Quick Review Math Handbook	**Lesson 6.1** Naming and Classifying Angles and Triangles **Lesson 6.2** Polygons and Polyhedrons	**Lesson 6.1** Naming and Classifying Angles and Triangles	**Lesson 6.4** Perimeter **Lesson 6.8** Circles
Print Resources	CRM Refresher Worksheets (pp. 3–14) CRM Study Guide and Intervention (p. 16) CRM Skills Practice (p. 17) CRM Problem-Solving Practice (p. 18) CRM Enrichment (p. 19) • Investigation Notebook and Reflection Journal • Differentiation Handbook	CRM Study Guide and Intervention (p. 28) CRM Skills Practice (p. 29) CRM Problem-Solving Practice (p. 30) CRM Enrichment (p. 31) • Investigation Notebook and Reflection Journal • Differentiation Handbook	CRM Study Guide and Intervention (p. 35) CRM Skills Practice (p. 36) CRM Problem-Solving Practice (p. 37) CRM Enrichment (p. 38) • Investigation Notebook and Reflection Journal • Differentiation Handbook
Technology Resources	TeacherWorks Plus Classroom Presentation Toolkit ExamView Assessment Suite StudentWorks Plus Math Online Brain Pops • Concepts in Motion	TeacherWorks Plus Classroom Presentation Toolkit ExamView Assessment Suite StudentWorks Plus Math Online Brain Pops • Concepts in Motion	TeacherWorks Plus Classroom Presentation Toolkit ExamView Assessment Suite StudentWorks Plus Math Online Brain Pops • Concepts in Motion

*Included in the Impact Mathematics Manipulative Kit

Assessment Resources

MARS Assessment: Teaching with Purpose

Merritt Bakery

In *Merritt Bakery,* students use circle diameter and circumference relationships to find out the amount of ribbon needed to decorate a cake. Students also write a formula or rule that expresses the length of the ribbon required in terms of the cake's diameter.

Targeting the Task

- **Diagnostic**—Use Exercises 1–3 in the *Merritt Bakery* assessment to determine students' understanding of how to use circle and circumference relationships and how to write a formula or rule for a linear relation. For those students who do not have this understanding, completing this unit is needed.

- **Formative**—Exercises 1–3 can be administered individually according to the lessons.

- **Summative**—Administer the complete *Merritt Bakery* performance-based assessment.

> **MARS Performance-Based Assessment** asks students to perform tasks or solve problems that appear in authentic (real-world) contexts.

CRM Chapter 1 MARS Assessment (pp. 61–63)

Assessment Planning Guide

Assessments are available for investigations, lessons, and chapters.

ExamView® Assessment Suite — Customize and create multiple versions of tests and quizzes.

	Student Edition	**Teacher Edition**	**Other Resources**
Diagnostic			CRM Course Pretest (p. 41) CRM Chapter 1 Pretest (p. 44) Math Online Online Chapter Quiz
Formative	Share & Summarize (pp. 8, 11, 15, 29, 34)	On the Spot Assessment (pp. 11, 14, 17, 31) Troubleshooting (pp. 7, 34, 47) Quick Check (pp. 22, 39, 51) Quick Quiz (pp. 23, 39, 51)	
Summative	Review & Self-Assessment (pp. 52–55)	The **Assessment Resources** displays the array of assessment opportunities, including materials in the Student Edition, Teacher Guide, and CRMs.	CRM Chapter 1 Test: Forms A and B (pp. 48–55) CRM Standardized Test Practice (p. 59)
Performance-Based	In Your Own Words (pp. 25, 39, 51)		CRM Chapter Performance Assessment (p. 56) CRM MARS Performance-Based Assessment (p. 61)

Differentiated Instruction
Reaching All Learners

Below are suggestions on differentiating the materials presented in this chapter. Additional modifications should be considered.

*For remediation or enrichment, the activities and modifications found on the **Differentiated Instruction** page provide additional options for use throughout the chapter.*

Approaching Level — AL

Lessons 1.1 and 1.2: Flash Cards Students having difficulty identifying polygons and/or angles may need extra practice. Use index cards to create flash cards showing a shape or angle on one side, and the correct term on the other side. Have students work in pairs or small groups. Tell them to take turns holding up a card and having the others identify the shape or angle shown. As students progress, have them show the side with the term while the other student draws an illustration of the term. If the flash cards are helpful to students, allow individuals to make a set of flashcards for themselves. Encourage them to take the cards home and practice with a family member.

Beyond Level — BL

Lesson 1.3: Draw It Some students will quickly grasp the concept of measuring around a polygon. Divide these students into pairs and tell them to take turns drawing a polygon for the other partner to measure around. Have each student draw a figure and determine whether the distance around it would be called the *perimeter* or the *circumference*. Then have them trade and find the specified measurements. Remind students to use formulas whenever possible, such as the formula for finding circumference. Once each student has found the measurement for the figure, have students trade back and check one another's work. Monitor for correct use of formulas and measurement strategies.

On Level — OL

Lesson 1.2: Triangles Remind students that any polygon can be split into triangles. Provide various polygons for students to trace onto their papers. After tracing the polygons, have students determine how the figure can be divided into triangles. Point out that the triangles can be drawn with different measurements, so students will need to think creatively. Allow students to work in pairs. Have them share their results with the class after they divide all the polygons. Compare each pair's findings and discuss how they are alike and different. Be sure to provide rulers for students to use as straightedges and to measure the triangles when reporting to the class about their work.

English Language Learners — ELL

Lesson 1.3: Measurements English Language Learners often need extra time to work on concepts that require new vocabulary. For students who are not comfortable with the terms in this lesson, such as circumference and perimeter, set up a time for them to practice identifying the proper terms. For example, call out "circumference" and "perimeter" and have students point to a polygon that could be measured with that term. In making students at ease with using the vocabulary, you will make grasping future related concepts much simpler for them. If they still need help, allow them to practice with a partner. Remind them that these terms are important because they will use them in many future lessons.

KEY

AL Approaching Level   OL On Level   BL Beyond Level   ELL English Language Learners

Intervention Planning Guide

CRM Assess students' prerequisite skills and knowledge using the
Chapter Pretest found in the Chapter 1 Resource Masters, p. 44.

Intensive Intervention two or more years below grade level	Strategic Intervention below grade level	On Level	Beyond Level
If students miss 75% of the exercises:	**If** students miss 50% of the exercises:	**If** students miss 25% of the exercises:	**If** students miss 0%–10% of the exercises:
Then use *Math Triumphs,* an intensive intervention	**Then** choose a resource:	**Then** choose a resource:	**Then** choose a resource:
Math Triumphs, Grade 6 • Chapter 10: Formulas	CRM Study Guide and Intervention (pp. 16, 28, 35) • Investigation Notebook and Reflection Journal • Differentiation Handbook **Math Online** Brain Pops • Concepts in Motion	CRM Skills Practice (pp. 17, 29, 36) CRM Problem-Solving Practice (pp. 18, 30, 37) • Investigation Notebook and Reflection Journal	CRM Enrichment (pp. 19, 31, 38) • Differentiation Handbook

*The **Intervention Planning Guide** prescribes both enrichment and remediation resources, including **Math Triumphs**.*

Literature Connections
Recommended Outside Reading for Students
Nonfiction

Long, Lynette. *Measurement Mania.* Wiley, John & Sons, Inc. 2001.

> This book provides 40 activities of measurement, providing instructions and black-and-white illustrations. Readers experience a progression of difficulty from the first activity to the last.

Fiction

Leedy, Loreen. *Measuring Penny.* Holt, Henry Books for Young Readers. 2000.

> Lisa has an important homework assignment—to measure something in several different ways. She measures her dog Penny using all sorts of units, such as pounds, inches, dog biscuits, and cotton swabs.

*The fiction and non-fiction books in **Literature Connections** offer opportunities for students to explore math concepts in contexts outside of the math classroom.*

 **Professional Development**

Targeted professional development has been articulated throughout the *IMPACT Mathematics* series. The **McGraw-Hill Professional Development Video Library** provides short videos that support the mathematics standards. Log on to **www.glencoe.com**.

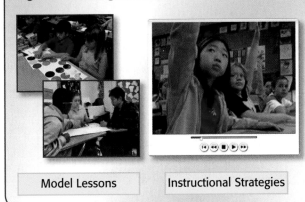

Model Lessons   Instructional Strategies

Real-Life Math

Geometry in Sports The shapes listed as examples on this page illustrate how geometric figures are used in many aspects of real life, including sports. Ask students to brainstorm different geometric shapes that are familiar and that are used in sports. Point out that there may be several geometric shapes related to one sport. For example, volleyball uses a sphere for the ball, a rectangle for the court, and a different rectangle for the net.

Think About It Suggest that students make a list of the sports they would like to consider. Then they should visualize playing the sport and list all the geometric figures that come to mind while playing the sport.

CHAPTER
1

Polygons, Angles, and Circles

Contents in Brief

Real-Life Math

Geometry in Sports Geometric figures are used in many aspects of everyday life, including sporting events. The shapes of soccer pitches, volleyball courts, and baseball diamonds are quadrilaterals. Spherical tennis balls are packaged in cylindrical cans. Skateboarding aerials and figure skating jumps are often named according to the number of revolutions performed by the athlete.

Think About It List as many other sports-related geometry examples as you can.

> **Math Online**
> Take the **Chapter Readiness Quiz** at glencoe.com.

2

---

*Each chapter has a separate **Chapter Resource Masters** booklet that contains lesson worksheets, chapter and lesson assessments, and chapter and lesson black-line masters.*

Chapter Resources

CRM Chapter 1 Resource Masters

CRM Refresher Worksheets, (pp. 3–14)

CRM English/Spanish Family Letter (pp. 1 and 2)

CRM Lesson Masters (pp. 21–27, 33–34, 40)

CRM Chapter 1 Pretest (pp. 44–47)

CRM Chapter 1 Tests (pp. 48–58)

Math Online Online Readiness Quiz • eGlossary

Dear Family,

Mathematics has been called the "science of patterns." Recognizing and describing patterns and using patterns to make predictions are important mathematical skills.

The class will begin by looking for patterns in geometry.

Key Concept—Polygons and Circles

Polygons are flat, two-dimensional, geometric figures that have the following characteristics.

- They are made of line segments.
- Each segment touches exactly two other segments, one at each endpoint.

The class will classify polygons by the number of their sides. A few polygons are shown below.

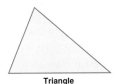
Triangle

Quadrilateral

Regular Pentagon

The class will explore circles. Even though circles are two-dimensional figures, they are not made of line segments. So, circles are not classified as polygons.

Chapter Vocabulary

angle	perpendicular
circumference	polygon
concave polygon	radius
diameter	regular polygon
line symmetry	right angle
perimeter	vertex

Home Activities

- Go on a family walk. Identify different-shaped objects around your home, in a neighborhood park, or along a city street.
- Look at a building or house and discuss the figures that you see.

Family Letter

Another version of the Family Letter, available in English and Spanish, is found in the Chapter 1 Resource Masters. You may want to send a copy of this letter home with your students.

Key Concept—Polygons and Circles

Introduce students to polygons by drawing several familiar polygons and classifying them by the number of sides. Start with a triangle and then name each polygon as you increase the number of sides.

Make a table showing a diagram of each polygon, the number of sides, and the name of the polygon.

Review the characteristics of polygons and draw several examples of shapes that are not polygons.

Home Activities

- Discuss different situations where it is important to identify different-shaped objects by name. These may be around your home or elsewhere. What geometric shapes are in the front view of your home?

- Each day, have your student cut out a different polygon from construction paper to post on the refrigerator. Have him or her label the polygon with its name.

Key Vocabulary

English (Spanish) *Introduce the most important terms from Chapter 1.*

angle (angulo) Two rays with the same endpoint. (p. 9)

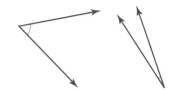

circumference (circunferencia) The perimeter of a circle (distance around the circle). (p. 44)

line symmetry (simetría lineal) A polygon has line symmetry if you can fold it in half along a line so that the two halves match exactly. The lines of symmetry are shown as dashed lines. (p. 12)

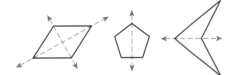

perimeter (perímetro) The distance around a two-dimensional shape. (p. 40)

regular polygon (polígono regular) A polygon with sides that are all the same length and angles that are all the same size. (p. 12)

vertex (vértice) A corner of a polygon, where two sides meet. (p. 4)

> **Mathematical Vocabulary** is highlighted and defined in context within each lesson.
> **Key Vocabulary** is listed before each chapter.

Patterns in Geometry

The **Overview** provides a synopsis of the investigations in the lesson and makes connections to content presented before or after the lesson.

Objectives

▶ To name polygons and classify them by regularity, concavity, and line symmetry

▶ To use Venn diagrams to classify objects

▶ To find the measures of identical angles summing to 90°, 180°, or 360°

▶ To estimate angle measures

▶ To determine whether three segments or angles could form a triangle

This lesson focuses on patterns in geometric shapes, specifically polygons and angles. Students are introduced to terminology of and relationships among geometric shapes and to well-established mathematical patterns and rules.

The first two investigations introduce students to polygons and angles. Students develop intuitions about angle measure as they use deduction and comparison to estimate the measures of angles. Students will use protractors in the next lesson.

Investigation 3 introduces students to new characteristics of polygons and the use of Venn diagrams. In the inquiry investigation, students discover the triangle inequality, although the formal name of the former is not used in this text. The inequality is discovered in a concrete manner by using linkage strips and physical triangles.

Advance Preparation

You may want to provide Lesson 1.1 Masters 1–7 to facilitate class discussion while presenting new topics, including angles, classifying polygons, and the triangle inequality.

	Summary	Materials	On Your Own Exercises (pp. 18–23)	Assessment Opportunities
Investigation 1 (p. 4) *Pacing: 2 days*	This investigation introduces students to polygons and the terminology used with them. Students identify polygons and name polygons using vertices.	Lesson 1.1 Masters 1–2, blank transparencies (optional), scissors (optional), Chapter 1 Master 1	Practice & Apply: 1–3 Connect & Extend: 16, 17 Mixed Review: 26–36	• Share & Summarize (p. 8) • Troubleshooting (p. 7)
Investigation 2 (p. 8) *Pacing: 1 day*	Students develop their sense of angle as they estimate angle measures by comparing angles to benchmarks: 90°, 180°, and 360°.	Lesson 1.1 Master 3, scissors (optional)	Practice & Apply: 4–11 Connect & Extend: 18–20 Mixed Review: 26–36	• On the Spot Assessment (p. 11) • Share & Summarize (p. 11)
Investigation 3 (p. 12) *Pacing: 1 day*	Students classify polygons using a variety of criteria. Venn diagrams are introduced as an organizational tool.	Lesson 1.1 Masters 4–6, scissors (optional), string (optional)	Practice & Apply: 12–15 Connect & Extend: 21–25 Mixed Review: 26–36	• On the Spot Assessment (p. 14) • Share & Summarize (p. 15)
Inquiry Investigation 4 (p. 16) *Pacing: 1 day*	Students focus on patterns in and special properties of triangles in this investigation, concluding with the triangle inequality. They also make conjectures about the sum of the angles in a triangle.	*linkage strips or Lesson 1.1 Master 7, scissors (optional), fasteners, rulers		• On the Spot Assessment (p. 17)

The concise table in the **Lesson Planner** includes a summary of the content, materials needed, and assessment opportunities for each investigation.

*Included in the Impact Mathematics Manipulative Kit

Leveled Lesson Resources

CRM *Available in:* **Chapter 1 Resource Masters**

Study Guide and Intervention (p. 16) **AL**

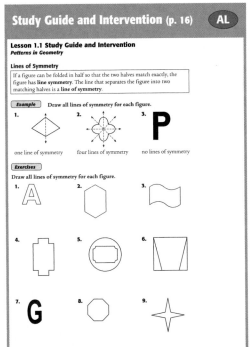

Skills Practice (p. 17) **AL** **OL**

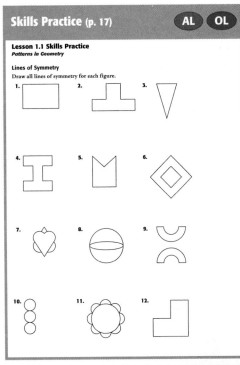

Problem-Solving Practice (p. 18) **AL** **OL**

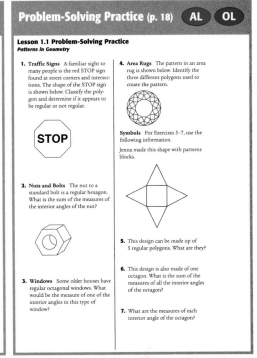

Enrichment (p. 19) **BL**

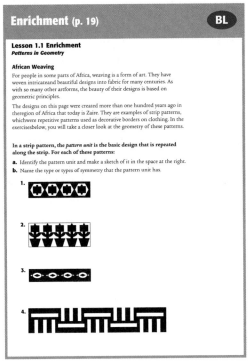

Lesson Quick Quiz (p. 20) **AL** **OL** **BL**

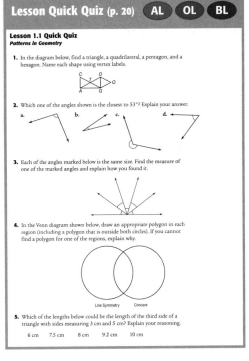

Lesson Masters 1–7 (pp. 21–27)

Lesson 1.1 Master 1
Patterns in Geometry

Investigation 1: Explore

*The page reductions on the **Leveled Lesson Resources** show the corresponding lesson worksheets, lesson masters, and the Quick Quiz from the Chapter Resource Masters (CRMs).*

Additional Lesson Resources

Teacher Tech Tools
- TeacherWorks
- ExamView Assessment Suite
- Classroom Presentation Toolkit
- Advance Tracker

Student Tech Tools
- StudentWorks Plus
- **Math Online** eGlossary •
  Concepts in Motion

Other Print Products
- Investigation Notebook
  and Reflection Journal
- Quick Review Math Handbook

LESSON 1.1 Patterns in Geometry

Explore

Suggested Grouping: Groups of 3 or 4

▶ **Prepare** Display a 4 × 4 square and ask students to write down the number of squares they see. If some students can find only 16 squares, point out one larger square.

▶ **Play** Ask students to find all of the possible squares. Encourage students to use the draw a picture or diagram problem-solving strategy. Use transparencies to outline a 2 × 2 square. Then move the transparency over the 4 × 4 square and match it up with as many 2 × 2 squares as possible. Do the same with 3 × 3 and 4 × 4 squares.

You can provide students with copies of Lesson 1.1 Master 1 or have them draw the squares themselves.

▶ **Report** Have a reporter from each group share their findings to the class. Discuss how to determine which groups are correct.

▶ **Score** Give each group a point for each square they find.

Investigation 1

On Your Own Exercises
Pages 18–23
Exercises 1–3, 16, 17

Polygons It is assumed in this investigation that students are familiar with the terms *segment, endpoint,* and *line.* Review how lines and segments are different. If you find that many students seem unfamiliar with these concepts, provide them with a reference sheet like Chapter 1 Master 1 for use in this lesson.

Think & Discuss

Discuss the examples of nonpolygons with the class.

Inv 1	Polygons	4
Inv 2	Angles	8
Inv 3	Classify Polygons	12
Inv 4	Triangle Sides	16

Investigation 1 Polygons

Vocabulary

polygon

vertex

① The first two shapes are not made from line segments. In the third shape, two of the segments touch only one other segment. In the fourth shape, some of the segments touch more than two other segments.

Reaching All Learners

ELL English Language Learners
English language learners may have difficulty remembering how to classify each polygon because the vocabulary is new. Encourage them to use note cards to write the names of polygons in English and in their native languages. Have them include examples on the note cards.

Patterns in Geometry

In this lesson, you will work with two-dimensional geometric figures. You will classify polygons and find angle measures.

Explore

How many squares are in this design? (Hint: The answer is more than 16.)
30 (sixteen 1 · 1 squares, nine 2 · 2 squares, four 3 · 3 squares, one 4 · 4 square)

Investigation 1 Polygons

Polygons are flat, two-dimensional geometric figures that have these characteristics.

- They are made of line segments.
- Each segment touches exactly two other segments, one at each of its endpoints.

These shapes are polygons.

These shapes are not polygons.

Think & Discuss

Look at the shapes above that are not polygons. Explain why each of these shapes does not fit the definition of a polygon. See ①.

Polygons can be classified according to the number of sides they have. You have probably heard many of these names.

Name	Sides	Examples
Triangle	3	
Quadrilateral	4	
Pentagon	5	
Hexagon	6	
Heptagon	7	
Octagon	8	
Nonagon	9	
Decagon	10	

Lesson 1.1 Patterns in Geometry   **5**

Prefixes Refer to the Real-World Link and discuss the names for different polygons. Point out the prefixes used in these names, and ask students what other words they can think of that use these prefixes. Some prefixes are used less frequently and students may not be able to provide examples. In those cases, give them the examples below and have them look up the words in the dictionary as homework.

Prefix	Examples
tri-	triangle, tripod
quad-	quadruple, quadrilateral
penta-	pentathlon, pentagram
hexa-	hexose, hexapod
hepta-	heptarchy, heptameter
octa-	octopus, octet
nona-	nonagenarian
deca-	decathalon, decapod

Also, ask students why there is not a name for a two-sided polygon. Point out that if two segments meet only at the endpoints, they must make a "V" or they must make a straight line segment, neither of which is a polygon because not all of the endpoints meet. If students argue that the line segments could be placed on top of one another so the endpoints meet, point out that the result is actually one segment, not two, so there is no such thing as a two-sided polygon.

Real-World Link
Emphasize that polygons are named only by their number of sides and not by their angle measures.

Real World Links engage students with interesting facts and add to the problem-solving context with examples from real life.

Teacher Tips give practical suggestions for teaching lessons, organizing materials, managing collaborative group work, and more.

Math Link
A *diagonal* is a segment that connects two vertices of a polygon but is not a side of the polygon. In quadrilateral *ABCD*, the diagonal is $\overline{AC}$.

Most polygons with more than ten sides have no special name. A polygon with 11 sides is described as an *11-gon*, a polygon with 12 sides is a *12-gon*, and so on. Each of the polygons below is a 17-gon.

Each corner of a polygon, where two sides meet, is called a **vertex**. The plural of vertex is *vertices*. Labeling vertices with capital letters makes it easy to refer to a polygon by name.

Example

This figure can be seen as two triangles and one quadrilateral.

To name one of the polygons in the figure, list its vertices in order as you move around it in either direction. One name for the white triangle is △*ABC*. Other names are possible, including △*BCA* and △*ACB*. One name for the green triangle is △*ADC*.

The quadrilateral in the figure could be named quadrilateral *ABCD*, or *BCDA*, or *DCBA*, or *DABC*. All of these names list the vertices in order as you move around the quadrilateral. The name *ACBD* is *not* correct.

Worked out **Examples** provide direct instruction when appropriate for the content.

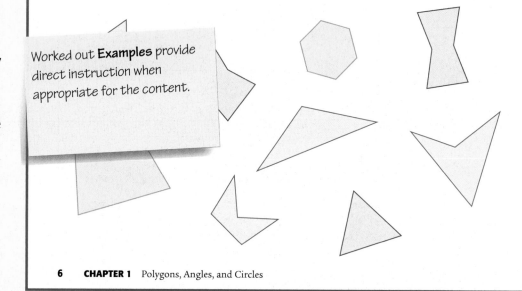

Reaching All Learners

OL On Level Some students may not think it is important to name the vertices in order for the quadrilateral in the example. Point out that if the vertices are not put in order, *ACBD* instead of *ABCD* for example, a diagonal of the quadrilateral may be included in the name.

Reaching All Learners strategies suggest adjustments for lessons and tailor instruction to encompass a wide variety of learning styles and modalities.

✓ Develop & Understand: A

You will now search for polygons in given figures. Each figure has a total score that is calculated by adding the following.

- 3 points for each triangle
- 4 points for each quadrilateral
- 5 points for each pentagon
- 6 points for each hexagon

As you work, try to discover a systematic way to find and list all the polygons in a figure. Be careful to give only one name for each polygon.

Record your work in a table like this one, which has already been started for Exercise 1.

Polygon	Names	Score
Triangle	ABC, ADC	6
Quadrilateral	ABCD	4
Pentagon		
Hexagon		
	Total Score	10

1. *See table above.*

2. *See below.*

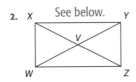

3. *See margin.*

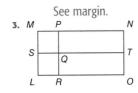

4. *See margin.*

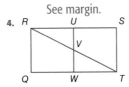

5. Now create your own figure that is worth at least 30 points. Label the vertices. List each of the triangles, quadrilaterals, pentagons, and hexagons in your figure. *See margin.*

2.

Polygon	Names	Score
Triangle	XYZ, XWZ, XYV, XWV, ZWV, ZVY, XYW, WYZ	24
Quadrilateral	WXYZ	4
Pentagon	YXWZV, XWZYV, WZYXV, ZYXWV	20
Hexagon		
	Total Score	48

Lesson 1.1 Patterns in Geometry **7**

Additional Answer

3.

Polygon	Names	Score
Triangle		
Quadrilateral	LMNO, LMPR, NORP, SMNT, LSTO, MPQS, NTQP, OTQR, LRQS	36
Pentagon		
Hexagon	PMLOTQ, PNOLSQ, RONMSQ, RLMNTQ	24

Additional Answers for Develop & Understand: A Exercises 4 and 5 are on page 55A.

✓ Develop & Understand: A

Suggested Grouping: Individuals

▶ **Exercise 1** Make sure students understand that the table shown on this page is for this exercise only. You may wish to give them copies of Lesson 1.1 Master 2, which has five blank copies of this table. Watch for students who do not name the quadrilateral correctly.

▶ **Exercises 2–4** Some students may need strategies to help them count the triangles and quadrilaterals and then look for their complements. For example, in Exercise 2, pentagon *YXWZV* includes everything in the figure except △*VYZ*. Others may choose one vertex (say, *X*) and count all the triangles that contain vertex *X* and then all the quadrilaterals that contain vertex *X*, and so on. Then they move on to vertex *Y* and count all the triangles that contain vertex *Y* but not vertex *X*, and so on. Point out that it is helpful to record all the names using the same direction, either clockwise or counterclockwise so they may notice if a polygon is listed more than once.

▶ **Exercise 3** Some students may think $\overline{SQ}$, $\overline{QT}$, $\overline{OR}$, and $\overline{RL}$ are sides of "quadrilateral" *LSQTORL*. Point out that *LSQTORL* is not a quadrilateral. A quadrilateral has exactly four vertices.

▶ **Exercise 5** Have students share their results for **Exercises 1–4** before doing this exercise and have them check how they named the polygons. This will help ensure that they understand the concepts. Use a transparency to highlight the polygons when there is a question because it may be difficult matching the names to the polygons without a visual connection.

Troubleshooting One of the difficulties some students encounter when studying geometric shapes is vocabulary. To help students keep the terminology clear, you may want to make a sheet of terms, with examples of each, or provide them with copies of Chapter 1 Master 1 for reference. Encourage students to add any new terms from future investigations to their vocabulary lists.

Share & **Summarize**

For **Exercise 1**, have students share their examples and explanations and make sure everyone agrees that they are correct.

For **Exercise 2**, the strategies students list are important. Students sometimes have difficulty explaining their strategies, so pair them up and have them explain the strategies to each other. Have them apply their strategies to example polygons they present.

The **Share & Summarize** *questions signal the end of each Investigation and are designed to bring closure to the day's activity.*

Share & Summarize

1. Draw two polygons. Also draw two shapes that are not polygons. Explain why the shapes that are not polygons do not fit the definition of a polygon.   Answers will vary.

2. In Exercises 1–5, you had to find ways to list all the polygons in a figure without repeating any. Describe one strategy you used.   See ①.

Investigation ② Angles

Vocabulary

angle

Materials

- paper polygons or pattern blocks

① Possible answer: I counted all the polygons containing a certain vertex first, then I moved on to other vertices. I counted a polygon and then counted the rest of the figure that did not contain that polygon. I always listed the vertices in counterclockwise order, so it was easier to spot repeats.

You probably already have a good idea about what an angle is. You may think about an angle as a rotation, or a turn, about a point. Examples include an arm bending at the elbow or hinged boards snapping shut at the start of a movie scene.

You may also think about an angle as two sides that meet at a point, like the hands of a clock or the vanes of a windmill.

Or you may think of an angle as a wedge, like a piece of cheese or a slice of pizza.

Investigation ②

On Your Own Exercises
Pages 18–23
Exercises 4–11, 18–20

Directions This investigation is designed to develop students' sense of angle as well as estimation techniques for angle measurement. Introduce angles informally by using the following activity.

Show students the path below, and ask them to write directions so that someone could follow this path exactly from A to B (without actually seeing the path).

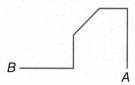

Possible directions: Walk two steps forward. Turn 90° to the left. Walk one step forward. Turn 45° to the left. Walk one step forward. Turn 45° to the left. Walk one step forward. Turn 90° to the right. Walk two steps forward.

Reaching All *Learners*

AL Approaching Level Ask students who still have difficulty identifying angles to give examples of real-life angles such as a partially opened book, the corner of a table or desk, or an open door.

In mathematics, an **angle** is defined as two rays with the same endpoint. A ray is straight, like a line. It has an endpoint where it starts, and it goes forever in the other direction.

Angles can be measured in *degrees*. Below are some angles with which you may be familiar.

- The angle at the vertex of a square measures 90°. You can think of a 90° angle as a rotation $\frac{1}{4}$ of the way around a circle.

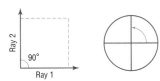

- Two rays pointing in opposite directions form a 180° angle. A 180° angle is a rotation $\frac{1}{2}$ of the way around a circle.

- A 360° angle is a rotation around a complete circle. In a 360° angle, the rays point in the same direction.

You can use 90°, 180°, and 360° angles to help estimate the measures of other angles. For example, the angle below is about a third of a 90° angle, so it has a measure of about 30°.

Angles Introduce the formal definition of *angle* using the concept of ray. You may need to discuss how a *ray* is different from a line or from a line segment.

Review the degree symbol (°) and discuss the benchmark angles 0°, 90°, 180°, and 360°. These angles provide a point of reference for measuring other angles. If there is a student in your class who likes to skateboard or snowboard, you might ask him or her to describe how those angles are used in the sport and demonstrate for the class what they mean.

Illustrate how to use benchmark angles to estimate the measures of other angles.

Real-World Link

Point out that the tip of the skateboard can be thought of as making a complete circle when there is a full turn (360°) and of as making a half-circle when there is a half turn (180°).

Reaching *All Learners*

OL **On Level** Students may notice that for each angle of 30° formed by a ray rotating counterclockwise, there is also an associated angle of 330° formed by the same ray rotating clockwise.

Think & Discuss

Ask students to offer as many ways as they can to figure out the angle measure that is marked in the star. In addition to the sample answer, some students may say that eight angles make 360°, so they divide 360° by 8. Others may say that two angles make 90°, so they divide 90° by 2.

You may find it helpful to have an overhead transparency of the design shown in the Think & Discuss. As you discuss the measures of the angles, fill in the angles that are adding to the benchmark in question so that students can visually see which angles have been included. For example, the figure below shows three angle measures that have been counted.

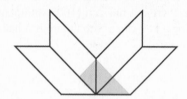

Teacher Tips In this exercise set, students develop their angle estimation skills. They will need pattern blocks or polygons cut from Lesson 1.1 Master 3.

✓ Develop & Understand: A

Suggested Grouping: Individuals

▶ **Exercise 1** Students may use one of these strategies to estimate the angle measures for these polygons.

Make designs like those in Think & Discuss by placing equal angles around a vertex. For example, in △ *FGE*, six equal angles measure 360°, so one angle measures 60°.

Compare benchmark angles. For example, the angles in square *ABCD* are 90°. Students can use a corner of a piece of paper or of an index card to confirm the measure.

Compare the angles to other angles whose sizes have already been determined. For example, ∠*KHI* is the same size as ∠*FGE*, so it is 60°. Similarly, ∠*LON* has the same measure as two of ∠*FGE*, so it is 120°.

① 45°; Possible explanation: Since there are eight identical angles that fill 360°, they must each measure 360 ÷ 8, or 45°.

Think & Discuss

Copies of the polygon at right can be arranged to form a star.

What is the measure of the angle that is marked in the star? How do you know?   See ①.

✓ Develop & Understand: A

1. You will be given several copies of each polygon below. Your job is to determine the angle measures for each polygon.

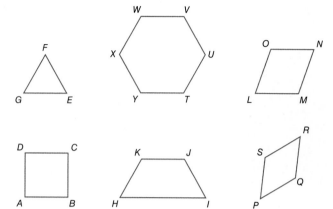

To find the measures of the angles, you can use 90°, 180°, and 360° angles as guides, and you can compare the angles of the polygons with one another.

Your answers should be a record of each vertex, *A–Y*, and the measure of the angle at that vertex. For many of the polygons, two or more of the angles are identical. So, you only have to find the measure of one of them.   See margin.

You will now use the angles you found in Exercise 1 to help estimate the measures of other angles.

Additional Answer

1.

Angles	Measure
P, R	30°
E, F, G, H, I, L, N	60°
A, B, C, D	90°
J, K, M, O, T, U, V, W, X, Y	120°
S, Q	150°

✅ Develop & Understand: B

Estimate the measure of each angle. To help make your estimates, you can compare the angles to 90°, 180°, and 360° angles and to the angles of the polygons in Exercise 1. For each angle, explain how you made your estimate.

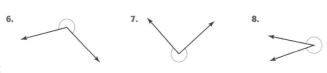

2. 45°; Possible explanation: It is about half the size of each angle of the square.

3. 210°; Possible answer: A circle can be completed with angle S, which is 150°.

4. 15°; Possible explanation: It is about half of angle R.

5. 300°; Possible explanation: A circle can be completed with the 60° angle of the triangle.

6. 240°; Possible explanation: It is the same as two of the 120° angles of the trapezoid, angles M and O.

7. 270°; Possible explanation: A circle can be completed with the 90° angle of the square.

8. 330°; Possible answer: The circle can be completed with one of the 30° angles of the rhombus, angle P or R.

Share & Summarize

1. Describe how you can estimate the measure of an angle.

2. Moria said the angles below have the same measure. Hannah said Angle 2 is larger than Angle 1. Who is correct? Explain.

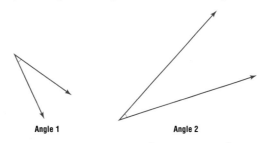

Angle 1   Angle 2

3. Explain the difference between a $\frac{1}{4}$-rotation and a $\frac{1}{2}$-rotation.

1. Possible answers: You can compare the angle to 90°, 180°, and 360° angles and to other angles whose measures you already know.

2. Moria; Possible explanation: An angle's size does not depend on the length of its rays, only the amount of the angle is "opened." The rays forming both angles actually go on forever. A picture shows only part of the rays.

3. Possible answer: A $\frac{1}{4}$-rotation is a 90° angle. A $\frac{1}{2}$-rotation is a 180° angle.

Lesson 1.1 Patterns in Geometry   **11**

On the Spot Assessment

Students may have trouble with the angles that are larger than 180°. Suggest that they extend one of the rays through the endpoint to indicate a 180° angle and estimate the measure of the angle formed by the new line and the ray that was not extended. Then they can add the two measures. For example, to estimate the measure of the angle in **Exercise 3**, extend the ray and estimate the measure of the small angle, about 30°. Add that measure to the measure of the straight angle, 180 ° + 30°, or 210°.

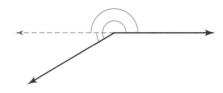

✅ Develop & Understand: B

Suggested Grouping: Pairs

▶ **Exercise 2** Emphasize that students should compare their angles to the angles of the polygons on page 10. Tell students they should look for fractions of benchmark angles. For example, this angle is about half the size of a 90° angle, so it is about 45°.

▶ **Exercises 3, 5, 6–8** When measuring angles greater than 180°, estimate the "other" smaller angle and then subtract the result from 360°. For example, for **Exercise 7**, the other angle is about 90°, so the angle to be measured is about 360° − 90°, or 270°.

▶ **Exercise 4** Compare the angle to ones whose measures are known. This angle is about half of the angle in **Exercise 2**, so it is about 22°.

Share & Summarize

For **Exercise 1**, have students list at least two different ways to estimate angles. If students do not mention the sample strategies listed in the notes for Develop & Understand, you may want to bring them up yourself.

Exercise 2 emphasizes the fact that the length of the rays does not affect the size of the angle. Students may argue that the Angle 2 picture is obviously larger; if so, clarify that when discussing whether an angle is larger, the *measure* of the angle is what is considered. Some students may better understand that the angles are the same if you ask them to draw an angle, estimate its measure, and then extend its rays. Ask students to estimate its measure again and determine whether the angle measure has changed.

Lesson 1.1 Patterns in Geometry   **11**

On Your Own Exercises
Pages 18–23
Exercises 12–15, 21–25

Classify Polygons In this investigation, students classify polygons according to type of shape as well as the following properties: concave/not concave, regular/not regular, line symmetry/no line symmetry. Students use circle diagrams as an organizational tool for classifying shapes.

Before students open their books, give them copies of Lesson 1.1 Master 4. This master shows the polygons on page 12. Ask students to quickly cut out the polygons and sort them into groups.

Many students will sort based on number of sides. Ask them to do it again, this time not using that characteristic. Explain there are other characteristics of polygons that can be used to group them together.

Teacher Tips Discuss the differences between *concave* and *convex* polygons. Point out the angles in the first set of figures that measure more than 180°.

Discuss the differences between *regular* and *irregular* polygons. Have students identify the characteristics of the irregular polygons on page 12. Demonstrate line *symmetry* with a paper rectangle. Show the two lines of symmetry by folding the rectangle lengthwise and widthwise. Ask students whether there are any other lines of symmetry. If students do not suggest folding along the diagonal, ask them why the diagonal is not a line of symmetry.

To determine if a polygon is concave or convex, stretch a rubber band around the polygon. The rubber band can touch all vertices of a convex polygon. A concave polygon will have a gap.

Example:

Gap ▷ ◁ Gap

Investigation ③ Classify Polygons

Vocabulary
concave polygon
line symmetry
regular polygon

Materials
- set of polygons and category labels
- large Venn diagram

Polygons can be divided into groups according to certain properties.

Concave polygons look like they are "collapsed" or have a "dent" on one or more sides. Any polygon with an angle measuring more than 180° is concave. The polygons below are concave.

The polygons below are not concave. Such polygons are sometimes called *convex polygons*.

Regular polygons have sides that are all the same length and angles that are all the same size. The polygons below are regular.

The polygons below are not regular. Such polygons are sometimes referred to as *irregular*.

A polygon has **line symmetry**, or *reflection symmetry*, when you can fold it in half along a line and the two halves match exactly. The "folding line" is called the *line of symmetry*.

Reaching All Learners

AL **Approaching Level** Have students who are having difficulty understanding line symmetry cut out the shapes in Lesson 1.1 Master 4 and work with folding them so the two halves match exactly. Monitor them so they make the folds accurately. Point out that the "folding line" is called the *line of symmetry*. Have them draw the line(s) of symmetry on the shapes.

The polygons below have line symmetry. The lines of symmetry are shown as dashed lines. Notice that three of the polygons have more than one line of symmetry.

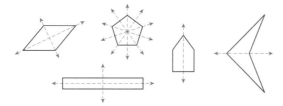

These polygons do not have line symmetry.

Think & Discuss

Consider the polygons below.

This diagram shows how these four polygons can be grouped into the categories *concave* and *not concave*.

 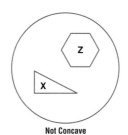

Concave   Not Concave

Now make a diagram to show how the four polygons can be grouped into the categories *line symmetry* and *not concave*. Use a circle to represent each category.   See margin.

Line Symmetry If students cannot find a line of symmetry, ask them to trace the polygon onto a sheet of paper, cut it out, and then try to find the line of symmetry by folding. Nonrectangular parallelograms may be especially tricky for some students, so ask students to experiment finding a line of symmetry with a paper parallelogram. If students do not understand why a regular hexagon has line symmetry, explain that the angles in the polygon have as much to do with line symmetry as the sides, and ask them to experiment with folding paper hexagons.

Think & Discuss

Ask students how to group the polygons as those with line symmetry and those that are not concave. If necessary, suggest that polygon Y must be placed outside both regions because it does not have either characteristic. Students should see that polygon Z fits both criteria. Some students may suggest adding an extra circle labeled *both;* others may suggest putting one copy of the shape in each region. Give your class time to suggest overlapping the circles, or discuss how using overlapping circles is an option.

Real-World Link
Point out that if a figure has line symmetry, it can be folded along the line of symmetry so that each side of the resulting "half" figure is identical.

Lesson 1.1   Patterns in Geometry   **13**

Additional Answer for the Think & Discuss
Possible answer (students may draw the circles with no overlap and draw polygon Z twice, once in each circle):

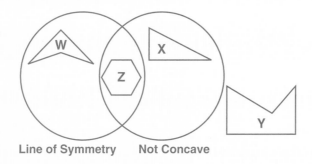

Line of Symmetry   Not Concave

⊘ Develop & Understand: A

Suggested Grouping: Groups of 3 or 4

▶ **Exercise 1** For this game, each group will need a copy of Lesson 1.1 Master 5, which reproduces the set of polygons and labels, and scissors. They might also use one copy of Lesson 1.1 Master 6 or make their own Venn diagrams to use when classifying polygons. Students can also use attribute or pattern blocks instead of the paper polygons on Lesson 1.1 Master 5. Emphasize that students can write the names of the polygons, rather than drawing the shapes, to record their work.

Math Link

For this game, the region where all three circles intersect represents the polygons that have the attributes common to all three circles.

> **Math Links** remind students about information they should already know.

Additional Examples See the polygons on page 14 or Lesson 1.1 Master 5 to answer the questions below.

1. What do polygons *G, H,* and *Q* have in common? They are all concave.

2. Complete a two-circle Venn diagram with the labels *quadrilateral* and *hexagon*.

3. There should be no polygons in the overlap of the circles for **Exercise 2**. Why? A polygon cannot be a quadrilateral and a hexagon at the same time.

> **Additional Examples** offer extra worked-out examples. Use them to assist struggling students or as an impromptu assessment tool.

⊘ Develop & Understand: A

You will now play a polygon-classification game with your group. Your group will need a set of polygons, category labels, and a large Venn diagram.

Here are the polygons used for the game.

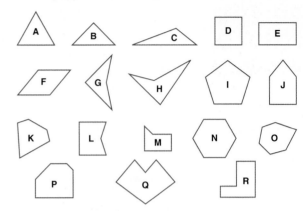

Math Link
A Venn diagram uses circles to represent relationships among sets of objects.

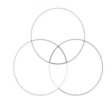

Here are the category labels.

Regular	Concave	Triangle
Not Regular	Not Concave	Not Triangle
Quadrilateral	Pentagon	Hexagon
Not Quadrilateral	Not Pentagon	Not Hexagon
Line Symmetry	No Line Symmetry	

1. As a warm-up for the game, put one of the labels *Regular, Concave,* and *Triangle* next to each of the circles on the diagram. Work with your group to place each of the polygons in the correct region of the diagram.

   Record your work. Sketch the three-circle diagram, label each circle, and record the polygons you placed in each region of the diagram. Record just the letters. You do not need to draw the polygons.

1.

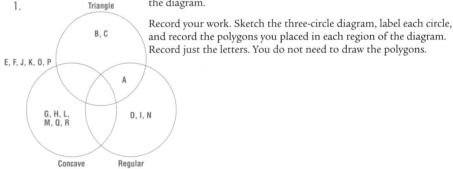

14   CHAPTER 1 Polygons, Angles, and Circles

2. Now you are ready to play the game. Choose one member of your group to be the leader. Use the following rules.   Answers will vary.

- The leader selects three category cards and looks at them *without showing them to the other group members.*
- The leader uses the cards to label the regions, placing one card *face down* next to each circle.
- The other group members take turns selecting a polygon. The leader places the polygon in the correct region of the diagram.
- After a player's shape has been placed in the diagram, he or she may guess what the labels are. The first player to guess all three labels correctly wins.

At the end of each game, work with your group to place the remaining shapes. Then copy the final diagram. Take turns being the leader until each member of the group has had a chance.

3. Work with your group to create a diagram in which no polygons are placed in an overlapping region, that is, no polygon belongs to more than one category.

4. Work with your group to create a diagram in which all of the polygons are placed either in the overlapping regions or outside the circles, that is, no polygon belongs to just one category.

Share & Summarize

1. Determine what the labels on this diagram must be. Use the category labels on page 14.

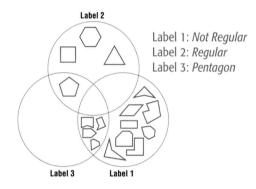

Label 2

Label 1: *Not Regular*
Label 2: *Regular*
Label 3: *Pentagon*

Label 3   Label 1

2. Explain why there are no polygons in the overlap of the Label 1 circle and the Label 2 circle.

3. Explain why there are no polygons in the Label 3 circle that are not also in one of the other circles.
Every pentagon must be either regular or not regular.

---

3. Possible answer: diagram with labels *Pentagon, Triangle,* and *Hexagon.*

4. Possible answer: diagram with labels *Not Pentagon, Not Triangle,* and *Not Hexagon*

Target Market

Men   18–34

Exercise 3–5 times per week

Ideal Customer: ☐
1.62 Million

Possible Customer: ▨
6.8 Million

Real-World Link
Venn diagrams are named after John Venn (1834–1923) of England, who made them popular. Venn diagrams are used in business to create visual models.

2. A polygon is either regular or not regular; it cannot be both.

▶ **Exercise 2** Students play the game. You may want to decide on a set amount of time for the game depending on the length of your class period. Be sure to leave time for students to complete **Exercises 3 and 4** as well as a Share & Summarize discussion.

▶ **Exercises 3 and 4** Students are told to create Venn diagrams using different categories than in **Exercise 2**. Ask students to explain how they chose their categories. They should understand that using "Not" to form a category (for example, Not Triangle) gives them a category that is the complement of a category (Triangle in this case).

Real-World Link
Point out that visual models like Venn diagrams are used because they can convey information quickly and concisely.

Share & Summarize
Use these questions to see whether students understand the vocabulary or how to use Vann diagrams. For **Exercise 1**, have students share answers and discuss any differences.

For **Exercises 2 and 3** point out the key features of a Venn diagram. Students' answers will show how well they understand Venn diagrams.

Reaching All Learners

ELL **English Language Learners** The directions for the game described in Exercise 2 may be difficult for some students to understand. Play the game once as a class, or condense the rules as follows:

- Leader picks three cards. Do *not* show them to the group.
- Leader places one card face down by each circle.
- Player picks a polygon and asks the leader where to place it. Leader answers.
- Player guesses what the cards say.

Inquiry
Investigation 4

Suggested Grouping: Individuals

Materials and Preparation

Students will need linkage strips and fasteners.

Triangle Sides In this investigation, students look at the relationship among the sides of a triangle.

Begin the investigation by showing students how to split various polygons into triangles. Challenge students to draw polygons on the board that cannot be split, and then let other students show how to split them.

Demonstrate how to make a triangle by using linkage strips to make a 2-unit-by-3-unit-by-4-unit triangle, perhaps projecting it on the overhead so all students can see. Explain how to measure the length of the sides using the linkage strips. (The distance from one hole to the next is one unit.) Ask students to name characteristics of the triangle such as *convex, irregular,* and *has no lines of symmetry.*

Build the Triangles

▶ **Exercise 1** Be sure students understand how to use linkage strips to make the triangles. Have students created their own linkage strips using copies of Lesson 1.1 Master 7 on card stock. As students try to build a different triangle, ask:

- Is it possible to connect the sides in a different order?

- Can you press on the sides of the triangle to change its shape?

> In **Inquiry Investigations,** which appear once per chapter, students explore and reinforce concepts through application of the scientific method.

Inquiry
Investigation 4 Triangle Sides

Materials
- linkage strips and fasteners

In many ways, triangles are the simplest polygons. They are the polygons with the fewest sides. Any polygon can be split into triangles. For this reason, learning about triangles can help you understand other polygons as well.

In this investigation, you will build triangles from linkage strips. The triangles will look like the one below. The sides of this triangle are 2, 3, and 4 units long. Notice that a "unit" is the space between two holes.

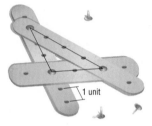
1 unit

Do you think any three segments can be joined to make a triangle? You will investigate this question.

Build the Triangles

1. Copy the table on the next page. Do the following steps for each row.
   - Try to build a triangle with the given side lengths.
   - In the "Triangle?" column, enter "yes" if you could make a triangle and "no" if you could not.
   - If you could make a triangle, try to make a *different* triangle from the same side lengths. (Hint: For two triangles to be different, they must have different shapes.) In the "Different Triangle?" column, enter "yes" if you could make another triangle and "no" if you could not.

Reaching All Learners

(AL) Approaching Level The directions for **Exercise 1** may be difficult. Reading them with the class and constructing the first triangle as an example can help. Make sure students understand that the column "Different Triangle?" is asking whether two or more different triangles can have the same side lengths. Two triangles are different if they cannot be turned or flipped so that they match up perfectly.

2. No; Possible explanation: If you connect the 4-unit segments in a straight line, they will not reach the ends of the 10-unit segment, so there is no way to bend them to reach the ends of the 10-unit segment.

3. Yes; Possible explanation: The 10-unit and 15-unit segments connected together are longer than the 16-unit segment, so you can bend them where they connect to reach the ends of the 16-unit segment.

Side 1	Side 2	Side 3	Triangle?	Different Triangle?
4 units	4 units	4 units	Yes	No
5 units	4 units	3 units	Yes	No
4 units	4 units	2 units	Yes	No
4 units	4 units	1 unit	Yes	No
4 units	3 units	1 unit	No	
4 units	2 units	2 units	No	
3 units	5 units	6 units	Yes	No
3 units	3 units	1 unit	Yes	No
3 units	2 units	2 units	Yes	No
3 units	2 units	1 unit	No	
3 units	1 unit	1 unit	No	

Analyze the Results

2. Do you think you could make a triangle with segments 4, 4, and 10 units long? Explain your answer.

3. Do you think you could make a triangle with segments 10, 15, and 16 units long? Explain your answer.

What Did You Learn? 4, 5. See margin.

4. Describe a rule you can use to determine whether three given segments will make a triangle. Test your rule on a few cases different from those in the table until you are convinced it is correct.

5. Do you think you can make more than one triangle with the same set of side lengths? Explain.

Analyze the Table Students should write "no" in the "Triangle?" column if the sum of each pair of two sides of the triangle is not greater than the third. For example, strips with length four units, three units, and one unit do not make a triangle because 3 + 1 is not greater than 4.

Analyze the Results

▶ **Exercises 2 and 3** Have students who are unsure of the relationship use linkage strips to try to make a model of each triangle. Encourage them to determine how long they would need to make the third side in order to make a triangle.

What Did You Learn?

▶ **Exercise 5** Students should draw conclusions based on what they have tried so far.

Teacher Tips After filling in the table for "Build the Triangles," point out the Triangle Inequality Theorem: The sum of the lengths of any two sides of a triangle is greater than the length of the third side. Give several examples of how to apply the theorem to three side lengths.

Additional Answers

4. Possible answer: If the sum of the lengths of the two shorter segments is greater than the length of the longest segment, the segments can make a triangle.

5. No; Possible explanation: In each case we tried, at most, one triangle was possible. We could not press in the sides or vertices to create a different shape.

On the Spot Assessment

For **Exercise 4**, watch for students who do not see the relationship between the sums of the side lengths. Encourage them to look back and think about why the triangle in **Exercise 2** could not be made.

On the Spot Assessment points out common errors and gives ideas for remediation. Teachers can quickly correct student errors before problems become persistent.

Investigation 1
Pages 4–8
Practice & Apply: 1–3
Connect & Extend: 16, 17

Investigation 2
Pages 8–11
Practice & Apply: 4–11
Connect & Extend: 18–20

Investigation 3
Pages 12–17
Practice & Apply: 12–15
Connect & Extend: 21–25

Assign Anytime
Mixed Review: 26–36

▶ **Exercises 1 and 3** You may want to make a transparency of each figure to facilitate discussion when reviewing the answers.

▶ **Exercise 2** It will be difficult to share the names of the polygons in the figure as a class because students will be using different letters to name the vertices. For this reason, you may want to collect answers and check each student's work.

▶ **Exercise 3** Ask students to name the different polygons they found. Make sure the class agrees that the naming is correct. You might also ask for other possible names for each polygon.

> **Practice & Apply** exercises provide opportunities for students to reinforce and directly apply the skills and concepts they learn in each Investigation.

> **On Your Own Exercises** at the end of each lesson offer daily opportunities for independent assignments and homework, and opportunities for teachers to assess student learning.

Practice & Apply

1. How many triangles are in this figure? Do not count just the smallest triangles. **13**

2a.

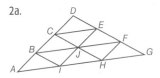

2. Look at the figure in Exercise 1.

a. Copy the figure. Label each vertex with a capital letter.

b. In your figure, find at least one of each of the following polygons.

- quadrilateral
- pentagon
- hexagon

Possible answer:
Quadrilateral *BCHI*,
Pentagon *CEFHA*,
Hexagon *DBIJHF*

Use your vertex labels to name each shape.

c. Find the polygon with the maximum number of sides in your figure. Use the vertex labels to name the shape. Possible answer:
Heptagon *IBCEFHJ*

3. List all the polygons in the figure below. Compute the figure's score using the following point values.

- 3 points for each triangle
- 4 points for each quadrilateral
- 5 points for each pentagon
- 6 points for each hexagon

Record your work in a table like the one below.

Polygon	Names	Score
Triangle	*EFC, BGF, BCF*	9
Quadrilateral	*ABCD, AGED, BGEC, BCEF, BCFG*	20
Pentagon	*ABFCD, ABFED, DCFGA*	15
Hexagon	*FGADCB, FEDABC*	12
	Total Score	56

4. 72°; Since 5 of the same angle make 360°, one has measure 360 ÷ 5.

5. 36°; Since 10 of the same angle make 360°, one has measure 360 ÷ 10.

6. 180°; Since 2 of the same angle make 360°, one has measure 360 ÷ 2.

7. About 51.4°; Since 7 of the same angle make 360°, one has measure 360 ÷ 7.

In Exercises 4–7, several identical angles have the same vertex. Find the measure of the marked angle. Explain how you found it.

4.

5.

6.

7.

Real-World Link
During a Ferris wheel ride, the wheel makes several complete rotations.

8. A 180° angle is sometimes called a *straight angle.* Explain why that name makes sense.   The two rays that make the angle form a straight line.

9. You know that a 360° rotation is one complete rotation around a circle. Find the degree measures for each of these rotations.

   a. half a rotation   180°

   b. two complete rotations   720°

   c. $1\frac{1}{2}$ rotations   540°

   d. three complete rotations   1,080°

   e. $2\frac{1}{4}$ rotations   810°

   f. five and one-half rotations   1,980°

10. Draw two angles that each measure more than 90°. Explain how you know they measure more than 90°.

11. Draw two angles that each measure less than 90°. Explain how you know they measure less than 90°.   Angles will vary. Possible explanation: They are smaller than the angle at the corner of a book.

10. Angles will vary. Possible explanation: They are larger than the angle at the corner of a book.

▶ **Exercises 4–7** Some students may just approximate the angle measures based on the activities completed on page 11. Although this is correct, explain that they can find the exact angle measure since they know all of the angles around the given vertex are the same size. Emphasize that the approximation is always a good first step because it helps to evaluate whether the calculation makes sense. This is especially useful when students divide incorrectly or do not remember where to place the decimal point. Students are most likely to make this mistake in **Exercise 7**.

Real-World Link
The Ferris wheel was introduced by George Ferris at the World's Columbian Exposition in 1893. A Ferris wheel typically carries 50 to 100 passengers.

► **Exercise 12 Extension** Ask students what kind of polygon would be placed in the three sections that do not have any figures. They should recognize that an equilateral triangle could be placed in the overlap of the three circles. No polygon can be placed in the overlap of the circles labeled *triangle* and *regular* since that figure would be an equilateral triangle with all three characteristics. No polygon can be placed in the circle labeled *regular* without also being placed in *line symmetry* because all regular polygons have line symmetry.

► **Exercises 13–15** If time permits, have students share their figures. There is only one possible shape for **Exercise 13** (a square), although it can be different sizes.

► **Exercise 16** When assigning this exercise, review the definition of *diagonal*. Have students look at the diagonal drawn for the polygon at the far right, and tell them that when a diagonal is outside of a polygon, the polygon is concave.

The exercises in **Connect & Extend** relate student learning to other mathematical topics and strands.

12a. Label 1: Regular
Label 2: Line Symmetry
Label 3: Triangle

12b. Shape A: in the overlap of all three circles
Shape E: in the Line Symmetry (Label 2) circle
Shape F: in the Line Symmetry (Label 2) circle

Connect & Extend

14. Possible polygon:

15. Any isosceles triangle that is not equilateral will work.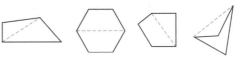

12. The diagram shows the result of one round of the game of polygon classification described on page 14.

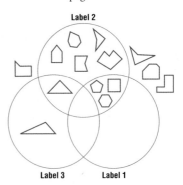

a. Figure out what the labels must be. Use the category labels from the polygon-classification game.

b. Where would you place each of these shapes?

In Exercises 13–15, draw a polygon that fits the given description, if possible. If it is not possible, say so.

13. a regular polygon with four sides

14. a concave polygon with a line of symmetry

15. a triangle with just one line of symmetry

16. A *diagonal* of a polygon is a segment that connects two vertices but is not a side of the polygon. In each polygon below, the dashed segment is one of the diagonals.

The number of diagonals you can draw from a vertex of a polygon depends on the number of vertices the polygon has.

a. Copy each of these regular polygons. On each polygon, choose a vertex. Draw every possible diagonal from that vertex.

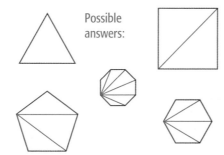

Possible answers:

b. Copy and complete the table.

Polygon	Vertices	Diagonals from a Vertex
Triangle	3	0
Quadrilateral	4	1
Pentagon	5	2
Hexagon	6	3
Heptagon	7	4
Octagon	8	5

16c. Number of diagonals = number of vertices − 3

16d. Possible answer: If you pick a vertex, you cannot draw a diagonal from the vertex to itself. You cannot draw a diagonal from the vertex to the vertices on either side of it. That leaves (number of vertices − 3) vertices to which you can draw a diagonal.

c. Describe a rule that connects a polygon's number of vertices to the number of diagonals that can be drawn from each vertex.

d. Explain how you know your rule will work for polygons with any number of vertices.

e. Challenge Describe a rule for predicting the *total number of diagonals* you can draw if you know the number of vertices in a polygon. Explain how you found your rule. Add a column to your table to help you organize your thinking.

Total Diagonals
0
2
5
9
14
20

17. Look for polygons in your home or school. Describe at least three different polygons that you find. Tell where you found them. Answers will vary.

Lesson 1.1 Patterns in Geometry **21**

▶ **Exercise 16b** When discussing students' answers, you may want to have the table for **Part b** already made to facilitate the discussion. Most students should be able to see the pattern for the number of diagonals from a vertex, but they may have difficulty finding the rule for the total number of diagonals in **Part e**.

The sequence rule (add 2, add 3, add 4, and so on) is the easiest for students to see, but the explicit rule, while easier to use, may require more explanation.

Additional Answer
16e. See completed column in Part e; Possible rules and explanations:
- total diagonals = number of vertices × (number of vertices − 3) ÷ 2; There are (number of vertices − 3) diagonals from each vertex, and there are (number of vertices) vertices. That makes (number of vertices − 3) × (number of vertices) diagonals. But this counts each diagonal twice (once for each vertex it connects), so divide by 2.
- The sequence in the second column is 0, 2, 5, 9, 14, 20, … . The pattern is add 2, add 3, add 4, and so on. This sequence can be continued to find the total number of diagonals for any polygon.

▶ **Exercise 19** Some students may mistake ∠*b* for a 90° angle. Point out that the angle mark indicates the larger angle.

▶ **Exercise 19 Extension** Make accurate drawings of 90°, 45°, and 30° angles on paper, and have students cut out their own copies. Using these angle wedges, have students sketch as many different angles as they can in 10 minutes. They can use an angle more than once. Have students order the angles they made from smallest to largest. Then give students a set of ten different angles, and ask them to estimate their measures using the angles they constructed.

▶ **Exercise 20** Students explore the relationship between the degree measure of a central angle and the fractional part of a circle formed by the rays of that angle, although they are not introduced to the terminology. For **Part b**, some students may determine the fractional part is $\frac{1}{6}$, because it is half the size of the $\frac{1}{3}$ wedge. Others may see that there are 360° in the whole circle. The other areas take up 120°, 90°, 45°, and 45°. This leaves 60° for the science wedge, and 60° is $\frac{1}{6}$ of 360°. A more extensive review of fractions follows in Chapter 2.

▶ **Exercise 23 Extension** You may want to share another pattern involving connecting midpoints, which leads to the famous fractal shape called the Sierpinski Gasket.

Quick Check
Informal Assessment Students should be able to:

✔ name polygons and classify them by regularity, concavity, and line symmetry

✔ use Venn diagrams to classify objects

✔ find the measures of identical angles summing to 90°, 180°, or 360°

✔ estimate angle measures

✔ determine whether three segments or angles could form a triangle

21. *Rule:* Draw a regular polygon with one more side than the preceding polygon.

23. *Rule:* Connect in order the midpoints of the innermost square of the preceding shape.

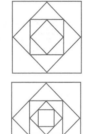

18. Find three angles in your home or school with measures equal to 90°, three with measures less than 90°, and three with measures greater than 90°. Describe where you found each angle. Answers will vary.

19. Order the angles below from smallest to largest. *a, d = e, c, b*

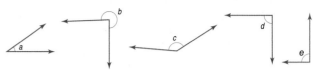

20. **Statistics** In a survey for the school yearbook, students were asked to name their favorite class. Conor made a circle graph to display the results. He forgot to label the wedges.

   a. Of the students surveyed, $\frac{1}{3}$ liked math best. Which color wedge represents these students? What is the angle measure of that wedge? Orange, 120°

   b. Conor remembers that he used light blue to represent students who like science best. What fraction of the students surveyed chose science as their favorite subject? $\frac{1}{6}$

   c. Drama and English tied with $\frac{1}{8}$ of the students choosing each. Which wedges represent drama and English? What is the angle measure of each wedge? Red and purple, 45°

In Exercises 21–23, describe a rule for creating each shape based on the preceding shape. Then draw the next two shapes.

21. 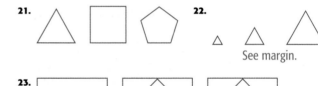   22.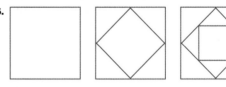

See margin.

23.

Additional Answer
22. Rule: Draw a regular triangle with sides twice as long as those of the preceding triangle.

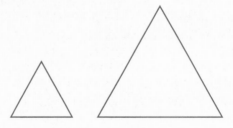

25. Possible answer: A polygon is a two-dimensional geometric figure. It can be identified by its number of sides. An angle is two rays with a common endpoint, which is the vertex. Angles are measured in degrees. A triangle is a polygon with three sides.

Mixed Review

31. Three hundred, twenty-four

32. Six hundred, fourteen

33. One thousand, twenty-five

34. Four thousand, six hundred, one

35. Ten thousand, eight hundred, nine

36. Twelve thousand, six hundred, forty

24. Circle diagrams, like those you used to classify polygons, are sometimes used to solve logic puzzles like this one.

   Camp Maple Leaf offers two sports, soccer and swimming. Of 30 campers, 24 play soccer, 20 swim, and 4 play no sport at all. How many campers both swim and play soccer?

   The diagram below includes a circle for each sport. The 4 outside the circles represents the four campers that do not play either sport. Use the diagram to help you solve the logic puzzle.

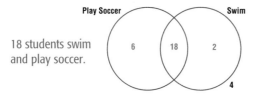

   18 students swim and play soccer.

25. **In Your Own Words** Explain what each of the following words means. Give at least two facts related to each word.

   • polygon   • angle   • triangle

For Exercises 26–28, find each sum or difference without using a calculator.

26. $5,853 - 788$ $5,065$ **27.** $1,054 + 1,492$ $2,546$ **28.** $47,745 - 2,943$ $44,802$

29. Write *thirty-two thousand, five hundred sixty-three* in standard form. $32,563$

30. Write *fourteen million, three hundred two thousand, two* in standard form. $14,302,002$

For Exercises 31–36, write each number in words.

31. 324   **32.** 614   **33.** 1,025

34. 4,601   **35.** 10,809   **36.** 12,640

For Exercises 37–42, find each product or quotient without using a calculator.

37. $15 \cdot 10$ 150 **38.** $24 \cdot 3$ 72 **39.** $51 \cdot 4$ 204

40. $72 \div 9$ 8 **41.** $56 \div 7$ 8 **42.** $480 \div 80$ 6

Additional Answers for Quick Quiz
4. Possible answer:

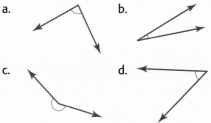

Line Symmetry   Concave

5. 6 cm or 7.5 cm; the sum of any two sides must be more than the third side. So, the third side must be less than 8 cm.

1. In the diagram below, find a triangle, a quadrilateral, a pentagon, and a hexagon. Name each shape using vertex labels.

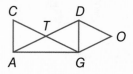

   Triangles: *CAT, CAG, GAT, GAD, GTD, DOG;*
   Quadrilaterals: *ADOG, TDOG;*
   Pentagon: *CAGDT;*
   Hexagon: *CAGODT*

2. Which one of the angles shown is the closest to 53°? Explain your answer.
   Angle *d*; it's only a little more than 45° while Angle *a* is nearly 90°, Angle *b* is far less than 45°, and Angle *c* is more than 180°.

   a.   b.

   c.   d.

   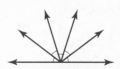

3. Each of the angles marked below is the same size. Find the measure of one of the marked angles and explain how you found it. The total of all 5 angles is 180°. So, each angle must measure 180° ÷ 5, or 36°.

4. In the Venn diagram shown, draw an appropriate polygon in each region (including a polygon that is outside both circles). If you cannot find a polygon for one of the regions, explain why.

5. Which of the lengths below could be the length of the third side of a triangle with sides measuring 3 cm and 5 cm? Explain your reasoning.

   6 cm   7.5 cm   8 cm   9.2 cm   10 cm

Angles

In this lesson, students get a brief review of the benchmark angles they studied in Lesson 1.1. They learn how to use a protractor to measure angles. They learn how to classify angles with measures greater than 0° and less than 180° as acute, right, or obtuse angles. Perpendicular lines and segments are defined as pairs of lines or segments that intersect to form right angles.

Students learn what is meant by vertical angles and learn that vertical angles have the same measure. Next, students measure angles of triangles and compute their angle sums. They confirm that the angle sum for any triangle is 180°. They also discover how to find the angle sums for polygons with more than three sides by dividing the polygons into triangles.

Objectives

▶ To measure angles by using a protractor

▶ To classify angles whose measures are greater than 0° and less than 180° as acute, right, or obtuse

▶ To find the sum of the angles of any polygon given the number of sides of the polygon

*The **Objectives** list summarizes the main mathematical concepts presented in the lesson.*

Advance Preparation

You may want to provide Lesson 1.2 Master 1 to facilitate class discussion while presenting new topics, including measuring angles and finding the sum of the interior angles of a polygon.

*The suggestions found in **Advance Preparation** give tips in preparing for the lesson that might not be apparent from reading the materials list.*

	Summary	Materials	On Your Own Exercises (pp. 35–39)	Assessment Opportunities
Investigation 1 (p. 25) Pacing: 2 days	Students learn to use a protractor to measure angles and to classify angles whose measures are greater than 0° and less than 180° as acute, right, or obtuse.	Lesson 1.2 Master 1, protractors, rulers	Practice & Apply: 1–13 Connect & Extend: 20, 21 Mixed Review: 25–31	• Share & Summarize (p. 29)
Investigation 2 (p. 30) Pacing: 1 day	Students measure angles and use reasoning to discover how measures of vertical angles are related; they then discover how to find the sum of the angle measures of any polygon, given the number of sides of the polygon.	rulers, protractors	Practice & Apply: 14–19 Connect & Extend: 22–24 Mixed Review: 25–31	• On the Spot Assessment (p. 31) • Share & Summarize (p. 34) • Troubleshooting (p. 34)

Leveled Lesson Resources

CRM *Available in:* **Chapter 1 Resource Masters**

Study Guide and Intervention (p. 28) AL

Lesson 1.2 Study Guide and Intervention
Angles

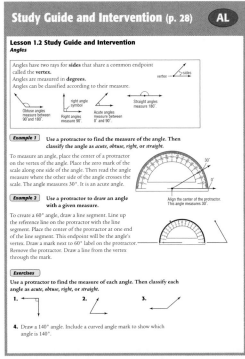

Angles have two rays for **sides** that share a common endpoint called the **vertex**.
Angles are measured in **degrees**.
Angles can be classified according to their measure.

Example 1 Use a protractor to find the measure of the angle. Then classify the angle as *acute, obtuse, right, or straight.*

To measure an angle, place the center of a protractor on the vertex of the angle. Place the zero mark of the scale along one side of the angle. Then read the angle measure where the other side of the angle crosses the scale. The angle measures 30°. It is an acute angle.

Example 2 Use a protractor to draw an angle with a given measure.

To create a 60° angle, draw a line segment. Line up the reference line on the protractor with the line segment. Place the center of the protractor at one end of the line segment. This endpoint will be the angle's vertex. Draw a mark next to 60° label on the protractor. Remove the protractor. Draw a line from the vertex through the mark.

Exercises

Use a protractor to find the measure of each angle. Then classify each angle as *acute, obtuse, right,* or *straight.*

1.   2.   3.

4. Draw a 140° angle. Include a curved angle mark to show which angle is 140°.

Skills Practice (p. 29) AL OL

Lesson 1.2 Skills Practice
Angles

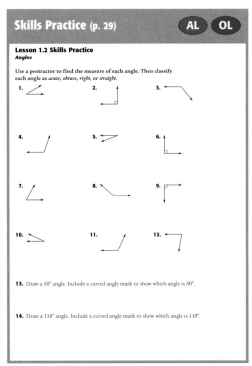

Use a protractor to find the measure of each angle. Then classify each angle as *acute, obtuse, right,* or *straight.*

1.   2.   3.

4.   5.   6.

7.   8.   9.

10.   11.   12.

13. Draw a 50° angle. Include a curved angle mark to show which angle is 50°.

14. Draw a 110° angle. Include a curved angle mark to show which angle is 110°.

Problem-Solving Practice (p. 30) AL OL

Lesson 1.2 Problem-Solving Practice
Angles

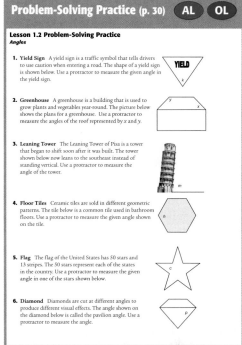

1. **Yield Sign** A yield sign is a traffic symbol that tells drivers to use caution when entering a road. The shape of a yield sign is shown below. Use a protractor to measure the given angle in the yield sign.

2. **Greenhouse** A greenhouse is a building that is used to grow plants and vegetables year-round. The picture below shows the plans for a greenhouse. Use a protractor to measure the angles of the roof represented by *x* and *y*.

3. **Leaning Tower** The Leaning Tower of Pisa is a tower that began to shift soon after it was built. The tower shown below now leans to the southeast instead of standing vertical. Use a protractor to measure the angle of the tower.

4. **Floor Tiles** Ceramic tiles are sold in different geometric patterns. The tile below is a common tile used in bathroom floors. Use a protractor to measure the given angle shown on the tile.

5. **Flag** The flag of the United States has 50 stars and 13 stripes. The 50 stars represent each of the states in the country. Use a protractor to measure the given angle in one of the stars shown below.

6. **Diamond** Diamonds are cut at different angles to produce different visual effects. The angle shown on the diamond below is called the pavilion angle. Use a protractor to measure the angle.

Enrichment (p. 31) BL

Lesson 1.2 Enrichment
Angles

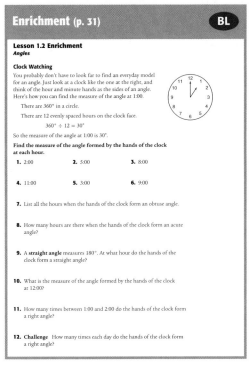

Clock Watching
You probably don't have to look far to find an everyday model for an angle. Just look at a clock like the one at the right, and think of the hour and minute hands as the sides of an angle. Here's how you can find the measure of the angle at 1:00.

There are 360° in a circle.

There are 12 evenly spaced hours on the clock face.

360° ÷ 12 = 30°

So the measure of the angle at 1:00 is 30°.

Find the measure of the angle formed by the hands of the clock at each hour.

1. 2:00   2. 5:00   3. 8:00

4. 11:00   5. 3:00   6. 9:00

7. List all the hours when the hands of the clock form an obtuse angle.

8. How many hours are there when the hands of the clock form an acute angle?

9. A **straight angle** measures 180°. At what hour do the hands of the clock form a straight angle?

10. What is the measure of the angle formed by the hands of the clock at 12:00?

11. How many times between 1:00 and 2:00 do the hands of the clock form a right angle?

12. **Challenge** How many times each day do the hands of the clock form a right angle?

Lesson Quick Quiz (p. 32) AL OL BL

Lesson 1.2 Quick Quiz
Angles

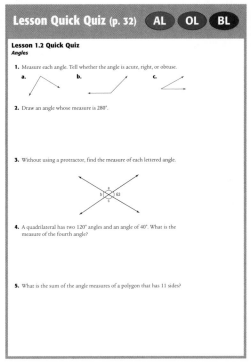

1. Measure each angle. Tell whether the angle is acute, right, or obtuse.

a.   b.   c.

2. Draw an angle whose measure is 280°.

3. Without using a protractor, find the measure of each lettered angle.

4. A quadrilateral has two 120° angles and an angle of 40°. What is the measure of the fourth angle?

5. What is the sum of the angle measures of a polygon that has 11 sides?

Lesson Masters 1–2 (pp. 33 and 34)

Lesson 1.2 Master 1
Angles

Investigation 1: Think & Discuss

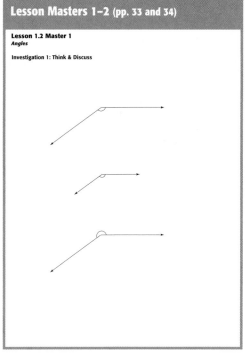

Additional Lesson Resources

Teacher Tech Tools
- TeacherWorks
- ExamView Assessment Suite
- Classroom Presentation Toolkit
- Advance Tracker

Student Tech Tools
- StudentWorks Plus
- Math Online eGlossary •
  Concepts in Motion

Other Print Products
- Investigation Notebook and Reflection Journal
- Quick Review Math Handbook

Introduce

Rotations Take time to review angles from Lesson 1.1 with the class. Using a yardstick, draw a long, horizontal segment on the board. Place the yardstick directly on top of the segment so that the left ends coincide. Then rotate the yardstick counterclockwise, keeping the two endpoints in contact with the board. Ask the class to call out "stop" when you reach the 90° position. Then continue the rotation. Ask the class to call out "stop" when you reach the 180° position.

Think & Discuss

Put the diagrams on the board and analyze them by asking additional questions: In the middle diagram, can you find a 60° angle? Yes

How many of them do you see? Two

Call on a volunteer to go to the board and point out the two 60° angles contained in the middle diagram.

Next, ask: How many 90° angles can you find in the third diagram? Three

Call on a volunteer to point them out. Then ask for angles of other sizes that can be found in the third diagram, and have volunteers highlight them. Some possibilities: 135°, 180°, 225°, 315°, and 360°

Math Link

You may need to point out that angle rotations are counterclockwise from a ray pointing to the right. This corresponds to lining up the ray on the reference line of a protractor, or the "0°" position of the protractor.

Math Link

You can think of an angle as a rotation. A 360° angle is a rotation around a complete circle. A 180° angle is a rotation $\frac{1}{2}$ of the way around a circle. A 90° angle is a rotation $\frac{1}{4}$ of the way around a circle.

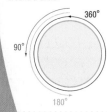

Angles

LESSON
1.2

In Lesson 1.1, you investigated angles. You learned that an angle is defined as two rays with a common endpoint called the *vertex*.

Angles are measured in degrees. In Lesson 1.1, you used 90°, 180°, and 360° angles as benchmarks to help estimate the measures of other angles.

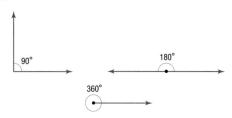

Think & Discuss

Each diagram is constructed from angles of the same size. Estimate the measure of each marked angle. Explain how you found it.

60°; Possible explanation: Together, the six equal angles make a 360° angle, so each must have measure 360 ÷ 6, or 60°.

30°; Possible explanation: Together, the three equal angles make a 90° angle, so each must have measure 90 ÷ 3, or 30°.

45°; Possible explanation: Together, the four equal angles make a 180° angle, so each must have measure 180 ÷ 4, or 45°.

Investigation 1 Measure Angles

Investigation 1

On Your Own Exercises
Pages 35–39
Exercises 1–13, 20, 21

Vocabulary

acute angle

obtuse angle

perpendicular

protractor

reference line

right angle

Materials

• protractor
• copies of the angles
• ruler

A **protractor** is a tool for measuring angles. A protractor has two sets of degree labels around the edge of a half circle or is sometimes a full circle. The line that goes through 0° is called the **reference line**.

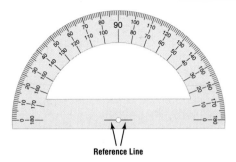

Reference Line

To measure an angle, follow these steps.
  • Place the bottom center of the protractor at the vertex of the angle.
  • Line up the reference line with one ray of the angle. Make sure the other ray can be seen through the protractor. You may need to extend this ray so that you can see where it meets the tick marks along the edge of the protractor.
  • Read the angle measurement.

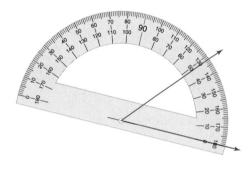

Real-World Link

When in-line skating, 360s, or full turns, and 540s, or one and a half turns, are two of the more difficult stunts.

Measuring Angles In this investigation, students use a protractor to measure angles. It is helpful to have a board protractor that you can use to demonstrate the steps involved in measuring an angle. Draw two angles with measures between 0° and 90° and two angles with measures between 90° and 180°. Before you demonstrate how to measure the angles, hold up the board protractor and point out the center point and the reference line. Then measure each angle. Each time, explain the steps you take so that students can relate them to the three steps on page 25.

Teacher Tips Discuss the fact that the protractor has two scales. Demonstrate which scale to use. Students should discuss which scale they should use when they read the measure for the angle. Tell them that they will take a good look at this question on page 26.

Real-World Link

Point out that angles can measure over 360°. They can be measured using a protractor by first subtracting the multiples of 360° until the angle is 180° or less. Then add the protractor measurement to the measure that was subtracted.

Lesson 1.2 Angles   **25**

There are two ways to decide on the appropriate scale to use when measuring an angle with a protractor.

- Use benchmark angles to determine which scale is correct.

- Make sure the ray is lined up with the reference line of the protractor and then check whether the ray passes through the 0° mark of the inside or outside scale. Once you have identified this scale, read the angle measure from the place where the other ray crosses this same scale.

Teacher Tips To measure the three angles shown at the bottom of the page, students will need to extend the rays to see where the rays cross the protractor scales. They can use the straight side along the bottom of the protractor to extend the sides. You may want to distribute copies of Lesson 1.2 Master 1, which contains the three angles. Be sure to discuss both methods given in the answers for finding the measure of the last angle on the page.

① A little more than 90°; Possible explanation: The angle is larger than the angle formed by a corner of a sheet of paper.

② 215°; Possible methods:
  - Measure the smaller angle (the unmarked angle) and subtract the result from 360°.
  - Extend one of the rays backward, dividing the angle into a 180° angle and a smaller angle. Measure the smaller angle, and add the result to 180°.

The angle below measures about 48°. Or is it 132°? How do you know which number to use? **48°; Possible explanation: The angle is clearly less than 90°.**

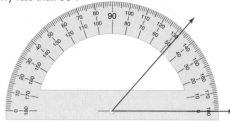

Is the measure of the angle below a little more than 90° or a little less than 90°? How do you know? **See ①.**

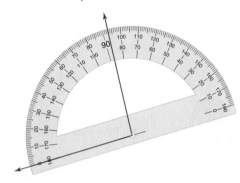

Measure these two angles. How do the measures compare? **Both measure 145°.**

Find the measure of the angle below. Describe the method that you used. **See ②.**

Reaching *All Learners*

BL **Beyond Level** Challenge students to measure the angle shown at the bottom of the page using a protractor and the sum of angles.

You have seen that when you measure an angle with a protractor, you must determine which of two measurements is correct. One way to decide is to compare the angle to a 90° angle, which is an important benchmark. Angles are sometimes classified by how their measures compare to 90°.

Acute angles measure less than 90°.

Obtuse angles measure more than 90° and less than 180°.

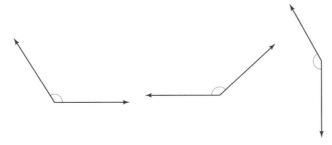

Right angles measure exactly 90°. Right angles are often marked with a small square at the vertex.

Two lines or segments that form a right angle are said to be **perpendicular**.

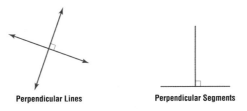

| Perpendicular Lines | Perpendicular Segments |

Vocabulary When you discuss the new vocabulary terms introduced on this page, be sure students understand that the terms *acute*, *right*, and *obtuse* are used only for angles with measures greater than 0° and less than 180°. Acute and obtuse angles can often be identified by simply looking at the angle. A corner of a sheet of paper or a protractor can be used to classify angles that are difficult to classify by simple visual inspection.

Teacher Tips Ask students to use a corner of a sheet of paper to confirm that all the angles formed by a pair of perpendicular lines or segments are right angles. Tell students that angles measuring 180° are called *straight angles*.

Real-World Link
Point out that the angle of elevation of the sun is the angle from your eyes at the horizontal to the sun as you are looking up.

Mathematical Background

The terms *acute*, *right*, and *obtuse* are important for classifying triangles as well as angles. In Investigation 2, students will gather evidence that the sum of the angle measures of any triangle is 180°. Any triangle falls into one of three categories: (1) three acute angles, or (2) two acute angles and one right angle, or (3) two acute angles and one obtuse angle. A triangle with three acute angles is called an *acute triangle*. A triangle with one right angle is called a *right triangle*. A triangle with one obtuse angle is called an *obtuse triangle*.

ⓥ *Develop & Understand: A*

Suggested Grouping: Pairs

▶ **Exercises 1–6** These exercises ask students to classify given angles as acute or obtuse. Indirectly, the exercise set also deals with right angles, since classifying an angle without a protractor implies that you have compared it to a right angle. Students should be able to decide what kind of angle is shown before measuring the angle. Often this can be done simply by looking. They can also use a corner of a sheet of paper to help them decide.

(Example) ·

Discuss the example, which shows how to draw on angle with a given measure. Be sure students understand that the scale to use is determined by which endpoint of the segment is used as the vertex of the angle. If there are two 25° labels, the one to use is the one that will result in an acute angle. When the center point of the protractor is placed as shown in the diagram, the 25° label on the outside scale is the correct one.

Teacher Tips Demonstrate how to draw various angles using a protractor. Have them label the point *A* at the center of the reference line. If students are having difficulty measuring angles with a protractor, work with them one-on-one. If you do not have time to do this yourself, ask a student who understands the procedure well to provide the help.

Point out that you can name an angle by the label of its vertex.

ⓥ *Develop & Understand: A*

Tell whether each angle is acute or obtuse. Then find its measure.

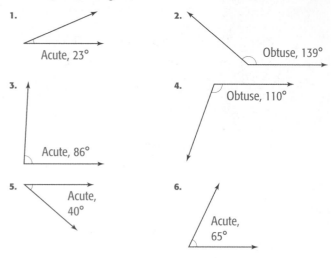

1. Acute, 23°
2. Obtuse, 139°
3. Acute, 86°
4. Obtuse, 110°
5. Acute, 40°
6. Acute, 65°

You have seen that a protractor is a useful tool for measuring angles. You can also use a protractor to draw angles with given measures.

Example

To create a 25° angle, start by drawing a line segment. This segment will be one side of the angle.

Line up the reference line of the protractor with the segment. Place the center of the protractor at one endpoint of the segment, which will be the angle's vertex.

Draw a mark next to the 25° label on the protractor. Be sure to choose the correct 25° label.

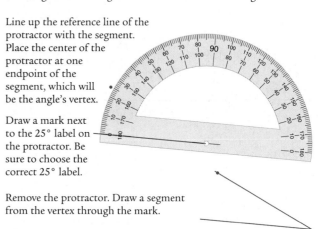

Remove the protractor. Draw a segment from the vertex through the mark.

7.

8.

10. Possible triangle:

11. Possible triangle:

15. Possible polygon:

✓ Develop & Understand: B

7. Draw a 160° angle. Include a curved angle mark to show which angle is 160°.

8. Draw a 210° angle. Include an angle mark to show which angle is 210°.

9. Draw two perpendicular segments.   See margin.

10. Draw a triangle in which one angle measures 50° and the other angles have measures greater than 50°. Label each angle with its measure.

11. Draw a triangle with one obtuse angle. Label each angle with its measure.

12. Draw a triangle with two 60° angles.   See margin.

13. Measure the sides of the triangle you drew in Exercise 12. What do you notice?   The sides all have the same length.

14. Draw a square. Make sure all the sides are the same length and all the angles measure 90°.   See margin.

15. Draw a polygon with any number of sides and one angle that has a measure greater than 180°. Mark that angle.

Share & Summarize

1. When you measure an angle with a protractor, how do you know which of the two possible numbers to choose?

2. The protractor on page 28 has a scale up to 180°. Describe how you would use such a protractor to draw an angle with a measure greater than 180°. Give an example if it helps you to explain your thinking.

1. Possible answer: Determine whether the angle is greater than 90° or less than 90°. Then choose the appropriate measure.

2. Possible answer: I would draw an angle with measure equal to 360° − (the angle measure). The correct angle would be the "outside" of this angle. For example, to draw a 230° angle, I would draw a 130° angle.

✓ Develop & Understand: B

Suggested Grouping: Pairs

▶ **Exercise 8** One approach is to draw a 150° angle and mark the "outside" of this angle. Another approach is to draw a line and mark a point on it to serve as the vertex of a 180° angle. Next, draw a 30° angle that has this same vertex and one of the rays of the 180° angle as the other side. Mark the sum of the 180° angle and the 30° angle.

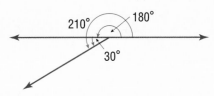

▶ **Exercise 9** Remind students that perpendicular segments meet to form four right angles.

▶ **Exercise 10** Students may need to draw a few triangles before they get one that works. Since the exercise requires a 50° angle, students should draw that angle first.

▶ **Exercise 12** After students have drawn the triangle, you may want to ask them to find the measure of the third angle of the triangle. If they have drawn the desired triangle accurately, the third angle will also have a measure of 60°.

Additional Answers

9. Possible answers:

12. Note: The size of the triangles will vary, but the triangle must be equilateral.

14. Note: Sizes will vary.

Share & Summarize

For **Exercise 1**, for students who say that either of the numbers can be chosen, point out that only one number should be chosen. Tell them they should estimate the angle to choose the number greater than 90° or less than 90°.

For **Exercise 2**, the example and explanation are important. Sometimes students have misconceptions about how to measure an angle, and their explanation can help you determine where they need help.

On Your Own Exercises
Pages 35–39
Exercises 14–19, 22–24

Sum of the Angles of a Triangle

- Ask students to draw a triangle.

- Have students tear off the three vertices of the triangle, as shown below.

- Tell students to arrange the vertices as shown below and give the measure of the angle they formed. 180°

- Tell them to compare their answers.

- Summarize the activity by saying that a rule relating the measures of the angles of any triangle is: The sum of the measures of the angles of a triangle is 180°.

✅ Develop & Understand: A

Suggested Grouping: Pairs

▶ **Exercise 1** Encourage students to use the shorthand notation for angles (∠) when they record the angle measures.

▶ **Exercise 2** Ask students to note the relative positions of the angles in these pairs. Define the pairs of angles as *vertical*.

▶ **Exercises 3 and 4** Ask students to draw their own pairs of lines and examine the measures of the angles formed.

▶ **Exercise 5** Watch for students who do not see that vertical angles are equal. Tell them to check their measurements.

Investigation ② **Angle Relationships**

Vocabulary
intersecting lines
vertical angles

Materials
- protractor
- ruler

You can refer to the angles in a drawing more easily if you label them with numbers or letters.

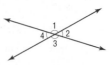

In the drawing above, the measure of Angle 1 is 135°. You can write this in symbols as $m\angle 1 = 135°$. The "m" stands for "measure," and ∠ is the symbol for "angle."

✅ Develop & Understand: A

Two lines that cross each other, like the lines in the drawing above, are called **intersecting lines**.

1. Measure angles 1, 2, 3, and 4 in the drawing above.

2. Which angles have the same measure?   1 and 3, 2 and 4

3. Use a ruler to draw another pair of intersecting lines. Measure each of the four angles formed. Label each with its measure.
   Answers will vary.

4. Draw one more pair of intersecting lines. Label each angle with its measure.   Answers will vary.

5. What patterns do you see relating the measure of the angles formed by two intersecting lines?

When two lines intersect, two angles that are not directly next to each other are called **vertical angles**. In the drawing below, $\angle a$ and $\angle c$ are vertical angles, and $\angle b$ and $\angle d$ are vertical angles.

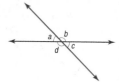

6. What do you think might be true about the measures of $\angle a$, $\angle b$, $\angle c$, and $\angle d$? Possible answers: $m\angle a = m\angle c$ and $m\angle b = m\angle d$; $m\angle a + m\angle b = 180°$; All angle measures add to 360°

1. $m\angle 1 = 135°$
   $m\angle 2 = 45°$
   $m\angle 3 = 135°$
   $m\angle 4 = 45°$

5. Possible answer: There are two pairs of equal angles. The angles that are not directly next to each other are equal. The measures of any two angles right next to each other add to 180°.

Reaching All Learners

BL **Beyond Level** If students notice that there are other pairs of angles besides vertical angles in the diagram on this page, ask them to focus on pairs of angles that have measures that add to 180°. These are called *supplementary angles*. Two intersecting lines always form supplementary angles.

Below, Conor explains the relationship he discovered.

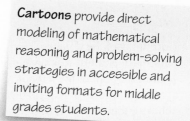
① Possible answer: ∠2 and ∠1 form a straight line, so their measures add to 180°. ∠4 and ∠1 form a straight line, so their measures add to 180°. So, $m\angle 2 + m\angle 1 = 180°$ and $m\angle 4 + m\angle 1 = 180°$. Since adding $m\angle 2$ to $m\angle 1$ gives 180°, and adding $m\angle 4$ to $m\angle 1$ also gives 180°, $m\angle 2$ must be equal to $m\angle 4$.

7–10. Measurements will vary. The sum should be very close or equal to 180°, 360°, 540°, and 720° consecutively.

Think & Discuss

In the cartoon, Conor showed that $m\angle 1 = m\angle 3$. Explain why $m\angle 2 = m\angle 4$.   See ①.

The *interior angles* of a polygon are the angles inside the polygon. In this quadrilateral, the interior angles are marked.

✓ Develop & Understand: B

The sum of the measures of the interior angles of any triangle is 180°. If you need a convincing argument for this, cut out any triangle, tear off the three vertices, and line the vertices up. What do you notice about the measure of the angles they form? In the following exercises, you will look for similar rules about the angle sums of other polygons.

7. Use a ruler and a pencil to draw a triangle. Measure each interior angle. Then find the sum of the three angles.

8. Draw a quadrilateral. Measure each interior angle. Then find the sum of the four angles.

9. Now draw a pentagon. Measure each interior angle. Find the sum of the five angles.

10. Finally, draw a hexagon. Measure each interior angle. Find the sum of the six angles.

Lesson 1.2 Angles   **31**

Think & Discuss

The key ideas for students to realize are that vertical angles have the same measure and that if two angles make a straight line, their measures add up to 180°. Discuss with the class how an argument similar to Conor's argument in the cartoon at the top of the page shows that the other pair of vertical angles in the cartoon has equal measures.

Introduce the term *interior angles* and show students examples of the interior angles in polygons.

✓ *Develop & Understand: B*

Suggested Grouping: Pairs

▶ **Exercises 7–10** Encourage students to draw polygons that are large enough to make it easy to measure the interior angles. Suggest that they write the measure of each interior angle inside the polygon, close to the vertex of the angle.

Teacher Tips Check students' work for any computational or measuring errors. Tell them to extend the side lengths of the polygon, if necessary, to measure the angles.

On the Spot Assessment

You can use the results of **Exercises 7–10** to identify particular difficulties students are having. If students get a sum that is not close to 360°, 540°, or 720°, check their work to see whether they made computational errors in finding the angle sum or if there were errors in measuring one or more of the angles. In this case, have students re-measure the angles while you observe to be sure they are positioning and reading the protractor correctly.

Suggested Grouping: Pairs

Students will use the look for a pattern, write a rule, and make and test a conjecture or prediction about the sum of the interior angles of a concave polygon. Urge pairs of students to compare their results with other students, and have a class discussion of their results. The class should be able to agree on a prediction of 360° for the angle sum of the quadrilateral and 720° for the hexagon.

Math Link

Students may need to see several examples of concave polygons before they understand how to draw one.

Teacher Tips When students are ready to consider the cartoon at the bottom of page 32, call their attention to the Math Link note in the margin. Ask students which segments in the cartoon are diagonals. The dashed segments

Discuss that the dashed diagonals divide the interior angles into two smaller angles.

---

① The angle sums for quadrilaterals are all about 360°. The angle sums for pentagons are all about 540°. The angle sums for hexagons are all about 720°.

Math Link

A *concave polygon* has at least one interior angle with measure greater than 180°. Concave polygons look "dented."

For Exercises 7–10, you and your classmates probably all drew different polygons. Compare the angle sums you found with the sums found by your classmates. What patterns do you see?   See ①.

Describe a rule that you could use to predict the sum of the interior-angle measures of a polygon when you know only the number of angles.   See ② in margin.

Use your rule to predict the interior-angle sums for each concave polygon below. Check your predictions by measuring the angles. Be sure to measure the interior angles.   360°, 720° (Note: The angle sums found by measuring may vary slightly.)

By now, you have probably concluded that the sum of the angle measures in a polygon depends only on the number of angles or the number of sides. You may have also discovered a rule for predicting the angle sum of any polygon when you know the number of angles.

Hannah and Jahmal wondered whether they could use what they know about the angle sum for triangles to think about the angle sums for other polygons.

32   CHAPTER 1   Polygons, Angles, and Circles

Additional Answer for Think & Discuss

② Possible rules:

- A triangle has an angle sum of 180°. Each time you add an angle to the polygon, you add 180° to the angle sum.

- angle sum = 180° × (number of angles − 2)

In the following exercises, you will investigate whether Hannah's strategy applies to other polygons. You will also see how her strategy leads to a rule for calculating angle sums.

Develop & Understand: C

11. First consider pentagons.

    a. Draw two pentagons. Make one of the pentagons concave. Divide each pentagon into triangles by drawing diagonals from one of the vertices.   Drawings will vary.

    b. Into how many triangles did you divide each pentagon?   3

    c. Use your answer to Part b to find the sum of the interior angles in a pentagon.   540°

12. Now consider hexagons.

    a. Draw two hexagons. Make one of the hexagons concave. Divide each hexagon into triangles by drawing diagonals from one of the vertices.   Drawings will vary.

    b. Into how many triangles did you divide each hexagon?   4

    c. Use your answer to Part b to find the sum of the interior angles in a hexagon.   720°

13. Suppose a quadrilateral has three 90° angles.

    a. What is the measure of the fourth angle? How do you know?

    b. What kind of quadrilateral is it?   Rectangle

14. Now think about octagons, which are 8-sided polygons.

    a. Without making a drawing, predict how many triangles you would divide an octagon into if you drew all the diagonals from one of the vertices. Explain how you made your prediction.

    b. Draw an octagon. Check your prediction.

    c. Use your answer to find the interior-angle sum for an octagon.   1,080°

15. Suppose you drew a 15-sided polygon and divided it into triangles by drawing diagonals from one of the vertices.

    a. How many triangles would you make?   13

    b. Use your answer to find the interior-angle sum for a 15-sided polygon.   2,340°

13a. 90°; the angles must add to 360°.

14a. Possible answer: 6; so far, I have been able to divide each polygon into the number of triangles equal to 2 less than the number of sides.

14b. Drawings will vary, but all should yield 6 triangles.

Math Link
A 15-sided polygon is called a *pentadecagon*.

Reaching All Learners

BL **Beyond Level** Ask students to trace the hexagon at the right and then draw the diagonals from vertex *A* so that the hexagon is divided into four triangles. What is the sum of the interior angles? 720°

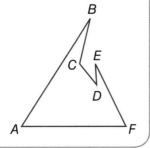

Develop & Understand: C

Suggested Grouping: Pairs

▶ **Exercise 11** Students may think that the diagonals can be drawn from any vertex. For some pentagons, this is not the case. For example, in pentagon *ABCDE* below, you would not want to use the diagonals from point *A*. The diagonal from *A* to *D* lies outside the pentagon, and the diagonal from *A* to *C* overlaps a side of the pentagon.

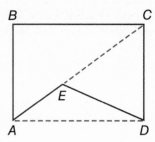

▶ **Exercise 11c** Students need to recall that the sum of the angle measures in each triangle is 180°.

▶ **Exercise 12c** It is possible to draw a hexagon that cannot be divided into suitable triangles by diagonals from a *single* vertex. If a student draws such a hexagon, simply relax the requirement that all the diagonals be drawn from the same vertex.

▶ **Exercise 13** Some students may draw a quadrilateral with three 90° angles. They may then measure the fourth angle to answer **Part a** and use the appearance of the diagram to answer **Part b**. While this approach can be used to obtain correct answers, it overlooks the fact that the exercise can be solved by reasoning. Encourage students to examine the use of reasoning.

▶ **Exercise 14** Students should not be too concerned if they sketch a concave octagon that cannot be divided into suitable triangles by drawing diagonals from a single vertex. Relax the requirement that all the diagonals be drawn from a single vertex.

Math Link
Remind students that not all polygons with over 10 sides have special names.

Share & Summarize

You can use these questions to check that students understand how to divide a polygon into triangles in order to find the sum of the measures of its angles. Make sure students can point to which angles are interior angles for **Exercise 1**. You may want to call on volunteers to read their answers to these questions. Discuss their answers with the class.

For **Exercise 2**, have students sketch a nonagon and then divide it into appropriate triangles by drawing diagonals. Help them see that they can find the sum of the angle measures of the polygon by counting the triangles and multiplying by 180°.

Additional Examples What is the sum of the angle measures of a decagon (10-sided polygon)? 1,440°

. . . .

Real-World Link

You may want to show students salt or sugar crystals under a microscope or magnified with an overhead projector. Ask students to describe the crystals in geometric terms.

. . . .

16a. Count the number of angles and subtract 2.

16b. Multiply the number of triangles you made by drawing diagonals by 180°.

1. Possible explanation: Some of the angles Martin is counting are in the center of the quadrilateral; they are not part of the angles of the quadrilateral.

. . . .

Real-World Link

Crystallographers are people who study the geometric properties and internal structures of crystals. They use reflecting goniometers to measure the angles between the faces of a crystal.

. . . .

16. Suppose you know the number of angles a polygon has.

a. How would you find the number of triangles you could make if you divided the polygon into triangles by drawing diagonals from one of the vertices?

b. How would you find the sum of the angle measures?

Share & Summarize

1. Martin said the sum of the angle measures for a quadrilateral must be 720° because a quadrilateral can be split into four triangles by drawing both diagonals.

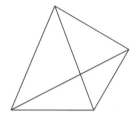 

Explain what is wrong with Martin's argument.

2. What is the sum of the angle measures of a nonagon, a 9-sided polygon? 1260°

Troubleshooting includes common misconceptions or procedural errors students might make and solutions to overcome those errors.

Troubleshooting

If students have difficulty with Exercise 1 in Share & Summarize, sketch the quadrilaterals on the board. In each diagram, mark one of the angles where the diagonals intersect and ask students whether it is part of an interior angle of the quadrilateral. Then point out angles that are part of an interior angle of the quadrilateral.

If students have difficulty with Exercise 2, have them sketch a nonagon and divide it into appropriate triangles by drawing the diagonals and then find the sum of the angle measures by multiplying the number of triangles by 180°.

Practice & Apply

Find the measure of each angle.

1.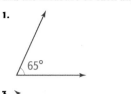

2.
44°

3.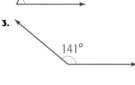
141°

4. 302°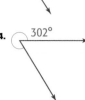

7.

Without measuring, find the missing angle measures.

5.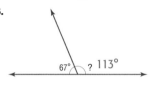
67° ? 113°

6.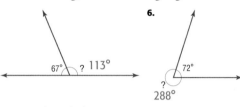
72°
?
288°

8.

Draw an angle with the given measure.

7. 17°   **8.** 75°   **9.** 164°   **10.** 290°

9.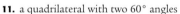

Draw the figure described. Label every angle in the figure with its measure.   11–13. See margin.

11. a quadrilateral with two 60° angles

12. a pentagon with two 90° angles

13. a quadrilateral with one 200° angle

10.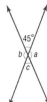

Without measuring, find the measure of each lettered angle.

14.
45°
b a
c

15.
b
107°
12°

16.
5°
15°
a
20°

14. $m\angle a = 135°$,
    $m\angle b = 135°$,
    $m\angle c = 45°$

15. $m\angle b = 61°$

16. $m\angle a = 320°$

Investigation 1
Pages 25–29
Practice & Apply: 1–13
Connect & Extend: 20, 21

Investigation 2
Pages 30–34
Practice & Apply: 14–19
Connect & Extend: 22–24

Assign Anytime
Mixed Review: 25–31

▶ **Exercises 14–16** Use these exercises to check that students understand the angle relationships for each figure. Encourage students to show their calculations so you can assess whether they used valid methods to find the angle measures.

Additional Answers

11. Possible quadrilateral:
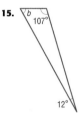
60°   140°   60°
100°

12. Possible pentagon:
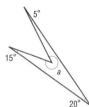
90°
130°
120°
90°   110°

13. Possible quadrilateral:

114°
23°   23°
200°

▶ **Exercise 17** Watch for students that are unsure about how to approach this exercise. You might help by asking the following questions:

• How many sides does this polygon have?

• From what you know about the number of sides, what can you say about the total of all of the measures of the interior angles?

• If you subtracted the sum of the known angle measures from that total, how many degrees would that leave for $\angle a$ and $\angle b$ combined?

• Since $\angle a$ and $\angle b$ have the same measure, what is the measure of each angle?

▶ **Exercise 20** When students trace the diagrams for this exercise, it would be good for them to use dots for the players rather than tracing each stick figure. Suggest that they mark the dots in a systematic way. They might, for example, place a dot at the head of each player or at the right foot of each player.

Math Link

Point out that if a polygon is regular, each angle can be found by dividing the sum of the interior angles by the number of sides.

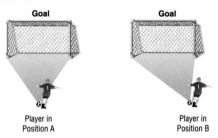

17. In this polygon, $\angle a$ and $\angle b$ have the same measure. What is it?   160°

18. What is the measure of each angle of a regular pentagon?   108°

19. What is the measure of each angle of a regular hexagon?   120°

Connect & Extend   **20.** The drawings below show angles formed by a soccer player and the goalposts. The greater the angle, the better chance the player has of scoring a goal. For example, the player has a better chance of scoring from Position A than from Position B.

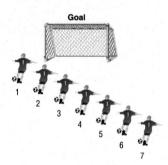

Math Link

In a regular polygon, all sides are the same length, and all angles the same measure.

In Parts a and b, it may help to trace the diagrams and draw and measure angles.

a. Seven soccer players are practicing their kicks. They are lined up as shown in front of the goalposts. Which player has the best, or greatest, kicking angle? Player 4

b. Now the players are lined up as shown. Which player has the best kicking angle? Player 3

21. The *diameter* of a circle is a segment that passes through the center of the circle and has both its endpoints on the circle. The four triangles below have all three vertices on a circle and the diameter as one side.

Diameter

Measure each numbered angle. What do the measures have in common?   All four angles measure 90°.

22a. $m\angle 1 = 75°$
   $m\angle 2 = 143°$
   $m\angle 3 = 142°$
   sum $= 360°$
22b. $m\angle 1 = 130°$
   $m\angle 2 = 77°$
   $m\angle 3 = 80°$
   $m\angle 4 = 73°$
   sum $= 360°$
22c. $m\angle 1 = 45°$
   $m\angle 2 = 79°$
   $m\angle 3 = 51°$
   $m\angle 4 = 81°$
   $m\angle 5 = 104°$
   sum $= 360°$
22d. $m\angle 1 = 50°$
   $m\angle 2 = 55°$
   $m\angle 3 = 63°$
   $m\angle 4 = 65°$
   $m\angle 5 = 45°$
   $m\angle 6 = 82°$
   sum $= 360°$

22. You discovered a rule about the sums of the interior angles of polygons. Polygons also have *exterior* angles, which can be found by extending their sides. In the drawings below, the exterior angles are marked.

In Parts a–d, find the measure of each exterior angle. Find the sum of the measures. Then describe any pattern you find in the measures.   The exterior-angle sum is always 360°.

a.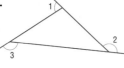

b.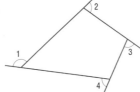

c.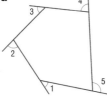

d.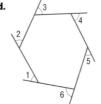

Lesson 1.2   Angles   **37**

▶ **Exercise 23** Ask students to trace the pool table shown and mark which angles are the angle of incidence and the angle of reflection. Then check that they identified the angles correctly.

Real-World Link

Ask students to use a protractor to measure and identify the angle of incidence and the angle of reflection for the diagrams they traced. Then ask, "Is the angle of incidence = the angle of reflection?"

Real-World Link

When light hits a mirror, it behaves in the same way as a pool ball hitting the side of a table. If light hits a mirror at an angle, it bounces off at the same angle. In physics, this law is often stated as "the angle of incidence = the angle of reflection."

23. The angle at which a pool ball hits the side of a table has the same measure as the angle at which it bounces off the side. This is shown in the drawing below. The marked angles have the same measure, and the arrow shows the ball's path.

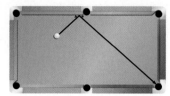

In Parts a–c, trace the drawing. Then use your protractor to find the path the ball will take when it bounces off the side. Tell whether the ball will go into a pocket or hit another side. Draw just one bounce.

a. 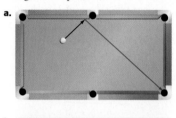 It will land in the corner pocket.

b. 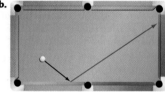 It will hit another side.

c. 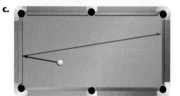 It will hit another side.

24. Possible answer: Divide the polygon's area into triangles. For each triangle, add 180 degrees. This works because the sum of the interior angles of a triangle equals 180 degrees.

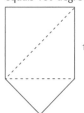

$180° + 180° + 180° = 540°$

d. Challenge Trace this drawing. Draw a path for which the ball will bounce off a side and land in the lower-right pocket.

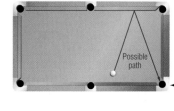

Possible path

Land Here

24. In Your Own Words Describe how you can find the interior-angle sum of any polygon without measuring any angles. Then explain how you know that your method works.

Mixed Review

25. 61.54
26. 2.542
27. 20.73
28. 268.44
29. 100
30. 68.7654

For Exercises 25–30, find each sum or difference without using a calculator.

25. $73.97 - 12.43$ **26.** $4.642 - 2.1$ **27.** $37.13 - 16.4$

28. $194.5 + 73.94$ **29.** $54.32 + 45.68$ **30.** $73.7654 - 5$

31. Lucida drew the following grid.

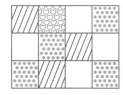

a. What fraction of the squares contain dots? $\frac{4}{12}$, or $\frac{1}{3}$

b. What percent of the squares are striped? 25%

c. What fraction of the squares have hearts? $\frac{1}{12}$

d. Describe how Lucita could fill in the blank squares to create a grid in which 50% of the squares contain dots, $\frac{1}{4}$ have hearts, and 25% have stripes. Fill in two with dots and two with hearts.

e. Describe how Lucita could fill in the blank squares to create a grid in which $\frac{2}{3}$ of the squares have the same pattern. Fill all four with dots.

▶ **Exercise 23d** Most students are likely to use a trial-and-error approach to solve **Part d**. Later, when students know more geometry, they will be able to use reasoning to solve the exercise.

▶ **Exercise 31** Some students may need a quick review of how to find and use percents, as well as the relationships among fractions, decimals, and percents. Students will learn more about fractions, decimals, and percents in Chapters 2, 4, and 6.

> **Quick Check** and **Quick Quiz** provide informal end-of-lesson opportunities for assessing students' understanding and progress.

Quick Check

Informal Assessment Students should be able to:

✔ measure angles by using a protractor

✔ classify angles whose measures are greater than 0° and less than 180° as acute, right, or obtuse

✔ find the sum of the angles of any polygon given the number of sides of the polygon

Quick Quiz

1. Measure each angle. Tell whether the angle is *acute, right,* or *obtuse.*

a. 90°; right

b. 135°; obtuse

c. 28°; acute

2. Draw an angle whose measure is 280°.

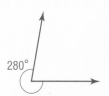

280°

3. Without using a protractor, find the measure of each lettered angle.

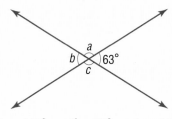

63°

$m \angle a = 117°$, $m \angle b = 63°$, $m \angle c = 117°$

4. A quadrilateral has two 120° angles and an angle of 40°. What is the measure of the fourth angle? 80°

5. What is the sum of the angle measures of a polygon that has 11 sides? 1,620°

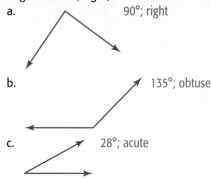

Lesson 1.2 Angles   **39**

Measure Around

Objectives

▶ To use the side lengths of a polygon to calculate the perimeter of the polygon

▶ To use polygons to approximate the perimeter of a shape with curved sides

▶ To understand and use formulas for the circumference of a circle

In this lesson, students learn to calculate perimeters of polygons. They use their knowledge of rectangles to write a formula for the perimeter of a rectangle. Students investigate how perimeters of polygons can be used to approximate perimeters of figures with curved sides.

Students use measuring tape to measure the diameter and circumference of circular objects. They use these measurements to discover that dividing the circumference by the diameter gives the same number for all circles. Students learn the meaning of π and learn to express the circumference and diameter of a circle in terms of π.

Advance Preparation

You may want to provide Lesson 1.3 Master 1 to facilitate class discussion while presenting new topics, including perimeter and circumference.

	Summary	Materials	On Your Own Exercises (pp. 48–51)	Assessment Opportunities
Investigation 1 (p. 40) *Pacing: 2 days*	This investigation introduces students to polygons and the terminology used with them. Students identify polygons and name polygons using vertices.	Metric rulers, Lesson 1.3 Master 1, string	Practice & Apply: 1–5 Connect & Extend: 10, 11 Mixed Review: 16–29	• Share & Summarize (p. 44)
Investigation 2 (p. 44) *Pacing: 1 day*	Students develop their sense of angle as they estimate angle measures by comparing angles to benchmarks: 90°, 180°, and 360°.	5 objects with circular faces, string or measuring tape, rulers, scissors	Practice & Apply: 6–9 Connect & Extend: 12–15 Mixed Review: 16–29	• Share & Summarize (p. 47) • Troubleshooting (p. 47)

Leveled Lesson Resources

CRM *Available in:* **Chapter 1 Resource Masters**

Also on
TeacherWorks™
Lesson 1.3

Study Guide and Intervention (p. 35) AL

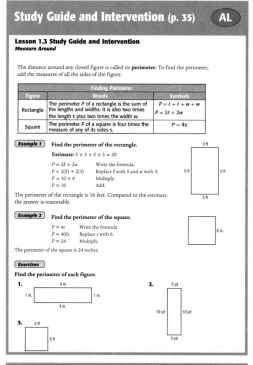

Lesson 1.3 Study Guide and Intervention
Measure Around

The distance around any closed figure is called its **perimeter**. To find the perimeter, add the measures of all the sides of the figure.

Finding Perimeter		
Figure	**Words**	**Symbols**
Rectangle	The perimeter *P* of a rectangle is the sum of the lengths and widths. It is also two times the length *l* plus two times the width *w*.	$P = l + l + w + w$ $P = 2l + 2w$
Square	The perimeter *P* of a square is four times the measure of any of its sides *s*.	$P = 4s$

Example 1 Find the perimeter of the rectangle.

Estimate: $5 + 5 + 5 + 5 = 20$

$P = 2l + 2w$ Write the formula.
$P = 2(5) + 2(3)$ Replace *l* with 5 and *w* with 3.
$P = 10 + 6$ Multiply.
$P = 16$ Add.

The perimeter of the rectangle is 16 feet. Compared to the estimate, the answer is reasonable.

Example 2 Find the perimeter of the square.

$P = 4s$ Write the formula.
$P = 4(6)$ Replace *s* with 6.
$P = 24$ Multiply.

The perimeter of the square is 24 inches.

Exercises

Find the perimeter of each figure.

1. 4 in., 1 in., 4 in.
2. 3 yd, 10 yd, 10 yd, 3 yd
3. 5 ft, 5 ft

Skills Practice (p. 36) AL OL

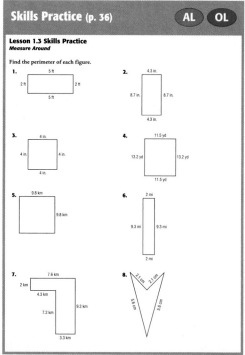

Lesson 1.3 Skills Practice
Measure Around

Find the perimeter of each figure.

1. 5 ft, 2 ft, 2 ft, 5 ft
2. 4.3 in., 8.7 in., 8.7 in., 4.3 in.
3. 4 in., 4 in., 4 in., 4 in.
4. 11.5 yd, 13.2 yd, 13.2 yd, 11.5 yd
5. 9.8 km, 9.8 km
6. 2 mi, 9.3 mi, 9.3 mi, 2 mi
7. 7.6 km, 2 km, 4.3 km, 9.2 km, 7.2 km, 3.3 km
8. 2.1 cm, 2.1 cm, 5.6 cm, 5.6 cm

Problem-Solving Practice (p. 37) AL OL

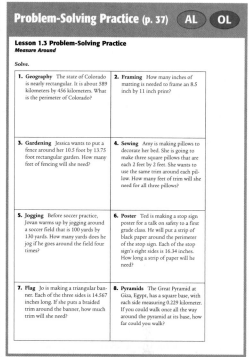

Lesson 1.3 Problem-Solving Practice
Measure Around

Solve.

1. **Geography** The state of Colorado is nearly rectangular. It is about 589 kilometers by 456 kilometers. What is the perimeter of Colorado?

2. **Framing** How many inches of matting is needed to frame an 8.5 inch by 11 inch print?

3. **Gardening** Jessica wants to put a fence around her 10.5 foot by 13.75 foot rectangular garden. How many feet of fencing will she need?

4. **Sewing** Amy is making pillows to decorate her bed. She is going to make three square pillows that are each 2 feet by 2 feet. She wants to use the same trim around each pillow. How many feet of trim will she need for all three pillows?

5. **Jogging** Before soccer practice, Jovan warms up by jogging around a soccer field that is 100 yards by 130 yards. How many yards does he jog if he goes around the field four times?

6. **Poster** Ted is making a stop sign poster for a talk on safety to a first grade class. He will put a strip of black paper around the perimeter of the stop sign. Each of the stop sign's eight sides is 16.34 inches. How long a strip of paper will he need?

7. **Flag** Jo is making a triangular banner. Each of the three sides is 14.567 inches long. If she puts a braided trim around the banner, how much trim will she need?

8. **Pyramids** The Great Pyramid at Giza, Egypt, has a square base, with each side measuring 0.229 kilometer. If you could walk once all the way around the pyramid at its base, how far could you walk?

Enrichment (p. 38) BL

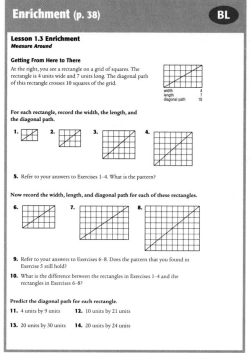

Lesson 1.3 Enrichment
Measure Around

Getting From Here to There

At the right, you see a rectangle on a grid of squares. The rectangle is 4 units wide and 7 units long. The diagonal path of this rectangle crosses 10 squares of the grid.

width   4
length   7
diagonal path   10

For each rectangle, record the width, the length, and the diagonal path.

1.   2.   3.   4.

5. Refer to your answers to Exercises 1–4. What is the pattern?

Now record the width, length, and diagonal path for each of these rectangles.

6.   7.   8.

9. Refer to your answers to Exercises 6–8. Does the pattern that you found in Exercise 5 still hold?

10. What is the difference between the rectangles in Exercises 1–4 and the rectangles in Exercises 6–8?

Predict the diagonal path for each rectangle.

11. 4 units by 9 units
12. 10 units by 21 units
13. 20 units by 30 units
14. 20 units by 24 units

Lesson Quick Quiz (p. 39) AL OL BL

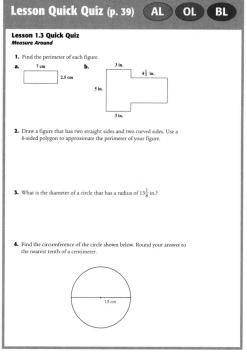

Lesson 1.3 Quick Quiz
Measure Around

1. Find the perimeter of each figure.
a. 7 cm, 2.5 cm
b. 3 in., $4\frac{1}{2}$ in., 5 in., 3 in.

2. Draw a figure that has two straight sides and two curved sides. Use a 6-sided polygon to approximate the perimeter of your figure.

3. What is the diameter of a circle that has a radius of $13\frac{1}{8}$ in.?

4. Find the circumference of the circle shown below. Round your answer to the nearest tenth of a centimeter.

15 cm

Lesson Master 1 (p. 40)

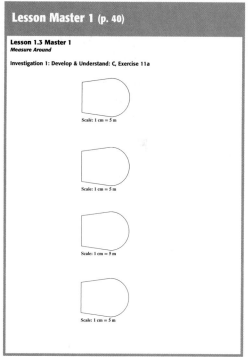

Lesson 1.3 Master 1
Measure Around

Investigation 1: Develop & Understand: C, Exercise 11a

Scale: 1 cm = 5 m
Scale: 1 cm = 5 m
Scale: 1 cm = 5 m
Scale: 1 cm = 5 m

Additional Lesson Resources

Teacher Tech Tools
- TeacherWorks
- ExamView Assessment Suite
- Classroom Presentation Toolkit
- Advance Tracker

Student Tech Tools
- StudentWorks Plus
- **Math Online** eGlossary •
  Concepts in Motion

Other Print Products
- Investigation Notebook and Reflection Journal
- Quick Review Math Handbook

LESSON 1.3 Measure Around

Introduce

Perimeter In this lesson, students learn to calculate perimeters of polygons. They use their knowledge of rectangles to write a formula for the perimeter of a rectangle. Students investigate how perimeters of polygons can be used to approximate perimeters of figures with curved sides.

Read the opening paragraph with the class. Discuss the meaning of the term *perimeter* and how to calculate the perimeter of the house by using the information in the diagram.

Think & Discuss

Have a class discussion of the questions. In the discussion, consider any difficulties that might arise in measuring the perimeter of the floor of the classroom. For example, are there heavy bookcases that get in the way? If so, how could the perimeter be found without moving those objects? Would a string or yardstick be more helpful, or would you need both? After a brief discussion of these matters, go on to Investigation 1.

Investigation 1

On Your Own Exercises
Pages 48–51
Exercises 1–5, 10–11

Perimeter In this investigation, students use a metric ruler to find the perimeters of several rooms in a floor plan by adding the lengths of the sides.

Introduce the term *scale drawing*. Point out that the diagram is a *scale drawing*. This means that the shapes of the actual classrooms are just like those in the floor plan, only larger. Call attention to the scale for the floor plan, which is just below the diagram.

LESSON 1.3 Measure Around

The **perimeter** of a two-dimensional shape is the distance around the shape. The perimeter of the shape to the right is 10.8 cm.

2 cm   2 cm
2 cm   2 cm
2.8 cm

Inv 1 Perimeter   40
Inv 2 Circumference   44

Vocabulary
perimeter

Think & Discuss

Describe as many methods as you can for measuring the perimeter of the floor of your classroom.
See ① in margin.

Which of your methods do you think will give the most accurate measurement?   Answers will vary.

Which of your methods do you think is the most practical?
Answers will vary.

Investigation 1 Perimeter

Vocabulary
formula

Materials
• metric ruler, ruler, string
• copies of the auditorium floor

To find the perimeter of a polygon, add the lengths of its sides.

✅ Develop & Understand: A

This is the floor plan of the second floor of Millbury Middle School. On the drawing, each centimeter equals 2 meters.

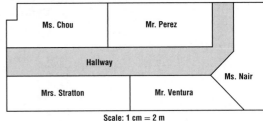

Ms. Chou   Mr. Perez
Hallway
Mrs. Stratton   Mr. Ventura   Ms. Nair

Scale: 1 cm = 2 m

Additional Answer for Think & Discuss
① Possible answer:
• Use a ruler, meterstick, or yardstick to measure each side, and add the measures.
• Wrap a string around the edges of the floor, and cut the string so its length equals the perimeter. Then measure the string with a ruler or yardstick.
• Wrap a long tape measure around the edges of the floor.

• Measure the pace of a student. Then count how many paces the student takes as he walks around the edge of the room, and multiply the result by the length of a pace.

★ indicates multi-step problem

1. Without measuring, tell whose classroom you think has the greatest perimeter. Explain why you think so.   Answers will vary.

2. Look at the floor plan for Ms. Nair's room.

   a. What type of polygon is the floor of Ms. Nair's room?   Hexagon

   b. Find the perimeter of Ms. Nair's floor plan to the nearest tenth of a centimeter. Then calculate the perimeter of the actual floor in meters.   11.4 cm, 22.8 m

4a. Yes; it has four right angles and its opposite sides have the same length.

4b. Possible answers: Measure the length and the width, double each, and add the results. Or, measure the length and the width, add them, and double the result.

3. Find the perimeter of Mrs. Stratton's floor plan to the nearest tenth of a centimeter. Then calculate the perimeter of the actual floor in meters.   12.6 cm, 25.2 m

4. Look at the floor plan for Mr. Perez's room.

   a. Is Mr. Perez's floor a rectangle? How do you know?

   b. Describe how to find the perimeter of Mr. Perez's floor plan by making only two measurements.

   c. Measure the perimeter of Mr. Perez's floor plan to the nearest tenth of a centimeter. Then calculate the perimeter of the actual floor in meters.   11.6 cm, 23.2 m

5. To find the perimeter of Ms. Chou's floor plan, Althea made the measurements labeled below. She claims these are the only measurements she needs to make.

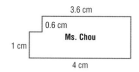

   a. Is Althea correct? If so, explain how to find the perimeter of Ms. Chou's room using only these measurements. If not, tell what other measurements you would need.   See margin.

★ **b.** Find the perimeter of Ms. Chou's floor plan to the nearest tenth of a centimeter. Then calculate the perimeter of the actual floor in meters.   11.2 cm, 22.4 m

★ **6.** Which teacher's classroom floor has the greatest perimeter? What is the greatest classroom perimeter?   Mrs. Stratton's, 25.2 m

Real-World Link
Many colleges and universities offer classes over the Internet. Students who are unable to travel to a college campus can earn college credits.

Additional Answer

5a. Yes; Possible explanations:
  • You can imagine "pushing out" the indented upper-left corner so the floor plan becomes a rectangle. The length of the rectangle would be 4 cm, and the width would be 1 cm + 0.6 cm, or 1.6 cm. Find the perimeter by adding twice the length to twice the width.
  • You can find the length of the right side by adding the two vertical lengths on the left; 0.6 cm + 1 cm, or 1.6 cm. Find the other missing length by subtracting the length of the top horizontal segment from the length of the bottom horizontal segment: 4 cm − 3.6 cm, or 0.4 cm. Then just add the side lengths.

 Develop & Understand: A

Suggested Grouping: Pairs

▶ **Exercise 1** Students are asked to tell which teacher's classroom they think has the greatest perimeter. Encourage students to come up with a thoughtful reply. Use students' answers to discover which features of the shapes guided them toward their answers.

▶ **Exercises 2–6** Encourage students to measure carefully.

▶ **Exercise 3** Some students may assume that the room is rectangular and measure only two sides. Ask whether it is safe to make that assumption, or whether it is safer to measure each side. (Remember, the instructions ask for a very accurate perimeter.)

▶ **Exercise 4** Students use the idea that a quadrilateral having four right angles is a rectangle.

▶ **Exercise 5** Students discover that the right-angle "dent" in the upper left-hand corner of Ms. Chou's room does not affect the perimeter. A rectangular room with the same overall length and width will have the same perimeter.

Teacher Tips Watch for students who have incorrect answers for **Exercise 5**. Students who simply added the four lengths shown in the diagram need to see that they have not accounted for the lengths of all parts of the polygon. Have these students count the number of sides in the polygon and the number of numbers they added.

Real-World Link
Ask students if they can give the name of a college or university with Internet classes.

Teacher Tips Discuss the explanation of the perimeter formulas for rectangles that is given at the top of the page. Students should not find it difficult to see why the two formulas are equivalent.

✓ Develop & Understand: B

Suggested Grouping: Pairs

▶ **Exercise 8** Students may arrive at their answers in different way. Some may guess a number for the length or width, double that number, subtract from 42, and then divide by 2 to get the other dimension.

Some may reason that if $2(L + W) = 42$, then $L + W = 21$. They can then look for pairs of numbers that have a sum of 21.

▶ **Exercise 9** Students will find it easy to get the answer once they remember that a square is a special rectangle in which the length and width are equal.

▶ **Exercise 10** Students may have different solution strategies. Some students may come up with the answer by noting that a square is a rectangle with four sides of equal lengths.

Other students may use one of the formulas for the perimeter of a rectangle, replace L and W with s, and simplify.

Both approaches are valid.

Teacher Tips The floor plan at the bottom of page 42 is used to focus students' attention on how to approximate the perimeter of a figure with curved sides. The Example on the next page uses the polygon approximation method.

In the previous exercises, you probably realized you could find the perimeter of a rectangle without measuring every side. This is because the opposite sides of a rectangle are the same length. If you measure the length and the width of a rectangle, you can find the perimeter using either of two rules.

Add the length and the width. Double the result.

Double the length and double the width. Add the results.

If you use P to represent the perimeter and L and W to represent the length and width, you can write these rules in symbols.

Geometric rules expressed using symbols, like those above, are often called **formulas**.

Perimeter of a Rectangle
$P = 2 \cdot (L + W)$ $P = 2L + 2W$

In these formulas, P represents the perimeter and L and W represent the length and width.

✓ Develop & Understand: B

7. Use one of the perimeter formulas to find the perimeter of a rectangle with length 5.7 meters and width 2.9 meters.   17.2 m

8. The floor of a rectangular room has a perimeter of 42 feet. What are three possibilities for the dimensions of the floor?

9. A square floor has a perimeter of 32.4 meters. How long are the sides of the floor?   8.1 m

10. Write a formula for the perimeter of a square, using P to represent the perimeter and s to represent the length of a side. Explain why your formula works.

This floor plan is of the auditorium at Marshville Middle School.

Since part of the floor is curved, it is difficult to find the perimeter using just a ruler. You could use a measuring tape or a piece of string to find the length of the curved part. Another method is to use a polygon to *approximate* the shape of the floor.

Scale: 1 cm = 5 m

---

8. Possible answer:
10 ft × 11 ft,
10.5 ft × 10.5 ft,
and 20 ft × 1 ft

10. $P = 4s$; This works because the four sides of a square are the same length, so to find the perimeter, you can multiply the side length of the square by 4.

Reaching *All Learners*

BL **Beyond Level** Refer students to **Exercise 8**. Ask them how many dimensions are possible for a rectangle that has a perimeter of 42 feet. Ask whether there are any limits on how large or how small the dimensions can be. If so, what are they? An unlimited number of dimensions are possible. Both dimensions must be greater than 0, and the greater dimension must be less than 24 feet.

Example

Luke drew a pentagon to approximate the shape of the floor.

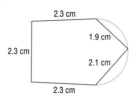

Scale: 1 cm = 5 m

Then he found the pentagon's perimeter.

$$2.3 + 2.3 + 2.3 + 1.9 + 2.1 = 10.9 \text{ cm}$$

✔ Develop & Understand: C

11. You can get a closer approximation than Luke's by using a polygon with more sides.

   a. Try using a hexagon, a polygon with six sides, to approximate the shape of the floor plan. What perimeter estimate do you get using a hexagon?

   b. Is the actual perimeter greater than or less than your estimate? Explain.

   c. Now try a heptagon, a polygon with seven sides, to approximate the shape of the floor plan. What perimeter estimate do you get using a heptagon? See margin.

   d. Is the actual perimeter greater than or less than your estimate? Explain. See margin.

   e. Using a polygon with more than seven sides, make another estimate. What is your estimate? See margin.

12. Wrap a piece of string around the floor plan. Try to keep the string as close to the sides of the floor plan as possible. Then mark the string to indicate the length of the perimeter. Measure the string's length up to the mark. What is your perimeter estimate?
Estimates will vary.

13. Which of your estimates do you think is most accurate? Explain.
Possible answer: The estimate I made with the string because I was able to get closer to the sides of the floor plan.

11a. Possible answer: The perimeter is about 11.2 cm.

11b. Greater; each side of the polygon along the curved part of the floor plan is shorter than the corresponding length of the floor plan.

Example

Discuss the example with the class. Ask students why a pentagon was used to approximate the shape of the floor. Could a hexagon be used?

✔ Develop & Understand: C

Suggested Grouping: Pairs

▶ **Exercise 11a** Distribute a copy of Lesson 1.3 Master 1. Students will probably get a variety of estimates, depending on where they select the two vertices that are on the curved side. You may want to have pairs of students compare their polygons and their estimates. Spacing the points evenly along the curve will give a good approximation.

▶ **Exercise 11b** Students will realize that no matter where they place the two vertices on the curved side, the perimeter of the polygon will be only an approximation of the perimeter of the floor plan.

▶ **Exercise 11c** The locations of the vertices on the curved side will again affect how good the approximation is. You may want to discuss with the class whether they think a heptagon can give a better approximation than a pentagon or a hexagon.

▶ **Exercises 12 and 13** Students wrap a piece of string around the floor plan and measure how much string it took to go around. Have students compare their estimates.

Additional Answers

11c. Possible answer: The perimeter is about 11.3 cm.

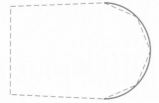

11d. Greater; each side of the polygon along the curved part of the floor plan is shorter than the corresponding length of the floor plan.

11e. Possible answer: The perimeter is about 11.4 cm.

Share & Summarize

After students have written their paragraphs for Share & Summarize, you may want to call on volunteers to read them to the class. If students' paragraphs make use of diagrams, have the students sketch them on the board. If they need more practice, have them create their own shapes with curved sides to measure.

Investigation 2

On Your Own Exercises
Pages 48–51
Exercises 6–9, 12–15

Circumference In this investigation, students learn several basic vocabulary terms related to circles. They measure the circumference and diameter of several circular objects and use their results to confirm that the circumference divided by the diameter is approximately equal to 3, regardless of the diameter of the object. They learn that the value of this quotient, assuming exact measures for the circumference and diameter, is called pi (π). They use this idea to write formulas for the circumference in terms of the diameter and radius. Finally, they apply these formulas to solve exercises.

Think & Discuss

When you go over these questions with the class, be sure students understand that all the points on a circle are the same distance from the center. Refer to the diagram on page 44 as you discuss the questions. When you discuss whether all diameters are the same length, use the diagram to point out that every diameter is made up of two radii. This idea makes it easy to write a rule that relates the radius to the diameter.

Teacher Tips Remind students again that a circle consists of the points on the curve and not the points in the interior region.

Share & Summarize   See margin.

Write a paragraph discussing what you know about finding the perimeter of two-dimensional shapes. Include the following.
- polygons and nonpolygons
- ruler measurements and string measurements
- formulas

Investigation 2   Circumference

Vocabulary
chord
circumference
diameter
radius

Materials
- 5 objects with circular faces (for example, a soup can, a coffee can, a roll of tape, a plate, and a quarter)
- string or measuring tape
- ruler
- scissors

In the last investigation, you found perimeters of polygons. You estimated perimeters of a shape with curved sides. In this investigation, you will focus on circles.

The perimeter of a circle is called its **circumference**. Although you can estimate the circumference of a circle by using string or by approximating with polygons, there is a formula for finding the exact circumference. Before you begin thinking about circumference, you need to learn some useful words for describing circles.

A **chord** is a segment connecting two points on a circle. The **diameter** is a chord that passes through the center of the circle. *Diameter* also refers to the distance across a circle through its center. The **radius** is a segment from the center to a point on the circle. *Radius* also refers to the distance from the center to a point on the circle. The plural of *radius* is *radii*.

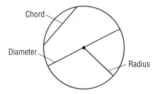

① No; The longest chords are those that pass through the center, the diameters.

Think & Discuss

Are all the chords of a circle the same length? If not, which are the longest?   See ①.

Are all the diameters of a circle the same length? Are all the radii the same length?   Yes; Yes

Describe the relationship between the radius of a circle *r* and its diameter *d*.   The radius is half the diameter, or the diameter is twice the radius.

44   CHAPTER 1 Polygons, Angles, and Circles

Additional Answer for Share & Summarize

Possible answer: Perimeter is the distance around a two-dimensional shape. You can find the perimeter of a polygon by measuring the lengths of its sides and adding them. For a rectangle, you can use the formula $P = 2 \cdot L + 2 \cdot W$, where L is the length and W is the width. You can approximate the perimeter of shapes with curved sides by using string or by drawing a polygon that closely matches the shape and finding its perimeter.

This quote from the novel *Contact* by Carl Sagan mentions a relationship between the circumference and diameter of any circle.

In whatever galaxy you happen to find yourself,
you take the circumference, divide it by its diameter,
measure closely enough, and uncover a miracle.

In the following exercises, you will examine the relationship that Sagan is describing.

✅ Develop & Understand: A

For Exercies 1–5, your group will need five objects with circular faces, for example, a soup can, a plate, or a quarter.

1. Follow these steps for each object.
   - Use string or a measuring tape to approximate the circumference of the object.
   - Trace the circular face of the object. Cut out the tracing. Fold it in half to form a crease along the diameter of the circle. Measure the diameter.

Record your measurements in a table like this one.   Tables will vary.

Object	Circumference, C	Diameter, d

2. Possible answer: The circumference is about 3 times the diameter.

3. Students should find that the quotient is about 3 for each object.

4. All groups should get values close to 3 for all the objects.

2. Do you see a relationship between the circumference and the diameter of each circle? If so, describe it.

3. The quotation from *Contact* mentions dividing the circumference by the diameter. Add a column to your table showing the quotient $C \div d$ for each object. Describe any patterns you see.

4. Share your group's $C \div d$ results with the class.

5. Does the $C \div d$ value depend on the size of the circle? Explain.
No; the $C \div d$ value is about the same for all the objects, regardless of their size.

✅ Develop & Understand: A

Suggested Grouping: Groups of 3 or 4

▶ **Exercise 1** Check with each group to be sure students are measuring the circumference and diameter correctly. Suggest measuring to the nearest tenth of a centimeter or to the nearest eighth of an inch.

Have some students measure in customary and others measure in metric.

▶ **Exercises 1 and 3** Prepare your own table for Exercises 1 and 3. The measurements and quotients that students record in their tables should be close to yours, although they do not need to be the same as yours. Ask students to express the quotients as decimals rounded to the nearest tenth.

▶ **Exercise 4** Have groups record the quotients from Exercise 3 on the board. This will facilitate class discussion with the results.

▶ **Exercise 5** Make sure the quotients students find are close to 3.

Teacher Tips Students may have made computational errors in **Exercise 3**. Students who are using measurements made in inches may have had difficulty with division of fractions. Students who used measurements made in centimeters may be having trouble placing decimal points in the correct position in quotients. You may need to provide some individual help to address these difficulties.

Wrap-Up Be sure to discuss the results from Exercises 4 and 5 with the class. The key observation is that all quotients are close to 3.

Reaching All Learners

OL **On Level** Some students may find the following approach helpful in measuring the diameter of a circular object. Have students trace the object on a sheet of paper, cut out the circle, and fold the cutout so that the two halves match. Students can then measure the straight edge of the cutout to find the diameter.

Teacher Tips Discuss the material on page 46 with the class. Students may be interested to know that the value of π has been calculated to many millions of decimal places.

Mathematicians have proved that the decimal for π never ends. The digits in this decimal never repeat in groups the way they do in decimals for fractions such as $\frac{1}{7}$ or $\frac{5}{9}$. This is why we use a special symbol when we want to talk about the exact value of the number.

The formulas for the circumference of a circle are easy to obtain if one accepts the fact that $C \div d$ is equal to π for all circles. Have students repeat that the *ratio* of the circumference to the diameter is π.

· ·

Math Link
Give students several examples of irrational numbers including π and $\sqrt{2}$.

· ·

Math Link
Decimal numbers that never end or repeat are called *irrational numbers*. Whole numbers, fractions, and the decimals with which you have worked to this point are called *rational numbers*.

No matter what size a circle is, the circumference divided by the diameter is always the same value. You probably discovered that this quotient is a little more than 3. The exact value is a decimal number whose digits never end or repeat. This value has been given the special name "pi" and is represented by the Greek letter π.

The symbol π is used to represent the ratio $\frac{C}{d}$, where C is the circumference of a circle and d is the diameter. The ratio $\frac{C}{d}$ can be written as $C \div d$.

Since the digits of π never end or repeat, it is impossible to write its exact numeric value. The number 3.14 is often used as an approximation of π. You can press the  key on your calculator to get a closer approximation.

Use the division equation $\pi = C \div d$ to write the related multiplication equation $C = \pi \cdot d$. This is the formula for computing the circumference C of a circle when you know its diameter d.

Circumference of a Circle
$C = \pi \cdot d$
In this formula, *C* is the circumference and *d* is the diameter. Since the diameter of a circle is twice the radius *r*, you can also write the formula in the following ways.
$C = \pi \cdot 2 \cdot r \qquad\qquad C = 2 \cdot \pi \cdot r$

Since the radius of this circle is 2.5 cm, the diameter is 5 cm.

$$C = \pi \cdot d$$
$$= \pi \cdot 5$$

2.5 cm

The exact circumference of the circle is $5 \cdot \pi$ cm. Although you cannot write the circumference as an exact numeric value, you can use the π key on your calculator to find an approximation.

$$C = \pi \cdot 5\text{cm} \approx 15.71 \text{ cm}$$

The symbol ≈ means "is approximately equal to."

Mathematical Background

π It has long been known that the decimal for π does not terminate and is not a repeating decimal. However, infinitely long decimals need not be repeating decimals for their digits to occur in some kind of pattern. Is there any kind of regular pattern in the decimal for π? No one knows!

★ indicates multi-step problem

✅ Develop & Understand: B

For Exercises 6 and 7, write your answer in terms of π.

6. Find the circumference of a circle with diameter 9 centimeters. 9π cm

7. Find the circumference of this circle where a radius has been drawn.   20π in.

10 in.

For Exercises 8 and 9, write your answer as a decimal rounded to the nearest hundredth. Use your calculator's [π] key to approximate π. If your calculator does not have a [π] key, use 3.14 as an approximation for π.

8. A circular pool has a circumference of about 16 meters. What is the pool's diameter?   About 5.09 m

9. The radius of Earth at the equator is about 4,000 miles.

   a. Suppose you could wrap a string around Earth's equator. How long would the string have to be to reach all the way around? Assume the equator is a perfect circle.
   About 25,132.74 mi

   ★ b. Now suppose you could raise the string one mile above Earth's surface. How much string would you have to add to your piece from Part a to go all the way around?
   About 6.28 mi

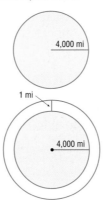

4,000 mi

1 mi

4,000 mi

Share & Summarize

Explain what π is in your own words. Be sure to discuss the following.   See margin.

   • how it is related to circles

   • its approximate value

✅ Develop & Understand: B

Suggested Grouping: Individuals or Pairs

▶ **Exercise 6** Students need only substitute 9 for *d* in the formula $C = \pi \cdot d$ and evaluate the resulting expression.

▶ **Exercise 8** Students use what they know about equivalent multiplication and division equations to solve $16 = \pi \cdot d$.

Share & Summarize

This Share & Summarize exercise is intended to help you assess how well students understand the meaning of π. You may want to add some related exercises that ask students to find the circumference of a circle, given its diameter or radius.

Troubleshooting Students sometimes confuse the radius and diameter when they solve exercises dealing with circles. Urge them to read exercises and examine diagrams carefully. If students are having trouble recalling the correct meaning of the words, remind them that both words refer to segments that contain the center of a circle. A radius is shorter than a diameter, and the word radius is shorter than the word diameter.

Teacher Tips Have students practice using the π key on their calculator when solving the exercises on this page.

Additional Answer for Share & Summarize

Possible answer: π is the number you get when you divide a circle's circumference by its diameter. So, if you multiply the diameter of a circle by π, you get the circle's circumference. The value of π is a little more than 3. The digits of π never end or repeat, so it is impossible to give the exact value of π. My calculator gives the approximation of 3.141592654.

★ indicates multi-step problem

Investigation 1
Pages 40–43
Exercises 1–5, 10–11

Investigation 2
Pages 44–47
Exercises 6–9, 12–15

Assign Anytime
Mixed Review 16–29

▶ **Exercise 1a** This is a good exercise for assessing how well students understand the use of polygons to estimate perimeters of figures with curved sides. All of the polygons students use for their approximations will have two or more vertices between the endpoints of the curved side of the infield. The closest approximations can be obtained by using vertices that are evenly spaced along the curved side.

▶ **Exercise 3a** In **Part a**, students can use string to measure the perimeter of the field. If they are using flexible plastic rulers, they can bend the ruler to measure the curved side and then add the lengths of the two straight sides.

▶ **Exercise 3b** In **Part b**, students can multiply the answer from **Part a** by 100 and then by 5 (for five laps) to find that the player will run slightly more than 5,560 ft. This is a distance of a little more than one mile.

Math Link
If one inch is 100 feet, 52.8 inches are 5,280 feet, or one mile.

Practice & Apply

In Exercises 1–3, use this diagram of a baseball field.

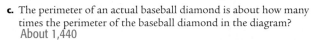

1. Consider the baseball diamond in this diagram.

  a. Find the perimeter of the diamond to the nearest $\frac{1}{4}$ inch. 3 in.

  b. An actual baseball diamond is a square with sides 90 feet long. What is the perimeter of an actual baseball diamond? 360 ft

  c. The perimeter of an actual baseball diamond is about how many times the perimeter of the baseball diamond in the diagram?
   About 1,440

2. Rosita approximated the perimeter of the infield using a quadrilateral. She found a perimeter of about $6\frac{3}{4}$ inches.

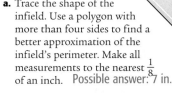

  a. Trace the shape of the infield. Use a polygon with more than four sides to find a better approximation of the infield's perimeter. Make all measurements to the nearest $\frac{1}{8}$ of an inch. Possible answer: 7 in.

  b. How does your approximation compare to Rosita's? It is more than hers, and it is closer to the actual perimeter.

3. Suppose the manager tells a player to run five laps around the entire baseball field, including the outfield. The player stays as close to the outer edge as possible.

  a. Measure the perimeter of the field in the diagram at the top of this page to the nearest $\frac{1}{8}$ of an inch. About $7\frac{1}{8}$ in.

★**b.** Suppose one inch on the diagram represents approximately 100 feet on the actual field. About how many miles will the player run in his five laps around the field? About $\frac{2}{3}$ mile

Math Link
1 mile = 5,280 feet

Real-World Link

Founded in 1800 in Washington, D.C., the Library of Congress is one of the greatest national libraries. In addition to 15,000,000 books, it houses impressive collections of manuscripts, music, prints, and maps.

4. This is the floor plan of the Harperstown Library. What is the perimeter of the floor? 130.6 ft

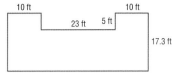

5. Give the dimensions of five rectangles that have a perimeter of 50 feet. See margin.

6. Find the circumference of a circle with diameter 7 meters. Write your answer in terms of π. 7 π m

7. Find the circumference of a circle with radius 4.25 inches. Write your answer in terms of π and as a decimal rounded to the nearest hundredth. 8.5 π in., 26.70 in.

8. The circumference of a tire is 150 inches. What is the tire's radius? Use the [π] key on your calculator or 3.14 to approximate π. Round your answer to the nearest hundredth. 23.87 in.

9. Challenge The radius of the wheel on Jahmal's bike is 2 feet.

★ **a.** If he rides 18.9 feet, how many full turns will the wheel make?

★ **b.** If the wheel on Jahmal's bike turned 115 times, how many feet did Jahmal ride? About how many miles is this?

★ **c.** If Jahmal rides 20 miles, how many times will his wheel turn? 9, 10. See margin.

Connect & Extend

10. Two shapes are *nested* when one is completely inside the other.

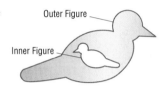

Outer Figure

Inner Figure

a. Draw two nested shapes so that the outer shape has a greater perimeter than the inner shape. Give the perimeters of both shapes.

b. Draw two nested shapes so that the inner shape has a greater perimeter than the outer shape. Give the perimeters of both shapes.

c. Draw two nested shapes so that the outer shape has the same perimeter as the inner shape. Give the perimeters of both shapes.

d. Look at your shapes from Parts a–c. In each case, which shape has more space inside, the inner shape or the outer shape? How do you know?

▶ **Exercise 4** Students should be careful to note that there are two 5 foot sides in this figure.

▶ **Exercises 6 and 7** The answers need to be exact, so suggest students do the calculations with paper and pencil using 3.14 for π.

▶ **Exercise 8** Answers may vary slightly, depending on whether students are using the π key on a calculator or are doing the calculations with paper and pencil.

▶ **Exercise 9** Ask students to show what expressions they evaluated to get their answers for each part of this exercise. This will help you check the validity of the approach they used to answer each question.

▶ **Exercise 10** This exercise lends itself easily to a guess-check-and-improve approach. It can also lead to some imaginative thinking about perimeter. The easiest figures to deal with are polygons. One approach is to use polygons in which all intersecting sides are perpendicular. Other types of polygons are certainly possible, as the sample answers demonstrate.

Real-World Link

Ask students to research the shape of the Library of Congress building. How would they find its perimeter?

Lesson 1.3 Measure Around **49**

Additional Answers

5. Possible answer: 20 ft × 5 ft, 10 ft × 15 ft, 12.5 ft × 12.5 ft, 8 ft × 17 ft, 1 ft × 24 ft

9a. About $1\frac{1}{2}$

9b. 460π, or about 1,445 ft; about 0.27 mi

9c. About 8,403 times

Additional Answers for Exercise 10 are on page 55A.

▶ **Exercise 11c Part c** of this exercise (and **Exercise 10d**) can be viewed as readiness builders for Lessons 7.1 and 7.2, which deal with area.

▶ **Exercise 12** Answers for this exercise may vary slightly, depending on whether students use the π key on a calculator or do the calculations with pencil and paper. The answer given here was obtained by using the calculator value of π.

11. Many artists incorporate mathematics into their artwork. The artwork at the right is a tessellation. A *tessellation* is a design made of identical shapes that fit together without gaps or overlaps.

One way to make a shape that will tessellate is to cut a rectangle into two pieces and slide one piece to the other side.

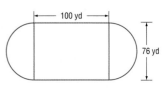

Original Shape   New Shape   Tessellation

a. Find the perimeter of the original shape in the artwork above. 10 cm

b. Trace the new shape. Estimate its perimeter by using a polygon approximation or a piece of string.   Possible answer: 10.6 cm

c. When the new shape is formed from the original, the space inside the shape, the *area,* stays the same. However, the perimeter changes. Explain why this happens.

11c. Possible answer: The curvy side of the new shape is longer than the corresponding straight side of the original rectangle. The space inside is the same because everything that was cut off was added back.

12. This is a diagram of the outer lane of the track at Albright Middle School. The lane is made of two straight segments and two semicircles, or half circles. Suppose a student runs one lap around the track in this lane. How many yards will she run?   About 438.76 yd

├── 100 yd ──┤

76 yd

13. Caroline wrapped a piece of string around the circumference of a circle with a diameter of 23 inches. She cut the string to the length of the circumference and then formed a rectangle with the string. Give the approximate dimensions of three rectangles she could make.   18.1 in. · 18 in., 30 in. · 6.1 in., 10 in. · 26.1 in.

14. A circle with radius 6.5 inches is cut into four wedges and rearranged to form another shape.

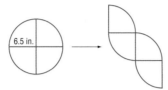

Does the perimeter change? How do you know? If it does change, by how much does it increase or decrease?   See margin.

15. In Your Own Words Describe what perimeter is and how to find it for various shapes. Give an example of a situation in which finding a shape's perimeter would be useful.

15. Possible answer: Perimeter is the distance around a polygon. It can be found by adding the side lengths. Perimeter can be used to find the amount of fencing needed for a schoolyard playground.

20. $\frac{10}{15}$, or $\frac{2}{3}$

Mixed Review

For Exercises 16–21, find each sum or difference.

16. $\frac{3}{7} + \frac{1}{7}$ $\frac{4}{7}$ **17.** $\frac{1}{4} + \frac{1}{4} + \frac{1}{4}$ $\frac{3}{4}$ **18.** $\frac{13}{32} + \frac{13}{32} + \frac{6}{32}$ 1

19. $\frac{9}{5} - \frac{6}{5}$ $\frac{3}{5}$ **20.** $\frac{12}{15} - \frac{1}{15} - \frac{1}{15}$ **21.** $\frac{5}{7} - \frac{2}{7} - \frac{3}{7}$ 0

Math Link
A *line of symmetry*, or a *reflection line*, divides a figure into mirror-image halves. If you fold a figure on a line of symmetry, the two halves match exactly.

Earth Science The symbols in Exercises 22–24 are used in *meteorology*, the study of weather. Copy each symbol, and draw all its lines of symmetry.

22. violent rain showers   **23.** ice pellets   **24.** hurricane

No lines of symmetry

Give the next four terms in each sequence.

25. 64, 32, 16, 8, ...   4, 2, 1, $\frac{1}{2}$ **26.** 4, 6, 5, 7, 6, 8, 7, ...   9, 8, 10, 9

Additional Answer
14. Yes; it increases because there are two extra segments on the "outside" of the shape. In the circle, these segments were inside. Since each of these segments is a 6.5-inch radius, the perimeter of the new shape is 2 · 6.5 in., or 13 in., greater than the perimeter of the circle.

Quick Check
Informal Assessment Students should be able to:

✔ use the side lengths of a polygon to calculate the perimeter of the polygon

✔ use polygons to approximate the perimeter of a shape with curved sides

✔ understand and use formulas for the circumference of a circle

Quick Quiz

1. Find the perimeter of each figure.

a.
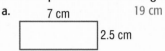

b.
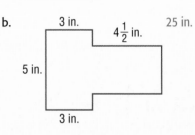

2. Draw a figure that has two straight sides and two curved sides. Use a 6-sided polygon to approximate the perimeter of your figure.   Check students' work.

3. What is the diameter of a circle that has a radius of $13\frac{1}{8}$ in.? $26\frac{1}{4}$ in.

4. Find the circumference of the circle shown below. Round your answer to the nearest tenth of a centimeter.   47.1 cm

Review & Self-Assessment

Review & Self-Assessment

Review & Self-Assessment allows students an opportunity to reflect on the important topics within the chapters and to prepare for formal assessment.

Chapter Summary
This summary helps students recall the major topics of the chapter.

Vocabulary
Students should be able to explain each of the terms listed in the vocabulary section.

▶ **Exercises 4–6 Extension** For each polygon, have students classify the figure.

Several formative assessment opportunities are found in the Chapter Resources Masters, including two equivalent **Chapter Test** forms as well as a **Performance Assessment** for each chapter and each semester.

Vocabulary

- **acute angle**
- **angle**
- **chord**
- **circumference**
- **concave polygon**
- **diameter**
- **formula**
- **intersecting lines**
- **line symmetry**
- **obtuse angle**
- **perimeter**
- **perpendicular**
- **polygon**
- **protractor**
- **radius**
- **reference line**
- **regular polygon**
- **right angle**
- **vertex**
- **vertical angles**

1. No; the figure is not made from straight segments.
3. No; each segment does not touch exactly two other segments.
4. Possible answer:

Chapter Summary

In this chapter, you focused on patterns in geometry. You learned to identify, name, and classify polygons. You worked with angles and studied some important properties about the side lengths and angle measures of triangles.

Next, you explored ideas about geometry and measurement. You started by working with angles. You measured angles and drew angles with given measures. You looked at relationships among the angles formed by intersecting lines. You explored the relationship between a polygon's number of angles or sides and the sum of its interior angles.

You then found the perimeters of polygons by adding side lengths. You estimated the perimeters of curved objects by using string and by approximating with polygons. You also learned that the ratio of the circumference of any circle to its diameter is equal to π.

Strategies and Applications

The questions in this section will help you review and apply the important ideas and strategies developed in this chapter.

Identifying, naming, and classifying polygons

Tell whether each figure is a polygon. If it is not, explain why.

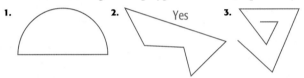

Draw a polygon that fits the given description, if possible. If it is not possible, say so.

4. a concave hexagon with line symmetry
5. a regular quadrilateral without line symmetry   Not possible
6. a concave pentagon with no line symmetry   Possible answer:

7. Possible answer: Add the two shorter lengths. If the sum is greater than the third length, the three segments can form a triangle. Segments of length 5, 6, and 7 can form a triangle. Segments of lengths 3, 3, and 10 cannot.

8. Subtract the sum of the two angle measures from 180°. This works because the sum of the angle measures for any triangle is 180°.

9a. Possible answer: The angle on the left is clearly less than 90°.

9b. Possible answer: When he measured the angle on the left, the ray passed through the mark labeled with both 50° and 130°. Victor must have read the wrong mark on the protractor.

9c. Possible answer: Before you measure the angle, think about whether it is greater than 90° or less than 90°. This will help you choose the correct angle measure.

Understanding and applying properties of triangles

7. Explain how you can tell whether three segments can be joined to form a triangle. Give the lengths of three segments that can form a triangle and the lengths of three segments that cannot form a triangle.

8. If you know the measures of two angles of a triangle, how can you find the measure of the third angle? Explain why your method works.

Measuring angles and drawing angles with given measures

9. Victor measured these angles with a protractor. He said both angles have measure of 130°.

   a. How do you know that Victor is incorrect?

   b. What mistake do you think Victor made?

   c. What advice would you give to help him measure angles correctly?

10. Draw an angle with measure 320°. Explain the steps you followed. See margin.

Demonstrating Skills

Find the measure of each angle.

11.
   23°

12.
   245°

13.
   100°

14.
   340°

Draw an angle with the given measure.

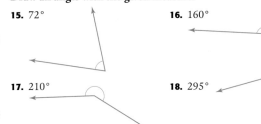

15. 72°

16. 160°

17. 210°

18. 295°

▶ **Exercise 7** Encourage students whose explanations state only that they can use the triangle inequality to write a more detailed answer and explain what the triangle inequality means.

▶ **Exercises 11–14** Remind students that they can use benchmark angles to estimate the angles, then use a protractor to give a more accurate measurement.

Additional Answer

10. Possible explanation: I drew a 40° angle. The angle "outside" the 40° has a measure of 320°, so I marked that angle.

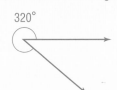
   320°

▶ **Exercise 21** Watch for students who do not identify the quadrilaterals that are concave.

▶ **Exercise 22** Watch for students who "start at" a different letter and think that gives a unique pentagon. Remind students to use the same direction as they identify the vertices.

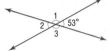

19. Find the measures of Angles 1, 2, and 3.
$m\angle 1 = m\angle 3 = 127°, m\angle 2 = 53°$

20. *ABG, BFG, BCD*
21. *ABFG, BDEF, ADEG, GBCE, GBDE, BCEF*
22. *ABCEG*

23. Quadrilateral, concave, line symmetry
24. Hexagon, concave
25. Quadrilateral, line symmetry
26. Pentagon, regular, line symmetry
27. Hexagon, regular, line symmetry
28. Triangle, line symmetry

In Exercises 20–22, refer to this figure.

20. Name all the triangles in the figure.

21. Name all the quadrilaterals in the figure.

22. Name all the pentagons in the figure.

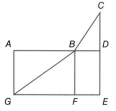

In Exercises 23–28, tell which of these terms describe each polygon. List all terms that apply.

triangle	pentagon	concave	line symmetry
quadrilateral	hexagon	regular	

23.   **24.**   **25.**

26.   **27.**   **28.**

Estimate the measure of each angle.

29.  60° **30.** 270° **31.** 45°

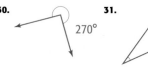

Tell whether the given measures could be the angle measures of a triangle.

32. 45°, 45°, 45° No   **33.** 80°, 40°, 80° No   **34.** 54°, 66°, 60° Yes

38. Sample answer: A concave polygon will have one angle measuring more than 180°.

35. Explain how you can determine if a polygon is concave.

36. Draw two angles that each measure more than 180°. Explain how you know they measure more than 180°.   Student answers will vary.

37. A quadrilateral has three angle measures of 45°, 60°, and 100°. What is the missing angle measure?   155°

38. A rectangle has a length of 4.2 meters and a width of 3.6 meters. What is its perimeter?   15.6 meters

For Exercises 39 and 40, write each answer in terms of π and as a decimal rounded to the nearest hundredth.

39. Find the circumference of a circle with a diameter of 5 inches.   5π, 15.71 inches

40. Find the circumference of this circle.   12π, 37.70 cm

6 cm

Test-Taking Practice

SHORT RESPONSE

1 Lisa is putting a fence around a circular garden. If the radius of the garden is 4 feet, how many feet of fencing will Lisa need around the garden?

Show your work.

Answer _____

Show your work:
Use $C = 2 \cdot \pi \cdot r$.
$C = 2 \cdot \pi \cdot 4 = 8\pi$

Answer: 8π, or 25.12 feet

MULTIPLE CHOICE

2 Which of the following could be the side lengths of a triangle?
  A 3, 5, 8
  B 5, 17, 9
  C 13, 4, 6
  (**D**) 14, 6, 10

3 Which term best describes the polygon shown?
  F octagon
  (**G**) hexagon
  H pentagon
  J regular

4 A triangle has two angle measures of 23° and 46°. What is the measure of the third angle of the triangle?
  A 21°
  B 69°
  (**C**) 111°
  D 157°

5 A rectangle has a length of 3.4 cm and a width of 1.2 cm. What is its perimeter?
  F 4.08 cm
  G 4.6 cm
  (**H**) 9.2 cm
  J 20.16 cm

▶ **Exercise 37** Remind students that the sum of the angles of a quadrilateral is 360°.

▶ **Exercises 39 and 40** Students' answers will vary slightly depending on whether a π key or 3.14 is used to approximate π.

Lesson 1.1, Develop & Understand: A (p. 7)

4.

Polygon	Names	Score
Triangle	RQT, RST, RUV, WVT	12
Quadrilateral	QRST, QRUW, TSUW, QRVW, TSUV	20
Pentagon	RQTVU, RSTWV	10
Hexagon	RQTSUV, RQWVTS	12
	Total Score	54

5. Possible answer:

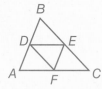

Polygon	Names	Score
Triangle	ABC, ADF, DEF, BED, ECF	15
Quadrilateral	BDFE, ADEF, CEDF, ADEC, BDFC, ABEF	24
Pentagon		
Hexagon		
	Total Score	39

Answers that do not fit on the student page or in the margin of the Teacher's Guide can be found in the **Answer Appendix** pages at the end of each chapter.

Lesson 1.3, On Your Own (p. 49)

10a. Possible answer: inner perimeter: 6.7 cm; outer perimeter: 17.6 cm

10b. Possible answer: inner perimeter: 14.3 cm; outer perimeter: 14.2 cm

10c. Possible answer: inner perimeter: 17.7 cm; outer perimeter: 17.7 cm

10d. The outer shape; it has all of the space in the inner shape plus more space outside the inner shape.

Notes

Fractions and Decimals

Chapter Overview

This chapter uses patterns to help students understand fractions and decimals. The lesson begins with models to visualize fractions and then explores how to write equivalent fractions using fraction families. Students will also estimate fractions using benchmarks and compare fractions using other patterns. Then they move from using patterns in fractions to discovering patterns in decimals.

In the second lesson, students use place value and the patterns revealed by multiplying or dividing decimals by powers of 10 to compare and order decimals and to perform some simple decimal calculations. They find patterns in decimal equivalents of fractions with the same denominator. They also work with repeating decimals. Finally, students use their understanding of equivalent decimals and fractions to order both fractions and decimals.

The **Big** Picture

Links to the Past	Chapter **2**	Links to the Future
Grade 5 Comparing fractions with like denominators. Finding fractions equivalent to simple fractions such as $\frac{1}{2}$ and $\frac{1}{4}$.	**Lesson 2.1** (p. 58) Patterns in Fractions	**Course 1, Chapter 4** Fraction and Decimal Operations (pp. 196–287) **Course 1, Chapter 5** Rate, Ratio, and Proportion (pp. 288–345) **Course 2, Chapter 10** Proportional Reasoning and Percents (pp. 492–555) **Course 3, Chapter 3** Percents and Proportions (pp. 110–143)
Grade 5 Understanding place value of whole numbers and decimals. Comparing whole numbers.	**Lesson 2.2** (p. 74) Patterns in Decimals	**Course 1, Chapter 4** Fraction and Decimal Operations (pp. 196–287) **Course 1, Chapter 6** Percents (pp. 346–395)
Grade 5 Dividing whole numbers. Understanding simple fraction and decimal equivalents.	**Lesson 2.3** (p. 88) Fraction and Decimal Equivalents	**Course 1, Chapter 4** Fraction and Decimal Operations (pp. 196–287)

Mathematical Background

Numerical patterns are at the heart of mathematics. In this chapter, students look at some fraction and decimal patterns. Throughout the chapter, the idea of equivalence is stressed as students learn the value of using equivalent numbers to see relationships and to compare numbers. They will extend these concepts when they calculate with fractions, decimals, and percents in Chapters 4 and 6.

Factors, multiples, primes, and relative primes have important roles in generating equivalent fractions that make calculations easier and relationships more obvious. The chapter uses the term *fraction family* to refer to a set of equivalent fractions such as $\frac{1}{8}, \frac{2}{16}, \frac{3}{24}, \frac{4}{32}$, and so on. Since equivalent representations have the same value, the representation used makes no difference, mathematically. In any particular situation, you can use a fraction in lowest terms if it makes the work simpler. In some situations, working with a fraction in lowest terms is easiest. In others, another form may be simpler.

Fraction Families You can find a fraction equivalent to a given fraction by multiplying or dividing the numerator and denominator by the same number. When a fraction is in *lowest terms*, the numerator and denominator are *relatively prime*. A fraction family is a grouping of equivalent fractions and is named for the member that is in lowest terms. For example, the fraction family for $\frac{3}{8}$ includes $\frac{3}{8}, \frac{6}{16}, \frac{9}{24}, \frac{12}{32}$, and so on. Stress the importance of using patterns to find other members of the family.

Change Fractions to Decimals One way to change a fraction to a decimal without doing long division is to find an equivalent fraction with a denominator of 100. For example, $\frac{32}{100}$ is equivalent to $\frac{8}{25}$. Therefore, $\frac{8}{25} = 0.32$.

The ideas in this chapter lay the groundwork for more extensive work with fractions and percents in Courses 2 and 3. In particular, students will find percentages and solve algebraic equations.

Additional Reading

Through twenty years of research, the Rational Number Project has found that the curriculum for learning fractions should include active involvement with multiple concrete models. In this chapter, students will use benchmark fractions and fraction models to help them learn. They will also compare fractions and decimals and use hundreds blocks.

Planning Guide
Lesson Resources

	Lesson 2.1 Pacing: 4 days	**Lesson 2.2** Pacing: 4 days	**Lesson 2.3** Pacing: 4 days
Lesson Title	**Patterns in Fractions** (p. 58)	**Patterns in Decimals** (p. 74)	**Fraction and Decimal Equivalents** (p. 88)
Lesson Objectives	• To write a fraction as a mixed number and a mixed number as a fraction • To find equivalent fractions • To write fractions in lowest terms • To compare and order fractions • To use benchmarks to estimate the values of other fractions	• To recognize decimal place value • To write decimals as fractions whose denominators are powers of 10 • To multiply and divide numbers by powers of 10 and represent the answers as decimals • To measure distance using the metric system and to convert among linear metric units • To compare and order decimals	• To estimate fraction and decimal equivalents • To find decimal equivalents to fractions • To find fraction equivalents to decimals • To demonstrate an understand of repeating decimals • To find patterns in decimal and fraction equivalents • To order and compare fractions and decimals
Materials	Lesson 2.1 Masters 1–3, scissors (optional), fraction pieces cut from colored paper	Lesson 2.2 Masters 1–3, metersticks, tape, Chapter 2 Master 1	Lesson 2.3 Masters 1–4, rulers, fraction calculators, 100-grids
Quick Review Math Handbook	**Lesson 2.1** Fractions and Equivalent Fractions **Lesson 2.2** Comparing and Ordering Fractions	**Lesson 2.5** Naming and Ordering Decimals	**Lesson 2.9** Fractions, Decimals, and Percent Relationships
Print Resources	CRM Study Guide and Intervention (p. 4) CRM Skills Practice (p. 5) CRM Problem-Solving Practice (p. 6) CRM Enrichment (p. 7) • Investigation Notebook and Reflection Journal • Differentiation Handbook	CRM Study Guide and Intervention (p. 12) CRM Skills Practice (p. 13) CRM Problem-Solving Practice (p. 14) CRM Enrichment (p. 15) • Investigation Notebook and Reflection Journal • Differentiation Handbook	CRM Study Guide and Intervention (p. 20) CRM Skills Practice (p. 21) CRM Problem-Solving Practice (p. 22) CRM Enrichment (p. 23) • Investigation Notebook and Reflection Journal • Differentiation Handbook
Technology Resources	TeacherWorks Plus Classroom Presentation Toolkit ExamView Assessment Suite StudentWorks Plus Math Online ▷ Brain Pops • Concepts in Motion	TeacherWorks Plus Classroom Presentation Toolkit ExamView Assessment Suite StudentWorks Plus Math Online ▷ Brain Pops • Concepts in Motion	TeacherWorks Plus Classroom Presentation Toolkit ExamView Assessment Suite StudentWorks Plus Math Online ▷ Brain Pops • Concepts in Motion

*Included in the Impact Mathematics Manipulative Kit

Assessment Resources

MARS Assessment: Teaching with Purpose

Sports Results
In *Sports Results,* students put two place decimals in order and correctly place them on a number line. Students list the scores of athletes in a High Jump contest and a 100 Meter Sprint.

Targeting the Task
- **Diagnostic**—Use Exercises 1–2 in the *Sports Results* assessment to determine students' understanding of how to put two place decimals in order. For those students who do not have this understanding, completing this unit is needed.

- **Formative**—Exercises 1–2 can be administered individually according to the lessons.

- **Summative**—Administer the complete *Sports Results* performance-based assessment.

Chapter 2 MARS Assessment
(pp. 49–52)

Assessment Planning Guide
Assessments are available for investigations, lessons, and chapters.

Customize and create multiple versions of tests and quizzes.

	Student Edition	Teacher Edition	Other Resources
Diagnostic			CRM Chapter 2 Pretest (p. 30) Math Online Online Chapter Quiz
Formative	Share & Summarize (pp. 60, 63, 65, 67, 79, 81, 91, 93, 97, 99)	Troubleshooting (pp. 60, 63, 65, 76, 79, 81, 92, 95, 99) On the Spot Assessment (pp. 59, 64, 66, 91, 93, 98) Quick Check (pp. 73, 87, 104) Quick Quiz (pp. 73, 87, 104)	
Summative	Review & Self-Assessment (pp. 105–107)		CRM Chapter 2 Test: Forms A and B (pp. 34–43) CRM Standardized Test Practice (p. 47)
Performance-Based	In Your Own Words (pp. 73, 85, 102)		CRM MARS Performance-Based Assessment (p. 49) CRM Chapter Performance Assessment (p. 44)

Differentiated Instruction

Reaching All Learners

Below are suggestions on differentiating the materials presented in this chapter. Additional modifications should be considered.

Approaching Level   **AL**

Benchmarks For students who have difficulty finding and/or using benchmark numbers, create and laminate a permanent number line that they can use repeatedly with wipe-off markers. On the bottom of the page, make lists of common benchmarks that are easy to remember. Show all three forms of each benchmark. Tell students to choose the closest number from the list to the numbers they need to plot on the number line. Have them practice placing the benchmarks on the number line until they are comfortable using those numbers. Remind students that it is important to be able to use all three forms of each number, and encourage them to practice using different benchmark numbers.

Beyond Level   **BL**

Move Ahead Tell students who grasp the concepts about numbers early that they can use the skills in this chapter to create an advertisement for a product. Have them choose any form of the number for the price and create a simple poster advertising their product. Allow them to present their products as part of the project. Encourage them to practice their presentations with a partner and to do their best to make others interested in the product they are selling. Then have students compare their posters, and determine whose product is cheapest by comparing the numbers. Remind them that numbers in different forms can still be compared and ordered.

On Level   **OL**

Visuals Have students create a poster that shows all the different forms of a number (decimal, fraction, and percent). The poster should include a model of the number, e.g. a 10×10, and a section for each form that shows how to write the number in that form. Encourage students to make the information concise and easy-to-read, so that other students can learn from their posters. The poster should be a concrete model for students to use in learning to write and use different forms of a number. Provide several different types of materials for students to use on their posters, and tell them to make the poster interesting and colorful. Then have them present their posters to the class.

English Language Learners   **ELL**

Consistent Vocabulary Some students may have difficulty reading several forms of a number. For example, it may be confusing to see 1.2 and read *one point two*, and then be told to read 1.23 as *one and twenty-three hundredths*, instead of *one point twenty-three*. Try to consistently read numbers the same way. It may be helpful to create a chart showing the different forms of a number and the correct way to read each form (decimal, percent, and fraction). Allow students to refer to the chart as they work. As practice, have partners take turns writing numbers for each other to read out loud. Tell students to listen to their partners and use the chart to determine if the readings were correct.

KEY

 Approaching Level   On Level   Beyond Level   **ELL** English Language Learners

Intervention Planning Guide

CRM Assess students' prerequisite skills and knowledge using the
Chapter Pretest found in the Chapter 2 Resource Masters, p. 30.

Intensive Intervention two or more years below grade level	Strategic Intervention below grade level	On Level	Beyond Level
If students miss 75% of the exercises:	**If** students miss 50% of the exercises:	**If** students miss 25% of the exercises:	**If** students miss 0%–10% of the exercises:
Then use *Math Triumphs,* an intensive intervention	**Then** choose a resource:	**Then** choose a resource:	**Then** choose a resource:
Math Triumphs, Grade 6 • Chapter 1: Fractions • Chapter 3: Decimals	CRM Study Guide and Intervention (pp. 4, 12, 20) • Investigation Notebook and Reflection Journal • Differentiation Handbook Math Online Brain Pops • Concepts in Motion	CRM Skills Practice (pp. 5, 13, 21) CRM Problem-Solving Practice (pp. 6, 14, 22) • Investigation Notebook and Reflection Journal	CRM Enrichment (pp. 7, 15, 23) • Differentiation Handbook

Literature Connections
Recommended Outside Reading for Students
Nonfiction

Tang, Greg. *The Grapes of Math: Mind Stretching Math Riddles.* Scholastic Trade, 2001.

Readers of this book learn creative ways of solving problems using patterns and number combinations. Colorful computer-generated art and riddles draw students into math as a game rather than a homework assignment.

Fiction

Sachar, Louis. *Sideways Arithmetic from Wayside School.* Apple, 1997.

This collection of stories from fictional Wayside school incorporates more than 50 mathematical brain teasers. These fun, real-life applications incorporate many math skills, including finding patterns and following the order of operations.

McGraw Hill Professional Development

Targeted professional development has been articulated throughout the *IMPACT Mathematics* series. The **McGraw-Hill Professional Development Video Library** provides short videos that support the mathematics standards. Log on to www.glencoe.com.

Model Lessons   Instructional Strategies

Real-Life Math

Market Place Values To introduce this chapter, provide students with pages from a newspaper that show stock values and discuss how these values are reported. Ask them to identify the stocks whose prices increased and those whose prices decreased. Discuss how the value of each share was traditionally shown in fractions, at one time going to as small an increment as $\frac{1}{16}$ of a dollar. Point out that this changed in 2000 when market values were reported as decimals.

Think About It Explain that when a stock price goes up, the change is reported as a positive number. A gain of $3 would be shown as 3.00, and a gain of $1.25 would be shown as 1.25. Show students where to find the change in stock value in a newspaper.

CHAPTER
2

Fractions and Decimals

Real-Life Math

Market Place Values *Buy low, sell high!* You may have heard this piece of wisdom about stock investing. Stocks allow people to own parts of companies, from fast-food chains to software developers to retail stores. Stockowners hope the value of their stock will rise over time, allowing them to sell their stocks at a higher price than they paid for them.

Think About It Stock-market reports use decimals to describe how a stock is doing. How might you show *a gain of $3* using a decimal? How about *a gain of $1.25*?

....

Contents in Brief

....

Math Online
Take the **Chapter Readiness Quiz** at glencoe.com.

Chapter Resources

CRM Chapter 2 Resource Masters

CRM English/Spanish Family Letter (pp. 1 and 2)

CRM Lesson Masters (pp. 3, 9–11, 17–19, 25–29)

CRM Chapter 2 Pretest (pp. 30–33)

CRM Chapter 2 Tests (pp. 34–46)

Math Online Online Readiness Quiz • eGlossary

Dear Family,

Chapter 2 extends mathematical ideas to look at patterns in fractions and decimals, numbers you use everyday.

Key Concept—Fractions and Decimals

There are many number patterns found in fractions and decimals. Here is a pattern shown by fractions with the same denominator. Try to predict the numbers in the next column.

Fraction	$\frac{1}{5}$	$\frac{2}{5}$	$\frac{3}{5}$	$\frac{4}{5}$	$\frac{5}{5}$	$\frac{6}{5}$	$\frac{7}{5}$	?
Decimal	0.2	0.4	0.6	0.8	1.0	1.2	1.4	?

Knowing these patterns and the decimal equivalents of common fractions will make it easier to calculate with fractions and decimals.

Chapter Vocabulary

decimal-fraction   mixed number

equivalent fractions   repeating decimal

improper fraction   terminating decimal

lowest terms

Home Activities

Fractions and decimals are everywhere.

- Ask your student to note the many ways fractions and decimals, in addition to money, are used in his or her day-to-day life.
- Discuss recipes as a meal is made. Compare the fractions used in different ingredients.
- When running an errand, have your student describe distances with fractions of miles.

Family Letter

Another version of the Family Letter, available in English and Spanish, is found in the Chapter 2 Resource Masters. You may want to send a copy of this letter home with your students.

Key Concept—Fractions and Decimals

Introduce students to fractions by using number patterns and decimals. Make a table showing fractions in fourths and give their decimal equivalents. Also, show students the pattern in tenths and their decimal equivalents.

Home Activities

- Discuss the relative sizes of different fractions of a pizza. Is a fourth of a pizza more or less than a fifth?

- Each day, have your student cut out a different circle from construction paper to post on the refrigerator. Have him or her label a fraction of the circle using $\frac{1}{2}, \frac{1}{3}, \frac{1}{4}, \frac{1}{6},$ and $\frac{1}{8}$.

Key Vocabulary

English (Spanish) *Introduce the most important terms from Chapter 2.*

decimal-fraction (decimal fracciones) A fraction that has a denominator of base 10; for example, $\frac{4}{10}$ is a decimal-fraction. (p. 93)

equivalent fractions (fracciones equivalents) Fractions that describe the same portion of a whole, or name the same number; for example, $\frac{3}{4}, \frac{9}{12},$ and $\frac{30}{40}$ are equivalent fractions. (p. 62)

improper fraction (fracción impropia) A fraction in which the numerator is greater than the denominator. (p. 60)

lowest terms (en términus reducidos o reducida) A fraction is in lowest terms if its numerator and denominator are relatively prime. For example, $\frac{5}{6}$ is in lowest terms because the only common factor of 5 and 6 is 1. (p. 62)

mixed number (número mixto) A whole number and a fraction; for example $12\frac{3}{4}$ is a mixed number. (p. 60)

repeating decimal (decimal periódico) A decimal with a pattern of digits that repeat without stopping; for example, 0.23232323... is a repeating decimal. (p. 95)

terminating decimal (decimal finito) A decimal whose equivalent fraction has a denominator in lowest terms with a prime factorization of only base 2 and base 5. For example, 0.024 is a terminating decimal. (p. 91)

Patterns in Fractions

Objectives

▶ To write a fraction as a mixed number and a mixed number as a fraction

▶ To find equivalent fractions

▶ To write fractions in lowest terms

▶ To compare and order fractions

▶ To use benchmarks to estimate the values of other fractions

Overview

In this lesson, students use fractions in a variety of settings as they find equivalent fractions, compare fractions, and approximate fractions.

They will apply these topics in this chapter and in Chapter 4 as they convert from fractions to decimals and from decimals to fractions.

Advance Preparation

You may want to a transparency of Lesson 2.1 Master 1 along with Lesson 2.1 Masters 1–3 to facilitate class activities and discussions for presenting new topics.

	Summary	Materials	On Your Own Exercises (pp. 68–73)	Assessment Opportunities
Investigation 1 (p. 59) *Pacing:* 1 day	Students review fractions and mixed numbers.	Transparency of Lesson 2.1 Master 1 (optional), Lesson 2.1 Masters 1–2 (optional), scissors (optional)	Practice & Apply: 1–5 Connect & Extend: 35, 36 Mixed Review: 48–52	On the Spot Assessment (p. 59) Share & Summarize (p. 60) Troubleshooting (p. 60)
Investigation 2 (p. 61) *Pacing:* 1 day	Students find equivalent fractions and write fractions in lowest terms.	Lesson 2.1 Master 3 or fraction pieces cut from different-colored paper	Practice & Apply: 6–21 Connect & Extend: 37–41 Mixed Review: 48–52	Share & Summarize (p. 63) Troubleshooting (p. 63)
Investigation 3 (p. 64) *Pacing:* 1 day	Students compare and order fractions by rewriting fractions with common denominators.		Practice & Apply: 22–29 Connect & Extend: 42–44 Mixed Review: 48–52	On the Spot Assessment (p. 64) Share & Summarize (p. 65) Troubleshooting (p. 65)
Investigation 4 (p. 66) *Pacing:* 1 day	Students use benchmarks to estimate the values of other fractions.		Practice & Apply: 30–34 Connect & Extend: 45–47 Mixed Review: 48–52	On the Spot Assessment (p. 66) Share & Summarize (p. 67)

Leveled Lesson Resources

CRM *Available in:* **Chapter 2 Resource Masters**

Study Guide and Intervention (p. 4) — AL

Lesson 2.1 Study Guide and Intervention
Patterns in Fractions

Fractions that name the same number are **equivalent fractions**. To find equivalent fractions, you can multiply or divide the numerator and denominator by the same nonzero number.

Example 1 Find a fraction that is equivalent to $\frac{5}{10}$.
Solution: Divide both the numerator and denominator by 5

$$\frac{5 \div 5}{10 \div 5} = \frac{1}{2}$$

A fraction is in lowest terms if its numerator and denominator are relatively prime. Fractions can be grouped into families of equivalent fractions named for the member that is in lowest terms.

Example 2 $\frac{12}{30}$ is a member of which fraction family?

$$\frac{12}{30} = \frac{2}{5} \quad \text{Divide the numerator and denominator by 6.}$$

$\frac{12}{30}$ is a member of the fraction family named $\frac{2}{5}$.

Exercises

Find a fraction equivalent to the given fraction in lowest terms.

1. $\frac{5}{15}$ 2. $\frac{12}{18}$ 3. $\frac{27}{42}$

Name the fraction family to which each of the given fractions belongs.

4. $\frac{6}{30}$ 5. $\frac{2}{3}$ 6. $\frac{6}{8}$

7. $\frac{21}{28}$ 8. $\frac{15}{30}$ 9. $\frac{7}{10}$

Skills Practice (p. 5) — AL OL

Lesson 2.1 Skills Practice
Patterns in Fractions

Find a fraction equivalent to the given fraction in lowest terms.

1. $\frac{7}{35}$ 2. $\frac{6}{15}$ 3. $\frac{4}{24}$

4. $\frac{10}{15}$ 5. $\frac{20}{45}$ 6. $\frac{4}{16}$

7. $\frac{27}{81}$ 8. $\frac{8}{28}$ 9. $\frac{18}{24}$

Name the fraction family to which each of the given fractions belongs.

10. $\frac{1}{2}$ 11. $\frac{8}{10}$ 12. $\frac{20}{60}$

13. $\frac{6}{15}$ 14. $\frac{15}{60}$ 15. $\frac{5}{8}$

16. $\frac{27}{81}$ 17. $\frac{7}{12}$ 18. $\frac{28}{36}$

Each set of fractions are in the same fraction family. Name one other member of the family.

19. $\frac{2}{3}, \frac{4}{6}, \frac{6}{9}$ 20. $\frac{2}{10}, \frac{9}{20}, \frac{6}{36}$ 21. $\frac{1}{4}, \frac{2}{8}, \frac{4}{16}$

22. $\frac{2}{7}, \frac{6}{21}, \frac{10}{35}$ 23. $\frac{14}{10}, \frac{21}{15}, \frac{28}{20}$ 24. $\frac{21}{24}, \frac{35}{40}, \frac{42}{48}$

25. $\frac{2}{5}, \frac{8}{20}, \frac{20}{50}$ 26. $1\frac{1}{4}, 1\frac{2}{8}, 1\frac{4}{16}$ 27. $\frac{3}{2}, \frac{15}{10}, \frac{18}{12}$

Replace each ○ with <, >, or = to make a true statement.

28. $\frac{10}{20} ○ \frac{1}{2}$ 29. $\frac{15}{19} ○ \frac{30}{38}$ 30. $\frac{20}{38} ○ \frac{21}{28}$

31. $1\frac{1}{2} ○ 1\frac{7}{8}$ 32. $\frac{37}{22} ○ \frac{18}{11}$ 33. $\frac{5}{2} ○ \frac{30}{12}$

Problem-Solving Practice (p. 6) — AL OL

Lesson 2.1 Problem-Solving Practice
Patterns in Fractions

For Exercises 1–3, rewrite each statement using one of the more familiar fractions $0, \frac{1}{4}, \frac{1}{3}, \frac{1}{2}, \frac{2}{3}, \frac{3}{4}$, or 1 to approximate the given fraction. Tell whether your fractions is a little greater than or a little less than the actual fractions.

1. $\frac{16}{30}$ of Hector's classmates have brown eyes.

2. $\frac{7}{24}$ of the cars that started the race finished the race.

3. $\frac{12}{17}$ of Rebbeca's family members attended the picnic.

4. **Animals** Lions sleep about 20 hours a day. Write $\frac{20}{24}$ as a fraction in lowest terms.

5. **Marbles** Carlota has 63 marbles. Twenty-eight of her marbles are aggies. What fraction of Carlota's marbles are aggies? Write the answer in lowest terms.

6. **Movies** Fourteen of the top thirty all time grossing children's films were animated films. Write $\frac{14}{30}$ as a fraction in lowest terms.

Enrichment (p. 7) — BL

Lesson 2.1 Enrichment
Patterns in Fractions

Fraction Mysteries
Here is a set of mysteries that will help you sharpen your thinking skills. In each exercise, use the clues to discover the identity of the mystery fraction.

1. My numerator is 6 less than my denominator.
   I am equivalent to $\frac{3}{4}$.

2. My denominator is 5 more than twice my numerator.
   I am equivalent to $\frac{1}{3}$.

3. Divide my numerator and denominator by 3.
   I am equivalent to $\frac{2}{5}$.

4. Divide my numerator and denominator by 5.
   I am equivalent to $\frac{4}{6}$.

5. My numerator and denominator are prime numbers.
   My numerator is one less than my denominator.

6. My numerator and denominator are prime numbers.
   The sum of my numerator and denominator is 24.

7. My numerator is divisible by 3.
   My denominator is divisible by 5.
   My denominator is 4 less than twice my numerator.

8. My numerator is divisible by 3.
   My denominator is divisible by 5.
   My denominator is 3 more than twice my numerator.

9. My numerator is a one-digit prime number.
   My denominator is a one-digit composite number.
   I am equivalent to $\frac{8}{32}$.

10. My numerator is a prime number.
    My denominator is divisible by 2.
    I am equivalent to $\frac{1}{5}$.

11. **Challenge** Make up your own mystery like the ones above. Be sure that there is only one solution. To check, have a classmate solve your mystery.

Lesson Quick Quiz (p. 8) — AL OL BL

Lesson 2.1 Quick Quiz
Patterns in Fractions

For Questions 1 and 2, write your answer as a fraction in lowest terms and as a mixed number.

1. Alex spent 75 minutes running errands. What fraction of an hour is this?

2. Carla has 8 quiches to share equally among 5 people. What portion will each person receive?

3. Write each fraction in lowest terms.
   a. $\frac{24}{36}$ b. $\frac{16}{20}$

   c. $\frac{125}{150}$ d. $\frac{60}{105}$

4. Compare each fraction. Write =,<, or >.
   a. $\frac{40}{75} ○ \frac{48}{90}$ b. $\frac{9}{10} ○ \frac{9}{15}$

   c. $\frac{21}{49} ○ \frac{7}{14}$ d. $\frac{8}{12} ○ \frac{5}{12}$

5. Rewrite each statement using a familiar fraction to approximate the actual fraction.
   a. Only $\frac{49}{72}$ of the concert tickets were sold.

   b. Pat has completed $\frac{13}{28}$ of the homework problems.

Lesson Masters 1–3 (pp. 9–11)

Lesson 2.1 Master 1
Patterns in Fractions

Investigation 1: Explore

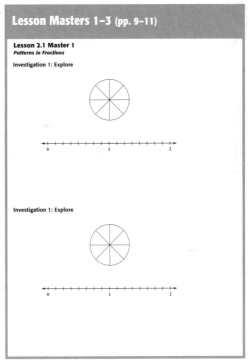

Investigation 1: Explore

Additional Lesson Resources

Teacher Tech Tools
- TeacherWorks
- ExamView Assessment Suite
- Classroom Presentation Toolkit
- Advance Tracker

Student Tech Tools
- StudentWorks Plus
- **Math Online** › eGlossary •
  Concepts in Motion

Other Print Products
- Investigation Notebook
  and Reflection Journal
- Quick Review Math Handbook

Introduce

Fractions Take time to review and discuss the definition of fraction. Make clear that fractions can be used to describe parts of a whole, and ask students to recall simple fractions that are familiar, like $\frac{1}{2}$ and $\frac{1}{4}$. Remind students that the numerator is the number above the fraction bar and the denominator is the number below the fraction bar.

Explore

Suggested Grouping: Individuals

▶ **Prepare** Provide students with copies of the circle and the number line from Lesson 2.1 Master 1 or have them trace the diagrams from their books.

▶ **Play** Ask students to trace around the circle and shade in $\frac{3}{4}$ of the area. Tell them to describe how their shaded area compares to the area in the book.

Have them also locate the number $\frac{12}{16}$ on the number line and compare its location with the location of $\frac{6}{8}$ on the number line.

▶ **Report** Discuss the questions with the class. Have each student check his or her answers and explanation. Ask a volunteer to present his or her findings.

▶ **Score** Give each student credit if his or her explanation is correct.

Patterns in Fractions

① The 8 represents the number of equal sections, the number of coins, and the number of divisions between 0 and 1. The 6 represents the number of shaded sections, the number of pennies, and the sixth division between 0 and 1.

②

The same amount of area is shaded. Possible explanation: My circle is divided into half as many sections, but each section is twice as big. So, shading three sections of my circle is the same as shading six sections of the original circle.

You probably know quite a bit about fractions already. A fraction can be used to describe part of a whole or to name a number between two whole numbers.

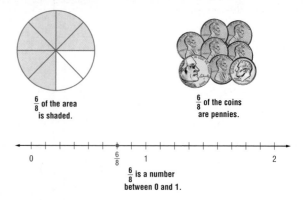

$\frac{6}{8}$ of the area is shaded.

$\frac{6}{8}$ of the coins are pennies.

$\frac{6}{8}$ is a number between 0 and 1.

Explore

In each representation above, what does the 8 in $\frac{6}{8}$ represent? What does the 6 represent?   See ①.

Trace the circle, and shade $\frac{3}{4}$ of its area. How does the area that you shaded compare to the above shaded area? Explain why your answer makes sense.   See ②.

Trace the number line. Indicate where $\frac{12}{16}$ is located. How does the location of $\frac{12}{16}$ compare with the location of $\frac{6}{8}$? Explain why your answer makes sense.   See ③.

In this lesson, you will see how factor and multiple relationships can help you think about and work with fractions.

③

$\frac{12}{16}$

The locations are the same. Possible explanation: My number line has twice as many divisions, but each is half as long. So, 12 divisions on my number line is the same as 6 on the original number line.

Investigation 1 Understand Fractions

Vocabulary

improper fraction

mixed number

In this investigation, you will review some ideas about fractions.

✓ Develop & Understand: A

The students in Mr. Jacobs' art class are sitting in four groups. Mr. Jacobs gives each group some bricks of clay to equally share among its members. All the bricks are the same size.

- Group 1 has 5 students and receives 4 bricks.
- Group 2 has 6 students and receives 4 bricks.
- Group 3 has 12 students and receives 9 bricks.
- Group 4 has 5 students and receives 6 bricks.

1. For each group, determine what fraction of a brick each student will get. Explain how you found your answers.

2. Did Mr. Jacobs pass out the clay fairly? Explain your answer.
   No; students in different groups received different amounts of clay.

The fraction of clay each member of Group 4 received was greater than 1. The next example shows how Miguel, Luke, and Hannah thought about dividing six bricks of clay among five students.

1. Group 1: $\frac{4}{5}$ of a brick; Group 2: $\frac{4}{6}$, or $\frac{2}{3}$, of a brick; Group 3: $\frac{9}{12}$, or $\frac{3}{4}$, of a brick; Group 4: $\frac{6}{5}$ of a brick, or $1\frac{1}{5}$ bricks. See teaching notes for possible strategies.

Example

First, I gave each student one brick. I divided the extra brick into fifths & gave $\frac{1}{5}$ to each student. So, each student got $1\frac{1}{5}$ bricks.

I drew 6 bricks and divided each into fifths. Each student got one of the fifths from each brick for a total of $\frac{6}{5}$.

I solved the division problem $6 \div 5$ and found that each student receives $1\frac{1}{5}$ bricks.

On the Spot Assessment

Point out that in a fraction the number below the bar tells how many equal-sized parts form a whole, and the number above the bar tells how many of the equal-sized parts are being discussed. Use the following example to remind students that some fractions are greater than 1:

How many quarters make a dollar? 4

If I have 3 quarters, how much of a dollar do I have? $\frac{3}{4}$

If I have 5 quarters, how much of a dollar do I have? $\frac{5}{4}$

Investigation 1

On Your Own Exercises
Pages 68–73
Exercises 1–5, 35, 36

Understand Fractions In this investigation, students review basic concepts about fractions in preparation for finding equivalent fractions and comparing fractions.

Teacher Tips Provide each group with a copy of Lesson 2.1 Master 2 to help them figure out how to share the clay. Students may use one of these strategies to divide the clay among the students in each group.

- Divide each brick of clay into the same number of equal-sized parts, with the number of equal parts equaling the number of students in the group. Then give one part of each brick to each student in the group.

- Give one brick to each student, when possible. Allocate the remaining bricks as described above.

- Divide the number of bricks by the number of students.

✓ Develop & Understand: A

Suggested Grouping: Small Groups

▶ **Exercise 1** Watch for students who answer incorrectly for Group 4.

▶ **Exercise 2** Ask students to compare fractions in the context of a situation. Mr. Jacobs divided the clay fairly if each student receives the same fraction of clay. Students should see that students did not receive the same amount. This is a preview of Investigation 2.

Wrap-Up Have students share their strategies for finding the fractional parts each of Mr. Jacobs' students received in Exercise 1 and their reasoning in Exercise 2.

Example

Summarize the strategies in the cartoon. Students may have shared some or all of the strategies when they discussed the exercises. If not, point this out as a review. Be sure students understand why the remainder can be expressed as a fraction.

Teacher Tips Discuss how to express a fraction greater than 1. Point out that one way is to use a *mixed number*, or a whole number and a fraction, and another way is to use an *improper fraction*.

✓ Develop & Understand: B

Suggested Grouping: Pairs

▶ **Exercise 3** Watch for students who give the reciprocal answer. Review mixed numbers if necessary.

▶ **Exercise 6** Some students may easily determine the mixed number but have difficulty determining the fraction. Suggest that they draw a rectangle model, like Luke's in the example on page 59, to help them.

Share & Summarize

Have volunteers share their word problems, and either have the class write the fraction and mixed number shown in the problem or verify that the two ways each volunteer gave are correct. This can provide an informal assessment of how your students are thinking about fractions.

Troubleshooting Use the activity below to reinforce students' basic ideas about fractions before going on to the next investigation.

Cut a sheet of paper into five equal strips.

- Label the beginning of each strip with 0 on the left end and one on the right end.

- Fold one of your strips in half, unfold it, and label the fold $\frac{1}{2}$. Write $\frac{2}{2}$ under one.

- Fold another strip in half, and then fold it in half again.

What fraction of the whole strip do you think you have created? Fourths

Unfold your strip, and label the folds with the appropriate fractions.

The example on page 59 shows two ways of expressing a fraction greater than 1. Luke's answer, $\frac{6}{5}$, is an **improper fraction**. This is a fraction in which the numerator is greater than the denominator. Miguel and Hannah's answer, $1\frac{1}{5}$, is a **mixed number**. A mixed number is a whole number and a fraction.

4. $\frac{18}{12}$, or $\frac{3}{2}$; $1\frac{6}{12}$, or $1\frac{1}{2}$

Real-World Link
The oldest known piece of pottery was made in China around 7900 B.C. The potter's wheel was invented in China around 3100 B.C.

✓ Develop & Understand: B

In Exercises 3–6, give your answer as a mixed number and as a fraction.

3. If 12 bricks of clay are divided among 5 students, what portion of a brick will each student receive? $2\frac{2}{5}$, $\frac{12}{5}$

4. Mr. Davis' geese laid 18 eggs. What fraction of a dozen is this?

5. Each grid below has 100 squares. What fraction of a grid is the entire shaded portion? $2\frac{33}{100}$, $\frac{233}{100}$

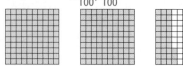

6. What number is indicated by the point? $5\frac{4}{7}$, or $\frac{39}{7}$

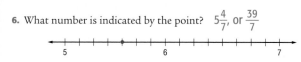

Share & Summarize

Write a word problem, like those in Exercises 3 and 4 above, that leads to a fraction greater than 1. Show two ways of expressing the fraction. Possible answer: 14 cans of juice are divided among 5 students. The fraction of a can each student gets can be expressed as $2\frac{4}{5}$ or $\frac{14}{5}$.

Mathematical Background

The text presents both improper fractions and mixed numbers somewhat interchangeably, since the "best" way to write a number depends on how the number is to be used. (Students are not expected to be familiar with the term improper fraction.) Sometimes it is best to express a quantity as an improper fraction to make calculations easier. Other times a mixed number is preferred because it can convey the value quickly. For example, most people get a sense of the size of $3\frac{3}{4}$ more quickly than $\frac{15}{4}$ because $3\frac{3}{4}$ is clearly between 3 and 4.

Investigation 2 — Equivalent Fractions

Vocabulary

equivalent fractions

lowest terms

In this investigation, you will see how different fractions can represent the same part of a whole and how different fractions can represent the same number.

✓ Develop & Understand: A

Casey, Collin, Manuel, Regina, and Jovan baked fruit bars in their Family and Consumer Science class. Each student cut his or her bar into a different number of equal pieces.

Casey

Collin

Manuel

Regina

Jovan

1. $\frac{2}{3}$ for $\frac{4}{6}$, $\frac{3}{3}$ for $\frac{6}{6}$

2. $\frac{2}{4}$ for $\frac{5}{10}$, $\frac{4}{4}$ for $\frac{10}{10}$

3. $\frac{1}{5}$ for $\frac{2}{10}$, $\frac{2}{5}$ for $\frac{4}{10}$, $\frac{3}{5}$ for $\frac{6}{10}$, $\frac{4}{5}$ for $\frac{8}{10}$, $\frac{5}{5}$ for $\frac{10}{10}$

4. Casey and Manuel, Casey and Collin, Casey and Jovan, Regina and Manuel, Collin and Manuel

1. Casey wants to trade some of her lemon bar for an equal portion of Regina's raspberry bar. She could trade $\frac{1}{3}$ of her bar for $\frac{2}{6}$ of Regina's bar.

   What other fair trades could they make? List all of the possibilities. Give your answers as fractions of fruit bars.

2. Collin wants to trade some of his apple bar for an equal portion of Jovan's peach bar. Describe all of the fair trades they could make.

3. Describe all of the fair trades Manuel and Jovan could make.

4. Which pairs of students can trade only whole fruit bars?

5. List some fractions of a fruit bar that are fair trades for $\frac{1}{2}$ of a bar.
   Possible answer: $\frac{2}{4}, \frac{3}{6}, \frac{5}{10}$

Lesson 2.1   Patterns in Fractions   **61**

Reaching All Learners

ELL **English Language Learners** As new terms are introduced, or whenever there is confusion over terms introduced in prior classes, have students make a "vocabulary card" for that word. Each card should include the word and a drawing, diagram, or labeled example that explains what the word means. The process of making the card will require students to think about the meaning of the word as they decide how best to represent it for others. They can also refer to any cards posted in the classroom or in their journals.

On Your Own Exercises
Pages 68–73
Exercises 6–21, 37–41

Equivalent Fractions Introduce the investigation by referring students to the circle on page 58. Remind students that in Explore, they shaded $\frac{3}{4}$ of a similar circle, and they should have found that the amount shaded was the same in each case. Tell students they will learn more about using different fractions to name the same part of a whole.

Teacher Tips Point out that this investigation introduces equivalent fractions, first through the context of trading parts of fruit bars and then as members of a "fraction family," which is a set of fractions all naming the same value. Students learn to generate or recognize equivalent fractions and fractions in lowest terms.

Explain that the fruit bars must be the same height for the exercises. The fruit bars have volume, so thickness (height) must be considered. Ask students if they can explain why the bars must have the same height.

✓ Develop & Understand: A

Suggested Grouping: Groups of Five

▶ **Exercises 1–5** Ask students to take the roles of students in the exercises and to model the exercises. Use Lesson 2.1 Master 3 to reproduce the fruit bars shown on this page. Remind students that the fruit bars can be cut only as shown; no other cuts are allowed.

▶ **Exercises 1–3** Remind students that they can write a fraction that describes a whole fruit bar.

Wrap-Up Have students share their answers and the strategies they used to find the fair trades. This discussion may lead into finding equivalent fractions by multiplying or dividing the numerator and denominator by the same number.

Equivalent Fractions Introduce the term *equivalent fractions*. Point out that the fractions in each pair that made a fair trade in the exercises on page 61 are equivalent. Remind students that they used models to find equivalent fractions in those problems, and let them know that there is another way to find equivalent fractions.

In the cartoon, Althea uses a visual argument to show that dividing the numerator and the denominator by the same number does not change the value of the fraction. Ask a volunteer to read Althea's argument, and then have the class discuss her reasoning. Ask students to explain how the models show each step.

Think & Discuss

Most students will easily make the translation to multiplying the numerator and denominator by the same number as a way of finding equivalent fractions. Encourage them to show their thinking visually on the board or overhead by drawing a diagram. You might want to show them how to find equivalent fractions symbolically.

$$\frac{2}{3} = \frac{2 \cdot 3}{3 \cdot 3} = \frac{6}{9}$$

Teacher Tips Discuss the meaning of *lowest terms* and explain *relatively prime*, if necessary. Ask students if a fraction with a prime number in the numerator and a different prime number in the denominator is in lowest terms, and have them explain their reasoning. Yes; the only common factor of two different prime numbers is 1.

In Exercises 1–5, $\frac{1}{5}$ of Manuel's fruit bar is the same as $\frac{2}{10}$ of Jovan's fruit bar. Fractions such as $\frac{1}{5}$ and $\frac{2}{10}$ *describe the same portion of a whole* or *name the same number*. Such fractions are called **equivalent fractions**.

You can find a fraction equivalent to a given fraction by multiplying or dividing the numerator and denominator by the same number. Althea worked out an example to convince herself that dividing by the same number gives an equivalent fraction.

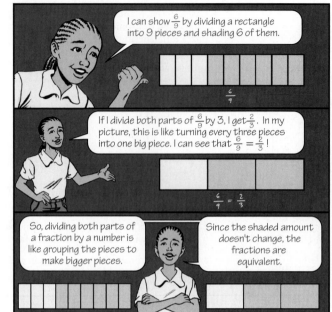

① Possible answer: Model $\frac{2}{5}$ by dividing a strip into five pieces and shading two. Multiplying both the numerator and denominator by 2 gives $\frac{4}{10}$. This is like dividing each piece into two equal pieces. There are twice as many pieces and twice as many are shaded, but the shaded amount remains the same, so $\frac{2}{5} = \frac{4}{10}$.

Think & Discuss

Use an argument similar to Althea's to convince yourself that multiplying the numerator and denominator of a fraction by a number gives an equivalent fraction. See ①.

A fraction is in **lowest terms** if its numerator and denominator are relatively prime. For example, the fractions $\frac{2}{3}$, $\frac{12}{18}$, and $\frac{20}{30}$ are all equivalent. However, only $\frac{2}{3}$ is in lowest terms because the only common factor of 2 and 3 is 1.

Mathematical Background

The *identity property of one* states that any number multiplied by one equals that number. This relates to finding equivalent fractions, because any fraction that has the same number in the numerator and the denominator is equal to one. When the numerator and the denominator of a fraction are multiplied by the same number, the fraction is essentially being multiplied by one. So, when performing the calculation $\frac{2}{3} \cdot \frac{3}{3} = \frac{6}{9}$, we are essentially multiplying $\frac{2}{3}$ by one and representing the answer in a different way.

Math Link

Two numbers are prime if their only common factor is 1.

Real-World Link

The sizes of wrenches and drill bits are often given as fractions.

6d. No; Possible explanation: 164 is not a multiple of 3.

7a. Possible answer: $\frac{18}{48}, \frac{21}{56}, \frac{24}{64}, \frac{30}{80}$

7b. $\frac{3}{8}, \frac{6}{16}, \frac{9}{24}, \frac{12}{32}$

8a. Possible answer: $\frac{5}{7}, \frac{10}{14}, \frac{30}{42}, \frac{35}{49}$

9, 10. See margin.

✓ Develop & Understand: B 6a–c. See margin.

6. Fractions can be grouped into "families" of equivalent fractions. A fraction family is named for the member that is in lowest terms. The following is part of the "$\frac{3}{4}$ fraction family."

$$\frac{3}{4} \quad \frac{6}{8} \quad \frac{9}{12} \quad \frac{12}{16} \quad \frac{15}{20} \quad \frac{18}{24} \quad \frac{21}{28} \quad \frac{24}{32} \quad \frac{27}{36} \quad \frac{30}{40}$$

a. What do the numerators of these fractions have in common? What do the denominators have in common?

b. How do you know that all of the fractions in this family are equivalent?

c. Find at least three more fractions in this family. Explain how you found them.

d. Is $\frac{164}{216}$ in this fraction family? Explain how you know.

7. Now consider the $\frac{3}{8}$ fraction family.

a. List four members of this family with numerators greater than 15.

b. List four members of this family with numerators less than 15.

8. The fractions below belong to the same family.

$$\frac{15}{21} \quad \frac{20}{28} \quad \frac{25}{35}$$

a. Find four more fractions in this family, two with denominators less than 21 and two with denominators greater than 35.

b. What is the name of this fraction family? The $\frac{5}{7}$ fraction family

9. How can you determine to which family a fraction belongs?

10. Are $\frac{6}{10}$ and $\frac{16}{20}$ in the same fraction family? Explain how you know.

Share & Summarize 1, 2. See margin.

1. In Exercises 1–5, how did you determine which trades could be made? Give an example to help explain your answer.

2. Explain how you can find fractions equivalent to a given fraction. Demonstrate your method by choosing a fraction and finding four fractions equivalent to it.

3. Describe a method for determining whether two given fractions are equivalent. Possible answer: Write each fraction in lowest terms. If the results are equal, the fractions are equivalent.

Lesson 2.1 Patterns in Fractions **63**

✓ Develop & Understand: B

Suggested Grouping: Pairs

▶ **Exercise 6** Remind students that the fraction family is named for the fraction that is in lowest terms.

▶ **Exercise 7** Encourage students to list the fractions in order with the numerator and denominator both increasing.

▶ **Exercise 10** Watch for students who think that $\frac{6}{10}$ and $\frac{16}{20}$ are in the same fraction family because the same number, 10, was added to the numerator and the denominator. Remind them that they can multiply or divide the numerator and the denominator by the same number to find equivalent fractions.

Math Link

Point out that the numbers 3 and 8 are relatively prime because their only common factor is 1.

Share & Summarize

For **Exercise 1**, most students will have used models to determine trades, but others may have looked for common factors for the total number of pieces in the fruit bars. Trades cannot be made if there is not a common factor for the denominator. When there is a common factor, some trades can be made. For example, a common factor for Collin's and Jovan's fruit bars is 2, and they could trade $\frac{1}{2}$ or $\frac{2}{2}$.

Troubleshooting If students have difficulty determining whether two fractions are equivalent, allow them to use fraction strips or other models to compare the fractions. Students can make fraction strips. For most students, a set of strips containing halves, thirds, fourths, fifths, sixths, eighths, tenths, and twelfths will suffice. Have them use the strips to find equivalent fractions and then write a number sentence describing each pair, such as $\frac{6}{12} = \frac{1}{2}$.

Additional Answers

6a. Possible answers: All the numerators are multiples of 3. All the denominators are multiples of 4.

6b. Possible answer: All the fractions are equivalent to $\frac{3}{4}$, so they are all equivalent to each other.

6c. Possible answer: $\frac{33}{44}, \frac{36}{48}, \frac{42}{56}$; I multiplied the numerator and denominator of other fractions in the family by the same number.

Additional Answers for Develop & Understand: B Exercises 9 and 10 and Share & Summarize Exercises 1 and 2 are on page 107A.

Compare Fractions In this investigation, students use what they have learned about equivalent fractions to compare fractions. The text presents two common methods for comparing fractions: writing the pair using a common denominator and writing the pair using a common numerator. Students have the conceptual understanding they need to see why these methods work.

✅ Develop & Understand: A

Suggested Grouping: Pairs

▶ **Exercise 1a** Tell students to use a common numerator or a common denominator to compare the fractions. There are more possible pairings with a common numerator than denominator.

▶ **Exercise 2b** Point out that students will need to make *two* comparisons and list a pair of fractions for each.

Wrap-Up Have students share their answers, focusing on the strategies they used to compare fractions. If students mention comparing fractions with common numerators or common denominators, use this as an opportunity to introduce the terms and lead into the comparisons shown in the diagram at the bottom of the page. If students do not mention these strategies, present them at the end of the discussion.

After discussing the *common denominator* and *common numerator* ways to compare fractions, point out how the rectangle model shows fractions greater than 1. You might also ask students to look for patterns in the two diagrams.

1a. Possible answers: $\frac{11}{77}$ and $\frac{14}{77}$ or $\frac{6}{42}$ and $\frac{6}{33}$

1b. $\frac{2}{11}$; Possible explanations: $\frac{11}{77}$ is less than $\frac{14}{77}$. $\frac{6}{33}$ is greater than $\frac{6}{42}$.

2a. Possible answer: $\frac{3}{4}, \frac{6}{8}, \frac{9}{12}, \frac{12}{16}, \frac{15}{20}, \frac{18}{24}, \frac{21}{28}$. $\frac{7}{12}, \frac{14}{24}, \frac{21}{36}, \frac{28}{48}, \frac{35}{60}, \frac{42}{72}$

2b. Possible answer: $\frac{9}{12}$ and $\frac{7}{12}$, or $\frac{21}{28}$ and $\frac{21}{36}$

Investigation ③ Compare Fractions

In Investigation 2, you explored families of equivalent fractions. You saw how you could find fractions equivalent to a given fraction by multiplying or dividing the numerator and denominator by the same number. You will now use what you learned to compare fractions.

✅ Develop & Understand: A

1. The following are some members of the $\frac{1}{7}$ and the $\frac{2}{11}$ fraction families.

The $\frac{1}{7}$ Fraction Family

| $\frac{1}{7}$ | $\frac{2}{14}$ | $\frac{3}{21}$ | $\frac{4}{28}$ | $\frac{5}{35}$ | $\frac{6}{42}$ | $\frac{7}{49}$ | $\frac{8}{56}$ | $\frac{9}{63}$ | $\frac{10}{70}$ | $\frac{11}{77}$ | $\frac{12}{84}$ |

The $\frac{2}{11}$ Fraction Family

| $\frac{2}{11}$ | $\frac{4}{22}$ | $\frac{6}{33}$ | $\frac{8}{44}$ | $\frac{10}{55}$ | $\frac{12}{66}$ | $\frac{14}{77}$ | $\frac{16}{88}$ | $\frac{18}{99}$ | $\frac{20}{110}$ |

a. Recall that all the fractions in the $\frac{1}{2}$ fraction family equal $\frac{1}{2}$. Choose a pair of fractions, one from each family above, that you could use to easily compare $\frac{1}{7}$ and $\frac{2}{11}$.

b. Which fraction is greater, $\frac{1}{7}$ or $\frac{2}{11}$? Explain how you know.

2. Consider the fractions $\frac{3}{4}$ and $\frac{7}{12}$.

a. List some members of their fraction families.

b. List two pairs of fractions you could use to compare $\frac{3}{4}$ and $\frac{7}{12}$.

c. Which fraction is greater, $\frac{3}{4}$ or $\frac{7}{12}$? $\frac{3}{4}$

You can compare two fractions by finding members of their fraction families with a *common denominator* or with a *common numerator*.

The diagram on the left shows how fractions with a common denominator of 10 compare. The diagram on the right shows how fractions with a common numerator of 7 compare.

Common Denominators		Common Numerators	
$\frac{2}{10}$		$\frac{7}{5}$	
$\frac{3}{10}$		$\frac{7}{6}$	
$\frac{4}{10}$		$\frac{7}{7}$	
$\frac{5}{10}$		$\frac{7}{8}$	
$\frac{6}{10}$		$\frac{7}{9}$	
$\frac{7}{10}$		$\frac{7}{10}$	

 Assessment

In Exercise 1, you may have found that students used different strategies to compare two fractions. Watch for students who confuse common denominators of fraction families. Present common numerator and denominator strategies if necessary.

Think & Discuss

If two fractions have the same denominator but different numerators, how can you tell which of the fractions is greater? Explain why your reasoning works. See ①.

If two fractions have the same numerator but different denominators, how can you tell which of the fractions is greater? Explain why your reasoning works. See ②.

When you are given two fractions to compare, how can you quickly find equivalent fractions with a common denominator? With a common numerator? See ③ below.

Develop & Understand: B

3. Rewrite $\frac{4}{17}$ and $\frac{3}{10}$ with a common denominator. Tell which fraction is greater. Possible answer: $\frac{40}{170}$, $\frac{51}{170}$; $\frac{3}{10}$

4. Rewrite $\frac{4}{9}$ and $\frac{8}{15}$ with a common numerator. Tell which fraction is greater. Possible answer: $\frac{8}{18}$ and $\frac{8}{15}$; $\frac{8}{15}$

5. Consider the fractions $\frac{5}{8}$ and $\frac{7}{10}$.
   a. Rewrite the fractions with the least common denominator. $\frac{25}{40}$, $\frac{28}{40}$
   b. Which fraction is greater, $\frac{5}{8}$ or $\frac{7}{10}$? $\frac{7}{10}$
   c. What is the relationship between the least common denominator and the multiples of the original denominators, 8 and 10? The least common denominator is the least common multiple of 8 and 10.

Replace each ◯ with <, >, or = to make a true statement.

6. $\frac{3}{4} \bigcirc \frac{7}{12}$

7. $\frac{8}{13} \bigcirc \frac{12}{19}$

8. $\frac{48}{120} \bigcirc \frac{12}{39}$

9. $\frac{17}{11} \bigcirc \frac{11}{7}$

10. $\frac{13}{12} \bigcirc \frac{6}{5}$

11. $\frac{19}{36} \bigcirc \frac{10}{24}$

Share & Summarize

Order these fractions from least to greatest using any method you like.

$$\frac{1}{3} \qquad \frac{2}{9} \qquad \frac{5}{3} \qquad \frac{5}{4} \qquad \frac{7}{9} \qquad \frac{1}{2} \qquad 1\frac{1}{8}$$

$$\frac{2}{9}, \frac{1}{3}, \frac{1}{2}, \frac{7}{9}, 1\frac{1}{8}, \frac{5}{4}, \frac{5}{3}$$

③ Possible answer: To write the fractions with a common denominator, multiply both parts of each fraction by the other fraction's denominator. To write the fractions with a common numerator, multiply both parts of each fraction by the other fraction's numerator.

Think & Discuss

Suggested Grouping: Individuals

This Think & Discuss provides two strategies for comparing fractions. Have students write their explanations and then share them with the class. As students explain why the common denominator and common numerator methods work, they may refer to the diagrams on page 64 or draw their own.

Be sure students have a strategy for comparing two fractions before they begin the Develop & Understand exercises.

Develop & Understand: B

Suggest Groupings: Individuals

▶ **Exercises 3–5** Point out that students are asked to use a specific method in these exercises.

▶ **Exercises 6–11** Encourage students to look in the margin if they need a reminder about which sign means "is greater than" and which means "is less than."

Wrap-Up Discuss Exercise 5c, which connects to prior investigations in this chapter. Point out that to compare fractions, finding the least common denominator is not necessary.

Share & Summarize

Have students explain how they determined the order of the fractions. Students may use the strategies below.

- Look for mixed numbers or fractions that can be written as mixed numbers. All mixed numbers and fractions whose numerators are greater than their denominators are greater than fractions whose numerators are less than their denominators.

- Write the fractions with a common denominator. The least common denominator is 72.

- Write the fractions with a common numerator. This method allows easy ordering of $\frac{5}{3}$ and $\frac{5}{4}$.

- Use benchmarks to estimate the value of some fractions.

Estimate with Fractions In this investigation, students estimate the size of unfamiliar fractions by comparing them to familiar, benchmark fractions. Using benchmark fractions in this way often involves choosing a familiar fraction whose numerator or denominator is close to that of the unfamiliar fraction. The two fractions are then close to one another as well.

Think & Discuss

Present the situation in the Think & Discuss activity as a warm-up for the investigation before students open their books. As students offer various strategies, note the different ways they suggest without comment. Then introduce the idea of using such benchmark fractions as $\frac{1}{4}, \frac{1}{3}, \frac{1}{2}, \frac{2}{3}, \frac{3}{4}$ along with 0 and 1, to estimate other fractions. Review how to use benchmarks to make an estimate if students did not suggest this method in the Think & Discuss. Then help students use this strategy to find out how Keisha can come closest to measuring $\frac{4}{9}$ cup using her measuring cups.

✅ Develop & Understand: A

Suggested Grouping: Pairs

▶ **Exercise 1** Ask students to focus on the fractional amount that the visual display represents, rather than its physical size. If students mention that the bars are different lengths, point out that it is the *fractional* part of each bar that is important. Some students may note that some computers do not display progress in "real time" but make jumps at seemingly random intervals.

Investigation 4 Estimate with Fractions

In this lesson, you will see how you can use familiar fractions to estimate the values of other fractions.

Think & Discuss

Keisha wants to make $\frac{1}{3}$ of a recipe of her grandmother's spaghetti sauce. When she divided the amount of each ingredient by 3, she found that she needed $\frac{4}{9}$ cup of olive oil. Keisha has only the measuring cups at right. How can she use these cups to measure *approximately* $\frac{4}{9}$ cup of oil? See ①.

① Possible answers:
- $\frac{4}{9}$ is a little more than $\frac{3}{9}$, which is equivalent to $\frac{1}{3}$. So, Keisha should use $\frac{1}{3}$ cup and a little more to compensate.
- $\frac{4}{9}$ is a little less than $\frac{1}{2}$ a cup, so Keisha could fill her $\frac{1}{2}$-cup measure almost all the way.

Most people are familiar with such fractions as $\frac{1}{4}, \frac{1}{3}, \frac{1}{2}, \frac{2}{3}$, and $\frac{3}{4}$, and have a good sense of their value. For this reason, familiar fractions like these, along with the numbers 0 and 1, are often used as benchmarks. *Benchmarks,* or reference points, can help you approximate the values of other fractions.

When you estimate with benchmark fractions, you should ask yourself questions like these.

- Is the fraction closest to 0, $\frac{1}{2}$, or 1?
- Is it greater than $\frac{1}{2}$ or less than $\frac{1}{2}$?
- Is it greater than $\frac{1}{4}$ or less than $\frac{1}{4}$?
- Is it greater than $\frac{2}{3}$ or less than $\frac{2}{3}$?

✅ Develop & Understand: A

Heather and Miranda were working in their school's computer lab. They began installing the same software program onto their computers at the same time. Each computer displayed a progress bar indicating how much of the program had been installed. The following shows what the progress bars looked like after one minute.

1. After one minute, about what fraction of the program had been installed on Miranda's computer? Explain how you made your estimate. Possible answer: $\frac{3}{4}$; three of the empty parts will fill the shaded part.

On the Spot Assessment

Watch for students who have difficulty understanding that the shaded portions of the bars represent different fractional amounts. Discourage them from making a side-by-side comparison. Point out that the two bars show the same event and that the whole of each bar is the data on the software program. When the program is fully loaded, the entire bar will be shaded whether it is a very small bar or a bar that fills the computer screen. The "part" of the fraction is the amount of the program that has been installed.

3. No; Heather's progress bar is longer so, although the lengths of the shaded parts are the same, hers represents a smaller fraction of the total length. Her computer has completed less of the installation.

4. No; if Heather's computer were half as fast, it would not be even halfway done yet.

2. After one minute, about what fraction of the program had been installed on Heather's computer? Explain how you made your estimate. **Possible answer: $\frac{2}{3}$; two of the empty parts would fill the shaded part.**

3. Heather noticed that after one minute the shaded parts of the progress bars were about the same length. She said, "Our progress bars are the same length. Your computer has completed just as much of the installation as my computer." Is she correct? Explain.

4. Miranda said, "Your computer is only $\frac{1}{2}$ as fast as my computer." Is she correct? Explain your reasoning.

Fractions involving real data can be unfamiliar and complicated. Using familiar fractions to approximate actual fractions often makes information easier to understand.

Think & Discuss

In a sixth-grade gym class, 28 out of the 40 students are girls. The gym teacher said, "Girls make up about $\frac{3}{4}$ of this class." Do you agree with this statement? Explain. **Yes; $\frac{3}{4}$ of 40 is 30, and 28 is close to 30.**

✓ Develop & Understand: B

5. Rewrite each statement using a more familiar fraction to approximate the actual fraction. Explain how you decided which fraction to use. Tell whether your approximation is a little greater than or a little less than the actual fraction. **See margin.**

  a. I have been in school for $\frac{43}{180}$ of the school year.

  b. Mrs. Stratton's class is $\frac{48}{60}$ of an hour long.

  c. The air distance from Washington, D.C., to Los Angeles is $\frac{2,300}{4,870}$ the air distance from Washington, D.C., to Moscow.

  d. The Volga River in Europe is $\frac{2,290}{3,362}$ the length of the Ob-Irtysh River in Asia.

6. Make up your own situation involving a "complicated" fraction. Tell which benchmark fraction you could use as an approximation. **Answers will vary.**

Share & Summarize

In what types of situations is it useful to approximate the value of a fraction with a more familiar fraction? **Possible answer: When an approximate measure is good enough, such as in cooking. When a fraction formed from real data is messy and you want to give others a sense of the fraction's value. When you want to compare two fractions.**

Real-World Link
The Volga River, the longest river in Europe, is located in western Russia. It is about 2,300 miles long (3,700 km).

Additional Answers

5a. Possible answer: I have been in school for about $\frac{1}{4}$ of the school year. I used $\frac{1}{4}$ because $\frac{1}{4}$ of 180 is 45, which is close to 43. $\frac{1}{4}$ is a little more than $\frac{43}{180}$.

5b. Possible answer: Mrs. Stratton's class is about $\frac{3}{4}$ of an hour long. I used $\frac{3}{4}$ because $\frac{3}{4}$ of an hour is 45 min, which is close to 48 min. $\frac{3}{4}$ is a little less than $\frac{48}{60}$.

Additional Answers for Develop & Understand: B Exercises 5c and 5d are on page 107A.

▶ **Exercise 3** Ask students to consider the appearance of the two status bars to compare the computers' progress. Although the length of the shaded portions of the bars is the same, the shaded portion on Heather's bar represents about $\frac{2}{3}$ of the length of the bar.

On Miranda's bar, the shaded portion represents about $\frac{3}{4}$ of the length.

▶ **Exercise 4** This exercise may cause students difficulty if they compare the shaded parts without considering the fractions they represent. They cannot compare the lengths of the status bars by dividing the shaded portion of Miranda's status bar in half and seeing if the result matches the shaded portion of Heather's. If a student suggests this, draw two rectangles, one about three times the length of the other. Shade $\frac{2}{3}$ of the longer rectangle and the entire shorter one.

Bar 1 [_____]

Bar 2 [_____]

Think & Discuss

Discuss the statement about approximating the fraction of girls in the gym class. Offer a few more examples in which students try to adjust the numerator or denominator to make a familiar fraction.

✓ Develop & Understand: B

Suggested Grouping: Individuals

▶ **Exercises 5c and 5d** Both have denominators that cannot be easily divided by 2, 3, or 4 mentally. Encourage students to look for more *compatible numbers* that are close to 4,870 and 3,362, such as 4,800 and 3,300.

Wrap-Up Have volunteers read their situations from Exercise 6 aloud.

Share & Summarize

Have students record their situations. Then discuss the questions as a class. You might post the responses, along with an example or two of how to estimate the size of a fraction.

Investigation 1
Pages 59–60
Practice & Apply: 1–5
Connect & Extend: 35, 36

Investigation 2
Pages 61–63
Practice & Apply: 6–21
Connect & Extend: 37–41

Investigation 3
Pages 64–65
Practice & Apply: 22–29
Connect & Extend: 42–44

Investigation 4
Pages 66–67
Practice & Apply: 30–34
Connect & Extend: 45–47

Assign Anytime
Mixed Review: 48–52

▶ **Exercises 6 and 7** If students have difficulty finding trades, suggest that they cut out four equal-sized rectangles. They can then divide one into ninths and another into sixths for Exercise 6, and one into 10ths and the last into 15ths for Exercise 7.

. . . .

Real-World Link
Kiwifruit was named after the kiwi, an indigenous bird to New Zealand, and one of the country's national symbols.

. . . .

Practice & Apply

2. $\frac{8}{6}$, or $\frac{4}{3}$; $1\frac{2}{6}$, or $1\frac{1}{3}$

3. $\frac{15}{10}$, or $\frac{3}{2}$; $1\frac{5}{10}$, or $1\frac{1}{2}$

5. $4\frac{37}{50}$, $\frac{237}{50}$

6. $\frac{3}{9}$ for $\frac{2}{6}$, $\frac{6}{9}$ for $\frac{4}{6}$, $\frac{9}{9}$ for $\frac{6}{6}$

7. $\frac{2}{10}$ for $\frac{3}{15}$, $\frac{4}{10}$ for $\frac{6}{15}$, $\frac{6}{10}$ for $\frac{9}{15}$, $\frac{8}{10}$ for $\frac{12}{15}$, $\frac{10}{10}$ for $\frac{15}{15}$

Real-World Link
Although kiwifruit was first grown in China over 700 years ago, it was not widely available in the United States until the 1970s.

. . . .

1. Suppose ten friends share four medium-sized pizzas. Each friend gets the same amount of pizza. What fraction of a pizza does each friend receive? $\frac{4}{10}$, or $\frac{2}{5}$

2. Suppose six people share eight submarine sandwiches. Each person gets the same amount. What fraction of a sandwich does each person receive? Express your answer as a fraction and as a mixed number.

3. Suppose ten people share fifteen cinnamon rolls. Each person gets the same amount. What fraction of a roll does each person receive? Express your answer as a fraction and as a mixed number.

4. What number is indicated by the point? Give your answer as a mixed number and as a fraction. $3\frac{2}{5}$, or $\frac{17}{5}$

5. A coin roll holds 50 pennies. What fraction of a roll is 237 pennies? Give your answer as a mixed number and as a fraction.

6. Althea baked a plum bar and cut it into ninths. What fair trades can she make with Regina, whose raspberry bar is divided into sixths?

Althea

Regina

7. Alicia's kiwifruit bar is divided into tenths, and Rob's strawberry bar is divided into fifteenths. List all the fair trades they could make.

Give two fractions that are equivalent to each given fraction.

8. $\frac{2}{3}$ Possible answer: $\frac{4}{6}$, $\frac{8}{12}$

9. $\frac{5}{8}$ Possible answer: $\frac{10}{16}$, $\frac{50}{80}$

10. $\frac{1}{5}$ Possible answer: $\frac{2}{10}$, $\frac{4}{20}$

11. The following are four members of the $\frac{5}{9}$ fraction family. List four more.

$\frac{5}{9}$ $\frac{10}{18}$ $\frac{15}{27}$ $\frac{20}{36}$ Possible answer: $\frac{25}{45}$, $\frac{30}{54}$, $\frac{45}{81}$, $\frac{50}{90}$

12. All of these fractions are in the same family.

$\frac{33}{27}$ $\frac{44}{36}$ $\frac{66}{54}$

   a. Find four more fractions in this family. Possible answer: $\frac{11}{9}$, $\frac{22}{18}$, $\frac{55}{45}$, $\frac{77}{63}$

   b. What is the name of this fraction family? The $\frac{11}{9}$ fraction family

13b. $\frac{3}{4}, \frac{6}{8}, \frac{9}{12}, \frac{12}{16}, \frac{15}{20},$
$\frac{18}{24}, \frac{21}{28}, \frac{24}{32}$

14. No; Possible explanation: $\frac{34}{64}$ is in the $\frac{17}{32}$ fraction family while $\frac{18}{36}$ is in the $\frac{1}{2}$ fraction family.

17. $5\frac{2}{3}$, or $\frac{17}{3}$

19. Yes; both are equivalent to $\frac{1}{2}$.

20. No; $\frac{4}{12}$ in lowest terms is $\frac{1}{3}$ while $\frac{8}{32}$ in lowest terms is $\frac{1}{4}$.

21. Yes; both are equivalent to $\frac{5}{6}$.

28. $\frac{3}{16}, \frac{3}{8}, \frac{3}{7}, \frac{3}{5}, \frac{3}{4}, \frac{3}{3}, \frac{3}{1}$

29. $\frac{1}{3}, \frac{2}{5}, \frac{1}{2}, \frac{2}{3}, \frac{3}{4}, \frac{7}{7}, \frac{11}{8}$

30b. A, C, B; Possible explanation: $\frac{3}{4} > \frac{1}{3} > \frac{1}{5}$

---

13. Consider the fraction $\frac{27}{36}$.
 a. To what fraction family does $\frac{27}{36}$ belong?   The $\frac{3}{4}$ fraction family
 b. List all the members of this fraction family with numerators less than 27.

14. Are $\frac{34}{64}$ and $\frac{18}{36}$ in the same fraction family? Explain how you know.

Rewrite each fraction or mixed number in lowest terms.
15. $\frac{12}{3}$ $\frac{4}{1}$, or 4   **16.** $\frac{9}{24}$ $\frac{3}{8}$ **17.** $5\frac{6}{9}$ **18.** $\frac{18}{45}$ $\frac{2}{5}$

Tell whether the fractions in each pair are equivalent. Explain how you know.
19. $\frac{4}{8}$ and $\frac{15}{30}$ **20.** $\frac{4}{12}$ and $\frac{8}{32}$ **21.** $\frac{50}{60}$ and $\frac{15}{18}$

Replace each $\bigcirc$ with <, >, or = to make a true statement.
22. $\frac{7}{8} \bigcirc \frac{2}{3}$ **23.** $\frac{5}{9} \bigcirc \frac{3}{5}$ **24.** $\frac{5}{16} \bigcirc \frac{5}{17}$
25. $\frac{90}{70} \bigcirc \frac{45}{35}$ **26.** $\frac{1}{2} \bigcirc \frac{7}{11}$ **27.** $\frac{13}{8} \bigcirc 1\frac{2}{3}$

Order each set of fractions from least to greatest.
28. $\frac{3}{4}, \frac{3}{3}, \frac{3}{8}, \frac{3}{5}, \frac{3}{16}, \frac{3}{7}, \frac{3}{1}$ **29.** $\frac{7}{7}, \frac{3}{4}, \frac{1}{2}, \frac{2}{5}, \frac{2}{3}, \frac{11}{8}, \frac{1}{3}$

30. Three computers begin installing the same program at the same time. The following are their progress bars after one minute.

  Computer A   Computer B   Computer C

 a. About what fraction of the installation has been completed by computer A? By computer B? By computer C? $\frac{3}{4}, \frac{1}{5}, \frac{1}{3}$
 b. Order the machines from fastest to slowest. Explain how you determined the ordering.

Tell whether each fraction is closest to 0, $\frac{1}{4}$, $\frac{1}{3}$, $\frac{1}{2}$, $\frac{2}{3}$, $\frac{3}{4}$, or 1. Explain how you decided.   31–33. See margin.
31. $\frac{5}{18}$ **32.** $\frac{1}{5}$ **33.** $\frac{9}{10}$

34. Determine whether $\frac{33}{40}$ is greater than or less than $\frac{21}{50}$ by comparing the fractions to benchmark fractions. Explain your thinking.
$\frac{33}{40} > \frac{21}{50}$; Possible explanation: $\frac{33}{40}$ is a little more than $\frac{3}{4}$, and $\frac{21}{50}$ is a little less than $\frac{1}{2}$.

▶ **Exercise 14** Have students share their explanations.

▶ **Exercise 30** Some students may use different fractions from the benchmark fractions in the suggested answer for **Part a**, which gives the exact fractional parts shaded. This should not affect the order in **Part b**.

Additional Answers
31. $\frac{1}{4}$; Possible explanation: $\frac{5}{18} = \frac{10}{36}$, which is close to $\frac{9}{36}$.

32. $\frac{1}{4}$; Possible explanation: $\frac{1}{5}$ is a little less than $\frac{1}{4}$.

33. 1; Possible explanation: $\frac{9}{10}$ is $\frac{36}{40}$ while $\frac{3}{4}$ is $\frac{30}{40}$, and 1 is $\frac{40}{40}$, so $\frac{9}{10}$ is closer to 1.

▶ **Exercise 35** Some students may not remember what it means to write a number in lowest terms or recall how to do this. Since this skill is reviewed in Investigation 2, you might want to have students write their answers without thinking about whether or not the fractional parts are in lowest terms, and then revisit the exercise after Investigation 2.

▶ **Exercise 36** These exercises prepare students for multiplication of mixed numbers. You should still assign this execise even if you have not taught multiplication yet. Suggest that students having difficulty draw a picture or use a number line to solve each part. These are number sense strategies.

▶ **Exercise 37** Point out that students must have some of their bar left over.

Connect & Extend

35. Measurement Five segments are shown above the yardstick. Give the length of each segment **in feet**. Give your answers as fractions or mixed numbers in lowest terms.

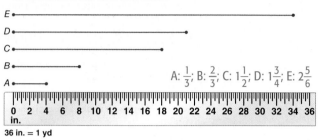

A: $\frac{1}{3}$; B: $\frac{2}{3}$; C: $1\frac{1}{2}$; D: $1\frac{3}{4}$; E: $2\frac{5}{6}$

36 in. = 1 yd

37a. Possible answer: I would cut my bar into 12 pieces. I would trade $\frac{6}{12}$ for $\frac{5}{10}$ of Jovan's and $\frac{4}{12}$ for $\frac{2}{6}$ of Regina's. I would have $\frac{2}{12}$ left.

37b. Possible answer: I would cut my bar into 3 pieces. I would trade $\frac{1}{3}$ for $\frac{1}{3}$ of Casey's and $\frac{1}{3}$ for $\frac{2}{6}$ of Regina's. I would have $\frac{1}{3}$ left.

37c. Possible answer: I would cut my bar into 15 pieces. I would trade $\frac{3}{15}$ for $\frac{1}{5}$ of Manuel's and $\frac{5}{15}$ for $\frac{1}{3}$ of Casey's. I would have $\frac{7}{15}$ left.

36. Number Sense People often use mixed numbers to compare two quantities or to describe how much something has changed or grown.

a. Dion's height is about $1\frac{1}{2}$ times his younger brother Jamil's height. Jamil is about 40 inches tall. How tall is Dion?   60 in.

b. Bobbi spends 40 minutes each night practicing her violin. She said, "That's $1\frac{1}{3}$ times the amount of time I spent last year." How much time did Bobbi practice each night last year?   30 min

c. The 2007 population of Seattle was about $7\frac{2}{5}$ times the 1900 population. Seattle's 1900 population was about 80,000. Estimate Seattle's population in 2007.   About 592,000

37. Imagine that you have baked a delicious mango-papaya bar the same size as the bars baked by the students in Investigation 2 on page 61.

Casey   Manuel   Your Bar

Regina   Jovan

a. You want to trade portions of your bar with Jovan and Regina and still have some left for yourself. Tell how many equal-sized pieces you would cut your bar into. Describe the trade you would make with each student. Tell what fraction of your bar you would have left.

b. Give the same information for trading with Casey and Regina.

c. Give the same information for trading with Casey and Manuel.

38. Ying baked a coconut bar and would like to trade with all three students.

Casey

Collin

Regina

38a. Possible answer: 24; Any multiple of 12 would work.

38b. Possible answer: $\frac{8}{24}$ for $\frac{1}{3}$ of Casey's, $\frac{4}{24}$ for $\frac{1}{6}$ of Regina's, and $\frac{6}{24}$ for $\frac{1}{4}$ of Collin's. This leaves $\frac{6}{24}$ for Ying.

39. Possible answer: $\frac{1}{4}$ is greater than $\frac{1}{5}$, so 3 pieces of $\frac{1}{4}$ is more than 3 pieces of $\frac{1}{5}$.

41a. 75%, 20%, 40%, 32%

a. Into how many equal-sized pieces should Ying divide her bar?

b. List the trades Ying could make. Tell how much of the bar she would have left for herself.

39. Prove It! Write a convincing argument to show that $\frac{3}{4}$ of a fruit bar is not a fair trade for $\frac{3}{5}$ of a fruit bar.

40. Biology Water makes up about $\frac{2}{3}$ of a person's body weight.

a. A student weighs 90 pounds. Determine how many pounds of the student's weight are attributed to water. Find a fraction equivalent to $\frac{2}{3}$ with a denominator of 90. $\frac{2}{3} = \frac{60}{90}$, 60 lb

b. A student weighs 75 pounds. Determine how many pounds of the student's weight are attributed to water.   50 lb

41. Preview Percent means "out of 100." You can think of a percent as the numerator of a fraction with a denominator of 100. For example, 25% means $\frac{25}{100}$. You can change a fraction to a percent by first finding an equivalent fraction with a denominator of 100.

a. Change the following fractions to percents: $\frac{3}{4}, \frac{1}{5}, \frac{20}{50}, \frac{8}{25}$.

b. In Eva's homeroom, 14 of the 20 students ride the bus to school. What percent of the students take the bus?   70%

c. Of the 500 people in the audience at the school play, 350 bought their tickets in advance. What percent of the audience bought tickets in advance?   70%

42. Measurement Between which two-twelfths of a foot will you find each measurement? For example, $\frac{1}{8}$ is between $\frac{1}{12}$ and $\frac{2}{12}$.

a. $\frac{3}{5}$ of a foot $\frac{7}{12}$ and $\frac{8}{12}$

b. $\frac{1}{10}$ of a foot $\frac{1}{12}$ and $\frac{2}{12}$

c. $\frac{5}{8}$ of a foot $\frac{7}{12}$ and $\frac{8}{12}$

▶ **Exercise 38** Have students share solution strategies. This exercise is a good opportunity to assess students' readiness to perform operations with fractions, which is introduced in Chapter 4.

▶ **Exercise 39** You may want to revisit this exercise after students have developed strategies for making comparisons of fractions having the same numerators. They will do that in Investigation 3.

▶ **Exercise 40** This exercise is a precursor to solving proportions, even though students will not formally set up a proportion at this time. Students will solve proportions in Chapter 5.

▶ **Exercise 41** You may want to have students share their answers. Percentages will be formally introduced in Chapter 6.

Lesson 2.1 Patterns and Fractions   **71**

▶ **Exercise 44** This exercise involves fractions with large numbers. You may want to discuss dividing by powers of ten to make equivalent fractions. For example, since $\frac{16,200,000}{58,300,000} \div \frac{100,000}{100,000} = \frac{162}{583}$, students can use $\frac{162}{183}$ in their calculations.

▶ **Exercise 45** If students are confused because some time periods are listed twice, tell them to assume that students reporting a time period that is exactly an hour or a multiple of an hour are included in the second group. For example, a student who does one hour of homework is included in the "1 to 2 hours" group.

45a. Yes; $\frac{57}{100}$ is close to $\frac{50}{100}$, which is $\frac{1}{2}$ of the students.

45b. No; $\frac{22}{100}$ is close to $\frac{25}{100}$, or $\frac{1}{4}$, of the students, which is considerably more than "hardly anyone."

43. Of the 560 students at Roosevelt Middle School, 240 participate in after-school sports. Of the 720 students at King Middle School, 300 participate in after-school sports.

   a. In which school does the greater *number* of students participate in sports? King

   b. In which school does the greater *fraction* of students participate in sports? Roosevelt

44. Statistics In a recent year, about 58,300,000 people lived in the western region of the United States. About 16,200,000 of these people were under 18 years of age. At the same time, about 23,900,000 of the 91,700,000 people living in the southern region were under 18 years of age. Which region had the greater fraction of children and teenagers? The western region

45. A survey asked all the sixth graders at Belmont Middle School how much time they spent on homework each week.

   a. Malik said, "About half of the students in the sixth grade spend five to six hours each week doing homework." Do you agree with this statement? Explain why or why not.

Time Spent Doing Homework	Fraction of Class
0 to 1 hours	$\frac{0}{100}$
1 to 2 hours	$\frac{1}{100}$
2 to 3 hours	$\frac{12}{100}$
3 to 4 hours	$\frac{3}{100}$
4 to 5 hours	$\frac{22}{100}$
5 to 6 hours	$\frac{57}{100}$
More than 6 hours	$\frac{5}{100}$

   b. Teresa said, "Hardly anyone spends four to five hours each week on homework." Do you agree with this statement? Explain why or why not.

47. Sample answer: You can find a fraction equivalent to a given fraction by multiplying or dividing the numerator and denominator by the same number.

46. **Challenge** The table shows the populations of the five most heavily populated countries in 2007.

2007 Population

Country	Population
China	1,320 million
India	1,169 million
United States	303 million
Indonesia	231 million
Brazil	187 million

    a. The world population in 2007 was about 6,671 million people. Which of these countries had about $\frac{1}{5}$ of the world population? China

    b. About what fraction of the total 2007 world population lived in the United States? Possible answer: About $\frac{1}{20}$

47. **In Your Own Words** Explain how factors and multiples can be used to find members of a fraction family.

Mixed Review

Find the measure of each angle.

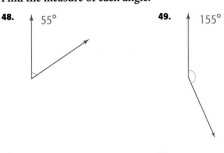

48. 55°

49. 155°

50. 15°

51. 100°

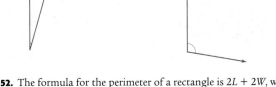

52. The formula for the perimeter of a rectangle is $2L + 2W$, where L is the length of the rectangle and W is the width. Find the perimeter of a rectangle with length 6 cm and width 2 cm. 16 cm

Lesson 2.1 Patterns and Fractions   73

▶ **Exercise 46** This exercise involves fractions with large numbers. Students may divide the numbers by one million before using them in their calculations. See the note for Exercise 44.

Quick Check

Informal Assessment Students should be able to:

✔ write a fraction as a mixed number and a mixed number as a fraction

✔ find equivalent fractions

✔ write fractions in lowest terms

✔ compare and order fractions

✔ use benchmarks to estimate the values of other fractions

Quick Quiz

For Exercises 1 and 2, write your answer as a fraction in lowest terms and as a mixed number.

1. Alex spent 75 minutes running errands. What fraction of an hour is this? $\frac{5}{4}$, $1\frac{1}{4}$

2. Carla has 8 quiches to share equally among 5 people. What portion will each person receive? $\frac{8}{5}$, $1\frac{3}{5}$

3. Write each fraction in lowest terms.
    a. $\frac{24}{36}$ $\frac{2}{3}$
    b. $\frac{16}{20}$ $\frac{4}{5}$
    c. $\frac{125}{150}$ $\frac{5}{6}$
    d. $\frac{60}{105}$ $\frac{4}{7}$

4. Compare each fraction. Write =, <, or >.
    a. $\frac{40}{75}$ = $\frac{48}{90}$ b. $\frac{9}{10}$ > $\frac{9}{15}$
    c. $\frac{21}{49}$ < $\frac{7}{14}$ d. $\frac{8}{12}$ > $\frac{5}{12}$

5. Rewrite each statement using a familiar fraction to approximate the actual fraction.
    a. Only $\frac{49}{72}$ of the concert tickets were sold. Possible answer: Only $\frac{2}{3}$ of the concert tickets were sold.
    b. Pat has completed $\frac{13}{28}$ of the homework problems. Possible answer: Pat has completed $\frac{1}{2}$ of the homework problems.

Lesson 2.1 Patterns in Fractions   **73**

Patterns in Decimals

Objectives

▶ To recognize decimal place value

▶ To write decimals as fractions whose denominators are powers of 10

▶ To multiply and divide numbers by powers of 10 and represent the answers as decimals

▶ To measure distance in the metric system and to convert among linear metric units

▶ To compare and order decimals

Overview

This lesson reviews basic concepts about decimal place values. Students begin by playing a game in which they try to make one dollar from various combinations of cents. Then they look at the patterns revealed when multiplying and dividing numbers by powers of ten and apply these patterns to convert units of metric measure. The lesson ends with students comparing and ordering decimals. These basic concepts will be important when students move on to operations with decimals in Chapter 4.

Advance Preparation

You may want to use dollar charts along with Lesson 2.2 Masters 1–3 to facilitate class activities and discussions for presenting new topics.

	Summary	Materials	On Your Own Exercises (pp. 84–87)	Assessment Opportunities
Investigation 1 (p. 75) *Pacing: 2 days*	Students review decimal place value and use patterns to multiply or divide numbers by powers of 10.	Lesson 2.2 Masters 1 and 2 or 10 × 10 grids, Transparency of Chapter 2 Master 1 (optional)	Practice & Apply: 1–11 Connect & Extend: 25–28 Mixed Review: 37–43	Share & Summarize (p. 79) Troubleshooting (pp. 76, 79)
Investigation 2 (p. 79) *Pacing: 1 day*	Students use metric units to measure lengths and use their knowledge of decimal place value to convert among metric units.	metersticks, tape	Practice & Apply: 12–21 Connect & Extend: 29–31 Mixed Review: 37–43	On the Spot Assessment (p. 80) Share & Summarize (p. 81) Troubleshooting (p. 81)
Inquiry Investigation 3 (p. 82) *Pacing: 1 day*	Students compare and order decimals.	Lesson 2.2 Master 3 (optional), Chapter 2 Master 1 (optional)	Practice & Apply: 22–24 Connect & Extend: 32–36 Mixed Review: 37–43	

Leveled Lesson Resources

CRM *Available in:* **Chapter 2 Resource Masters**

Also on
TeacherWorks™
Lesson 2.2

Study Guide and Intervention (p. 12) **AL**

Lesson 2.2 Study Guide and Intervention
Patterns in Decimals

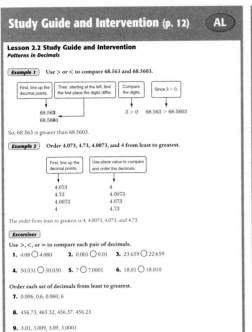

Example 1 Use > or < to compare 68.563 and 68.5603.

First, line up the decimal points. → Then, starting at the left, find the first place the digits differ. → Compare the digits. → Since 3 > 0,

68.563
68.5603

3 > 0   68.563 > 68.5603

So, 68.563 is greater than 68.5603.

Example 2 Order 4.073, 4.73, 4.0073, and 4 from least to greatest.

First, line up the decimal points. → Use place value to compare and order the decimals.

4.073	4
4.73	4.0073
4.0073	4.073
4	4.73

The order from least to greatest is 4, 4.0073, 4.073, and 4.73.

Exercises

Use >, <, or = to compare each pair of decimals.
1. 4.08 ◯ 4.080   2. 0.001 ◯ 0.01   3. 23.659 ◯ 22.659
4. 50.031 ◯ 50.030   5. 7 ◯ 7.0001   6. 18.01 ◯ 18.010

Order each set of decimals from least to greatest.
7. 0.006, 0.6, 0.060, 6
8. 456.73, 465.32, 456.37, 456.23
9. 3.01, 3.009, 3.09, 3.0001
10. 45.333, 45.303, 45.03, 45.003, 45.0003

Skills Practice (p. 13) **AL** **OL**

Lesson 2.2 Skills Practice
Patterns in Decimals

Use >, <, or = to compare each pair of decimals.
1. 2.4 ◯ 2.04   2. 6.23 ◯ 6.32   3. 0.02 ◯ 0.020
4. 12.05 ◯ 12.50   5. 0.92 ◯ 0.095   6. 39.21 ◯ 39.021
7. 0.849 ◯ 0.0851   8. 12.1 ◯ 12.10   9. 21.967 ◯ 2.1968
10. 0.0128 ◯ 0.128   11. 1.4601 ◯ 1.460   12. 19.08 ◯ 19.079

Predict the value of each product without doing any calculations.
13. $8.3 \cdot 100$ 14. $19.2 \cdot \frac{1}{10}$ 15. $0.24 \cdot 10,000$
16. $623 \cdot \frac{1}{100}$ 17. $15.07 \cdot 10$ 18. $1.02 \cdot \frac{1}{10} \cdot \frac{1}{10}$

Order each set of decimals from least to greatest.
19. 1.25, 1.52, 1.02, 1.50   20. 67.39, 68.004, 67.039, 67.04
21. 15.0421, 14.52, 14.521, 15.421   22. 0.0012, 0.0211, 0.0002, 0.0022

Order each set of decimals from greatest to least.
23. 4.99, 4.001, 5.0, 4.01   24. 12.0012, 120.012, 12.012, 12.12
25. 3.5, 3.05, 3.55, 3.555   26. 45.0, 40.5, 40.09, 49.5

Problem-Solving Practice (p. 14) **AL** **OL**

Lesson 2.2 Problem-Solving Practice
Patterns in Decimals

Music For Exercises 1–4, use the table below.
The table shows the percent of the music market for each type of music.

| Music Industry Sales Statistics, 2001 | |
Type of Music	Percent of Market
Pop	12.1
Country	10.5
Rock	24.4
Rap/Hip-Hop	11.4
R&B	10.6

1. Use > or < to compare the percents for pop and rap/hip-hop. Which is greater?

2. Use > or < to compare the percents for country and R&B. Which is greater?

3. If you owned a store that sells CDs, which kind of music would you want to sell, based on the table? Explain.

4. Suppose children's songs have 12.05 percent of the market. Is this greater or less than the percent for pop music? Explain.

5. Alberto is setting out four boards of lumber. The lengths of the boards are 4.5 meters, 4.52 meters, 4 meters, and 4.505 meters. Order the lengths from longest to shortest.

6. Ella set out a board of pine lumber that was 0.8 feet long and a board of cedar lumber that was 0.80 feet long. Alberto said the cedar board was longer. Is he correct? Explain.

Enrichment (p. 15) **BL**

Lesson 2.2 Enrichment
Patterns in Decimals

A Look at Nutrients
The table below gives data about a few of the nutrients in an average serving of some common foods.

Food	Protein (grams)	Fat (grams)	Carbohydrates (grams)	Vitamins (milligrams) B	B-1	B-2	Minerals† (milligrams) Na	K	Ca
apple (medium)	0.3	0.5	21.1	8	0.02	0.02	1	159	10
chocolate bar (1.02 oz)	2.2	9.4	16.5	0	0.02	0.08	29	119	55
cola (12 fl oz)	0.0	0.0	40.7	0	0.00	0.00	20	7	11
hamburger (1 medium)	21.8	14.5	0.0	0	0.13	0.15	40	382	6
orange juice (8 fl oz)	1.7	0.1	26.8	97	0.20	0.05	2	474	22
peas (1/2 cup)	4.5	0.4	10.8	19	0.22	0.09	128	137	17
wheat bread (1 slice)	2.3	1.0	11.3	0	0.11	0.08	129	33	30
whole milk (8 fl oz)	8.0	8.2	11.4	2	0.09	0.40	120	370	291

*Na = sodium, K = potassium, Ca = calcium

Use the data in the table to answer each question.
1. Is there more potassium in one apple or in one serving of peas?
2. Does one serving of milk contain more fat or more carbohydrates?
3. Which foods contain less than 0.05 milligram of vitamin B-2?
4. Which foods contain an amount of carbohydrates between 15 grams and 25 grams?
5. Which food contains the least amount of calcium?
6. Which food contains the greatest amount of vitamin B-1?
7. List the foods in order of their protein content from least to greatest.
8. List the foods in order of their fat content from greatest to least.
9. Make up two questions about the data in the table. Exchange questions with a classmate. Then answer your classmate's questions.

Lesson Quick Quiz (p. 16) **AL** **OL** **BL**

Lesson 2.2 Quick Quiz
Patterns in Fractions

1. Find each quantity without using a calculator.
   a. $3.12 \cdot 1,000$
   b. $\frac{1}{1,000}$ of 3.12
   c. $3.12 \div 1,000$

2. Write 6.1521 as a mixed number.

3. Write 0.432 meter in centimeters as a fraction or mixed number and as a decimal.

4. Write each measure in meters as a fraction or mixed number and as a decimal.
   a. 36 cm
   b. 25.1 mm

5. Order these numbers from least to greatest.
   14.7, 19.26, 15.138, 14.28, 16.9, 19.85, 15.01

Lesson Masters 1–3 (p. 17–19)

Lesson 2.2 Master 1
Patterns in Fractions

Explore and Investigation 1: Develop & Understand: A, Exercises 1-3

Dollar Charts

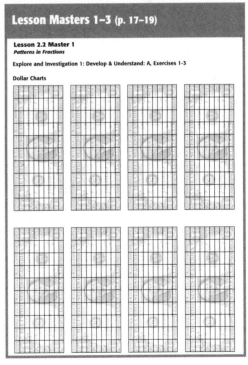

Additional Lesson Resources

Teacher Tech Tools
- TeacherWorks
- ExamView Assessment Suite
- Classroom Presentation Toolkit
- Advance Tracker

Student Tech Tools
- StudentWorks Plus
- **Math Online** ▷ eGlossary •
  Concepts in Motion

Other Print Products
- Investigation Notebook and Reflection Journal
- Quick Review Math Handbook

Introduce

Decimals and Place Values As students work through this lesson, encourage them to name decimals by their place values; for example, saying "one and five tenths" rather than "one point five." This will help students make the connection between decimals and fractions, reinforce what decimals mean, and provide a helpful way of thinking as they begin to order and compare decimals.

Explore ·

Suggested Grouping: Groups of 3 or 4

▶ **Materials and Preparation** Create sets of 54 *Spare Change* cards with the following values shown in the chart on the bottom of p. 75. You will need one set of cards for each group.

▶ **Prepare** Read through the rules with the class, and then play a few turns to model the game. A transparency of Lesson 2.2 Master 1 would help you demonstrate how to fill in the dollar chart, or draw a 10 × 10 grid on the board. Students can use dollar charts cut from the master or draw their own 10 × 10 grids for playing the game.

▶ **Play** The key to winning the game is to watch all players' dollar charts. As a player gets closer to completely filling in the dollar chart, he or she will choose smaller values in order to get close to, but not over, $1.00. When an opponent is in this situation, taking the card that would place him or her closest to $1.00 may keep the player from winning.

▶ **Report** Discuss the game with the class and bring out things to remember such as lining up the decimal points when adding, and helpful tips such as including trailing zeros so that each decimal has the same number of places after the decimal point. Ask a volunteer to describe his or her strategies.

▶ **Score** The player in the group who has shaded the amount closest to a dollar at the end of the game is the winner.

Patterns in Decimals

Materials

- Spare Change cards
  (1 set per group)
- dollar charts (1 per player)

① Possible answer: I always chose the greatest value I could, or I would try to choose a value that would not allow my opponent to get $1.00 perfectly. When I was closer to a dollar than my partner, I could sometimes choose a card so that all the remaining cards would put my partner over a dollar.

② Possible answer: I learned to look carefully at the decimal places. $0.5 is 50 cents, not 5 cents.

You encounter decimals everyday. Prices displayed in stores and statistics in the sports section of the newspaper are often given as decimals. In this lesson, you will review the meaning of decimals. You will also practice working with decimals in a variety of situations.

Explore ·

Read the rules of the *Spare Change* game. Play two rounds with your group.

Spare Change Game Rules

- Place four *Spare Change* cards face up on the table. Place the rest of the deck face down in a pile.

- To take a turn, a player chooses one of the four cards showing and shades that fraction of a dollar on his or her dollar chart. The player then places the card on the bottom of the deck and replaces it with the top card from the deck.

- Play continues until one player has shaded the entire card or is unable to shade any of the four amounts showing on the face up cards.

- The player who has shaded the amount closest to a dollar at the end of the game is the winner.

Describe some strategies you used while playing the game. See ①.

Discuss what you learned about decimals.   See ②.

Reaching *All Learners*

ELL **English Language Learners**
Read the game directions carefully and make sure students understand what to do.

Materials
- dollar charts

Decimals are equivalent to fractions whose denominators are 10, 100, 1,000, 10,000, and so on. Each decimal place has a name based on the fraction it represents.

Math Link

The prefix "deci" comes from the Latin word *decem*, meaning "ten."

Decimal	Equivalent Fraction	In Words
0.1	$\frac{1}{10}$	one tenth
0.01	$\frac{1}{100}$	one hundredth
0.001	$\frac{1}{1,000}$	one thousandth
0.0001	$\frac{1}{10,000}$	one ten-thousandth

Example

How is 9.057 different from 9.57?

These decimals look similar, but they represent different numbers. You can see this by looking at the place values of the digits.

1000	100	10	1	0.1	0.01	0.001
thousands	hundreds	tens	ones	tenths	hundredths	thousandths
			9	0	5	7
			9	5	7	

9.057 means $9 + \frac{0}{10} + \frac{5}{100} + \frac{7}{1,000}$,

or $9\frac{57}{1,000}$,

or $\frac{9,057}{1,000}$.

9.57 means $9 + \frac{5}{10} + \frac{7}{100}$,

or $9\frac{57}{100}$,

or $\frac{957}{100}$.

The number 9.057 is read "nine and fifty-seven thousandths."
The number 9.57 is read "nine and fifty-seven hundredths."

Lesson 2.2 Patterns in Decimals **75**

$0.01	$0.01	$0.02	$0.02	$0.03	$0.03
$0.04	$0.04	$0.05	$0.05	$0.06	$0.06
$0.07	$0.07	$0.08	$0.08	$0.09	$0.09
$0.10	$0.10	$0.11	$0.11	$0.12	$0.12
$0.13	$0.13	$0.14	$0.14	$0.15	$0.15
$0.16	$0.16	$0.17	$0.17	$0.18	$0.18
$0.19	$0.19	$0.20	$0.20	$0.25	$0.25
$0.25	$0.50	$0.50	$0.50	$0.75	$0.75
$0.75	$0.38	$0.43	$0.46	$0.61	$0.79

On Your Own Exercises
Pages 84–87
Exercises 1–11, 25–28

Understand Decimals This investigation presents decimal place value and fractional equivalents of decimals, which will be a review for most students. During the investigation, students should connect decimal place values to the dollar charts used in the *Spare Change* game on page 74, and then go on to look at the patterns that can be seen when multiplying or dividing numbers by powers of 10.

Analyze the Table Review the decimals and equivalent fractions in the table, stressing that both forms have the same name.

(Example)

To assess students' initial understanding of decimals, pose the question in the text: "How is 9.057 different from 9.57?" Use students' responses to decide how much detail you will go into when discussing the place value chart and the value of each decimal. Be sure to review the different meanings of each number.

You may also want to use a transparency of Chapter 2 Master 1, Place Value Chart, in your discussion. To give students extra help identifying numbers, write a number on the transparency, one digit per box, and show the students the number with the place value names covered. You can then ask questions about specific digits. You can also use the transparency as an overlay and write a number on another transparency with the digits appropriately spread. Then overlay the place value table and have students read the number. You can move the place value table so the digit appears in a different position, and have students read the new number.

Math Link

Words using "deci" include decimeter and decibel. What do these words mean?

Teacher Tips If students were able to explain the difference between 9.057 and 9.57 on page 75 clearly, assign the exercises as an independent review. If they were confused, work through the exercises as a class and have students explain the answers whenever possible, or take the opportunity to explain the ideas yourself when they cannot.

 Develop & Understand: A

Suggested Grouping: Individuals

▶ **Exercises 1–3** You may wish to provide students with copies of dollar charts cut from Lesson 2.2 Master 1 and related On Your Own Exercises 1 and 2, if assigned. If you choose not to use the master, have students draw 10 × 10 grids to represent the dollar charts.

In Exercises 1–3, students' dollar charts may be visually different from the sample answers, but all should have the same number of shaded parts.

▶ **Exercise 2** Students may use one of the following strategies.

- Count the unshaded parts. Write the number as the numerator with a denominator of 100 and as a decimal money amount.

- Subtract the shaded parts from 100. Write the result as the numerator with a denominator of 100. Then write an equivalent decimal amount.

- Subtract the money amounts: $1.00 − $0.93.

Math Link

Point out, for example, that 1 234 567.89 would be the same number as 1,234,567.89.

1b. $0.3 = $ $\frac{3}{10}$ dollar,

$0.03 = \frac{3}{100}$ dollar

1c. Possible chart:

....

Math Link

In many countries, a *decimal comma* is used instead of a decimal point, and a space is used to separate groups of three digits.

....

2a. Possible chart:

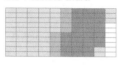

In Exercises 1–3, you will see how the ideas discussed in Investigation 1 relate to the *Spare Change* game.

 Develop & Understand: A

1. Consider the values $0.3 and $0.03.

   a. Are these values the same? No

   b. Explain your answer to Part a by writing both amounts as fractions.

   c. Illustrate your answer to Part a by shading both amounts on a dollar chart.

2. In her first four turns of the *Spare Change* game, Kristina chose $0.45, $0.1, $0.33, and $0.05.

   a. Complete a dollar chart showing the amount Kristina should have shaded after the first four turns.

   b. What part of a dollar is shaded on Kristina's chart? Express your answer as a fraction and as a decimal. $\frac{93}{100}$, 0.93

   c. How much more does Kristina need to have $1.00? Express your answer as a decimal and as a fraction. $\frac{7}{100}$ dollar, $0.07

3. How could you shade a dollar chart to represent $0.125?
   Shade 12 whole rectangles and $\frac{1}{2}$ of another.

Now you will explore how multiplying or dividing a number by 10, 100, 1,000, and so on changes the position of the decimal point.

Troubleshooting

In Exercise 1, watch for students who interpret $0.3 as 3 cents. Review how to use zero as a placeholder. Remind students that money amounts always have two decimal places, so 3 cents is written as $0.03 and 30 cents is written as $0.30. Then show a correctly shaded dollar chart to demonstrate how the two values differ.

4. Copy the table.

Calculation		Result
81.07	= 81.07 • 1	81.07
81.07 • 10	= 81.07 • 10	810.7
81.07 • 10 • 10	= 81.07 • 100	8,107
81.07 • 10 • 10 • 10	= 81.07 • 1,000	81,070
81.07 • 10 • 10 • 10 • 10	= 81.07 • 10,000	810,700
81.07 • 10 • 10 • 10 • 10 • 10	= 81.07 • 100,000	8,107,000

a. Enter the number 81.07 on your calculator. Multiply it by 10. Record the result in the second row of the table.

b. Find 81.07 • 100 by multiplying your result from Part a by 10. Record the result in the table.

c. Continue to multiply each result by 10 to find 81.07 • 1,000; 81.07 • 10,000; and 81.07 • 100,000. Record your results.

d. Describe how the position of the decimal point changed each time you multiplied by 10.   It moved one place to the right.

5. In Parts a–c, predict the value of each product without doing any calculations. Check your prediction by using your calculator.

a. 7.801 • 10,000
78,010

b. 0.003 • 100
0.3

c. 9,832 • 1,000
9,832,000

d. When you predicted the results of Parts a–c, how did you determine where to put the decimal point?   Possible answer: I moved the decimal point one place to the right for each 0.

6. Think about how the value of a number changes as you move the decimal point to the right.

a. How does the value of a number change when you move the decimal point one place to the right? Two places to the right? Three places to the right? (Hint: Look at your completed table from Exercise 5, or test a few numbers to see what happens.)

b. **Challenge** In general, what is the relationship between the number of places a decimal is moved to the right and the change in the value of the number?   Possible answer: The value of the number is multiplied by 10 for each decimal place moved.

7. Tell what number you must multiply the given number by to get 240. Explain how you found your answer.

a. 2.4

b. 0.24

c. 0.00024

6a. It is multiplied by 10. It is multiplied by 100. It is multiplied by 1,000.

7a. 100; Possible explanation: To get from 2.4 to 240, the decimal point is moved two places to the right.

7b. 1,000; Possible explanation: To get from 0.24 to 240, the decimal point is moved three places to the right.

7c. 1,000,000; To get from 0.00024 to 240, the decimal point is moved six places to the right.

Suggested Grouping: Pairs

▶ **Exercises 4–7** Students should have calculators for these exercises. You may also wish to provide them with copies of Lesson 2.2 Master 2, which reproduces the tables.

▶ **Exercise 7** Students have to find missing power-of-ten factors. Students may use one of these strategies.

• Count the number of places the decimal point must move to get from the given factor to the given product. Then use the relationship between how many places a decimal point moves and the number of zeros in the power-of-ten factor to determine the other factor.

• Find a missing factor: 2.4 × ? = 240.

• Divide 240 by the number in each problem. For example, 240 ÷ 2.4 = 100.

Analyze the Table Discuss the pattern in the factors of 10 in each row of the table. Point out that each additional factor of 10 moves the decimal point one place to the right.

Wrap-Up Have students share the patterns they found in Exercise 4d, their descriptions of how the value of a number changes when the decimal point is moved in Exercise 6, and how they used what they learned to find missing factors in Exercise 7.

A transparency of Chapter 2 Master 1 might help in your discussion. Write 8107000 with the digits spread out, and then overlay the transparency so that the decimal point is between the one and the first zero. You can demonstrate moving the decimal point by moving the overlay.

Reaching All Learners

BL **Beyond Level** Have students who finish early use exponents to write each multiple of 10 shown in the table.

Lesson 2.2   Patterns in Decimals   **77**

Teacher Tips

Teacher Tips Point out that this exercise set is analogous to the exercises on page 77, but with division by powers of 10 rather than multiplication.

Students are also informally introduced to how to rewrite a division problem by multiplying the dividend by the reciprocal of the divisor. If students had difficulty with those exercises, you may want to work through this problem set as a class.

The second table on Lesson 2.2 Master 2 is a copy of the table in Exercise 8.

✅ Develop & Understand: C

Suggested Grouping: Pairs

▶ **Exercises 8–10** If students had difficulty with the exercises on page 77, you may want to work through this exercise set as a class. Use Lesson 2.2 Master 2 to reproduce the table for Exercise 8.

Analyze the Table Discuss the pattern in the divisors of 10 in each row of the table. Point out that each additional divisor of 10 moves the decimal point one place to the left.

Wrap-Up Discuss the patterns students found in Exercise 8d, and discuss how moving the decimal point changes the value of a number in Exercise 10.

A transparency of Chapter 2 Master 1 may be helpful.

✅ Develop & Understand: C

8. Copy the table.   9a–c. See table.

Calculation		Result
81.07		81.07
$81.07 \div 10$	$= \frac{1}{10}$ of 81.07	8.107
$81.07 \div 10 \div 10$	$= \frac{1}{100}$ of 81.07	0.8107
$81.07 \div 10 \div 10 \div 10$	$= \frac{1}{1,000}$ of 81.07	0.08107
$81.07 \div 10 \div 10 \div 10 \div 10$	$= \frac{1}{10,000}$ of 81.07	0.008107
$81.07 \div 10 \div 10 \div 10 \div 10 \div 10 = \frac{1}{100,000}$ of 81.07		0.0008107

a. Find $\frac{1}{10}$ of 81.07 by entering 81.07 on your calculator and dividing by 10. Record the result in the second row of the table.

b. Find $\frac{1}{100}$ of 81.07 by dividing your result from Part a by 10. Record the result in the table.

c. Continue to divide each result by 10 to find $\frac{1}{1,000}$ of 81.07, $\frac{1}{10,000}$ of 81.07, and $\frac{1}{100,000}$ of 81.07. Record your results.

d. Describe how the position of the decimal point changed each time you divided by 10, that is, each time you found $\frac{1}{10}$. It moved one place to the left.

9. In Parts a–c, predict each result without doing any calculations. Check your prediction by using your calculator.

a. $\frac{1}{10,000}$ of 14.14   **b.** $34,372 \div 100$ **c.** $\frac{1}{1,000}$ of 877
 0.001414   343.72   0.877

d. When you predicted the results of Parts a–c, how did you determine where to put the decimal point?   Possible answer: I moved the decimal point one place to the left for each 0.

10. Think about how the value of a number changes as you move the decimal point to the left.

10a. It is divided by 10. It is divided by 100. It is divided by 1,000.

a. How does the value of a number change when you move the decimal point one place to the left? Two places to the left? Three places to the left? (Hint: Look at your completed table from Exercise 8, or test a few numbers to see what happens.)

b. Challenge In general, what is the relationship between the number of places a decimal is moved to the left and the change in the value of the number?   Possible answer: The value of the number is divided by 10 for each decimal place moved.

Mathematical Background

The relationship between the two sides of each equation shown in the "Calculation" column of the table can be explained by thinking of division as being shown by fractions, and whole numbers being written as fractions with a denominator of 1.

For example, $81.07 \div 10$ can be thought of as the fraction $\frac{81.07}{10}$. At the same time, $\frac{81.07}{1} \cdot \frac{1}{10}$ is equal to $\frac{81.07}{10}$.

11a. 10; Possible explanation: To get from 18 to 1.8, the decimal point is moved one place to the left.

11b. 100; Possible explanation: To get from 180 to 1.8, the decimal point is moved two places to the left.

11. Tell what number you must divide the given number by to get 1.8. Explain how you found your answer.

   a. 18   **b.** 180   **c.** 18,000

Share & Summarize

1. A shirt is on sale for $16.80. Write $16.80 as a mixed number. See below.
2. A big-screen television costs 100 times as much as the shirt. How much does the TV cost? $1,680
3. A fresh-cooked pretzel costs $\frac{1}{10}$ as much as the shirt. How much is the pretzel? $1.68

1. Possible answer: $16\frac{80}{100}$ dollars

Investigation 2 — Measure with Decimals

Materials
- tape
- meterstick

Math Link
The abbreviation for meter is m.

The abbreviation for centimeter is cm.

The abbreviation for millimeter is mm.

11c. 10,000; Possible explanation: To get from 18,000 to 1.8, the decimal point is moved four places to the left.

① 0.01, $\frac{1}{100}$

② 0.1, $\frac{1}{10}$

③ 0.001, $\frac{1}{1,000}$

④ 0.05, $\frac{5}{100}$

⑤ 1.5, $1\frac{1}{2}$

⑥ 0.015, $\frac{15}{1,000}$

In the metric system, units of measure are based on the number 10. This makes converting from one unit to another as easy as moving a decimal point.

The basic unit of length in the metric system is the meter. Each meter can be divided into 100 centimeters.

Each centimeter can be divided into 10 millimeters. (Note: Ruler is not to scale.)

1 cm = 10 mm

Think & Discuss

Fill in the blanks. Give your answers as both decimals and fractions.

1 cm = ①____ m   1 mm = ②____ cm   1 mm = ③____ m

5 cm = ④____ m   15 mm = ⑤____ cm   15 mm = ⑥____ m

Reaching All Learners

AL Approaching Level You may want to supply metersticks now rather than waiting until later. You also may want to have students tell how many centimeters and how many millimeters are on a meterstick. Then have them find the marks for 10 cm, 10 mm, 5 cm, 5 mm, and 50 mm on their metersticks.

▶ **Exercise 11** Point out that students should look at the number to *divide* by, so the answer should be a whole number, not a fraction.

Share & Summarize

Have students work individually on these questions and then explain how they found their answers to **Exercises 2 and 3**. Ask students who moved the decimal point by following the patterns they found in the problem sets to explain *why* the pattern works.

Troubleshooting If students are struggling with decimal and fraction equivalencies, review the table on page 75 with them. Remind students that both forms have the same name—one tenth, one hundredth, and so on—and the same value. Review the relationship between the place values on either side of one in the place value chart. For example, the place values on either side of one are ten and tenths.

Investigation 2

On Your Own Exercises
Pages 84–87
Exercises 12–21, 29–31

Measure with Decimals The focus of this investigation is to use decimals to relate units of metric measure.

Review meter, centimeter, millimeter. You may want to supply metersticks now and have students tell how many centimeters and how many millimeters are on a meterstick. Then have them find the marks for 10 cm, 10 mm, 5 cm, 5 mm, and 50 mm on their metersticks.

Think & Discuss
Suggested Grouping: Individuals

Ask students to answer the questions independently before discussing their answers as a class. In the discussion, stress the connection to the previous investigation, in particular, to moving the decimal point.

✅ **Develop & Understand: A**

Suggested Grouping: Pairs

▶ **Exercises 1–5** Encourage students to express answers in both fraction and decimal form. Students often do not think of metric measurement as fractions, so using both forms may help them avoid the overgeneralization that all measurement sub-units have a direct correspondence to place value. This overgeneralization becomes a problem if students extend it to the customary measurement systems; for example, they may think that one foot 6 inches is equal to 1.6 feet instead of 1.5 feet. On Your Own Exercise 31 on page 86 addresses this issue.

▶ **Exercise 5a** Students may enjoy challenging each other to see who can find a set of objects that come closest to measuring exactly one meter. If you choose to make these problems a contest, be sure to allow students enough time to try different possibilities.

Math Link
Alternately, light travels 299,792,458 meters in one second.

✅ **Develop & Understand: A**

Convert each measurement to meters. Write your answers as fractions and as decimals.

1. 35 cm   **2.** 9 mm   **3.** 23 mm

4. Give the lengths of segments A and B **in meters**. Express your answers as fractions and as decimals.

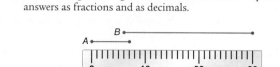

For Exercises 5–6, tape four sheets of paper together lengthwise. Tape a meterstick on top of the paper as shown, so you can draw objects above and below the meterstick.

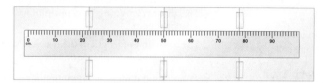

5. Collect objects whose lengths you can measure, such as pencils, books, staplers, and screwdrivers.

  a. Place the objects end to end along your meterstick until the combined length is as close to one meter as possible. Sketch the objects *above* the meterstick at their actual lengths. Sketches will vary.

  b. Find the length of each object to the nearest millimeter. Label the sketch of each object with its length in millimeters, centimeters, and meters.   Answers will vary.

Math Link
Since 1983, the meter has been defined as the distance light travels in a vacuum in $\frac{1}{299,792,458}$ of a second.

1. $\frac{35}{100}$ m, 0.35 m

2. $\frac{9}{1,000}$ m, 0.009 m

3. $\frac{23}{1,000}$ m, 0.023 m

4. A: 0.07 m, $\frac{7}{100}$ m;
   B: 0.24 m, $\frac{24}{100}$ m

On the Spot Assessment

Watch for students who look only at the right end of Segment B in Exercise 4 to determine its length and say the length is 30 cm. Point out that they must also look at where the left end lies. Remind them that when the left end aligns with 0 on the measuring tool, as with Segment A, then the length is determined by looking at the number below the right end of the segment. However, when the left end is not aligned with the 0 mark, one must subtract the number corresponding to the left end of the segment from the number corresponding to the right end.

6. In this exercise, you will try to find the combination of the following objects with a length as close to one meter as possible.

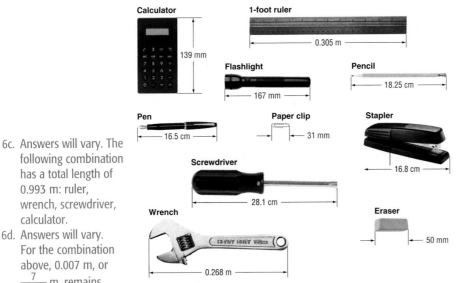

Calculator — 139 mm

1-foot ruler — 0.305 m

Flashlight — 167 mm

Pencil — 18.25 cm

Pen — 16.5 cm

Paper clip — 31 mm

Stapler — 16.8 cm

Screwdriver — 28.1 cm

Wrench — 0.268 m

Eraser — 50 mm

6c. Answers will vary. The following combination has a total length of 0.993 m: ruler, wrench, screwdriver, calculator.

6d. Answers will vary. For the combination above, 0.007 m, or $\frac{7}{1,000}$ m, remains.

6e. Ruler, paper clip; Possible explanation: I changed all the measurements to the same unit and compared them.

1. Move the decimal point two places to the left. Possible explanation: There are 100 cm in 1 m, so the measurement in meters is $\frac{1}{100}$ of the measurement in centimeters. Finding $\frac{1}{100}$ of a number moves the decimal point two places to the left.

a. Choose one of the objects. Below your meterstick, begin at 0 and sketch the object at its actual length.   Answers will vary.

b. Choose a second object. Starting at the right end of the previous drawing, sketch the second object at its actual length.
Answers will vary.

c. Continue to choose objects and sketch them until the total length is as close to one meter as possible.

d. How much of a meter is left? Express your answer as a decimal and as a fraction.

e. Which object is longest? Which object is shortest? Explain how you found your answers.

Share & Summarize

Suppose you are given a measurement in centimeters.

1. How would you move the decimal point to change the measurement to meters? Explain why this technique works.

2. How would you move the decimal point to change the measurement to millimeters? Explain why this technique works.
Move the decimal point one place to the right. Possible explanation: There are 10 mm in 1 cm, so the measurement in millimeters is 10 times the measurement in centimeters. Finding 10 times a number moves the decimal point one place to the right.

Lesson 2.2   Patterns in Decimals   **81**

▶ **Exercise 6** Students may enjoy challenging each other to see who can find a set of objects that come closest to measuring exactly one meter.

Share & Summarize

Discuss the questions. You may want to extend the discussion to have students generalize their answers to conversion to a larger or smaller unit: the decimal point moves to the left when converting to a larger metric unit and to the right when converting to a smaller metric unit.

Troubleshooting If students are having difficulty relating the units of metric measure to the decimal patterns they found in the prior investigation, it might be because the *decimeter*, which corresponds to $\frac{1}{10}$ of a meter, was not presented. Introduce the unit to resolve this discrepancy. When decimeters are considered, the pattern for metric units mirrors the decimal pattern.

$$1 \text{ dm} = \frac{1}{10} \text{ m}$$
$$1 \text{ cm} = \frac{1}{10} \text{ dm} = \frac{1}{100} \text{ m}$$
$$1 \text{ mm} = \frac{1}{10} \text{ cm} = \frac{1}{100} \text{ dm} = \frac{1}{1,000} \text{ m}$$

If the trouble seems to be with measuring or the names of units, you might have them practice measuring real objects. Have them measure using different units and give help as needed.

Inquiry
Investigation ③

Suggested Grouping: Pairs

Materials and Preparation
Students will need paper and pencil. You may want to provide each student with at least two copies of Lesson 2.2 Master 3, which contains a record sheet for the game.

Guess My Number Open the investigation by playing with the class a game of *Guess My Number* using whole numbers. Tell students you are thinking of a whole number from one to ten, and challenge them to guess it by asking no more than five yes-or-no questions. Record their guesses in a table on the board or overhead.

After they guess the number point out that they should try to think of strategies to help them find decimals that lie between other decimals as they play *Guess My Number*.

Teacher Tips As you play the game, point out that students should think of numbers with decimal places, not just whole numbers like you used. Encourage them to write something in the last column after each guess.

Try It Out
▶ **Exercises 1 and 2** Ask students to explain and apply their game strategies.

▶ **Exercise 3** Ask students to discuss any patterns they noticed.

Inquiry
Investigation ③ Compare and Order Decimals

You will now play a game that will give you practice finding decimals between other decimals.

Guess My Number

1. Possible answer: I would start asking about numbers that were far apart on the number line. Then I would guess numbers that were closer together so that I could try to find what two numbers it was between.

2. Possible answer: For each question, I know the number is between two other numbers. I always ask if the number is greater than the number halfway between the two numbers. For example, if I know the number is between 1 and 2, I ask, "Is it more than 1.5?" This eliminates half the remaining possibilities.

Guess My Number Game Rules
• Player 1 thinks of a number between 0 and 10 with no more than four decimal places and writes it down so that Player 2 cannot see it.
• Player 2 asks "yes" or "no" questions to try to figure out the number. Player 2 writes down each question and answer on a record sheet.

Question	Answer	What I Know about the Number
Is the number greater than 6?	No	It is less than or equal to 6.
Is the number less than 3?	No	It is between 3 and 6 including 3 and 6.

• Play continues until Player 2 guesses the number. Player 1 receives one point for each question Player 2 asked.
• The winner is the player with the most points after four rounds.

Try It Out
Play four rounds with your partner, switching roles for each round. Then, with your partner, look closely at your record sheet for the game.

1. What strategies did you find helpful when you asked questions?

2. Once you knew which whole numbers the answer was between, did your strategy change? Explain.   Answers will vary.

3. Who was able to ask the least questions to find the numbers? What pattern, if any, did you notice?   Answers will vary.

Reaching *All Learners*

AL **Approaching Level** If students have difficulty with this game, discuss strategies and possible questions about the game or questions about the number being guessed. Encourage the partners to discuss strategies before you do.

4a. Possible answer: She is asking too many questions. She could have eliminated the first three questions by asking, "Is it between 5 and 10?" or "Is it between 0 and 5?"

4. Jessica and Kali are playing *Guess My Number*. Kali is the Asker. Here is her record sheet.

Question	Answer
Is it greater than 1?	Yes
Is it between 4 and 10?	Yes
Is it between 5 and 10?	Yes
Is it greater than 8?	No
Is it between 7 and 8?	Yes

a. What do you think of Kali's questions? What, if anything, do you think she should have done differently?

b. What question do you think Kali should ask next?
Possible answer: "Is it greater than 7.5?"

What Did You Learn?

5. Suppose you have asked several questions and you know the number is between 4.71 and 4.72. List at least four possibilities for the number.   Possible answer: 4.711, 4.712, 4.7112, 4.719

6. What is the greatest decimal that can be made in this game? What is the least decimal that can be made in this game?   9.9999, 0.0001

▶ **Exercise 4** Ask students to explain and apply the questions they think Kali should ask next.

What Did You Learn?

▶ **Exercise 5** Discuss the game. Ask students to share their answers after you discuss strategies and possible questions for the game. Emphasize the unlimited possibilities once students consider adding more decimal places.

▶ **Exercise 6** Ask students to discuss the game and how they answered this question.

Lesson 2.2 *Patterns in Decimals* **83**

Investigation 1
Pages 75–79
Practice & Apply: 1–11
Connect & Extend: 25–28

Investigation 2
Pages 79–81
Practice & Apply: 12–21
Connect & Extend: 29–31

Inquiry Investigation
Pages 82–83
Practice & Apply: 22–24
Connect & Extend: 32–36

Assign Anytime
Mixed Review: 37–43

▶ **Exercises 1 and 2** Students will need dollar charts to complete these exercises. You may want to have students use Lesson 2.2 Master 1 or draw 10 × 10 grids.

▶ **Exercise 2** This exercise introduces the idea of a fraction of a penny. You may want to ask students what they think $0.115 actually represents before you assign this exercise.

▶ **Exercises 2b, 4, and 5** Students may write their answers in lowest terms or as another equivalent fraction.

▶ **Exercise 15** Student measures may differ slightly from the printed answer as long as the conversions are correct.

▶ **Exercises 16–21** These exercises prepare students for ordering decimals in the Inquiry Investigation.

Practice & Apply

12. $\frac{50}{100}$ m, or $\frac{1}{2}$ m; 0.5 m

13. $\frac{50}{1,000}$ m, or $\frac{1}{20}$ m; 0.05 m

14. $\frac{700}{1,000}$ m, or $\frac{7}{10}$ m; 0.7 m

1. In his first two turns in the *Spare Change* game, Maurice chose $0.03 and $0.8.

   a. Complete a dollar chart showing the amount Maurice should have shaded after his first two turns.   See margin.

   b. What part of a dollar is shaded on Maurice's chart? Express your answer as a fraction and as a decimal. $\frac{83}{100}$, 0.83

   c. How much more does Maurice need to have $1.00? Express your answer as a fraction and as a decimal. $\frac{17}{100}$ dollar, $0.17

2. Ms. Picó added cards with three decimal places to the *Spare Change* game deck. In her first three turns, Una chose $0.77, $0.1, and $0.115.

   a. Complete a dollar chart showing the amount Una should have shaded after her first three turns.   See margin.

   b. What part of a dollar is shaded on Una's chart? Express your answer as a fraction and as a decimal. $\frac{985}{1,000}$, 0.985

Write each decimal as a mixed number.

3. 1.99 $1\frac{99}{100}$

4. 7.016 $7\frac{16}{1,000}$

5. 100.5 $100\frac{5}{10}$, or $100\frac{1}{2}$

Find each product without using a calculator.

6. 100 · 0.0436   4.36

7. 100,000 · 754.01   75,401,000

8. 1,000 · 98.9   98,900

Find each quantity without using a calculator.

9. $\frac{1}{10}$ of 645   64.5

10. 7.7 ÷ 1,000   0.0077

11. $\frac{1}{10,000}$ of 55.66   0.005566

Measurement In Exercises 12–14, convert each measurement to meters. Write your answers as both fractions and decimals.

12. 50 cm

13. 50 mm

14. 700 mm

15. Give the length of the baseball bat in centimeters and in meters. 91 cm, 0.91 m

Give the nearest tenths of a centimeter that each given measurement is between, such as 3.66 is between 3.6 and 3.7.

16. 5.75 cm   5.7 cm and 5.8 cm

17. 0.25 cm   0.2 cm and 0.3 cm

18. 1.01 cm   1.0 cm and 1.1 cm

Give the nearest hundredths of a meter that each given measurement is between, such as 2.865 is between 2.86 and 2.87.

19. 0.555 m   0.55 m and 0.56 m

20. 1.759 m   1.75 m and 1.76 m

21. 0.0511 m   0.05 m and 0.06 m

Additional Answers

1a.
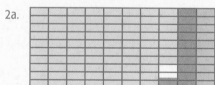

2a.

Order each set of numbers from least to greatest.

22. 7.31, 7.4, 7.110, 7.3, 7.04, 7.149   7.04, 7.110, 7.149, 7.3, 7.31, 7.4

23. 21.5, 20.50, 22.500, 20.719, 21.66, 21.01, 20.99
20.50, 20.719, 20.99, 21.01, 21.5, 21.66, 22.500

24. Participants in the school gymnastics meet are scored on a scale from 1 to 10 with 10 being the highest score. To the right are the scores for the first event. Ryan has not yet had his turn.

Student	Score
Kent	9.4
Elijah	8.9
Santiago	9.25
Matthew	8.85
Ernesto	9.9
Ryan	
Tyler	9.1
Craig	8.0
Alvin	8.7
Pierce	9.2

    a. List the students from highest score to lowest score. Ernesto, Kent, Santiago, Pierce, Tyler, Elijah, Matthew, Alvin, Craig

    b. Ryan is hoping to get third place in this event. List five possible scores that would put him in third place. Possible answers: 9.26, 9.27, 9.3, 9.35, 9.38

Connect & Extend

25. Economics The FoodStuff market is running the following specials.

- Bananas: $0.99 per pound
- Swiss cheese: $3.00 per pound
- Rolls: $0.25 each

    a. Jenna paid $9.90 for bananas. How many pounds did she buy? 10

    b. Allie bought $\frac{1}{10}$ of a pound of Swiss cheese. How much did the cheese cost? $0.30

    c. Ms. Washington is organizing the school picnic. How many rolls can she purchase with $250?   1,000

    d. Ms. Washington decides to buy some rolls, cheese, and bananas for $250. What combination of food could she buy without going over her budget?

26. Economics A grocery store flyer advertises bananas for 0.15¢ each. Does this make sense? Explain.

27. In Your Own Words Explain the purpose of the decimal point in decimal numbers.   Possible answer: A decimal separates a whole number from its fractional part.

28. Today is Tony's 10th birthday. His parents have decided to start giving him a monthly allowance, but they each suggest a different plan.

- Tony's mother wants to give him $0.01 each month this year, $0.10 each month next year, $1.00 each month the third year, and so on, multiplying the monthly amount by 10 each year until Tony's 16th birthday.

25d. Sample answer: She could buy 150 bananas, 200 rolls, and 17 pounds of swiss cheese. This would cost her $249.50

26. No; Possible explanation: 0.15 cent is $\frac{15}{100}$ of a penny.

28. Possible answer: His mother's plan. Although his father's plan would give him the most money now, over the six-year period, Tony would receive $2,520 on his father's plan and $13,333.32 on his mother's plan.

▶ **Exercise 24b** Accept any answers between 9.25 and 9.4.

▶ **Exercise 26** Using both the decimal and the cent sign to represent cents is a common error that some students may overlook because they have seen and interpreted signs containing it. After discussing this exercise, you might challenge students to bring in examples of this error.

▶ **Exercise 28** To find the total allowance Tony would receive from each plan, students may add the monthly allowance for each of the six years and then multiply by 12, or multiply each monthly allowance by 12 and add the sums.

▶ **Exercise 29** You may want to briefly discuss decimal place value to the billionths place before students work these exercises. Also, some students may not write their fractions in lowest terms, choosing to write $\frac{10}{1,000,000}$ m so the denominator is the same as the definition of 1 micron as 1 millionth of a meter.

▶ **Exercise 31** This problem addresses a common mistake that students make: reading fractions of feet as inches because they are the next smallest customary measurement unit. If students are confused about how to convert these kinds of measurement units, you may want to give them other examples, such as 6.2 hours, which is neither 6 hours 2 minutes nor 6 hours 20 minutes, but 6 hours 12 minutes.

Real-World Link
A nanoguitar is about the size of a human being's white blood cell.

· ·

29a. 0.00001 m, $\frac{1}{100,000}$ m

29c. $\frac{350}{1,000,000,000}$ m, 0.00000035 m

30. 0.003 m, or 3 mm

31. No; Possible explanation: 12 cm is $\frac{12}{100}$ of a meter, but 5 in. is not $\frac{5}{10}$ of a foot. It is $\frac{5}{12}$ of a foot.

• Tony's father wants to give him $10 each month this year, $20 each month next year, $30 each month the next year, and so on, adding $10 to the monthly amount each year until Tony's 16th birthday.

His parents told Tony he could decide which plan to use. Which plan do you think he should choose? Explain your reasoning.

29. **Science** *Nanotechnology* is a branch of science that focuses on building very small objects from molecules. These tiny objects are measured with units such as microns and nanometers.

• 1 micron = 1 millionth of a meter

• 1 nanometer = 1 billionth of a meter

a. The photo to the left is a nanoguitar. Although this guitar is only 10 microns long, it actually works. However, the sound it produces cannot be heard by the human ear. Express the length of the nanoguitar in meters. Give your answer as a decimal and as a fraction.

b. Two human hairs, side by side, would be about 0.001 meter wide. What fraction of this width is the length of the nanoguitar? $\frac{1}{100}$

c. Microchips inside the processors of computers can have widths as small as 350 nanometers. Express this width in meters. Give your answer as a fraction and as a decimal.

d. A paper clip is about 0.035 meter long. What fraction of the length of a paper clip is the width of a microchip? $\frac{1}{100,000}$

30. How much greater than 5.417 meters is 5.42 meters?

31. If a person is 2 meters 12 centimeters tall, we can say that he is 2.12 meters tall. If a person is 5 feet 5 inches tall, can we say that she is 5.5 feet tall? Why or why not?

Economics The table below gives the value of foreign currencies in U.S. dollars in 2007.

Currency	Value in U.S. Dollars
Australian dollar	0.8989
British pound	2.0486
Canadian dollar	1.0326
Chinese renminbi	0.1333
Danish krone	0.1913
Russian rouble	0.0402
Mexican new peso	0.0923
Singapore dollar	0.6837

BUREAU DE CHANGE
RATES PER £1.00	WE SELL	WE BUY
U.S.A.	1.52	1.60
BELGIUM	47.87	51.47
CANADA	2.035	2.24
DENMARK	8.75	9.65
FRANCE	7.80	8.40
GERMANY	2.30	2.53
IRELAND	0.96	1.05
ITALY	2350	2548
JAPAN	165	181
NETHERLANDS	2.60	2.80
PORTUGAL	2.39	2.56
SPAIN	192.00	208.13
SWEDEN	10.20	11.10
SWITZERLAND	1.86	2.02
MIN' CHARGE £	3.00	3.00
COM' RATE %	2.00	5.00

32. If you exchanged one Canadian dollar for U.S. currency, how much money would you receive? Assume that values are rounded to the nearest penny. $1.03

33. Of those listed in the table, which currency is worth the most in U.S. dollars?   The British pound

34. Of those listed in the table, which currency is worth the least in U.S. dollars?   The Russian rouble

35. The Canadian dollar; $0.0326 more, or about $0.03 more

35. Which currency listed in the table is worth closest to one U.S. dollar? How much more or less than one U.S. dollar is this currency worth?

36. How many Russian roubles could you exchange for one dime?   2

Mixed Review

Geometry Draw a polygon matching each description, if possible. If it is not possible, say so.

37. Possible polygon:

37. a concave pentagon

38. a triangle with exactly two lines of symmetry   Not possible

39. a quadrilateral that is not regular and that has two lines of symmetry

39. Possible polygon:

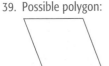

Geometry Find the perimeter of each figure.

40.

2.19 cm

3.65 cm

11.68 cm

41.

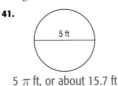

5 ft

5 π ft, or about 15.7 ft

42.

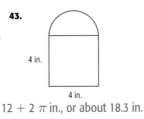

2 cm

4 cm

1 cm

2 cm

2 cm

5 cm

26 cm

43.

4 in.

4 in.

12 + 2 π in., or about 18.3 in.

Quick Check

Informal Assessment Students should be able to:

✔ recognize decimal place value

✔ write decimals as fractions whose denominators are powers of ten

✔ multiply and divide numbers by powers of ten and represent the answers as decimals

✔ measure distance in the metric system and convert among linear metric units

✔ compare and order decimals

Quick Quiz

1. Find each quantity without using a calculator.
   a. $3.12 \cdot 1{,}000$ 3,120
   b. $\frac{1}{1000}$ of 3.12 0.00312
   c. $3.12 \div 1{,}000$ 0.00312

2. Write 6.1521 as a mixed number.
   $6\frac{1{,}521}{10{,}000}$

3. Write 0.432 meter in centimeters as a fraction or mixed number and as a decimal. $43\frac{2}{10}$ cm, or $43\frac{1}{5}$; 43.2 cm

4. Write each measure in meters as a fraction or mixed number, and as a decimal.
   a. 36 cm $\frac{36}{100}$m, or $\frac{9}{25}$m; 0.36 m
   b. 25.1 mm $\frac{251}{10{,}000}$m, or 0.0251 m

5. Order these numbers from least to greatest. 14.7, 19.26, 15.138, 14.28, 16.9, 19.85, 15.01 14.28, 14.7, 15.01, 15.138, 16.9, 19.26, 19.85

Fraction and Decimal Equivalents

Objectives

▶ To estimate fraction and decimal equivalents

▶ To find decimal equivalents to fractions

▶ To demonstrate an understanding of repeating decimals

▶ To find patterns in decimal and fraction equivalents

▶ To order and compare fractions and decimals

Overview

This lesson continues students' work with fraction and decimal equivalencies. Students start by using labeled number lines to compare values of fractions and decimals. Then they find decimal equivalents for fractions, work with repeating decimals, and discover patterns in a table showing the decimal representations of fractions from wholes to tenths. Students should be able to move efficiently between decimals and fractions by the end of this lesson.

Advance Preparation

You may want to use Lesson 2.3 Masters 1–5 to facilitate class discussion while presenting new topics. Transparencies of Lesson 2.3 Masters 1–5 and an overhead calculator would also be useful.

	Summary	Materials	On Your Own Exercises (pp. 100–104)	Assessment Opportunities
Investigation 1 (p. 88) *Pacing: 1 day*	Students use number lines to estimate fractions and decimal equivalents.	Lesson 2.3 Master 1, Transparency of Lesson 2.3 Master 1 (optional), rulers or other straightedges (optional)	Practice & Apply: 1–5 Connect & Extend: 30–32, 35–43 Mixed Review: 53–62	• Share & Summarize (p. 91)
Investigation 2 (p. 91) *Pacing: 1 day*	Students explore how to write fractions as decimals, and they order numbers in both fraction and decimal form.	100-grids, Lesson 2.3 Master 5	Practice & Apply: 6, 7, 33, 34 Connect & Extend: 44 Mixed Review: 53–62	• On the Spot Assessment (pp. 91, 93) • Share & Summarize (p. 93) • Troubleshooting (p. 92)
Investigation 3 (p. 94) *Pacing: 1 day*	Students find exact decimal and fraction equivalents and identify repeating decimals.	Overhead calculator (optional), Lesson 2.3 Masters 2 and 3 (optional), Transparencies of Lesson 2.3 Masters 2 and 3 (optional), fraction calculators	Practice & Apply: 8–17 Mixed Review: 53–62	• Share & Summarize (p. 97) • Troubleshooting (p. 95)
Investigation 4 (p. 97) *Pacing: 1 day*	Students find patterns in a fraction and decimal equivalents chart. They write and compare fraction and decimal equivalents to make a fraction tower.	Lesson 2.3 Master 4 (optional), Transparency of Lesson 2.3 Master 4 (optional)	Practice & Apply: 18–29, 44 Connect & Extend: 45–52 Mixed Review: 53–62	• On the Spot Assessment (p. 98) • Share & Summarize (p. 99) • Troubleshooting (p. 99)

Leveled Lesson Resources

Also on
TeacherWorks™
Lesson 2.3

CRM *Available in:* **Chapter 2 Resource Masters**

Study Guide and Intervention (p. 20) — AL

Lesson 2.3 Study Guide and Intervention
Fraction and Decimal Equivalents

Fractions can be written as decimals by dividing the numerator by the denominator. If the division ends, or terminates, when the remainder is 0, it is a terminating decimal. If the decimal number repeats without end, it is a repeating decimal.

Example 1 Write each decimal as a fraction. Simplify each fraction.
a. 0.8 $0.8 = \frac{8}{10} = \frac{2 \cdot 2 \cdot 2}{2 \cdot 5} = \frac{4}{5}$ **b.** $12\frac{10}{25}$ $12\frac{2 \cdot 5}{5 \cdot 5} = 12\frac{2}{5}$

Example 2 Use your calculator to find a decimal for each fraction. Tell whether each fraction is a terminating or repeating decimal.
a. $\frac{7}{8} = 0.875$ **b.** $\frac{4}{9}$
0.875 is a terminating decimal. $0.4\ldots$ or $0.\overline{4}$ is a repeating decimal.

Exercises
Write each fraction or mixed number as a decimal. Use a bar to show a repeating decimal.
1. $\frac{7}{20}$ **2.** $\frac{2}{11}$ **3.** $\frac{5}{9}$
4. $\frac{5}{6}$ **5.** $\frac{6}{25}$ **6.** $\frac{5}{20}$
7. $8\frac{3}{5}$ **8.** $3\frac{7}{25}$ **9.** $\frac{4}{15}$

Write each decimal as a fraction. Simplify each fraction.
10. 1.2   **11.** 71.53   **12.** 24.6
13. 0.5   **14.** 103.7   **15.** 88.66
16. 101.1   **17.** 0.31   **18.** 9.4

Use your calculator to find a decimal approximation for each fraction. Tell whether each fraction is a terminating or a repeating decimal.
19. $\frac{9}{5}$ **20.** $\frac{4}{7}$ **21.** $\frac{5}{10}$

Skills Practice (p. 21) — AL OL

Lesson 2.3 Skills Practice
Fraction and Decimal Equivalents

Write each fraction or mixed number as a decimal. Use a bar to show a repeating decimal.
1. $\frac{3}{5}$ **2.** $\frac{1}{8}$
3. $\frac{9}{11}$ **4.** $\frac{3}{14}$
5. $\frac{3}{40}$ **6.** $\frac{8}{11}$
7. $\frac{5}{12}$ **8.** $\frac{1}{3}$
9. $\frac{7}{9}$ **10.** $\frac{11}{15}$

Write each decimal as a fraction. Simplify each fraction.
11. 0.7   **12.** 8.2
13. 212.5   **14.** 19.91
15. 17.01   **16.** 0.88
17. 61.3   **18.** 49.48
19. 0.6   **20.** 18.101

Use your calculator to find a decimal approximation for each fraction. Tell whether each fraction is a terminating or repeating decimal.
21. $\frac{2}{3}$ **22.** $\frac{5}{8}$
23. $\frac{15}{20}$ **24.** $4\frac{3}{8}$
25. $\frac{8}{9}$ **26.** $\frac{33}{100}$

27. Order $\frac{4}{9}$, $\frac{444}{1000}$ and 0.4 from least to greatest.
28. Order $\frac{8}{9}$, $\frac{8}{10}$, and $0.\overline{80}$ from least to greatest.
29. Opinion In a school survey, 787 out of 1000 students preferred hip-hop music to techno. Is this figure more or less than $\frac{7}{9}$ of those surveyed? Explain.

Problem-Solving Practice (p. 22) — AL OL

Lesson 2.3 Problem-Solving Practice
Fraction and Decimal Equivalents

1. Tax Ted pays $\frac{2}{7}$ of his salary in taxes, while Carl pays $\frac{5}{16}$ of his salary in taxes. Who pays more of his salary in taxes?

2. Rocks Jan and Bob are classifying rocks in geology class. They begin the classification by finding the weight of each rock. Jan's rock weighs $\frac{6}{100}$ kg while Bob's weighs 0.016 kg. Whose rock is heavier?

3. Building Lot The two one-acre lots in the diagram below are subdivided equally by the lines shown. The shaded areas in each lot have been set aside for housing.

Northfield   Southfield

Which of the two lots, Northfield or Southfield, has the greater area of land set aside for housing? To the nearest hundredth, what is the total acreage of land within both lots that is set aside for housing?

4. Tests Petra earned scores of $\frac{30}{40}$, $\frac{54}{60}$, and $\frac{49}{50}$ on her last three English quizzes. Find each score as a decimal. Arrange the fractions in order from least to greatest.

Paint For Exercises 5–7, use the following information.
Angie is mixing together yellow paint and blue paint to make 2 shades of green paint. She will mix the paint in two 5-liter canisters.
In canister A, she will pour $2\frac{4}{9}$ liters of yellow paint; in canister B, she will pour 2.46 liters of yellow paint. She fills the rest of each can with blue paint.

5. In which canister will Angie pour more yellow paint?

6. To the nearest hundredth of a liter, how much more blue paint than yellow paint does Angie use in all?

7. Angie can paint one room with $3\frac{2}{9}$ liters of one shade of green paint. She will need $1\frac{5}{8}$ liters of the same shade of green paint for a second room. Does Angie have enough of this shade of green paint to finish the second room? If not, how much additional paint will she need? Express your answer in decimal form.

Enrichment (p. 23) — BL

Lesson 2.3 Enrichment
Fraction and Decimal Equivalents

Matching Equivalent Fractions and Decimals

Cut out the pieces below and match the edges so that equivalent fractions and decimals meet. The pieces form a 4 × 6 rectangle. The outer edges of the rectangle formed will have no fractions or decimals.

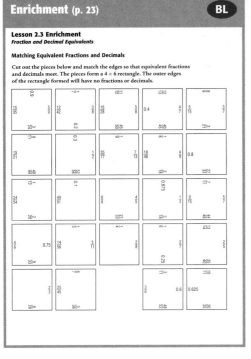

Lesson Quick Quiz (p. 24) — AL OL BL

Lesson 2.3 Quick Quiz
Fraction and Decimal Equivalents

1. a. Which of the following decimals is closest to $87\frac{3}{5}$?
87.5   87.58   87.61   87.7

b. Which of the following fractions is closest to $0.2\overline{2}$?
$\frac{1}{5}$ $\frac{23}{100}$ $\frac{3}{10}$

2. Find a fraction or mixed number equivalent to each decimal. Simplify each fraction.
a. 0.8

b. 2.75

c. 1.6

3. Find a decimal equivalent for each fraction.
a. $\frac{4}{9}$

b. $2\frac{1}{3}$

c. $1\frac{2}{8}$

4. Order these numbers from least to greatest.
0.875, 0.7, $\frac{2}{5}$, $\frac{6}{8}$, $\frac{5}{6}$, $0.\overline{6}$

Lesson Masters 1–5 (p. 25–29)

Lesson 2.3 Master 1
Fraction and Decimal Equivalents

Investigation 1: Decimal and Fraction Number Lines

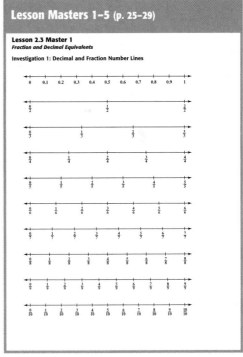

Additional Lesson Resources

Teacher Tech Tools
- TeacherWorks
- ExamView Assessment Suite
- Classroom Presentation Toolkit
- Advance Tracker

Student Tech Tools
- StudentWorks Plus
- **Math Online** eGlossary •
- Concepts in Motion

Other Print Products
- Investigation Notebook and Reflection Journal
- Quick Review Math Handbook

Lesson 2.3 Fraction and Decimal Equivalents   **88B**

LESSON 2.3 Fraction and Decimal Equivalents

Introduce

Fraction and Decimal Equivalents
Introduce this lesson by asking students what fraction and decimal equivalents they already know. Many students will know that $\frac{1}{2} = 0.5$, $\frac{1}{4} = 0.25$, and $\frac{3}{4} = 0.75$, and you can use their responses to introduce the Think & Discuss.

Think & Discuss

This activity reviews benchmark fractions and decimals, and may give you a good idea of students' conceptual understanding of the relationship between the two representations. If students have difficulty, suggest they estimate a fraction by folding a copy of the number line to break it into equal parts.

Investigation 1

On Your Own Exercises
Pages 100–104
Exercises 1–5, 35–43

Estimate Equivalents Have students look at the number lines on page 89 or on Lesson 2.3 Master 1. Point out that they can use this diagram to approximate fraction and decimal equivalents. Ask them what they notice about all the fractions on each number line. They should notice that they all have the same denominator. Tell students they will use these number lines as they work through the exercises on this page.

✅ Develop & Understand: A

Suggested Grouping: Pairs

▶ **Exercises 1 and 2** Students compare fractions and decimals on labeled number lines to estimate equivalent values and compare values. Answer these questions as a class. Have students show how to find the equivalents in **Exercise 2b**. See sample strategies on page 89, side column.

LESSON 2.3 Fraction and Decimal Equivalents

Fractions and decimals are two ways of expressing quantities that are not whole numbers. You already know how to write a decimal in fraction form by thinking about the place values of its digits. In this lesson, you will find decimals that estimate the values of fractions. You will also learn to write fractions in decimal form.

Think & Discuss

Use both a fraction and a decimal to describe the approximate location of each point. See ①.

```
        A B           C
 |------•-•----------•----|
 0                        1
```

What methods did you use to make your estimates? Possible answers: I divided the interval between 0 and 1 into equal parts. Or, I estimated the decimal first, and then converted to get a fraction. Or, I estimated the fraction first, and converted to get a decimal.

Investigation 1 Estimate Equivalents

Materials

- copy of the number-line diagram

① Possible answers:
Point A: $\frac{1}{4}$; Decimal should be between 0.2 and 0.3.
Point B: $\frac{1}{3}$; Decimal should be between 0.3 and 0.4.
Point C: $\frac{9}{10}$; Decimal should be about 0.9.

Number lines can help you understand the relationship between decimals and fractions. The diagram on page 89 shows ten number lines. The first is labeled with decimals, and the others are labeled with fractions. The fractions on each number line have the same denominator.

✅ Develop & Understand: A

1. Describe at least two patterns you notice in the diagram on page 89. See margin.
2. Consider decimal values greater than 0.5.

   a. Choose any decimal greater than 0.5 and less than 1. Answers will vary.
   b. Find all the fractions in the diagram that appear to be equivalent to the decimal that you chose. State if there are no equivalent fractions.   Answers will vary.

   c. Find two fractions in the diagram that are a little less than your decimal and two fractions that are a little greater. Try to find fractions as close to your decimal as possible. Answers will vary.

88   CHAPTER 2 Fractions and Decimals

Additional Answer

1. Possible answer: Only the number lines for fractions with even denominators have fractions that line up exactly with $\frac{1}{2}$. The larger the denominator, the more fractions that are close to a particular decimal. Each number line has an equal number of fractions on either side of 0.5.

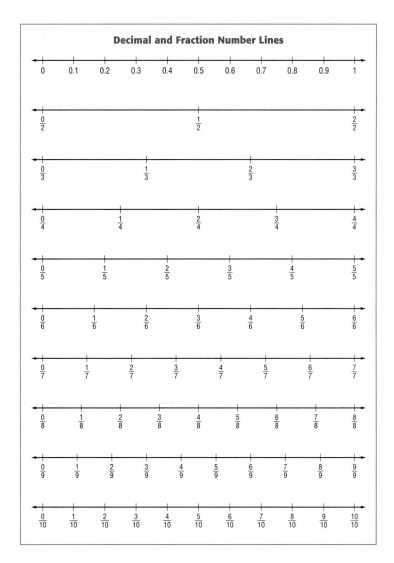

Decimal and Fraction Number Lines

The key to using the number-line diagram successfully is to line up the decimal and fraction marks carefully. If students use Lesson 2.3 Master 1, they may use one of these methods to approximate the equivalencies.

• Use a ruler or straightedge to draw vertical lines through the number lines.

• Fold the number lines on the decimal marks, creating folds that serve as perpendicular straightedges.

• Cut out all the number lines and then match up the decimal number line with the fraction number lines.

Discuss the ways in which students may use the decimal and fraction number lines chart. You may want to facilitate the discussion by providing Lesson 2.3 Master 1 or by making a transparency of the master.

Lesson 2.3   Fraction and Decimal Equivalents   **89**

▶ **Exercises 3c and 3d** Students' answers may not be accurate to the hundredths place since they are estimating. For example, students may think that $\frac{2}{3}$ is between 0.65 and 0.66. Accept any answers that you feel are reasonable.

Wrap-Up Discuss the answers to Exercise 4. While it is likely that many students will choose 0.25, 0.5, or 0.75 as benchmarks, some may prefer other decimals. Be sure they can explain why they chose these decimals as benchmarks. There is no correct answer, although some decimals are more convenient than others to use as benchmarks. Chosen decimals should be used easily to approximate a range of fractions between zero and one. With practice, students may decide that the benchmarks they have chosen are not as useful as they first thought and choose others instead.

Teacher Tips Point out that all the fractions and decimals in the exercises on page 89 were less than one, but that students can use similar strategies to find equivalent fractions and decimals greater than one in the exercises on this page.

✓ Develop & Understand: B

Suggested Grouping: Pairs

▶ **Exercises 5–7** This exercise set extends the estimation ideas in Exercises 1–4 to mixed numbers. Ask students to refer to the number lines on page 89 or Lesson 2.3 Master 1 as they work through the exercise set.

▶ **Exercise 8** Some students may know that $0.\overline{3}$ is the decimal equivalent to $\frac{1}{3}$ and use that knowledge as part of the explanation.

3a–d. Answers will vary.
4a. Possible answer: 0, 0.25, 0.5, 0.75, 1; I am very sure about what these decimals mean.
4b. Possible answer: Fractions that are halfway between two benchmarks are listed twice.

$0: \frac{1}{8}, \frac{1}{9}, \frac{1}{10}$

$0.25: \frac{1}{3}, \frac{1}{4}, \frac{1}{5}, \frac{1}{6}, \frac{2}{6}, \frac{1}{7}, \frac{2}{7}, \frac{1}{8}, \frac{2}{8}, \frac{3}{8}, \frac{2}{9}, \frac{3}{9}, \frac{2}{10}, \frac{3}{10}$

$0.5: \frac{1}{2}, \frac{2}{4}, \frac{2}{5}, \frac{3}{5}, \frac{3}{6}, \frac{3}{7}, \frac{4}{7}, \frac{3}{8}, \frac{4}{8}, \frac{5}{8}, \frac{4}{9}, \frac{5}{9}, \frac{4}{10}, \frac{5}{10}, \frac{6}{10}$

$0.75: \frac{2}{3}, \frac{3}{4}, \frac{4}{5}, \frac{4}{6}, \frac{5}{6}, \frac{5}{7}, \frac{6}{7}, \frac{5}{8}, \frac{6}{8}, \frac{7}{8}, \frac{6}{9}, \frac{7}{9}, \frac{7}{10}, \frac{8}{10}$

$1: \frac{2}{2}, \frac{3}{3}, \frac{4}{4}, \frac{5}{5}, \frac{6}{6}, \frac{7}{7}, \frac{7}{8}, \frac{8}{8}, \frac{8}{9}, \frac{9}{9}, \frac{9}{10}, \frac{10}{10}$

8a. 3.3; Possible explanation: Since $\frac{3}{10}$ is a little less than $\frac{1}{3}$, and $\frac{4}{10}$ is a little more than $\frac{1}{3}$, $3\frac{1}{3}$ is between 3.3 and 3.4. So, of the choices given, it is closest to 3.3.

---

3. Refer to the diagram on page 89. Consider the fractions that are not equivalent to $\frac{1}{2}$.

   a. Choose any fraction in the diagram that is not equivalent to $\frac{1}{2}$.

   b. Name the fraction on each of the other fraction number lines that is closest to the fraction that you chose.

   c. If possible, find an exact decimal value for your fraction to the hundredths place. If this is not possible, tell which two decimals your fraction is between, to the hundredths place.

   d. Repeat Parts a–c for two more fractions. Each fraction you choose should have a different denominator.

4. Decimals that are familiar make good benchmarks for estimating the values of other decimals and fractions.

   a. Which decimals do you think would be useful as benchmarks? Explain why you chose those numbers

   b. For each fraction labeled in the diagram, find the benchmark decimal from Part a closest to that fraction. Organize your answers in any way you like.

In Exercises 5–10, you will estimate fractions and decimals greater than 1.

✓ Develop & Understand: B

For Exercises 5–7, use both a mixed number and a decimal to describe the approximate location of each point.

5. 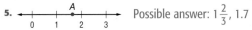 Possible answer: $1\frac{2}{3}$, 1.7

6.  Possible answer: $4\frac{1}{4}$, 4.3

7.  Possible answer: $7\frac{9}{10}$, 7.9

8. Consider the mixed number $3\frac{1}{3}$.

   a. Which of the following decimals is closest to $3\frac{1}{3}$? Explain how you decided.

   3.1   3.2   3.3   3.5

   b. Find a decimal that is even closer to $3\frac{1}{3}$. Explain how you found your answer. Possible answer: 3.31; $\frac{31}{100}$ is closer to $\frac{1}{3}$ than $\frac{30}{100}$, so 3.31 is closer to $3\frac{1}{3}$ than is 3.3.

Reaching All Learners

OL **On Level** For **Exercise 4b**, suggest that students make an organized list. They should shade or use different colors of pencils to show fractions close to each benchmark. This can help them keep track of which fractions they have classified, and the visual representation can help them decide which fractions are closest to each benchmark.

9a. 81.8; Possible
explanation: I used
the number-line
diagram to see that $\frac{5}{6}$
is between 0.8 and
0.9 but closer to 0.8.

9b. Possible answer:
81.81; I used the
number-line diagram.

① Answer 1 is incorrect
because $\frac{2}{3}$ is
approximately 0.7.
Answer 3 is also
incorrect because $\frac{1}{5}$ is
less than 1, so it could
not possibly be 2.

9. Consider the mixed number $81\frac{5}{6}$.

   a. Which of the following decimals is closest to $81\frac{5}{6}$? Explain how you decided.

      81.5   81.6   81.8   81.9

   b. Find a decimal that is even closer to $81\frac{5}{6}$. Explain how you found your answer.

10. Use your estimation skills to order these numbers from least to greatest. $\frac{2}{5}$, 0.5, 0.7, $\frac{5}{6}$, 3.1, $3\frac{1}{3}$, 3.6, 5.2

    $\frac{5}{6}$ 0.7 $\frac{2}{5}$ 3.1   0.5 $3\frac{1}{3}$ 3.6   5.2

Share & Summarize

Below is part of a student's homework assignment. Using your estimation skills, find the answers that are definitely incorrect. Explain how you know.   See ①.

1. $\frac{2}{3} = 0.9$ **2.** $3\frac{7}{10} = 3.7$ **3.** $\frac{1}{5} = 2.0$ **4.** $2\frac{3}{4} = 2.75$

Investigation 2 Change Decimals to Fractions

Vocabulary

terminating decimal

Materials

• 100-grid

In this investigation, you will explore the process for writing fractions as decimals. You will also look at problems that involve ordering numbers in both decimal and fraction form as you consider the merits of each.

✓ Develop & Understand: A

1. In each of the following, represent the shaded portion as a decimal. Then write the decimal as a fraction. How does place value help you do this?

   a.

   0.45; $\frac{45}{100}$. I know that two places after the decimal point is the hundredths place. So, 0.45 is the same as $\frac{45}{100}$.

1b. 0.4; $\frac{4}{10}$. I know that one place after the decimal point is the tenths place. So, 0.4 is the same as $\frac{4}{10}$.

   b. ▭▭▭▭▭▭

   c.

   0.17; $\frac{17}{100}$. I know that two places after the decimal point the hundredths place. So, 0.17 is the same as $\frac{17}{100}$.

Lesson 2.3   Fraction and Decimal Equivalents   **91**

On the Spot Assessment

Watch for students who do not read the hundreds block carefully. Remind them that each column has ten squares and that the basic fraction for shaded squares will have a denominator of 100 before being simplified.

▶ **Exercise 10** Students may approach this exercise in different ways.

• Order the decimals first and then insert the fractions into the sequence.

• Order the fractions and then insert the decimals into the sequence.

• Write all the numbers written as fractions as mixed numbers, then group and order the numbers with the same whole number part; that is, order all fractions less than 1, order all fractions with a whole number of 3, and so on.

Wrap-Up Discuss students' answers to Exercises 8 and 9. Have them share their strategies for ordering the numbers in Exercise 10.

Share & Summarize

Have students write answers on their own so that you can see how they are thinking about fraction and decimal equivalents. Remind them that they can use the set of number lines to help them make the comparisons. You may want to discuss their ideas after they complete the questions, and then take up their written answers so you can assess them individually.

Investigation 2

On Your Own Exercises
Pages 100–104
Exercises 6, 7, 33, 34, 44

Change Decimals to Fractions In this investigation, students use 100-grids as models to write fractions for both terminating and repeating decimals. You may want to provide students with copies of Lesson 2.3 Master 5, 100 grids.

✓ Develop & Understand: A

Suggested Grouping: Pairs

▶ **Exercises 1–4** As they work through the exercises, help students see the patterns that occur in terminating decimals. Reinforce the importance of understanding the relationship between fractions and decimals.

Suggested Grouping: Pairs

▶ **Exercises 5 and 6** Have students explain their strategies to each other. Have them compare their strategies for finding a decimal halfway between two others.

▶ **Exercises 7 and 8** Have students test their strategies from Exercises 5–6 on this exercise. Ask them to explain how they adjusted their strategies to accommodate fractions.

▶ **Exercise 8** You may want to discuss this exercise as a class. Make sure students understand that they can always find another decimal between two others by using their "halfway strategy."

Teacher Tips You may want to demonstrate the game on this page before having the students play it. Have a student be your partner.

A decimal that terminates, stops, or ends is called a **terminating decimal**. Some examples of terminating decimals are 0.25, 1.38, 4.5.

2. Copy or draw blank grids. Shade in the following decimals.

   a. 0.3   Students should shade in 30 blocks.

   b. 0.62   Students should shade in 62 blocks.

   c. 1.07   Students should shade in 1 whole grid plus 7 blocks.

   d. 0.065   Students should shade in 6.5 blocks.

3. Write each of the following decimals as a fraction in simplest form.

   a. 0.34 $\frac{34}{100}$; $\frac{17}{50}$

   b. 0.453 $\frac{453}{1000}$

   c. 1.3 $1\frac{3}{10}$

   d. 0.2875 $\frac{2875}{10000}$; $\frac{23}{80}$

4a. 0.2875, 0.34, 0.453, 1.3

4b. Answers will vary. Sample answer: decimals; All you have to do is compare relative placeholders.

4. Look at the decimals you converted to fractions in Exercise 3.

   a. Write the decimals in order from least to greatest.

   b. Would it be easier to order these numbers as decimals or as fractions? Explain your thinking.

Develop & Understand: B

5. Name a decimal between 0.99 and 1. Explain the strategy you used.
   Sample answer: 0.998   Answers will vary.

6. Name the decimal which is exactly halfway between 0.99 and 1.
   0.995

7. Name a decimal between 2.34 and 2.341. Explain the strategy you used.   Sample answer: 2.3402   Answers will vary.

8. Name the decimal that is exactly halfway between 2.34 and 2.341.   2.3405   Answers will vary.

9. Answers will vary. Sample answer: There are an unlimited, infinite number of fractions between two numbers.

9. How many fractions are there between 2.34 and 2.341? Explain your thinking.

Here is a game that you can play with a partner. It will sharpen your skills with decimals and fractions.

   • Label you and your partner A and B. Player A will go first.

   • You will be given two decimals for each game.

Troubleshooting

Watch for students who may still be struggling with finding a decimal between two others. Encourage students to use a place value chart (you can provide one with Chapter 2 Master 1) to help them see how decimals compare. Point out that to find a decimal between two others, they need to go out one decimal place further to the right on the chart.

Round 1: Player A states a decimal that is between the two given decimals.

Player B also states a decimal (different from Players A's choice) that is between the two given decimals. Players A and B check each other to see if he or she has given correct decimals.

Round 2: Player B states a decimal between the two decimals that were provided by Players A and B in the first round. Player A does the same. Players A and B check each other to see if he or she has given correct decimals.

Round 3: The selection continues for three more rounds. Play five rounds total. Players should alternate who goes first in each round.

Players score 1 point if they:
- correctly identify a decimal between the two decimals in any given round
- find a mistake that the other player made

Here are decimals you can use for playing the game.

Game 1: 1.5 and 1.6

Game 2: 0.71 and 0.72

Repeat the same game, but use fractions this time. Here are fractions you can use for playing the game.

Game 1: $\frac{3}{5}$ and $\frac{4}{5}$

Game 2: $\frac{5}{11}$ and $\frac{6}{11}$

10. Which game do you think is easier? Explain.

Share & Summarize

1. Explain the process for converting decimals to fractions.

2. When comparing numbers, is it easier to compare them as fractions or as decimals? Explain your reasoning.

10. Sample answer: The first game was easier because we were using decimals. It is easier to figure out a decimal in between two other decimals. It was difficult to find a fraction in between two fractions.

1. Sample answer: Decimals can be converted into a fraction by using the decimal's place value to guide you. If you have 0.15, you know that two decimal places after the decimal is the hundredths place. You can place the 15 over 100. Then simplify the fraction. So, $0.15 = \frac{15}{100} = \frac{3}{20}$.

2. It is easier to compare the numbers as decimals. You can easily line up the decimal points to order them. When comparing fractions, you must first find a common denominator for each fraction before you can order them.

Share & Summarize

Discuss the steps used to convert a decimal to a fraction for **Exercise 1**. Have students explain their reasoning for choosing fractions or decimals as easier to compare in **Exercise 2**. Ask them why lining up the decimal points is convenient to do.

Assessment

Students who have trouble understanding how to find a fraction between two others for the game may need to find equivalent fractions by multiplying the numerator and denominator by $\frac{2}{2}$ or $\frac{10}{10}$, for example. Remind them that decimals are like fractions with a denominator of 100. For decimals, remind them to notice whether they should be using tenths, hundredths, or thousandths.

Investigation ③

On Your Own Exercises
Pages 100–104
Exercises 8–17

Change Fractions to Decimals Introduce the investigation by having a volunteer summarize how he or she found decimal approximations for fractions in Investigation 1. Use this to lead into students finding exact decimal equivalents in the Think & Discuss.

Think & Discuss

Suggested Grouping: Individuals

Have students find the decimal equivalents, and then discuss their answers and the ways they determined the equivalents. Most students will use their knowledge of decimal place value to write $\frac{47}{1,000}$ and $\frac{59}{10}$ as decimals. For $\frac{7}{20}$ and $\frac{3}{5}$, whose denominators are not powers of 10, many students will find the equivalent fraction by multiplying numerator and denominator by the same number to find a denominator that is a power of 10. Others may use division.

Example

Have students read the cartoon to see how Jing and Marcus thought about finding a decimal equivalent to $\frac{7}{20}$. Then compare these strategies to the ones students used to find decimal equivalents in the Think & Discuss. Encourage them to try Jing's and Marcus' methods for at least one problem as they work through the exercises.

✓ Develop & Understand: A

Suggested Grouping: Pairs

▶ **Exercises 1–4** Point out that the decimals in these exercises are terminating decimals.

Investigation ③ Change Fractions to Decimals

Vocabulary

repeating decimal

In Investigation 1, you found decimals approximations for given fractions. Now you will find exact decimal values for fractions.

Think & Discuss

Find a decimal equivalent to each fraction.

$\frac{47}{1,000}$ 0.047 $\frac{59}{10}$ 5.9

$\frac{7}{20}$ 0.35 $\frac{3}{5}$ 0.6

Here is how Jing and Marcus found a decimal equivalent to $\frac{7}{20}$.

Example

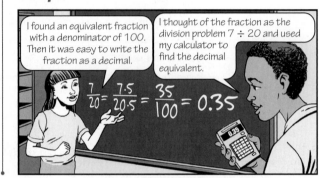

✓ Develop & Understand: A

Find a decimal equivalent to each given fraction.

1. $\frac{16}{25}$ 0.64

2. $\frac{5}{8}$ 0.625

3. $\frac{320}{200}$ 1.6

4. $\frac{8}{125}$ 0.064

Reaching All Learners

ELL English Language Learners
There are several words students need to understand in order to succeed in this lesson. Make a list of the following terms: diagram, decimal-fraction, repeating decimal, terminating decimal. Review the terms with the students. Make sure they fully understand each word. Ask them to make note cards if necessary.

5. Without using a calculator, try to find a decimal equivalent to $\frac{2}{3}$ by dividing. What happens?   0.66666 …; The 6 keeps repeating. The division never "stops."

When you divided to find a decimal equivalent to $\frac{2}{3}$, you got 0.6666 …, where the 6s repeat forever. Decimals with a pattern of digits that repeat without stopping are called **repeating decimals**. Repeating decimals are usually written with a bar over the repeating digits.

- $0.\overline{6}$ means 0.66666 …
- $3.1\overline{24}$ means 3.1242424 …

All fractions whose numerators and denominators are whole numbers have decimal equivalents that end, like 0.25, or that repeat forever, like $0.4\overline{6}$.

Calculators are useful for determining whether a fraction is equivalent to a repeating decimal. However, because the number of digits a calculator can display is limited, you sometimes cannot be certain.

Think & Discuss

Use your calculator to find a decimal approximation for each fraction below. Write your answers exactly as they appear in the calculator's display.   See ① in margin.

$$\frac{6}{9} \qquad \frac{6}{13} \qquad \frac{6}{15}$$

$$\frac{6}{17} \qquad \frac{6}{21} \qquad \frac{666}{1,000}$$

Which of the fractions above definitely *are* equivalent to repeating decimals?

Which of the fractions definitely *are not* equivalent to repeating decimals?   See ②.

Which of the fractions above do you *think* might be repeating decimals? How could you find out for sure?   See ③ in margin.

② Answers will vary. Most students will see that $\frac{6}{9}$ repeats; however, if their calculator rounds off the last digit to 7, they may need help understanding this. They may also say that $\frac{6}{13}$ and $\frac{6}{21}$ repeat. Only students with large displays will see that $\frac{6}{17}$ repeats. $\frac{6}{15}$ and $\frac{666}{1,000}$ are not repeating decimals.

Troubleshooting

Watch for students who always divide the greater number by the lesser number regardless of their positions in the fraction. Remind them to always divide the numerator by the denominator. Encourage students to look at the relative values of the decimal and the fraction to make sure that they are reasonable. Point out that a fraction less than one would not have a decimal equivalent greater than one.

▶ **Exercise 5** Point out that the decimal is repeating.

Teacher Tips Some students think you must write a couple of patterns under the bar. For example 0.33 … would have a bar over 33 or 0.866 … would have a bar over 66. Point out that they should only write the minimum needed to show the pattern, or 0.33 … = $0.\overline{3}$ or 0.866 … = $0.8\overline{6}$.

Wrap-Up Discuss Exercises 1–4 and ask students which method they preferred to find each decimal. Then have them share their results for Exercise 5. Encourage students to predict how they could show the non-ending decimal.

Think & Discuss

Suggested Grouping: Individuals

Recognizing repeating decimals is something students often take for granted. Some may assume that whenever they divide a fraction and the answer fills the calculator display, the digits shown must be either the only digits in the decimal or the digits that make up the repeating part of the decimal. This exercise should help dispel that notion.

Have students find the equivalent decimals and answer the questions independently. When discussing their results as a class, you might use an overhead projection of the calculator display to show each decimal equivalent.

Note that $\frac{6}{13}$ is equivalent to $0.\overline{461538}$ and $\frac{6}{21}$ is equivalent to $0.\overline{285714}$.

Additional Answers for Think & Discuss

① Answers will vary depending on the number of digits the calculator displays and whether the calculator rounds or truncates. Possible answers:

$\frac{6}{9} \approx$ 0.66666666 or 0.66666667,
0.66666667,

$\frac{6}{13} \approx$ 0.461538461 or 0.461538462,

$\frac{6}{15} =$ 0.4, $\frac{6}{17} \approx$ 0.352941176,

$\frac{6}{21} \approx$ 0.285714285 or 0.285714286,

$\frac{666}{1,000} =$ 0.666

③ Most students should respond $\frac{6}{13}, \frac{6}{17},$ and $\frac{6}{21}$. Possible answer: You could do the division by hand.

✅ Develop & Understand: B

Suggested Grouping: Pairs

▶ **Exercise 6** Lesson 2.3 Master 2 reproduces the chart of fractions, and Lesson 2.3 Master 3 is a completed chart with decimal equivalents. Provide students with copies of Lesson 2.3 Master 2 so that they can work directly on the chart and then keep it for future reference. Depending upon your class, you may also want to provide students with copies of Lesson 2.3 Master 3 after they have completed this exercise so that they have a clean copy to use as reference for other problems and exercises; you may prefer to let them use their own completed charts.

▶ **Exercise 8** Discuss this exercise to help students discover any computational errors they made in Exercise 6. Have them correct the errors in their charts so they will be useable later.

Teacher Tips Have students find benchmarks by shading decimal grids for terminating decimals such as halves, fourths, fifths, and tenths. Have them write equivalent fractions for each shaded part. An example is shown here.

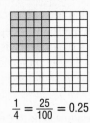

$$\frac{1}{4} = \frac{25}{100} = 0.25$$

Analyze the Table Ask students to describe patterns they see in the table. Summarize them as a class.

✅ Develop & Understand: B

6. Copy the chart below. Fill in the decimal equivalents for each fraction in the chart. Some of the cells have been filled for you. Start by writing the decimal equivalents you know. Then use your calculator to find the others.

$\frac{0}{1}=0$	$\frac{0}{2}=0$	$\frac{0}{3}=0$	$\frac{0}{4}=0$	$\frac{0}{5}=0$	$\frac{0}{6}=0$	$\frac{0}{7}=0$	$\frac{0}{8}=0$	$\frac{0}{9}=0$	$\frac{0}{10}=0$
$\frac{1}{1}=1$	$\frac{1}{2}=0.5$	$\frac{1}{3}=0.\overline{3}$	$\frac{1}{4}=0.25$	$\frac{1}{5}=0.2$	$\frac{1}{6}=0.1\overline{6}$	$\frac{1}{7}=0.\overline{142857}$	$\frac{1}{8}=0.125$	$\frac{1}{9}=0.\overline{1}$	$\frac{1}{10}=0.1$
$\frac{2}{1}=2$	$\frac{2}{2}=1$	$\frac{2}{3}=0.\overline{6}$	$\frac{2}{4}=0.5$	$\frac{2}{5}=0.4$	$\frac{2}{6}=0.\overline{3}$	$\frac{2}{7}=0.\overline{285714}$	$\frac{2}{8}=0.25$	$\frac{2}{9}=0.\overline{2}$	$\frac{2}{10}=0.2$
$\frac{3}{1}=3$	$\frac{3}{2}=1.5$	$\frac{3}{3}=1$	$\frac{3}{4}=0.75$	$\frac{3}{5}=0.6$	$\frac{3}{6}=0.5$	$\frac{3}{7}=0.\overline{428571}$	$\frac{3}{8}=0.375$	$\frac{3}{9}=0.\overline{3}$	$\frac{3}{10}=0.3$
$\frac{4}{1}=4$	$\frac{4}{2}=2$	$\frac{4}{3}=1.\overline{3}$	$\frac{4}{4}=1$	$\frac{4}{5}=0.8$	$\frac{4}{6}=0.\overline{6}$	$\frac{4}{7}=0.\overline{571428}$	$\frac{4}{8}=0.5$	$\frac{4}{9}=0.\overline{4}$	$\frac{4}{10}=0.4$
$\frac{5}{1}=5$	$\frac{5}{2}=2.5$	$\frac{5}{3}=1.\overline{6}$	$\frac{5}{4}=1.25$	$\frac{5}{5}=1$	$\frac{5}{6}=0.8\overline{3}$	$\frac{5}{7}=0.\overline{714285}$	$\frac{5}{8}=0.625$	$\frac{5}{9}=0.\overline{5}$	$\frac{5}{10}=0.5$
$\frac{6}{1}=6$	$\frac{6}{2}=3$	$\frac{6}{3}=2$	$\frac{6}{4}=1.5$	$\frac{6}{5}=1.2$	$\frac{6}{6}=1$	$\frac{6}{7}=0.\overline{857142}$	$\frac{6}{8}=0.75$	$\frac{6}{9}=0.\overline{6}$	$\frac{6}{10}=0.6$
$\frac{7}{1}=7$	$\frac{7}{2}=3.5$	$\frac{7}{3}=2.\overline{3}$	$\frac{7}{4}=1.75$	$\frac{7}{5}=1.4$	$\frac{7}{6}=1.1\overline{6}$	$\frac{7}{7}=1$	$\frac{7}{8}=0.875$	$\frac{7}{9}=0.\overline{7}$	$\frac{7}{10}=0.7$
$\frac{8}{1}=8$	$\frac{8}{2}=4$	$\frac{8}{3}=2.\overline{6}$	$\frac{8}{4}=2$	$\frac{8}{5}=1.6$	$\frac{8}{6}=1.\overline{3}$	$\frac{8}{7}=1.\overline{142857}$	$\frac{8}{8}=1$	$\frac{8}{9}=0.\overline{8}$	$\frac{8}{10}=0.8$
$\frac{9}{1}=9$	$\frac{9}{2}=4.5$	$\frac{9}{3}=3$	$\frac{9}{4}=2.25$	$\frac{9}{5}=1.8$	$\frac{9}{6}=1.5$	$\frac{9}{7}=1.\overline{285714}$	$\frac{9}{8}=1.125$	$\frac{9}{9}=1$	$\frac{9}{10}=0.9$
$\frac{10}{1}=10$	$\frac{10}{2}=5$	$\frac{10}{3}=3.\overline{3}$	$\frac{10}{4}=2.5$	$\frac{10}{5}=2$	$\frac{10}{6}=1.\overline{6}$	$\frac{10}{7}=1.142871$	$\frac{10}{8}=1.25$	$\frac{10}{9}=1.\overline{1}$	$\frac{10}{10}=1$

8. Possible answer: Ignoring the top row, the main diagonal is all 1s. In the columns for denominators 2, 4, and 8, all the decimal parts end in 0 or 5. In the column for denominator 5, the digits after the decimal repeat in the pattern 0, 2, 4, 6, 8. In the ninths column, the decimal equivalents for the fractions less than 1 have the numerator as a repeating digit.

7. Which columns contain fractions equivalent to repeating decimals?
   The columns for denominators 3, 6, 7, and 9

8. Describe at least two patterns that you see in the completed chart.

Save your chart for the On Your Own Exercises and for Investigation 4.

Investigation 4 · Patterns in Fractions and Decimals

Materials
- completed fraction and decimal equivalents chart

In Exercises 1–14, you will look for patterns in your chart of fraction and decimal equivalents from Investigation 3.

✓ Develop & Understand: A

For Exercises 1–2, find all of the fractions in the chart that are equivalent to each given decimal.

1. 1.25 $\frac{5}{4}, \frac{10}{8}$

2. $0.\overline{6}$ $\frac{2}{3}, \frac{4}{6}, \frac{6}{9}$

3. **Possible answer:** They form a diagonal going down and to the right, from one cell to another, down one cell and over two. This happens because each time you add 1 to the numerator, you need to add 2 to the denominator to keep the fraction $\frac{1}{2}$.

3. Color all of the cells with fractions equivalent to $\frac{1}{2}$. What pattern do you notice? Why does this happen?

4. Does the chart have a column showing fractions with a denominator of 0? Why or why not?   You cannot divide by 0.

5. Look at the column containing fractions with denominator 10.

   a. Describe the pattern in the decimals in this column. Explain why this pattern occurs.   See margin.

   b. Write $5\frac{7}{10}$ as a decimal.   5.7

   c. Write 68.3 as a mixed number. $68\frac{3}{10}$

6. Look at the column containing fractions with denominator 2.

   a. How do the decimal values change as you move down the column? Why?   See margin.

   b. Use the pattern from Part a to find the decimal equivalent of $\frac{11}{2}$, the number that would be next in the chart if a row was added.
   5.5

Investigation 4

On Your Own Exercises
Pages 100–104
Exercises 18–29, 44–52

Patterns in Fractions and Decimals
Introduce the investigation by referring students to the chart of fraction and decimal equivalents they made for Investigation 3 on page 94.

✓ Develop & Understand: A

Suggested Grouping: Pairs

▶ **Exercise 3** Point out that students should look at the pattern of the *cells* and use their knowledge of fractions to help explain the pattern.

▶ **Exercise 4** Have students use their calculators to try to divide by zero. The result will be an error message.

Wrap-Up If students extended their tables on page 96, have them use the patterns in Exercises 6 and 7 to check that the decimal equivalents in their charts are correct.

Additional Answers

5a. Possible answer: As you move down the column, the decimal values increase by 0.1. This happens because with each cell, the fraction increases by $\frac{1}{10}$, and $\frac{1}{10} = 0.1$

6a. Possible explanation: They increase by 0.5. With each cell, the fraction increases by $\frac{1}{2}$, and $\frac{1}{2} = 0.5$.

► **Exercise 8** Watch for students who focus only on the decimal parts of 0 and 0.5 in **Parts a** and **b**.

► **Exercises 13 and 14** Have students use the look for a pattern problem-solving strategy.

Wrap-Up Discuss the patterns students found in Exercises 7 and 8. You might extend the discussion of Exercise 3 on page 97 by asking these questions.

- Why do fractional equivalents to $\frac{1}{2}$ appear in every other column rather than in every column? Every other column contains a fraction with an even denominator that is twice the numerator. The alternate columns have odd denominators. Since all the numerators in the chart are whole numbers and there are no whole numbers that can be doubled to equal an odd number, there can be no fraction or decimal representing $\frac{1}{2}$ with those denominators.

- Do similar patterns hold for other equivalent fractions? Explain. Yes; every third column includes a fraction that represents $\frac{1}{3}$, every fourth column includes a fraction representing $\frac{1}{4}$, and the fifth and tenth columns include fractions representing $\frac{1}{5}$.

Encourage students to think of these patterns to determine equivalent fractions and decimals.

Point out that they can use these equivalencies to compare fractions and decimals in the next exercise set.

Real-World Link
If $\frac{4}{5}$ of a number is 40, then the number is 50. The lion has a maximum speed of 50 mph.

Additional Answer
8d. Possible answer: For a given denominator, you are adding $\frac{1}{denominator}$, $\frac{2}{denominator}$, and so on, until you get $\frac{denominator}{denominator}$, which is 1. When you add 1 to a number, the decimal part does not change, so you are back with the decimal part you started with and the pattern starts to repeat.

7a. Possible explanation: They increase by 0.25. With each cell, the fraction increases by $\frac{1}{4}$, and $\frac{1}{4} = 0.25$.

8a. The decimal part repeats every fourth number according to this pattern: 0.25, 0.5, 0.75, 0.

8b. The decimal part seems to repeat every sixth number according to this pattern: $0.1\overline{6}$, $0.\overline{3}$, 0.5, $0.\overline{6}$, $0.8\overline{3}$, 0.

Real-World Link
Lions and hyenas are the zebra's main predators in the wild. Zebras have a maximum speed of 40 mph, which is $\frac{4}{5}$, or 0.8, of the maximum speed of a lion. Hyenas and zebras have the same maximum speed.

7. Look at the column containing fractions with denominator 4.

a. How do the decimal values change as you move down the column? Why?

b. Use the pattern from Part a to find the decimal equivalent of $\frac{11}{4}$, the number that would be next in the chart if a row was added. 2.75

8. Look again at the fractions with denominator 2. The decimals in this column are 0, 0.5, 1, 1.5, 2, 2.5, 3, 3.5, 4, 4.5, 5. Notice that the "decimal parts" alternate between 0 (no decimal part) and 0.5.

a. Look for a similar pattern in the column for fractions with denominator 4. Describe the pattern.

b. Look for a similar pattern in the column for fractions with denominator 6. Describe the pattern.

c. Look at a few other columns. Do similar patterns hold? Answer will vary.

d. **Challenge** Explain why these patterns occur. See margin.

Use the chart to help find the decimal equivalent for each fraction or mixed number.

9. $10\frac{1}{2}$ 10.5

10. $32\frac{7}{9}$ $32.\overline{7}$

11. $62\frac{4}{5}$ 62.8

12. $23\frac{5}{6}$ $23.8\overline{3}$

Use the chart to help find a fraction equivalent to each decimal.

13. 14.125 Possible answer: $14\frac{1}{8}$, or $\frac{113}{8}$

14. $4.\overline{6}$ Possible answer: $4\frac{2}{3}$, or $\frac{14}{3}$

98   **CHAPTER 2**   Fractions and Decimals

 Assessment

In **Exercises 8a and 8b**, watch for students who focus on the pattern for fractions with denominators of 2 when describing the patterns for fractions with denominators of 4 and 6. These students may state that the pattern 0 (no decimal part) and 0.5 repeats for every other fraction for fourths and every third fraction for sixths. Acknowledge that this is a valid observation, and encourage them to extend each pattern so that it describes all the fractions in the respective column.

☑ Develop & Understand: B

In Exercises 15–16, you will use what you have learned about comparing and converting between fractions and decimals to build a fraction tower.

Building a Fraction Tower

- Choose a fraction less than 1 whose numerator and denominator are whole numbers between 1 and 9. Write both the fraction and its decimal equivalent on the bottom level of the tower.
- Choose another fraction whose numerator and denominator are between 1 and 9 and that is *less than* the fraction in the bottom level. Write the fraction and its decimal equivalent on the next level of the tower.
- Continue this process of choosing fractions and adding levels until you are unable to make a fraction with a value less than the fraction in the top level.

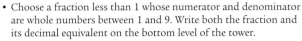

$$\frac{1}{4} = 0.25$$

$$\frac{2}{5} = 0.4$$

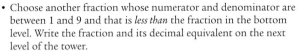

$$\frac{4}{9} = 0.\overline{4}$$

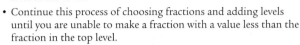

$$\frac{5}{7} = 0.\overline{714285}$$

Real-World Link

The tallest building in the world, as measured to the top of the roof, is the Burj Dubai in Dubai, United Arab Emirates, at 1,885 feet.

15. Work with your partner to build several fraction towers. Record each tower that you build. Try to build the highest tower possible.
    Towers will vary.

16. What strategies did you use when building your towers?   **See below.**

Share & Summarize

1. Choose a pattern in the chart of fraction and decimal equivalents. It can be a pattern you discussed in class or a new pattern you have discovered. Describe the pattern, and explain why it occurs.
   Answers will vary.

2. Write a letter to a student who is just learning how to build fraction towers. Explain strategies that he or she might use to build a high tower.   **Answers will vary.**

16. Possible answer: We changed the fractions to decimals so they were easier to compare. We wrote down all the fractions with denominators that differed by 1 $\left(\frac{8}{9}, \frac{7}{8}, \frac{6}{7}, \frac{5}{6}, \text{and so on}\right)$ and their decimal equivalents. We did the same for fractions whose numerator and denominator differed by 2, 3, and so on. When we were done, we had listed all the possibilities, and we just needed to put them in order to make the tower.

Lesson 2.3 Fraction and Decimal Equivalents   **99**

☑ Develop & Understand: B

Suggested Grouping: Pairs

▶ **Exercises 15 and 16** Suggest that students build their towers without relying on the fraction and decimal equivalents charts, if possible. To assist lower-level readers, you may want to read the directions for building towers and construct a simple tower as a class. You can draw rectangles for each layer or use a transparency of Lesson 2.3 Master 4 to construct the sample tower. You may wish to provide students with copies of Lesson 2.3 Master 4, which has two blank towers with 28 levels each for students to record their towers.

▶ **Exercise 16** Suggest that students use a systematic approach for finding all possible combinations of numerator and denominator within the parameters of the problem.

Real-World Link

You may want students to research the heights of the tallest buildings in the world.

Share & Summarize

Have students share any new patterns they described in **Exercise 1**.

You may want to have students share their letters and strategies for **Exercise 2** with the class or in small groups to make sure every student has a chance to present his or her letter and discuss the effectiveness of the strategies recommended.

Troubleshooting To help students compare decimal and fraction equivalents, have them write the decimal equivalent for each fraction shown on Lesson 2.3 Master 1, Decimal and Fraction Number Lines. Encourage them to use one of the methods discussed in the lesson, such as dividing the numerator by the denominator or finding equivalent fractions with a denominator that is a multiple of 10, when finding the equivalents.

Reaching *All Learners*

BL **Beyond Level** Challenge students to find all 27 levels of the tallest possible tower for the exercises without using the fraction and decimal equivalents chart. The numbers, in order, are as follows:

$\frac{8}{9} = 0.\overline{8}, \frac{7}{8} = 0.875, \frac{6}{7} \approx 0.86, \frac{5}{6} = 0.8\overline{3}, \frac{4}{5} = 0.8, \frac{7}{9} = 0.\overline{7}, \frac{3}{4} \text{ or } \frac{6}{8} = 0.75; \frac{5}{7} \approx 0.71;$

$\frac{2}{3} \text{ or } \frac{4}{6} \text{ or } \frac{6}{9} = 0.\overline{6}; \frac{5}{8} = 0.625; \frac{3}{5} = 0.6; \frac{4}{7} \approx 0.57; \frac{5}{9} = 0.\overline{5}; \frac{1}{2} \text{ or } \frac{2}{4} \text{ or } \frac{3}{6} \text{ or } \frac{4}{8} = 0.5;$

$\frac{4}{9} = 0.\overline{4}; \frac{3}{7} \approx 0.43; \frac{2}{5} = 0.4; \frac{3}{8} = 0.375; \frac{1}{3} \text{ or } \frac{2}{6} \text{ or } \frac{3}{9} = 0.\overline{3}; \frac{2}{7} \approx 0.29; \frac{1}{4} \text{ or } \frac{2}{8} = 0.25;$

$\frac{2}{9} = 0.\overline{2}; \frac{1}{5} = 0.2; \frac{1}{6} = 0.1\overline{6}; \frac{1}{7} \approx 0.14; \frac{1}{8} = 0.125; \frac{1}{9} = 0.\overline{1}$

Investigation 1
Pages 88–91
Practice & Apply: 1–5, 30–32
Connect & Extend: 35–43

Investigation 2
Pages 91–93
Practice & Apply: 6, 7, 33, 34
Connect & Extend: 44

Investigation 3
Pages 94–97
Practice & Apply: 8–17

Investigation 4
Pages 97–99
Practice & Apply: 18–29, 44
Connect & Extend: 45–52

Assign Anytime
Mixed Review: 53–62

▶ **Exercises 2 and 3** Students' answers may vary slightly from the answers provided, but each student's answer to Exercise 3 should be greater than his or her answer to Exercise 2.

▶ **Exercise 5** Encourage students having difficulty to write the fraction as a mixed number and then find the closest decimal.

▶ **Exercises 8 and 9** You may want to point out that the notation … indicates a repeating digit or digits. Students must look at the pattern to determine exactly which digit or digits repeat.

Practice & *Apply*

1. $\frac{4}{5}, \frac{7}{9}, \frac{8}{10}$ (Note: It is hard to tell precisely, so students may think $\frac{3}{4}, \frac{5}{6}$, and $\frac{6}{8}$ are among the three closest.)

2. Possible answer: 0.85 and 0.86

3. Possible answer: 0.87 and 0.88

4. Possible answer:
   A: $3\frac{2}{3}$ and 3.7;
   B: $5\frac{3}{4}$ and 5.8;
   C: $4\frac{3}{8}$ and 4.38

5a. 2.1; Possible explanation: $\frac{17}{8} = 2\frac{1}{8}$, and I can see from the number-line diagram that $\frac{1}{8}$ is closer to 0.1 than to 0.2.

5b. Possible answer: 2.13; I used my number-line diagram.

6. 0.52, $\frac{52}{100} = 1 \cdot 2 \cdot 2 \cdot \frac{13}{1} \cdot 2 \cdot 2 \cdot 5 \cdot 5;$ $\frac{52}{100} = \frac{13}{25}$

For Exercises 1–3, use the number-line diagram on page 89.

1. Name the three fractions in the diagram that are closest to 0.8.

2. Tell which two decimals $\frac{6}{7}$ is between, to the hundredths place.

3. Tell which two decimals $\frac{7}{8}$ is between, to the hundredths place.

4. Use a mixed number and a decimal to approximate the location of each point.

5. Consider the fraction $\frac{17}{8}$.

   a. Which of these decimals is closest to $\frac{17}{8}$? Explain how you decided.

   2.1   2.2   2.8   2.9   17.1   17.8

   b. Give a decimal that would be even closer to $\frac{17}{8}$. Explain how you found your answer.

Write the decimal and fraction from the model. Simplify each fraction.

6.

7. $0.6, \frac{6}{10} = 1 \cdot 2 \cdot \frac{3}{1} \cdot 2 \cdot 5;$ $\frac{6}{10} = \frac{3}{5}$

8. Which of the following is equivalent to $1.2\overline{34}$?

   1.23412341234 …   (1.23434343434 …)   1.23444444 …

9. Which of the following is equivalent to 2.393939 …?

   $2.3\overline{9}$ ($2.\overline{39}$)

Find a decimal equivalent for each fraction or mixed number.

10. $\frac{16}{5}$ 3.2

11. $\frac{15}{11}$ $1.\overline{36}$

12. $\frac{70}{250}$ 0.28

13. $\frac{33}{24}$ 1.375

14. $\frac{14}{3}$ $4.\overline{6}$

15. $\frac{376}{20,000}$ 0.0188

16. $5\frac{1}{16}$ 5.0625

17. $\frac{9}{12}$ 0.75

18a. Possible answer: The cells form a diagonal line going down and to the right, from one cell to the next, down one cell and over three. This happens because each time you add 1 to the numerator, you need to add 3 to the denominator to keep the fraction $\frac{1}{3}$.

18. In the chart you completed for page 96, color all of the cells with fractions equivalent to $\frac{1}{3}$.

   a. What pattern do you notice? Why does this happen?

   b. Why doesn't every column have a colored cell?

Use the chart that you completed for page 96 to help find a decimal equivalent to each fraction or mixed number.

19. $\frac{12}{5}$ 2.4   **20.** $32\frac{7}{10}$ 32.7 **21.** $65\frac{2}{3}$ $65.\overline{6}$ **22.** $3\frac{1}{7}$ $3.\overline{142857}$

Use the chart you completed for page 96 to help find a fraction or mixed number equivalent to each decimal. Possible answers:

23. 4.125   **24.** 32.5   **25.** 4.75   **26.** $8.\overline{1}$
    $4\frac{1}{8}$, or $\frac{33}{8}$ $32\frac{1}{2}$, or $\frac{65}{2}$ $4\frac{3}{4}$, or $\frac{19}{4}$ $8\frac{1}{9}$, or $\frac{73}{9}$

27. Refer to the chart that you completed for page 96. Look at the column containing fractions with denominator 5.

   a. How do the decimal values change as you move down the column? Why? See below.

   b. Use the pattern in Part a to find the decimal equivalent of $\frac{11}{5}$, the number that would be next in the chart if a row was added. 2.2

In Exercises 28 and 29, the start of a fraction tower is given. If you want to build the highest tower possible, what number should you choose for the next level? Explain your answer. Give your number in both fraction and decimal form.

Real-World Link

Devils Tower National Monument in northeast Wyoming rises 1,267 feet above the nearby Belle Fourche River.

. . . .

18b. Possible answer: Only columns containing denominators that are multiples of 3 contain a fraction equivalent to $\frac{1}{3}$.

28.

| $\frac{6}{9} = 0.\overline{6}$ |
| $\frac{7}{9} = 0.\overline{7}$ |
| $\frac{8}{9} = 0.\overline{8}$ |

$\frac{5}{8} = 0.625$;
It is the next smallest fraction you can make.

29.

| $\frac{3}{9} = 0.\overline{3}$ |
| $\frac{4}{5} = 0.8$ |

$\frac{3}{10} = 0.3$;
It is the next smallest fraction you can make.

Represent each number as a fraction or mixed number. Simplify each fraction.

30. Twenty-eight and six-tenths $28\frac{6}{10}$; $28\frac{3}{5}$

31. Nine and two-hundredths $9\frac{2}{100}$; $9\frac{1}{50}$

32. One hundred fifteen and twelve-thousandths $115\frac{12}{1000}$; $115\frac{3}{250}$

27a. Possible explanation: They increase by 0.2. With each cell, the fraction increases by $\frac{1}{5}$, and $\frac{1}{5} = 0.2$.

▶ **Exercises 19–27** Students need to refer to their completed charts from the exercises on page 96.

▶ **Exercises 19–26** If time permits, you might have students explain how they found the equivalent decimals and fractions.

▶ **Exercises 28 and 29** Encourage students to work though these exercises without referring to a decimal and fraction chart. Suggest that they use the chart to check their answers when possible.

▶ **Exercises 36c and 36d** Discuss students' answers. Make sure they understand the relative values of fractions whose numerators (or denominators) differ by 1, since this can help them more easily compare some fractions.

▶ **Exercise 37** Have students share their strategies for finding the fractions that each decimal is between. One possible strategy is recognizing that, for odd denominators, the two fractions whose numerators are consecutive numbers that sum to the denominator are on opposite sides of 0.5 on a number line. Another strategy is to divide the implied denominator (for example, in **Part b**, the denominator is 7) by 2, giving the numerator (in each case, not a whole number) that would make a fraction equivalent to 0.5. Then choose the next lesser and next greater whole numbers for numerators.

---

33. Order these numbers from least to greatest. $2.05, \frac{11}{5}, 2.3, 2\frac{3}{7}$

$2.3 \qquad \frac{11}{5} \qquad 2\frac{3}{7} \qquad 2.05$

34. In Your Own Words Explain how to find a fraction between any two given fractions. Give an example to illustrate your method.

Connect & Extend

34. Possible answer: You can draw a number line. Plot the two fractions on the number line. Divide the number line into equal parts. Place a point on a fraction between your two given fractions.

35. Copy the number line. Mark and label the point corresponding to each number.

Point A: 2.4   Point B: $3\frac{8}{9}$ Point C: 0.67   Point D: 1.2

36. Look back at the number-line diagram on page 89. Imagine creating two more number lines to represent 11ths and 12ths.

a. Is $\frac{1}{11}$ less than or greater than 0.1? How do you know?

b. Is $\frac{1}{12}$ less than or greater than $\frac{1}{11}$? How do you know?

c. Is $\frac{10}{11}$ less than or greater than 0.9? How do you know?

d. Is $\frac{11}{12}$ less than or greater than $\frac{10}{11}$? How do you know?

36a. Less; Possible explanation: Since $\frac{1}{10}$ and $\frac{1}{11}$ have the same numerator, the fraction with the smaller denominator is greater. So, $\frac{1}{10} = 0.1 > \frac{1}{11}$.

36b–d. See margin.

37. Look back at the number-line diagram on page 89. Notice that 0.5 is between $\frac{1}{3}$ and $\frac{2}{3}$.

a. Between which two fifths is 0.5? $\frac{2}{5}$ and $\frac{3}{5}$

b. Between which two sevenths is 0.5? $\frac{3}{7}$ and $\frac{4}{7}$

c. Between which two ninths is 0.5? $\frac{4}{9}$ and $\frac{5}{9}$

Now think beyond the diagram.

d. Between which two 15ths is 0.5? $\frac{7}{15}$ and $\frac{8}{15}$

e. Between which two 49ths is 0.5? $\frac{24}{49}$ and $\frac{25}{49}$

In each pair, tell which fraction is closer to 0.5.

38. $\frac{2}{5}$ or $\frac{3}{7}$ $\frac{3}{7}$

39. $\frac{4}{9}$ or $\frac{11}{23}$ $\frac{11}{23}$

40. $\frac{2}{5}$ or $\frac{4}{5}$ $\frac{2}{5}$

41. $\frac{4}{9}$ or $\frac{6}{9}$ $\frac{4}{9}$

42. $\frac{3}{17}$ or $\frac{16}{17}$ $\frac{3}{17}$

43. $\frac{19}{44}$ or $\frac{27}{44}$ $\frac{19}{44}$

Additional Answers

36b. Less; Possible explanation: Since $\frac{1}{11}$ and $\frac{1}{12}$ have the same numerator, the fraction with the smaller denominator is greater.

36c. Greater; Possible explanation: The positions of fractions whose numerator and denominator differ by 1? such as $\frac{1}{2}$ and $\frac{2}{3}$ move right as you move down the number lines. So, $\frac{10}{11}$ would be farther right than $\frac{9}{10}$, or 0.9.

36d. Greater; Possible explanation: The positions of fractions whose numerator and denominator differ by 1? such as $\frac{1}{2}$ and $\frac{2}{3}$ move right as you move down the number lines. So, $\frac{11}{12}$ would be farther to the right than $\frac{10}{11}$.

44. Answers will vary: Sample answer: $\frac{21}{25}$ terminating, $\frac{8}{10}$ terminating, $\frac{2}{60}$ repeating, $\frac{5}{18}$ repeating. When the denominator factors into a base 2 or base 5 the decimal will be terminating. If it factors into any other number besides base 2 of base 5 it will be repeating.

45d. $0.\overline{0001}$, $0.\overline{0005}$, $0.\overline{0008}$

46a. Possible pattern: $0.\overline{09}$, $0.\overline{18}$, $0.\overline{27}$, $0.\overline{36}$, $0.\overline{45}$; The repeating digits are 9 times the numerator.

47. Possible answer: The fractions with numerator 10 are 10 times those with numerator 1, and multiplying by 10 corresponds to moving the decimal point one place to the right.

44. Use prime factorization to name two fractions that are repeating decimals, and two fractions that are terminating decimals. Explain how you know.

45. Refer to your completed chart from page 96.   45a–c. See margin.

  a. Look at the column containing fractions with denominator 9. What pattern do you see as you move down this column?

  b. Find the decimal equivalents of $\frac{1}{99}$, $\frac{2}{99}$, $\frac{3}{99}$, and so on, up to $\frac{9}{99}$. What pattern do you see?

  c. Find the decimal equivalents of $\frac{1}{999}$, $\frac{2}{999}$, $\frac{3}{999}$, and so on, up to $\frac{9}{999}$. What pattern do you see?

  d. Predict the decimal equivalents for $\frac{1}{9,999}$, $\frac{5}{9,999}$, and $\frac{8}{9,999}$. Use your calculator to check your prediction.

46. Consider fractions with denominator 11.

  a. Find decimal equivalents for $\frac{1}{11}$, $\frac{2}{11}$, $\frac{3}{11}$, $\frac{4}{11}$, and $\frac{5}{11}$. What pattern do you see?

  b. Use the pattern you discovered to predict the decimal equivalents of $\frac{7}{11}$ and $\frac{9}{11}$. $0.\overline{63}$, $0.\overline{81}$

47. Refer to your completed chart from page 96. Compare the *row* containing fractions with *numerator* 10 to the row containing fractions with numerator 1. The decimals for fractions with numerator 10 are the same as those for fractions with numerator 1, except the decimal point is moved one place to the right. Explain why.

48. In your completed chart from page 96, color the cells containing fractions equivalent to 1. Use a different color.

  a. Describe the pattern you see.   A diagonal extending from $\frac{1}{1}$ to $\frac{10}{10}$

  b. The numbers below the line of 1s are greater than 1. The numbers above the line of 1s are less than 1. Why?
  Possible answer: The numbers below the line have numerators greater than their denominators, making the fractions greater than 1. The numbers above the line have numerators less than their denominators, making the fractions less than 1.

Lesson 2.3   Fraction and Decimal Equivalents   **103**

▶ **Exercise 45** Students will need their completed chart for decimals and fractions to complete this exercise.

▶ **Exercise 45 Extension** You may want to ask students to generalize how to write a decimal equivalent for a fraction with a numerator of one to nine and a denominator that has only nines in it. Possible answer: The number of zeros to the right of the decimal point is one fewer than the number of nines in the denominator. The last digit is the same number as the numerator.

▶ **Exercise 46** You may want to encourage students to use this information to add a column for elevenths to their decimal and fraction chart from page 96.

▶ **Exercises 47 and 48** Students need their completed charts from page 96.

▶ **Exercises 48–52** Point out that while some of the rules for building fraction towers change in these exercises, the basic idea that the value of the fraction decreases with each level added to the top of the tower remains the same.

Additional Answers

45a. Possible answer: The decimal equivalents are the repeating decimals $0.\overline{1}$, $0.\overline{2}$, $0.\overline{3}$, and so on, with the repeating part increasing by 0.1 each time. Until you reach $\frac{9}{9}$, the repeating digit is the numerator of the fraction.

45b. $0.\overline{01}$, $0.\overline{02}$, $0.\overline{03}$, $0.\overline{04}$, $0.\overline{05}$, $0.\overline{06}$, $0.\overline{07}$, $0.\overline{08}$, $0.\overline{09}$; The repeating part is 0 followed by the numerator of the fraction.

45c. $0.\overline{001}$, $0.\overline{002}$, $0.\overline{003}$, $0.\overline{004}$, $0.\overline{005}$, $0.\overline{006}$, $0.\overline{007}$, $0.\overline{008}$, $0.\overline{009}$; The repeating part is two 0s followed by the numerator of the fraction.

Quick Check

Informal Assessment Students should be able to:

✔ estimate fraction and decimal equivalents

✔ find decimal equivalents to fractions

✔ demonstrate an understanding of repeating decimals

✔ find patterns in decimal and fraction equivalents

✔ order and compare fractions and decimals

Quick Quiz

1. a. Which of the following decimals is closest to $87\frac{3}{5}$?
   87.5 87.58 87.61 87.7 87.61

   b. Which of the following fractions is closest to $0.2\overline{2}$?
   $\frac{1}{5}$ $\frac{23}{100}$ $\frac{3}{10}$ $\frac{23}{100}$

2. Find a fraction or mixed number equivalent to each decimal. Simplify each fraction.
   a. 0.8 $\frac{4}{5}$
   b. 2.75 $2\frac{3}{4}$ or $\frac{11}{4}$
   c. 1.6 $1\frac{3}{5}$ or $\frac{8}{5}$

3. Find a decimal equivalent for each fraction.
   a. $\frac{4}{9}$ $0.\overline{4}$
   b. $2\frac{1}{3}$ $2.\overline{3}$
   c. $1\frac{2}{8}$ 1.25

4. Order these numbers from least to greatest. 0.875, 0.7, $\frac{2}{5}$, $\frac{6}{8}$, $\frac{5}{6}$, $0.\overline{6}$
   $\frac{2}{5}$, $0.\overline{6}$, 0.7, $\frac{6}{8}$, $\frac{5}{6}$, 0.875

In Exercises 49–52, the rules for building a fraction tower have been changed. Tell what fraction you would choose as your starting number in order to build the tallest possible tower.

49. Use whole numbers between 1 and 20 for numerators and denominators. As before, fractions must be less than 1. $\frac{19}{20}$

50. Use whole numbers between 1 and 9 for numerators and denominators. There is no limit on the value of the fraction. $\frac{9}{1}$

51. Use whole numbers between 1 and 9 for numerators and denominators. The fractions must be less than $\frac{1}{2}$. $\frac{4}{9}$

52. Suppose the rules for building a fraction tower are changed so you can choose only numbers between 1 and 4 for numerators and denominators. Fractions still must be less than 1. Draw a tower with the maximum number of levels. Explain why it is the maximum.

Mixed Review

52. Tower:

Possible explanation: There are only six possible fractions you can make with different numerator and denominator:
$\frac{1}{2}, \frac{1}{3}, \frac{1}{4}, \frac{2}{3}, \frac{2}{4}, \frac{3}{4}$.
However, since $\frac{1}{2}$ = $\frac{2}{4}$, there are only five different fractions.

Geometry Estimate the measure of each angle.

53. 90°

54. 45°

55. 30°

56.  225°

Use the fact that 13 · 217 = 2,821 to find each product *without* using a calculator.

57. 1.3 · 217 282.1

58. 13 · 2.17 28.21

59. 0.013 · 21.7 0.2821

60. 0.13 · 0.217 0.02821

61. 1,300 · 2,170 2,821,000

62. 13 · 0.0217 0.2821

Review & Self-Assessment

Chapter Summary

In this chapter, you used what you learned about factors and multiples to find *equivalent fractions* and to compare fractions. You also saw how you could use *benchmark fractions* like $\frac{1}{4}$, $\frac{1}{2}$, and $\frac{2}{3}$ to estimate the values of more complicated fractions.

You reviewed the meaning of decimals, and you investigated how multiplying or dividing by 10, 100, 1,000, 10,000, and so on affects the position of the decimal point. Then you compared and ordered decimals and found a number between two given decimals.

You saw how you could write a fraction as a decimal. You discovered that sometimes the decimal representation of a fraction is a *repeating decimal* with a pattern of digits that repeats forever.

Strategies and Applications

The questions in this section will help you review and apply the important ideas and strategies developed in this chapter.

Finding equivalent fractions and comparing fractions

1. Find two fractions equivalent to $\frac{4}{6}$. Use diagrams or another method to explain why the fractions are equivalent to $\frac{4}{6}$.

2. Explain what it means for a fraction to be in *lowest terms*. Then describe a method for writing a given fraction in lowest terms.

3. Describe two methods for comparing fractions. Then use one of the methods to determine whether $\frac{7}{10}$ is greater than, less than, or equal to $\frac{8}{11}$.   See margin.

Understanding and comparing decimals

4. Describe a rule for comparing two decimals. Demonstrate your rule by comparing 307.63 with 308.63 and by comparing 3.786 with 3.779.   See margin.

5. How does the value of a number change when you move the decimal point three places to the right? Illustrate your answer with an example.

6. How does the value change when you move the decimal point two places to the left? Illustrate your answer with an example.
It decreases to $\frac{1}{100}$ its value; Possible example: If you start with 4.34 and move the decimal point two places to the left, you get 0.0434, which is $\frac{1}{100}$ of 4.34.

Vocabulary

- equivalent fractions
- lowest terms
- mixed number
- repeating decimal

1. Possible answer: $\frac{2}{3}$, $\frac{8}{12}$

    $\frac{2}{3}$

    $\frac{4}{6}$

    $\frac{8}{12}$

2. Possible answer: A fraction is in lowest terms if the only common factor of the numerator and denominator is 1. Possible method: If a fraction is not in lowest terms, write it in lowest terms by dividing both the numerator and denominator by the greatest common factor.

5. It increases 1,000 times; Possible example: If you start with 4.34 and move the decimal point three places to the right, you get 4,340, which is 4.34 · 1,000.

Review & Self-Assessment

Chapter Summary
This summary helps students recall the major topics of the chapter.

Vocabulary
Students should be able to explain each of the terms listed in the vocabulary section.

▶ **Exercise 3** If time permits, have students share their methods.

▶ **Exercises 5 and 6** Point out that students should look at how the values change, not just determine what the new number will be after the decimal point is moved.

Additional Answers

3. Possible answer: Write the fractions with a common denominator. Then compare the numerators. The fraction with the greater numerator is greater. Or, write the fractions with a common numerator. Then compare the denominators. The fraction with the lesser denominator is greater. $\frac{7}{10} = \frac{56}{80}$ and $\frac{8}{11} = \frac{56}{77}$, so $\frac{8}{11}$ is greater. Or, $\frac{7}{10} = \frac{77}{110}$ and $\frac{8}{11} = \frac{80}{110}$, so $\frac{8}{11}$ is greater.

4. Possible answer: Compare the whole-number parts. If they are not the same, the number with the greater whole-number part is greater. If they are the same, compare the tenths digits. If they are not the same, the number with the greater tenths digit is greater. If they are the same, compare the hundredths digits. Continue this process, moving to the right one digit each time, until you find two digits that are different. The number with the greater digit is greater. 308.63 > 307.63 because 308 > 307. 3.786 > 3.779 because 8 > 7.

▶ **Exercises 11 and 12 Extension** Have students write each fraction in lowest terms if they did not include it as an equivalent fraction: $\frac{13}{39} = \frac{1}{3}, \frac{32}{720} = \frac{2}{45}$.

▶ **Exercises 16 and 17** Remind students that they can align the decimal points as they list the numbers to help them compare and order the numbers.

▶ **Exercises 25 and 26** You may want to remind students that for these exercises, repeating decimals are written with a bar above the repeating digits.

7. Possible answer: Think about the place value of the digits. 0.97 is 97 hundredths, or $\frac{97}{100}$. 0.003 is 3 thousandths, or $\frac{3}{1000}$.

8. Possible answer: Divide the numerator by the denominator. For example, $3 \div 4 = 0.75$, so $\frac{3}{4} = 0.75$.

9. Possible answer: A repeating decimal is a decimal with a pattern of digits that repeats forever. For example, $\frac{5}{9}$ is equivalent to 0.555 ... , or $0.\overline{5}$.

16. 0.754, 0.7541, 0.75411, 0.7641, 1.754

Converting decimals to fractions and fractions to decimals

7. Explain how you would write a decimal in fraction form. Illustrate by writing 0.97 and 0.003 as fractions.

8. Explain how you would find a decimal equivalent to a given fraction. Give an example.

9. Explain what a *repeating decimal* is. Give an example of a fraction that is equivalent to a repeating decimal.

List three fractions equivalent to each given fraction.

10. $\frac{6}{7}$ Possible answer: $\frac{12}{14}, \frac{18}{21}, \frac{60}{70}$

11. $\frac{13}{39}$ Possible answer: $\frac{1}{3}, \frac{2}{6}, \frac{26}{78}$

12. $\frac{32}{720}$ Possible answer: $\frac{16}{360}, \frac{8}{180}, \frac{4}{90}$

Replace each $\bigcirc$ with <, >, or = to make a true statement.

13. $\frac{5}{16} \bigcirc \frac{7}{24}$

14. $\frac{14}{22} \bigcirc \frac{35}{55}$

15. $\frac{9}{49} \bigcirc \frac{3}{14}$

Order each set of decimals from least to greatest.

16. 0.7541, 1.754, 0.754, 0.75411, 0.7641

17. 251.889, 249.9, 251.9, 251.8888, 252.000001
    249.9, 251.8888, 251.889, 251.9, 252.000001

Compute each result mentally.

18. $0.00012 \cdot 1,000$
    0.12

19. $\frac{1}{10,000}$ of 344
    0.0344

20. $100 \cdot 77.5$
    7,750

Find a number between each given pair of numbers.

21. 11.66 and 11.67   Possible answer: 11.665

22. 0.0001 and 0.001   Possible answer: 0.0002

23. 3.04676 and 3.04677   Possible answer: 3.046765

Write each fraction or mixed number in decimal form.

24. $\frac{7}{8}$ 0.875

25. $\frac{8}{6}$ $1.\overline{3}$

26. $\frac{11}{15}$ $0.7\overline{3}$

27. $5\frac{17}{20}$ 5.85

Represent each number as a fraction or mixed number. Simplify each fraction.

28. forty-two hundredths $\frac{42}{100} = \frac{1 \cdot 2 \cdot 3 \cdot 7}{1 \cdot 2 \cdot 2 \cdot 5 \cdot 5} = \frac{21}{50}$

29. six and eight tenths $6\frac{8}{10} = \frac{1 \cdot 2 \cdot 2 \cdot 2}{1 \cdot 2 \cdot 5} = 6\frac{4}{5}$

Give your answer as a mixed number and a fraction.

30. $\frac{7}{2}$, or $3\frac{1}{2}$, slices

31. $\frac{3}{2}$, or $1\frac{1}{2}$, days

32. Sample answer: $\frac{1}{3}$,

$\frac{6}{18} \cdot \frac{1}{3} = \frac{1 \cdot 3}{3 \cdot 3} = \frac{3}{9}$;

$\frac{6}{18} = \frac{6 \div 2}{18 \div 2} = \frac{3}{9}$

30. If 14 slices of pizza are divided among four people, what portion of pizza will each person receive?

31. Joan worked for 36 hours last week. What portion of a day is this?

32. Find two fractions equivalent to $\frac{3}{9}$. Use diagrams or another method to explain why the fractions are equivalent to $\frac{3}{9}$.

Replace each $\bigcirc$ with <, >, or = to make a true statement.

33. $\frac{9}{36} \ominus \frac{10}{40}$

34. $\frac{17}{4} \oslash \frac{9}{12}$

35. $\frac{28}{52} \oslash \frac{12}{50}$

36. $\frac{72}{27} \ominus \frac{8}{3}$

Write each fraction or mixed number in decimal form.

37. $\frac{3}{5}$ 0.6

38. $\frac{4}{12}$ $0.33\overline{3}$

39. $\frac{70}{15}$ $4.66\overline{6}$

40. $\frac{52}{8}$ 6.5

Test-Taking Practice

SHORT RESPONSE

1 Determine whether $\frac{5}{7}$ is greater than, less than, or equal to $\frac{7}{9}$.

   Show your work.

   Answer _____

Show your work:
The fractions can be compared by finding a common denominator. The LCD of 7 and 9 is 63. Rewrite both fractions using a denominator of 63, then compare numerators.
$\frac{5}{7} = \frac{45}{63}$ and $\frac{7}{9} = \frac{49}{63}$.
Since 45 is less than 49, $\frac{5}{7}$ is less than $\frac{7}{9}$.

Answer: $\frac{5}{7}$ is less than $\frac{7}{9}$

MULTIPLE CHOICE

2 Which set of fractions are equivalent?

A $\frac{6}{24}, \frac{3}{8}, \frac{12}{36}, \frac{5}{16}$

B $\frac{20}{32}, \frac{5}{9}, \frac{15}{24}, \frac{10}{18}$

C $\frac{4}{5}, \frac{8}{10}, \frac{15}{20}, \frac{11}{15}$

D $\frac{18}{21}, \frac{6}{7}, \frac{12}{14}, \frac{30}{35}$

3 Which list shows the decimals in order from the least to the greatest?

F   0.362   0.252   0.237   0.31   0.27

G   0.27   0.31   0.237   0.252   0.362

H   0.237   0.252   0.27   0.31   0.362

J   0.362   0.31   0.27   0.252   0.237

4 Which of the following is equivalent to 0.0037 · 100?

A 0.000037

B 0.003700

C 0.037

D 0.37

5 Which decimal is equivalent to $\frac{7}{12}$?

F $0.58\overline{3}$

G $0.\overline{583}$

H 0.712

J 1.714285

▶ **Exercise 32** Have student pairs compare their diagrams or methods for this exercise.

▶ **Exercises 37–40** You may want students to use calculators to check their decimals for these exercises.

Lesson 2.1, Develop & Understand: B (p. 63)

9. Possible answer: Write the fraction in lowest terms by dividing the numerator and denominator by common factors until they are relatively prime. (You can do this in one step if you divide by the greatest common factor.)

10. No: Possible explanation: By writing both fractions in lowest terms, I know that $\frac{6}{10}$ is in the $\frac{3}{5}$ fraction family and that $\frac{16}{20}$ is in the $\frac{4}{5}$ fraction family.

Lesson 2.1, Share & Summarize (p. 63)

1. Possible answer: I looked for portions that were the same size. For example, for Caroline and Rosita, I could see that one piece of Caroline's bar $\left(\frac{1}{3}\right)$ was the same size as two pieces of Rosita's $\left(\frac{2}{6}\right)$.

2. Possible answer: Multiply or divide the numerator and the denominator of the given fraction by the same number. The following fractions are equivalent to $\frac{6}{9}$.

$$\frac{2}{3} = \frac{6 \div 3}{9 \div 3} \quad \frac{12}{18} = \frac{6 \cdot 2}{9 \cdot 2} \quad \frac{30}{45} = \frac{6 \cdot 5}{9 \cdot 5} \quad \frac{600}{900} = \frac{6 \cdot 100}{9 \cdot 100}$$

Lesson 2.1, Develop & Understand: B (p. 67)

5c. Possible answer: The air distance from Washington, DC, to Los Angeles is about $\frac{1}{2}$ the air distance from Washington, DC, to Moscow. I used $\frac{1}{2}$ because 2,300 is half of 4,600, which is close to 4,870. $\frac{1}{2}$ is a little more than $\frac{2,300}{4,870}$.

5d. Possible answer: The Volga River is about $\frac{2}{3}$ the length of the Ob-Irtysh River. I chose $\frac{2}{3}$ because $\frac{1}{3}$ of 3,362 is about 1,100 and so $\frac{2}{3}$ is about 2,200. This is close to 2,290. $\frac{2}{3}$ is a little less than $\frac{2,290}{3,362}$.

Notes

Patterns, Numbers, and Rules

Chapter Overview

In this chapter, students will study numbers in the millions and billions and learn to use different strategies to extend and generalize patterns in a variety of contexts, including Pascal's triangle. In studying a broad range of patterns, students will develop stronger understandings of the mathematical concepts underlying the patterns. Students also learn about some properties of real numbers and review the order of operations.

The **Big** Picture

Links to the Past	Chapter **3**	Links to the Future
Grade 5 Developing number sense for large numbers; multiplying whole numbers such as 5 · 5.	**Lesson 3.1** (p. 110) Number Sense	**Course 2, Chapter 4** Magnitude of Numbers (pp. 172–209) **Course 3, Chapter 4** Exponents and Exponential Variation (pp. 144–203)
Grade 4 Recognizing, describing, and extending repetitive patterns of numbers and shapes.	**Lesson 3.2** (p. 120) Patterns	**Course 2, Chapter 8** Linear Relationships (pp. 366–433) **Course 3, Chapter 1** Linear Relationships (pp. 2–63)
Grade 5 Writing multiplication number models for rectangular arrays; using algebraic expressions such as $n + 2$.	**Lesson 3.3** (p. 143) Variables and Rules	**Chapter 9** Equations (pp. 532–575) **Course 2, Chapter 1** Expressions (pp. 2–71) **Course 3, Chapter 10** Functions and Their Graphs (pp. 522–575)
Grade 5 Reading a clock; using the distributive property to multiply mentally.	**Lesson 3.4** (p. 174) Apply Properties	**Course 2, Chapter 1** Expressions (pp. 2–71) **Course 3, Chapter 7** Inequalities and Linear Systems (pp. 310–371)

Mathematical Background

How many is a million? How about a billion? A trillion? Which is more, 100 million or 1 billion? Chapter 3 introduces students to ways of understanding extremely large numbers by writing them in exponential form.

An important part of algebra is developing facility in manipulating expressions, regardless of the real quantities they represent. In this chapter, the investigations deliberately activate kinesthetic, concrete, and visual styles of learning, particularly in the bags-and-blocks model. In addition, students will learn some ways in which expressions can be manipulated, especially those related to the distributive property of multiplication over addition and over subtraction.

In this chapter, students create and identify a few of the patterns found in Pascal's triangle, especially the connection between the entries in each row and the two entries above it. If any two adjacent entries are added, the sum equals the entry below them. The triangle has practical applications, which students will learn in later years in areas of mathematics such as combinatorics and algebra.

A common thread in this chapter is rule writing. Students are asked to describe the patterns and to use their descriptions to predict terms if the patterns were extended. Generally, there are two types of rules: recursive and explicit. A recursive rule states the pattern using previous terms or outcomes, while an explicit (or direct) rule describes the pattern independently of the previous terms or outcomes. For example, there are many rules to describe the sequence 1, 2, 3, 4, 5, …

A recursive rule could be "Add 1 to the previous term." An explicit rule could be "Each term is equal to its term number." Explicit rules are more useful for finding the nth term of a sequence. Some patterns, like the Fibonacci sequence, are most easily described recursively. Both approaches are acceptable ways of generalizing a pattern, and students should be encouraged to recognize both ways of rule writing.

Variables and Rules Students will often look at a sequence of dots or numbers and come up with different rules. Each student can show that his or her rule is correct by explaining why it will work for any sequence. The rules are then said to be *equivalent*. Students learn to write symbolic expressions in equivalent forms by using properties and relationships between basic number operations.

A fun way in this chapter for students to practice recognizing patterns and finding rules is to play the game *What's My Rule?* One student thinks of a rule about numbers and the other students in the group try to guess the rule.

Order of Operations The order of operations is a pattern for calculation that allows everyone to consistently arrive at the same answer to a given calculation or problem. Students should recognize that although the order of operations could have been different, they must follow it as it is since the order has already been set. Because order of operations is a pattern imposed to create an order for calculations, it is slightly different from the other patterns in the chapter, where the pattern exists and students uncover it.

The ideas in this chapter lay the groundwork for more extensive work with variables and equations in Courses 2 and 3.

Additional Reading

According to Grouws and Cebulla in *Improvising Student Achievement in Mathematics,* if students focus on number sense, they may be encouraged to use problem-solving strategies that reflect number sense. In Lesson 3.1, students use number sense to work with large numbers and exponents.

Planning Guide
Lesson Resources

	Lesson 3.1 **Pacing:** 2 days	Lesson 3.2 **Pacing:** 5 days	Lesson 3.3 **Pacing:** 7 days	Lesson 3.4 **Pacing:** 4 days
Lesson Title	**Number Sense** (p. 110)	**Patterns** (p. 120)	**Variables and Rules** (p. 143)	**Apply Properties** (p. 174)
Lesson Objectives	• To understand the relationship between a million, a billion, and a trillion • To write a number in exponential form	• To create Pascal's triangle and describe patterns that aid in the creation • To evaluate and compare expressions using the order of operations • To write rules for a constructed pattern	• To write symbolic rules for a number or dot sequence and show how each term relates to the term number • To recognize when rules for a pattern are equivalent • To use letters for variables to write rules for real-life situations	• To apply the commutative and associative properties • To perform numerical calculations using the distributive property • To use the additive identity and the multiplicative identity
Materials	calculators, one quarter, ruler	Lesson 3.2 Masters 1–3, Chapter 3 Master 3, *counters, scientific calculators, calculators, newpaper sections, computer with spreadsheet software, toothpicks	Chapter 3 Master 1–3 paper bags, *blocks	Lesson 3.4 Master 1
Quick Review Math Handbook	**Lesson 3.1** Powers and Exponents	**Lesson 1.3** Order of Operations	**Lesson 1.3** Order of Operations; Ⓐ	**Lesson 5.2** Simplifying Expressions
Print Resources	CRM Study Guide and Intervention (p. 6) CRM Skills Practice (p. 7) CRM Problem-Solving Practice (p. 8) CRM Enrichment (p. 9) • Investigation Notebook and Reflection Journal • Differentiation Handbook	CRM Study Guide and Intervention (p. 11) CRM Skills Practice (p. 12) CRM Problem-Solving Practice (p. 13) CRM Enrichment (p. 14) • Investigation Notebook and Reflection Journal • Differentiation Handbook	CRM Study Guide and Intervention (p. 19) CRM Skills Practice (p. 20) CRM Problem-Solving Practice (p. 21) CRM Enrichment (p. 22) • Investigation Notebook and Reflection Journal • Differentiation Handbook	CRM Study Guide and Intervention (p. 24) CRM Skills Practice (p. 25) CRM Problem-Solving Practice (p. 26) CRM Enrichment (p. 27) • Investigation Notebook and Reflection Journal • Differentiation Handbook
Technology Resources	TeacherWorks Plus Classroom Presentation Toolkit ExamView Assessment Suite StudentWorks Plus **Math Online** Brain Pops • Concepts in Motion	TeacherWorks Plus Classroom Presentation Toolkit ExamView Assessment Suite StudentWorks Plus **Math Online** Brain Pops • Concepts in Motion	TeacherWorks Plus Classroom Presentation Toolkit ExamView Assessment Suite StudentWorks Plus **Math Online** Brain Pops • Concepts in Motion	TeacherWorks Plus Classroom Presentation Toolkit ExamView Assessment Suite StudentWorks Plus **Math Online** Brain Pops • Concepts in Motion

*Included in the Impact Mathematics Manipulative Kit   Ⓐ **Lesson 5.1** Writing Expressions and Equations

Assessment Resources

MARS Assessment: Teaching with Purpose

Design a Logo

In *Design a Logo,* students draw a logo and complete a table that shows the number of tiles needed to make logos of different sizes.

Targeting the Task

- **Diagnostic**—Use Exercises 1–5 in the *Design a Logo* assessment to determine students' understanding of how to find and use a number pattern. For those students who do not have this understanding, completing this unit is needed.

- **Formative**—Exercises 1–5 can be administered individually according to the lessons.

- **Summative**—Administer the complete *Design a Logo* performance-based assessment.

CRM **Chapter 3 MARS Assessment** (pp. 49–52)

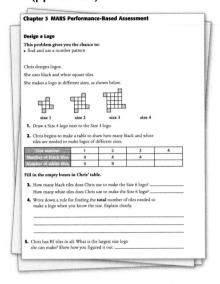

Assessment Planning Guide

Assessments are available for investigations, lessons, and chapters.

 **ExamView®** Assessment Suite — Customize and create multiple versions of tests and quizzes.

	Student Edition	Teacher Edition	Other Resources
Diagnostic			CRM Chapter 3 Pretest (p. 30) Math Online Online Chapter Quiz
Formative	Share & Summarize (pp. 113, 116, 125, 129, 132, 135, 148, 152, 156, 162, 165, 178, 183, 186)	Troubleshooting (pp. 116, 121, 125, 129, 132, 135, 148, 152, 156, 162, 165, 178, 183, 185) On the Spot Assessment (pp. 111, 114, 127, 128, 130, 135, 145, 176, 177, 180, 182) Quick Check (pp. 119, 142, 173, 190) Quick Quiz (pp. 119, 142, 173, 190)	
Summative	Review & Self-Assessment (pp. 191-195)		CRM Chapter 3 Test: Forms A and B (pp. 34–43) CRM Standardized Test Practice (p. 47)
Performance-Based	In Your Own Words (pp. 119, 139, 140, 142, 173, 190)		CRM MARS Performance-Based Assessment (p. 49) CRM Chapter Performance Assessment (p. 44)

Differentiated Instruction

Reaching All Learners

Below are suggestions on differentiating the materials presented in this chapter. Additional modifications should be considered.

Approaching Level AL

Lesson 3.2: Pascal's Triangle For students who have difficulty with the patterns and rules in Pascal's Triangle, you can create a larger version on chart paper. Have students work in pairs or small groups to find patterns in the triangle. Allow them to take turns identifying patterns. Keep a list to show their findings. Make sure students understand that the patterns they find would keep repeating, no matter how large the triangle grows. Then, have each group choose one pattern and create their own triangle. Instruct them to highlight the pattern throughout their triangle. Discuss how the highlighted areas constantly form a pattern. Display the triangles in the classroom.

Beyond Level BL

Rules Students who have a strong grasp of the concepts in this chapter can work with a group to create their own "Input/Output machines." Provide materials for them to use, such as shoeboxes and construction paper. Have groups create a rule and write it on the side of their Input/Output machine. Then have them list several numbers to put in and solve with the rule. Have other students try the numbers with the rule. Discuss whether they found the correct answers, and have students write two sentences about the rule and why it worked. Have students read their sentences out loud to each other and discuss their answers. Display the Input/Output machines where others can see them and try the problems.

On Level OL

Lesson 3.4: Properties Have students choose one property to explore. In pairs or small groups, give students index cards. Have them write notes about the property they chose on each card. Tell them to write the definition of the property on one card, an example on another card, and any important words for learning the property on another (identity element, etc.). Tell them to take turns studying their index cards to learn about each property. Then have them trade with someone who chose a different property, and study those cards. Remind students that this is a good study technique that they can use for other concepts, too. Before the Chapter Test, allow students to review their cards.

English Language Learners ELL

Lesson 3.3: Inv. 4, Crossing a Bridge This investigation focuses on variations of a word problem. English Learners may need help with vocabulary involved in order to solve each problem. Create a sketch of the basic problem on chart paper. Label each part of the picture – hikers, adults, children, bridge, across, and so on. Make sure students know the meanings of all the words in the problems, and have them point out any they are not sure of as they read. The sketch will prove helpful in illustrating the vocabulary in the problems for students who are not completely comfortable with the English language, and you can use it as a visual aid for each variation of the problem.

KEY

 Approaching Level On Level Beyond Level **ELL** English Language Learners

Intervention Planning Guide

CRM Assess students' prerequisite skills and knowledge using the
Chapter Pretest found in the Chapter 3 Resource Masters, p. 30.

Intensive Intervention two or more years below grade level	Strategic Intervention below grade level	On Level	Beyond Level
If students miss 75% of the exercises:	**If** students miss 50% of the exercises:	**If** students miss 25% of the exercises:	**If** students miss 0%–10% of the exercises:
Then use *Math Triumphs,* an intensive intervention	**Then** choose a resource:	**Then** choose a resource:	**Then** choose a resource:
Math Triumphs, Grade 6 • Chapter 9: Variables and Expressions	CRM Study Guide and Intervention (pp. 6, 11, 19, 24) • Investigation Notebook and Reflection Journal • Differentiation Handbook **Math Online** Brain Pops • Concepts in Motion	CRM Skills Practice (pp. 7, 12, 20, 25) CRM Problem-Solving Practice (pp. 8, 13, 21, 26) • Investigation Notebook and Reflection Journal	CRM Enrichment (pp. 9, 14, 22, 27) • Differentiation Handbook

Literature Connections
Recommended Outside Reading for Students
Nonfiction

Tang, Greg. *The Grapes of Math: Mind Stretching Math Riddles.* Scholastic Trade, 2001.

Readers of this book learn creative ways of solving problems using patterns and number combinations. Colorful computer-generated art and riddles draw students into math as a game rather than a homework assignment. It provides an interesting supplement to Lessons 1-1, 1-7a, and 1-7. In addition, it relates to those lessons incorporating the finding of patterns such as Lessons 1-2 and 1-8.

Fiction

Sachar, Louis. *Sideways Arithmetic from Wayside School.* Apple, 1997.

This collection of stories from fictional Wayside school incorporates more than 50 mathematical brain teasers. These fun, real-life applications incorporate many math skills, including finding patterns and following the order of operations.

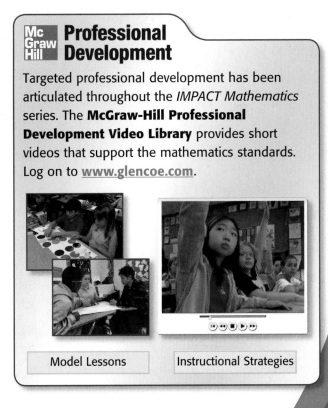

Mc Graw Hill Professional Development

Targeted professional development has been articulated throughout the *IMPACT Mathematics* series. The **McGraw-Hill Professional Development Video Library** provides short videos that support the mathematics standards. Log on to **www.glencoe.com**.

Model Lessons   Instructional Strategies

Real-Life Math

A Bee Tree Ask students to think about the existence of patterns in their lives by brainstorming different kinds of patterns they have seen in nature. You might need to offer a few examples, such as the changing of the seasons, the rising and setting of the sun, or the three-leaf structure of poison ivy. After you have discussed general patterns, have students read "A Bee Tree." Point out that numerical patterns like the Fibonacci sequence are interesting not only to mathematicians (and mathematics teachers) but also to others, such as scientists and business people. Identifying patterns in a situation helps people understand the situation and make predictions.

Think About It You might have students use pine cones to help discover the pattern of adding the two previous terms to get the next term in the Fibonacci sequence. Students should count how many spirals are on each cone, tracing each spiral with a permanent marker to be sure one is not counted twice.

Patterns, Numbers, and Rules

Contents in Brief

Real-Life Math

A Bee Tree Although a female honeybee has two parents, a male honeybee has only a mother. The family tree of a male honeybee's ancestors reveals an interesting pattern of numbers.

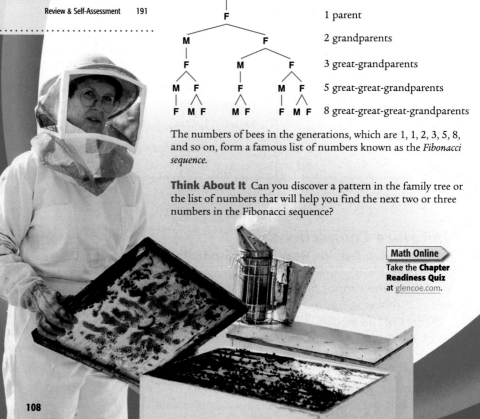

M	1 male bee
F	1 parent
M F	2 grandparents
F M F	3 great-grandparents
M F M F	5 great-great-grandparents
F M F M F F M F	8 great-great-great-grandparents

The numbers of bees in the generations, which are 1, 1, 2, 3, 5, 8, and so on, form a famous list of numbers known as the *Fibonacci sequence*.

Think About It Can you discover a pattern in the family tree or the list of numbers that will help you find the next two or three numbers in the Fibonacci sequence?

Math Online
Take the **Chapter Readiness Quiz** at glencoe.com.

108

Chapter Resources

- CRM Chapter 3 Resource Masters
- CRM English/Spanish Family Letter (pp. 1 and 2)
- CRM Lesson Masters (pp. 3–5, 16–18, 29)
- CRM Chapter 3 Pretest (pp. 30–33)
- CRM Chapter 3 Tests (pp. 34–46)

Math Online Online Readiness Quiz • eGlossary

Dear Family,

In this chapter, students will study two important mathematical concepts, number sense and patterns. The chapter begins with a discussion of millions, billions, and trillions. The class will ponder questions such as, "How high would a stack of one million quarters reach?"

Next, students will look for patterns in diagrams, in sequences of numbers, and in a triangular array. Your student will use patterns to write mathematical rules. Mathematics has been called the "science of patterns." Recognizing and describing patterns and using patterns to make predictions are important mathematical skills.

Key Concepts—Patterns and Rules

Patterns can be represented using diagrams, words, numbers, and equations.

□   □□   □□□

Diagram

Words	Numbers	Equation
A square is added each time.	4, 8, 12	Let s represent the number of squares. Let t represent the total number of sides. $t = 4s$

Chapter Vocabulary

exponent	property
input	sequence
order of operations	term
output	variable

Home Activities

- Look and listen for real-world references that use millions, billions, and trillions. Discuss the size of these numbers.
- Work together to represent a pattern using a diagram, words, numbers, and an equation.
- Challenge your student to a game of *What's My Rule*.
- Apply properties to simplify daily calculations.

Family Letter

Another version of the Family Letter, available in English and Spanish, is found in the Chapter 3 Resource Masters. You may want to send a copy of this letter home with your students.

Key Concept—Patterns and Rules

Introduce students to patterns and rules by giving them toothpicks and asking them to construct the images on this page—one square, then two squares, then three squares. Ask them to predict the number of toothpicks they would need to construct a total of six squares. How did they determine the number of toothpicks?

Home Activities

- Each day, have your student look at the business pages of a newspaper and cut out references to stocks. How many stocks were traded in each day of the last week?

- Have your student find all the ways he or she can continue the pattern 2, 4, … . What is the next number?

Key Vocabulary

English (Spanish) *Introduce the most important terms from Chapter 3.*

associative property (propiedad associative) The grouping of addends (or factors) does not change the sum (product). (p. 178)

commutative property (propiedad conmutative) The order in which two numbers are added (multiplied) does not change the sum (product). (p. 176)

distributive property (propiedad distributiva) To multiply a sum by a number, you can multiply each addend by the number and add the products. (p. 181)

exponent (exponente) A small, raised number that tells how many times a factor is multiplied. For example in 10^3, the exponent 3 tells you to multiply 3 factors of 10: $10 \cdot 10 \cdot 10 = 1,000$. (p. 114)

order of operations (orden de las operaciones) A convention for reading and evaluating expressions. (p. 130)

sequence (sucesión) An ordered list. For example, 2, 5, 8, 11, … is a sequence. (p. 122)

variable (variable) A quantity that varies, or changes. For example, in a problem about the size of buildings, the height and width of the buildings would be variables. (p. 144)

Number Sense

Objectives

▶ To understand the relationship between a million, a billion, and a trillion

▶ To write a number in exponential form

Overview

This lesson presents students with some useful ways of dealing with large numbers. First, students get a sense of the difference between millions, billions, and trillions, and then they explore some real-world contexts for these numbers.

Students are then introduced to exponents. They use an "Input-Output Machine" to explore exponents and rules and to write products of factors in exponential form.

Advance Preparation

You may want to provide calculators to facilitate class discussion while presenting new topics, including large numbers and exponents.

	Summary	Materials	On Your Own Exercises (pp. 117–119)	Assessment Opportunities
Investigation 1 (p. 111) *Pacing:* 1 day	Students calculate characteristics of a million quarters: how high they will stack, how far they will reach, and how much area they will cover.	calculators, one quarter, rulers	Practice & Apply: 1, 2 Connect & Extend: 17–20 Mixed Review: 25–33	• On the Spot Assessment (p. 111) • Share & Summarize (p. 113)
Investigation 2 (p. 115) *Pacing:* 1 day	Students use an Input/Output machine as a tool to help them see patterns and rules in numbers. They also explore exponents and exponential notation.		Practice & Apply: 3–16 Connect & Extend: 21–24 Mixed Review: 25–33	• On the Spot Assessment (p. 114) • Share & Summarize (p. 116) • Troubleshooting (p. 116)

Leveled Lesson Resources

Also on
TeacherWorks™
Lesson 3.1

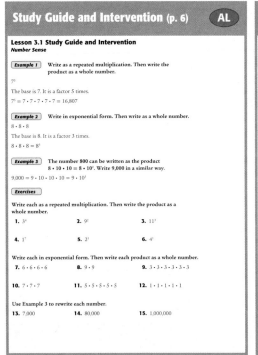

Study Guide and Intervention (p. 6) AL

Lesson 3.1 Study Guide and Intervention
Number Sense

Example 1 Write as a repeated multiplication. Then write the product as a whole number.

7^5

The base is 7. It is a factor 5 times.

$7^5 = 7 \cdot 7 \cdot 7 \cdot 7 \cdot 7 = 16,807$

Example 2 Write in exponential form. Then write as a whole number.

$8 \cdot 8 \cdot 8$

The base is 8. It is a factor 3 times.

$8 \cdot 8 \cdot 8 = 8^3$

Example 3 The number 800 can be written as the product $8 \cdot 10 \cdot 10 = 8 \cdot 10^2$. Write 9,000 in a similar way.

$9,000 = 9 \cdot 10 \cdot 10 \cdot 10 = 9 \cdot 10^3$

Exercises

Write each as a repeated multiplication. Then write the product as a whole number.

1. 3^4 **2.** 9^2 **3.** 11^3

4. 1^7 **5.** 2^5 **6.** 4^1

Write each in exponential form. Then write each product as a whole number.

7. $6 \cdot 6 \cdot 6 \cdot 6$ **8.** $9 \cdot 9$ **9.** $3 \cdot 3 \cdot 3 \cdot 3 \cdot 3 \cdot 3$

10. $7 \cdot 7 \cdot 7$ **11.** $5 \cdot 5 \cdot 5 \cdot 5 \cdot 5$ **12.** $1 \cdot 1 \cdot 1 \cdot 1 \cdot 1$

Use Example 3 to rewrite each number.

13. 7,000   **14.** 80,000   **15.** 1,000,000

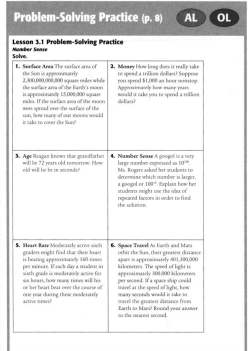

Skills Practice (p. 7) AL OL

Lesson 3.1 Skills Practice
Number Sense

Write as a repeated multiplication. Then write the product as a whole number.

1. 5^5 **2.** 12^2

3. 8^4 **4.** 2^2

5. 5^1 **6.** 1^9

7. 4^5 **8.** 3^7

9. 10^5 **10.** 5^8

Write in exponential form. Then write as a whole number.

11. $3 \cdot 3 \cdot 3 \cdot 3$ **12.** $5 \cdot 5 \cdot 5 \cdot 5 \cdot 5$

13. $6 \cdot 6 \cdot 6 \cdot 6 \cdot 6 \cdot 6 \cdot 6$ **14.** $1 \cdot 1 \cdot 1 \cdot 1 \cdot 1 \cdot 1 \cdot 1 \cdot 1 \cdot 1$

15. $7 \cdot 7 \cdot 7 \cdot 7 \cdot 7$ **16.** $2 \cdot 2 \cdot 2 \cdot 2 \cdot 2 \cdot 2 \cdot 2 \cdot 2$

17. $8 \cdot 8 \cdot 8 \cdot 8 \cdot 8 \cdot 8 \cdot 8$ **18.** $10 \cdot 10 \cdot 10 \cdot 10 \cdot 10 \cdot 10$

19. $23 \cdot 23$ **20.** 9

Write each of the following as a power of 10.

21. 100

22. 1,000

23. 1,000,000

24. 1,000,000,000

25. 1,000,000,000,000

Problem-Solving Practice (p. 8) AL OL

Lesson 3.1 Problem-Solving Practice
Number Sense
Solve.

1. Surface Area The surface area of the Sun is approximately 2,300,000,000,000 square miles while the surface area of the Earth's moon is approximately 15,000,000 square miles. If the surface area of the moon were spread over the surface of the sun, how many of our moons would it take to cover the Sun?

2. Money How long does it really take to spend a trillion dollars? Suppose you spend $1,000 an hour nonstop. Approximately how many years would it take you to spend a trillion dollars?

3. Age Reagan knows that grandfather will be 72 years old tomorrow. How old will he be in seconds?

4. Number Sense A googol is a very large number expressed as 10^{100}. Ms. Rogers asked her students to determine which number is larger, a googol or 100^{10}. Explain how her students might use the idea of repeated factors in order to find the solution.

5. Heart Rate Moderately active sixth graders might find that their heart is beating approximately 160 times per minute. If each day a student in sixth grade is moderately active for six hours, how many times will his or her heart beat over the course of one year during these moderately active times?

6. Space Travel As Earth and Mars orbit the Sun, their greatest distance apart is approximately 401,300,000 kilometers. The speed of light is approximately 300,000 kilometers per second. If a space ship could travel at the speed of light, how many seconds would it take to travel the greatest distance from Earth to Mars? Round your answer to the nearest second.

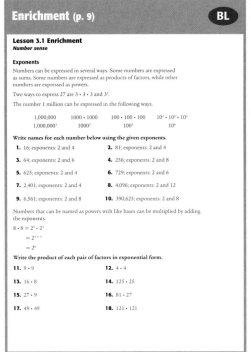

Enrichment (p. 9) BL

Lesson 3.1 Enrichment
Number sense

Exponents

Numbers can be expressed in several ways. Some numbers are expressed as sums. Some numbers are expressed as products of factors, while other numbers are expressed as powers.

Two ways to express 27 are $3 \cdot 3 \cdot 3$ and 3^3.

The number 1 million can be expressed in the following ways.

1,000,000	$1000 \cdot 1000$	$100 \cdot 100 \cdot 100$	$10^2 \cdot 10^2 \cdot 10^2$
$1,000,000^1$	1000^2	100^3	10^6

Write names for each number below using the given exponents.

1. 16; exponents: 2 and 4   **2.** 81; exponents: 2 and 4

3. 64; exponents: 2 and 6   **4.** 256; exponents: 2 and 8

5. 625; exponents: 2 and 4   **6.** 729; exponents: 2 and 6

7. 2,401; exponents: 2 and 4   **8.** 4,096; exponents: 2 and 12

9. 6,561; exponents: 2 and 8   **10.** 390,625; exponents: 2 and 8

Numbers that can be named as powers with like bases can be multiplied by adding the exponents.

$8 \cdot 8 = 2^3 \cdot 2^3$
$\quad\quad = 2^{3+3}$
$\quad\quad = 2^6$

Write the product of each pair of factors in exponential form.

11. $9 \cdot 9$ **12.** $4 \cdot 4$

13. $16 \cdot 8$ **14.** $125 \cdot 25$

15. $27 \cdot 9$ **16.** $81 \cdot 27$

17. $49 \cdot 49$ **18.** $121 \cdot 121$

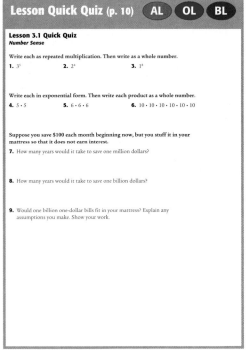

Lesson Quick Quiz (p. 10) AL OL BL

Lesson 3.1 Quick Quiz
Number Sense

Write each as repeated multiplication. Then write as a whole number.

1. 3^5 **2.** 2^4 **3.** 1^8

Write each in exponential form. Then write each product as a whole number.

4. $5 \cdot 5$ **5.** $6 \cdot 6 \cdot 6$ **6.** $10 \cdot 10 \cdot 10 \cdot 10 \cdot 10$

Suppose you save $100 each month beginning now, but you stuff it in your mattress so that it does not earn interest.

7. How many years would it take to save one million dollars?

8. How many years would it take to save one billion dollars?

9. Would one billion one-dollar bills fit in your mattress? Explain any assumptions you make. Show your work.

Additional Lesson Resources

Teacher Tech Tools
- TeacherWorks
- ExamView Assessment Suite
- Classroom Presentation Toolkit
- Advance Tracker

Student Tech Tools
- StudentWorks Plus
- **Math Online** eGlossary •
  Concepts in Motion

Other Print Products
- Investigation Notebook
  and Reflection Journal
- Quick Review Math Handbook

LESSON 3.1 Number Sense

Introduce

Billions Begin the lesson by reminding students that they have already heard of large numbers. If someone says the Earth is 5 billion years old, students should know that this is not an exact figure, but a rounded figure. Students should have the sense that a billion is much larger than a million (a billion is one thousand million).

Think & Discuss

Allow students a few minutes to think about millions, billions, and trillions in Think & Discuss. Ask them if they have a sense of how many groups of 300 million would equal 6.6 billion. How many times larger than the population of the United States is the population of China if China has a population of over one billion?

Number Sense

LESSON 3.1

Can you imagine what a million quarters look like? If you stacked a million quarters, how high would they reach? How long is a million seconds? How old is someone who has been alive a billion seconds? How much money is a trillion dollars?

In this lesson, you will explore these questions, and you will learn a new tool for writing large numbers.

Think & Discuss

Consider the following numbers. Which number is the greatest?   9 trillion

| 9 trillion | 300 million | 6.6 billion |

> This newspaper says the national debt is 9 trillion dollars!

> Can you believe that there are 300 million people in the United States?

> The world's population is estimated to be 6.6 billion people.

Investigation 1 — Millions, Billions, and Trillions

Materials
• a quarter

It is difficult to understand just how large one million, one billion, and one trillion are. It helps to think about these numbers in contexts that you can imagine. The exercises in this investigation will help you get a better sense of the size of a million, a billion, and a trillion.

Think & Discuss

How many zeros follow the 1 in 1 million?   6

How many zeros follow the 1 in 1 billion?   9

How many millions are in 1 billion?   1,000

Develop & Understand: A

★ **1.** How old is someone who has been alive one million seconds?   About $11\frac{1}{2}$ days

2. About 31 years $8\frac{1}{2}$ months

★ **2.** How old is someone who has been alive one billion seconds?

3. Find the diameter of a quarter in inches. Give your answer to the nearest inch.   About 1 in.

Math Link
5,280 feet = 1 mile

4. The distance around Earth's equator is about 24,830 miles.

   a. If you lined up one million quarters end to end, how far would they reach? Give your answer in miles.   About 15.8 mi

   b. Would they reach around the equator? If not, how many quarters would you need to reach around the equator?   See below.

5. How many quarters do you need to make a stack one inch high?   16

6. The average distance from Earth to the moon is 238,855 miles.

   a. If you stacked one million quarters, how high would they reach?   About 5,208 ft, or about 1 mi

   b. Would they reach the moon? If not, how many quarters would you need to reach the moon? Estimate your answer without using a calculator. Explain how you found your answer.   No; 1 million quarters forms a stack about a mile high, so you would need about 238,855 · 1,000,000 = about 239,000,000,000 quarters.

4b. No; About $1,000,000 \cdot \dfrac{24,830}{15.8}$ = about 1,570,000,000 quarters

Lesson 3.1 Number Sense   **111**

On the Spot Assessment

Watch for students who multiply rather than divide when converting inches to feet and feet to miles. Ask students to use common sense to decide whether the answer is reasonable. For example:
Would you expect the number of miles to be more or less than the number of feet? Less If you multiply by 5,280, is the product greater or less? Greater

---

Investigation 1

Millions, Billions, and Trillions In this investigation, students gain a better sense of big numbers, including the fact that a million, a billion, and a trillion are quite different. "Order of magnitude" is important in mathematics, and few people understand it.

Think & Discuss

These questions should be familiar to students, but it is worth taking a few minutes to discuss them.

Develop & Understand: A

Suggested Grouping: Small Groups

▶ **Exercise 1** Stop the class after most groups have finished working on this exercise and ask several volunteers to give their answers and explain their calculations. Students may be tempted to answer Exercise 1 in years and get a value of about 0.031. Encourage them to answer in whatever unit gives them a sense for the age.

▶ **Exercise 2** Give students the option of doing the calculations individually or in small groups. Ask students whether any of them found a shortcut method for determining the answer to Exercise 2. Point out that since a billion is 1,000 millions, you can simply take the converted value of a million seconds, multiply by 1,000, and divide by 365 to get an answer for a billion seconds expressed in years.

▶ **Exercises 3–6** As students work, encourage them to check that their answers make sense. Point out that when converting inches to feet, they should always get a smaller number, about $\frac{1}{10}$ as much. You also get a smaller number when converting feet to miles.

Teacher Tips Students will need about 20 quarters per group. If students use disks other than quarters, be sure to adjust answers accordingly.

Lesson 3.1 Number Sense   **111**

▶ **Exercise 7** Point out that the unit conversion is more complicated in this exercise because students have to deal with square feet rather than linear feet. Here are some strategies students might use.

• Convert all measurements to inches before starting, and thus use 1,080 inches for 90 feet.

• Compute the area of the infield in terms of quarters. The area in square feet is 902, so students have to find the number of quarters needed to cover a square foot. A square foot of quarters would have 12 quarters along each side, and 144 quarters would cover one square foot. Then students should multiply 144 by 90^2 to see whether a million quarters are enough.
$144 \cdot 90^2 = 1{,}166{,}400$, so a million quarters is not quite enough.

Teacher Tips Since a trillion is a million millions, work with your students to help them envision one million before doing Think & Discuss. Point out, for example, that if each of 25 students brings in 222 pennies on each of the 180 days of school, they would be 1,000 pennies short of 1 million: $25 \times 222 \times 180 = 999{,}000$.

Think & *Discuss*

Write out 1 trillion as the number 1 followed by 12 zeros. Try to emphasize that 1 trillion is a very large number. For example, another way to picture a million is to use centimeter cubes. Find or create a box with 1-meter edges and put a few centimeter cubes inside. Students can then "see" what 1 million cubes would look like, as one million centimeter cubes would exactly fill the box. Then emphasize that it would take one million of these boxes to equal a trillion!

⊘ *Develop & Understand: B*

Suggested Grouping: Small Groups

▶ **Exercises 8–10** Before students answer the questions, have them brainstorm the answers in their groups.

7. No; Possible explanation: 1,000 quarters extend about 83 ft, so 1 million quarters will cover a square measuring 83 ft on a side.

7. A baseball diamond is a square, 90 feet on each side. Would one million quarters spread out cover a baseball diamond? Explain how you found your answer.

Hint: Think of one million quarters forming a square with 1,000 quarters on each side. Since quarters are round, they do not fit together exactly. Do not worry about the extra space left uncovered.

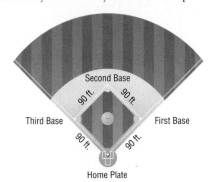

Now you will think about one trillion in a real-world context to help you get a better sense of its size. As with one million and one billion, it can be difficult to understand how large one trillion is.

Think & *Discuss*

How many zeros follow the 1 in 1 trillion?   12

How many billions are in 1 trillion?   1,000

How many millions are in 1 trillion?   1,000,000

⊘ *Develop & Understand: B*

Consider the following statistics. Use this information for Exercises 8–10.

• In 2006, the real median household income in the United States was about $50,000.

• During the 2006–2007 basketball season, the median salary for a player on the San Antonio Spurs team was $3,000,000.

• In 2007, the United States national debt was estimated at 7 trillion dollars.

8. How many years would an American family work to earn the amount of money earned by a San Antonio Spurs player in one year?   60

Additional Example Work with your students to describe other distances that are the same as the length of a million quarters. For example, a million quarters laid end to end reach almost 16 miles. That is about a 20-minute drive on the highway. Similarly, a million quarters form a tower almost a mile high. That is the elevation (above sea level) of Denver!

★ indicates multi-step problem

1. Since 1 million quarters form a stack about a mile high, about 93,000,000 · 1,000,000 = about 93,000,000,000,000 quarters would be needed.

9. About how many years would a San Antonio Spurs player work to earn 1 trillion dollars? Over 300,000

10. About how many years would a San Antonio Spurs player work to earn enough money to pay off the 7 trillion dollar national debt? Over 2,300,000

Share & Summarize

★ 1. The average distance from Earth to the Sun is about 93,000,000 miles. How many quarters would you need to stack for the pile to reach the sun?

2. Why do you think many people do not understand the difference between a million, a billion, and a trillion? Answers will vary.

Investigation 2 Exponents

Vocabulary
exponent
factor
input
output

In Investigation 1, you worked with millions, billions, and trillions. In this lesson, you will learn an operation that can be used to represent big numbers.

Imagine a machine that takes in a number called an **input**. The machine applies a rule to the input. After the rule is applied, a number comes out of the machine. The number that comes out of the machine is called an **output**.

Suppose the rule is take any input and multiply it by itself. You can use □ to represent the original number and □ · □ to represent the rule. Let 3 be the input number. The rule, input, and resulting output are shown below.

Reaching All Learners

BL **Beyond Level** Ask interested students to create their own input-output machines using exponents. Encourage them to create example machines for finding other powers of numbers and for finding other number patterns.

Share & Summarize

Exercise 1 asks students ask students to do a computation similar to the exercises on page 111 but for a greater distance. Have students work on this individually and then share their answers with partners. Consider asking students to read their answers out loud to check their understanding of larger numbers.

Exercise 2 asks students why people make mistakes with large numbers. There are certainly many reasonable answers. Some may say that both numbers are so big that the difference between them is confusing. Others may say that people are not careful with what they say. Or others may say that people have trouble deciding whether to add or to multiply; they think of a billion as more like "a few million" rather than "a thousand million."

Investigation 2

On Your Own Exercises
Pages 117–119
Exercises 3–16, 21–24

Exponents In this investigation, students are introduced to exponents through the use of repeated multiplication. They will see that writing exponents is much simpler than writing repeated multiplication. This lesson helps reinforce the meaning and use of exponents. It is important that students learn these concepts to enable proper understanding of future exponential operations.

Point out how students have to imagine how an input-output machine works. You many want to do several more examples of the "squaring machine" shown on this page.

✅ *Develop & Understand: A*

Suggested Grouping: Pairs

▶ **Exercises 1–5** These exercises provide a chance for students to practice using common exponents. Encourage them to memorize these facts because they will be using them regularly.

▶ **Exercise 6** Students may have difficulty with repeated multiplication of the number 1. Since the factors and the product are the same, they may need an illustration to help them understand the fact. Point out that one times one is the same as one group of one object.

Think & Discuss

Ask students to think quickly about how they can write the repeated multiplication in shorter form. Allow them to express their thoughts; then work the repeated multiplication problems on the board. Show how the repeated multiplication results in the same answer as using an exponent. Discuss the relationship between the two forms.

✅ *Develop & Understand: A*

For Exercises 1–6, input the following numbers into the □ · □ machine. Find the output for each input number.

1. 2 4	**2.** 5 25	**3.** 8 64
4. 4 16	**5.** 7 49	**6.** 1 1

A **factor** is a number that divides into another number without a remainder. For example, 5 is a factor of 30 because 30 ÷ 5 equals 6.

When a factor is repeated, you can use an *exponent* to write the multiplication in a shorter form. An **exponent** is a small, raised number that tells how many times a factor is multiplied.

2 is the exponent.

3^2

3^2 is read "3 to the second power" or "three squared."

Think & Discuss

What do you think? How can Luke use Althea's idea to write $5 \cdot 5 \cdot 5 \cdot 5$ in a shorter form? 5^4

How can Althea's idea be used to write $2 \cdot 2 \cdot 2 \cdot 2 \cdot 2$ in a shorter form? 2^5

🔵 On the Spot Assessment

Monitor for signs of understanding in students. Create an example of an expression in exponential form and ask students to explain why the example applies to the repeated multiplication fact as well. Use their answers to help you see who needs further help with exponents.

Develop & Understand: B

Write each multiplication in exponential form. Then write each product as a whole number.

7. $6 \cdot 6$ 6^2; 36

8. $2 \cdot 2$ 2^2; 4

9. $7 \cdot 7$ 7^2; 49

10. $10 \cdot 10$ 10^2; 100

11. $5 \cdot 5 \cdot 5$ 5^3; 125

12. $3 \cdot 3 \cdot 3$ 3^3; 27

13. $4 \cdot 4 \cdot 4$ 4^3; 64

14. $2 \cdot 2 \cdot 2 \cdot 2$ 2^4; 16

15. $10 \cdot 10 \cdot 10 \cdot 10 \cdot 10$ 10^5; 100,000

16. $1 \cdot 1 \cdot 1 \cdot 1 \cdot 1 \cdot 1$ 1^6; 1

Math Link

The products $3 \cdot 3$ and $5 \cdot 5 \cdot 5 \cdot 5$ are written as repeated multiplications, and 3^2 and 5^4 are written in exponential form.

Write each of the following as repeated multiplication. Then write each product as a whole number.

17. 5^2 $5 \cdot 5$; 25

18. 9^2 $9 \cdot 9$; 81

19. 12^2 $12 \cdot 12$; 144

20. 10^3 $10 \cdot 10 \cdot 10$; 1,000

21. 6^3 $6 \cdot 6 \cdot 6$; 216

22. 2^3 $2 \cdot 2 \cdot 2$; 8

23. 1^4 $1 \cdot 1 \cdot 1 \cdot 1$; 1

24. 10^4 $10 \cdot 10 \cdot 10 \cdot 10$; 10,000

25. 4^5 $4 \cdot 4 \cdot 4 \cdot 4 \cdot 4$; 1,024

26. 3^6 $3 \cdot 3 \cdot 3 \cdot 3 \cdot 3 \cdot 3$; 729

In Exercises 1–6, you were given the rule and input to find the output. In the following exercises, you will be given the input and output. Your challenge is to find the missing rule.

Develop & Understand: C

For Exercises 27–34, find the missing rule. Write each rule as repeated multiplication and in exponential form. Use □ to represent the factor when writing each rule.

Real-World Link

Earthquake strength can be measured using the Richter scale. Suppose an earthquake registers a 7.0 on the Richter scale. It would do considerably more damage than an earthquake registering a 5.0 because it is 10^2, or 100, times stronger.

27.

9 → ? → 81

□ · □; $□^2$

28.

2 → ? → 8

□ · □ · □; $□^3$

Develop & Understand: B

Suggested Grouping: Pairs

▶ **Exercises 7–16** Remind students to pay close attention to the number of factors in each repeated multiplication sentence.

▶ **Exercises 17–26** Make sure students use repeated multiplication to find the product in each problem. Remind students not to multiply the factor by the exponent, such as using $3 \cdot 2$ to get 3^2.

Teacher Tips Students will need to be able to use the multiplication facts for numbers 1 through 12 both quickly and easily. For students who have difficulty, use flashcards to review the facts. Drill and practice as necessary to make sure students can use multiplication.

Develop & Understand: C

Suggested Grouping: Pairs

▶ **Exercises 27 and 28** Students may have more trouble finding the rule when the input and output are given. Remind them that they can keep multiplying the input until they reach the output, then count the factors.

Real-World Link

Tell students that earthquake strength is how strongly the Earth shakes in an earthquake. Ask students which they think would do more damage: a measure of 6.0 or 9.0?

Reaching *All Learners*

ELL **English Language Learners** For students new to the English language, learning to read the same problem in more than one way can be confusing. Write "3 to the second power," and "three squared" around a larger "3^2" in the center of a piece of paper. Show students how all three represent the same amount, and then encourage students to keep it in their notebooks and use it as a reference.

▶ **Exercises 29 and 30** These exercises
require students to multiply farther to find
the missing rule. Monitor to be sure they do
not let simple multiplication mistakes cause
them to miss the whole exercise.

▶ **Exercises 31 and 32** Point out to students
that when finding exponents for powers of
ten, it is important to write the correct
number of zeros. Write out the repeated
multiplication for each problem, and have
students count the zeros in each factor and
in the products.

▶ **Exercise 34** Ask students to generalize that
no matter how many times one is
multiplied by itself, the answer is one.

Share & Summarize

When students use words to explain a
mathematical concept such as writing a
number in exponential form, they need to
use proper terms. Remind them to use
repeated multiplication, exponent, and
exponential form in their explanations. Write
example problems on the board for
students to refer to when telling their
answers.

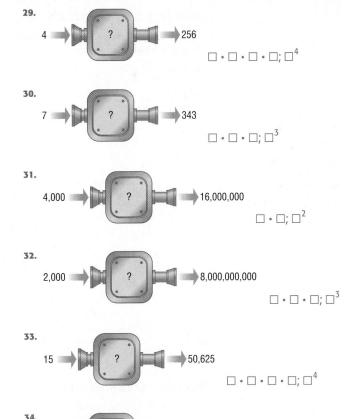

29.

4 ⟶ ? ⟶ 256

□ · □ · □ · □; □⁴

30.

7 ⟶ ? ⟶ 343

□ · □ · □; □³

31.

4,000 ⟶ ? ⟶ 16,000,000

□ · □; □²

32.

2,000 ⟶ ? ⟶ 8,000,000,000

□ · □ · □; □³

33.

15 ⟶ ? ⟶ 50,625

□ · □ · □ · □; □⁴

34.

1 ⟶ ? ⟶ 1

34. Answers will vary.
Students should
realize that there
are many different
answers since no
matter how many
times 1 is multiplied
by itself, the answer
is one.

Share & Summarize

Explain the difference between writing a number in exponential
form and as repeated multiplication.
Possible answer: In exponential form, the base indicates the factor
and the exponent indicates the number of times the factor is
multiplied by itself. In 5^2, 5 is the factor, and it is being multiplied
2 times. As a repeated multiplication, the factors are multiplied
out. 5^2 equals $5 \cdot 5$.

Troubleshooting

For students who understand the concept of exponents, but have trouble using
and distinguishing the raised numbers that show exponents, use index cards to
make the concept more concrete. Write a different one-digit number on each of
several cards. Have students choose two cards, place one as a number and the
other raised number as the exponent. Then have them find the product.

Practice & Apply

2a. Answers will vary. An average stride is between 2 ft and 3 ft.

2e. Possible answer: I may walk 1 million steps but I will not walk 1 billion. If I walk 5 mi a week, or 260 mi a year, for 60 yr, I will walk 15,600 mi in my lifetime. This is somewhere between 27 million and 41 million steps. To walk 1 billion steps, I would have to walk 24 to 37 times as many miles, or between 120 mi and 185 mi every week for 60 yr.

13. $6 \cdot 6 \cdot 6 \cdot 6 \cdot 6$; 7,776
14. $1 \cdot 1 \cdot 1 \cdot 1 \cdot 1 \cdot 1 \cdot 1$; 1

1. How many millimeters are in a kilometer?   1 million

2. In this exercise, you will figure out how far you would walk if you took 1 million steps, if you took 1 billion steps, and if you took 1 trillion steps.

   a. Measure or estimate the length of a single step you take.

   b. If you took 1 million steps, about how far would you walk? Give your answer in miles.   Between 379 mi and 568 mi

   c. If you took 1 billion steps, about how far would you walk? Give your answer in miles.   Between 379,000 mi and 568,000 mi

   d. If you took 1 trillion steps, about how far would you walk? Between 379,000,000 mi and 568,000,000 mi

   e. Do you think you will walk 1 million steps in your lifetime? What about 1 billion steps? Explain your answers.

In Exercises 3–8, write each multiplication expression in exponential form. Then write each product as a whole number.

3. $9 \cdot 9$ 9^2; 81   4. $4 \cdot 4$ 4^2; 16   5. $12 \cdot 12$ 12^2; 144

6. $6 \cdot 6 \cdot 6$ 6^3; 216   7. $3 \cdot 3 \cdot 3 \cdot 3$ 3^4; 81   8. $5 \cdot 5 \cdot 5 \cdot 5 \cdot 5$ 5^5; 3,125

In Exercises 9–14, write each of the following as repeated multiplication. Then write each product as a whole number.

9. 7^2 $7 \cdot 7$; 49   10. 11^2 $11 \cdot 11$; 121   11. 2^3 $2 \cdot 2 \cdot 2$; 8

12. 8^3 $8 \cdot 8 \cdot 8$; 512   13. 6^5 14. 1^7

For Exercises 15 and 16, find the missing rule. Write each rule as repeated multiplication and in exponential form. Use □ when writing each rule.

15.

$\square \cdot \square \cdot \square \cdot \square \cdot \square$; $\square^5$

16.

$\square \cdot \square$; $\square^2$

Investigation 1
Pages 111–113
Practice & Apply: 1, 2
Connect & Extend: 17–20

Investigation 2
Pages 113–116
Practice & Apply: 3–16
Connect & Extend: 21–24

Assign Anytime
Mixed Review: 25–33

▶ **Exercise 1** Another way to picture a million is to show a meter stick. One thousand meters contain 1 thousand thousands, or 1 million, millimeters.

▶ **Exercise 2** Students may not know the lengths of their paces, but they should be able to make a reasonable estimate of one to two feet per step. The goal is to relate what they have learned, especially lengths of time related to one million seconds and one billion seconds, and to realize it is unlikely, though possible, that anyone will take a billion steps in a lifetime. Student responses may include some of the following reasoning:

A reasonable estimate is that it takes 1 second to take a step. If this is the case, walking one million steps would be equivalent to walking for 11 straight days. Over a lifetime, most people probably do walk that much. A billion steps, however, would be equivalent to walking for more than 30 years without a break. It is possible that someone who lived a long time and spent a lot of time walking could accomplish that, but most people would not.

▶ **Exercise 17** This exercise helps students get a sense for what a million dollars will buy. Why is it that lottery winners could spend all of their winnings within a few years? It is not that hard to do. You can ask the question, "If you had a million dollars, what would you do with it? How long would it last?" It is also a nice comparison with someone who has billions of dollars. That is much more money.

▶ **Exercises 18–20** Ask students which of these exercises they found particularly interesting. Ask them to explain why they chose the exercise and which problem-solving strategy they used.

Connect & Extend

17. Economics In this exercise, you will investigate what you could buy if you had $1 million. To answer these questions, it might help to look at advertisements in the newspaper.

  a. How many cars could you buy? Tell how much you are assuming each car costs.   Possible answer: 50 cars at $20,000 each

  b. How many houses could you buy? Tell how much you are assuming each house costs.   Possible answer: 4 houses at $250,000 each

  c. Make a shopping list of several items that total about $1 million. Give the price of each item.   Lists will vary.

18. Astronomy The average distance from Earth to the Sun is 93,000,000 miles. How many of you, stacked on top of yourself, would it take to reach to the Sun? Explain how you found your answer.

19. How many dollars is 1 million quarters? $250,000

20. Count the number of times your heart beats in 1 minute.

  a. At your current heart rate, approximately how many times has your heart beaten since your birth?   Answers will vary.

  b. How many times will your heart have beaten when you reach age 20?   Answers will vary.

  c. How many times will your heart have beaten when you reach age 80?   Answers will vary.

18. Possible answer: I am about 5 ft 3 in. tall, or 5.25 ft. It would take 5,280 ÷ 5.25 ≈ 1,000 of me to reach 1 mi, so it would take 93,000,000 · 1,000 = 93,000,000,000 of me to reach the sun.

21. The number 400 can be written as the product $4 \cdot 10 \cdot 10$, or $4 \cdot 10^2$. Write each of the following products two ways, one with exponents and one without.

  a. 700 $7 \cdot 10 \cdot 10$; $7 \cdot 10^2$

  b. 3,000 $3 \cdot 10 \cdot 10 \cdot 10$; $3 \cdot 10^3$

  c. 80,000 $8 \cdot 10 \cdot 10 \cdot 10 \cdot 10$; $8 \cdot 10^4$

  d. 2,000,000 $2 \cdot 10 \cdot 10 \cdot 10 \cdot 10 \cdot 10 \cdot 10$; $2 \cdot 10^6$

  e. 9,000,000,000

  f. 6,000,000,000,000
  $6 \cdot 10 \cdot 10 \cdot 10 \cdot 10 \cdot 10 \cdot 10 \cdot 10 \cdot 10 \cdot 10 \cdot 10 \cdot 10 \cdot 10$; $6 \cdot 10^{12}$

21e. $9 \cdot 10 \cdot 10 \cdot 10 \cdot 10 \cdot 10 \cdot 10 \cdot 10 \cdot 10 \cdot 10$; $9 \cdot 10^9$

22. Refer to Exercise 21. What relationship do you see between each number and its products? The number of zeros in the original number equals the number of times 10 is used as a factor.

23. **In Your Own Words** Are the expressions $3 \cdot 4$ and 3^4 equal? Why or why not? No; The expression $3 \cdot 4$ equals 12. The expression 3^4 equals $3 \cdot 3 \cdot 3 \cdot 3$, or 81.

24. **Preview** In Lesson 3.2, you will be working with patterns. Give the next three terms of each sequence.

    a. 1, 3, 5, 7, 9, ...   11, 13, 15

    b. 2, 6, 18, ...   54, 162, 486

    c. 800, 400, 200, ...   100, 50, 25

    d. 10, 15, 14, 19, 18, 23, 22, ...   27, 26, 31

Mixed Review

25. From the following list, identify each fraction that simplifies to $\frac{1}{2}$.

$$\frac{10}{20} \qquad \frac{15}{35} \qquad \frac{8}{14} \qquad \frac{2}{6} \qquad \frac{2}{14} \qquad \frac{3}{6} \qquad \frac{10}{12}$$

26. In the number 35,217, which digit is in the thousands place?   5

27. In the number 73.412, which digit is in the tenths place?   4

28. In the number 892,341.7, which digit is in the tens place?   4

29. Write 322 in words.   Three hundred twenty-two

30. Write 10,010 in words.   Ten thousand ten

31. List the following numbers in order from least to greatest.

$$\frac{3}{2} \qquad 0.\overline{3} \qquad \frac{2}{4} \qquad 1\frac{1}{5} \qquad 0.3$$

In Exercises 32 and 33, give your answer as a mixed number and as a fraction.

32. Evelyn ran 17 miles in four days. How many miles per day did she run?

33. Seven people order one large pizza. If a large pizza has 16 slices, what portion of the pizza will each person receive?

Answers

25. $\frac{10}{20}, \frac{3}{6}$

31. $0.3, 0.\overline{3}, \frac{2}{4}, 1\frac{1}{5}, \frac{3}{2}$

32. $\frac{17}{4}$, or $4\frac{1}{4}$ miles per day

33. $\frac{16}{7}$, or $2\frac{2}{7}$ pieces

Lesson 3.1 Number Sense   **119**

▶ **Exercise 22** This exercise is a precursor to scientific notation, which is explored in Course 2, Chapter 4.

Quick Check

Informal Assessment Students should be able to:

✔ understand the relationship between a million, a billion, and a trillion

✔ write a number in exponential form

Quick Quiz

Write each as repeated multiplication. Then write as a whole number.

1. 3^5 $3 \cdot 3 \cdot 3 \cdot 3 \cdot 3 = 243$

2. 2^4 $2 \cdot 2 \cdot 2 \cdot 2 = 16$

3. 1^8 $1 \cdot 1 \cdot 1 \cdot 1 \cdot 1 \cdot 1 \cdot 1 \cdot 1 = 1$

Write each in exponential form. Then write each product as a whole number.

4. $5 \cdot 5$ $5^2 = 25$

5. $6 \cdot 6 \cdot 6$ $6^3 = 216$

6. $10 \cdot 10 \cdot 10 \cdot 10 \cdot 10 \cdot 10$ $10^6 = 1,000,000$

Suppose you save $100 each month beginning now, but stuff it in your mattress so that it does not earn interest.

7. How many years would it take to save 1 million dollars? About 833 years

8. How many years would it take to save 1 billion dollars? About 833,334 years

9. Would one billion one-dollar bills fit in your mattress? Explain any assumptions you make and show your work. Answers will vary.

Patterns

Overview

This lesson introduces patterns by having students construct Pascal's triangle, identify some of the patterns within the triangle, and use those patterns to extend the triangle. Students then look at a variety of patterns in sequences, including repeating patterns, patterns in geometric sequences, and patterns in numeric sequences. They write informal descriptions or rules for these patterns and use the patterns to find missing terms. It is important to note that students need not master pattern identification or rule writing in this lesson, although they should be familiar with strategies for finding patterns. They will study patterns and rules more extensively throughout the rest of this chapter and in subsequent chapters.

Advance Preparation

You may want to provide students with toothpicks, counters, and Lesson 3.2 Masters 1–3 to facilitate class discussion while presenting new topics, including patterns and order of operations.

	Summary	Materials	On Your Own Exercises (pp. 136–142)	Assessment Opportunities
Investigation 1 (p. 121) *Pacing: 2 days*	Students construct Pascal's triangle and describe some of the patterns in the triangle. They develop strategies for finding patterns in geometric and numeric sequences and write informal rules for some of the sequences.	Lesson 3.2 Master 1, toothpicks (optional), counters (optional), Lesson 3.2 Master 2 (optional), Chapter 3 Master 3	Practice & Apply: 1–8 Connect & Extend: 36–40 Mixed Review: 57–70	• Share & Summarize (p. 125) • Troubleshooting (p. 121, 125)
Investigation 2 (p. 126) *Pacing: 1 day*	Students use the order of operations to evaluate expressions. They also review how fraction bars can be used as grouping symbols.	scientific calculators	Practice & Apply: 9–16 Connect & Extend: 41–45 Mixed Review: 57–70	• On the Spot Assessment (p. 127, 128) • Share & Summarize (p. 129) • Troubleshooting (p. 129)
Investigation 3 (p. 130) *Pacing: 1 day*	Students investigate order of operations with exponents and will do calculations using exponents.	calculator	Practice & Apply: 17–31 Connect & Extend: 46–49 Mixed Review: 57–70	• On the Spot Assessment (p. 130) • Share & Summarize (p. 132) • Troubleshooting (p. 132)
Investigation 4 (p. 133) *Pacing: 1 day*	Students use words to write rules that connect two variables. They find patterns in tables and write rules describing the patterns.	Lesson 3.2 Master 3 (optional), newspaper sections, computer with spreadsheet software (optional)	Practice & Apply: 32–35 Connect & Extend: 50–56 Mixed Review: 57–70	• On the Spot Assessment (p. 135) • Share & Summarize (p. 135) • Troubleshooting (p. 135)

Leveled Lesson Resources

CRM Available in: **Chapter 3 Resource Masters**

Study Guide and Intervention (p. 11)   AL

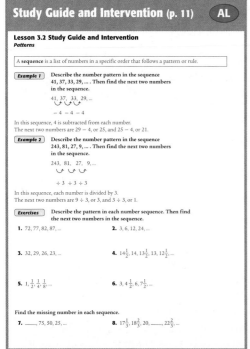

Lesson 3.2 Study Guide and Intervention
Patterns

A **sequence** is a list of numbers in a specific order that follows a pattern or rule.

Example 1 Describe the number pattern in the sequence 41, 37, 33, 29, ... Then find the next two numbers in the sequence.

41, 37, 33, 29, ...
$-4 \quad -4 \quad -4$

In this sequence, 4 is subtracted from each number.
The next two numbers are 29 − 4, or 25, and 25 − 4, or 21.

Example 2 Describe the number pattern in the sequence 243, 81, 27, 9, ... Then find the next two numbers in the sequence.

243, 81, 27, 9, ...
$\div 3 \quad \div 3 \quad \div 3$

In this sequence, each number is divided by 3.
The next two numbers are 9 ÷ 3, or 3, and 3 ÷ 3, or 1.

Exercises Describe the pattern in each number sequence. Then find the next two numbers in the sequence.

1. 72, 77, 82, 87, ...
2. 3, 6, 12, 24, ...
3. 32, 29, 26, 23, ...
4. $14\frac{1}{2}, 14, 13\frac{1}{2}, 13, 12\frac{1}{2}, ...$
5. $1, \frac{1}{2}, \frac{1}{4}, \frac{1}{8}, ...$
6. $3, 4\frac{1}{2}, 6, 7\frac{1}{2}, ...$

Find the missing number in each sequence.

7. _____, 75, 50, 25, ...
8. $17\frac{1}{3}, 18\frac{2}{3}, 20, $ _____, $22\frac{2}{3}, ...$

Skills Practice (p. 12)   AL   OL

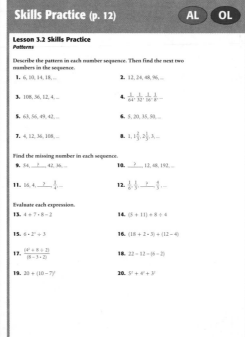

Lesson 3.2 Skills Practice
Patterns

Describe the pattern in each number sequence. Then find the next two numbers in the sequence.

1. 6, 10, 14, 18, ...
2. 12, 24, 48, 96, ...
3. 108, 36, 12, 4, ...
4. $\frac{1}{64}, \frac{1}{32}, \frac{1}{16}, \frac{1}{8}, ...$
5. 63, 56, 49, 42, ...
6. 5, 20, 35, 50, ...
7. 4, 12, 36, 108, ...
8. $1, 1\frac{2}{3}, 2\frac{1}{3}, 3, ...$

Find the missing number in each sequence.

9. 54, _____, 42, 36, ...
10. _____, 12, 48, 192, ...
11. 16, 4, _____, $\frac{1}{4}, ...$
12. $\frac{1}{6}, \frac{1}{3}, $ _____, $\frac{4}{3}, ...$

Evaluate each expression.

13. $4 + 7 \cdot 8 - 2$
14. $(5 + 11) + 8 \div 4$
15. $6 \cdot 2^4 \div 3$
16. $(18 + 2 \cdot 3) + (12 - 4)$
17. $\frac{(4^2 + 8 \div 2)}{(8 - 3 \cdot 2)}$
18. $22 - 12 - (6 - 2)$
19. $20 + (10 - 7)^2$
20. $5^2 + 4^2 + 3^2$

Problem-Solving Practice (p. 13)   AL   OL

Lesson 3.2 Problem-Solving Practice
Patterns
Solve.

1. **Sports** Shakia is getting in shape for track. He is starting with a 2-mile run and will increase the run by $\frac{1}{2}$ mile each week for 4 weeks. What will his distance be for the second, third, and fourth weeks?

2. **Water** Miguel is pumping water from a small pond into a water tank. At 9 A.M. the water level was 2 inches. At 11 A.M. it was $3\frac{1}{2}$ inches. At 1 P.M. it was 5 inches. If the pattern continues, what will the level be at 3 P.M.? Explain.

3. **Backpacking** A group of backpackers started with 5 pounds of cheese. On the second day, they had only $2\frac{1}{2}$ pounds. On the third day, they had $1\frac{1}{4}$ pounds. If the pattern continues, how much will they have on the fourth day? Explain.

4. **Frogs** The frog population in a Japanese garden is growing at an alarming rate. The counts taken show there were 14 frogs to start, then 28, then 56, then 112. If they continue to grow at this rate, what will be the next count? Explain.

5. **Money** Noshi borrowed $315 from his parents for a snowboard. He agreed to pay them back in monthly payments. In February, he owed $265. In March, he owed $215. In April, he owed $165. What are his monthly payments? How much will he owe in August?

6. **Travel** Jessica is on a road trip. At noon, she still had 372 miles to go. At 1 P.M. she had 307 miles to go. At 2 P.M. she had 242 miles to go. At this rate, how many miles will Jessica have left to go at 5 P.M.? Explain.

Enrichment (p. 14)   BL

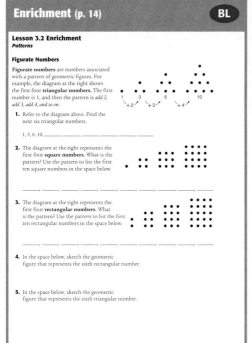

Lesson 3.2 Enrichment
Patterns

Figurate Numbers

Figurate numbers are numbers associated with a pattern of geometric figures. For example, the diagram at the right shows the first four **triangular numbers**. The first number is 1, and then the pattern is *add 2, add 3, add 4,* and so on.

1. Refer to the diagram above. Find the next six triangular numbers.

1, 3, 6, 10, _____

2. The diagram at the right represents the first four **square numbers**. What is the pattern? Use the pattern to list the first ten square numbers in the space below.

3. The diagram at the right represents the first four **rectangular numbers**. What is the pattern? Use the pattern to list the first ten rectangular numbers in the space below.

4. In the space below, sketch the geometric figure that represents the sixth rectangular number.

5. In the space below, sketch the geometric figure that represents the sixth triangular number.

Lesson Quick Quiz (p. 15)   AL   OL   BL

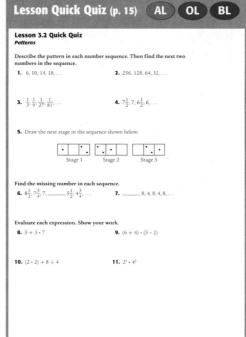

Lesson 3.2 Quick Quiz
Patterns

Describe the pattern in each number sequence. Then find the next two numbers in the sequence.

1. 6, 10, 14, 18, ...
2. 256, 128, 64, 32, ...
3. $\frac{1}{3}, \frac{1}{9}, \frac{1}{27}, \frac{1}{81}, ...$
4. $7\frac{1}{2}, 7, 6\frac{1}{2}, 6, ...$

5. Draw the next stage in the sequence shown below.

Stage 1   Stage 2   Stage 3

Find the missing number in each sequence.

6. $8\frac{1}{2}, 7\frac{3}{4}, 7, $ _____, $5\frac{1}{2}, 4\frac{3}{4}, ...$
7. _____, 8, 4, 8, 4, 8, ...

Evaluate each expression. Show your work.

8. $5 + 3 \cdot 7$
9. $(6 + 4) \cdot (5 - 2)$
10. $(2 \cdot 2) + 8 \div 4$
11. $2^3 \cdot 4^2$

Lesson Masters 1–3 (pp. 16–18)

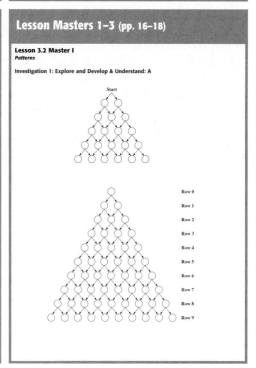

Lesson 3.2 Master I
Patterns

Investigation 1: Explore and Develop & Understand: A

Start

Row 0
Row 1
Row 2
Row 3
Row 4
Row 5
Row 6
Row 7
Row 8
Row 9

Additional Lesson Resources

Teacher Tech Tools
- TeacherWorks
- ExamView Assessment Suite
- Classroom Presentation Toolkit
- Advance Tracker

Student Tech Tools
- StudentWorks Plus
- Math Online › eGlossary •
  Concepts in Motion

Other Print Products
- Investigation Notebook and Reflection Journal
- Quick Review Math Handbook

Introduce

Patterns Introduce the investigation by discussing patterns students see in the room, such as the layout of the wall bricks or floor tiles and patterns they might see outside in nature. Lead into the Explore, in which students determine paths that will help them construct Pascal's triangle.

Explore

Suggested Grouping: Pairs

▶ **Prepare** It is useful to have a transparency of Lesson 3.2 Master 1 as you help students understand the diagram. A copy of the master for each student can help them record their results.

Discuss how to use the diagram with students and make sure they understand that all paths start at the word "Start" and can only follow the directions indicated by the arrows. Point out that there is more than one path to many letters in the diagram.

▶ **Play** Ask students to work in pairs to answer the questions in the Explore. These questions guide students to find the total number of paths to each letter in the diagram and ultimately to construct Pascal's triangle.

▶ **Report** Have students think of their own notations to describe paths through the diagram. Have the class vote on a style they like best and use that throughout the lesson. As students finish constructing Pascal's triangle, bring them together for a brief discussion about the results they found and the connections among the different numbers of paths.

▶ **Score** Give students credit for doing the Explore activity.

LESSON 3.2

Patterns

Materials

- toothpicks (optional)
- counters (optional)

① 3; Start → A → C → G;
Start → A → D → G;
Start → B → D → G.

② Start → A → C → F → K;
Start → A → C → G → K;
Start → A → D → G → K;
Start → B → D → G → K.

Patterns are everywhere. You can see patterns in wallpaper, fabric, buildings, flowers, and insects. You can hear patterns in music and song lyrics and even in the sound of a person's voice. You can follow patterns to catch a bus or a train or to locate a store with a particular address.

Patterns are an important part of mathematics. You use them every time you read a number, perform a mathematical operation, interpret a graph, or identify a shape. In this lesson, you will search for, describe, and extend many types of patterns.

Explore

In this diagram, you can begin at "Start." Trace a path down the diagram, following the arrows, to any of the letters.

How many paths are there from Start to A? Describe each path.
1; Start → A

How many paths are there from Start to D? Describe each path.
2; Start → A → D, Start → B → D

How many paths are there from Start to G? Describe each path.
See ①.

There are four paths from Start to K. Describe all four. See ②.

Copy the diagram. Add another row of circles following the pattern of arrows and letters. How many paths are there from Start to S? Describe them. See ③ in margin.

On a new copy of the diagram, replace each letter with the number of paths from Start to that letter. For example, replace A with 1 and K with 4. See ④ in margin.

The triangle of numbers you just created is quite famous. You will learn more about the triangle and the patterns it contains in Investigation 1.

Additional Answers

③

5; Start → A → D → H → M → S,
Start → B → D → H → M → S,
Start → B → E → H → M → S,
Start → B → E → I → M → S,
Start → B → E → I → N → S

Additional Answers for Explore ④ is on p. 195A

Vocabulary

sequence

term

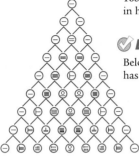

The number triangle is shown as it appears in *Precious Mirror of the Four Elements*, written by Chinese mathematician Chu Shih-Chieh in 1303.

The number triangle that you created in Explore has fascinated mathematicians for centuries because of the many patterns it contains. Chinese and Islamic mathematicians worked with the triangle as early as 1100 A.D. Blaise Pascal, a French mathematician who studied it in 1653, called it the *arithmetic triangle*. It is now known as *Pascal's triangle* in his honor.

✓ Develop & Understand: A

Below is a copy of the diagram you made in Explore. The word "Start" has been replaced by the number 1, and the rows have been labeled.

					1						Row 0
				1		1					Row 1
			1		2		1				Row 2
		1		3		3		1			Row 3
	1		4		6		4		1		Row 4
1		5		10		10		5		1	Row 5

There are many patterns in this triangle. For example, each row reads the same forward as it does backward.

1. Describe as many patterns in the triangle as you can.   See margin.

2. To add more rows to the triangle, you could count paths as you did in Explore. But that might take a lot of time. Instead, use some of the patterns you found in Exercise 1 to extend the triangle to Row 7. You may not be able to figure out all the numbers, but fill in as many as you can.   See the answer to Exercise 4, which shows the triangle completed to Row 9.

3. The first and last numbers in Row 4 are 1. Each of the other numbers is the sum of the numbers above it to the left and right. The rule works for all rows.

3. One way to add new rows to the triangle is to consider how each number is related to the two numbers just above it to the left and right. Look at the numbers in Rows 3 and 4. Describe a rule for finding the numbers in Row 4 from those in Row 3. Does your rule work for other rows of the triangle as well?

4. Use your rule from Exercise 3 to complete the triangle to Row 9. See margin.

Reaching All Learners

BL Beyond Level Provide each student with one or two copies of Lesson 3.2 Master 2, Pascal's Triangle to Row 15, or have them create four copies of the triangle through Row 15. Ask them to find visual patterns in the triangle by shading the following sets of numbers. Answers for the first three are given on page 195A.

1. Shade all even numbers.
2. Shade all odd numbers.
3. Shade all multiples of 5.
4. Find your own visual pattern.

Additional Answers for Reaching All Learners are on page 195A.

On Your Own Exercises
Pages 136–142
Exercises 1–8, 36–40

Pascal's Triangle In this investigation, students examine some of the patterns in Pascal's triangle. They identify visual and numeric patterns and use them to extend the triangle beyond the fifth row. Discuss the history of Pascal's triangle. Tell students that they will discover some of the patterns in the triangle in the next exercise set. You may want to review the term *symmetric* before starting the exercise set to help students describe some patterns more effectively.

✓ Develop & Understand: A

Suggested Grouping: Pairs

▶ **Exercises 1 and 2** Students list patterns they see and then use their patterns to extend Pascal's triangle to Row 7. Since students extend only patterns that they see, they may not be able to determine each number in the triangle. You may want to distribute Lesson 3.2 Master 1 (if you have not already done so).

▶ **Exercise 3** Teachers can tell students, "If you look at the circle with 4, for example, the only two paths that lead to 4 are from 3 and 1. Therefore it makes sense to add 3 and 1 to get the total number of paths to 4."

▶ **Exercise 4** Students should be able to extend Pascal's triangle to any row past Row 9 completely.

Wrap-Up Ask students to describe some patterns they found in Exercise 1. Discuss Exercises 3 and 4 to make sure all students know at least one way to extend the triangle.

Troubleshooting Watch for students who have difficulty seeing the patterns from one row in Pascal's triangle to the next. Have them focus on interpreting the numbers in each row as the numbers of paths to that spot.

Additional Answers for Develop & Understand: A Exercises 1 and 4 are on page 195A.

Pascal's triangle has many interesting patterns in it. You have probably worked with other patterns in the form of puzzles like the following.

> Fill in the blanks.
>
> **Puzzle A:** 2, 5, 8, 11, __, __, __
>
> **Puzzle B:** 16, 8, 4, 2, __, __, __
>
> **Puzzle C:** 3, 2, 3, 2, __, __, __
>
> **Puzzle D:** ★, ✳, ★, ✳, __, __, __

To solve these puzzles, you need to find a pattern in the part of the list given and use it to figure out the next few items. Ordered lists like these are called **sequences**. Each item in a sequence is called a **term**. When patterns consist of shapes that build from one to the next, we sometimes refer to each term as a *stage*.

Think & Discuss

Here is Puzzle A. Describe a rule you can follow to get from one term to the next.

$$2, 5, 8, 11, \_\_, \_\_, \_\_ \quad \text{Add 3.}$$

According to your rule, what are the next three terms? 14, 17, 20

Now look at Puzzle B. Describe the pattern you see. See ①.

$$16, 8, 4, 2, \_\_, \_\_, \_\_$$

According to the pattern you described, what are the next three terms? $1, \frac{1}{2}, \frac{1}{4}$

What pattern do you see in Puzzle C: 3, 2, 3, 2, __, __, __?
The combination 3, 2 is repeated.
According to the pattern, what are the next three terms? 3, 2, 3

Sequences do not always involve numbers. Look at Puzzle D, for example.

$$★, ✳, ★, ✳, \_\_, \_\_, \_\_$$

Describe the pattern, and give the next three terms. The combination ★, ✳ is repeated. The next three terms are ★, ✳, ★.

In Puzzles A and B, each term is found by applying a rule to the term before it. In Puzzles C and D, the terms or stages follow a repeating pattern. In the following exercises, you will explore more sequences of both types.

① Each number is half of the preceding number.

✓ *Develop & Understand: B*

5. The sequences in Parts a–e follow a repeating pattern. Give the next three terms or stages of each sequence.

a.

b. 3, 6, 9, 3, 6, 9, 3, 6, ...   9, 3, 6

c.

d. 7, 1, 1, 7, 1, 1, 7, 1, 1, ...   7, 1, 1

e. $\frac{1}{2}, \frac{2}{3}, \frac{1}{2}, \frac{2}{3}, \frac{1}{2}, \frac{2}{3}, \cdots$ $\frac{1}{2}, \frac{2}{3}, \frac{1}{2}$

6. In Parts a–e, each term or stage in the sequence is found by applying a rule to the one before it, the *preceding* term or stage. Give the next three terms or stages of each sequence.

a. 3, 6, 9, 12, ...   15, 18, 21

b.

 See margin.

c. 100, 98.5, 97, ...   95.5, 94, 92.5

d. 3, 5, 8, 12, ...   17, 23, 30

e. $\frac{1}{2}, \frac{1}{3}, \frac{1}{4}, \frac{1}{5}, \cdots$ $\frac{1}{6}, \frac{1}{7}, \frac{1}{8}$

Additional Answer
6b.

  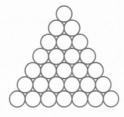

Teacher Tips Partners are very important for Exercise 7, since each works on a different geometric pattern that can be described by the same number sequence.

▶ **Exercise 7** If you have students construct the patterns in Exercise 7, each pair will need 30 toothpicks and 30 counters. Encourage students to quickly sketch each stage after they construct it. Students should recognize that the two different geometric patterns can be described by the same rule and sequence of numbers.

▶ **Exercise 8** Have students describe the pattern visually, numerically, or in both ways. A numerical description tells how the value of the decimal is changing, such as each number is $\frac{1}{10}$ of the preceding value. Making this connection emphasizes the meaning of the decimal point or fraction bar and develops a stronger sense of number. Students often describe patterns with decimals and fractions visually by describing how to move the decimal point or how to change the denominator. In this problem, students might say that the pattern is to add another 0 between 1 and the decimal point. Such rules are correct, but you may want to encourage students to find an arithmetic connection and state the rule numerically.

▶ **Exercise 9** If students do not understand what is meant by the 30th term, it may be helpful for you to write the term number under each term in the sequence. If students are having trouble predicting the 100th term, you may want to first ask them to find a single block of symbols that is repeated in this sequence. They should see that this block of five symbols is repeated:

$$\triangle, \triangle, \triangle, \Omega, \Omega$$

Then ask them how they could use this block to determine what the 20th term or 35th term would be, as a way of leading up to the 100th term.

7d. Possible answer: The number sequences are the same even though the patterns they came from look different. In both cases, you add 3 to get the next stage.

8a. Each term is 7 more than the preceding term; 33, 40, 47.

8b. Each term is 9 more than the preceding term; 36, 45, 54.

8c. Each term is double the preceding term; 500, 2,000, 4,000.

8d. Possible descriptions: Each term is $\frac{1}{10}$ the preceding term. *Or,* from one term to the next, the decimal point moves one place to the left. Missing terms: 0.01, 0.0001, 0.000001.

8e. Add 2, then 3, then 2, then 3, and so on; 21, 24, 26.

9a. $\triangle, \triangle, \triangle, \Omega, \Omega, \triangle$

Math Link
The symbols in Exercise 9 are letters of the Greek alphabet. $\triangle$ is the letter *delta,* and Ω is the letter *omega.* Greek letters are used frequently in physics and advanced mathematics.

7. Below are two sequences, one made with toothpicks and the other with counters. You and your partner should each choose a different sequence. Do Parts a–c on your own using your sequence.

Sequence A

Sequence B

a. Make or draw the next three stages of your sequence.   See margin.

b. How many toothpicks or counters will be in the tenth stage? Check by making or drawing the tenth stage.
30 toothpicks, 30 counters

c. Give a number sequence that describes the number of toothpicks or counters in each stage of your pattern.   See below.

d. Compare your answers to Parts a–c with those of your partner. What is the same about your answers? What is different?

8. Describe the pattern in each number sequence. Use the pattern to fill in the missing terms.

a. 5, 12, 19, 26, __, __, __

b. 0, 9, 18, 27, __, __, __

c. 125, 250, __, 1,000, __, __, 8,000

d. 1, 0.1, __, 0.001, __, 0.00001, __

e. 4, 6, 9, 11, 14, 16, 19, __, __, __

9. Consider this sequence of symbols.

$$\triangle, \triangle, \triangle, \Omega, \Omega, \triangle, \triangle, \triangle, \Omega, \Omega, \triangle, \triangle, \triangle, \Omega, \Omega, \dots$$

a. If this repeating pattern continues, what are the next six terms?

b. What is the 30th term? Ω

c. How could you find the 100th term without drawing 100 symbols? What is the 100th term?   The pattern repeats the five symbols $\triangle, \triangle, \triangle, \Omega, \Omega$ over and over. In 100 terms, this group of symbols is repeated 20 times, so the hundredth term is Ω.

7c. Sequence A: 3, 6, 9, 12, ... Sequence B: 3, 6, 9, 12, ...

Additional Answer
7a. Sequence A

Sequence B

10b. Possible answer:
To find a term,
add the two terms
immediately
preceding it.

1. Each number in
Pascal's triangle is
the number of
paths from the
topmost 1
(corresponding to
Start) to the
corresponding
position in the
triangle.

2. To get to any
letter, you must
go through one of
the letters above
it, so the number
of paths to a letter
is the sum of the
numbers of paths
to the two letters
just above it.

10. The sequence below is known as the *Fibonacci sequence* after the mathematician who studied it. The Fibonacci sequence is interesting because it appears often in both natural and manufactured things.

$$1, 1, 2, 3, 5, 8, 13, \ldots$$

a. Study the sequence carefully to see whether you can discover the pattern. Give the next three terms of the sequence. **21, 34, 55**

b. Write instructions for continuing the Fibonacci sequence.

Share & Summarize

1. The diagram from Explore on page 120 is repeated below. How is Pascal's triangle related to the number of paths from Start to each letter in this diagram?

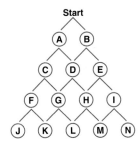

2. You discovered that each number in Pascal's triangle is the sum of the two numbers just above it. Explain what this means in terms of the number of paths to a particular letter in the diagram.

3. Describe some strategies you use when searching for a pattern in a sequence. **See margin.**

Lesson 3.2 Patterns **125**

Additional Answer
Share & Summarize

3. Possible answer: Look to see if the pattern involves a repetition. If you do not see a repeating pattern, look for an operation (e.g., adding the same thing, doubling) you can apply to each term to get the next. If not, look for more complicated patterns. For example, in the sequence 9, 10, 8, 9, 7, 8, 6, ..., the operations applied to the terms alternate, add 1, subtract 2, add 1, subtract 2, and so on.

▶ **Exercise 10** Students are introduced to the Fibonacci sequence in this exercise. Some students may have difficulty describing this sequence numerically because it requires them to look at two preceding terms instead of only one. Depending on student interest, you may want to provide some examples of Fibonacci numbers in nature.

Share & Summarize

These exercises help students connect the patterns they found in Pascal's triangle in the exercises on page 121 and the original paths they found in Explore. A discussion of **Exercise 2** should bring out this connection.

In **Exercise 3**, students review strategies they used in previous exercises in finding patterns. Students often think about sequences and patterns recursively from one term to the next, and the strategies they describe will probably reflect this. Patterns that cannot be described recursively, such as the one in Exercise 9 on page 124, may cause students difficulty. As you discuss the different strategies used, be sure to ask about the patterns in Exercises 9 and 10 on pages 124 and 125. These patterns are specifically aimed at having students think about other ways to look at patterns and sequences. Students will become more proficient at determining non-recursive rules with more practice. They will look at patterns and rules later in this and subsequent chapters.

Troubleshooting Encourage students having trouble determining and describing patterns to use the techniques presented in this investigation, such as looking for an operation that is used to get from one term to the next or looking for repeating patterns within a sequence. They will come back to patterns and rules in later chapters and can perfect these skills at that time.

Order of Operations This investigation introduces students to one of the most widely used rules of mathematics: the order of operations. Discuss the notion of a *convention* by pointing out some conventions that students follow in their own lives, such as eating three meals a day or wearing casual clothes to school. Point out that everyday conventions can differ by region or country. They are not unchangeable like the physical law, "When you drop an object, it falls to the ground." People can agree to change a convention and do something different.

Use this discussion to lead into the idea of mathematical conventions. Before students open their books, give them the expression $5 + 3 \cdot 7$ and ask them how many different ways they can interpret it. They should realize that evaluating the expression in different ways leads to different answers. Without conventions, the value of the expression is ambiguous. Introduce the order of operations as a convention that makes all expressions unambiguous. Discuss the order of operations and how to use the order to evaluate expressions. Then discuss the Example on page 127. If students are familiar with powers, you may want to include them now in the order of operations.

Math Link

Point out that evaluating an expression is not the same as solving an equation.

Investigation 2 Order of Operations

Vocabulary

order of operations

A *convention* is a rule people have agreed to follow because it is helpful or convenient for everyone to do the same thing. The rules, "When you drive, keep to the right" and "In the grocery store, wait in line to pay for your selections," are two conventions.

Reading across the page from left to right is a convention that English-speaking people have adopted. When you see the words "dog bites child," you know to read "dog" then "bites" then "child" and not "child bites dog." Not all languages follow this convention. For example, Hebrew is read across the page from right to left, and Japanese is read down the page from left to right.

To do mathematics, you need to know how to read mathematical expressions. For example, how would you read this expression?

$$5 + 3 \cdot 7$$

There are several possibilities.

- *Left to right:* Add 5 and 3 to get 8 and then multiply by 7. The result is 56.
- *Right to left:* Multiply 7 and 3 to get 21 and then add 5. The result is 26.
- *Multiply and then add:* Multiply 3 and 7 to get 21 and then add 5. The result is 26.

Math Link

Evaluating a mathematical expression means finding its value.

To communicate in the language of mathematics, people follow a convention for reading and evaluating expressions. The convention, called the **order of operations**, says that expressions should be evaluated in this order.

- Evaluate expressions inside parentheses.
- Simplify exponents.
- Do multiplications and divisions from left to right.
- Do additions and subtractions from left to right.

To evaluate $5 + 3 \cdot 7$, you multiply first and then add.

$$5 + 3 \cdot 7 = 5 + 21 = 26$$

If you want to indicate that the addition should be done first, you would use parentheses.

$$(5 + 3) \cdot 7 = 8 \cdot 7 = 56$$

Example

These calculations follow the order of operations.

$$15 - 3 \times 4 = 15 - 12 = 3$$

$$1 + 4 \cdot (2 + 3) = 1 + 4 \cdot 5 = 1 + 20 = 21$$

$$3 + 6 \div 2 - 1 = 3 + 3 - 1 = 6 - 1 = 5$$

Another convention in mathematics involves the symbols used to represent multiplication. You are familiar with the $\times$ symbol. An asterisk or a small dot between two numbers also means to multiply. So, each of the following expressions means "three times four."

$$3 \times 4 \qquad 3 \cdot 4 \qquad 3 * 4$$

✅ Develop & Understand: A

In Exercises 1–4, use the order of operations to decide which of the expressions are equal.

1. $(8 \cdot 4 + 6)$ $(8 \cdot 4) + 6$ $8 \times (4 + 6)$

2. $(2 + 8 \cdot 4 + 6)$ $(2 + 8) \times (4 + 6)$ $(2 + (8 \cdot 4) + 6)$

3. $(10 - 4) \times 2$ $(10 - (4 * 2))$ $(10 - 4 * 2)$

4. $(24 \div 6 * 2)$ $(24 \div 6) \times 2$ $24 \div (6 \cdot 2)$

5. Create a mathematical expression with at least three operations. Calculate the result. Then write your expression on a separate sheet of paper. Trade expressions with your partner. Evaluate your partner's expression, and have your partner check your result.
Answers will vary.

6. Most modern calculators follow the order of operations.

   a. Use your calculator to compute $2 + 3 \times 4$. What is the result? Did your calculator follow the order of operations?

   b. Use your calculator to compute $1 + 4 \times 2 + 3$. What is the result? Did your calculator follow the order of operations? 12; Students' scientific calculators should follow the order of operations.

As a rule, the small dot will be used to indicate multiplication in this course.

6a. 14; Students' scientific calculators should follow the order of operations.

 Assessment

Even though multiplication and division are written in the same step of the order of operations, many students confuse this and think it means to do multiplication first and then do division next. In Exercise 4, students making this error will likely select $24 \div 6 \cdot 2$ and $24 \div (6 \cdot 2)$ as having equal values. This error also occurs with addition and subtraction. Students may think that they should do all addition first and then do all subtraction. If you find students doing this, use Exercise 4 to review the sequence in the order of operations.

Example

You may want to present each expression in the Example and challenge students to evaluate them before you go over the Example. As you work through these three examples in detail, write the steps vertically on the board or overhead so that students can see the stages more clearly. You can have students compare their original answers to those in the Example and discuss any mistakes.

Troubleshooting Point out that many errors occur when students try to evaluate too quickly and do not think about the order of operations. To help students who make this mistake, have students circle the operation they are going to do first, then rewrite the problem. If there are still more operations in the problem, they should repeat the process.

✅ Develop & Understand: A

Suggested Grouping: Individuals

▶ **Exercises 1–4** Point out that students will compare three expressions with similar numbers and operations but with different uses of parentheses. As students work, ask them to explain their reasoning.

▶ **Exercise 5** Have students get in pairs for this exercise so they can exchange expressions.

▶ **Exercise 6** Most calculators follow the order of operations. In this exercise, students should discover whether their calculators do or do not. If their calculators do follow the order of operations, you may want to ask students how they would calculate $(2 + 3) * 5$. If the calculator does not have parentheses keys, students should recognize that they need to enter $2 + 3$ ☐=☐, followed by ☐×☐ 5 ☐=☐.

Wrap-Up Ask volunteers to write their expressions from Exercise 5 on the board along with the evaluated results. Discuss the evaluations or have students use calculators to check their results.

Teacher Tips In this exercise set, students look at how a calculator that does not use the order of operations gives a different answer from the actual answer.

✅ Develop & Understand: B

Suggested Grouping: Individuals

▶ **Exercises 8 and 9** Watch for students who do not realize that the calculator used by the treasurer does not follow the order of operations. Remind them that the answer should be reasonable.

Wrap-Up Have some students share their explanations for Exercises 8 and 9. Some students may not perform precise calculations to solve the problem, instead using number-sense reasoning or estimation.

✅ Develop & Understand: B

A middle school student council is holding a fundraiser for a local charity. Teachers and students are donating paperback and hard cover books to sell. The student council will sell books according to the following rule.

Charge $2 for each paperback book and $3 for each hard cover book.

7. The student council collected 410 paperbacks and 180 hard cover books. If the student council sells all of the donated books, how much will it collect from the book sale? **$1,360**

8. The student council treasurer uses a calculator to determine the fundraiser expenses. The calculator *does not* use the order of operations. Instead, the calculator evaluates the operations in the order they are entered.

   To figure out the book sale total, the treasurer enters the expression below. Will the result be correct, too little, or too much? Explain.

   $$410 \cdot 2 + 180 \cdot 3$$

8. Too much; if the calculations are done left to right, the result is $3,000.

9. Suppose the treasurer enters the calculation below instead. Will the result be correct, too little, or too much? Explain. **Too much; if the calculations are done left to right, the result is $148,140.**

   $$2 \cdot 410 + 3 \cdot 180$$

On the Spot *Assessment*

Watch for students who do not make the correct entries in their calculators. Students tend to believe that if they get an answer from an electronic device, it must be the correct answer. Point out that they should try to estimate the answer first.

A fraction bar is often used to indicate division. For example, the expressions below both mean "divide 10 by 2" or "10 divided by 2."

$$10 \div 2 \qquad \frac{10}{2}$$

Sometimes a fraction bar is used in more complicated expressions.

$$\frac{2+3}{4+4}$$

In expressions such as this, the bar not only means "divide," it also acts as a grouping symbol, grouping the numbers and operations above the bar and grouping the numbers and operations below the bar. It is as if the expressions above and below the bar are inside parentheses.

The expression $\frac{2+3}{4+4}$ means "Add 2 + 3. Next, add 4 + 4. Then divide the results." So, this expression equals $\frac{5}{8}$, or 0.625.

This more complete order of operations includes the fraction bar.
- Evaluate expressions inside parentheses and above and below fraction bars.
- Simplify exponents.
- Do multiplications and divisions from left to right.
- Do additions and subtractions from left to right.

✅ Develop & Understand: C

Find the value of each expression.

10. $\frac{2+2}{1+1}$ 2

11. $2 + \frac{2}{1+1}$ 3

12. Your calculator does not have a fraction bar to serve as a grouping symbol. So, you have to be careful when entering expressions like $\frac{2+2}{1+1}$.

12a. The calculator does the $\frac{2}{1}$ division first, so you get 2 + 2 + 1, or 5.

    a. What result does your calculator give if you enter 2 + 2/1 + 1 or 2 + 2 ÷ 1 + 1? Can you explain why you get that result?

    b. What should you enter to evaluate $\frac{2+2}{1+1}$?   (2 + 2)/(1 + 1)

Share & Summarize

Why is it important to learn mathematical conventions such as the order of operations? Possible answer: So that everyone who evaluates the same expression will get the same result, and so that people can communicate mathematical information with one another and know that everyone is interpreting it in the same way.

Lesson 3.2 Patterns   **129**

Reaching All Learners

OL **On Level** Note that many students can apply order of operations properly when they are specifically doing an order of operations lesson, but they may not think about it in other situations. For this reason, order of operations should be revisited on a regular basis.

Teacher Tips Remind students that a fraction bar can be considered to represent division. Next, point out how fraction bars can be used to indicate grouping in the same way that parentheses do. Discuss how to incorporate fraction bars into the order of operations.

✅ Develop & Understand: C

Suggested Grouping: Individuals

▶ **Exercises 10 and 11** You may want to discuss how these exercises are different from each other. If students feel out of practice with fractions, you might assure them that they will review fractions and decimals in more detail in Chapter 4.

Share & Summarize

This exercise can be used to summarize the order of operations and its importance in making expressions unique. Be sure the points in the sample answer are discussed in class. You might also ask:

What would happen if some people used the rule "multiply first and then add" and other people used the rule "add first then multiply"? Possible answer: People would get different results even though they were evaluating the same expression.

Imagine that when the order of operations was established, people had agreed to add and subtract before multiplying and dividing. Would this be all right? As long as everyone agreed, it would be fine.

Troubleshooting If students are confused about how to apply the order of operations, have them do additional practice problems. A mnemonic device such as "Please, My Dear Aunt Sally" (parentheses, multiplication and division, addition and subtraction), or with exponents "Please Excuse My Dear Aunt Sally," might be helpful for some students.

Order of Operations with Exponents
Discuss the order of operations rules shown in the box on page 130. Stress that evaluating the parts of an expression that involve exponents should come before doing multiplication, division, addition, and subtraction. Then go directly to the Think & Discuss.

Think & Discuss

When you discuss how to evaluate the two expressions, point out that the numbers that occur in the expressions are exactly the same. Go through the order of operations rules, in order, for each expression. Ask questions as you work on the first expression.

- Are there parentheses or fractions? No

- Are there exponents, and if so, where?
  Yes, in 11 squared

- What is 11 squared? 121

- What multiplication do you need to do next? 2 times 121

- What is the product? 242

Develop & Understand: A

Suggested Grouping: Pairs

▶ **Exercise 1** Watch how students evaluate $(3 + 5)^2$. Some may square 5 and add the result to 3 to get 28. Remind them that the expression in parentheses must be evaluated first.

▶ **Exercise 2** Again check that students evaluate the expression in parentheses first. Some students may try to evaluate $(5 \cdot 3)^2$ by first squaring 3 and then multiplying by 5.

▶ **Exercise 3** Students may be a bit unsure how to handle $(5 \cdot x)^2$ since this is the first time a variable is used. In this case, a variable is used to show a generalization. The term *variable* is formally defined on p. 144.

Investigation **3** **Order of Operations with Exponents**

Squaring is an operation, just like addition, subtraction, division, and multiplication. In Investigation 2, you learned about *order of operations*, a rule that specifies the order in which the operations in an expression should be performed. Below, the rule has been extended to include squares and other exponents.

Order of Operations
- Evaluate expressions inside parentheses and above and below fraction bars.
- Evaluate all exponents, including squares.
- Do multiplications and divisions from left to right.
- Do additions and subtractions from left to right.

Think & Discuss

Evaluate each expression.

$$\underset{242}{2 \cdot 11^2} \qquad \underset{484}{(2 \cdot 11)^2}$$

Explain how the order in which you performed the operations is different for the two expressions. See ①.

Develop & Understand: A

① For the first expression, I squared 11 and multiplied the result by 2. For the second expression, I multiplied 2 by 11 and squared the result.

1. Does $(3 + 5)^2$ have the same value as $3^2 + 5^2$? Explain. No; Possible explanation: $(3 + 5)^2 = 64$, but $3^2 + 5^2 = 34$.

2. Does $(5 \cdot 3)^2$ have the same value as $5^2 \cdot 3^2$? Explain. Yes; Possible explanation: Both expressions are equal to 225.

3. Is $(5 \cdot x)^2$ equivalent to $5^2 \cdot x^2$? Explain. Yes; Possible explanation: $(5 \cdot x)^2 = 5 \cdot x \cdot 5 \cdot x = 5 \cdot 5 \cdot x \cdot x = 5^2 \cdot x^2$.

On the Spot Assessment

For the second expression in the Think & Discuss, students should realize that the multiplication 2 · 11 should be done first because it is in parentheses. After multiplying 2 and 11 to get 22, square the result. Students should note that the results for the two sets of calculations are quite different.

4. This equation is *not* true.

$$2 \cdot 5 + 2^2 = 11^2 - 23$$

    a. Show that the equation above is not true by finding the value of each side. $2 \cdot 5 + 2^2 = 14$, $11^2 - 23 = 98$

    b. Challenge Place one pair of parentheses in the equation to make it true. Show that your equation is true by finding the value of each side. $2 \cdot (5 + 2)^2 = 11^2 - 23$; $2 \cdot (5 + 2)^2 = 2 \cdot 49 = 98$ and $11^2 - 23 = 98$

5. Consider the four digits of the year in which you were born. Write at least three expressions using these four digits and any combination of parentheses, squaring, addition, subtraction, multiplication, and division. Use each digit only once in an expression. Evaluate each expression.   See below.

 Develop & Understand: B

In Exercises 6–13, you will compare squaring to doubling.

You and a partner will play the game *Square to a Million.* The object of the game is to get a number as close to 1 million as possible, without going over, using only the operation of squaring.

Here are the rules for the game.

- Player 1 enters a number greater than 1 into a calculator.
- Starting with Player 2, players take turns choosing to continue or to end the game. In either case, the player states his or her decision and then presses $\boxed{x^2}$ $\boxed{\text{ENTER}}$.

    If the player chooses to continue the game and the result is greater than or equal to 1 million, the player loses the round. If the result is less than 1 million, it is the other player's turn.

    If the player chooses to end the game and the result is greater than or equal to 1 million, the player wins. If it is less than 1 million, the player loses.

Play six games with your partner, switching roles for each round.

6. On your turn, how did you decide whether to continue or to end the game?

7. What is the greatest whole number whose square is less than 1 million?   999

5. Possible answer for 1999: $1 + 9 + 9 + 9 = 28$,
    $1 \cdot 9 \cdot 9 \cdot 9 = 729$, $9 \div 9 \div 9 \div 1 = \dfrac{1}{9}$,
    $1 \div 9 \div 9 \div 9 = 0.00137$,
    $1^2 + 9^2 + 9^2 + 9^2 = 244$

Lesson 3.2 Patterns   **131**

Math Link

The convention of using raised exponents was introduced by René Descartes, a French mathematician, philosopher, and scientist. Descartes invented the Cartesian coordinate system.

6. If the number was greater than 1,000, I ended the game because the square would be over 1 million. If it was less than 1,000, I squared it.

▶ **Exercise 4b** Point out that that there is no way to get an expression that makes sense by inserting parentheses on the right side of the equation. From Exercise 4a, we know that $11^2 - 23 = 98$. So in Exercise 4b, the object is to insert parentheses on the left side of the original equation to get an expression whose value is 98. Students can use trial and error until they find a way to do this that works.

Math Link

The carat key $\boxed{\wedge}$ on a calculator is used to raise an expression to a power.

Teacher Tips In this exercise set, students play a game that involves squaring numbers. Students must decide whether the current number being used has a square that equals or exceeds 1 million. Each pair of students should have a calculator.

Do not give any hints about winning strategies. Students will quickly wonder whether there is an easy way to ensure a win. Realizing that $1,000^2 = 1,000,000$ is the key. Before students get started, point out that the rules do not prohibit decimals.

✔ Develop & Understand: B

Suggested Grouping: Pairs

▶ **Exercise 7** Point out that since $1,000^2$ is equal to 1 million, 999 is the greatest whole number whose square will not equal or exceed 1 million.

▶ **Exercise 8** Ask students to use their result from Exercise 7 on page 131 and look for the greatest whole number whose square is less than or equal to 999. They can likewise make successive use of previous answers to answer Exercise 9 and then Exercise 10.

▶ **Exercise 11** Students should observe that if they use one or a number between 0 and 1, the game will never end.

Wrap-Up Review student answers to Exercises 12 and 13 as a class. Have them discuss the differences between squaring and doubling numbers.

Share & Summarize

You may want to have students work in pairs or groups of three on these exercises. Students can have others in their group evaluate the expressions they write for **Exercise 1**.

You will find it worthwhile to discuss the table in **Exercise 2** with the entire class. Students may base their answers in each row on only one or two numerical examples. Use the class discussion to assess where they are able to use reasoning to support their answers. For rows 1 and 2, they should be able to see that the answers in columns 2 and 3 force the answer to be "doubling" in column 4. The last three rows are more difficult to answer by using reasoning alone. If students are able to construct a graph that shows values of $2x$ and x^2, they may feel more confident of the answers for column 4.

Troubleshooting If students are still having trouble applying the order of operations rules, you might give them a few more expressions containing parentheses, fractions, and exponents to evaluate. They may need to refer back to the list on page 129.

11. The game would go on forever because you could never get to 1,000,000. If you started with 1, the result will always be 1, no matter how many times you pressed x^2. If you started with a number less than 1, the number would get smaller every time you pressed x^2, getting further away from 1 million.

8. What is the greatest whole number with which you could start, press x^2 twice, and get a number less than 1 million?   31

9. What is the greatest whole number with which you could start, press x^2 three times, and get a number less than 1 million?   5

10. What is the greatest whole number with which you could start, press x^2 four times, and get a number less than 1 million?   2

11. What would happen if you started the game with a positive number less than or equal to 1?

12. Imagine you are playing the game *Double to a Million,* in which you double the number in the calculator instead of squaring it. If you start with the given number, how many times will you have to double until you produce a number greater than or equal to 1 million?

   a. 50   15   **b.** 5   18

   c. 1   20   **d.** 0.5   21

13. For each part of Exercise 12, describe what would happen if you repeatedly squared the result instead of doubling it.   See margin.

1. Possible answer:
$4 + 2 \cdot 3^2 - (6 - 4)$; To evaluate the expression, first do the subtraction in the parentheses: $4 + 2 \cdot 3^2 - 2$. Then do the squaring: $4 + 2 \cdot 9 - 2$. Then multiply: $4 + 18 - 2$. Finally, add and subtract from left to right: $22 - 2 = 20$.

Share & Summarize

1. Write an expression that involves parentheses, squaring, and at least two other operations. Explain how to use order of operations to evaluate your expression.

2. Copy the table. Fill in the missing information. The first row has been completed for you.

Number	Double It Is the result greater than, less than, or equal to the original number?	Square It Is the result greater than, less than, or equal to the original number?	Which gives the greater result, squaring or doubling?
Between 0 and 1	greater than	less than	doubling
1	greater than	equal to	doubling
Between 1 and 2	greater than	greater than	doubling
2	greater than	greater than	results are the same
Greater than 2	greater than	greater than	squaring

Additional Answer

13a. It would take only two presses.

13b. It would take only four presses.

13c. I would never reach one million; the result will always be one.

13d. The result will get smaller and smaller, so it will never reach one million.

Investigation 4 Find the Rule

A fun way to practice recognizing patterns and finding rules is to play a game called *What's My Rule*. In this game, one player thinks of a rule about numbers. The other players try to guess the rule.

Example

Hannah, Jahmal, and Miguel were playing *What's My Rule*.

Find the Rule This investigation builds students' skills in finding non-recursive rules for patterns and using those rules to make predictions about the patterns. In particular, students will learn how to find patterns in, and write rules for, related numbers in tables. They will also play *What's My Rule*. This game models mathematical functions, in the sense that students supply inputs and are given unique outputs. From this, they try to guess the rule, or function, that fits the inputs and outputs.

Example

Use the cartoon to discuss how to play *What's My Rule*. If you like, you may have students act out the cartoon. Point out that once students think they know the rule, they should test the rule before stating it in words. Many students may be familiar with the game, and if so, you should start them working. If not, play a round or two as a class to be sure everyone understands. You might first take the role of rule-maker and have the class guess the rule. Then allow one of the students to be rule-maker.

Develop & Understand: A

Suggested Grouping: Groups of 3 or 4

▶ **Exercises 1 and 2** As students play the game, encourage them to record their guesses in a table like the ones on Lesson 3.2 Master 3 (which you might hand out) to help them more easily identify the pattern.

Teacher Tips Make sure all students get a chance to be rule-maker. Suggest to the rule-maker that he or she write the rule on a paper no one else can see. They can do any necessary calculations on this piece of paper. When students write their rules, they may write them in words or in mathematical notation. For example, they might write *multiply by 2*, or *2 × the number*.

You may want to model how to use variables to write rules so that students become familiar with writing rules in this way.

Wrap-Up Discuss the strategies students listed in Exercise 2 to find the rules.

Think & Discuss

Read the Think & Discuss activity with the class. You may want to show them how to organize the inputs and outputs in a table.

Input	Output
6	20
3	11
10	32
11	35

If you have a computer available, you might instead simulate the "rule" machine with a computer spreadsheet program. Have students compare the new table or spreadsheet to the table they used to record guesses and results in *What's My Rule.* Emphasize the similarities between the two tables. Give students sufficient time to determine the rule shown by the table. Then have volunteers share their rules.

1. Answers will vary.
2. Possible answer:
   - Come up with as many rules as you can for each new pair of numbers, and look for rules that fit more than one of the number pairs.
   - Look for a relationship in the table of guesses and results.
   - Guess the number 0. The result often tells you the number that is added in the rule.
   - Make the guesses in order (0, 1, 2, 3, and so on), and look for a pattern in the results.

Now you will have a chance to play *What's My Rule.* As you play, try to come up with some strategies for finding the rule quickly.

Develop & Understand: A

1. Play *What's My Rule* at least six times with your group. Take turns making up the rule. Do the following for each game you play.
   - Write down the name of the person who made up the rule.
   - Make a table showing the numbers the players guess and the results the rule gives for those numbers.
   - After a player correctly guesses the rule, write it down.

2. Work with your group to create a list of strategies for playing *What's My Rule.*

In the *What's My Rule* game, you try to guess a rule created by another student. Now you will play a rule-guessing game that does not require a partner.

To play, imagine a machine like the one that you used in Lesson 1. This machine has taken some *input* numbers, applied a rule to each one, and given the resulting *output* numbers. Your job is to guess the rule the machine used.

Think & Discuss

Here are the outputs one machine gave for the inputs 6, 3, 10, and 11. What rule did the machine use?   output = 3 · input + 2

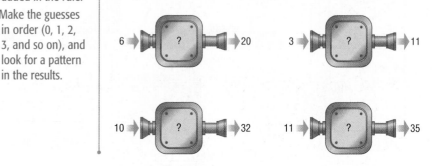

Reaching All Learners

BL   Beyond Level Have groups trade copies of one guess-and-result table. Encourage them to determine the rule from the table without looking at the rule. This exercise previews the next investigation, in which students try to create a rule directly from a table without being able to make guesses.

✓ Develop & Understand: B

Each table shows the outputs a particular machine produced for the given inputs. Find a rule the machine could have used. Check to make sure your rule works for all the inputs listed.

3.

Input	3	5	8	4	1
Output	2	4	7	3	0

output = input − 1

4.

Input	4	7	10	3	0
Output	2	3.5	5	1.5	0

output = input ÷ 2

5.

Input	10	6	3	4	0	100
Output	23	15	9	11	3	203

output = 2 · input + 3

Share & Summarize

1. In one round of the *What's My Rule* game, the first clue was "2 gives 4." Write at least two rules that fit this clue.

2. The next clue in the same game was "3 gives 9." Write at least two rules that fit this clue. Do any of the rules you wrote for the first clue work for this clue as well?

3. The third clue was "10 gives 100." Give a rule that fits all three clues. How did you find the rule?

4. Describe some strategies that you use to find a rule for an input/output table. Possible answer: I look for many rules that fit the first pair and then see which fit the other pairs as well. Or, I look for a rule that fits both the first and second pairs and then check whether it fits the rest of the table.

1. Possible answer:
   - Double the number.
   - Add 2 to the number.
   - Multiply the number by itself.

2. Possible answer:
   - Triple the number.
   - Add 6 to the number.
   - Multiply the number by itself. The last rule fits both clues.

3. Multiply the number by itself. Possible strategy: "Multiply by 2" fit the first clue, "multiply by 3" fit the second clue, and "multiply by 10" fit the third clue. In each case, multiply by the number guessed.

Develop & Understand: B

Suggested Grouping: Individuals

▶ **Exercises 3–5** This exercise set provides practice in finding rules for given inputs and outputs in table form. The rules in these exercises contain only one operation. Exercise 5 is more challenging, since the rule involves two operations.

Wrap-Up Have students share the rules they found, and have the class verify each rule. Discuss the differences among the rules for the three tables. Students may note that Exercise 3 uses subtraction only, Exercise 4 uses division only, and Exercise 5 uses both addition and multiplication.

Share & Summarize

For **Exercises 1 and 2**, encourage students to write several rules to describe each clue. Point out that one possibility is multiply a number by itself.

Exercise 4 allows students to share some strategies that they found helpful.

Troubleshooting If students are struggling with finding rules, use the strategy below. Have them practice the strategy with the tables in the exercises or other similar tables.

Add or subtract: See what value can be added to or subtracted from the first input to get the first output. Then see if that same value can be added to or subtracted from each input and to get its related output.

Multiply or divide: See what value the first input can be multiplied or divided by to get the first output. Then see if all other inputs can be multiplied or divided by that same value to get their related outputs.

Combinations: If none of the above strategies results in a rule, try using more than one operation. Some combinations students can try are to first multiply, then add or subtract another value from the product; or to first add, then multiply or divide the sum by another value. Remind students to check that the rule works for all pairs in the table.

On the Spot Assessment

Watch for students who write a rule based on only one pair of input/output values. Remind them that the rule must work for all pairs of values in the table.

Investigation 1
Pages 121–125
Practice & Apply: 1–8
Connect & Extend: 36–40

Investigation 2
Pages 126–129
Practice & Apply: 9–16
Connect & Extend: 41–45

Investigation 3
Pages 130–132
Practice & Apply: 17–31
Connect & Extend: 46–49

Investigation 4
Pages 133–135
Practice & Apply: 32–35
Connect & Extend: 50–56

Assign Anytime
Mixed Review: 57–70

▶ **Exercise 1d Extension** Ask students if the middle number would appear once or twice for other rows, like row 100 (once) or row 101 (twice). Ask them to generalize this pattern (in even-numbered rows the middle number appears once, while in odd-numbered rows it appears twice).

▶ **Exercise 7** This problem includes negative numbers as a diagnostic to help you assess students' experiences. Negative numbers are not presented formally in this text.

▶ **Exercises 9–12** Be sure students understand that they should follow the order of operations unless told to do otherwise. This applies not only to these exercises, but to all mathematics.

Practice & Apply

Real-World Link
Pascal's triangle is named for Blaise Pascal (1623–1662).

1. Here are the first few rows of Pascal's triangle.

			1				Row 0
		1		1			Row 1
	1		2		1		Row 2
1		3		3		1	Row 3

a. How many numbers are in each row shown? Row 0: 1; Row 1: 2; Row 2: 3; Row 3: 4

b. How many numbers are in Row 4? In Row 5? In Row 6? 5, 6, 7

c. If you are given a row number, how can you determine how many numbers are in that row? Add 1 to the row number.

d. In some rows, every number appears twice. Other rows have a middle number that appears only once. Will Row 10 have a middle number? Will Row 9? How do you know?

2. A certain row of Pascal's triangle has 252 as the middle number and 210 just to the right of the middle number.

   ... ? ? ? ? 252 210 ? ? ? ...

a. What is the number just to the left of the middle number? How do you know? 210; Pascal's triangle is symmetric about a line down the center.

b. What is the middle number two rows later? How do you know?

Describe the pattern in each sequence. Use the pattern to find the next three terms.

3. 3, 12, 48, 192, ___, ___, ___
   Each term is 4 times the preceding term; 768, 3,072, 12,288.

4. 0.1, 0.4, 0.7, 1.0, ___, ___, ___
   Each term is 0.3 more than the preceding term; 1.3, 1.6, 1.9.

5. 2, 5, 4, 7, 6, 9, ___, ___, ___ The terms are generated by alternately adding 3 and subtracting 1; 8, 11, 10.

6. $\triangle, \infty, \triangle, \triangle, \infty, \triangle, \triangle, \triangle, \infty,$ ___, ___, ___

7. $-5, -4, -3, -2,$ ___, ___, ___
   Each term is 1 more than the preceding term; -1, 0, 1.

8. a, c, e, g, ___, ___, ___
   The sequence is every other letter of the alphabet; i, k, m.

Evaluate each expression.

9. $3 + 3 \cdot 2 + 2$ 11

10. $(3 + 3) \cdot (2 + 2)$ 24

11. $(3 + 3) + 2 \div 2$ 7

12. $\dfrac{7 + 6 - 2 \cdot 6}{11 - 5 \cdot 2}$ 1

1d. Yes; No; Possible explanation: Even rows have an odd number of numbers, so they have a middle number. Odd rows have an even number of numbers, so they do not have a middle number.

2b. 924; The next row has 252 + 210, or 462, on each side of the middle number, and the row after that has 462 + 462, or 924, as the middle number.

6. The sequence alternates between a group of $\triangle$s and a single ∞, and each group of $\triangle$s contains one more ∞ than the preceding group; $\triangle, \triangle, \triangle.$

Tell whether each expression was evaluated correctly using the order of operations. If not, give the correct result.

13. $10 \cdot (6 - 5) + 7 = 80$
Incorrect, 17

14. $54 - 27 \div 3 = 45$
Correct

15. $(16 - 4 \cdot 2) - (14 \div 2) = 5$
Incorrect, 1

16. $100 - 33 \cdot 2 - (4 + 8) = 22$
Correct

Find the value of each expression.

17. $5 \cdot 3^2 - 2$ 43 **18.** $2 \cdot (5^2 - 10)$ 30 **19.** $3^2 - 2^2$ 5 **20.** $7 + \dfrac{6^2}{3}$ 19

21–23. See margin.

21. Does $(1 + 3)^2$ have the same value as $1^2 + 3^2$? Explain.

22. Does $(4 - 2)^2$ have the same value as $4 - 2^2$? Explain.

23. Does $(11 \cdot 7)^2$ have the same value as $11^2 \cdot 7^2$? Explain.

24. Challenge Place one pair of parentheses in the equation below to make it true. Show that it is true by computing the value of each side.

$$22 - (7 - 5)^2 \cdot 2 = 2 \cdot 3^2 - 4$$

25. Suppose you are playing *Square to a Million*. You chose the starting number 5, and your partner squared it. Now it is your turn. Should you continue or end the game? Explain. See margin.

26. Suppose you are playing *Square to a Million*. Your partner chose the starting number 1,001. Should you continue or end the game? Explain. End the game; 1,001 squared is 1,002,001, which is more than 1 million.

In Exercises 27–31, suppose you square the number. Without doing any calculations, tell whether the result will be *less than*, *greater than*, or *equal to* the original number. 27–31. See margin.

27. 0.75 **28.** $\dfrac{2}{3}$ **29.** 1 **30.** 1.5 **31.** 5

Find a rule that works for all the pairs in each input/output table. Use your rule to find the missing outputs.

32.

Input	0	1	2	5	8	12
Output	4	5	6	9	12	16

output = input + 4

33.

Input	3	24	36	12	45	60
Output	1	8	12	4	15	20

output = input ÷ 3

34.

Input	2	10	16	22	32	44
Output	0	4	7	10	15	21

Possible rules: output = (input − 2) ÷ 2, output = input ÷ 2 − 1

35.

Input	1	2	3	4	6	10
Output	9	19	29	39	59	99

output = 10 · input − 1

Lesson 3.2 Patterns **137**

▶ **Exercises 17–20** If students have mistakes in these exercises, there is a good chance that either they are not observing the correct order of operations or they are using the exponent 2 as a factor. If students did not show all steps for the calculations, ask them to do so. This will help you pinpoint the source of the problem.

▶ **Exercises 27–31** If necessary, have students check their work with a calculator using the ⌧ x^2 key.

▶ **Exercise 34** The rule involves division and subtraction. Ask students to share their strategies for finding the rule. You may want to suggest that students having difficulty finding the rule divide the inputs by 2 and then see if they can find a pattern in the results.

Additional Answers

21. No; Possible explanation: $(1 + 3)^2 = 16$ while $1^2 + 3^2 = 10$.

22. No; Possible explanation: $(4 - 2)^2 = 4$ while $4 - 2^2 = 0$.

23. Yes; Possible explanation: $(11 \cdot 7)^2$ and $11^2 - 7^2$ are both 5,929.

25. Continue the game; after my partner's turn, 25 is showing in the display. $25^2 = 625$, which is less than 1,000,000.

27. Less than the original number

28. Less than the original number

29. Equal to the original number

30. Greater than the original number

31. Greater than the original number

▶ **Exercise 36** This pattern involves sums of rows. If students are familiar with powers of two, you may want to help them describe the pattern this way: $2^{\text{row number}}$ = row sum.

▶ **Exercises 37 and 38** Have students share their strategies as part of a class discussion.

▶ **Exercise 38** One way to explain the pattern is that the last number of each row (when the first row is considered Row 1) is the row number times itself (1 × 1, 2 × 2, 3 × 3, and so on). So, 100 should be at the end of the 10th row and 121 should be at the end of the 11th row. Students can work backwards from 121 to see which number would be beneath 100.

▶ **Exercise 39** Some students may be confused by the directions in **Part a**. You may want to read over this exercise with the class before assigning it, perhaps making a transparency of the grid and having students shade in the squares for different numbers of steps in front of the whole class. For **Part b**, you may want to help students develop a table to assist them in recognizing patterns. Some students may notice that if the grid were extended forever, the number of squares for each number of steps would be 4 × number of steps.

Additional Answer

39b. Possible answer: Squares of the same color form a square (or diamond) around Square A. In the part of the grid shown, the number of squares of each color goes up and then down in a symmetric pattern: 4, 8, 12, 12, 8, 4. In each row and column, the numbers count down and then up again. The first and seventh rows and columns match, the second and sixth rows and columns match, and so on.

Connect & Extend

36b. Possible answer: The total for the first row is 1. The total for each of the other rows is twice the total for the preceding row.

37. 100; Possible explanation: Every third number goes on the top line. Since 99 is divisible by 3, part of the pattern would look like this:

```
    99
97  98  100
```

39a. See the grid, which shows the number of steps to get to each square.

36. Some patterns in Pascal's triangle appear in unexpected ways. For example, look at the pattern in the sums of the rows.

					1					Row 0 Sum = 1
				1	+	1				Row 1 Sum = 2
			1	+	2	+	1			Row 2 Sum = 4
		1	+	3	+	3	+	1		
	1	+	4	+	6	+	4	+	1	
1	+	5	+	10	+	10	+	5	+	1

a. Find the sum of each row shown above.   1, 2, 4, 8, 16, 32

b. Describe the pattern in the row sums.

37. The pattern below involves two rows of numbers. If the pattern continued, what number would be directly to the right of 98? Explain how you know.

```
    3      6      9     12     15     18
1   2   4   5   7   8   10  11  13  14  16  17
```

38. Look at this pattern of numbers. If it continued, what number would be directly below 100?   120

```
              1
           2  3  4
        5  6  7  8  9
    10 11 12 13 14 15 16
```

39. Imagine that an ant is standing in the square labeled A on the grid below. The ant can move horizontally or vertically, with each step taking it one square from where it started.

```
6 5 4 3 4 5 6
5 4 3 2 3 4 5
4 3 2 1 2 3 4
3 2 1 A 1 2 3
4 3 2 1 2 3 4
5 4 3 2 3 4 5
6 5 4 3 4 5 6
```

a. On a copy of the grid, color each square, except the center square, according to the least number of steps it takes the ant to get there. Use one color for all squares that are one step away, another color for all squares that are two steps away, and so on.

b. What shapes are formed by squares of the same color? How many squares of each color are there? What other patterns do you notice? See margin.

40a.

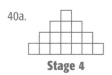

Stage 4

40c. Each number is 2 more than the preceding number.

Stage	Squares in Bottom Row
5	9
6	11

40f. The total number of squares is the stage number times itself. Stage 10 would contain 100 squares.

40. For this exercise, you may want to draw the shapes on graph paper.

a. Find the next stage in this sequence.

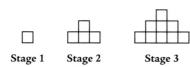

Stage 1　　**Stage 2**　　**Stage 3**

b. This table shows the number of squares in the bottom rows of stages 1 and 2. Copy and complete the table to show the number of squares in the bottom rows of the next two stages.

Stage	Squares in Bottom Row
1	1
2	3
3	5
4	7

c. Look at your table carefully. Describe the pattern of numbers in the second column. Use your pattern to extend the table to show the number of squares in the bottom rows of stages 5 and 6.

d. Predict the number of squares in the bottom row of stage 30.　59

e. Now make a table to show the *total number of squares* in each of the first five stages.

Stage	Total Number of Squares
1	1
2	4
3	9
4	16
5	25

f. Look for a pattern in your table from Part e. Use the pattern to predict the total number of squares in stage 10.

41. In Your Own Words What is a pattern? Is every sequence of numbers a pattern? Is every sequence of shapes a pattern? Explain your answers.　A pattern is a regular, repeating design or sequence of shapes or numbers. A sequence is an ordered list. In order for a sequence to be a pattern, there must be a rule to find the next term in the sequence.

Lesson 3.2　Patterns　**139**

▶ **Exercise 40** You may want to supply graph paper or copies of Chapter 3 Master 3 to students when you assign this exercise.

Have students share their strategies as part of a class discussion. Students should be able to see the rule in **Part c**. However, if they wrote a recursive rule, they may need help applying it in **Part d** because the rule requires that they know the number of squares for stage 29. Since students are not expected at this point to develop an explicit rule, you may want to either lead students to the rule or just present it to them and ask if it works: 2 × stage number − 1. Students should recognize that using this rule to find the total number of squares is much easier and faster than using a recursive rule.

▶ **Exercise 45** Many students who do not recall what *integer part* and *fractional part* mean will derive the definitions from the context of the exercise. For other students, you may want to review the definitions of these terms.

You may want to point out that many countries use a comma to separate the integer and decimal parts. In some countries, periods are used to separate thousands, millions, billions, and so on in the same way commas are used in the United States.

▶ **Exercise 47** Students may find it helpful to make a table to show what each child would receive as his or her new allowance under each option.

Additional Answers

48. 5; 5 is the only digit that can be squared to make a number that ends in 5.

49. 4 or 6; Both numbers square to give a number that ends in 6.

In Exercises 42–45, tell whether each rule is a convention or a rule we cannot change.

42. Nine times a number is equal to the difference between ten times the number and the number.   A rule we cannot change

43. A convention

43. In an expression involving only addition and multiplication and no parentheses, such as $2 \cdot 3 + 4 \cdot 5 + 6$, do the multiplication first.

44. $4 + 3 = 7$ A rule we cannot change

45. Use a decimal point to separate the integer part of a number from the fractional part.   A convention

46. This computation gives the same result whether you compute correctly, using order of operations, or whether you do the computations from left to right.

46a. Correct:
$16 - 12 - 3 =$
$4 - 3 = 1$
Left to right:
$10 \cdot 2 - 15 \div 5 =$
$20 - 15 \div 5 =$
$5 \div 5 = 1$

$$16 - 6 \cdot 2 - 15 \div 5$$

  a. Find the value of the expression both ways. Show that you get the same result.

  b. Find another computation that you should *not* evaluate from left to right but that gives the correct result if you do.   Answers will vary.

47. Marcela, Option II because 2^2 is more than $2 + 1$. Omar, Option II because 3^2 is more than $3 + 1$. Stella, Option I because $1 + 1$ is more than 1^2.

47. Marcela receives \$2 a week as an allowance. Her older brother Omar gets \$3 each week. Her younger sister Stella receives \$1 each week. All three children have asked their parents for larger allowances. Their parents have given them these choices.

- Option I: Add \$1 to your current weekly allowance.
- Option II: Square your current weekly allowance.

Which option should each child choose? Why?

48. Randall squared a number and got 390,625. Without using your calculator, find the possible ones digits of his original number. Explain.   See margin.

49. Marlene squared a number and got 15,376. Without using your calculator, find the possible ones digits of her original number. Explain.   See margin.

50. 3 or 7; Both numbers square to give a number that ends in 9.

50. Courtney squared a number and got 284,089. Without using your calculator, find the possible ones digits of her original number. Explain.

51. Add $1 + 4$. Raise the sum to the second power. Multiply this value by 5. Add 3 to the product.

51. **In Your Own Words** Explain the order you would perform the operations in the expression. $3 + 5(1 + 4)^2$.

52. Not all input/output tables involve numbers. In this table, the inputs are words and the outputs are letters.

52c. The output is the third letter in the word.

52d. Yes; a word with fewer than three letters would not have an output.

Input	Alice	Justin	Darren	Jarvis	Jimmy	Mara
Output	i	s	r	r	m	r

a. Complete the last two columns of the table.

b. What would be the output for your name?   Answers will vary.

c. Describe a rule for finding the output letter for any input word.

d. Are there input words that have no outputs? Explain your answer.

53. In this input/output table, the inputs are numbers and the outputs are letters.

Input	1	2	3	4	5	6
Output	O	T	T	F	F	S

a. What would be the outputs for the inputs 7 and 8?   S and E

b. Describe a rule for finding the output letter for any input number. The output is the first letter in the spelling of the number.

54. Camille was trying to find a relationship between the number of letters in a word and the number of different ways the letters can be arranged. She considered only words in which all the letters are different.   See margin.

Number of Letters	Example	Number of Arrangements
1	A	1 (A)
2	OF	2 (OF, FO)
3	CAT	6 (CAT, CTA, ACT, ATC, TAC, TCA)

a. Continue Camille's table, finding the number of arrangements of four different letters. You could use MATH as your example, since it has four different letters.

b. **Challenge** Predict the number of arrangements of five different letters. Explain how you found your answer.

Additional Answer

54a. There are 24 arrangements of MATH:

MATH ATHM THMA HMAT
MAHT ATMH THAM HMTA
MTHA AHTM TMHA HAMT
MTAH AHMT TMAH HATM
MHAT AMTH TAHM HTMA
MHTA AMHT TAMH HTAM

Additional Answer for Exercise 54b is on page 195B.

▶ **Exercises 52 and 53** You may want to help students get started on these in class since these rules involve relationships among letters, words, and numbers, which is a new situation for students. If students need a hint for Exercise 53, you could suggest that they write out the word names for the numbers. For users of the Spanish text, the outputs for this problem will be U, D, T, Q, C, and S. The answer to 53a would be S and O.

▶ **Exercise 54** Some students may need to review how to make an organized list. You may want to model how to derive and list all the combinations for the letters in CAT and possibly start the list for the combinations for the letters in MATH.

▶ **Exercise 54 Extension** You may want to introduce a tree diagram to help students visualize and organize the possibilities for the letters in CAT. Students will work more with tree diagrams in later courses.

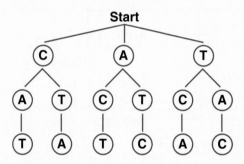

Start

You can also introduce *factorials*. Have students multiply the number of branches at each level: 3 · 2 ·1. Explain that multiplying all the numbers from 1 to some whole number can be more easily written as (number!). For example, 3! is 3 · 2 · 1. Students usually like this notation since it represents a clear pattern. You might ask students to calculate 10! on their calculators (3,628,800) and then point out that this is how many different anagrams could be made with 10 letters. Students will work more with combinations and factorials in Course 3.

Quick Check

Informal Assessment Students should be able to:

✔ create Pascal's triangle and describe patterns that aid in the creation

✔ evaluate and compare expressions using the order of operations

✔ write rules for a constructed pattern

Quick Quiz

Describe the pattern in each number sequence. Then find the next two numbers in the sequence.

1. 6, 10, 14, 18, … Add 4; 22, 26

2. 256, 128, 64, 32, … Divide by 2; 16, 8

3. $\frac{1}{3}, \frac{1}{9}, \frac{1}{27}, \frac{1}{81},$ … Multiply by $\frac{1}{3}; \frac{1}{243}, \frac{1}{729}$

4. $7\frac{1}{2}, 7, 6\frac{1}{2}, 6,$ … Subtract $\frac{1}{2}; 5\frac{1}{2}, 5$

5. Draw the next stage in the sequence shown below.

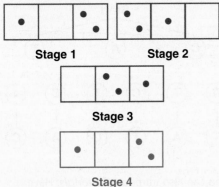

Find the missing number in each sequence.

6. $8\frac{1}{2}, 7\frac{3}{4}, 7,$ _____, $5\frac{1}{2}, 4\frac{3}{4},$ … $6\frac{1}{4}$

7. _____, 8, 4, 8, 4, 8, … 4

Evaluate each expression. Show your work.

8. $5 + 3 \cdot 7$ 26

9. $(6 + 4) \cdot (5 - 2)$ 30

10. $(2 \cdot 2) + 8 \div 4$ 6

11. $2^3 \cdot 4^2$ 128

55. In Your Own Words How is looking for a rule similar to looking for a pattern?

56. Preview In Lesson 3.3, you will be working with *variables*. You will substitute values for variables to find the value of an expression. For example, when $x = 0$, the expression $5x + 1$ equals $5(0) + 1$, or 1.

Determine the value of the expression $5x + 1$ for each value of x.

a. $x = 1$ 6 **b.** $x = 2$ 11

c. $x = 10$ 51 **d.** $x = 25$ 126

Geometry Tell what fraction of each figure is shaded.

57. $\frac{4}{15}$ **58.** 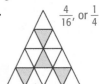 $\frac{4}{16}$, or $\frac{1}{4}$

Mixed Review

55. Answers will vary. Possible answer: Both involve finding the common link. To look for a rule, you find what operation is performed on each input to get each output. To look for a pattern, you find the change from one stage or term to the next stage or term.

67. Possible answer: $\frac{3}{5}, \frac{12}{20}, \frac{60}{100}$

Replace each ○ with <, >, or = to make a true sentence.

59. $\frac{7}{8} \bigcirc \frac{7}{10}$ **60.** $\frac{2}{7} \bigcirc \frac{2}{9}$

61. $\frac{9}{15} \bigcirc \frac{9}{12}$ **62.** $\frac{6}{5} \bigcirc 1.2$

63. $0.37 \bigcirc \frac{7}{20}$ **64.** $\frac{13}{18} \bigcirc \frac{7}{10}$

65. $0.0375 \bigcirc \frac{3}{80}$ **66.** $\frac{23}{24} \bigcirc \frac{24}{25}$

67. Write three fractions that are equivalent to $\frac{6}{10}$.

Write each multiplication expression in exponential form. Then write each product as a whole number.

68. $3 \cdot 3$ 3^2; 9 **69.** $4 \cdot 4 \cdot 4$ 4^3; 64 **70.** $2 \cdot 2 \cdot 2 \cdot 2 \cdot 2$ 2^5; 32

Variables and Rules

Overview

The concept of a *variable* is one of the fundamental concepts of algebra, and well before students begin their study of algebra, the concept has many uses. Although the term can have various meanings, it is introduced in this lesson with its most basic meaning, namely that of a quantity that changes.

Students also learn how variables can be used to describe and study patterns. They write rules for patterns in symbolic form, and they learn how to present convincing arguments that their rules will always work. They also learn to recognize equivalent rules—that is, different rules that generate the same pattern. These understandings will prove useful in problem solving and in later courses involving mathematical proof.

Advance Preparation

You may want to provide students with paper bags to facilitate class discussion.

	Summary	Materials	On Your Own Exercises (pp. 166–173)	Assessment Opportunities
Investigation 1 (p. 144) *Pacing: 2 days*	Students translate between expressions and bags-and-blocks situations.	Chapter 3 Master 1, 3 paper bags, blocks	Practice & Apply: 1–6 Connect & Extend: 25–27 Mixed Review: 35–44	• On the Spot (p. 145) • Share & Summarize (p. 148) • Troubleshooting (p. 148)
Investigation 2 (p. 149) *Pacing: 1 day*	Students identify variables in sequences and use symbols to write rules that describe how the variables are related to the term number.		Practice & Apply: 7–11 Connect & Extend: 28, 29 Mixed Review: 35–44	• Share & Summarize (p. 152)
Investigation 3 (p. 152) *Pacing: 1 day*	Students use diagrams and reasoning to explain how they know whether two rules are equivalent.		Practice & Apply: 12–14 Connect & Extend: 30 Mixed Review: 35–44	• Share & Summarize (p. 156) • Troubleshooting (pp. 152, 156)
Inquiry Investigation 4 (p. 157) *Pacing: 1 day*	Students discover and write rules that relate three variables in a real-life situation.		Mixed Review: 35–44	
Investigation 5 (p. 160) *Pacing: 1 day*	Students use symbols to describe rules for games of *What's My Rule?*		Practice & Apply: 15–19 Connect & Extend: 31–32 Mixed Review: 35–44	• Share & Summarize (p. 162) • Troubleshooting (p. 162)
Investigation 6 (p. 163) *Pacing: 1 day*	Students analyze situations and use letters to write rules describing how the variables in the situations are related.		Practice & Apply: 20–24 Connect & Extend: 33, 34 Mixed Review: 35–44	• Share & Summarize (p. 165) • Troubleshooting (p. 165)

Leveled Lesson Resources

Also on
TeacherWorks™
Lesson 3.3

CRM *Available in:* **Chapter 3 Resource Masters**

Study Guide and Intervention (p. 19) — AL

Lesson 3.3 Study Guide and Intervention
Variables and Rules

Example 1 Algebra Write a rule for each table using the given letters to represent the variable.

a.
w	1	2	3	4
g	3	6	9	12

b.
x	2	4	6	8
z	5	9	13	17

$g = 3 \cdot 1 = 3$ $z = 2 \cdot 2 + 1 = 5$
$g = 3 \cdot 2 = 6$ $z = 2 \cdot 4 + 1 = 9$
$g = 3 \cdot 3 = 9$ $z = 2 \cdot 6 + 1 = 13$
$g = 3 \cdot 4 = 12$ $z = 2 \cdot 8 + 1 = 17$
$g = 3w$ $z = 2x + 1$

Example 2 Algebra Evaluate each expression when $a = 2$ and $c = 5$.

a. $4a + 5$ b. $3(c + 2)$

$4a + 5 = 4 \cdot 2 + 5$ Replace a with 2. $3(c + 2) = 3(5 + 2)$ Replace c with 5.
     $= 8 + 5$ Multiply. $= 3 \cdot 7$ Evaluate ( ).
     $= 13$ Add. $= 21$ Multiply.

Exercises

Write a rule for each table using the given letters to represent the variable.

1.
m	3	5	7	9
n	8	10	12	14

2.
p	1	2	3	4
q	6	10	14	18

Evaluate each expression when $n = 3$, $p = 4$, and $q = 5$.

3. $5n - 3$ 4. $1 + 2p$ 5. $3(q + 1)$

6. $p + p + p + 2$ 7. $9 - n$ 8. $p \div 2$

Translate each phrase into an algebraic expression.

9. eight inches taller than Mycala's height

10. twelve more than four times a number

Skills Practice (p. 20) — AL OL

Lesson 3.3 Skills Practice
Variables and Rules

Write a rule for each table using the given letters to represent the variable.

1.
u	3	5	7	9
v	21	35	49	63

2.
w	1	2	3	4
y	5	8	11	14

3.
m	2	4	6	8
n	18	16	14	12

4.
p	3	4	5	6
q	9	11	13	15

5.
x	1	2	3	4
y	2	6	10	14

6.
t	2	4	6	8
r	4	16	36	64

Evaluate each expression when $w = 2$, $x = 3$, and $y = 4$.

7. $3w + 1$ 8. $5x$ 9. $20 - 2y$

10. $(x + 15) \div 2$ 11. $8 - 2w$ 12. $y \div 4$

13. $2y - 1$ 14. $1 + 2x$ 15. $4(w + 3)$

16. $x + x + 5$ 17. $9 + 3y$ 18. $5w \div 2$

19. $3(w + 1)$ 20. $18 - 2y$ 21. $x + (2x - 1)$

22. $4x - x$ 23. $w(w - 1)$ 24. y^2

Translate each phrase into an algebraic expression.

25. three times a number minus eight

26. the product of seventy and a number

Problem-Solving Practice (p. 21) — AL OL

Lesson 3.3 Problem-Solving Practice
Variables and Rules

Solve.

1. **Drought** The farmers in Ravin's town complained about the lack of rain during the growing season. Ravin did some research to find out how much rain typically falls during the growing season compared to the amount of rain during this growing season. She learned that it had rained 7 inches less than normal this season. Write an expression that represents the amount of rain this growing season.

2. **Repairs** Deidre's car needs to be repaired. The cost of the repair is going to be $40 per hour for labor and an additional $120 for parts. Write an expression that would represent the cost of getting the car repaired if a mechanic works on it for h hours.

3. **Retail sales** Amara works in his parents' clothing shop after school. Sometimes, he prices new merchandise to sell. He uses the table below to determine what the retail price of a piece of clothing should be. Based on the prices in the table, write an expression that Amara could use to calculate the retail price (R) given the cost price (C).

Cost	Retail
14	21
18	27
24	36
30	45
100	150

4. **Temperature** The formula that is used to convert Fahrenheit (F) to Celsius (C) is $C = (F - 32) \div 1.8$. Convert 77°F to degrees Celsius.

Nutrition For Exercises 5–7, use the information in the table below.

Mr. Jacobs is teaching a unit on nutrition. The class has learned that each gram of fat contains 9 calories, each gram of carbohydrates has 4 calories, and each gram of protein has 4 calories. He has his students research the nutritional facts of sandwiches served in the school lunch room.

Nutrition Facts	Fat (g)	Total Calories
Hamburger	29	580
Grilled chicken sandwich	7	360
Tuna wrap	32	440
Meatball sub	24	560
Veggie wrap	8	390
Turkey breast wrap	6	190

5. Write an expression to determine the grams of protein and carbohydrates of a grilled chicken sandwich.

6. How many calories of fat are in a meatball sub?

7. What percent of the total calories in a veggie wrap come from fat?

Enrichment (p. 22) — BL

Lesson 3.3 Enrichment
Variables and Rules

Hypatia

Hypatia, pronounced *hi PAY sha*, was the first woman to be mentioned in the history of mathematics. Born about A.D. 370, Hypatia lived in Alexandria and served as a professor at the famous Library of Alexandria. She wrote important commentaries on the works of the mathematician Appollonius and the scientist Ptolemy. She also excelled in the fields of astronomy, medicine, and philosophy.

Egypt was in great political turmoil during Hypatia's lifetime. Because of her influence among scholars of the day, she became the target of criticism from those who equated science with paganism. In A.D. 415, she was murdered by an angry mob. Soon after her death, the library was destroyed and the Dark Ages began. The serious study of mathematics was limited for the next 500 years.

One of the things Hypatia studied was the relationship between number patterns and geometry. Investigate these geometric patterns.

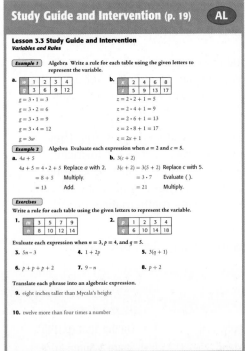

Triangular Numbers

Square Numbers

1. Draw the fifth and sixth figures in the pattern of triangular numbers. Then write the first six triangular numbers.

2. Draw the fifth and sixth figures in the patterns of square numbers. Then write the first six square numbers.

3. Draw the first four pentagonal and hexagonal numbers.

4. Use counters or drawings to determine if there is a number that is both square and triangular.

Lesson Quick Quiz (p. 23) — AL OL BL

Lesson 3.3 Quick Quiz
Variables and Rules

1. Consider the toothpick sequence of U-shapes whose first three stages are shown below.

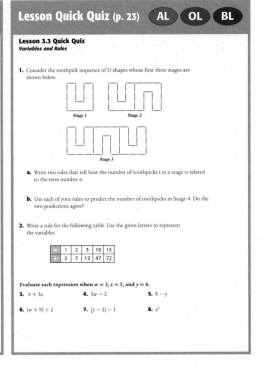

Stage 1   Stage 2

Stage 3

a. Write two rules that tell how the number of toothpicks t in a stage is related to the term number n.

b. Use each of your rules to predict the number of toothpicks in Stage 4. Do the two predictions agree?

2. Write a rule for the following table. Use the given letters to represent the variables.

m	1	2	3	10	15
k	2	7	12	47	72

Evaluate each expression when $w = 3$, $x = 5$, and $y = 6$.

3. $4 + 3x$ 4. $5w - 2$ 5. $8 - y$

6. $(w + 9) \div 2$ 7. $(y - 2) - 1$ 8. x^2

Additional Lesson Resources

Teacher Tech Tools
- TeacherWorks
- ExamView Assessment Suite
- Classroom Presentation Toolkit
- Advance Tracker

Student Tech Tools
- StudentWorks Plus
- Math Online > eGlossary •
- Concepts in Motion

Other Print Products
- Investigation Notebook and Reflection Journal
- Quick Review Math Handbook

Variables and Rules

Vocabulary

variable

① Start with the number in the first bag, add the number in the second bag, plus the number in the third bag, plus 2. Or, since the number in each of the bags is the same, multiply this number by 3 and add 2.

Every day, people are confronted with problems that they have to solve. Some of these situations involve such quantities as the amount of spice to add to a recipe, the cost of electricity, and interest rates. In some situations, it helps to have a way to record information without using many words. For example, both expressions in the box present the same idea.

To find the circumference of a circle, multiply the radius length by 2π.

$$C = 2\pi r$$

While the statement on the top may be easier to read and understand at first, the statement on the bottom has several advantages. It is shorter and easier to write. It shows clearly how the quantities, radius and circumference, are related. It allows you to try different radius values and compute the corresponding circumferences.

In this lesson, you will see that by using a few simple rules, you can write powerful algebraic expressions and equations for a variety of situations.

Think & Discuss

Shaunda, Kate, and Simon are holding bags of blocks. Isabel has just two blocks.

Suppose you know how many blocks are in each bag. How can you figure out how many blocks there are altogether? See ①.

Introduce

Use Expressions Tell students that they will be learning how to use expressions to describe situations. Read the opening paragraphs with students. You may wish to review the definition of an expression, a mathematical phrase that uses numbers and/or variables and operations.

Students may find that some material introduced in the first lesson is a review. If your students are familiar with writing expressions and using flowcharts, you may want to move quickly through these investigations.

Think & Discuss

One way to introduce the bags-and-blocks scenario is to have students participate in setting up the problem. This should help them remember the model. Have four students come to the front of the room and form a line facing the class. Have 3 bags and 30 blocks placed on a desk. Hand 2 blocks to the student on the right. Give each of the other three students an empty bag to hold. Students now mirror the arrangement in the illustration in the text.

Show the class that the bags are empty. Then ask the class:

- How many blocks do these four students have altogether? 2

Now place 5 blocks in each of the bags. Ask students:

- What is the total number of blocks now? 17

Encourage students to predict the total number of blocks by asking:

- What would be the total number of blocks if there were 8 blocks in each bag? 26

Suppose there were 100 blocks in each bag.

- What is the total number of blocks now? 302

- When you know how many blocks are in each bag, how do you find the total number of blocks? Multiply the number of blocks in each bag by 3, and then add 2.

Teacher Tips Students should understand that since the number of blocks in each bag can change, or vary, the quantity can be represented by a variable. They should be aware that it is customary to use letters to represent a number, such as the varying quantity of blocks in each bag. On the board, draw a picture of 3 bags and 2 blocks and write the letter *n* on each of the bags. Ask students questions such as:

• How can we add to find the total number of blocks? Add *n* three times, then add 2. $n + n + n + 2$

• What is another way to find the total number of blocks? Multiply 3 by *n*, then add 2.

• How can you write the expression using multiplication? $3n + 2$

Continue the demonstration by having students find how many blocks are in each bag when there are 29 blocks altogether. Leave 29 blocks on the desk. Tell students that one student will have 2 blocks and the remaining blocks will be divided evenly among the bags. Encourage students to provide ways to find the number of blocks that will be in each bag. Some students may suggest that you give 2 blocks to the student on the right and divide the remaining 27 blocks equally among the three students.

Investigation (1)

On Your Own Exercises
Pages 166–173
Exercises 1–6, 25–27

Variables and Expressions In this investigation, students use a bags-and-blocks model to write and evaluate algebraic expressions. Continue to use the 3-bags-and-2-blocks model from the introduction. Ask students:

• What rule could you use to find the total number of blocks if you know how many blocks are in each bag? $3n + 2$

Write the rule on the board. Tell students that this rule is an example of an algebraic expression, since it contains variables and operations.

If you know the number of blocks in each bag, it is possible to express the total number of blocks. For example, if there are 20 blocks in each bag, you can add as shown below.

$$20 + 20 + 20 + 2 = 62$$

Or, you can multiply and add.

$$3 \cdot 20 + 2 = 62$$

What if you do not know the number in each bag? First, notice that, in this situation, the number of bags and the number of loose blocks do not change, but the number of blocks in each bag can change. **Variables** represent unknown values and quantities that can change, or vary.

In algebra, letters are often used to represent variables. For example, you can let the letter *n* stand for the number of blocks in each bag.

Now you can find the total number of blocks as you did before, by adding.

$$n + n + n + 2$$

Or, you can multiply and add.

$$3 \cdot n + 2$$

In algebra, the multiplication symbol between a number and a variable is usually not shown. So, $3 \cdot n + 2$ can be written $3n + 2$.

Math Link
Multiplication can be shown in several ways.
$3 \times n$ $3(n)$
$3 \cdot n$ $3 * n$

Investigation (1) **Variables and Expressions**

Vocabulary

algebraic expression

In the bags-and-blocks situation above, you can think of $3n + 2$ as a rule for finding the total number of blocks when you know the number of blocks in each bag. Substitute the number in each bag for *n*. For example, for 100 blocks in each bag, the total number of blocks is as follows.

$$3n + 2 = 3 \cdot 100 + 2 = 302$$

Rules written with numbers and symbols, such as $n + n + n + 2$ and $3n + 2$, are called **algebraic expressions**.

As you progress in your study of mathematics, you will often work with algebraic expressions. Using bags and blocks is a good way to start thinking about expressions. Imagining the variable as a bag into which you can put any number of blocks can help you see how the value of an expression changes as the value of the variable changes.

Develop & Understand: A

In these exercises, you will continue to explore the situation in which there are three bags, each containing the same number of blocks plus two extra blocks.

1. Copy and complete the table.

Number of Blocks in Each Bag, n	0	1	2	3	4	5
Total Number of Blocks, $3n + 2$	2	5	8	11	14	17

2. If $n = 7$, what is the value of $3n + 2$?   23

3. If $n = 25$, what is the value of $3n + 2$?   77

4. If there are 50 blocks in each bag, how many blocks are there altogether?   152

5. If there are 20 blocks altogether, how many blocks are in each bag?   6

6. Copy and complete the table.

n	10	5	40	25	100	7	30	22	42	1,047
$3n + 2$	32	17	122	77	302	23	92	68	128	3,143

7. Compare the tables in Exercises 1 and 6. Which table do you think was more difficult to complete? Why?   Possible answer: The tables use the same rule, but the table in Exercise 1 has inputs that are in order and only missing outputs. The table in Exercise 6 was more difficult because the numbers are not in order. We had to find some inputs as well as outputs.

 Assessment

Watch for students who add 3 and the number representing n when evaluating the expression $3n + 2$. Review the meaning of the notation in which a number followed by a variable indicates multiplication. You might wish to have students use bags and blocks to find the value of the expression $3n + 4$ when n has these values:

$n = 5$ $3 \cdot 5 + 4 = 19$
$n = 2$ $3 \cdot 2 + 4 = 10$
$n = 6$ $3 \cdot 6 + 4 = 22$

Develop & Understand: A

Suggested Grouping: Pairs

▶ **Exercises 1–7** These exercises provides students practice evaluating the expression $3n + 2$ for different values of n. Students also informally practice backtracking, or working backward, to find the value of n when given the total number of blocks.

▶ **Exercise 1** Circulate around the room to make sure students know how to complete the table. You may want to complete the table as a whole-class activity, having volunteers complete individual table entries on the board. You may wish to use Chapter 3 Master 1, Input/Output Tables, as a means of having students record their answers in an orderly fashion.

▶ **Exercise 5** The reasoning processes students use to solve this exercise are essential for solving equations. Here students work from the total number of blocks to the number of blocks in each bag. Many students may have previous experiences in solving this kind of problem. In the later investigations, students will learn the technique of backtracking more formally. At this stage, students may employ these strategies:

• Work with the blocks and bags. Students may model the problem by counting out 20 blocks, and then putting 2 blocks aside. The remaining 18 blocks must be divided equally among the 3 bags. Students can find the number of blocks in each bag by either physically counting and putting the blocks in each bag or by simplifying $\frac{18}{3}$.

• Use guess-check-and-improve.

Encourage students to explain their solving strategies.

Analyze the Table Describe these tables as "Input-Output" tables and show students how to substitute values of n into the output expression to find the output values.

▶ **Exercise 8** Students may use one of the following strategies to solve this exercise.

• Use bags and blocks to model the problem. They may need to put blocks in the bags to discover that the situation is impossible with whole units. As students reconstruct the problem in these concrete or visual terms, they should find it easier to understand the question.

• Use number sense. They may subtract the 2 blocks first and then realize that 16 is not divisible by 3.

• Use logical reasoning. They may recognize that since 3 · 6 = 18, there must be fewer than 6 blocks in each bag. If there were 5 blocks in each bag, there would only be 17 blocks in all. If each bag held fewer than 5 blocks, the total number of blocks would be less than 17. Therefore, it is not possible to have exactly 18 blocks in all.

Wrap-Up Students should understand how the expression $3n + 2$ relates to the bags-and-blocks model before doing the next exercise set. Check their work on Exercises 8–10 before proceeding.

✅ Develop & Understand: B

Suggested Grouping: Pairs

▶ **Exercises 11–14** Point out that the focus is on relating expressions with bags-and-blocks situations. Students are asked to explain what the numbers and variables in expressions represent for a given situation. They are introduced to the use of letters other than *n* as variables, and they write simple expressions for models. They also explore the meaning of subtracting a constant.

8. No; Possible explanation: If 5 blocks are in each bag, there are a total of 17 blocks. If 6 blocks are in each bag, there are a total of 20 blocks. The number that gives a total of 18 must be between 5 and 6. Since the number of blocks must be a whole number, it is not possible to have a total of 18 blocks.

9. If the bags contained different numbers of blocks, the number of blocks in a bag could not be represented by a single variable, *n*.

10a. Five bags, each containing the same number of blocks, plus 6 extra blocks

10b. The 5*n* represents the 5 bags with *n* blocks each, and the 6 represents the 6 extra blocks.

---

8. Could the total number of blocks in this situation be 18? Explain.

9. To represent the number of blocks in three bags plus two extra blocks with the expression $3n + 2$, you need to assume that all the bags contain the same number of blocks. Why?

10. The expression $3n + 2$ describes the total number of blocks in three bags, each with the same number of blocks plus two extra blocks.

   a. Describe a bags-and-blocks situation that can be represented by the expression $5n + 6$.

   b. Explain how the expression fits your situation.

You have explored the number of blocks in three bags plus two extra blocks. Now you will investigate some other bags-and-blocks situations.

✅ Develop & Understand: B

11. Here are five bags and four extra blocks.

   a. What is the total number of blocks if each bag contains three blocks? If each bag contains ten blocks?   **19, 54**

   b. Using *n* to represent the number of blocks in each bag, write an algebraic expression for the total number of blocks.   **5*n* + 4**

   c. Find the value of your expression for $n = 3$ and $n = 10$. Do you get the same answers you found in Part a?   **19, 54, yes**

12. Now suppose you have four bags, each with the same number of blocks plus two extra blocks.

   a. Draw a picture of this situation.

   b. Write an expression for the total number of blocks.   **4*n* + 2**

13. Write an expression to represent seven bags, each with the same number of blocks plus five extra blocks.   **7*n* + 5**

14. Write an expression to represent ten bags, each with the same number of blocks plus one extra block.   **10*n* + 1**

15. Any letter can be used to stand for the number of blocks in a bag. Match each expression below with a drawing.

$$2c + 4 \qquad 4m + 2 \qquad 4y + 5 \qquad 2f + 5$$

a.  $4m + 2$

b.  $2f + 5$

c. $2c + 4$

d. $4y + 5$

16. Rebecca wrote the expression $3b + 1$ to describe the total number of blocks represented in this picture.

16a. The number of blocks in each bag

a. What does the variable b stand for in Rebecca's expression?

b. What does the 3 represent? The number of bags

c. What does the 1 represent? The number of loose blocks

d. Complete the table for Rebecca's expression.

b	1	2	3	10	4	25	100
$3b + 1$	4	7	10	31	13	76	301

▶ **Exercise 15** Point out that this exercise gives students their first exposure in this course to using a letter other than *n* as a variable when they match expressions to drawings. You may wish to discuss various ways to approach the exercise. Some students may look at a picture and then find the expression that describes it. Others may choose an expression and look for a drawing that matches that expression. Some students may count the bags in a picture and find expressions that have the correct corresponding coefficient. Then they can count the number of blocks to narrow their choices and choose the correct expression. Others may approach it from the constant perspective, counting the blocks first, narrowing their search, and then looking at the bags to find the correct expression.

▶ **Exercise 16** In this exercise, students define different components of a given expression. They also think forward and backward to complete a table. Students will get more formal practice with working backward in the subsequent investigations. Be sure students understand what each variable and each equation represents.

► **Exercise 17** In this exercise, students are exposed to the limitations of models. Students may question how the situation in **Part b** can occur if there is only 1 block in each bag. Since there would only be 5 blocks in all, they may wonder how it would be possible to have 7 fewer blocks. In this case, the model does not make sense. Point out that the bags-and-blocks model is merely one way to help us think about a situation. Remind them that this model, like most models, sometimes has limitations.

► **Exercise 17c** Students are given the total number of blocks and take away bags of blocks.

► **Exercises 18a and 18b** Students are given the number of blocks for Len. They can then use that information to find how many blocks Blake and Ramon have. Then they add the number of blocks each boy has to find the total number of blocks. Some students may focus on finding the number of blocks held by Blake and Ramon and forget to add Patrick's blocks when finding the total quantity.

► **Exercise 18d** This exercise is more challenging. Students may reason that if there are 29 blocks altogether, they can take away two blocks for Patrick. That leaves 24 blocks to be divided among the other three boys. Since $\frac{24}{3} = 8$, Len has 8 blocks, Blake has one fewer block, or 7 blocks, and Ramon has one more, or nine blocks.

► **Exercises 18e–g** In this exercise, students must realize that the expressions with c and s name the same total quantity. However, since c and s stand for the number of blocks for different people, the written expressions are not the same. Students may choose to verify their answers using different values for Len's blocks.

Share & Summarize

These three exercises ask students to make their own bag-and-block drawing and write an expression describing it. Ask students to share their pictures with partners, and have the partners write expressions that represent the pictures.

17c. Possible answer: the number of blocks left after 3 bags' worth are removed from a group of 14 blocks

18d. The total, 26, is 3 times the number Len has, plus 2. So, 3 times the number Len has must be 24. Len must have 8 blocks. So, Blake has 7, Ramon has 9, and Patrick has 2.

18e. Blake: $l − 1$; Len: l; Ramon: $l + 1$; Patrick: 2; total: $(l − 1) + l + (l + 1) + 2$, or $3l + 2$

18f. Blake: b; Len: $b + 1$; Ramon: $(b + 1) + 1$; Patrick: 2; total: $b + b + b + 5$, or $3b + 5$

18g. $3l + 2$ tells the total number of blocks in terms of the number Len has. $3b + 5$ tells the total number of blocks in terms of the number Blake has. They are different because the variables l and b stand for different values.

17. Brandi thought of the following situation.

"Imagine that the total number of blocks is two blocks less than three bags' worth. This is hard to draw, but I just described it easily in words. I can write it algebraically as $3n − 2$."

   a. Describe a situation that $4n − 1$ could represent.
   Possible answer: 1 block less than 4 bags' worth
   b. Describe a situation that $5x − 7$ could represent.
   Possible answer: 7 blocks less than 5 bags' worth
   c. Describe a situation that $14 − 3p$ could represent.

18. Len has one more block than Blake. Ramon has one more block than Len. Patrick has two blocks.

   a. If Len has six blocks, how many blocks does each boy have? How many do they have altogether?
   Blake: 5; Len: 6; Ramon: 7; Patrick: 2; total: 20
   b. If Len has 15 blocks, how many blocks does each boy have? How many do they have altogether?
   Blake: 14; Len: 15; Ramon: 16; Patrick: 2; total: 47
   c. If you know how many blocks Len has, how can you determine the total number of blocks without figuring out how many blocks each of the other boys has?
   The total is 3 times the number Len has, plus 2.
   d. If the boys have 26 blocks altogether, how many does each boy have? Explain how you arrived at your answer.

   e. Let l stand for the number of blocks that Len has. Write an expression for the number each boy has. Then write an expression for the total number of blocks.

   f. Let b stand for the number of blocks that Blake has. Write an expression for the number each boy has. Then write an expression for the total number of blocks.

   g. Your expressions for Parts e and f both tell how many blocks the group has. Yet, the expressions are different. Explain why.

Share & Summarize   Answers will vary.

1. Make a bags-and-blocks drawing.

2. Write an expression that describes your drawing.

3. Explain how you know your expression matches your drawing.

Troubleshooting

If students are still having difficulty understanding expressions, they may need more experience modeling bags-and-blocks situations. As students experiment with different quantities, have them record their answers in a table. Start by giving each group of students 2 bags and 3 extra blocks. Have them find the total number of blocks if each bag has 7 blocks. Continue with different numbers of blocks per bag. They can use their tables to help them find a rule and write an expression.

Investigation ② Variables, Sequences, and Rules

In Lesson 3.2, you explored sequences involving numbers, symbols, and shapes. Consider the following sequence.

| Stage 1 | Stage 2 | Stage 3 | Stage 4 |

The toothpick sequence can be represented by the following numerical sequence.

$$4, 7, 10, 13, 16, \dots$$

Making a table is a good way to study the relationship between two quantities. This table shows the stage number and the number of toothpicks for the first five stages.

Stage Number	1	2	3	4	5
Number of Toothpicks	4	7	10	13	16

You can sometimes write a rule to show how two variables are related. Here is one possible rule relating the number of toothpicks to the stage number.

$$\text{number of toothpicks} = 3 \cdot \text{stage number} + 1$$

In the following exercises, you will make tables and find rules for variables in the toothpick sequence.

Math Link

An *arithmetic* sequence is created by adding each term by the same number to get the next term. Here are two arithmetic sequences.

1, 2, 3, 4, 5, …
4, 7, 10, 13, 16, …

✔ Develop & Understand: A

1. In Parts a–d, make a table showing the values of the given variable for the first four stages of the toothpick sequence shown above. The first table has been started for you.

   a. number of squares

Stage Number	1	2	3	4
Number of Squares	1	2	3	4

   b. number of vertical toothpicks   See margin.

   c. number of horizontal toothpicks   See margin.

   d. number of rectangles (Hint: In each stage, count the squares, the rectangles made from two squares, the rectangles made from three squares, and so on.)

Stage Number	1	2	3	4
Number of Rectangles	1	3	6	10

Lesson 3.3 Variables and Rules   **149**

Additional Answer

1b.

Stage Number	1	2	3	4
Number of Vertical Toothpicks	2	3	4	5

1c.

Stage Number	1	2	3	4
Number of Horizontal Toothpicks	2	4	6	8

Variables, Sequences, and Rules This investigation introduces letters to represent variables and describe relationships between variable quantities. Using letters for variables to express general relationships and patterns is one of the basic differences between algebra and ordinary arithmetic. Some students may already have used letters as a shorthand for numbers, but for other students the idea may be new. Before students begin the exercises, copy the table from the top of page 149 onto the board. Ask students if they can find a rule that relates the stage number to the number of toothpicks used to make that stage of the sequence. Ask: If you are told a stage number, how can you figure out the number of toothpicks in that stage? Encourage students to describe their rules in ordinary language. Lead them to see that one rule that seems to work is the rule presented in the paragraph just above the exercise set.

Math Link
What is a pattern in the sequence?
Add 3 for the second sequence.

Teacher Tips This exercise set provides opportunities for students to discover rules that describe how the values of two variables are related. Students test their rules and consider whether the rules will always work. Working in pairs allows students to discuss their thinking as they arrive at their answers.

✔ Develop & Understand: A

Suggested Grouping: Pairs

▶ **Exercise 1** Point out that the top row of each table should contain the stage numbers one through four.

► Exercise 2 Point out that students will write rules to describe how the variables in their tables are related. The rules can be stated using words alone or with a combination of words and symbols. The rule in **Part d** may be difficult for many students. You might suggest that students consider how the values of the second variable change from one stage to the next. Discovering the pattern +1, +2, +3, may lead students to state the rule as follows

number of rectangles = sum of the whole numbers from one through the stage number

Some students may also notice that this sum can be found by calculating

stage number $\cdot \dfrac{\text{stage number} + 1}{2}$

► Exercise 3 This exercise asks students to check their rules from Exercise 2 by using them to predict the value of Term 5. Remind students that checking a rule in this way lets them see whether the rule works once again for the next stage in the sequence. It does not prove for all instances that the rule will *always* work. If students have come up with a rule that works for the first four stages but not for stage 5, they will need to revise their rule.

► Exercise 4 This exercise has students explain why their first three rules for Exercise 3 will always work. This assumes that they have indeed arrived at rules that work for the first five stages for each situation. Putting their reasoning into words may be difficult, but being able to do so is the main way for students to be confident that their thinking is correct. It is also important in communicating their thinking to others.

Wrap-Up After students have finished work on the problems, you may want the whole class to discuss and compare results.

- -

Math Link

Remind students about the order of operations rules.

- -

2. For each table from Exercise 1, try to find a relationship between the stage number and the other variable. Then write a rule to describe the relationship.

  a. number of squares = Stage number

  b. number of vertical toothpicks =

  c. number of horizontal toothpicks =

  d. Challenge number of rectangles =

2b. Possible rules:
1 + stage number,
2 + (stage number − 1)

2c. Possible rules:
2 · stage number,
stage number + stage number

3. To check your rules, you can test them for a particular stage number. Although this will not tell you for certain that a rule is correct, it is a good way to find mistakes. For each part of Exercise 2, use your rule to predict the value of the variable for stage 5. Then draw stage 5. Check your predictions. See margin.

4. Explain how you know that the rules that you wrote in Parts a–c of Exercise 2 will work for every stage. See margin.

2d. Possible rules:
stage number $\cdot \dfrac{\text{stage number} + 1}{2}$,
$\dfrac{\text{stage number} \cdot (\text{stage number} + 1)}{2}$

As you have seen, letters are often used to represent variables. For example, consider this rule.

number of toothpicks = 3 · stage number + 1

If you use the letter n to represent the stage number and the letter t to represent the number of toothpicks, you can write the rule as shown.

$$t = 3 \cdot n + 1$$

- - - - - - - - - - - - - - - - - - -

Math Link

Remember to follow the order of operations when simplifying expressions.

· Evaluate expressions inside parentheses and above and below fraction bars.

· Do multiplications and divisions from left to right.

· Do additions and subtractions from left to right.

- - - - - - - - - - - - - - - - - - -

This rule is shorter than the original rule.

When a number is multiplied by a variable, the multiplication symbol is often not shown. So, you can write the rule above in an even shorter form.

$$t = 3n + 1$$

You can use any letter to represent a variable, as long as you say what the letter represents. For example, you could let w represent the stage number and z represent the number of toothpicks and write the rule as $z = 3w + 1$.

A single rule can usually be written in many ways. Here are six ways to write the rule for the number of toothpicks in a stage.

$t = n \cdot 3 + 1$ $t = (n * 3) + 1$ $t = 1 + 3n$

$t = 1 + (3 \cdot n)$ $t = 1 + n \cdot 3$ $t = 3 \times n + 1$

None of the rules above need parentheses because the order of operations states to multiply before you add. However, it is not incorrect to include them. Since some rules do need parentheses, be careful when you write your rules.

Additional Answer

3.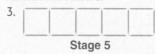

Stage 5

  a. Number of squares = stage number = 5
  b. Number of vertical toothpicks = stage number + 1 = 5 + 1 = 6
  c. Number of horizontal toothpicks = 2 · stage number = 2 · 5 = 10
  d. Number of rectangles = stage number $\cdot \dfrac{\text{stage number} + 1}{2} = 5 \cdot \dfrac{6}{2} = 15$

Additional Answer for Develop & Understand: A Exercise 4 is on page 195B.

Develop & Understand: B

5. Rewrite your rules from Exercise 2 in a shorter form by using *n* for the stage number and a different letter for the other variable. Make sure to state what variable each letter represents.   See margin.

6. Consider this toothpick sequence.

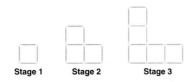

Stage 1   Stage 2   Stage 3

6a. Possible variables: number of toothpicks, number of squares, number of outer toothpicks, number of inner toothpicks

6b–c. See margin.

7–8. See margin.

a. Choose a variable other than the stage number.

b. Create a table showing the value of your variable for each stage.

Stage Number, *n*	1	2	3	4
Your Variable				

c. Try to find a rule that connects the stage number and your variable. Write the rule as simply as you can, using *n* to represent the stage number and a different letter to represent your variable.

7. Complete Parts a–c of Exercise 6 for this sequence of toothpicks.

Stage 1   Stage 2   Stage 3   Stage 4

8. Complete Parts a–c of Exercise 6 for this sequence of dots.

Stage 1   Stage 2   Stage 3   Stage 4

Math Link
Remember when a number is multiplied by a quantity in parentheses, the multiplication symbol is often left out. So, $2 \cdot n$ can be written as $2n$, and $3 \cdot (n + 1)$ can be written $3(n + 1)$.

9. Consider the rule $t = 4 \cdot n + 2$, where *n* represents the stage number and *t* represents the number of toothpicks in a sequence.

a. Write the first four numbers in the sequence.   6, 10, 14, 18

b. Draw a toothpick sequence that fits the rule.   See margin.

10. Consider the rule $d = 3 \cdot (n + 1)$, where *n* represents the stage number and *d* represents the number of dots in a sequence.

a. Write the first four numbers in the sequence.   6, 9, 12, 15

b. Draw a dot sequence that fits the rule.
Possible sequence:

Stage 1   Stage 2   Stage 3   Stage 4

Lesson 3.3   Variables and Rules   **151**

Additional Answer

5. Possible answer:
   a. $s = n$, where *s* represents the number of squares
   b. $v = n + 1$, where *v* represents the number of vertical toothpicks
   c. $h = n \cdot 2$, where *h* represents the number of horizontal toothpicks
   d. $r = n \cdot \frac{n + 1}{2}$, where *r* represents the total number of rectangles

Additional Answers for Develop & Understand: B Exercises 6–9 are on page 195B.

Teacher Tips This exercise set gives more practice in identifying variables in toothpick sequences and finding rules that relate the values of the variables to the stage numbers. In these exercises, students work with rules that are written in symbolic form.

Develop & Understand: B

Suggested Grouping: Individuals

▶ **Exercise 5** Students are asked to write their rules from the exercises on page 150 in shorter, symbolic forms by using letters for the variables. They use *n* to represent the first variable (the stage number), but they may choose any other letter for the other variable. A helpful convention is to choose a letter that will serve as a reminder of what the letter represents. For example, *s* (the first letter of "square") might be used if the number of squares is the second variable. Any letter (other than *n*) can be used for the second variable provided the students states clearly what the letter represents.

▶ **Exercises 6–8** Point out students are given new toothpick sequences and a dot sequence. They identify a second variable suggested by the figures in each sequence and make a table that shows the values of the second variable. They then find a rule that relates the stage number to the value of the second variable and write the rule in symbolic form.

▶ **Exercises 9 and 10** These exercises have students take the opposite approach: students use a rule expressed in symbolic form and use it to list the first four stages in the number sequence. They then try to discover and draw a toothpick sequence or dot sequence that fits the rule and the number sequence. Students may find this a bit challenging. In Exercise 9, a helpful approach may be to imagine a toothpick sequence that starts with 6 toothpicks and then imagine how to generate subsequent figures by adding on 4 new toothpicks each time. A similar hint applies to Exercise 6.

Wrap-Up Ask students to share their variables from Exercises 6–8 and their sequences from Exercises 9 and 10.

Give students time to write out their answers to these exercises. For **Exercise 1**, you may want to suggest that students show at least four stages in their toothpick or dot sequence.

In **Exercise 2**, the variables should be described clearly in words. Each description should make it possible for the student or another person to easily determine the value of the variable for any desired stage of the sequence.

In **Exercise 3**, students should express their rules in clear and accurate symbolic form. They should check that the rules are written in agreement with order of operations rules.

Investigation 3

On Your Own Exercises
Pages 166–173
Exercises 12–14, 30

Equivalent Rules In this investigation, students see that they can use different symbolic expressions to describe the same sequence. Their explanations of the rules should show that the rules must work for any stage in the sequence. Their roles will typically describe how to build the same toothpick or dot sequence in different ways. Such rules are said to be *equivalent*.

Look at the given toothpick sequence with the class, and read the two rules written to describe the sequence.

Think & Discuss
Suggested Grouping: Pairs

Students need to understand that stating three instances in which a rule works is not enough to prove that the rule *always* works.

Troubleshooting Some students may have difficulty performing the calculations in Think & Discuss. Encourage them to show all their work. This will help you determine the source of any errors students have made. If there are errors involving order of operations, you may need to remind them of the order-of-operations rules.

Share & Summarize

1. Draw a toothpick or dot sequence. Make sure your sequence changes in a predictable way.   See below.

2. Name two variables in your sequence.

3. For each variable you named, try to write a rule relating the stage number to the variable. Use letters to represent the variables. Tell what each letter represents.   Possible answer: $t = n \cdot n + 1$, where t is the total number of dots and n is the stage number; $b = n$, where b is the number of dots in the bottom row and n is the stage number

2. Possible variables: total number of dots, stage number, number of dots in bottom row

Investigation 3 Equivalent Rules

Sometimes people can write different rules for the same pattern. You and your classmates may have written different rules in the last investigation.

Consider this toothpick sequence.

Stage 1   Stage 2   Stage 3   Stage 4

Math Link
It is not enough to show that a rule works in a few specific cases. Try to explain why it works based on how the terms are built.

Rosita and Conor wrote rules for the number of toothpicks in each stage. Both students used n to represent the stage number and t to represent the number of toothpicks.

Rosita's rule: $t = 3 + 2 \cdot (n - 1)$ Conor's rule: $t = 1 + 2n$

Think & Discuss

Use the two rules to find the number of toothpicks in stage 10. Check your results by drawing stage 10 and counting toothpicks. See ① in margin.
Show that both rules give the same result for stage 20 and for stage 100.   See ②.

Do you think the rules will give the same result for every stage? Answers will vary.

One way to show that the two rules will give the same result for every stage is to explain why both rules must work for any stage in the sequence.

② Rosita's rule:
$t = 3 + 2 \cdot (20 - 1)$
$= 41, t = 3 + 2 \cdot (100 - 1) = 201$
Conor's rule:
$t = 1 + 2 \cdot 20 = 41,$
$t = 1 + 2 \cdot 100 = 201$

1. Possible sequence:

Stage 1   Stage 2   Stage 3   Stage 4

Additional Answer
Think & Discuss
①

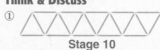

Stage 10

There are 21 toothpicks in stage 10. Rosita's rule gives $t = 3 + 2 \cdot (10 - 1) = 21$, and Conor's rule gives $t = 1 + 2 \cdot 10 = 21$. Both rules give the correct result.

Example

Rosita explains why her rule works.

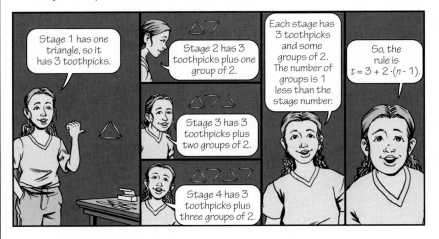

Conor explains why his rule works.

Rosita's and Conor's rules both correctly describe the toothpick sequence, so they *will* give the same result for every stage. Two rules that look different but describe the same relationship are said to be *equivalent*.

Discuss the example presented in the cartoon with the class. Discuss the different rules presented and how they are equivalent. This example demonstrates clearly that the toothpick sequence on page 152 can be constructed in two different ways. Rosita's rule describes one of these ways, and Conor's rule describes the other. Since the same sequence results no matter which rule is used, the rules are equivalent.

✅ *Develop & Understand: A*

Suggested Grouping: *Small Groups*

▶ **Exercises 1 and 2** In this exercise set, students use toothpick sequences and dot sequences to consider equivalent rules. You should allow plenty of time for these exercises, since students may find them challenging.

▶ **Exercise 1** Students are given a toothpick sequence and two equivalent rules that describe the sequence. A diagram is provided to show why one of the rules correctly describes the number of toothpicks in stage *n*. Students are asked to use diagrams to explain why the other rule also works. They may need to make sketches and try several ideas before give an explanation for the second rule.

▶ **Exercise 2** Suggest to students that they use the draw a diagram problem-solving strategy for this exercise.

✅ *Develop & Understand: A*

1. Consider this sequence.   See margin.

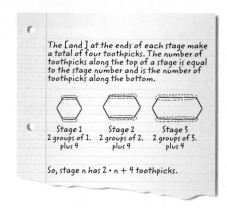

Mariana and Kendra wrote equivalent rules for this sequence. Both students used *n* to represent the stage number and *t* to represent the number of toothpicks.

Mariana's rule: $t = 2 \cdot n + 4$ Kendra's rule: $t = 2 \cdot (n + 2)$

Mariana used diagrams to explain why her rule is correct.

Use diagrams to help explain why Kendra's rule is correct.

2. Consider this sequence.

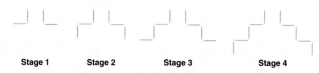

Nadia and Uma wrote equivalent rules for this sequence. Both girls used *n* to represent the stage number and *t* to represent the number of toothpicks.

Nadia's rule: $t = 2n + 2$ Uma's rule: $t = 2 \cdot (n + 1)$

The Mayan temple of Kukulcan is on the Yucatan Peninsula, Mexico.

Additional Answer

1. Possible explanation: Each stage has two halves, and each half has a number of toothpicks equal to the stage number plus 2. So, stage *n* has $2 \cdot (n + 2)$ toothpicks.

Stage 1
2 groups of 3

Stage 2
2 groups of 4

Stage 3
2 groups of 5

a. Copy and complete the table to show that both rules work for the first five stages of the sequence.

Stage Number, n	1	2	3	4	5
Number of Toothpicks, t	4	6	8	10	12
$2n + 2$	4	6	8	10	12
$2 \cdot (n + 1)$	4	6	8	10	12

b. Use words and diagrams to explain why Nadia's rule is correct.
See margin.
c. Use words and diagrams to explain why Uma's rule is correct.
See margin.

3. Consider this sequence.

Stage 1   Stage 2   Stage 3

a. Write two equivalent rules for the number of toothpicks in each stage.   Possible rules: $t = 2 \cdot (n + 2)$, $t = 4 + 2n$

b. Use words and diagrams to explain why each rule is correct.
See margin.

4. Consider this sequence.

Stage 1   Stage 2   Stage 3

a. Write two equivalent rules for the number of dots in each stage.
Possible rules: $d = 2 + 4n$, $d = 2 \cdot (2n + 1)$
b. Use words and diagrams to explain why each rule is correct.
See margin.

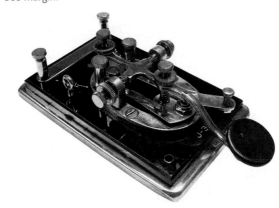

Morse code is a system of communication in which letters, numbers, and punctuation marks are represented by combinations of dots, dashes, and spaces. Morse code messages are transmitted as electrical pulses of various lengths. A short pulse represents a dot, and a long pulse represents a dash.

▶ **Exercises 3 and 4** In these exercises, students are given sequences and are asked first to write two equivalent rules for the sequence and then to explain why each rule is correct. Point out that there is no sure way to come up with rules or explanations. To find a rule for a sequence, it is often helpful to make a table of values. In these problems, tables that show the stage number in the top row, and the number of toothpicks or dots in the second row may suggest a rule for the sequence. A good approach is to observe how the numbers in the second row change from one stage to the next. One can also inspect the toothpick or dot sequence itself to look for a pattern. It may be helpful to use both approaches in conjunction.

Analyze the Table Ask students to recheck their answers if the answer rows are not identical. Both rules should work for the first five terms of the sequence.

Real-World Link
What would be Morse code for SOS, the international distress signal?

Additional Answer
2b. Possible answer: Each stage has two vertical toothpicks at the top, and two equal groups of toothpicks. The number of toothpicks in each group is equal to the stage number. So, the number of toothpicks in stage n is $2n + 2$.

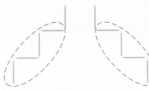

Stage 1
2 groups of 1,
plus 2

Stage 2
2 groups of 2,
plus 2

Stage 3
2 groups of 3,
plus 2

Stage 4
2 groups of 4,
plus 2

Additional Answers for Develop & Understand: A
Exercises 2c, 3b, and 4b are on pages 195B and 195C.

▶ **Exercise 5** Students should note that Rosita's rule uses the number of hexagons and not the stage number. However, the toothpick diagrams make it clear that the number of hexagons in a stage is the same as the term number. Students can quickly rule out Jahmal's rule. If they make tables of values for each rule, they can see that Jahmal's rule does not correctly predict the number of toothpicks in Stages 2 and 3. Students may want to test whether Conor's and Rosita's rules correctly predict the number of toothpicks in Stages 4 and 5. Next, they can examine the sequence more closely to give a reasoned explanation of why these two rules always work.

Wrap-Up Having students share some of their rules and explanations for Exercises 3 and 4 on page 155 might be helpful. Coming up with rules and explanations of why the rules work can take time and patience. Students must be willing to try different ideas. With practice, they can improve their ability to solve problems of this kind.

Share & Summarize

These exercises will help students focus on what it takes to be confident that two rules are equivalent. You may want to have students work on these exercises in small groups. Then have the groups present their answers in a discussion with the whole class.

Troubleshooting Thinking about rules that can be directly linked to a visual pattern can be helpful for many visual learners.

---

5. Conor, Jahmal, and Rosita each wrote a rule for this sequence.

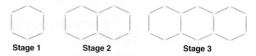

Stage 1   Stage 2   Stage 3

Conor's rule:
$t = 5n + 1$, where t is the number of toothpicks and n is the stage number

Jahmal's rule:
$t = 3 \cdot n + 3$, where t is the number of toothpicks and n is the stage number

Rosita's rule:
$t = 6h - (h - 1)$, where t is the number of toothpicks and h is the number of hexagons

Determine whether each rule correctly describes the sequence. If it does, explain how you know it is correct. If it does not, explain why it is incorrect.   See margin.

6a. Possible rule:
$t = 3 + 7 \cdot k$, where k is the number of T-shapes and t is the number of toothpicks

1. Possible answer: Show that both rules correctly describe the sequence. If both rules are correct, they must be equivalent.

2. No; Possible example: Suppose the rules are $d = n + 4$ and $d = 2 \cdot n$, where n is the stage number and d is the number of dots. Both rules give eight dots for stage 4, but the first rule gives five dots for stage 1 while the second gives two.

6. Consider strips of T-shapes like this one in which a strip can have any number of T-shapes.

a. Find a rule that connects the number of toothpicks in a strip to the number of T-shapes.

b. Explain why your rule is correct. Use diagrams if they help you to explain.   See margin.

Share & Summarize

1. How can you show that two rules for a sequence are equivalent?

2. Suppose two different rules give the same number of dots for stage 4 of a sequence. Can you conclude that the two rules are equivalent? Give an example to support your answer.

Additional Answers

5. See page 195C.

6b. Possible explanation: You can think of starting with three toothpicks and adding seven more to form each T-shape. So, a strip with k T-shapes would have $3 + 7 \cdot k$ toothpicks.

3   + 7   + 7   + 7

Investigation (4) Crossing a Bridge

1a. Possible explanation: Repeat the following steps until all the adults are across:

- The two children cross the bridge.
- One child brings back the flashlight, and one stays on the other side.
- The child that returned gives an adult the flashlight, and the adult crosses.
- The adult gives the flashlight to the child on the other side, and that child crosses back.

After all the adults are across, the two children cross together.

2a. Yes; use the same process as the first group (2 children cross, 1 child returns with the flashlight, 1 adult crosses, the other child brings back the flashlight).

While walking at night, a group of eight hikers, made up of six adults and two children, arrives at a rickety wooden bridge. A sign says the bridge can hold a maximum of 200 pounds. The group estimates that this means the following.

- one child can cross alone
- one adult can cross alone
- two children can cross together

Anyone crossing the bridge will need to use a flashlight. Unfortunately, the group has only one flashlight.

Maximum Capacity 200 Pounds

Try It Out

1. Find a way to get all the hikers across the bridge in the fewest number of trips. Count one trip each time one or two people walk across the bridge.

   a. Describe your plan using words, drawings, or both.

   b. How many trips will it take for everyone in the group to get across the bridge?   25

2. A second group of hikers approaches the bridge. This group has ten adults, two children, and one flashlight.

   a. Can everyone in this group get across the bridge? If so, describe how.

   b. What is the least number of trips it will take for this group to cross the bridge?   41

 Go on

Trip Number	First Side	Second Side
1	2A	2C
2	2A, 1C	1C
3	1A, 1C	1A, 1C
4	1A, 2C	1A
5	1A	1A, 2C
6	1A, 1C	1A, 1C
7	1C	2A, 1C
8	2C	2A
9		2A, 2C

Investigation (4)

Suggested Grouping: Small Groups

Materials and Preparation

To introduce this investigation, you may want to have a group of students act out the first few moves. Have eight students (two designated as the children) stand on one side of the room. Use a small object to represent the flashlight which must be carried on each trip. Have the class tell the group who should cross for the first few stages. If one adult walks over with the flashlight, what happens then? How does the flashlight get back to the group that needs it? Do not take time to get the whole group to the other side of the room. Have the class demonstrate that they understand the procedure needed to get everyone across. Make sure students understand that each crossing counts as one trip. Then have students work in groups to answer the questions in the investigation.

Try It Out

▶ **Exercise 1** Students can answer **Part a** by describing how to act out the problem. **Part b** may prove to be more difficult. Students who see the pattern may arrive at the answer quickly. Others may feel it necessary to devise a way to record what happens for each trip and to count the number of trips. Another approach is to see what would happen if there were only one adult and two children, and then to increase the number of adults one step at a time.

The table at the left (illustrated for two adults and two children) makes it easy to keep track of the trips needed to get everyone across the bridge. Each row in the body of the table shows where the adults and children are after the trip number for that row. For example, after trip 4, there will be one adult and two children on the first side of the bridge, and there will be one adult on the second side.

Use the same method for **Exercise 2**.

▶ **Exercise 3** This exercise should be easy for students who have been successful in seeing the pattern to which Exercises 1 and 2 are pointing.

▶ **Exercise 4** This exercise asks students to write, in symbols, the rule they have discovered in their work on Exercises 1–3. Students will probably benefit from a discussion of why the rule works. If students have any difficulty explaining this, you may want to use tables of trips (like the one shown on page 159) to make the point that each additional adult requires four more trips.

▶ **Exercise 5** This exercise is important because it shows that the bridge problem has no solution if there is only one child in the group.

Teacher Tips Allow students to use objects such as counters to model the situation, if needed.

Try It Again

▶ **Exercises 6–9** Point out that students will now consider what happens when the number of children changes.

▶ **Exercise 6** Students consider the number of trips needed to get various numbers of children across the bridge. They may use methods similar to those used for earlier exercises. Students should note that this exercise assumes that no adults are in the group crossing the bridge.

▶ **Exercise 7** Point out that students look for a pattern that generalizes what they discovered in Exercise 6.

5. No; A group needs at least two children to get across so there can be one child on the other side to return the flashlight when an adult brings it across.

3. In Parts a–c, find the least number of trips it would take for the group to get across the bridge. Assume each group has only a single flashlight.

   a. 8 adults and 2 children   33

   b. 1 adult and 2 children   5

   c. 100 adults and 2 children   401

4. Suppose a group has two children, *a* adults, and one flashlight. Write a rule that relates these two variables, the least number of trips *t* needed to get everyone across and the number of adults.
   $t = 4a + 1$

5. Could a group with 15 adults, one child, and one flashlight cross the bridge? Explain.

Try It Again

Now you will explore how the number of children in a group affects the number of trips needed for the group to cross the bridge. You will start by thinking about groups with no adults at all.

6. Tell how many trips it would take to get each of these groups across the bridge. (Hint: First figure out a method for getting everyone across and then think about how many trips it would take.)

   a. 2 children   1   **b.** 3 children   3

   c. 6 children   9   **d.** 10 children   17

7. Look for a pattern relating the number of children to the number of trips.

   a. Write rule that relates the number of trips *t* to the number of children in the group *c*. Assume the group has no adults, more than one child, and just one flashlight. $t = 2c - 3$

   b. Part a states that the group must have more than one child. How many trips would it take a single child to get across the bridge? Does your rule give the correct result for one child?   1, no

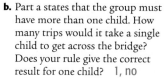

Reaching *All Learners*

AL Approaching Level Tactile learners may find it helpful to explore the bridge-crossing problem by using small pieces of paper to represent the people. Have students tear a sheet of paper into 8 or 10 pieces. Next, have them write the letter *C* on two pieces of paper and the letter *A* on the other pieces. The pieces can represent the children and adults, respectively.

Real-World Link
The world's longest overwater bridge is the Lake Pontchartrain Causeway, which connects Mandeville and Metairie, Louisiana. The bridge is almost 24 miles long.

8. Tell how many trips it would take to get each of the following groups across the bridge.

   a. 6 adults and 2 children   25   **b.** 6 adults and 3 children   27

   c. 6 adults and 6 children   33   **d.** 8 adults and 10 children   49

9. **Challenge** Write a rule that relates the number of trips to the number of children and adults in the group. Assume the group has at least two children and exactly one flashlight. $t = 4a + 2c - 3$, where a is the number of adults and c is the number of children

What Did You Learn?

A second bridge has the following weight restriction.

   • one adult can cross alone

   • one child can cross alone

   • one adult and one child can cross together

   • two children can cross together

10. With these new rules, a group might be able to use a different method to get across the bridge.

    a. Find a way to get a group of eight adults and two children across the bridge in the fewest trips. Describe your method using words, pictures, or both.

    b. How many trips does it take for everyone to get across the bridge?
    17
    c. How does the number of trips needed to get the group across this bridge compare to the number of trips needed for the first bridge? See your answer for Part a of Exercise 3.

11. A group of 15 adults and one child could not get across the first bridge. Could this group cross the second bridge? If so, explain how. Tell how many trips it would take.

12. Tell how many trips it would take each of these groups to get across the second bridge.

    a. 3 adults and 1 child   5

    b. 5 adults and 1 child   9

    c. 100 adults and 1 child   199

13. Write a rule that relates the number of trips needed to cross the second bridge to the number of adults in the group. Assume the group has one child and one flashlight. $t = 2a - 1$, where t is the number of trips and a is the number of adults

10a. Possible answer: An adult crosses with a child. The adult stays behind while the child cross back over. This is repeated until all the adults have crossed. Finally, the two children cross together.

10c. This bridge requires 16 fewer trips.

11. Yes; one adult and the child could cross, and then the child could return and get another adult. This is repeated until everyone has crossed. It would take 29 trips.

▶ **Exercise 8** Students may need to think about how to handle variation in the number of both adults and children. After some thought and experimentation, they should realize that they can get all of the children across and then address the problem of getting all the adults across.

▶ **Exercise 9** Students may reason that getting c children from one side to the other will require $2c - 3$ trips (assuming that c is 2 or greater). If there are adults in the group, each adult will require another 4 trips.

What Did You Learn?

These exercises allow students to apply their methods from earlier questions to a situation involving different restrictions on the number of people who can cross a bridge at one time. You may want to take time to discuss the new restrictions with the class. Students should note that if only one person needs to cross the second bridge, then one trip will do. But the problem is really about trying to get a *group* of people across the bridge. Use a discussion to help students see that to get everyone in a group of two or more across the bridge, there must be at least one child. Methods similar to those used for Exercises 1–3 can be helpful with **Exercises 10–12**. Encourage students to make a table to help them develop a rule. Some students may discover that if there are p people in the group (where p is at least 2 and the group includes at least one child), then $2p - 3$ trips are required to get everyone across.

▶ **Exercise 13** Ask student to make a table to help them develop the rule $t = 2a - 1$. You may want to discuss that this rule assumes at least one adult is in the group.

On Your Own Exercises
Pages 166–173
Exercises 15–29, 31–32

Use Inputs and Outputs In this investigation, students take another look at the *What's My Rule.* game in Lesson 3.2. However, now they are asked to state their rules by using letters to represent input and output variables. Remind students that rules that describe the same relationship are equivalent. Knowing that two rules give the same outputs for a limited number of inputs is not sufficient to prove that the rules are equivalent. On the other hand, a single instance of rules that give different outputs for the same input is enough to show that the rules are *not* equivalent. Review the directions for playing *What's My Rule.* with the class. Discuss the idea of writing rules for the game by using letters to represent the input and output variables.

Think & Discuss

This introduction focuses on the idea that symbolically written rules can be used to find outputs for given inputs in games of *What's My Rule.* Use a class discussion to draw attention to the similarities among the rules that Rosita, Jahmal, and Althea are using. You may want to put input-output tables for the rules on the board. Label these *Rosita's Table*, *Jahmal's Table*, and *Althea's Table*. Use the same input values in each table. Guide the discussion to help students observe that the order in which they perform the operations is the only significant difference between Rosita's and Jahmal's rules. In the case of Rosita's and Althea's rules, there is a superficial difference in the notation.

Teacher Tips Remind students that the multiplication symbol is often left out when a number is multiplied by a variable. So, $3b$ is the same as $3 \cdot b$.

In this investigation, you will play the game *What's My Rule.* Here is how you play.

- One player, the rule-maker, thinks of a secret rule for calculating an output number from a given input number. An example follows.

  To find the output, add 3 to the input and multiply by 4.

- The other players take turns giving the rule-maker input numbers. For each input, the rule-maker calculates the output and says the result out loud.

- By comparing each input to its output, the players try to guess the secret rule. The first player to guess the rule correctly wins.

In the *What's My Rule* game, the input and output are variables. In this investigation, you will play *What's My Rule* using letters to represent these variables. For example, if you let i represent the input and o represent the output, you can write the rule above as follows.

$$o = (i + 3) \cdot 4$$

Think & Discuss

Rosita, Jahmal, and Althea are playing *What's My Rule*. Rosita's secret rule is $a = 3b + 4$, where a is the output and b is the input.

- Jahmal guesses that the rule is $a = 4 + 3b$, where a is the output and b is the input.
- Althea guesses that the rule is $x = 3y + 4$, where x is the output and y is the input.

Rosita is not sure whether the rules Jahmal and Althea wrote are the same as her secret rule. Tell whether each rule is correct. Explain how you know. See ①.

① Both rules are correct. In Jahmal's rule, the addition is written before the multiplication. Since order of operations states that multiplication is done first, his and Rosita's rules will always give the same result. Althea's rule simply uses different letters to represent the variables.

Reaching All Learners

AL Approaching Level Although the use of different letters for the input and output is only a superficial difference, some students may not see it that way. Auditory learners may find it helpful to describe to you in their own words what each rule says should be done to find the output for a given input. Check their explanations for clarity, and help them check whether the verbal description matches the symbolic rule.

1. Possible answer: I found that guessing numbers in order, starting with 0, helped me guess the rule. After the first guess, I wrote down several rules that might work and then checked to see if any of them worked for the second guess. Rules that have only one operation are easiest to guess. Rules with many operations or parentheses are harder. To see if two rules were the same, we first checked that both gave the same outputs for all of the inputs we used. If they did, we tried to explain why they were the same, like we did in the last lesson. Sometimes, we could not show they were the same. We decided that if they gave the same output for four or five different inputs, we would say they were the same.

✅ Develop & Understand: A

1. Play *What's My Rule* with your group, using these added rules.
   - The rule-maker should write the secret rule with symbols, using letters for the variables.
   - The other players should make a table to keep track of the inputs and outputs.
   - When a player guesses the rule, he or she should write it with symbols, using letters for the variables.

Take turns being the rule-maker so everyone has a chance. As you play, you may have to decide whether a guessed rule is equivalent to the secret rule even though it looks different.

After your group has played several games, write a paragraph describing what you learned while playing. In your paragraph, you might discuss the following.
- strategies you used to help you guess the rule
- a description of what makes a rule easy to guess and what makes a rule difficult to guess
- strategies you used to decide whether two rules were equivalent even when they looked different

✅ Develop & Understand: B

These tables were made during games of *What's My Rule*. Two rules are given for each table. Determine whether each rule could be correct. Explain how you know.   2–4. See below.

2.

q	1	2	3	10
P	7	11	15	43

$p = q + q + q + 4$
$p = 4 \cdot q + 3$

3.

s	1	2	5	10
t	10	20	50	100

$t = 4 \cdot s + 6 \cdot s$
$t = 10s$

4.

k	0	2	5	10
j	1	17	101	402

$j = 5 \cdot k^2 + 1$
$j = 5 \cdot k \cdot k + 1$

In the following exercises, you will try to figure out the rules for some *What's My Rule* games.

2. Possible explanation: $p = q + q + q + 4$ is not correct because it works only for $q = 1$ and $p = 7$. $p = 4 \cdot q + 3$ could be correct because it works for all the values in the table.
3. Possible explanation: Both rules could be correct because they work for all the values in the table.
4. Neither rule is correct. Possible explanation: Both rules give an output of 21 for an input of 2, but the table lists 17 as the output for an input of 2.

Lesson 3.3 Variables and Rules   **161**

✅ Develop & Understand: A

Suggested Grouping: Small Groups

▶ **Exercise 1** Suggest that the players agree each time on what letters to use for the input and output variables. The first of the additional rules for these games requires the rule-maker to write the secret rule in symbols. This rule is intended, in part, to limit the rules that are easily expressed in terms of fundamental arithmetical operations. It is possible that students will limit their inputs to whole numbers, although they do not have to do it.

Wrap-Up The groups' observations about strategies may vary widely. Therefore, it may be helpful to have a class discussion of results. You might ask the groups to keep track of the rules that were easiest and hardest to discover and to comment on what makes a rule easy or hard to guess.

✅ Develop & Understand: B

Suggested Grouping: Small Groups

▶ **Exercise 2** In this exercise set, students use given tables of inputs and outputs and test proposed rules to see whether they could be correct. For this exercise, some students may observe that the first rule they test is equivalent to $p = 3 \cdot q + 4$. This should be enough for them to see that the first and second rules cannot both be correct.

▶ **Exercise 3** Help students observe that the rules are equivalent because they say the same thing in a slightly different form. Therefore, as soon as they determine that the first rule does not apply, they know that the second rule does not apply.

Teacher Tips In this exercise set, students must discover a rule that relates the inputs and outputs that are presented in each of several tables. Students should test each rule they propose to be sure it gives the correct output for each input shown. The inputs in the tables have been selected more or less at random. As a result, it may take time for students to come up with a rule for some of the tables.

✅ Develop & Understand: C

Suggested Grouping: Pairs

▶ **Exercise 5** It may help students to look at what happens if the inputs are arranged in order from least to greatest. It appears that increasing the input by one causes the output to increase by four.

▶ **Exercise 6** The first three inputs are whole numbers that increase by one each time. When the input increases by one, the output increases by five. This may help students get started in their search for a rule.

▶ **Exercises 7 and 8** Point out that the fractions and decimals suggest rules that involve division.

Wrap-Up For each problem, have students share the various rules they wrote. Remind them that rules that look different but describe the same relationship are said to be equivalent.

Share & Summarize

Give students time to write out their answers to the questions. Then have volunteers read their answers. Discuss the answers with the class. For **Exercise 1**, be sure students make appropriate use of parentheses when they write Jade's rule in symbols.

Troubleshooting If students are having difficulty generating rules for tables, review specific strategies that might help. For example, suggest putting inputs in order in the input-output tables. Remind students to think about multiples and squares when looking for rules.

✅ Develop & Understand: C

These tables were made during games of *What's My Rule*. In each table, the values in the top row are the inputs and the values in the bottom row are the outputs.

Write a rule for each table, using the given letters to represent the variables.

5.

a	2	5	3	6	1
b	9	21	13	25	5

Possible rule:
$b = 4a + 1$

6.

y	4	5	6	1	$\frac{3}{5}$
z	18	23	28	3	1

Possible rule:
$z = 5y - 2$

7.

w	$\frac{12}{7}$	11	19	4	7
g	$\frac{2}{7}$	$1\frac{5}{6}$	$3\frac{1}{6}$	$\frac{2}{3}$	$1\frac{1}{6}$

Possible rule:
$g = w \div 6$

8.

q	10	5.5	1	2	3
p	6	3.75	1.5	2	2.5

Possible rule:
$p = (q \div 2) + 1$

9.

c	100	42	17	1	0.3
d	10,000	1,764	289	1	0.09

Possible rules:
$d = c^2$, or $d = c \cdot c$

10.

s	1	3.1	10	5	6.5
t	3	11.61	102	27	44.25

Possible rules:
$t = s^2 + 2$, or
$t = s \cdot s + 2$

Share & Summarize

Jade and Diego were playing *What's My Rule*. Diego's secret rule was "To get the output, multiply the input by itself and subtract 1." Jade guessed that the rule was "Subtract 1 from the input, and multiply the result by itself."

1. Diego's rule:
$m = n^2 - 1$, or
$m = n \cdot n - 1$;
Jade's rule:
$m = (n - 1)^2$, or
$m = (n - 1) \cdot (n - 1)$

1. Write both rules with symbols. Use m to represent the output and n to represent the input.

2. Is Jade's rule equivalent to Diego's rule? Explain.
No; the two rules give the same output only when the input is 1.

Investigation 6 Translate Words into Symbols

Writing a rule for a real-life situation can be difficult, even when the situation is fairly simple. It is easy to make a mistake if you do not pay close attention to the details.

Think & Discuss

A spider has eight legs. If S represents the number of spiders and L represents the number of legs, which of the following rules is correct? How do you know?   See ① below.

$$S = 8 \cdot L \qquad L = 8 \cdot S$$

In the spider situation, it is easy to confuse the two rules. The example shows how Luke thought about the situation.

Example

Creating a table and looking for a pattern can make finding a rule a little easier. Notice that, after Luke wrote his rule, he checked it by testing a value for which he knew the answer. It is a good idea to test a value whenever you write a rule. Although this will not guarantee that your rule is correct, it is a helpful way to uncover mistakes.

① $L = 8 \cdot S$; Possible explanation: There are 8 legs per spider, so the number of legs is 8 times the number of spiders. This is what the second rule says.

Lesson 3.3 Variables and Rules   **163**

Investigation 6

On Your Own Exercises
Pages 166–173
Exercises 20–24, 33, 34

Translate Words into Symbols This investigation addresses some of the difficulties students have when they try to translate quantitative relationships from everyday language into the more compact symbolic language of mathematics.

Think & Discuss

Read the question out loud to the class. After a short time, ask for a show of hands of those who selected each of the rules. Then ask volunteers from each group explain the answer they selected. Ask students to identify the variables in the situation. Be sure they understand that the variables are not spiders and legs but the number of spiders (S) and the number of legs (L). Watch for students who say that since there are eight times as many legs as spiders, the rule is $S = 8 \cdot L$. These students are replacing words for the things (legs, spiders) with the symbols for the variables. They are focusing narrowly on the word order rather than thinking about the mathematical relationship between the variables. Point out that if $S = 8 \cdot L$ were correct, there would be more spiders than legs.

Example

The table in this example should help students see why $L = 8 \cdot S$ is the correct rule. Discuss why testing the rule is a good idea. Students will be using the make and test a conjecture problem-solving strategy. Ask questions to achieve closure.

In any spider collection, will there be more spiders or more legs?   More legs

The table tells you that three spiders will have how many legs?   24 legs

How many times 3 is 24?   8

Teacher Tips For each exercise, students are to identify the two variables in the situation, make a table of values, describe how to calculate the values of one variable from the values of the other, and write a rule in symbolic form. By working in pairs, students will be able to discuss and check their thinking at each stage.

✅ Develop & Understand: A

Suggested Grouping: Pairs

▶ **Exercise 1a** Tell students to be careful to identify the variables as the *number* of blue tiles and the *number* of white tiles (as opposed to simply blue tiles and white tiles).

▶ **Exercise 1b** Some students may think that only whole tiles should be used. This may influence the values they choose for variables in their tables but is not likely to present any difficulty when they get to **Parts c and d**.

▶ **Exercise 5** Students must use a price greater than $3 for an adult's ticket.

▶ **Exercise 6** The situation requires that students use only whole-number values for the variables when they make the table for **Part b**. (One does not want a fraction of a hamster.)

Wrap-Up Have students share the various rules they wrote for each situation. Review the idea that even though two equations may use different variables, they are still equivalent if they describe the same relationship.

Additional Answers

1b. Possible table:

White Tiles	1	2	3	4	5
Blue Tiles	2	4	6	8	10

2a. Number of pink mints, number of green mints

2b. Possible table:

Pink Mints	1	2	3	4	5
Green Mints	4	8	12	16	20

Additional Answers for Develop & Understand: A Exercises 2–6 are on pages 195C and 195D.

✅ Develop & Understand: A

1. To tile his bathroom, Mr. Drury needs twice as many blue tiles as white tiles.

   a. What are the two variables in this situation?
   Number of white tiles, number of blue tiles
   b. Make a table of values for the two variables.   See margin.

   c. Look for a pattern in your table. Describe how to calculate the values of one variable from the values of the other.

   d. Write a rule for the relationship between the two variables. Use letters to represent the variables. Tell what each letter represents. Be sure to check your rule by testing a value.

   In Exercises 2–6, complete Parts a–d of Exercise 1.   2–6. See margin.

1c. Possible answers: To find the number of blue tiles, multiply the number of white tiles by 2. *Or,* to find the number of white tiles, divide the number of blue tiles by 2.

1d. $b = 2w$, or $w = \frac{1}{2} \cdot b$, or $w = b \div 2$, where b represents the number of blue tiles and w represents the number of white tiles

2. In packages of Cool Breeze mints, there are four green mints for every pink mint.

3. In a toothpick sequence, the total number of toothpicks in a term is four more than twice the number of vertical toothpicks in the term.

4. In a factory, each assembly worker earns one seventh as much money as his or her manager.

5. A community theater charges $3 less for a child's ticket than for an adult's ticket.

6. A pet store always carries six times as many fish as hamsters.

Reaching *All Learners*

BL **Beyond Level** Students may have noted that for some of the situations in Exercises 1–6, it is possible to identify more than two variables. It is usually clear which variables to focus on, but other choices are possible. For example, in Exercise 2, a student could let m be the total number of mints in a package, g be the number of green mints, and p be the number of pink mints. A rule relating m to g would then be $m = p + g$. A rule relating m to p is $m = p + 4p$ (since $g = 4p$). A rule relating m to g is $m = \frac{1}{4}g + g$ (since $p = \frac{1}{4}g$).

Develop & Understand: B

Below are more situations involving rules. Make a table whenever you feel it will help you better understand. Also, be sure to test all your rules.

7. Nick and his friends collect the prizes hidden in boxes of Flako cereal. Joel has twice as many prizes as Nick. Ruben has three more prizes than Nick. Andrea has half as many prizes as Nick.

  a. If Nick has six prizes, how many prizes do the other friends have?
Joel has 12. Ruben has 9. Andrea has 3.

  b. Write a rule for the relationship between the number of prizes Joel has j and the number of prizes Nick has n. $j = 2n$

  c. Write a rule for the relationship between the number of prizes Ruben has r and the number Nick has n. $r = 3 + n$

  d. Write a rule for the relationship between the number of prizes Andrea has a and the number Nick has n. $a = \frac{1}{2} \cdot n$, or $a = n \div 2$

8. Suppose Germaine has two more prizes than Joel.

  a. Write a rule for the relationship between the number of prizes Germaine has g and the number Joel has j. $g = j + 2$

  b. If Nick has 19 prizes, how many prizes does Joel have? How many does Germaine have?   Joel has 38. Germaine has 40.

  c. Describe in words the relationship between the number of prizes Germaine has and the number of prizes Nick has.   Germaine has twice as many as Nick, plus 2.

  d. Write a rule for the relationship between the number of prizes Germaine has g and the number Nick has n. $g = 2 \cdot n + 2$

Share & Summarize

1. How can making a table help you find a rule for a situation?

2. Once you have written a rule, how can you test it to check for mistakes?   **Possible answer:** Test the rule for a case for which you know the result.

1. Possible answer: If I make a table, I can look for patterns and relationships in the values. I can think of the values as inputs and outputs and try to find a rule that fits them, as I did when I played *What's My Rule*.

Develop & Understand: B

Suggested Grouping: Pairs

▶ **Exercise 7** Point out that students who make a table to help them write the rule may write a correct rule but have tables that do not meet all the conditions of the problem. For example, a table that shows a value of 3 for n and $1\frac{1}{2}$ for a does not make sense, since Andrea cannot have $1\frac{1}{2}$ prizes. You may want to discuss this with students, and commend students who arrive at the correct rule in **Part d**.

▶ **Exercise 8** Students may need help with **Part d**. One approach is to make a table of values for n and g. However, it would be good for students to see that they can use the rule from Exercise 7b, $j = 2n$, and the rule from Part a of this exercise, $g = j + 2$, to get $g = 2n + 2$. Simply replace j with $2n$ in $g = j + 2$.

Share & Summarize

After students have had time to write their answers to these questions, have volunteers read their answers. You may also want to ask students to give some examples to illustrate what they say. They can refer to the problems in the Exercises on page 164.

Troubleshooting If students are having difficulty writing rules for situations given in words, it may help to provide more practice with this skill.

Additional Example There are five times as many boys as girls in a class. Let b stand for the number of boys, g for the number of girls, and t for the total number of students in the class.

What rule describes how the variable b is related to the variable g? Possible rule: $b = 5g$

What rule describes how t is related to b and g? Possible rule: $t = b + g$

What rule describes how t is related to g? Possible rule: $t = 5g + g$, or $t = 6g$

▶ **Exercise 5** Some students will substitute directly into the expression to find the total number of blocks. Others, however, may need to go back to the concrete image of 4 bags and 5 extra blocks to compute the total.

Practice & Apply

For each picture, write an expression for the total number of blocks. Assume each bag contains the same number of blocks.

1. $3n + 4$
2. $2n + 3$
3. $n + 5$
4. $5n + 5$

5. Consider the expression $4n + 5$.

5a.

   a. Draw a bags-and-blocks picture for this expression.

   b. Copy and complete the table.

n	0	1	2	3	26	66	79
4n + 5	5	9	13	17	109	269	321

   c. If $n = 7$, what is the value of $4n + 5$? 33

   d. If $n = 25$, what is the value of $4n + 5$? 105

6. A particular bags-and-blocks situation can be represented by the expression $5n + 3$. What is the value of $5n + 3$ if there are 38 blocks in each bag? 193

7. Consider this sequence of toothpick "houses."

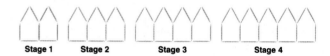

Stage 1   Stage 2   Stage 3   Stage 4

   a. Write a number sequence for the number of houses in each stage.
   2, 3, 4, 5, . . .

   b. Write a rule that connects the number of houses to the stage number. Use letters to represent the variables. Tell what each letter represents. Possible rule; $h = n + 1$, where h represents the number of houses and n represents the stage number

8. Consider this dot sequence.

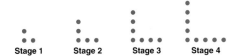

Stage 1   Stage 2   Stage 3   Stage 4

a. Write a number sequence for the number of dots in each stage.
3, 5, 7, 9, …
b. Write a rule that connects the number of dots to the stage number. Use letters to represent the variables. Tell what each letter represents. $d = 2n + 1$, where d represents the number of dots and n represents the stage number

In Exercises 9 and 10, give the first four numbers in the sequence. Then draw a sequence of toothpicks or dots that fits the rule.

9. $t = 4 \cdot (k + 1)$, where t represents the number of toothpicks and k represents the stage number   See margin.

10. $d = 3 \cdot p - 2$, where d represents the number of dots and p represents the stage number

10. 1, 4, 7, 10, …
   Possible sequence:

Stage 1 Stage 2 Stage 3 Stage 4

11. Consider this sequence.

Stage 1   Stage 2   Stage 3   Stage 4

11a. Possible rules:
   $t = 2 \cdot n + 1$,
   $t = 3 + 2 \cdot (n - 1)$,
   where t is the number of toothpicks and n is the stage number

a. Write two equivalent rules for the number of toothpicks in each stage.

b. Use words and diagrams to explain why each of your rules is correct.   See margin.

12. Three students wrote rules for this dot sequence. Determine whether each rule correctly describes the pattern. If it does, explain how you know it is correct. If it does not, explain why it is not correct.

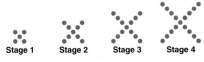

Stage 1   Stage 2   Stage 3   Stage 4

a. Ilsa's rule: $d = 5 \cdot m$, where d is the number of dots and m is the stage number   Incorrect; Possible explanation: Her rule gives $d = 5 \cdot 2 = 10$ dots in stage 2, but there are only 9.
b. Mattie's rule: $d = 1 + 4k$, where d is the number of dots and k is the stage number   See margin.

c. Mauricio's rule: $d = 4 \cdot (j - 1) + 5$, where d is the number of dots and j is the stage number   See margin.

Lesson 3.3 Variables and Rules   **167**

▶ **Exercise 11** Students may find it helpful to make a table showing stage numbers and stage values as they search for rules. Their rules may suggest how diagrams can be used to argue that the rules always work.

▶ **Exercise 12** Point out that to eliminate the rule in **Part a**, students need only find one case in which it fails to predict the stage value correctly. However, students should confirm that the rules in **Parts b and c** give correct values for all four stages shown in the dot sequence. They must then explain why the rules will continue to give correct values.

Additional Answers

12b. Correct; Possible explanation: Each stage has one center dot and four "arms." The number of dots in each arm is equal to the stage number. So, the number of dots in stage k is $1 + 4k$.

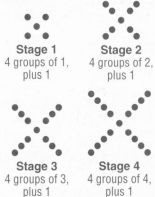

Stage 1   Stage 2
4 groups of 1,   4 groups of 2,
   plus 1   plus 1

Stage 3   Stage 4
4 groups of 3,   4 groups of 4,
   plus 1   plus 1

9. 8, 12, 16, 20, . . .
   Possible sequence:

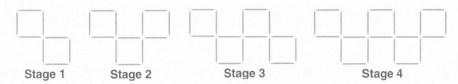

Stage 1   Stage 2   Stage 3   Stage 4

Additional Answers for Exercises 11b and 12c are on page 195D.

▶ **Exercise 13** This exercise is different from the preceding exercises in which students were asked to find a rule that gives the value of a stage in terms of the stage number. Here, the value of b (the number of blue tiles) is always an even number. Students should notice that each number in the second row of the table for **Part a** is 5 times the number of blue tiles.

▶ **Exercise 14** Another rule that students may give is $c = (n + 2)^2 - n^2$.

Additional Answer

14b. Possible explanation for $c = 4 + 4 \cdot n$: Each stage has four corner cubes. If you remove these cubes, each side has a number of cubes equal to the stage number. So, stage n has $4 + 4 \cdot n$ cubes.

Stage 1
4 groups of 1,
plus 4

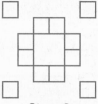

Stage 2
4 groups of 2,
plus 4

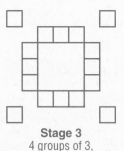

Stage 3
4 groups of 3,
plus 4

13b. Possible rule:
$w = 5 \cdot b$, where
b is the number
of blue tiles and
w is the number
of white tiles

13c. Possible explanation:
Each section of the
design has five times
as many white tiles
as blue tiles (2 blue
and 10 white).
When the sections
are put together,
there will always
be five times as
many white tiles
as blue tiles.

14a. Possible rule:
$c = 4 + 4 \cdot n$,
where c is the
number of cubes
and n is the stage
number

13. When tiling a walkway, a particular contractor surrounds each pair of blue tiles with white tiles as shown at right. Four copies of this design are put together below.

a. Copy and complete the table to show the number of white tiles needed for each given number of blue tiles.

Blue Tiles	2	4	6	8	20	100
White Tiles	10	20	30	40	100	500

b. Find a rule that describes the connection between the number of white tiles and the number of blue tiles. Use letters for the variables in your rule. Tell what each letter represents.

c. Explain how you know your rule is correct. Use diagrams if necessary.

14. Consider this sequence of cubes.

Stage 1   Stage 2   Stage 3

a. Find a rule for the number of cubes in each stage. You may want to make a table first. Use letters for the variables in your rule. Tell what each letter represents.

b. Explain how you know your rule is correct. Use diagrams if necessary.   See margin.

15. In a round of the *What's My Rule* game, Hiam's secret rule was $a = b^2 \cdot 3$, where b is the input and a is the output. Complete the table to show the outputs for the given inputs.

b	8	0	15	7	4
a	192	0	675	147	48

The tables below were made during games of *What's My Rule*. The values in the top row are inputs, and the values in the bottom row are outputs. Write a rule for each table, using the given letters to represent the variables.

16.

f	11	4	1	7	2
g	43	22	13	31	16

Possible rule:
$g = 10 + 3f$

17.

j	12	9	2	16	23
k	6	5.25	3.5	7	8.75

Possible rule:
$k = j \cdot \dfrac{1}{4} + 3$ or
$k = j \div 4 + 3$

The tables in Exercises 18 and 19 were made during games of *What's My Rule*. Two rules are given for each table. Determine whether each rule could be correct, and explain how you know.

18.

s	2	5	11	7	10
t	5	14	32	20	29

$s = (t - 1) \cdot 3$
$t = 2s + (s - 1)$

See margin.

19.

p	2	5	1	4	3
m	10	127	3	66	29

$m = 2 + p \cdot p \cdot p$
$m = p^3 + 2$

19. Possible explanation: Both rules could be correct because they work for all the values in the table.

20. Economics Tickets for a school play cost $3.75 each. Write a rule connecting the total cost in dollars *c* and the number of tickets bought *t*. Make a table if necessary. Check your rule by testing a value. $c = 3.75 \cdot t$

21. The cooking time for a turkey is 18 minutes for every pound plus an extra 20 minutes.

a. How long will it take to cook a 12-pound turkey?
236 min, or 3 h 56 min

b. Write a rule for this situation, using *m* for the number of minutes and *p* for the number of pounds. Make a table if necessary. Check your rule by testing a value. $m = 18p + 20$

22. Three students wrote rules for the relationship between the number of eyes and the number of noses in a group of people. Each student used *e* to represent the number of eyes and *n* to represent the number of noses. Which of the rules are correct? Explain how you decided. See margin.

Miguel's rule: $2 \cdot e = n$

Althea's rule: $n \times 2 = e$

Hannah's rule: $n = e \div 2$

▶ **Exercises 18 and 19** These exercises make the point that a valid rule must work in every case.

▶ **Exercise 21** Check that students are using a correct procedure to change 236 min to hours and minutes. You may want to discuss why a cook would find 3 h 56 min a more useful result than either 236 min or 3.93 h.

▶ **Exercise 22** Students who have difficulty selecting the correct rules may find it helpful to ask themselves, "Which rule says that there are more eyes than noses?"

Additional Answers

18. Possible explanation: $s = (t - 1) * 3$ is not correct because it gives an *s* value of 12 for a *t* value of 5. $t = 2s + (s - 1)$ could be correct because it works for all the values in the table.

22. Althea's and Hannah's rules are correct. Possible explanation: According to Miguel's rule, there would be four noses if there are two eyes. This is not correct. Althea's rule says there are twice as many eyes as noses, which is correct. Hannah's rule says there are half as many noses as eyes, which is correct.

▶ **Exercise 23e** You may wish to call on volunteers to explain how they found the distance Alma ran.

▶ **Exercise 25** You may wish to have students show their work on Chapter 3 Master 1, Input and Output Tables.

23a. $j = 2a$, where j represents the number of miles Juan ran

23b. $k = a + 3$, where k represents the number of miles Kai ran

23c. $t = \frac{2}{3} \cdot a$, where t represents the number of miles Toshio ran

Connect 🔗 Extend

23d. $m = 2 \cdot a$, where m represents the number of miles Melissa ran

23. Alma and her friends are training for a marathon. Today, Alma ran *a* miles. In Parts a–d, write a rule expressing the relationship between the number of miles a friend ran and the number of miles Alma ran. Be sure to state what the letters in your rules represent. Make a table if necessary. Check your rule by testing a value.

   a. Juan ran twice as far as Alma.

   b. Kai ran 3 miles more than Alma.

   c. Toshio ran $\frac{2}{3}$ as far as Alma.

   d. Challenge Melissa ran three times as far as Toshio. Remember, your rule should relate Melissa's distance to Alma's distance.

24. In football, a team receives six points for a touchdown, one point for making the kick after a touchdown, and three points for a field goal.

   a. If a team scores three touchdowns, makes two of the kicks after the touchdowns, and scores two field goals, what is the team's total score?   26 points

   b. Write a rule for a team's total score S if the team gets t touchdowns, makes p kicks after touchdowns, and scores g field goals. Be sure to check your rule by testing it for a specific case. $S = 6 \cdot t + p + 3 \cdot g$

25. Consider this expression.

   $$3n - 2$$

   a. Why is it difficult to draw a picture of bags and blocks for this expression?   It is difficult to draw subtracted blocks.

   b. Copy and complete the table.

n	15	24	30	38	45	60
$3n - 2$	43	70	88	112	133	178

26. Orlando and Tate are packing the 27 prizes left in their booth after the school fair. They have four boxes, and each box holds eight prizes.

a. How many boxes can they fill completely?   3

b. After they fill all the boxes they can, will they have any prizes left to fill another box? If so, how many prizes will be in that box?
Yes, 3

c. How many empty boxes will there be, if any?   None

27. Claudio has two bags and a box. Each bag contains the same number of blocks. The box contains ten more blocks than a bag contains.

27a.

a. Draw a sketch of this situation. Label each part of your sketch with an expression showing how many blocks that part contains.

b. Write an expression for the total number of blocks Claudio has.
$n + n + n + 10$, or $3n + 10$

c. If Claudio has a total of 49 blocks, how many blocks are in each bag?
13

28. Here are the first and fifth stages of a toothpick sequence.

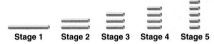

a. What might stages 2, 3, and 4 look like?   See margin.

b. Write a rule that connects the stage number and the number of toothpicks in your sequence. Use letters to represent the variables.
See margin.

29. Each stage of this sequence is made from a one-inch straw cut into equal-sized pieces.

29a. $10, \frac{1}{10}$

29b. $p = n$, where p represents the number of pieces and n represents the stage number

29c. $L = \frac{1}{n}$, where L represents the length of each piece and n represents the stage number

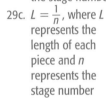

a. How many pieces of straw will be in stage 10? What fraction of an inch will the length of each piece be?

b. Write a rule that connects the number of straw pieces to the stage number.

c. Write a rule that connects the length of each straw piece in a stage to the term number.

▶ **Exercise 28** Encourage students to make a table of stage numbers and number of toothpicks. This will help them draw the middle three stages and subsequently, find the rule.

Additional Answer

28a. Possible answer:

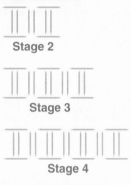

28b. Possible rule: $t = 4 + 6 \cdot (n - 1)$, where t represents the number of toothpicks and n represents the stage number

▶ **Exercise 30** This exercise is unlike preceding exercises in that the rules involve three rather than two variables. In **Part b**, students may realize that $2 \cdot L \cdot W$ does not represent the perimeter of the rectangle but rather twice the area of the rectangle.

▶ **Exercise 31** This exercise should help students recall how multiplication and division are related. If no one mentions the possibility of using fractions, you may want to discuss the fact that the rule in **Part b** can also be written as $m = \frac{1}{13} n$.

Additional Answers

30a. Gage's formula is correct. Possible explanation: The rectangle can be broken into two lengths and two widths, so the perimeter is $2L + 2W$.

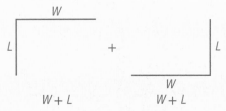

Tara's formula is correct. Possible explanation: The rectangle can be broken into two parts made of one length and one width. So, the perimeter is $2 \cdot (L + W)$.

32c. Yes; after 60 min, Adan will have walked $N = \frac{60}{3}$, or 20, blocks, and Danilo will have walked $N = \frac{60 - 20}{2} = \frac{40}{2}$, or 20, blocks. The boys will reach the 20-block point at the same time.

Math Link

The *perimeter* of a figure is the distance around it.

30b. No; Possible explanation: A rectangle with width 2 cm and length 5 cm has perimeter 14 cm, but this formula gives a perimeter of 20 cm.

31c. Possible answer: The first rule says that n is equal to 13 times m. If this is true, then m must equal n divided by 13, which is what the second rule says. The two rules are just different ways of expressing the same relationship.

Real-World Link

In race walking, a competitor's leading leg must be straight from the time his heel hits the ground until his leg is under his hip, and one foot must be in contact with the ground at all times.

---

30. **Geometry** Gage and Tara wrote formulas for the perimeter of a rectangle. Both students used P for the perimeter, L for the length, and W for the width.

Gage's formula: $P = 2 \cdot L + 2 \cdot W$

Tara's formula: $P = 2 \cdot (L + W)$

   a. Tell whether each formula is correct. If it is correct, draw diagrams showing why it is correct. If it is not correct, explain what is wrong.   See margin.

   b. Gage said, "I wonder whether I could just write my formula as $P = 2 \cdot L \cdot W$." Does this formula give the correct perimeter for a rectangle? Explain how you know.

31. This table shows values of the variables m and n.

m	6	0	11	7	3
n	78	0	143	91	39

   a. Complete this rule for the relationship between m and n.

   $$n = \underline{\quad 13m \quad}$$

   b. Complete this rule for the relationship between m and n.

   $$m = \underline{\quad n \div 13 \quad}$$

   c. Explain how your two rules describe the same relationship.

32. Danilo and his brother Adan are having a walking race. Since Adan is younger, Danilo gives him a head start. The table shows the number of minutes after the start of the race that each boy has reached the given distance. The boys are walking at a steady pace, and all the blocks are about the same length.

Number of Blocks	1	4	6	10
Adan's Time (min)	3	12	18	30
Danilo's Time (min)	22	28	32	40

   a. Write a rule for finding the number of minutes M that it takes Adan to reach N number of blocks. $M = 3 \cdot N$

   b. Write a rule for finding the number of minutes M, after the start of the race, that it takes Danilo to reach N number of blocks.   Possible rule: $M = 20 + 2 \cdot N$

   c. If both boys stop walking an hour after the race began, will Danilo catch up to Adan? Explain.   See margin.

33. In a children's story, peacocks and rabbits lived in a king's garden. A peacock has two legs, and a rabbit has four legs.

a. Complete the table to show the total number of legs in the garden for the given numbers of peacocks and rabbits.

Peacocks	2	4	6	8	10
Rabbits	3	6	9	12	15
Legs	16	32	48	64	80

b. Describe how you calculated the total number of legs for each group of animals.

c. Use letters and symbols to write a rule to calculate the total number of legs in the garden if you know the number of rabbits and the number of peacocks. Tell what variable each letter represents.

33b. I multiplied the number of peacocks by 2 and the number of rabbits by 4 and added the results.

34. In Your Own Words Write a paragraph explaining what you have learned about writing rules for real-life situations. Be sure to discuss the following. Answers will vary. Check students' work.
• strategies for making rule-writing easier
• how to tell whether a rule is correct

Mixed Review

33c. $L = 4 \cdot r + 2 \cdot p$, where L is the total number of legs, r is the number of rabbits, and p is the number of peacocks.

35. Order the following 40-meter-dash times from slowest to fastest.

4.52   5.01   4.82   5.1   5.26   6.00   5.24
6.00, 5.26, 5.24, 5.1, 5.01, 4.82, 4.52

Write each fraction or mixed number as a decimal.

36. $\frac{3}{5}$ 0.6   **37.** $\frac{132}{10,000}$ 0.0132   **38.** $\frac{7}{9}$ $0.\overline{7}$

39. $3\frac{17}{20}$ 3.85   **40.** $\frac{72}{2,500}$ 0.0288   **41.** $\frac{173}{12}$ $14.41\overline{6}$

Geometry Find each missing angle measure in Exercises 42–43.

42. 105°, ?, 30°, 45°

43.  80°, ?, 50°, 50°

44. Write the next three terms in the sequence 1, 3, 4, 7, 11, 18, 29, ...
47, 76, 123

2. Write a rule for the following table. Use the given letters to represent the variables. $k = 5m - 3$

m	1	2	3	10	15
k	2	7	12	47	72

Evaluate each expression when $w = 3$, $x = 5$, and $y = 6$.

3. $4 + 3x$ 19   **4.** $5w - 2$ 13   **5.** $8 - y$ 2

6. $(w + 9) \div 2$ 6   **7.** $(y - 2) - 1$ 3   **8.** x^2 25

Informal Assessment Students should be able to:

✔ write symbolic rules for a toothpick or dot sequence and show how the number of toothpicks or dots in each term relates to the term number

✔ recognize when rules for a pattern are equivalent

✔ use letters for variables to write rules for real-life situations

Quick Quiz

1. Consider the toothpick sequence of U-shapes whose first three terms are shown below.

Stage 1

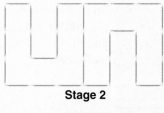
Stage 2

Stage 3

a. Write two rules that tell how the number of toothpicks t in a stage is related to the stage number n.
Possible rules: $t = 3 + 13n$, $t = 16 + 13(n - 1)$

b. Use each of your rules to predict the number of toothpicks in stage 4. Do the two predictions agree? 55, 55; yes

Apply Properties

Overview

This lesson expands numbers, patterns, and variables to the more general statements of the commutative property and the associative properties of addition and multiplication. Students explore the identity and inverse elements for number systems and write equations that show the properties. Students also work with groupings of dots to understand the distributive property and then use the distributive property to help them do calculations mentally. Finally, students use clock systems to help them understand the meaning of "identity element" and "inverse element" for a number system.

Advance Preparation

You may want to provide students with dot diagrams to facilitate class discussion while presenting new topics, including the commutative, associative, and distributive properties. Use Lesson 3.4 Master 1 for the clock system exercises.

Objectives

▶ To apply the commutative and associative properties

▶ To perform numerical calculations using the distributive property

▶ To use the additive identity and the multiplicative identity

	Summary	Materials	On Your Own Exercises (pp. 187–190)	Assessment Opportunities
Investigation 1 (p. 175) Pacing: 2 days	Students investigate the commutative and associative properties of addition and multiplication.		Practice & Apply: 1–12 Connect & Extend: 31, 35 Mixed Review: 38–47	• On the Spot Assessment (pp. 176, 177) • Share & Summarize (p. 178) • Troubleshooting (p. 178)
Investigation 2 (p. 179) Pacing: 1 day	Students use the distributive property to do calculations mentally and to simplify expressions.		Practice & Apply: 13–26 Connect & Extend: 29, 30, 32–34, 37 Mixed Review: 38–47	• On the Spot Assessment (pp. 180, 182) • Share & Summarize (p. 183) • Troubleshooting (p. 183)
Investigation 3 (p. 184) Pacing: 1 day	Students use a clock system to explore the identity element and the inverse element.	Lesson 3.4 Master 1	Practice & Apply: 27, 28 Connect & Extend: 36 Mixed Review: 38–47	• Share & Summarize (p. 186) • Troubleshooting (p. 185)

Leveled Lesson Resources

Also on
TeacherWorks™
Lesson 3.4

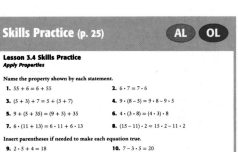

CRM *Available in:* **Chapter 3 Resource Masters**

Study Guide and Intervention (p. 24) **AL**

Lesson 3.4 Study Guide and Intervention
Apply Properties

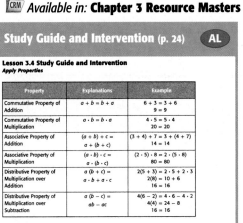

Property	Explanations	Example
Commutative Property of Addition	$a + b = b + a$	$6 + 3 = 3 + 6$ $9 = 9$
Commutative Property of Multiplication	$a \cdot b = b \cdot a$	$4 \cdot 5 = 5 \cdot 4$ $20 = 20$
Associative Property of Addition	$(a + b) + c =$ $a + (b + c)$	$(3 + 4) + 7 = 3 + (4 + 7)$ $14 = 14$
Associative Property of Multiplication	$(a \cdot b) \cdot c =$ $a \cdot (b \cdot c)$	$(2 \cdot 5) \cdot 8 = 2 \cdot (5 \cdot 8)$ $80 = 80$
Distributive Property of Multiplication over Addition	$a (b + c) =$ $a \cdot b + a \cdot c$	$2(5 + 3) = 2 \cdot 5 + 2 \cdot 3$ $2(8) = 10 + 6$ $16 = 16$
Distributive Property of Multiplication over Subtraction	$a (b - c) =$ $ab - ac$	$4(6 - 2) = 4 \cdot 6 - 4 \cdot 2$ $4(4) = 24 - 8$ $16 = 16$

Example 1 Name the property shown: $5 \cdot 7 = 7 \cdot 5$.

Suppose $a = 5$ and $b = 7$.
$a \cdot b = b \cdot a$
$5 \cdot 7 = 7 \cdot 5$
$35 = 35$

Exercises
Name the property shown by each statement.

1. $75 + 25 = 25 + 75$ 2. $2 \cdot (3 \cdot 4) = (2 \cdot 3) \cdot 4$

3. $5 (7 - 3) = 5 \cdot 7 - 5 \cdot 3$ 4. $2 (8 + 1) = 2 \cdot 8 + 2 \cdot 1$

5. $6 + (5 + m) = (6 + 5) + m$ 6. $2 \cdot 6 = 6 \cdot 2$

7. $(5 \cdot 9) \cdot 2 = 2 \cdot (5 \cdot 9)$ 8. $(9 + 3) \cdot 4 = 9 \cdot 4 + 3 \cdot 4$

Skills Practice (p. 25) **AL** **OL**

Lesson 3.4 Skills Practice
Apply Properties

Name the property shown by each statement.

1. $55 + 6 = 6 + 55$ 2. $6 \cdot 7 = 7 \cdot 6$

3. $(5 + 3) + 7 = 5 + (3 + 7)$ 4. $9 \cdot (8 - 5) = 9 \cdot 8 - 9 \cdot 5$

5. $9 + (5 + 35) = (9 + 5) + 35$ 6. $4 \cdot (3 \cdot 8) = (4 \cdot 3) \cdot 8$

7. $6 \cdot (11 + 13) = 6 \cdot 11 + 6 \cdot 13$ 8. $(15 - 11) \cdot 2 = 15 \cdot 2 - 11 \cdot 2$

Insert parentheses if needed to make each equation true.

9. $2 \cdot 5 + 4 = 18$ 10. $7 - 3 \cdot 5 = 20$

11. $8 + 11 \cdot 6 = 114$ 12. $4 \cdot 7 \cdot 2 = 56$

13. $18 - 7 - 5 = 6$ 14. $9 \cdot 4 - 2 = 18$

15. $11 + 4 + 20 = 35$ 16. $18 - 8 \cdot 4 = 40$

Determine which of the following expressions are commutative. If the expression is commutative, use the commutative property to write an equivalent expression. If the expression is not commutative, write "not commutative."

17. $11 \cdot 2$ 18. $8 \div 4$

19. $9 - 7$ 20. $14 + 3$

Find each sum or product mentally.

21. $15 + 23 + 35$ 22. $13 + 8 + 7 + 2$

23. $50 \cdot 7 \cdot 2$ 24. $55 \cdot 6 \cdot 0$

25. $2 \cdot 13 \cdot 5$ 26. $44 + 57 + 6$

27. $25 \cdot 7 \cdot 4$ 28. $76 + 33 + 24$

Problem-Solving Practice (p. 26) **AL** **OL**

Lesson 3.4 Problem-Solving Practice
Apply Properties

Solve.

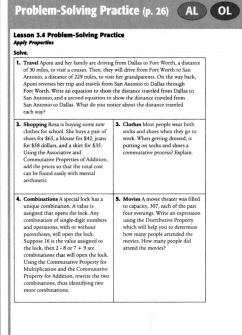

1. **Travel** Aponi and her family are driving from Dallas to Fort Worth, a distance of 30 miles, to visit a cousin. Then, they will drive from Fort Worth to San Antonio, a distance of 229 miles, to visit her grandparents. On the way back, Aponi reverses her trip and travels from San Antonio to Dallas through Fort Worth. Write an equation to show the distance traveled from Dallas to San Antonio, and a second equation to show the distance traveled from San Antonio to Dallas. What do you notice about the distance traveled each way?

2. **Shopping** Rosa is buying some new clothes for school. She buys a pair of shoes for $65, a blouse for $42, jeans for $58 dollars, and a skirt for $35. Using the Associative and Commutative Properties of Addition, add the prices so that the total cost can be found easily with mental arithmetic.

3. **Clothes** Most people wear both socks and shoes when they go to work. When getting dressed, is putting on socks and shoes a commutative process? Explain.

4. **Combinations** A special lock has a unique combination. A value is assigned that opens the lock. Any combination of single-digit numbers and operations, with or without parentheses, will open the lock. Suppose 16 is the value assigned to the lock, then $2 \cdot 8$ or $7 + 9$ are combinations that will open the lock. Using the Commutative Property for Multiplication and the Commutative Property for Addition, rewrite the two combinations, thus identifying two more combinations.

5. **Movies** A movie theater was filled to capacity, 307, each of the past four evenings. Write an expression using the Distributive Property which will help you to determine how many people attended the movies. How many people did attend the movies?

Enrichment (p. 27) **BL**

Lesson 3.4 Enrichment
Apply Properties

You can use the distributive property to make it easier to multiply whole numbers.

Example 1

$45 \cdot 52 = (40 + 5) \cdot (50 + 2)$
$= 40 \cdot (50 + 2) + 5 \cdot (50 + 2)$
$= (40 \cdot 50) + (40 \cdot 2) + (5 \cdot 50) + (5 \cdot 2)$
$= 2,000 + 80 + 250 + 10$
$= 2,340$

Example 2

$37 \cdot 59 = (30 + 7) \cdot (60 - 1)$
$= 30 \cdot (60 - 1) + 7 \cdot (60 - 1)$
$= (30 \cdot 60) - (30 \cdot 1) + (7 \cdot 60) - (7 \cdot 1)$
$= 1,800 - 30 + 420 - 7$
$= 2,183$

Using the idea presented in the examples find the products. Show your work.

1. $23 \cdot 92$

2. $41 \cdot 68$

3. If you completed Exercise 2 by simplifying the expression $(40 + 1) \cdot (60 + 8)$, redo the problem by simplifying the expression $(40 + 1) \cdot (70 - 2)$. Did you get the same answer?

4. During a thunderstorm, rain ruined a section of your basement ceiling measuring 23 inches by 89 inches. Using the idea presented above, what is the area of the ceiling that was ruined?

Lesson Quick Quiz (p. 28) **AL** **OL** **BL**

Lesson 3.4 Quick Quiz
Apply Properties

In Exercises 1–6, name the property shown.

1. $4 + (11 + 2) = (4 + 11) + 2$

2. $5 \cdot 7 = 7 \cdot 5$

3. $10 \cdot (8 + 6) = 10 \cdot 8 + 10 \cdot 6$

4. $16 \cdot (14 \cdot 11) = (16 \cdot 14) \cdot 11$

5. $2 \cdot (10 - 4) = 2 \cdot 10 - 2 \cdot 4$

6. $9 + 11 = 11 + 9$

Insert parentheses if needed to make each equation in Exercises 7–10 true. If no parentheses are need, indicate so by writing "no parentheses needed."

7. $2 \cdot 5 + 7 = 24$

8. $18 - 2 - 6 = 10$

9. $12 - 6 \cdot 5 = 30$

10. $4 \cdot 7 \cdot 2 = 56$

11. Most wide receivers in football score touchdowns by catching a pass. Order the given events listed below that lead to this touchdown. Is the order commutative? Explain.

   a. wide receiver catches a pass

   b. quarterback throws a pass to the wide receiver

   c. wide receiver scores a touchdown

Lesson Master 1 (p. 29)

Lesson 3.4 Master 1
Apply Properties

Investigation 3: Develop & Understand: B

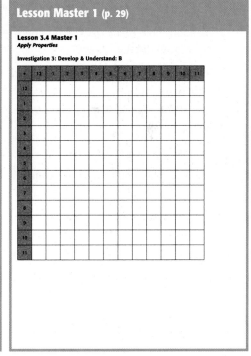

Additional Lesson Resources

Teacher Tech Tools
- TeacherWorks
- ExamView Assessment Suite
- Classroom Presentation Toolkit
- Advance Tracker

Student Tech Tools
- StudentWorks Plus
- **Math Online** eGlossary •
- Concepts in Motion

Other Print Products
- Investigation Notebook and Reflection Journal
- Quick Review Math Handbook

Introduce

Apply Properties Tell students that in this lesson they will apply numbers, patterns, and rules as general statements called *properties*. Students will study both the commutative and associative properties.

Teacher Tips The goal of this Explore is for students to observe that the sum of the page numbers for any sheet in the same newspaper section is the same and then to use this observation to generalize how to find the sum of the page numbers for any section.

If groups do not realize that the sums of the page numbers are the same for each sheet, you may want to suggest that they add the page numbers to see what patterns they can find.

If students are struggling with the last question, you may want to give them one or more of these hints.

- Think about how many sheets there are in the section.

- Think about how many pairs of numbers with the same total there are.

- Try to find the total by multiplying instead of adding.

Explore ·······························

Suggested Grouping: Groups of Six

▶ **Prepare** You will need to provide sections of a newspaper for each group of students.

▶ **Play** Ask each group to distribute one page from the same section of a newspaper to each member of the group. Tell each student to compare the page numbers of their page of the newspaper and describe any patterns that fit the page numbers.

▶ **Record** Ask groups to describe the patterns for the pages in their groups and how they found the sum of all the page numbers.

▶ **Score** Give students credit for doing the activity.

Apply Properties

In previous lessons, you learned to use patterns to write mathematical rules. In this lesson, you will see that certain number patterns can be expanded to more general statements. These types of statements are called **properties**.

Vocabulary

properties

Real-World Link
Carl Friedrich Gauss (1777–1855) made many contributions to the fields of mathematics, physics, and astronomy. His accomplishments included predicting the orbit of the asteroid Ceres.

The page numbers of a newspaper form a pattern that will help you find the sum of any number of counting numbers.

Explore ··············

Each person in your group should take one sheet from the same section of a newspaper.

Notice that your sheet contains four printed pages, two on each side. Write down the pair of page numbers on one side of the sheet and the pair of page numbers on the other side.

Compare the two page numbers on one side with the two on the other side. Describe any patterns you notice.

Next, compare your two pairs of numbers with those of the other students in your group. Describe any patterns that fit every pair of numbers.

Now work with your group to find the following sum.

A section of the newspaper has 48 pages that are numbered from 1 to 48. Without adding all the page numbers in the section, find the sum of all the page numbers. Explain how you found your answer.

At a very young age, German mathematician Carl Friedrich Gauss used the strategy you discovered using the newspaper pattern to find the sum of the first 100 counting numbers.

Gauss' strategy involved rearranging and regrouping numbers. In this lesson, you will work with several properties, including the commutative and associative properties, which can be used to simplify computations.

174 **CHAPTER 3** Patterns, Numbers, and Rules

Reaching All Learners

BL **Beyond Level** Point out that the sum of the first 100 counting numbers is 5,050. The sum can be found by applying the commutative and associative properties to rearrange and group terms, as Gauss did. Have students use the rule to calculate the sum of all whole numbers from 49 to 100. Possible methods: Find the sum from 1 to 48 ($49 \cdot 24 = 1,176$), and then find the sum from 1 to 100 ($101 \cdot 50 = 5,050$). Subtract the two sums: $5,050 - 1,176 = 3,874$.

Investigation 1 — Commutative and Associative Properties

Investigation 1

Vocabulary

- associative property
- commutative property
- identity element
- inverse element

In this chapter, you have studied a number of patterns. In this investigation, you will continue to use patterns to explore several important mathematical relationships, or properties.

Think & Discuss

Are there everyday situations in which the order that you perform certain actions makes a difference?

When you are getting dressed for school, can you put on your shoes before your socks? When you are eating cereal, does it matter if you put the milk in your bowl before the cereal?

Think about situations that occur in your daily life. Give an example of a situation in which the order of your actions makes a difference. Give an example of a situation in which the order of your actions does not make a difference.

✓ Develop & Understand: A

Consider the following table, where ☆ is an operation on the given shapes. For example, ⬭ ☆ ☐ equals ⬭.

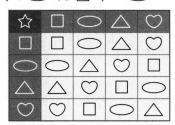

1. Perform the following operations. The first shape comes from the table's columns and the second shape comes from the table's rows.

a. △ ☆ ⬭ ♡
b. ⬭ ☆ △ ♡
c. ☐ ☆ ☐ ☐
d. ☐ ☆ ⬭ ⬭
e. ☐ ☆ △ △
f. ☐ ☆ ♡ ♡
g. ⬭ ☆ ♡ ☐
h. ♡ ☆ ⬭ ☐

2. Answers will vary.
Possible answers:
 any shape equals the shape;
 equals
; Every cell in the diagonal from bottom left to top right has ♡.

2. Describe at least one relationship you see in the table.

Lesson 3.4 Apply Properties **175**

Reaching All Learners

AL Approaching Level It may be hard for students to understand properties if students still have difficulty with rules. Review Input/Output tables, and provide some examples for students. When they are confident in using rules, it should be easier for them to work with properties.

On Your Own Exercises
Pages 187–190
Exercises 1–12, 31–35

Commutative and Associative Properties In this investigation, students explore how patterns in mathematical relationships are known as properties. They will be using shapes and numbers to see that some operations will always give predictable answers. Make sure students see that the commutative and associative properties are useful because they help us find mathematical answers more quickly and easily.

Think & Discuss

Discuss these questions with the class. Students should see that some questions will have different possible answers because order does not affect those activities. Some activities must be done in a certain order, however. Help students relate their discussion to the necessity for order in mathematical operations.

Students may debate whether milk or cereal should be first put in the bowl. The focus here is on the order of events, and this leads to an exploration of the commutative property.

✓ Develop & Understand: A

▶ **Exercise 1** Using the shapes in the chart should reinforce the importance of order and patterns for students. Make sure they understand how the chart works before starting the exercises.

▶ **Exercise 2** Students will not all find the same relationships, but they should see that each of the relationships is still valid and correct. Point out that the operations given allow for several different answers.

Lesson 3.4 Apply Properties **175**

Real-World Link

Discuss that the order of the trip to and from school does not change the actual distance.

✅ Develop & Understand: B

Suggested Grouping: Pairs

▶ **Exercise 3** Help students relate the word *commutative* to the star operation. Have them tell the meaning of *commutative* in their own words.

▶ **Exercise 4** Identity elements can be confusing; students may need some visual aids to help them understand why performing an operation can result in the same number as the original. Have pairs tell each other what makes an identity element.

▶ **Exercise 5** Make sure students understand inverse elements and their relationship to identity elements. Have them explain how they identified each inverse element in the chart.

Explore

Suggested Grouping: Groups

Work the first set of operations for two numbers on the board. Tell students to write the equations on their papers. Make sure students simplify each side of the equations and compare them to see which equations are true. Then have them work in groups to find which statements are true for other pairs of numbers. Also have them check their expressions for commutativity.

3. Yes; Possible explanation: The first shape ☆ the second shape equals the second shape ☆ the first shape.
4. ☐; Any shape ☆ ☐ equals the original shape.
5. ♡, ⬭; ♡ ☆ ⬭ and ⬭ ☆ ♡ equal ☐, which is the identity element.

① Check students' answers for all three pairs of numbers; addition, multiplication.

Real-World Link

Many students commute to and from school daily. Suppose you reverse the path you take to school for your return trip. Your distances to and from school will be the same.

The **commutative property** states that the order that any two numbers are combined does not make a difference.

✅ Develop & Understand: B

Refer to the table on page 175 for Exercises 3–5.

3. Do you think the ☆ operation is commutative? How can you tell?

Number systems have **identity elements**. When an operation is performed on a number and an identity element, the result is the original number.

4. Examine your answers to Parts c–f in Exercise 1. Which shape acts like an identity element in the ☆ operation? How do you know?

Number systems also have **inverse elements**. When the identity element is the result of an operation being performed on a pair of numbers, the numbers are said to be inverses.

5. Examine your answers to Parts g and h in Exercise 1. Which shapes appears to be inverses in the ☆ operation? How do you know?

Explore

Think of two numbers x and y. Let x represent the first number and y represent the second number.

Determine which of the following statements are true.

a. $x + y = y + x$ 　　**b.** $x - y = y - x$
c. $x \cdot y = y \cdot x$ 　　**d.** $x \div y = y \div x$

With two other pairs of numbers, repeat Parts a–d. Based on your results, for which operations does the commutative property hold? See ①.
Write two expressions that are commutative. Then write two expressions that are not commutative.
Answers will vary. Check students' answers.

176 　**CHAPTER 3** 　Patterns, Numbers, and Rules

On the Spot Assessment

Watch students to see if they have trouble comparing the statements in Exercises 5a–c. Have them first practice writing the statements with numbers instead of variables, if necessary.

176 　**CHAPTER 3** 　Patterns, Numbers, and Rules

Without using a calculator, work with a partner to find the following sums and products. See if you can find a shortcut for the calculator.

25 + 75 + 29   129   16 + 81 + 84   181

22 + 41 + 8   71   4 · 23 · 25   2,300

20 · 5 · 8   800   5 · 18 · 2   180

The ☆ table from page 175 is shown below. Use the ☆ table to perform the following operations. An example is provided below the table.

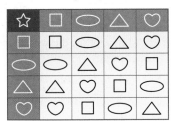

= □

Math Link

The order of operations states you to simplify expressions inside grouping symbols, such as parentheses, first.

6. (□ ☆ ◯) ☆ △   ♡

7. □ ☆ (◯ ☆ △)   ♡

8. (♡ ☆ △) ☆ ♡   □

9. ♡ ☆ (△ ☆ ♡)   □

10. (△ ☆ □) ☆ △   □

11. △ ☆ (□ ☆ △)   □

On the Spot Assessment

You can see from students' answers to each question in Exercise 7 if they are correctly using the shape chart. If they understand the properties, and they are clear on the rules of grouping, then they should answer most of the questions correctly. If not, review in detail any information you see they do not understand.

Think & Discuss

Students need to be able to find compatible numbers in order to simplify calculations. Have volunteers tell which numbers they grouped to make each problem simpler. Discuss how it helped them in each problem. If students are having difficulty finding the sums and products, you may want to give them some additional examples below.

Additional Examples Determine which of the following expressions in Exercises 1–6 are commutative. If the expression is commutative, use the commutative property to write an equivalent expression.

1. 3 + 2 2 + 3

2. 10 ÷ 2 not commutative

3. 15 · 6 6 · 15

4. 4 · 5 5 · 4

5. 8 − 6 not commutative

6. 25 ÷ 5 not commutative

Teacher Tips Compatible numbers can be used to simplify calculations in Think & Discuss. Numbers in the second column can be rearranged and grouped to create pairs of compatible numbers.

▶ **Exercises 6–11** Each of these exercises requires students to use the star table to solve equations. Make sure they understand that the equations that work for the shapes would also work with correctly substituted numbers. Help students relate the star chart to the commutative and associative properties.

Teacher Tips When working with properties, tell students to pay close attention to the order in which they solve problems. Point out that working in a certain order helps us simplify problems and will save time and effort. Have students tell how the properties can save them time and effort. Make sure they understand why the properties are important.

Develop & Understand: C

Suggested Grouping: Pairs

▶ **Exercise 12** Students use the star chart to identify the associative property. Have them tell the characteristics of the associative property before they look at the chart, to be sure they are looking for the correct facts.

Develop & Understand: D

Suggested Grouping: Pairs

▶ **Exercises 15–22** Make sure students understand that in these problems, the operation is the same throughout each problem. Because there are no other operations, the order does not change the answer. However, remind students that it is still important to work the numbers inside the parentheses first, because in some problems, it does affect the answer.

Troubleshooting If students are still having difficulty with the commutative or associative property, give them the following exercises as an alternative strategy.

1. Use the numbers 2, 3, and 4, written in any order and two addition symbols to create as many expressions as possible. Find the sum of each expression. What do you notice? The sum is always the same.

2. Now find the product of each expression. What do you notice? The product is always the same.

Share & Summarize

To help you discuss these questions, make a two-column chart on the board, and label the columns *Commutative Property* and *Associative Property*. Use the chart to list facts about each property, and then compare the two properties. Have students tell how the two properties are alike or different based on the chart.

12. Yes; Possible explanation: When adding three numbers, the sum is always the same regardless of which two numbers you add first.

13. Yes; Possible explanation: When multiplying three numbers, the product is always the same regardless of which two numbers you multiply first.

14. Yes; Possible explanation: Shapes are grouped differently in Parts a and b, Parts c and d, and Parts e and f. In each case, the result is the same.

15. $(29 + 21) + 88$; 138

16. $12 + (9 + 91)$; 112

17. $45 + (63 + 7)$; 115

18. $(24 + 6) + 133$; 163

19. $18 \cdot (5 \cdot 20)$; 1,800

20. $(5 \cdot 2) \cdot 129$; 1,290

21. $7 \cdot (25 \cdot 4)$; 700

22. $(50 \cdot 2) \cdot 37$; 3,700

The **associative property** states that numbers can be grouped differently when they are combined and the result will be the same.

In other words, $(1 + 2) + 3 = 1 + (2 + 3)$.

Develop & Understand: C

12. Do you think addition is associative? Why or why not?

13. Do you think multiplication is associative? Why or why not?

14. Do you think the ☆ operation is associative? How can you tell?

Develop & Understand: D

By applying the associative property, calculations can be made easier by grouping compatible numbers. Consider the following examples.

$$15 + (85 + 24) = (15 + 85) + 24 = 100 + 24 = 124$$

$$(7 \cdot 2) \cdot 5 = 7 \cdot (2 \cdot 5) = 7 \cdot 10 = 70$$

Without using your calculator, use the associative property and compatible numbers to write an equivalent expression to find the following sums and products.

15. $29 + (21 + 88)$

16. $(12 + 9) + 91$

17. $(45 + 63) + 7$

18. $24 + (6 + 133)$

19. $(18 \cdot 5) \cdot 20$

20. $5 \cdot (2 \cdot 129)$

21. $(7 \cdot 25) \cdot 4$

22. $50 \cdot (2 \cdot 37)$

Share & Summarize

How are the commutative and associative properties alike? How are they different? See ③ in margin.

Explain how you can use the commutative and associative properties and compatible numbers to find the sum of $(81 + 24) + 19$. Group 24 and 19. Change the order to add 19 and 24. Group 81 and 19.

③ Possible explanation: The properties are alike because both hold true for addition and multiplication. They are different because the commutative deals with the order of numbers, while the associative deals with the grouping of numbers.

Reaching *All Learners*

ELL **English Language Learners**
Students may need help with the parentheses. Make sure they understand that parentheses are used to show order, so that the numbers inside are dealt with first. Point out that the associative property is used to show that the grouping in these problems does not change the answer.

Investigation ② Distributive Property

Vocabulary

distributive property

In previous lessons, you have used different rules to represent the same situation. In this investigation, you will use different groupings to represent the same value.

One way to find different rules is to look at different groupings of quantities. For example, you can think of the diagram below as a single rectangular array of dots or as two rectangular arrays put together.

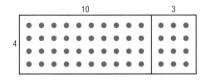

These two ways of thinking about the diagram lead to two ways of calculating the total number of dots in the diagram.

- The total number of dots can be found by noting that there are four rows with 10 + 3 dots each.

$$4(10 + 3)$$

- The total number of dots can be found by adding the number of dots in the left rectangle to the number of dots in the right rectangle.

$$4 \cdot 10 + 4 \cdot 3$$

Both $4(10 + 3)$ and $4 \cdot 10 + 4 \cdot 3$ describe the total number of dots in the diagram.

$$4(10 + 3) = 4 \cdot 10 + 4 \cdot 3$$

✓ Develop & Understand: A

1. Possible answer: Multiply the number of rows by the number of dots in each row to get $5(2 + 3)$, or find the number of dots in each small rectangle and then add to get $5 \cdot 2 + 5 \cdot 3$.

1. Describe two ways to find the number of dots in this diagram. Write an expression for each method.

Investigation ②

On Your Own Exercises
Pages 187–190
Exercises 13–26, 29, 30, 32–34, 37

Distributive Property In this investigation, students practice using the distributive property in various contexts. First, dot diagrams are used to show two ways to think about grouping numbers. Next, students receive a formal introduction to the distributive property. They use the distributive property to simplify some calculations. Then they test to see whether the distributive property works for various combinations of operations.

Call students' attention to the dot diagram on page 179. Discuss how the dot diagram shows different groupings. Some students will be familiar with this way to show the distributive property. Others will need a more comprehensive discussion. Discuss the two ways to think about the groupings shown in the dot diagram. Use dot paper or grid paper to model the shown rectangular array.

Additional Example Relate the dot diagram to students' earlier work. Write $4 \cdot 24$ on the board. Have students tell how they could make a dot diagram to show how to find the product. Students should describe two adjacent rectangles. The first rectangle has 4 rows with 20 dots in each row. The second rectangle has 4 rows of 4 dots each. You may wish to have students use Chapter 3 Master 2, Centimeter Dot Paper, to model this example.

✓ Develop & Understand: A

Suggested Grouping: Pairs

▶ **Exercise 1** You may want to use the problem-solving strategy of solving a simpler problem to help students describe ways to find the number of dots in a diagram. Use a simple 2 × 3 square full of dots and have students count the dots and find the number of dots by multiplying. Then extend the ideas to include the distributive property.

Teacher Tips

Teacher Tips In the exercises, students will interpret and make dot diagrams to show the distributive property visually. They could use Chapter 3 Master 2, Centimeter Dot Paper, when answering **Exercises 2 and 5b**. They are given a dot diagram and asked to solve for a variable. Students use dot diagrams to explain why an equation is false.

▶ **Exercise 2** Students create a dot diagram. Although this is a new skill, students should able to work independently to draw the diagram.

▶ **Exercises 3 and 4** Students find the value of two variables in each picture. Students can discuss their strategies as a class in the Wrap-Ups.

Students may use one of these strategies to find the variables in this exercise.

- Some students may find the value of r first and then use that information to find the value of t. Students find $5 \cdot 10 = 50$, the number of dots in the first rectangle. They find $80 - 50 = 30$, the number of dots in the second rectangle. Then they use this information to find the value of the variables: $5 \cdot r = 30$, so $r = 6$, and $t = 10 + 6$, or 16.

- Other students may find the value of t first and then use that information to find the value of r. Students think $5t = 80$, so $t = 16$. Then they use this information to find the value of r: $t - 10 = r$, or $16 - 10 = 6$.

▶ **Exercise 5** Students correct a common error and ignore the parentheses in an expression. Students will study the use of parentheses in the next investigation.

▶ **Exercise 6** Students are asked to interpret a dot diagram with three smaller rectangles.

Wrap-Up Have students discuss the way they determined the value of the variables in Exercises 3 and 4.

2.

2a.

5a. $5(10 + 6) = 80$,
  $5 \cdot 10 + 6 = 56$

5b.

---

2. Create a dot diagram to show that $3(4 + 5) = 3 \cdot 4 + 3 \cdot 5$.

In the diagrams below, the dots are not shown, but the total number of dots is given. Labels indicate the number of rows and columns. Use the clues to determine the value of each variable.

3. 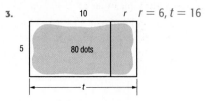 $r = 6, t = 16$

4. 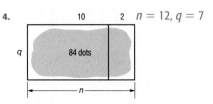 $n = 12, q = 7$

5. Jane wrote $5(10 + 6) = 5 \cdot 10 + 6$ in her notebook.

  a. Find the value of the expression on each side to show that Jane's statement is incorrect.

  b. Make a dot diagram you could use to explain to Jane why her statement does not make sense.

6. Describe two ways to find the number of dots in this diagram. Write an expression for each method.

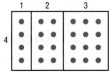

Multiply the number of rows by the number of dots in each row to get $4(1 + 2 + 3)$, or find the number of dots in each small rectangle and then add to get $4 \cdot 1 + 4 \cdot 2 + 4 \cdot 3$.

On the Spot Assessment

Watch for students whose diagram for Exercise 2 does not show that $3(4 + 5) = 3 \cdot 4 + 3 \cdot 5$. Some students may draw two diagrams to show that each side of the equation has the same number of dots. This would show that the two expressions are equivalent, but it is not the model used in this text. Review the example on page 179 with these students.

Dot diagrams help you see how different groupings can give equivalent expressions. In this lesson, you have seen many pairs of equivalent expressions like $3(10 + 9)$ and $3 \cdot 10 + 3 \cdot 9$, or $2(n - 3)$ and $2n - 2 \cdot 3$.

When you rewrite an expression like $3(10 + 9)$ or $3(20 - 1)$ as a sum or difference of products, you are using the **distributive property**.

Think & Discuss

What does it mean to distribute something? A dictionary might help. See ①.

What is being distributed in the following equations?

$$3(10 + 9) = 3 \cdot 10 + 3 \cdot 9 \qquad \text{The 3}$$

$$5(8 + 4) = 5 \cdot 8 + 5 \cdot 4 \qquad \text{The 5}$$

$$9(3 + 1) = 9 \cdot 3 + 9 \cdot 1 \qquad \text{The 9}$$

$$7(4 - 2) = 7 \cdot 4 - 7 \cdot 2 \qquad \text{The 7}$$

$$10(25 - 21) = 10 \cdot 25 - 10 \cdot 21 \qquad \text{The 10}$$

At the beginning of this lesson, you read about shortcuts that can be used to compute numbers mentally. Such shortcuts are examples of the distributive property.

Shortcut in Words	Shortcut in Symbols
It is $4 \cdot 20$ plus $4 \cdot 4$.	$4 \cdot 24 = 4(20 + 4) = 4 \cdot 20 + 4 \cdot 4$
It is 4 less than $4 \cdot 25$.	$4 \cdot 24 = 4(25 - 1) = 4 \cdot 25 - 4 \cdot 1$

Sometimes a calculation can be simplified by using the distributive property in reverse.

Example

The example shows a shortcut for calculating $12 \cdot 77 + 12 \cdot 23$.

$$12 \cdot 77 + 12 \cdot 23 = 12(77 + 23)$$
$$= 12(100)$$
$$= 1{,}200$$

① Possible answer: to pass something around or to give something out

Discuss the meaning of *distribute*. Although the mathematical usage is more precise than the common usage, this association can help students remember the basic concept of the *distributive property*. Direct students' attention to the equation in Think & Discuss. Have them tell what is being distributed in $3(10 + 9) = 3 \cdot 10 + 3 \cdot 9$. The 3

Discuss the shortcuts. You may wish to have students provide other examples of how to use these shortcuts to find products mentally.

Example

Write the expression $12 \cdot 77 + 12 \cdot 23$ on the board. Ask students:

Which number is distributed in the expression? How do you know? 12; it is a factor in both multiplication steps.

Walk students through the shortcut in the example. Students should see that by writing the equation in this manner, they can use mental math to simplify the expression.

Develop & Understand: B

Suggested Grouping: Individuals

▶ **Exercises 7–12** Use these exercises to reinforce students' mental calculation techniques.

▶ **Exercises 13–16** Students must use the order of operations to make each equation true. Parentheses and order of operations were introduced in Lesson 3.2. Parentheses can now play a role in understanding the distributive property.

▶ **Exercises 17–20** Point out that students use the distributive property to rewrite expressions and show shortcuts.

Wrap-Up Have students explain their grouping methods to a partner. Students who are having difficulty placing the parentheses in Exercises 13–16 will have the opportunity to work on this skill in future investigations.

Teacher Tips Have students recall which operations have been used together in the problems they have seen in this lesson. Most of the exercises use multiplication and addition. Tell students that these problems are examples of the *distributive property of multiplication over addition*. Write the general form of this property on the board: $n(a + b) = na + nb$

Some students will recall problems that use multiplication and subtraction. Tell students that these problems are examples of the *distributive property of multiplication over subtraction*. Write the general form of this property on the board: $n(a - b) = na - nb$

Tell students that they will explore whether the distributive property is applicable to other pairs of operations.

Develop & Understand: B

Use the distributive property to help you do each calculation mentally. Write the grouping that shows the method you used.

7. $5 \cdot 17$

8. $6 \cdot 41$

9. $4 \cdot 19$

10. $7 \cdot 27$

11. $6 \cdot 45$

12. $9 \cdot 38$

Copy each equation, inserting parentheses if needed to make the equation true.

13. $4 \cdot(8 + 3) = 44$

14. $4 \cdot 8 + 3 = 35$ No parentheses needed

15. $3 \cdot 7 + 4 = 25$

16. $3 \cdot(7 + 4) = 33$

Find a shortcut for doing each calculation. Use parentheses to show your shortcut.

17. $9 \cdot 2 + 9 \cdot 8$ $9(2 + 8)$

18. $19 \cdot 2 + 19 \cdot 8$ $19(2 + 8)$

19. $12 \cdot 4 + 12 \cdot 6$ $12(4 + 6)$

20. $7 \cdot \frac{3}{5} + 3 \cdot \frac{3}{5}$ $(7 + 3)\frac{3}{5}$

You have been rewriting expressions as sums or differences of products using two versions of the *distributive property*. Each version has its own name.

When addition is involved, you use the *distributive property of multiplication over addition*. The general form of this property states that for any numbers *n*, *a*, and *b*,

$$n(a + b) = na + nb.$$

The distributive property you have used to write an expression as a difference of products is the *distributive property of multiplication over subtraction*. The general form of this property states that for any numbers *n*, *a*, and *b*,

$$n(a - b) = na - nb.$$

Each of these more specific names mentions two operations, multiplication and either addition or subtraction. You distribute the number that multiplies the sum or difference to each part of the sum or difference.

In the next exercise set, you will explore whether distribution works for several combinations of operations.

Possible answers:
7. 85; 5(10 + 7) or 5(20 − 3)
8. 246; 6(40 + 1)
9. 76; 4(20 − 1)
10. 189; 7(20 + 7) or 7(30 − 3)
11. 270; 6(40 + 5) or 6(50 − 5)
12. 342; 9(40 − 2)
15. No parentheses needed

Assessment

Watch for students who insert parentheses around the factors in Exercises 14 and 15. Remind them that this is not necessary since multiplication comes before addition in the order of operations.

✅ Develop & Understand: C

21. The expressions in the following statement involve division rather than multiplication.

$$\frac{a+b}{c} = \frac{a}{c} + \frac{b}{c}$$

Choose some values for a, b, and c. Test the statement to see whether it is true. For example, you might try $a = 2$, $b = 5$, and $c = 7$. Try several values for each variable. Do you think the statement is true for all values of a, b, and c? **The statement is true for all values of the variables, provided c ≠ 0.**

22. The expressions in the statement below are like those in Exercise 21, but they involve multiplication rather than addition.

$$\frac{ab}{c} = \frac{a}{c} \cdot \frac{b}{c}$$

Choose some values for a, b, and c. Test the statement to see whether it is true. Try several values for each variable. Do you think the statement is true for all values of a, b, and c? **The statement is not true.**

23. Choose some values for a and b, and test this statement.

$$(a+b)^2 = a^2 + b^2$$

Do you think the statement is true for all values of a and b? **No (It works only when $a = 0$ or $b = 0$.)**

Share & Summarize

1. Make a dot diagram to show that
$6 \cdot 3 + 6 \cdot 2 = 6(3 + 2)$.

2. Give examples of calculations that look difficult but are easy to do mentally by using the distributive property. For each example, explain how the distributive property can be used to simplify the calculation. **Answers will vary.**

1.
```
  3   2
┌───┬──┐
│•••│••│
│•••│••│
6 │•••│••│
│•••│••│
│•••│••│
│•••│••│
└───┴──┘
```

Reaching All Learners

BL Beyond Level Students who finish early may want to explore distributing with other pairs of operations, such as addition and subtraction or division and subtraction. Encourage students to write an expression using variables, try values for the variables, and decide whether the statement is true for all values of the variables.

Teacher Tips This problem set addresses the misconception that any operation distributes over any other operation. This is an important consideration for students since it may affect their basic math computations when they solve more complex problems.

✅ Develop & Understand: C

Suggested Grouping: Pairs

▶ **Exercise 21** Students determine whether division can be distributed over addition.

▶ **Exercise 22** Students find that division does not distribute over multiplication.

▶ **Exercise 23** Students look at expressions involving exponents, which do not distribute over addition.

Wrap-Up Have students share their answers to Exercises 21–23. You may want to point out which operation is distributing over another for each exercise.

Share & Summarize

These exercises focus on the basic concepts in this investigation. **Exercise 1** asks students to make a dot diagram. They can use Chapter 3 Master 2, Centimeter Dot Paper.

Exercise 2 asks students to show how to use the distributive property to find answers mentally. You may want to provide students with additional practice by having students share the parts of their calculations that look difficult. Then have the class use the distributive property to simplify the calculation.

Troubleshooting If students are having difficulty showing the groupings of the distributive property, have them use concrete materials to model some of the problems in this investigation. Students may need to use bags and blocks in order for them to internalize the concepts. Once they have a basic grasp of the concepts, they can move on to symbolic representations.

Clock Systems In this investigation, students will be using the clock system to add and subtract time. They will count hours from or to a specified time, and they will learn that adding 12 to any number brings you back to the same number. Since telling time is such a necessary life skill, it is important to make sure students have a firm grasp on this material. If students are only familiar with digital clocks instead of analog clocks, you may want to spend some time explaining how to read an analog clock.

✅ Develop & Understand: A

Suggested Grouping: Pairs

▶ **Exercise 1** When students begin adding hours that take them past the 12, they must learn to start again at 1. Count from 1 to 12 as a class several times as practice to get them thinking of counting in this different way.

▶ **Exercise 2** This method of counting time reinforces for students that adding or subtracting 12 always brings you back to the number you started counting with. As long as students understand this, they can move forward in counting time.

▶ **Exercise 3** Have students write their answers to this question. Then have them read their answers after you discuss the exercise with the class. Tell them to see where they were correct or incorrect in their thinking.

▶ **Exercise 4** Have students write the addition equations individually, then trade with their partners to check. Watch to see that they are using the clock system correctly when adding.

Additional Answers
1c. 1 o'clock; 11 o'clock; Possible answers: 5 + 20 − 12 − 12, 5 + 30 − 12 − 12 or an explanation that includes passing twelve o'clock twice and starting over at 1 o'clock.

Investigation ③ Clock Systems

Vocabulary
- additive identity
- additive inverse
- identity property of multiplication

In this investigation, you will study a new number system so you can think more about the number system with which you are familiar. The number system you are going to explore is a clock system.

✅ Develop & Understand: A

Our method of telling time uses hours from 1 through 12. A number system based on the way we tell time can be called the clock-12 system.

Real-World Link
Atomic clocks tell time based on the frequencies of electromagnetic waves emitted by certain atoms. They can be accurate to within one second in more than a million years.

· ·

1b. 1 o'clock; 3 o'clock; 5 o'clock; Possible answers: 5 + 8 − 12, 5 + 10 − 12, 5 + 12 − 12 or an explanation that includes passing the twelve o'clock hour and starting over with 1 o'clock

1. Suppose it is now 5 o'clock.
   a. What time will it be in 2 hours? In 5 hours? In 7 hours? How did you find your answers? 7 o'clock; 10 o'clock; 12 o'clock; 5 + 2, 5 + 5, 5 + 7
   b. What time will it be in 8 hours? In 10 hours? In 12 hours? How did you find your answers?
   c. What time will it be in 20 hours? In 30 hours? How did you find your answers? See margin.

2. Brianna says she can find the time h in hours after 5 o'clock by computing $5 + h$ and then subtracting 12 until her answer is between 1 and 12. Does her method work? Explain. See margin.

3. Your answers to Parts a, b, and c in Exercise 1 should have been a number from 1 to 12. Explain why. Clock hours only go to 12 and then start over again at 1.

Suppose the time is 9 o'clock. To find the time in five hours, you would first add 9 and 5 to get 14. Then, you would subtract 12 to find that the time will be 2 o'clock. So, in the clock-12 system, $9 + 5 = 2$.

4. Write an addition equation to represent the following times.
   a. It is now 3 o'clock. What time will it be in 7 hours? $3 + 7 = 10$; 10 o'clock
   b. It is now 2 o'clock. What time will it be in 12 hours? $2 + 12 = 2$; 2 o'clock
   c. It is now 10 o'clock. What time will it be in 6 hours? $10 + 6 = 4$; 4 o'clock

2. Yes, it works every time; Possible explanation: When you go all the way around the clock, that is 12 hours. So, you can take off 12 hours and be at the same time.

Reaching *All Learners*

AL **Approaching Level** Adding on the clock-12 system can be especially hard for some students. It may be helpful to create and laminate a drawing of a clock face, and have students use wipe-off markers to mark off as they count around the clock. Tell them to use it as much as they want at first, but then have them gradually use it less and less until they are comfortable without it.

In Exercise 4, you wrote addition equations to represent times in the clock-12 system. For example, in Part a, you wrote $10 + 6 = 4$.

✅ *Develop & Understand: B*

5. Copy and complete the addition table to show *all* the possible sums in the clock-12 system.

+	12	1	2	3	4	5	6	7	8	9	10	11
12	12	1	2	3	4	5	6	7	8	9	10	11
1	1	2	3	4	5	6	7	8	9	10	11	12
2	2	3	4	5	6	7	8	9	10	11	12	1
3	3	4	5	6	7	8	9	10	11	12	1	2
4	4	5	6	7	8	9	10	11	12	1	2	3
5	5	6	7	8	9	10	11	12	1	2	3	4
6	6	7	8	9	10	11	12	1	2	3	4	5
7	7	8	9	10	11	12	1	2	3	4	5	6
8	8	9	10	11	12	1	2	3	4	5	6	7
9	9	10	11	12	1	2	3	4	5	6	7	8
10	10	11	12	1	2	3	4	5	6	7	8	9
11	11	12	1	2	3	4	5	6	7	8	9	10

6. **Yes; Possible explanation:** Choose any row and any column. You get the same sum whether you add the row number to the column number or the column number to the row number.

6. Examine the table. Is addition commutative in the clock-12 system? How do you know?

7. Examine the table again. What happens when you add 12 to any number? *You get that number*

In the clock-12 system, the sum of twelve and any number equals the original number. For example, $2 + 12 = 2$ and $12 + 3 = 3$. So, 12 is the **additive identity** in the clock-12 system.

Math Link
The product of one and any number is the original number. For example, $5 \cdot 1 = 5$. This relationship is an example of the **identity property of multiplication**.

✅ *Develop & Understand: B*

Suggested Grouping: Pairs

▶ **Exercise 5** This addition table can be very useful to students when they work with time. Use Lesson 3.4 Master 1. Remind them to copy it carefully to avoid errors, and have them keep it in their notebooks for future use.

▶ **Exercise 6** Students should see that the order of adding (a row to a column or a column to a row) does not change the sum. Have them explain the commutative property and why it applies to this table to their partners.

▶ **Exercise 7** Have partners each choose one number on the clock and show how adding 12 to it brings you back to the same number.

Teacher Tips There are many possible examples to use when teaching time. Even students who have difficulty using clocks and telling time usually understand that time is important. Have students give an example of a time that is important, such as getting to school by 8 am. Create problems based on the times they name to help them grasp the concepts in this investigation.

Point out to students that the whole numbers are the counting numbers plus zero, {0, 1, 2, 3, … }.

Math Link
Help students see that *multiplicative identity* simply means the number that can be multiplied by 1 without changing the original number.

Troubleshooting

The clock-12 system requires students to readjust their thinking. Help those who have difficulty adjusting by writing a schedule for the day on the board. Have students tell the number of hours from an early event to a late event. Allow students to use the chart from Exercise 5.

✅ Develop & Understand: C

Suggested Grouping: Pairs

▶ **Exercise 9** One way to help students make use of the clock table would be to copy a larger one for each student, and have them cross out the 12s with a light color. Give them another copy of Lesson 3.4 Master 1, if necessary.

▶ **Exercises 9 and 10** Remind students that an additive inverse can be used to make 12 on the clock system. Have them shade each pair of additive inverses a different color on the clock table.

▶ **Exercise 9** Point out that asking which pair of numbers adds to zero is the same as asking which pair of numbers adds to 12.

Share & Summarize

Have partners discuss the question. Then discuss their answers. Comparing and contrasting the clock-12 system and the base-10 system can be accomplished as a class by drawing a Venn diagram on the board and labeling each side with the name of one counting system. Have students tell the features of each system and where they fit in the diagram.

Real-World Link

Explain how sundials used the location and direction of shadows to determine the time. You may want to shine a flashlight down on a student or object from different angles, and ask students to tell how that might be used with the sun to make a sundial.

Math Link
The whole numbers are the counting numbers plus zero, (0, 1, 2, 3, ...).

8. 0, 0; 1, 11; 2, 10; 3, 9; 4, 8; 5, 7; 6, 6

① Answers will vary. Possible answer: The two systems are alike because they both have additive identities. They are different because 0 is the additive identity in our number system, while 12 is the additive identity in the clock-12 system.

Real-World Link
The first clocks were used in ancient Egypt. They were shadow clocks, an early version of a sundial.

In the whole number system, zero is the identity element for addition, or *additive identity*. The sum of zero and any number equals the original number. For example, $2 + 0 = 2$ and $0 + 3 = 3$.

✅ Develop & Understand: C

Consider your table from page 185. Cross out the 12s in your table and replace them with 0s.

8. Find the diagonal of 0s in your table. Which pairs of numbers add to zero?

In any number system, pairs of numbers whose sum is the *additive identity* are known as **additive inverses**. In the clock-12 system, 2 and 10 are additive inverses.

9. What is the additive inverse of 5 in the clock-12 system? 7

10. What is the additive inverse of 6 in the clock-12 system? 6

Share & Summarize

How is the clock-12 system like the whole number system? How are the two systems different? See ①.

Explain why $6 + 12 = 6$ is a true statement in the clock-12 system. Possible answer: Twelve is the additive identity in the clock-12 system.

186   CHAPTER 3 Patterns, Numbers, and Rules

Reaching *All Learners*

BL **Beyond Level** Students who already have a strong command of adding time can create a schedule for "the perfect day." Have them tell what they would do at each time for one day, and create questions for their schedules that involve adding time. Then have them trade and work each other's problems.

Practice & Apply

For Exercises 1–6, determine which of the following expressions are commutative. If the expression is commutative, use the commutative property to write an equivalent expression. If the expression is not commutative, write "not commutative."

1. $7 \cdot 9$ $9 \cdot 7$

2. $3 + 10$ $10 + 3$

3. $8 \div 4$ Not commutative

4. $18 + 6$ $6 + 18$

5. $12 \cdot 6$ $6 \cdot 12$

6. $30 - 14$ Not commutative

For Exercises 7–12, without using your calculator, use compatible numbers and the associative property to write an equivalent expression and find the following sums and products.

7. $32 + (18 + 12)$

8. $(31 + 12) + 88$

9. $(21 + 34) + 6$

10. $91 + (9 + 57)$

11. $(31 \cdot 2) \cdot 50$

12. $2 \cdot (5 \cdot 8)$

7. $(32 + 18) + 12$; 62
8. $31 + (12 + 88)$; 131
9. $21 + (34 + 6)$; 61
10. $(91 + 9) + 57$; 157
11. $31 \cdot (2 \cdot 50)$; 3,100
12. $(2 \cdot 5) \cdot 8$; 80
13. $a = 10$, $b = 126$
14. $g = 18$, $h = 4$
17. Parentheses not needed
19. 170; Possible grouping: $17(2 + 8)$
20. 48; Possible grouping: $(16 - 4)4$
21. 100; Possible grouping: $(11 + 9)5$
22. $\frac{100}{87}$; Possible grouping: $\frac{1}{87}(20 + 80)$
23–26. See margin.

Use the clues on each dot diagram to find the unknown values.

13.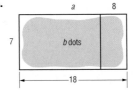

14.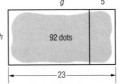

Copy each equation, inserting parentheses when needed to make the equation true.

15. $5 \cdot (2 + 3) = 25$

16. $(12 + 3) \cdot 7 = 105$

17. $11 + 8 \cdot 4 = 43$

18. $(0.2 + 0.2) \cdot 0.2 = 0.08$

Use the distributive property to help you do each calculation mentally. Write the grouping that shows the method you used.

19. $17 \cdot 2 + 17 \cdot 8$

20. $16 \cdot 4 - 4 \cdot 4$

21. $11 \cdot 5 + 5 \cdot 9$

22. $\frac{20}{87} + \frac{80}{87}$

Decide whether each equation is true for all values of the variable. Justify your answers.

23. $6(W + 2) = 6W + 2$

24. $(y + 176) \div 8 = \frac{y}{8} + \frac{176}{8}$

25. $2.5(B + 12) = 2.5B + 30$

26. $(a + 3) \cdot 7 = a \cdot 7 + 3$

Lesson 3.4 Apply Properties **187**

Investigation 1
Pages 176–178
Practice & Apply: 1–12
Connect & Extend: 31, 35

Investigation 2
Pages 179–183
Practice & Apply: 13–26
Connect & Extend: 29, 30, 32–34, 37

Investigation 3
Pages 184–186
Practice & Apply: 27, 28
Connect & Extend: 36

Assign Anytime
Mixed Review: 38–47

▶ **Exercises 13 and 14** Many students will find these exercises to be an interesting challenge. However, if some students have difficulty, refer them to pages 179 and 180.

Additional Answers

23. Not true; $6(w + 2) = 6w + 12$
24. True; Valid use of of the distributive property.
25. True; Valid use of the distributive property.
26. Not true; $(a + 3) \cdot 7 = 7a + 21$

▶ **Exercise 27a**
Adding in the Clock-6 System
Students now apply the strategies they used with the clock-12 system to a new system, clock-6. (Note that 0 is used in place of 6 from the very beginning.) They create an addition table, look at additive inverses in this system, and finally solve equations in the system. You can use this section as an assessment of their understanding of what they learned in the clock-12 system.

27. This clock face is for the clock-6 system.

The clock-6 system works in a similar way to the clock-12 system. Consider the following examples.

$$1 + 3 = 4 \qquad 2 + 4 = 0 \qquad 3 + 5 = 2$$

a. Create an addition table for the clock-6 system.

+	0	1	2	3	4	5
0	0	1	2	3	4	5
1	1	2	3	4	5	0
2	2	3	4	5	0	1
3	3	4	5	0	1	2
4	4	5	0	1	2	3
5	5	0	1	2	3	4

b. Which pairs of numbers add to 0 in the clock-6 system?
1, 5; 2, 4; 3, 3

28. Find each sum in the clock-6 system.

a. 2 + 3   5

b. 5 + 1   0

c. 4 + 5   3

d. (3 + 4) + (0 + 1)   2

e. What is the additive inverse of 4 in the clock-6 system?   2

29. Yes; Possible explanation: In each case, you would multiply to find the total number of seats. The commutative property of multiplication states that $n \cdot 45$ equals $45 \cdot n$.

Connect & Extend

29. An auditorium has 45 rows with n seats in each row. Suppose a second auditorium has n rows with 45 seats in each row. Would the two auditoriums have the same number of seats? Explain your answer.

30. Does the associative property hold for division? Provide at least one example to support your conjecture.   No; Possible example: $(8 \div 4) \div 2 \neq 8 \div (4 \div 2)$

31. In this exercise, you will use the commutative and associative properties to explore the volume of two rectangular prisms made from cubes. To find the volume of a rectangular prism, you would multiply the length times the width times the height.

a. Find the volume of the following rectangular prism. 24 cubes

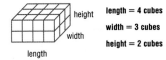

length = 4 cubes

width = 3 cubes

height = 2 cubes

31b. Answers may vary.
Possible answer:
length = 8 cubes,
width = 3 cubes,
height = 1 cube

b. Find three different measurements for the length, width, and height of a rectangular prism that has the same volume as the rectangular prism in Part a.

c. Find the volume of a rectangular prism that has a length of 9 cubes, a width of 2 cubes, and a height of 2 cubes. 36 cubes

31d. Answers may vary.
Possible answer:
length = 6 cubes,
width = 2 cubes,
height = 3 cubes

d. Find three different measurements for the length, width, and height of a rectangular prism that has the same volume as the rectangular prism in Part c.

32. Possible answer:

a	*b*	*c*
3	20	8
5	16	10
11	10	16
15	8	20
27	5	32
35	4	40

32. This dot diagram is missing information, and many sets of numbers will work. Find at least three sets of values for *a, b,* and *c.*

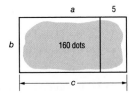

a   5

b   160 dots

c

33. Addition does not distribute over multiplication.
For example,
$2 + (3 \cdot 1) \neq$
$(2 + 3) \cdot (2 + 1)$
because $5 \neq 15$.

33. You have learned that multiplication distributes over addition. Do you think addition distributes over multiplication? That is, does $a + (b \cdot c) = (a + b) \cdot (a + c)$? Support your idea with numerical examples.

34. Marcus says he knows a shortcut for multiplying by 99 in his head. He claims he can mentally multiply any number by 99 within 5 seconds.

a. Find Marcus' shortcut for multiplying by 99. Possible answer: Multiply the number by 100, then subtract the number.

b. Using symbols, explain why his shortcut works. (Hint: His shortcut uses the distributive property.)
$99n = (100 - 1)n = 100n - n$

▶ **Exercise 32** Many students enjoy working on problems such as these in which they must use logical reasoning to find the answer. The basis for the logical reasoning involves familiarity with the distributive property.

Quick Check

Informal Assessment At the end of the lesson, students should be able to:

✔ apply the commutative and associative properties of addition and multiplication

✔ perform numerical calculations using the distributive property

✔ use the additive identity and the multiplicative identiy

Quick Quiz

In Exercises 1–6, name the property shown.

1. $4 + (11 + 2) = (4 + 11) + 2$
Associative Property of Addition

2. $5 \cdot 7 = 7 \cdot 5$ Commutative Property of Multiplication

3. $10 \cdot (8 + 6) = 10 \cdot 8 + 10 \cdot 6$
Distributive Property of Multiplication over Addition

4. $16 \cdot (14 \cdot 11) = (16 \cdot 14) \cdot 11$
Associative Property of Multiplication

5. $2 \cdot (10 - 4) = 2 \cdot 10 - 2 \cdot 4$
Distributive Property of Multiplication over Subtraction

6. $9 + 11 = 11 + 9$ Commutative Property of Addition

Insert parentheses if needed to make each equation in Exercises 7–10 true. If no parentheses are needed, indicate so by writing "no parentheses needed."

7. $2 \cdot (5 + 7) = 24$

8. $18 - 2 - 6 = 10$ No parentheses needed

9. $(12 - 6) \cdot 5 = 30$

10. $4 \cdot 7 \cdot 2 = 56$ No parentheses needed

11. Most wide receivers in football score touchdowns by catching a pass. Order the given events listed below that lead to this touchdown. Is the order commutative? Explain.
a. Wide receiver catches a pass.
b. Quarterback throws a pass to the wide receiver.
c. Wide receiver scores a touchdown
b, a, c; the order is not commutative because it cannot be changed

35. For each *What's My Rule* table, fill in the missing numbers and find the rule. (Hint: Consider exponents when you are looking for the rules.)

Possible rule: n^2

a.

Input	0	1	2	3	5	8	10	25
Output	0	1	4	9	25	64	100	625

b.

Input	0	1	2	3	4	5	7	10
Output	3	4	7	12	19	28	52	103

Possible rule: $n^2 + 3$

36. Challenge In Investigation 3, you learned that pairs of numbers whose sum is the identity element are additive inverses. In the clock-12 system, 12 is the additive identity element. Two additive inverses are 10 and 2.

In the whole number number system, 0 is the additive identity element. To find additive inverses for whole numbers, you use negative numbers. Think about a number line. Just as numbers start from zero and increase to the right of zero, there are numbers that start from zero and decrease to the left of zero.

a. Copy the following number line. Find the missing values.

$$\overleftrightarrow{-8 \ -7 \ -6 \ -5 \ -4 \ -3 \ -2 \ -1 \ \ 0 \ \ 1 \ \ 2 \ \ 3 \ \ 4 \ \ 5 \ \ 6 \ \ 7 \ \ 8}$$

b. Use your number line to find each additive inverse.

i. $1 \quad -1$ **ii.** $5 \quad -5$ **iii.** $7 \quad -7$

iv. $-2 \quad 2$ **v.** $-6 \quad 6$ **vi.** $-4 \quad 4$

37. In Your Own Words Assume you are talking to a student two years younger than you are. Explain why $3(b + 4) = 3b + 12$, not $3b + 4$. You might want to draw a picture to help explain the idea.

37. Possible answer: You need to distribute the 3, which means that you multiply b and 4 by 3.

Mixed Review

Find each sum or difference without using a calculator.

38. $165.7 + 47.5$ **39.** $3.179 - 0.238$ **40.** $976{,}556 + 0.002$

41. $87.78 + 94.76$ **42.** $10.0101 + 1.101$ **43.** $9.02 - 7.34$

44. Order these numbers from least to greatest $6.05, 6.2, 6\frac{1}{4}, \frac{26}{4}$

$$6\frac{1}{4} \qquad 6.2 \qquad \frac{26}{4} \qquad 6.05$$

38. 213.2
39. 2.941
40. 976,556.002
41. 182.54
42. 11.1111
43. 1.68

Convert each fraction to a decimal and each decimal to a fraction or mixed number.

45. $0.36 \quad \frac{36}{100}$ or $\frac{9}{25}$ **46.** $\frac{17}{20} \quad 0.85$ **47.** $1.4 \quad 1\frac{2}{5}$

Review & Self-Assessment

Chapter Summary

In this chapter, you worked with expressions that helped you develop a sense of large numbers, like a million, a billion, and a trillion. You also learned how to write repeated multiplication expressions using exponents.

Next, you explored patterns and rules. You began by searching for patterns in Pascal's triangle and in sequences. You looked for ways to describe and extend the patterns you found. You then followed common rules and rules for creating sequences. You wrote rules for others to follow. You also learned about the *order of operations,* a convention for evaluating and writing mathematical expressions.

In an *algebraic expression,* symbols, usually letters, are used as variables. *Variables* can be quantities that change or unknown quantities. By investigating different values for a variable, you can explore what happens in a situation as the variable changes.

You found that the same situation can often be described with several *equivalent expressions.* Then, you focused on writing rules connecting two quantities, such as the term number and the number of toothpicks in the term, and the inputs and outputs in a game of *What's My Rule.*

You used the commutative and associative properties to simplify calculations. Next, you saw that you could change expressions into equivalent expressions by using the *distributive property* to *expand* and *factor* expressions. Lastly, you used a 12-clock system to explore *identities* and *inverses.*

Vocabulary

additive identity

additive inverse

algebraic expression

associative property

commutative property

distributive property

exponent

factor

identity element

identity property of multiplication

input

inverse element

order of operations

output

property

sequence

term

variable

Strategies and Applications

The questions in this section will help you review and apply the important ideas and strategies developed in this chapter.

Developing a sense of large numbers

1. What repeater machine will stretch a stick one million miles long into a stick one billion miles long? $\times 10^3$

2. What repeater machine will stretch a stick one million miles long into a stick one trillion miles long? $\times 10^6$

3. Which is worth more, a billion $1 bills or a 100 million $1 bills?
   A billion $1 bills

Review & Self-Assessment

Chapter Summary
This summary helps students recall the major topics of the chapter

Vocabulary
Students should be able to explain each of the terms listed in the vocabulary section.

▶ **Exercises 1–3** Make sure students see the relationship between one million and one billion.

▶ **Exercises 4 and 5** Make sure students write each exponent correctly. For example, watch to see that they do not write 7 · 3 instead of 7^3.

▶ **Exercise 6c** Remind students that they will need to extend the pattern to find the answer. Make sure they have the correct pattern base before working very far into the exercise.

▶ **Exercise 7c** Have students determine how much money Lakita would make for each method of charging. Discuss which method they would prefer, and why they chose it.

6c. 3; Possible explanation: In 24 products, the sequence 3, 9, 7, 1 repeats four full times. The 25th product will thus have a ones digit of 3.

Understanding Exponents

Write each multiplication in exponential form. Then write each product as a whole number.

4. 7 · 7 · 7 7^3, 343   **5.** 10 · 10 · 10 · 10 10^4, 10,000

Recognizing, describing, and extending patterns

6. Use your calculator to help you complete this table.

Number of 3s	Expression	Whole Number
1	3	3
2	3 · 3	9
3	3 · 3 · 3	27
4	3 · 3 · 3 · 3	81
5	3 · 3 · 3 · 3 · 3	243
6	3 · 3 · 3 · 3 · 3 · 3	729
7	3 · 3 · 3 · 3 · 3 · 3 · 3	2,187
8	3 · 3 · 3 · 3 · 3 · 3 · 3 · 3	6,561

a. Look at the ones digits of the products. What pattern do you see? The sequence 3, 9, 7, 1 repeats.
b. Predict the ones digits of the product of nine 3s and the product of ten 3s. Use your calculator to check your predictions.   3, 9

c. What is the ones digit of the product of twenty-five 3s? Explain.

Following common rules and rules for sequences

7. Lakita works as a word processor. She charges customers according to this rule.

Charge $7.50 for the project plus $2 per page.

a. Kaylee hired Lakita to type an eight-page term paper. How much did Lakita charge him? $23.50

b. Ms. Thompson hired Lakita to type a business report. Lakita charged her $67.50 for the job. How many pages were in the report?   30

c. Lakita thinks she might get more customers if she does not charge the fixed rate of $7.50. She decides to use this new rule.

Charge $2.50 per page.

How much more or less would Kaylee and Ms. Thompson have been charged if Lakita had used this new rule?   Kaylee: $3.50 less; Ms. Thompson: $7.50 more

10a.

Stage	1	2	3	4	5
Squares	3	5	7	9	11

10c. Possible rule: number of squares = 1 + stage number × 2; stage 6 has 13 squares and stage 7 has 15 squares.

10d. Each stage has a corner squares with two "arms" attached. Each arm has "stage number" squares, so the number of squares is 2 × stage number + 1.

8. Consider this starting stage and rule.

    Starting stage: ▲

    Rule: Add three triangles to the preceding stage.

a. Give the first four stages of two sequences that fit this rule. See margin.

b. Rewrite the rule so that only one of your sequences is correct. Add three triangles to the right of the preceding figure to form a straight line.

Applying the order of operations

9. Start with this string of numbers.

    3   4   6   2   4   3

a. Copy the string of numbers. Create a mathematical expression by inserting operation symbols ($+, -, \times, \div$) and parentheses between the numbers. Evaluate your expression. Possible answer: $3 \cdot 4 \div (6 - 2) + 4 - 3 = 4$

b. Copy the string two more times. Create and evaluate two more mathematical expressions so that each of your three expressions gives a different result. Possible answers: $(3 + 4) \cdot 6 \div 2 \div (4 + 3) = 3$, $(3 \div 4)(6 \cdot 2) + 4 \cdot 3 = 21$

Writing rules that connect two quantities

10. Here are the first three stages of a sequence made from squares.

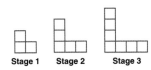

Stage 1   Stage 2   Stage 3

a. Figure out how many squares are in each of the first five stages. Record your results in a table.

b. How many squares are needed for stage 100? 201

c. Write a rule that connects the number of squares to the stage number. Use your rule to predict the number of squares in stages 6 and 7. Check your predictions by drawing those stages. If your rule does not work, revise it until it does.

d. Explain why your rule will work for any stage number.

Applying Properties

Without using a calculator, use the commutative property to find the following sums and products.

11. $32 + 15 + 18$ 65
                   12. $5 \cdot 16 \cdot 20$ 1,600

13. $2 \cdot 11 \cdot 5$ 110
                   14. $57 + 62 + 38$ 157

CHAPTER 3 Review & Self-Assessment   **193**

▶ **Exercise 8** Make sure students understand that rules are only correct if the entire pattern fits; when they rewrite the rule, they must check the patterns to be sure which one fits.

▶ **Exercises 9 and 10** Have partners check each other's strings of numbers to see if the results for each are different.

▶ **Exercise 10** Have partners test each other's rules to see if they will work for other numbers.

▶ **Exercises 11–14** Remind students to look for compatible number pairs first, and then add or multiply the final number.

Additional Answers

8a. Possible answer:

Sequence A

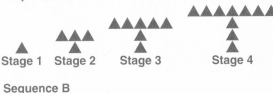

Stage 1   Stage 2   Stage 3   Stage 4

Sequence B

Stage 1
Stage 2
Stage 3
Stage 4

▶ **Exercises 15–18** Make sure students remember to work the operation inside the parentheses first.

▶ **Exercises 19 and 20** Have pairs work together to create the rules and additional terms for each sequence.

▶ **Exercises 21–24** Have students write the order or operations using symbols ($\times, \div, +, -$) in the margin of their papers to help them evaluate the expressions correctly.

▶ **Exercises 25 and 26** Remind students that 6 inches is exactly half of one foot.

▶ **Exercises 27–29** Make sure students write the appropriate number of factors in each repeated multiplication expression.

▶ **Exercises 30 and 31** Some students may choose different numbers to use in distributing the multiplication; make sure the pairs add to the total original number, such as 5 and 8 or 10 and 3 for 13.

▶ **Exercises 32 and 33** Have students work the equation without parentheses and discuss their answers with a partner to determine where to place parentheses.

▶ **Exercise 35** Check students' equations to be sure they understand the distributive property.

▶ **Exercises 36–38** Remind students to look at the clock. Make sure they use the first number as the starting point and use the second number to determine how many places to count around.

Without using your calculator, use the associative property to write an equivalent expression to find the following sums and products.

15. $(8 \cdot 4) \cdot 25$ $8 \cdot (4 \cdot 25)$, 800   **16.** $15 + (15 + 28)$ $(15 + 15) + 28$, 58

17. $25 + (75 + 92)$ $(25 + 75) + 92$, 192   **18.** $50 \cdot (2 \cdot 135)$ $(50 \cdot 2) \cdot 135$, 13500

Demonstrating Skills

Describe a rule for creating each sequence. Give the next three terms.

19. Add 3; 17, 20, 23.

19. 2, 5, 8, 11, 14,...   **20.** 1, 4, 2, 5, 3, 6, 4,...
Alternately add 3 and subtract 2; 7, 5, 8.

Evaluate each expression.

21. $6 + 4 - 5 \div 5$ 9   **22.** $5 \cdot (4 + 5) + 3$ 48

23. $2 + \dfrac{7 \cdot 4}{5 + 2}$ 6   **24.** $2 \cdot 3 + 2 \cdot 3 + 2$ 14

For Exercises 25 and 26, use the fact that a dollar bill is approximately six inches long.

25. If you lined up one million dollar bills, how far would they reach? Give your answer in miles.   About 95 miles

26. Approximately how many dollars would you need to lay end to end in order to reach from Earth to the moon 238,855 miles away?
2,522,308,800 dollars

Write each of the following as repeated multiplication. Then write each product as a whole number.

27. 11^2 $11 \cdot 11$, 121   **28.** 5^3 $5 \cdot 5 \cdot 5$, 125   **29.** 3^2 $3 \cdot 3$, 9

Use the distributive property to help you do each calculation mentally. Write the grouping that shows the method you used.

30. $4 \cdot 29$
$4(25 + 4) = 100 + 16 = 116$ **31.** $5 \cdot 13$
$5(10 + 3) = 50 + 15 = 65$

Copy each equation, inserting parentheses if needed to make the equation true.

32. $7 \cdot 10 + 5 = 105$
$7(10 + 5) = 105$ **33.** $15 \cdot 2 + 8 = 38$
No parentheses needed

34. Claire, Danny, and Jena each bought a $5 ticket and a $3 program at the school play.

  a. Write an equation using the distributive property to determine how much total money was spent by the three students.
$3(5 + 3) = 3 \cdot 5 + 3 \cdot 3$
  b. Determine how much total money was spent. $24

Find each sum in the clock-12 system.

35. $11 + 4$ 3   **36.** $2 + 8$ 10

37. $7 + 12$ 7   **38.** $9 + 3$ 12

39. Possible answers: total number of toothpicks, number of top and bottom toothpicks

39b. Possible table:

Stage Number	1	2	3
Number of Top and Bottom Toothpicks	3	6	9

39c. Possible rules:
$t = 4n + 1$, where t is the number of toothpicks
$b = 3 \cdot n$, where b is the number of top and bottom toothpicks

Writing and interpreting rules for sequences and input/output tables

39. Consider this toothpick pattern.

Stage 1   Stage 2   Stage 3

a. Choose a variable other than the stage number.

b. Create a table showing the value of your variable for each stage.

c. Try to find a rule that connects the stage number and your variable. Write the rule as simply as you can, using n to represent the stage number and another letter to represent your variable.

40. Write two different rules to express the relationship between a and b.

a	0	1	2	3	4
b	3	6	9	12	15

Possible answer: $b = 3a + 3$, $b = 3 \cdot (a + 1)$

Test-Taking Practice

SHORT RESPONSE

1 Mr. Brunney works as a plumber. He charges customers according to this rule.

Charge $50.00 for the work plus $25.00 per hour.

Maxim hired Mr. Brunney to fix a leak in his kitchen sink. Mr. Brunney charged him $125.00 for the job. How many hours did Mr. Brunney work?

Show your work.

Answer _____

Show your work:
Write an equation to represent the rule, letting T = the total charge and h = the number of hours: $T = 50 + 25h$. Substitute and solve for h: $125 = 50 + 25h$; $75 = 25h$; $3 = h$; Mr. Brunney worked for 3 hours.

Answer: 3 hours

MULTIPLE CHOICE

2 Which algebraic expression represents the sequence 4, 7, 12, 19, …?

A $3n$

B $n(n + 3)$

C $n^2 + 3$

D $3n^2$

3 Which operation should you do first when evaluating the expression below?

$$32 - 6 + 9 \div 3 \cdot 2$$

E add

F subtract

G multiply

H divide

▶ **Exercises 39 and 40** Have pairs work with the rules and sequences. Discuss their answers and why each rule or sequence students used is appropriate.

Lesson 3.2, Explore (p. 120)

④

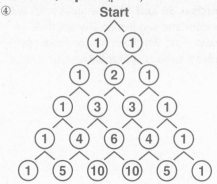

Lesson 3.2, Develop & Understand: A (p. 121)

1. Possible answer:
   - Each row starts and ends with one and is symmetric—that is, each number on the left side is the same as the corresponding number on the right side.
   - The diagonals that form the sides of the triangle contain all ones. The numbers in the diagonals just inside these increase by one as you move down the diagonal.
   - Each entry that is not at the beginning or end of a row is the sum of the two numbers above it to the right and left.

4.

								1										Row 0
							1		1									Row 1
						1		2		1								Row 2
					1		3		3		1							Row 3
				1		4		6		4		1						Row 4
			1		5		10		10		5		1					Row 5
		1		6		15		20		15		6		1				Row 6
	1		7		21		35		35		21		7		1			Row 7
1		8		28		56		70		56		28		8		1		Row 8
1	9		36		84		126		126		84		36		9		1	Row 9

Lesson 3.2, Reaching All Learners (p. 121)

1.

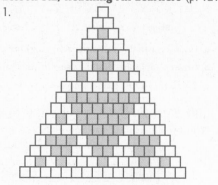

2.

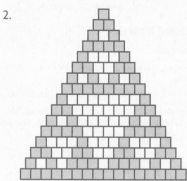

3.

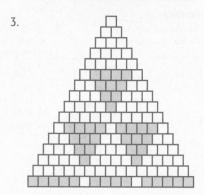

Lesson 3.2, On Your Own Exercises (p. 141)

54b. 120; Possible explanations:

- Pick the first letter of an arrangement. Once you choose that, you know (from Part a) there are 24 ways to arrange the four remaining letters. Since there are 5 choices for first letter, there are 5 × 24 arrangements.
- Look for a pattern in this table:

Input (number of letters)	1	2	3	4	5
Output (number of arrangements)	1	2	6	24	?

A given output is the preceding output times the current input ($6 = 2 \cdot 3$, $24 = 6 \cdot 4$, and so on).

- The number of arrangements of a given number of letters is the product of all the numbers of letters up to that number: $2 = 1 \cdot 2$, $6 = 1 \cdot 2 \cdot 3$, $24 = 1 \cdot 2 \cdot 3 \cdot 4$.

Lesson 3.3, Develop & Understand: A (p. 150)

4. Possible answer:

a. Stage 1 has one square, and one square is added with each stage, so the number of squares always equals the stage number.

b. You can imagine that the pattern starts with one vertical toothpick. For stage 1, one vertical toothpick is added to this starting toothpick. For stage 2, two vertical toothpicks are added to the starting toothpick, and so on. So, the number of vertical toothpicks equals 1 plus the stage number.

c. The horizontal toothpicks are the tops and bottoms of the squares. Each square has one top toothpick and one bottom toothpick, for a total of two. The number of squares in each stage is the stage number. So, you multiply the stage number by 2 to get the number of toothpicks on the top and bottom.

Lesson 3.3, Develop & Understand: B (p. 151)

6b. Possible table:

Stage Number, n	1	2	3	4
Your Variable	4	10	16	22

6c. Possible rules:

$t = 6n - 2$, where t is the number of toothpicks

$s = 2n - 1$, where s is the number of squares

$o = 4n$, where o is the number of outer toothpicks

$j = 2n - 2$, where j is the number of inner toothpicks

7a. Possible variables: number of toothpicks, number of triangle vertices, number of inner toothpicks

7b. Possible table:

Stage Number, n	1	2	3	4
Your Variable	0	1	2	3

Lesson 3.3, Develop & Understand: B (p. 151) Continued

7c. Possible rules:

$t = 2n + 1$, where t is the number of toothpicks

$v = n + 2$, where v is the number of triangle vertices

$j = n - 1$, where j is the number of inner toothpicks

8a. Possible variables: number of dots, number of dots in the top row

8b. Possible table:

Stage Number, n	1	2	3	4
Your Variable	1	3	5	7

8c. Possible rules:

$d = 2n - 1$, where d is the number of dots

$t = n - 1$, where t is the number of dots in the top row

9b. Possible sequence:

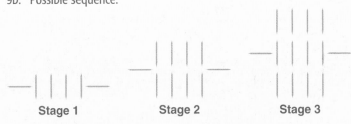

Stage 1   Stage 2   Stage 3

Lesson 3.3, Develop & Understand: A (p. 155)

2c. Possible answer: Each stage is made up of two halves, each containing a number of toothpicks equal to the stage number plus 1. So, the number of toothpicks in stage n is $2 \cdot (n + 1)$.

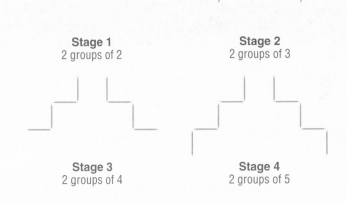

Stage 1
2 groups of 2

Stage 2
2 groups of 3

Stage 3
2 groups of 4

Stage 4
2 groups of 5

Lesson 3.3, Develop & Understand: A (p. 155) Continued

3b. Possible explanation for $t = 2 \cdot (n + 2)$: Each stage has two halves. The number of toothpicks in each half is equal to the stage number plus 2. So, the number of toothpicks in stage n is $2 \cdot (n + 2)$.

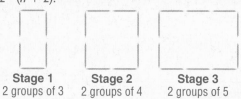

Stage 1 **Stage 2** **Stage 3**
2 groups of 3 2 groups of 4 2 groups of 5

Possible explanation for $t = 2n + 4$: Each stage has two toothpicks on the left and two on the right, for a total of four. The top and bottom each have a number of toothpicks equal to the stage number. So, the number of toothpicks in stage n is $2n + 4$.

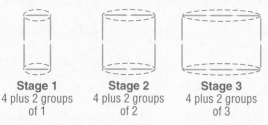

Stage 1 **Stage 2** **Stage 3**
4 plus 2 groups 4 plus 2 groups 4 plus 2 groups
of 1 of 2 of 3

4b. Possible explanation for $d = 2 + 4n$: Each stage has two dots in the center and four "arms," each with a number of dots equal to the stage number. So, stage n has $2 + 4n$ dots.

Stage 1 **Stage 2** **Stage 3**
2 plus 4 groups 2 plus 4 groups 2 plus 4 groups
of 1 of 2 of 3

Possible explanation for $d = 2 \cdot (2n + 1)$: Each stage has two halves. Each half has one dot at the "point" and two "arms," each with a number of dots equal to the stage number. So, stage n has $2 \cdot (2n + 1)$ dots.

Stage 1 **Stage 2** **Stage 3**
2 groups of 2 groups of 2 groups of
(2 groups of 1, plus 1) (2 groups of 2, plus 1) (2 groups of 3, plus 1)

Lesson 3.3, Develop & Understand: A (p. 156)

5. Conor's rule is correct. Possible explanation: Each stage has one toothpick, plus (stage number) groups of five toothpicks. So, stage n has $5n + 1$ toothpicks.

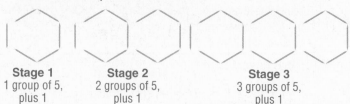

Stage 1 **Stage 2** **Stage 3**
1 group of 5, 2 groups of 5, 3 groups of 5,
plus 1 plus 1 plus 1

Jahmal's rule is incorrect. For stage 2, his rule gives $t = 3 \cdot 2 + 3 = 9$, but stage 2 actually has 11 toothpicks. Rosita's rule is correct. Possible explanation: The one-hexagon shape has 6 toothpicks. The two-hexagon shape has $2 \cdot 6$ toothpicks minus one because the hexagons share a side. The three-hexagon shape has $3 \cdot 6$ hexagons, minus 2 for the two shared sides. The h-hexagon shape will have $h - 1$ shared sides, so the total number of toothpicks is $6h - (h - 1)$.

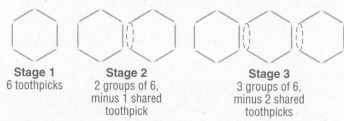

Stage 1 **Stage 2** **Stage 3**
6 toothpicks 2 groups of 6, 3 groups of 6,
minus 1 shared minus 2 shared
toothpick toothpicks

Lesson 3.3, Develop & Understand: A (p. 164)

2c. Possible answers: To find the number of green mints, multiply the number of pink mints by 4. *Or*, to find the number of pink mints, divide the number of green mints by 4.

2d. $g = 4p$, or $p = \frac{1}{4} \cdot g$, or $p = g \div 4$, where g is the number of green mints and p is the number of pink mints

3a. Number of vertical toothpicks, total number of toothpicks

3b. Possible table:

Vertical Toothpicks	1	2	3	4	5
Total Toothpicks	6	8	10	12	14

3c. Possible answer: To find the total number of toothpicks, multiply the number of vertical toothpicks by 2 and add 4.

3d. $t = 2 \cdot v + 4$, where t represents the number of toothpicks in the stage and v represents the number of vertical toothpicks

4a. Manager's earnings, worker's earnings

4b. Possible table:

Manager's Earnings	$50.00	$100.00	$150.00	$200.00	$250.00
Worker's Earnings	$7.14	$14.29	$21.43	$28.57	$35.71

Lesson 3.3, Develop & Understand: A (p. 164) Continued

4c. Possible answers: To find the worker's earnings, divide the manager's earnings by 7 or multiply the manager's earnings by $\frac{1}{7}$. *Or,* to find the manager's earnings, multiply the worker's earnings by 7.

4d. $w = \frac{m}{7}$, or $w = \frac{1}{7} \cdot m$, or $m = 7w$, where m represents the amount the manager earns and w represents the amount the assembly worker earns

5a. Cost of a child's ticket, cost of an adult's ticket

5b. Possible table:

Adult's Ticket Cost	$5	$6	$7	$8	$9
Child's Ticket Cost	$2	$3	$4	$5	$6

5c. Possible answers: To find the cost of a child's ticket, subtract $3 from the cost of an adult's ticket. *Or,* to find the cost of an adult's ticket, add $3 to the cost of a child's ticket.

5d. $c = a - 3$, or $a = c + 3$, where a represents the price of an adult's ticket and c represents the price of a child's ticket

6a. Number of fish, number of hamsters

6b. Possible table:

Hamsters	1	2	3	4	5
Fish	6	12	18	24	30

6c. Possible answers: To find the number of fish, multiply the number of hamsters by 6. *Or,* to find the number of hamsters, divide the number of fish by 6.

6d. $f = 6h$, $h = \frac{1}{6} \cdot f$, $h = f \div 6$, where h is the number of hamsters and f is the number of fish

Lesson 3.3, On Your Own Exercises (p. 167)

11b. Possible explanation for $t = 2 \cdot n + 1$: Each stage has one vertical toothpick plus two slanted sides. The number of toothpicks in each slanted side is equal to the stage number. So, the number of toothpicks in stage n is $2 \cdot n + 1$.

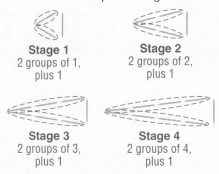

Stage 1
2 groups of 1, plus 1

Stage 2
2 groups of 2, plus 1

Stage 3
2 groups of 3, plus 1

Stage 4
2 groups of 4, plus 1

Possible explanation for $t = 2 \cdot (n - 1) + 3$: You can separate the three rightmost toothpicks from the rest of the stage. The rest of the stage has two slanted segments, each with a number of toothpicks equal to 1 less than the stage number. So, the number of toothpicks in stage n is $2 \cdot (n - 1) + 3$.

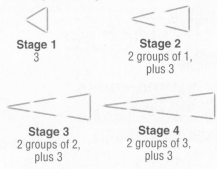

Stage 1
3

Stage 2
2 groups of 1, plus 3

Stage 3
2 groups of 2, plus 3

Stage 4
2 groups of 3, plus 3

12c. Correct; Possible explanation: Each stage has five center dots and four "arms." The number of dots in each arm is equal to the stage number minus 1. So, the number of dots in stage j is $4 \div (j - 1) + 5$.

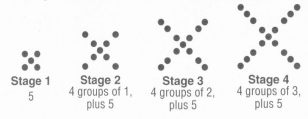

Stage 1
5

Stage 2
4 groups of 1, plus 5

Stage 3
4 groups of 2, plus 5

Stage 4
4 groups of 3, plus 5

Fraction and Decimal Operations

Chapter Overview

In this chapter, students extend their knowledge of arithmetic to adding and subtracting fractions and mixed numbers with unlike denominators, multiplying and dividing fractions and mixed numbers, and multiplying and dividing decimals. This chapter builds on fraction and decimal experience gained in Chapter 2 and in earlier courses. In the last lesson, students learn the measures of central tendency (mode, median, and mean) and dispersion (range) to help them describe what is typical in a data set, and they consider how changing or adding data values affects these statistical measures.

The **Big** Picture

Links to the Past	Chapter **4**	Links to the Future
Grade 5 Adding and subtracting fractions with like denominators.	**Lesson 4.1** (p. 198) Add and Subtract Fractions	**Course 2, Chapter 3** Signed Numbers (pp. 124–168)
Grade 5 Finding simple fractions of a whole number (for example, $\frac{1}{2}$ of 16 or $\frac{1}{3}$ of 24); dividing whole numbers.	**Lesson 4.2** (p. 216) Multiply and Divide Fractions	**Course 2, Chapter 10** Proportional Reasoning and Percents (pp. 492–555)
		Course 2, Chapter 3 Signed Numbers (pp. 124–168)
		Course 3, Chapter 12 Algebraic Fractions (pp. 626–657)
Grade 5 Understanding and applying algorithms for multiplying and dividing whole numbers.	**Lesson 4.3** (p. 242) Multiply and Divide Decimals	**Course 1, Chapter 6** Percents (pp. 346–395)
Course 1, Chapter 2 Multiplying and dividing by powers of 10.		**Course 2, Chapter 3** Signed Numbers (pp. 124–168)
Grade 5 Display and interpret data.	**Lesson 4.4** (p. 265) What Is Typical?	**Course 2, Chapter 6** Data and Probability (pp. 260–317)
		Course 3, Chapter 11 Data and Probability (pp. 576–601)

Mathematical Background

This chapter relies on students' prior knowledge of fractions and decimals. Students already know how to find equivalent fractions, reduce fractions to simplest terms, compare fractions, and convert fractions to decimals and decimals to fractions.

Research has shown that understanding of fractions and methods for computation with fractions are some of the least understood aspects of elementary mathematics. Some reasons include:

- Fractions have many uses and meanings, including part-whole relationships, division of whole numbers, ratios and proportions, scale factors, and unit conversions.

- The same fractional relationship can have many names, for example, $\frac{1}{2}$, $\frac{7}{14}$, 0.5, 0.500, and 50%.

The chapter strikes a balance between developing conceptual understanding of fraction and decimal computations and offering practice of the methods needed to carry them out. Students will work with fractions and decimals in the rest of this course, and these opportunities for reinforcement will help students master the concepts and arithmetical methods introduced here.

Also in this chapter are lessons about the three measures of central tendency, or measures of the center, the mean, median, and mode. The mean is often called the *average*, but statisticians use the term average to refer to any measure of central tendency.

Adding and Subtracting Fractions The chapter begins with an area model for adding and subtracting fractions, using paper pieces of different sizes to represent fractional parts. The pieces represent halves, thirds, fourths, sixths, and twelfths. All sums and differences of pieces from this set can be represented using others in the set. For example, $\frac{1}{3} + \frac{1}{2} = \frac{5}{6}$ and $\frac{3}{4} - \frac{1}{3} = \frac{5}{12}$. The visual and concrete aspects of this model will help students develop their number sense with fractions. After working with the fraction pieces, students develop arithmetical methods for adding and subtracting.

Measures of Central Tendency The three measures of central tendency may give different ideas about a set of data because each measure reflects a different aspect of the data. The values differ because the mean is sensitive to outliers, or isolated values at the extremes of the data set, whereas the median is not. For example, if the number of hours a student watches television in a week were 4, 3, 5, 5, 3, 4, 4, the median and mean are both 4. However, if the last 4 were changed to 8, the median would still be 4, but the mean would increase.

The ideas in this chapter lay the groundwork for more extensive work with data analysis in Courses 2 and 3. In particular, students will find ways to display data.

Additional Reading

According to Grouws and Cebulla in *Improving Student Achievement in Mathematics,* students perform best if they develop conceptual understanding early. Students rely on prior knowledge and use money and other models to help them understand decimals in this chapter.

Planning Guide
Lesson Resources

	Pacing: 5 days **Lesson 4.1**	Pacing: 6 days **Lesson 4.2**	Pacing: 6 days **Lesson 4.3**	Pacing: 4 days **Lesson 4.4**
Lesson Title	**Add and Subtract Fractions** (p. 198)	**Multiply and Divide Fractions** (p. 216)	**Multiply and Divide Decimals** (p. 242)	**What Is Typical?** (p. 265)
Lesson Objectives	• To use fraction models • To find common denominators, add and subtract fractions, and write the answers in lowest terms • To use a calculator to add and subtract fractions	• To multiply fractions by whole numbers • To model fraction multiplication • To multiply and divide fractions	• To multiply whole numbers and decimals • To multiply decimals as fractions • To multily and divide decimals	• To find the mode, median, mean, and range of a data set • To make line plots and use them to describe a data set • To predict how changing a value in a data set impacts the mean and median
Materials	fraction calculator, scissors, fraction cards, fraction mat, Fraction Match cards, *number cubes, Lesson 4.1 Masters 1–8	Chapter 4 Master 1, colored pencils, rulers or straightedges	Lesson 4.3 Masters 1–2	Lesson 4.4 Master 1
Quick Review Math Handbook	**Lesson 2.3** Addition and Subracting of Fractions	**Lesson 2.4** Multiplication and Division of Fractions	**Lesson 2.6** Decimal operations	**Lesson 4.3** Statistics
Print Resources	CRM Study Guide and Intervention (p. 4) CRM Skills Practice (p. 5) CRM Problem-Solving Practice (p. 6) CRM Enrichment (p. 7) • Investigation Notebook and Reflection Journal • Differentiation Handbook	CRM Study Guide and Intervention (p. 17) CRM Skills Practice (p. 18) CRM Problem-Solving Practice (p. 19) CRM Enrichment (p. 20) • Investigation Notebook and Reflection Journal • Differentiation Handbook	CRM Study Guide and Intervention (p. 22) CRM Skills Practice (p. 23) CRM Problem-Solving Practice (p. 24) CRM Enrichment (p. 25) • Investigation Notebook and Reflection Journal • Differentiation Handbook	CRM Study Guide and Intervention (p. 29) CRM Skills Practice (p. 30) CRM Problem-Solving Practice (p. 31) CRM Enrichment (p. 32) • Investigation Notebook and Reflection Journal • Differentiation Handbook
Technology Resources	TeacherWorks Plus Classroom Presentation Toolkit ExamView Assessment Suite StudentWorks Plus Math Online Brain Pops • Concepts in Motion	TeacherWorks Plus Classroom Presentation Toolkit ExamView Assessment Suite StudentWorks Plus Math Online Brain Pops • Concepts in Motion	TeacherWorks Plus Classroom Presentation Toolkit ExamView Assessment Suite StudentWorks Plus Math Online Brain Pops • Concepts in Motion	TeacherWorks Plus Classroom Presentation Toolkit ExamView Assessment Suite StudentWorks Plus Math Online Brain Pops • Concepts in Motion

*Included in the Impact Mathematics Manipulative Kit

Assessment Resources

MARS Assessment: Teaching with Purpose

Costumes for the Play
In *Costumes for the Play,* students use division with fractions to calculate the number of costumes that can be made using different fabrics. Students are asked how they determined which fabric is used up first.

Targeting the Task
- **Diagnostic**—Use Exercises 1–2 in the *Costumes for the Play* assessment to determine students' understanding of how to use division with fractions. For those students who do not have this understanding, completing this unit is needed.

- **Formative**—Exercises 1–2 can be administered individually according to the lessons.

- **Summative**—Administer the complete *Costumes for the Play* performance-based assessment.

CRM **Chapter 4 MARS Assessment**
(pp. 53–55)

Name _____ Date _____

Chapter 4 MARS Performance-Based Assessment

Costumes for the Play
This problem gives you the chance to:
• use division with fractions

Gail makes costumes for the school play. There are a lot of people playing rabbit roles in the play.

Each rabbit costume needs one and half yards of white fur fabric, a yard of blue striped fabric, and a quarter of a yard of pink felt for the ears.

1. Gail needs to make *eight* rabbit costumes.
How much material does she need?

White fur fabric _____ yards

Blue striped fabric _____ yards

Pink felt _____ yards

2. Gail has ten yards of white fur fabric, seven yards of blue striped fabric, and one and three quarter yards of pink felt.

How many rabbit costumes can Gail make? _____

Say what type of fabric Gail uses up first and show how you figured this out.

_____
_____
_____

Assessment Planning Guide
Assessments are available for investigations, lessons, and chapters.

 **ExamView®** Assessment Suite

Customize and create multiple versions of tests and quizzes.

	Student Edition	Teacher Edition	Other Resources
Diagnostic			CRM Chapter 4 Pretest (p. 35) Math Online Online Chapter Quiz
Formative	Share & Summarize (pp. 201, 204, 207, 219, 221, 225, 229, 232, 245, 247, 250, 254, 256, 268, 271, 275)	Troubleshooting (pp. 198, 199, 201, 207, 217, 219, 221, 225, 243, 245, 247, 250, 254, 256, 267, 268, 272, 275) On the Spot Assessment (pp. 201, 203, 207, 220, 221, 222, 223, 226, 227, 267) Quick Check (pp. 215, 241, 264, 282) Quick Quiz (pp. 215, 241, 264, 282)	
Summative	Review & Self-Assessment (pp. 283–387)		CRM Chapter 4 Test: Forms A and B (pp. 39–48) CRM Standardized Test Practice (p. 51)
Performance-Based	In Your Own Words (pp. 214, 241, 264, 281)		CRM MARS Performance-Based Assessment (p. 53) CRM Chapter Performance Assessment (p. 49)

Differentiated Instruction

Reaching All Learners

Below are suggestions on differentiating the materials presented in this chapter. Additional modifications should be considered.

Approaching Level `AL`

Lesson 4.1: Moving Forward In this chapter, students begin to move forward in using fractions, leaving behind the consistent use of fraction pieces as concrete models. It may be difficult for students to grasp concepts with fractions that cannot be easily modeled with the fraction pieces, so it is important to consistently model all the steps in every process. Create a step-by-step model for the most common addition and/or subtraction processes, and display it where students can refer to it. Tell students to write the steps the same each time, so that they can develop a routine for working problems with fractions. Then have them practice by using the chart to work several problems of the same type.

Beyond Level `BL`

Lesson 4.3: Real-Life Decimals Tell students who grasp the concept of multiplying decimals early to think of a time in real life when they may have to use the skills they have learned. Divide students into pairs or small groups and have them create a word problem that requires the reader to multiply decimals. Then have them trade problems with another pair or group and solve each other's problem. Check to see that the groups agree on the answer to the problem. Then have them work to illustrate the problem they wrote. Tell them to show the steps involved in solving the problem, and to make as clear as possible the best way to do the work. Display all the problems in the classroom.

On Level `OL`

Lesson 4.3: Multiplication Students are learning to use multiplication to get a fraction with a whole number numerator and denominator. To reinforce this skill, show a problem with decimals in both top and bottom, and ask students to divide the numbers. Explain that multiplying is a way to make the problem much simpler. To help students determine the number to multiply by, tell them to choose the number with the most decimal places and multiply by the number it takes to make that number a whole number. As an example, have students take turns demonstrating sample problems on the board. Allow each student to work a problem, with other students helping when necessary.

English Language Learners `ELL`

Money English learners may have trouble with constantly changing forms of numbers, but money is a constant that they can use as well as other students. Allow them to name items that their families buy on a regular basis, and use those items to create addition, subtraction, multiplication, and division problems. Have students tell the quantity of items they usually buy, and how much an item usually costs. Putting the problem into the student's perspective makes learning the mathematical concepts much easier. If possible, have students create an illustration of a problem, showing sketches or sale paper clippings of the items they are using and step-by-step problem solving.

KEY

 Approaching Level   On Level   Beyond Level   English Language Learners

Intervention Planning Guide

CRM Assess students' prerequisite skills and knowledge using the
Chapter Pretest found in the Chapter 4 Resource Masters, p. 35.

Intensive Intervention two or more years below grade level	Strategic Intervention below grade level	On Level	Beyond Level
If ➤ students miss 75% of the exercises:	**If** ➤ students miss 50% of the exercises:	**If** ➤ students miss 25% of the exercises:	**If** ➤ students miss 0%–10% of the exercises:
Then ➤ use *Math Triumphs,* an intensive intervention	**Then** ➤ choose a resource:	**Then** ➤ choose a resource:	**Then** ➤ choose a resource:
Math Triumphs, Grade 6 • Chapter 2: Operations with Fractions	CRM Study Guide and Intervention (pp. 4, 17, 22, 29) • Investigation Notebook and Reflection Journal • Differentiation Handbook Math Online ➤ Brain Pops • Concepts in Motion	CRM Skills Practice (pp. 5, 18, 23, 30) CRM Problem-Solving Practice (pp. 6, 19, 24, 31) • Investigation Notebook and Reflection Journal	CRM Enrichment (pp. 7, 20, 25, 32) • Differentiation Handbook

Literature Connections

Recommended Outside Reading for Students

Forte, Imogene. *BASIC/Not Boring Fractions & Decimals.* Incentive Publications, Inc., 1999.

Mayfield-Ingram, Karen, and Thompson, Virginia. *Family Math: The Middle School Years, Algebraic Reasoning and Number Sense.* Equals, 1998.
   This book is the middle school version of the very popular book for younger children, *Family Math.* Families can work together to learn mathematical concepts through games and activities.

Fiction

Enzenberger, Hans Magnus. *The Number Devil: A Mathematical Adventure.* Henry Holt & Company, 2000.
   Story of a boy who must use math skills to solve problems he encounters as the number devil leads him on adventure. Provides fun way to learn about meaning of decimals and fractions, as well as other topics.

Sachar, Louis. *More Sideways Arithmetic from Wayside School.* Apple, 1997.

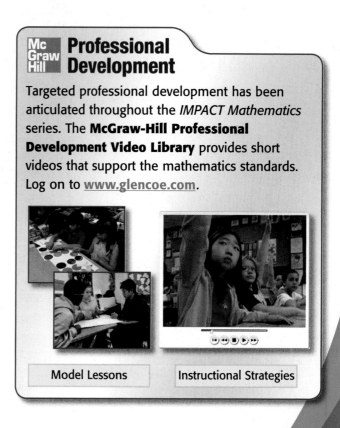

McGraw Hill Professional Development

Targeted professional development has been articulated throughout the *IMPACT Mathematics* series. The **McGraw-Hill Professional Development Video Library** provides short videos that support the mathematics standards. Log on to www.glencoe.com.

| Model Lessons | Instructional Strategies |

Fraction and Decimal Operations

Real-Life Math

The House that Fractions Built The example listed on this page to build a house shows students how fractions are used in real-life. Ask students to brainstorm different uses of fractions and decimals. Tell the class that there are many uses for fractions and decimals, such as their examples and the construction of buildings, and that they will learn ways to multiply fractions and mixed numbers in this chapter.

Think About It To represent a floor with dimensions 12 feet by 16 feet, the architect needs to multiply 12 and 16 by $\frac{1}{4}$. The dimensions of the drawing should be 3 inches by 4 inches.

CHAPTER 4

Fraction and Decimal Operations

Real-Life Math

Contents in Brief

The House that Fractions Built Did you know that planning and building a house requires calculations with fractions and decimals? Architects and contractors need to know how to add, subtract, multiply, and divide fractions and mixed numbers to make and read blueprints.

Think About It Blueprints are detailed drawings of the floorplan, front, back, and side views of a building. They are drawn to a particular scale. Suppose $\frac{1}{4}$ inch on a blueprint represents 1 foot on the actual house. What dimensions could you use on the drawing to represent a floor with dimensions 12 feet by 16 feet?

Math Online ▷
Take the **Chapter Readiness Quiz** at glencoe.com.

196

Chapter Resources

CRM Chapter 4 Resource Masters

CRM English/Spanish Family Letter (pp. 1 and 2)

CRM Lesson Masters (pp. 3, 9–16, 27 and 28, 34)

CRM Chapter 4 Pretest (pp. 35–38)

CRM Chapter 4 Tests (pp. 39–50)

Math Online ▷ Online Readiness Quiz • eGlossary

Dear Family,

Many real-life trades, such as construction, cooking, and sewing, use fractions. In this chapter, your student will add, subtract, multiply, and divide fractions while exploring real-world situations. They will use their fraction knowledge to explore data, using measures such as the mean, median, and mode.

Key Concept—Adding Fractions

Suppose you have two boards of lengths $\frac{3}{4}$ yard and $\frac{1}{8}$ yard. How much total lumber do you have? The sum $\frac{7}{8}$ yard is found by adding $\frac{3}{4}$ yard and $\frac{1}{8}$ yard.

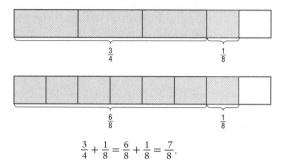

$$\frac{3}{4} + \frac{1}{8} = \frac{6}{8} + \frac{1}{8} = \frac{7}{8}.$$

Since we live in a computer age, it is becoming more and more likely that a number is represented as a decimal. For example, $\frac{7}{8}$ yard of lumber is the same as 0.875 yard. Your student will also be multiplying and dividing decimals.

Chapter Vocabulary

mean	outlier
median	range
mode	reciprocal

Home Activities

- Work with measurements, customary or metric, when you are measuring, sewing, or doing carpentry work.
- In the grocery store, find the unit cost, like the cost of 1 ounce, 1 liter, or 1 piece, of different brands or different packaging for the same item. Decide which is the better value.
- Figure out the correct quantities when doubling or halving a recipe.

Family Letter

Another version of the Family Letter, available in English and Spanish, is found in the Chapter 4 Resource Masters. You may want to send a copy of this letter home with your students.

Key Concept-Adding Fractions Introduce students to adding fractions by having them model the two boards of length $\frac{3}{4}$ yard and $\frac{1}{8}$ yard with strips of paper. Have them brainstorm how to represent the total length.

Ask students to write an equivalent fraction for $\frac{3}{4}$ in eighths. Can the total length now be represented as eighths?

Ask students to conjecture how to add two fractions with unlike denominators.

Home Activities

- Have students measure the perimeter of room in your house using a ruler or yardstick. Do they have to know how to add fractions? What unit of measure is most convenient, customary or metric?

- Each day, have your student cut out a different rectangular strip of paper 12 inches long and then remove a fraction of the paper. Use the fractions $\frac{1}{2}$, $\frac{1}{3}$, $\frac{1}{4}$, and $\frac{1}{6}$. What are the lengths of paper that remain?

Key Vocabulary

English (Spanish) *Introduce the most important terms from Chapter 4.*

mean (media) The number you get by distributing the total of the values in a data set among the members of the data set. You can compute the mean by adding the values and dividing by the total number of values. For example, for the data set 5, 6, 6, 8, 8, 8, 9, 10, 12, the *mean* is 8. (p. 270)

median (mediana) The middle value when all the values in a data set are ordered from least to greatest. For example, for the data set 4.5, 6, 7, 8.5, 10.5, 12, 12, 14.5, the *median* is 8.5. (p. 266)

mode (moda) The value in a data set that occurs most often. For example, for the data set 4.5, 6, 7, 7, 7, 8.5, 10.5, 12, 12, the *mode* is 7. (p. 266)

outlier (valor atipico) A value that is much greater than or much less than most of the other values in a data set. For example, for the data set 6, 8.2, 9.5, 11.6, 14, 30, the value 30 is an *outlier*. (p. 274)

range (rango) The difference between the minimum and maximum values of a data set. For example, for the data set 4.5, 6, 7, 7, 7, 8.5, 10.5, 12, 12, the range is $12 - 4.5 = 7.5$. (p. 266)

reciprocal (recíproco) Two numbers are reciprocals if their product is one. For example, the reciprocal of $\frac{5}{7}$ is $\frac{7}{5}$. (p. 231)

LESSON 4.1

Add and Subtract Fractions

Objectives

▶ To use fraction models

▶ To find common denominators, add and subtract fractions, and write the answers in lowest terms

▶ To use a calculator to add and subtract fractions

Overview

In this lesson, students build on their understanding of the meaning of fractions to develop techniques for adding and subtracting fractions with different denominators. Students begin by using fraction mats and fraction pieces to model the process. This provides them with a solid visual and conceptual basis for understanding and internalizing the steps of the algorithms they eventually use.

Advance Preparation

You may want to provide copies of Lesson 4.1 Masters 1–8 to facilitate class discussion while presenting these topics, including adding and subtracting fractions.

	Summary	Materials	On Your Own Exercises (pp. 210–215)	Assessment Opportunities
Investigation 1 (p. 198) *Pacing: 2 days*	Students use fraction models to explore addition and subtraction of fractions with denominators of 2, 3, 4, 6, and 12.	Lesson 4.1 Master 1, Fraction Pieces, Lesson 4.1 Master 2, Fraction Mats, transparencies of Lesson 4.1 Masters 1–2, scissors (optional)	Practice & Apply: 1–14 Connect & Extend: 32–35 Mixed Review: 54–68	• On the Spot Assessment (p. 201) • Share & Summarize (p. 201) • Troubleshooting (pp. 198, 199, 201)
Investigation 2 (p. 201) *Pacing: 1 day*	Students find a common denominator to add and subtract fractions symbolically. They create magic squares.	Lesson 4.1 Masters 3 and 4, scissors, *number cubes (optional), self-stick notes (optional)	Practice & Apply: 15–24 Connect & Extend: 36–43, 48 Mixed Review: 54–68	• On the Spot Assessment (p. 203) • Share & Summarize (p. 204)
Investigation 3 (p. 205) *Pacing: 1 day*	Students add and subtract mixed numbers with regrouping.		Practice & Apply: 25–31 Connect & Extend: 44–47, 49–53 Mixed Review: 54–68	• On the Spot Assessment (p. 207) • Share & Summarize (p. 207) • Troubleshooting (p. 207)
Inquiry Investigation 4 (p. 208) *Pacing: 1 day*	Students explore using fraction calculators	Lesson 4.1 Masters 5–8, scissors, fraction calculators		

*Included in the Impact Mathematics Manipulative Kit

Leveled Lesson Resources

Also on
TeacherWorks™
Lesson 4.1

Study Guide and Intervention (p. 4) AL

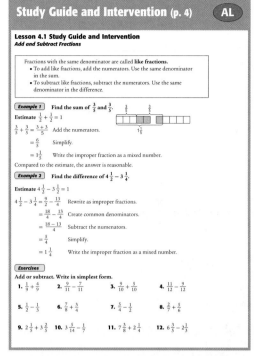

Lesson 4.1 Study Guide and Intervention
Add and Subtract Fractions

Fractions with the same denominator are called **like fractions.**
- To add like fractions, add the numerators. Use the same denominator in the sum.
- To subtract like fractions, subtract the numerators. Use the same denominator in the difference.

Example 1 Find the sum of $\frac{3}{5}$ and $\frac{3}{5}$.

Estimate $\frac{1}{2} + \frac{1}{2} = 1$

$\frac{3}{5} + \frac{3}{5} = \frac{3+3}{5}$ Add the numerators.

$= \frac{6}{5}$ Simplify.

$= 1\frac{1}{5}$ Write the improper fraction as a mixed number.

Compared to the estimate, the answer is reasonable.

Example 2 Find the difference of $4\frac{1}{2} - 3\frac{1}{4}$.

Estimate $4\frac{1}{2} - 3\frac{1}{2} = 1$

$4\frac{1}{2} - 3\frac{1}{4} = \frac{9}{2} - \frac{13}{4}$ Rewrite as improper fractions.

$= \frac{18}{4} - \frac{13}{4}$ Create common denominators.

$= \frac{18-13}{4}$ Subtract the numerators.

$= \frac{5}{4}$ Simplify.

$= 1\frac{1}{4}$ Write the improper fraction as a mixed number.

Exercises

Add or subtract. Write in simplest form.

1. $\frac{1}{9} + \frac{4}{9}$ 2. $\frac{9}{11} - \frac{7}{11}$ 3. $\frac{9}{10} + \frac{5}{10}$ 4. $\frac{11}{12} - \frac{9}{12}$

5. $\frac{1}{2} - \frac{1}{3}$ 6. $\frac{7}{8} + \frac{3}{4}$ 7. $\frac{5}{4} - \frac{1}{2}$ 8. $\frac{2}{7} + \frac{5}{6}$

9. $2\frac{1}{5} + 3\frac{2}{5}$ 10. $3\frac{5}{14} - \frac{1}{7}$ 11. $7\frac{3}{8} + 2\frac{1}{4}$ 12. $6\frac{3}{5} - 2\frac{1}{3}$

Skills Practice (p. 5) AL OL

Lesson 4.1 Skills Practice
Add and Subtract Fractions

Add or subtract. Write in simplest form.

1. $\frac{2}{3} + \frac{5}{6}$ 2. $\frac{5}{6} + \frac{3}{4}$

3. $\frac{2}{3} - \frac{1}{6}$ 4. $\frac{1}{2} + \frac{2}{8}$

5. $\frac{4}{7} - \frac{1}{2}$ 6. $\frac{1}{6} - \frac{1}{12}$

7. $\frac{5}{8} - \frac{1}{4}$ 8. $\frac{1}{3} + \frac{5}{7}$

9. $\frac{1}{5} + \frac{5}{6}$ 10. $\frac{3}{4} + \frac{11}{12}$

11. $\frac{1}{2} - \frac{2}{5}$ 12. $\frac{11}{12} - \frac{3}{4}$

13. $8\frac{5}{8} - 4\frac{2}{5}$ 14. $1\frac{5}{7} + \frac{2}{7}$

15. $11\frac{1}{4} + 3\frac{3}{8}$ 16. $6\frac{5}{9} - 2\frac{1}{18}$

17. $14\frac{1}{3} + 5\frac{4}{5}$ 18. $10\frac{3}{4} - 2\frac{2}{3}$

19. How much more is $\frac{3}{8}$ gallon than $\frac{1}{4}$ gallon?

20. How much more is $\frac{3}{4}$ ounce than $\frac{1}{3}$ ounce?

21. Evaluate $x - y$ if $x = \frac{7}{10}$ and $y = \frac{3}{5}$.

22. Evaluate $s + t$ if $s = \frac{2}{3}$ and $t = \frac{5}{6}$.

Problem-Solving Practice (p. 6) AL OL

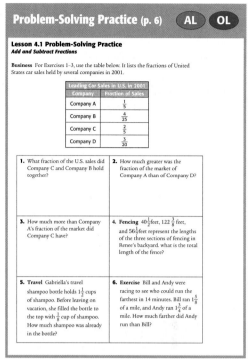

Lesson 4.1 Problem-Solving Practice
Add and Subtract Fractions

Business For Exercises 1–3, use the table below. It lists the fractions of United States car sales held by several companies in 2001.

Leading Car Sales in U.S. in 2001	
Company	Fraction of Sales
Company A	$\frac{1}{5}$
Company B	$\frac{4}{25}$
Company C	$\frac{2}{5}$
Company D	$\frac{3}{20}$

1. What fraction of the U.S. sales did Company C and Company B hold together?

2. How much greater was the fraction of the market of Company A than of Company D?

3. How much more than Company A's fraction of the market did Company C have?

4. **Fencing** $40\frac{1}{2}$ feet, $122\frac{3}{8}$ feet, and $56\frac{1}{2}$ feet represent the lengths of the three sections of fencing in Renee's backyard. what is the total length of the fence?

5. **Travel** Gabriella's travel shampoo bottle holds $1\frac{1}{2}$ cups of shampoo. Before leaving on vacation, she filled the bottle to the top with $\frac{1}{6}$ cup of shampoo. How much shampoo was already in the bottle?

6. **Exercise** Bill and Andy were racing to see who could run the farthest in 14 minutes. Bill ran $1\frac{5}{8}$ of a mile, and Andy ran $1\frac{3}{4}$ of a mile. How much farther did Andy run than Bill?

Enrichment (p. 7) BL

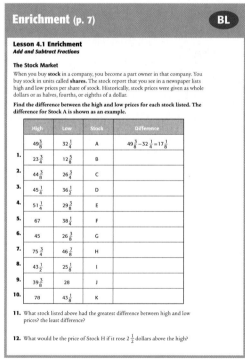

Lesson 4.1 Enrichment
Add and Subtract Fractions

The Stock Market

When you buy **stock** in a company, you become a part owner in that company. You buy stock in units called **shares.** The stock report that you see in a newspaper lists high and low prices per share of stock. Historically, stock prices were given as whole dollars or as halves, fourths, or eighths of a dollar.

Find the difference between the high and low prices for each stock listed. The difference for Stock A is shown as an example.

	High	Low	Stock	Difference
	$49\frac{3}{8}$	$32\frac{1}{4}$	A	$49\frac{3}{8} - 32\frac{1}{4} = 17\frac{1}{8}$
1.	$23\frac{3}{4}$	$12\frac{5}{8}$	B	
2.	$44\frac{3}{8}$	$26\frac{3}{8}$	C	
3.	$45\frac{1}{4}$	$36\frac{1}{2}$	D	
4.	$51\frac{1}{4}$	$29\frac{3}{8}$	E	
5.	67	$38\frac{1}{4}$	F	
6.	45	$26\frac{3}{8}$	G	
7.	$75\frac{3}{4}$	$46\frac{7}{8}$	H	
8.	$43\frac{1}{2}$	$25\frac{1}{8}$	I	
9.	$39\frac{3}{8}$	28	J	
10.	78	$43\frac{1}{8}$	K	

11. What stock listed above had the greatest difference between high and low prices? the least difference?

12. What would be the price of Stock H if it rose $2\frac{1}{2}$ dollars above the high?

Lesson Quick Quiz (p. 8) AL OL BL

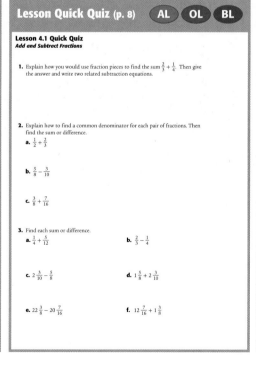

Lesson 4.1 Quick Quiz
Add and Subtract Fractions

1. Explain how you would use fraction pieces to find the sum $\frac{2}{3} + \frac{1}{4}$. Then give the answer and write two related subtraction equations.

2. Explain how to find a common denominator for each pair of fractions. Then find the sum or difference.

a. $\frac{1}{2} + \frac{2}{3}$

b. $\frac{5}{8} - \frac{3}{10}$

c. $\frac{3}{8} + \frac{7}{16}$

3. Find each sum or difference.

a. $\frac{1}{4} + \frac{5}{12}$ b. $\frac{2}{3} - \frac{1}{4}$

c. $2\frac{3}{10} - \frac{5}{8}$ d. $1\frac{5}{8} + 2\frac{3}{10}$

e. $22\frac{3}{8} - 20\frac{7}{16}$ f. $12\frac{7}{16} + 1\frac{3}{8}$

Lesson Masters 1–8 (pp. 9–16)

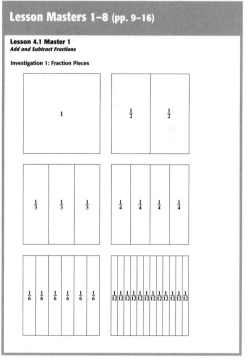

Lesson 4.1 Master 1
Add and Subtract Fractions

Investigation 1: Fraction Pieces

Additional Lesson Resources

Teacher Tech Tools
- TeacherWorks
- ExamView Assessment Suite
- Classroom Presentation Toolkit
- Advance Tracker

Student Tech Tools
- StudentWorks Plus
- Math Online eGlossary •
- Concepts in Motion

Other Print Products
- Investigation Notebook and Reflection Journal
- Quick Review Math Handbook

Introduce

Fractions Begin the lesson by reminding students that they have already computed with fractions. To prove this point, the Think & Discuss activity poses some simple addition and subtraction problems that students can solve mentally.

Think & Discuss

As students review adding and subtracting fractions with the same denominator, they will need to recall how to express one as various fractions with different denominators such as $\frac{5}{5}$, $\frac{6}{6}$, and $\frac{3}{3}$.

Spend some time discussing students' methods for solving these problems. If students do not have a good understanding of addition and subtraction of fractions with the same denominator, they will have difficulty following the ideas in this lesson. If necessary, provide additional problems after you have discussed how to find the answers.

Investigation ①

On Your Own Exercises
Pages 210–215
Exercises 1–14, 32–35

Use Fraction Models In this investigation, students use fraction pieces to add and subtract fractions with different denominators. Introduce the fraction pieces and the fraction mat model. Ask students how many one-fourth pieces would be needed to cover the square mat. 4

Provide each pair of students with either fraction manipulatives or scissors and one copy each of Lesson 4.1 Masters 1 and 2 Remind students that they need to cut carefully so that the pieces fit together exactly.

---

① Possible answer: Find a fraction with the same denominator as the given fraction such that the sum of the two numerators equals the denominator.

LESSON 4.1 Add and Subtract Fractions

You know how to compare fractions and how to find equivalent fractions. Now you will begin to think about adding and subtracting fractions. You already know how to add and subtract fractions with the same denominator.

Think & Discuss

Solve each problem in your head.

$$\frac{1}{5} + \frac{2}{5} = \frac{3}{5} \qquad \frac{5}{7} - \frac{2}{7} = \frac{3}{7} \qquad \frac{1}{2} + \frac{1}{2} = \frac{2}{2}, \text{ or } 1$$

$$\frac{1}{3} + \frac{2}{3} = 1 \qquad \frac{4}{6}, \text{ or } \frac{2}{3} + \frac{2}{6} = 1 \qquad \frac{5}{8} + \frac{3}{8} = 1$$

$$1 - \frac{1}{3} = \frac{2}{3} \qquad 1 - \frac{3}{8} = \frac{5}{8} \qquad 1 - \frac{1}{6} = \frac{5}{6}$$

Explain how to add or subtract fractions with the same denominator. Add or subtract the numerators while keeping the denominator the same.

Explain how to find a fraction that adds to another fraction with the same denominator to produce a 1. See ①.

Explain how to subtract a fraction from 1. Possible answer: Rename 1 as $\dfrac{\text{denominator of given fraction}}{\text{denominator of given fraction}}$ and subtract.

Investigation ① Use Fraction Models

Materials
- set of fraction pieces and whole square

You can use models to add and subtract fractions.

The square represents the whole, or 1.

The rectangles represent fractions of the whole, or fraction pieces.

Troubleshooting

If students have difficulty representing fractions using fraction models, make transparencies of Lesson 4.1 Masters 1 and 2 and cut out the fraction pieces so you can model their use and discuss any problems. Coloring the transparent fraction pieces using overhead markers might be helpful.

Point out as you use the models what each fraction represents.

Example

One $\frac{1}{2}$ piece and three $\frac{1}{6}$ pieces cover the square. Represent this with the addition equation.

$$\frac{1}{2} + \frac{3}{6} = 1$$

Removing three $\frac{1}{6}$ pieces leaves a $\frac{1}{2}$ piece. Represent this with the subtraction equation.

$$1 - \frac{3}{6} = \frac{1}{2}$$

✓ Develop & Understand: A

1. Choose fraction pieces with two different denominators.

   a. Find as many ways as you can to cover the whole square with those two types of fraction pieces. Rearranging the same pieces in different positions does *not* count as a new way to cover the square. **Answers will vary.**

   For each combination you find, make a sketch and write an equation. Each equation should be a sum of two fractions equal to 1. For example, the equation in the example above is $\frac{1}{2} + \frac{3}{6} = 1$. **Answers will vary.**

   b. Choose another pair of denominators. Look for ways to cover the square with those two types of fraction pieces. Record a sketch and an equation for each combination. **Answers will vary.**

   c. Continue this process until you think you have found all the ways to cover the square with two types of fraction pieces.

1c. These are the 16 possible equations:

$$\frac{1}{2} + \frac{2}{4} = 1, \quad \frac{1}{2} + \frac{3}{6} = 1,$$
$$\frac{1}{2} + \frac{6}{12} = 1, \quad \frac{1}{3} + \frac{4}{6} = 1,$$
$$\frac{1}{3} + \frac{8}{12} = 1, \quad \frac{2}{3} + \frac{2}{6} = 1,$$
$$\frac{2}{3} + \frac{4}{12} = 1, \quad \frac{1}{4} + \frac{9}{12} = 1,$$
$$\frac{2}{4} + \frac{3}{6} = 1, \quad \frac{2}{4} + \frac{6}{12} = 1,$$
$$\frac{3}{4} + \frac{3}{12} = 1, \quad \frac{1}{6} + \frac{10}{12} = 1,$$
$$\frac{2}{6} + \frac{8}{12} = 1, \quad \frac{3}{6} + \frac{6}{12} = 1,$$
$$\frac{4}{6} + \frac{4}{12} = 1, \quad \frac{5}{6} + \frac{2}{12} = 1$$

2. For each addition equation, you can write two related subtraction equations. In the example above, the sixths pieces were removed to get $1 - \frac{3}{6} = \frac{1}{2}$. You could instead remove the $\frac{1}{2}$ piece to get $1 - \frac{1}{2} = \frac{3}{6}$.

   Choose three of the addition equations you wrote in Exercise 1. Write two related subtraction equations for each. **Answers will vary.**

3. Now find as many ways as you can to cover the square with *three* different types of fraction pieces. Record a sketch and an equation for each combination. **See margin.**

Lesson 4.1 Add and Subtract Fractions **199**

Additional Answer

3. There are 20 possible equations:

$$\frac{1}{2} + \frac{1}{4} + \frac{3}{12} = 1, \quad \frac{1}{2} + \frac{1}{3} + \frac{1}{6} = 1,$$
$$\frac{1}{2} + \frac{1}{3} + \frac{2}{12} = 1, \quad \frac{1}{2} + \frac{1}{6} + \frac{4}{12} = 1,$$
$$\frac{1}{2} + \frac{2}{6} + \frac{2}{12} = 1, \quad \frac{1}{3} + \frac{1}{4} + \frac{5}{12} = 1,$$
$$\frac{1}{3} + \frac{2}{4} + \frac{1}{6} = 1, \quad \frac{1}{3} + \frac{2}{4} + \frac{2}{12} = 1,$$
$$\frac{1}{3} + \frac{1}{6} + \frac{6}{12} = 1, \quad \frac{1}{3} + \frac{2}{6} + \frac{4}{12} = 1,$$
$$\frac{1}{3} + \frac{3}{6} + \frac{2}{12} = 1, \quad \frac{2}{3} + \frac{1}{6} + \frac{2}{12} = 1,$$
$$\frac{2}{3} + \frac{1}{4} + \frac{1}{12} = 1, \quad \frac{1}{4} + \frac{1}{6} + \frac{7}{12} = 1,$$

$$\frac{1}{4} + \frac{2}{6} + \frac{5}{12} = 1, \quad \frac{1}{4} + \frac{3}{6} + \frac{3}{12} = 1,$$
$$\frac{1}{4} + \frac{4}{6} + \frac{1}{12} = 1, \quad \frac{2}{4} + \frac{1}{6} + \frac{4}{12} = 1,$$
$$\frac{2}{4} + \frac{2}{6} + \frac{2}{12} = 1, \quad \frac{3}{4} + \frac{1}{6} + \frac{1}{12} = 1$$

Have students use their fraction models to show the addition and subtraction in the Example. For most students, this Example will be straightforward and will help to clarify how they can use fraction pieces to add and subtract. You might also ask:

- How are the two equations similar and how are they different? Possible answer: Both use the same numbers and fraction pieces, but they use different operations, and their answers are different.

Point out that the relationship between addition and subtraction of fractions is the same as the one for whole numbers.

✓ Develop & Understand: A

Suggested Grouping: Pairs

▶ **Exercise 1–3** Make sure students save their work from these exercises so they can use them in Investigation 2.

▶ **Exercises 1 and 3** Some students may reverse the order of the addends in these exercises and present them as different equations. When discussing these exercises, remind students that the commutative property states that changing the order of the addends does not change the sum, and that this property applies to all addition expressions regardless of the type of numbers added.

▶ **Exercise 2** Use this exercise to reinforce the inverse relationship between addition and subtraction of fractions.

Troubleshooting Watch for students who have difficulty deciding whether they have found all the equations in **Exercises 1c and 3**. Discuss how to organize the data, including a table or a list. Ask volunteers to write their equations from these exercises on the board and have the class check that each equation is accurate and different from the other equations.

Lesson 4.1 Add and Subtract Fractions **199**

Teacher Tips Tell students that while all the sums they have worked with so far have been equal to one, they can also use fraction pieces to find sums greater than one and sums less than one.

Example Ask students how they can use fraction pieces to find $\frac{2}{4} + \frac{1}{6}$ before they look at the Example. Someone will likely present the solution shown in the Example, and if so, you can point that out.

Another solution would be to find a fraction piece or pieces to fill the square. In this case, a $\frac{1}{3}$ piece will fill it, so the sum must be $1 - \frac{1}{3}$, or $\frac{2}{3}$.

Otherwise, you can discuss the Example by having students use their fraction pieces to model the addition and subtraction equations. Make sure they understand how to use the models to form sums less than one. If they seem uncertain, you might let them practice on other problems, such as $\frac{3}{8} + \frac{1}{2}$.

✅ *Develop & Understand: B*

Suggested Grouping: Pairs

▶ **Exercises 4 and 5** Ask for different combinations of sums. You may want to point out that some combinations will have the same sum. For example, $\frac{1}{6} + \frac{1}{3} = \frac{1}{2}$ and $\frac{1}{4} + \frac{3}{12} = \frac{1}{2}$ are both acceptable answers.

Teacher Tips Be sure students save their work from this exercise set and their fraction pieces and fraction mats to use in Investigation 2.

All of the sums in Exercises 1–3 on page 199 equal 1. You can also use your fraction pieces to form sums greater than or less than 1.

┌─ **Example**

Use fraction pieces to find $\frac{2}{4} + \frac{1}{6}$.

Choose the appropriate pieces. Arrange them on your fraction mat.

Look for a set of identical fraction pieces that cover the same area. You could use two $\frac{1}{3}$ pieces.

So, $\frac{2}{4} + \frac{1}{6} = \frac{2}{3}$.

The addition equation above has two related subtraction equations.

$$\frac{2}{3} - \frac{2}{4} = \frac{1}{6} \qquad \frac{2}{3} - \frac{1}{6} = \frac{2}{4}$$

✅ *Develop & Understand: B* 4, 5. Answers will vary.

4. Form sums less than 1 by combining two different types of fraction pieces. Find at least six different combinations.

   a. Record each combination by drawing a sketch and writing an addition equation.

   b. For each addition equation you wrote in Part a, write two related subtraction equations.

5. Now combine two different types of fraction pieces to form sums greater than 1. Find at least six different combinations.

   a. Record a sketch and an addition equation for each combination.

   b. For each addition equation you wrote in Part a, write two related subtraction equations.

Reaching All Learners

OL **On Level** Some students may have difficulty finding the sum of two different types of fraction pieces. Suggest that they try to cover the area using only halves, only thirds, only fourths, and so on until they find a set that covers the same area as the two different types of fraction pieces.

Point out that they will improve with practice. For example, $\frac{1}{6} + \frac{2}{3}$ is greater than $\frac{1}{2}$ and less than 1, and when students recognize this fact, they will not need to see whether halves can cover the same area.

6b. Possible answer:
$\frac{1}{3} + \frac{1}{4} = \frac{7}{12}$

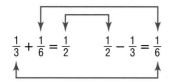

1. Combine two $\frac{1}{3}$ pieces and one $\frac{1}{4}$ piece and compare the total area to the area of ten $\frac{1}{12}$ pieces.

6. Look for a pair of fractions with sum $\frac{7}{12}$.

   a. Use the $\frac{1}{12}$ pieces to cover $\frac{7}{12}$ of the square.   See students' work.

   b. Look for a combination of two types of fraction pieces that cover $\frac{7}{12}$ of the square. Record the result with a sketch and an addition equation.

   c. Write two related subtraction equations for the addition equation.   Possible answer: $\frac{7}{12} - \frac{1}{3} = \frac{1}{4}$, $\frac{7}{12} - \frac{1}{4} = \frac{1}{3}$

Share & Summarize

Consider the equation $\frac{2}{3} + \frac{1}{4} = \frac{10}{12}$.

1. Explain how you could use fraction pieces to determine whether the equation is true.

2. Is the equation true? If it is not, change it to a true equation by replacing one of the fractions in it.   No; possible true equation:
   $\frac{2}{3} + \frac{1}{4} = \frac{11}{12}$

Investigation 2 — Common Denominators

Materials
- fraction cards
- 3-by-3 grid

You have used fraction pieces to add and subtract fractions with unlike denominators. What do you do if you do not have your fraction pieces or if you want to add fractions with denominators other than 2, 3, 4, 6, or 12?

Explore

Try to find this sum without using fraction pieces or writing anything.

$$\frac{1}{6} + \frac{3}{4}$$

Were you able to calculate the sum in your head? If so, what strategy did you use? If not, why did you find the problem difficult?
Answers will vary.
The sum would be much easier to find if the fractions had the same denominator.

Now use your fraction pieces or another method to find two fractions with the same denominator. The fractions should be equivalent to $\frac{1}{6}$ and $\frac{3}{4}$. Then add the two fractions in your head.
$\frac{1}{6} = \frac{2}{12}$ and $\frac{3}{4} = \frac{9}{12}$, $\frac{2}{12} + \frac{9}{12} = \frac{11}{12}$

On the Spot Assessment

To help write related equations, have students use arrows to show how the position of each number relates. In the example below, point out that the sum and the number to be subtracted from are the same $\left(\frac{1}{2}\right)$, and that the addends are the number subtracted $\left(\frac{1}{3}\right)$ and the difference $\left(\frac{1}{6}\right)$, in either order.

$$\frac{1}{3} + \frac{1}{6} = \frac{1}{2} \qquad \frac{1}{2} - \frac{1}{3} = \frac{1}{6}$$

▶ **Exercise 6b** Encourage students to use their knowledge of equivalent fractions, logical reasoning, or guess-check-and-improve to do this exercise.

Share & Summarize

Discuss approaches to **Exercise 1**. Challenge students to find more than one true equation for **Exercise 2** and have them justify each answer using fraction pieces.

Again, be sure students save their work from this investigation. They will need it in Investigation 2.

Troubleshooting If students are having difficulty using the fraction pieces to add and subtract, have them use only pieces of the same size to model addition and subtraction of fractions with like denominators. Since this activity does not require students to find equivalent fractions, students may find it easier to concentrate on how to use the models and how the equations are represented by each model.

Investigation 2

On Your Own Exercises
Pages 210–215
Exercises 15–24, 36–43, 48

Explore Have the class try adding the two fractions with different denominators without using fraction pieces. Most students will likely be unsuccessful. The problem is meant to motivate students to discover how to use common denominators to add fractions.

After students have tried to solve the problem, remind them that they already know how to find fractions equivalent. Ask them to use fraction pieces to find fractions equivalent to $\frac{1}{6}$ and $\frac{3}{4}$ that have the same denominator and then add these equivalent fractions. Then encourage students to think of ways to find the sum without using fraction pieces.

Discuss with students whether they were able to find the sum of the fractions in their head. Have them share their strategies.

✅ Develop & Understand: A

Suggested Grouping: *Individuals*

▶ **Exercises 1–4** Students will need fraction pieces and fraction mats, or any other fraction manipulatives they used in the prior investigation, to work through the exercises. Point out that they will need to refer to the work from previous exercises on pages 199 and 200.

▶ **Exercise 4** Students are asked to rewrite equations that have sums greater than 1. If students have difficulty rewriting these equations, they may find it easier if they change the mixed numbers to fractions and then find the common denominators.

Wrap-Up Have students share some of their original and rewritten equations. To reinforce their learning, encourage them to explain how they rewrote the equations.

Point out that all the fractions that students have added and subtracted have common denominators that can be found by using their fraction pieces. Tell them that they can use common denominators to find sums and differences for other fractions as well.

✅ Develop & Understand: B

Suggested Grouping: *Pairs*

▶ **Exercises 5–11** Students may use different methods to find each answer. They can find equivalent fractions using one of the methods from Lesson 2.1. Other methods will be reviewed in the Example on page 203. Point out all answers should be written in lowest terms.

▶ **Exercise 11** Be sure students understand that Daniela uses $\frac{1}{3}$ of a full bag of potting soil, not $\frac{1}{3}$ of the amount of potting soil she has in her bag. The second interpretation would involve multiplication and subtraction: $\frac{1}{2} - \left(\frac{1}{3} \cdot \frac{1}{2}\right) = \frac{1}{3}$.

Math Link Using lowest terms to express a fraction narrows the answer to one instead of all the possible equivalent fractions.

✅ Develop & Understand: A

In Exercises 1–4, use your fraction pieces or any other method you know to help rewrite the fractions. **1–4. Answers will vary.**

1. Choose two of the addition equations that you wrote for Exercise 1 on page 199. Rewrite each equation so the fractions being added have a common denominator. Check to be sure each sum is equal to 1. An example follows.

$$\frac{1}{3} + \frac{8}{12} = 1 \quad \longrightarrow \quad \frac{4}{12} + \frac{8}{12} = \frac{12}{12} = 1$$

2. Choose two of the addition equations that you wrote for Exercise 3 on page 199. Rewrite each equation so the fractions being added have a common denominator. Check to be sure that each sum is equal to 1.

3. Choose two of the addition equations that you wrote for Exercise 4 on page 200. Rewrite each equation and the two related subtraction equations using common denominators. Check each equation to make sure that it is correct.

4. Choose two of the addition equations you wrote for Exercise 5 on page 200. Rewrite each equation and the two related subtraction equations using common denominators. Check that each equation is correct.

Many of the following expressions would be difficult or impossible to solve using fraction pieces. Use what you know about common denominators and equivalent fractions to rewrite the sums and differences.

✅ Develop & Understand: B

Rewrite each expression using a common denominator. Then find the sum or difference. Give your answers in lowest terms. If an answer is greater than 1, write it as a mixed number.

5. $\frac{1}{2} + \frac{7}{8}$ 6. $\frac{2}{5} + \frac{2}{3}$ 7. $\frac{1}{9} + \frac{5}{6}$

8. $\frac{4}{5} - \frac{1}{4}$ 9. $\frac{7}{8} - \frac{2}{3}$ 10. $\frac{5}{9} - \frac{1}{3}$

5. $\frac{4}{8} + \frac{7}{8} = \frac{11}{8} = 1\frac{3}{8}$

6. $\frac{6}{15} + \frac{10}{15} = \frac{16}{15} = 1\frac{1}{15}$

7. $\frac{2}{18} + \frac{15}{18} = \frac{17}{18}$

8. $\frac{16}{20} - \frac{5}{20} = \frac{11}{20}$

9. $\frac{21}{24} - \frac{16}{24} = \frac{5}{24}$

10. $\frac{5}{9} - \frac{3}{9} = \frac{2}{9}$

11. Daniela has $\frac{1}{2}$ of a bag of potting soil. She uses $\frac{1}{3}$ of a bag to plant some flower seeds. How much of the bag remains? $\frac{1}{6}$

Reaching All Learners

AL **Approaching Level** If students have difficulty finding common denominators, remind them that they can use their knowledge of fraction families to find equivalent fractions with a common denominator. Have them write out several fractions in each family until they find one in each family with the same denominator.

Discuss students' answers and discuss how they found each pair of common denominators.

Example

Jahmal, Marcus, and Caroline discuss some strategies that they use to find common denominators.

I use the product of the two denominators. Then I just multiply both parts of each fraction by the denominator of the other fraction.

$$\frac{2}{5} + \frac{2}{3} = \frac{2 \cdot 3}{5 \cdot 3} + \frac{2 \cdot 5}{3 \cdot 5}$$
$$= \frac{6}{15} + \frac{10}{15}$$

When one denominator is a factor of the other, I use the greater number as the common denominator. To find $\frac{1}{2} + \frac{7}{8}$, I used 8.

$$\frac{1}{2} + \frac{7}{8} = \frac{1 \cdot 4}{2 \cdot 4} + \frac{7}{8}$$
$$= \frac{4}{8} + \frac{7}{8}$$

I use the least common multiple of the denominators. To find $\frac{1}{9} + \frac{5}{6}$, I used 18.

$$\frac{1}{9} + \frac{5}{6} = \frac{1 \cdot 2}{9 \cdot 2} + \frac{5 \cdot 3}{6 \cdot 3}$$
$$= \frac{2}{18} + \frac{15}{18}$$

As you work the following exercises, you might try some of the methods described in the above example.

✔ Develop & Understand: C

Find each sum or difference and show each step of your work. Give your answers in lowest terms. If an answer is greater than 1, write it as a mixed number.

12. $\frac{1}{3} + \frac{3}{7}$ $\frac{16}{21}$

13. $\frac{1}{4} + \frac{3}{9}$ $\frac{7}{12}$

14. $\frac{4}{5} - \frac{3}{8}$ $\frac{17}{40}$

15. $\frac{13}{27} - \frac{2}{9}$ $\frac{7}{27}$

16. $\frac{7}{15} + \frac{1}{3} + \frac{1}{5}$ 1

17. $\frac{11}{12} + \frac{3}{8}$ $1\frac{7}{24}$

18. $1 - \frac{3}{4} - \frac{1}{5}$ $\frac{1}{20}$

19. $1\frac{31}{42} + \frac{17}{21}$ $2\frac{23}{42}$

20. $1\frac{3}{4} - \frac{5}{8}$ $1\frac{1}{8}$

21. $\frac{32}{75} + \frac{32}{50}$ $1\frac{1}{15}$

On the Spot Assessment

Watch for students who do not rewrite each fraction with a common denominator before adding or subtracting. Some students may simply add or subtract the numerators and write the answer over a common denominator. Others may add or subtract the numerators and the denominators.

Encourage students to use benchmarks to estimate their answers, and to compare their answers to the estimates.

Discuss the three strategies for finding common denominators. Be sure to acknowledge whether students have suggested one or more of these strategies for Exercises 5–11 on page 202. If necessary, discuss how to use multiplication to rewrite fractions.

If your class seemed to have difficulty with the exercises on page 202, you may want to spend more time on the strategies in this Example.

- Have students compare the methods Marcus and Caroline used. Some students may note that Marcus also finds the least common multiple of the denominators, but needs to rewrite only one fraction.

- Ask students when they might use Caroline's method instead of Jamal's method. Make sure that their responses include situations in which the denominators are greater numbers and the likelihood of a multiplication error is greater.

- Encourage students to try each of the methods in the Example at least one time as they work through the exercise set.

✔ Develop & Understand: C

Suggested Grouping: Pairs

▶ **Exercises 19 and 20** Point out that students may rewrite the mixed numbers as fractions. Others may add and subtract the fractions separately from the whole numbers.

▶ **Exercise 21** Discuss how writing $\frac{32}{50}$ in lowest terms first can help to simplify the calculations. Determining a common denominator becomes much easier, and using 75 as the common denominator makes the calculations more manageable. Using the product of the denominators would result in a common denominator of 3,750, and using the least common multiple would result in a common denominator of 150.

Wrap-Up Have students present the methods they used to solve the exercises. Since there is more than one correct method, this can help students see various approaches to solving fraction problems.

Teacher Tips Introduce *magic squares* and review the terms *row*, *column*, and *diagonal*. Do this by drawing a magic square on a transparency or the board and drawing lines to show each term or by having students read the numbers in each row, column, and diagonal of the magic square on page 204. Then have students verify that each sum is 15.

If students are not familiar with magic squares, ask them to create a different 3-by-3 magic square that contains the numbers 1–9, so they can see how magic squares work without fractions.

You might want to distribute copies of Lesson 4.1 Masters 3 and 4 to each pair of students.

✅ Develop & Understand: D

Suggested Grouping: Pairs

▶ **Exercise 22** Point out that the denominators are factors of 15, and only four of the nine fractions have denominators that are not 15.

▶ **Exercise 23** Point out that this exercise is more complex since students work with six different denominators that are factors of 36. The correct magic square for each of these fractions will be a rotation or reflection of the possible answer given. For example, the square shown here is a reflection, along the diagonal from top left to bottom right, of the magic square shown for Exercise 23.

$\frac{7}{36}$	$\frac{2}{9}$	$\frac{1}{12}$
$\frac{1}{18}$	$\frac{1}{6}$	$\frac{5}{18}$
$\frac{1}{4}$	$\frac{1}{9}$	$\frac{5}{36}$

Share & Summarize

Encourage students to write an explanation of the steps they would take to solve Exercise 1 mentally or with paper and pencil, not with fraction pieces. Have them share their explanations.

For **Exercise 2**, make sure students understand that if the denominators of two fractions are different, you must find the common denominator first.

---

22. Possible magic square:

$\frac{2}{5}$	$\frac{1}{15}$	$\frac{8}{15}$
$\frac{7}{15}$	$\frac{1}{3}$	$\frac{1}{5}$
$\frac{2}{15}$	$\frac{3}{5}$	$\frac{4}{15}$

23. Possible magic square:

$\frac{7}{36}$	$\frac{1}{18}$	$\frac{1}{4}$
$\frac{2}{9}$	$\frac{1}{6}$	$\frac{1}{9}$
$\frac{1}{12}$	$\frac{5}{18}$	$\frac{5}{36}$

A *magic square* is a square grid of numbers in which every row, column, and diagonal has the same sum. This magic square has a sum of 15.

8	1	6
3	5	7
4	9	2

✅ Develop & Understand: D

You can create your own magic squares using a set of fraction cards and a grid.

22. Arrange the following numbers into a magic square with a sum of 1. Record your grid.

$\boxed{\frac{1}{15}}$ $\boxed{\frac{2}{15}}$ $\boxed{\frac{4}{15}}$ $\boxed{\frac{7}{15}}$ $\boxed{\frac{8}{15}}$ $\boxed{\frac{1}{5}}$ $\boxed{\frac{2}{5}}$ $\boxed{\frac{3}{5}}$ $\boxed{\frac{1}{3}}$

23. Arrange the following numbers into a magic square with a sum of $\frac{1}{2}$. Record your grid.

$\boxed{\frac{5}{36}}$ $\boxed{\frac{7}{36}}$ $\boxed{\frac{1}{18}}$ $\boxed{\frac{5}{18}}$ $\boxed{\frac{1}{12}}$ $\boxed{\frac{1}{9}}$ $\boxed{\frac{2}{9}}$ $\boxed{\frac{1}{6}}$ $\boxed{\frac{1}{4}}$

Share & Summarize

1. Use an example to help explain the steps you follow to add or subtract two fractions with different denominators.

2. Mandy wrote the following statement on her homework paper.

$$\frac{2}{7} + \frac{9}{4} + \frac{11}{11} = 1$$

Is Mandy correct? Explain your reasoning.

1. Possible answer: To add $\frac{1}{2} + \frac{2}{3}$, I would use a common denominator of 2 · 3, or 6. To rewrite the equation, I need to multiply both parts of $\frac{1}{2}$ by 3 and both parts of $\frac{2}{3}$ by 2:

$$\frac{1}{2} + \frac{2}{3} = \frac{1 \cdot 3}{2 \cdot 3} = \frac{2 \cdot 2}{3 \cdot 2} = \frac{3}{6} + \frac{4}{6} = \frac{7}{6} = 1\frac{1}{6}$$

2. No; Mandy did not find a common denominator before adding. Also, you never add denominators when adding fractions.

Reaching All Learners

AL **Approaching Level** If some students have difficulty creating magic squares, suggest that they find a common denominator that could be used to add all the given fractions and use it to write all the fractions with that common denominator. Then students need to consider only the sums of the numerators when creating their squares.

★ indicates multi-step problem

Investigation ③ Add and Subtract Mixed Numbers

In this investigation, you will apply what you have learned about adding and subtracting fractions to solve exercises involving mixed numbers.

Explore

Rosita is making a box to hold her pencils. She needs one piece of wood for the bottom and four pieces of wood for the sides. The top of the box will be open.

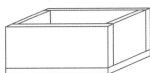

Rosita plans to cut the five pieces from a long wooden board that is 4 inches wide and $\frac{5}{8}$ inch thick. New pencils are about $7\frac{1}{2}$ inches long. Rosita wants to make the inside of the box $\frac{3}{4}$ inch longer, so it is easy to take out the pencils.

She made this sketch of the top view of the box. All measurements are in inches.

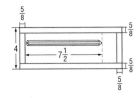

① Ends: $4 - \left(\frac{5}{8} + \frac{5}{8}\right) = 2\frac{3}{4}$ in.; sides and bottom: $7\frac{1}{2} + \frac{3}{4} + \frac{5}{8} + \frac{5}{8} = 9\frac{1}{2}$ in.

★• What lengths will Rosita need to cut for the bottom, ends, and sides of her box? Give your answers as fractions or mixed numbers. Show how you found your answers. See ①.

• What will be the height of the box? $4\frac{5}{8}$ in.

Lesson 4.1 Add and Subtract Fractions **205**

Reaching *All Learners*

OL **On Level** Encourage students to use a model to solve the Explore exercises by providing students with a 3-foot-long, 4-inch-wide strip of foam board or thick cardboard and then letting them construct the box. This may help them visualize how the thickness of the wood can affect the measurements. Students are not expected to make a perfect scale model of the box, but rather to see how the dimensions of a rectangular solid determine the measures of each of its sides.

Investigation ③

On Your Own Exercises
Pages 210–215
Exercises 25–31, 44–47, 49–53

Add and Subtract Mixed Numbers In this investigation, students develop additional strategies for adding and subtracting mixed numbers as they solve problems that require regrouping. It is important for students to have a conceptual understanding of this kind of problem so that they will not be relying entirely on memorizing one particular technique.

Explore

Suggested Grouping: Pairs

The problem of how to cut a board to build a box of a certain size is more complex than it may appear at first glance. Even if all of the measurements were whole numbers, students might find it challenging to determine the length of each piece. After students have found the appropriate length, width, and height of the whole box, they still need to determine which of these dimensions form the length of the different rectangular sides.

Discuss the facts in the Explore as a class. Point out that the pieces of wood forming the sides of the box are placed on top of the base rather than at each side of the base. While the second interpretation is reasonable, it does not match the illustration.

Have students work in pairs to find the lengths. Then discuss their answers as a class, focusing on the strategies students used to solve the exercises.

Teacher Tips You may want to use cardstock to make a model of the box in the Explore.

Lesson 4.1 Add and Subtract Fractions **205**

Develop & Understand: A

Suggested Grouping: Pairs

▶ **Exercises 1, 3, 4** Remind students that subtraction is not commutative, so they cannot automatically subtract the lesser fraction from the greater fraction. For example, in Exercise 1, students may find equivalent fractions and then subtract $\frac{4}{8}$ from $\frac{7}{8}$ to find an incorrect answer of $30\frac{3}{8}$. Remind these students that when subtracting, the order of the numbers matters.

▶ **Exercises 1–4** Students may use one or more of the following strategies:

- Use a meterstick, measuring tape, or number line. Locate the greater measure and count forward or backward to find the final measure.

- Change any or all mixed numbers into fractions and calculate.

- Add or subtract the whole-number parts and the fractional parts of the mixed numbers separately, regrouping one whole as fractional parts when necessary.

- Use fraction pieces to model each problem.

- Measure strips of paper such as adding machine tape. Measure and mark the length to be cut off or the lengths of pieces to be taped, depending upon the problem. Measure the final length of the strip.

Think & Discuss

Suggested Grouping: Individuals

Have students answer Think & Discuss questions independently before discussing their answers with the class. Most students should not have trouble understanding Althea's approach, and they should easily show how to finish her solution. However, they may not see why Jing says that $3\frac{2}{3}$ is equal to $2\frac{5}{3}$. You may want to use mathematical reasoning or fraction pieces to illustrate the equivalency: $3\frac{2}{3} = 2 + \frac{3}{3} + \frac{2}{3} = 2\frac{5}{3}$. Then have students share how they finished Jing's solution.

Develop & Understand: A

1. Suppose a piece of wood $6\frac{7}{8}$ inches long is cut from a $36\frac{1}{2}$-inch board. How much of the board is left? Explain how you found your answer.   See margin.

2. Juana needs two red ribbons for a costume she is making. One ribbon must be $2\frac{1}{3}$ feet long, and the other must be $3\frac{1}{2}$ feet long. What total length of red ribbon does she need? $5\frac{5}{6}$ ft

3. Juana has a piece of blue ribbon $6\frac{1}{2}$ feet long. She cuts off a piece $3\frac{3}{4}$ feet long. How much blue ribbon will be left? $2\frac{3}{4}$ ft

4. Juana has a length of green ribbon that is $3\frac{2}{3}$ yards long. Suppose she cuts off a piece $1\frac{3}{4}$ yards long. How many yards of green ribbon will remain? $1\frac{11}{12}$ yd

Real-World Link
Sewing originated more than 20,000 years ago. The earliest sewing was done using animal tendons for thread and needles made from bones or horns.

Althea and Jing are comparing how they thought about Exercise 4.

Think & Discuss

Althea changed both mixed numbers to fractions. Finish her solution. $\frac{11}{3} - \frac{7}{4} = \frac{44}{12} - \frac{21}{12} = \frac{23}{12} = 1\frac{11}{12}$

Jing changed $3\frac{2}{3}$ to $2\frac{5}{3}$. Explain why these two numbers are equal. How does this step help Jing find the solution?   See ① in margin.

Finish Jing's solution.
$(2 - 1) + \left(\frac{5}{3} - \frac{3}{4}\right) = 1 + \left(\frac{20}{12} - \frac{9}{12}\right) = 1\frac{11}{12}$

Additional Answers

1. $29\frac{5}{8}$ in., Possible explanation: First I subtracted 6 from $36\frac{1}{2}$ to get $30\frac{1}{2}$. I still had to subtract $\frac{7}{8}$. Subtacting $\frac{4}{8}$, or $\frac{1}{2}$, left 30 in., and subtracting the remaining $\frac{3}{8}$ left $29\frac{5}{8}$ in.

Think & Discuss

① Possible explanation: If you start with $3\frac{2}{3}$, you can "borrow" 1, or $\frac{3}{3}$, from the whole number part and give it to the fraction part: $3\frac{2}{3} = 3 + \frac{2}{3} = 2 + \frac{3}{3} + \frac{2}{3} = 2 + \frac{5}{3} = 2\frac{5}{3}$.

Doing this makes the fraction part of the first number greater than the fraction part of the second number, so Jing could easily subtract them.

✅ *Develop & Understand: B*

Use any method you like to solve these exercises.

5. Jahmal organized a foot-long sub sandwich sale as a student council fundraiser. At lunch, students could purchase whole sandwiches or portion of sandwiches. The amounts sold during the four lunch periods are listed below.

Lunch A	Lunch B	Lunch C	Lunch D
$5\frac{3}{4}$ ft	$7\frac{1}{8}$ ft	$7\frac{1}{2}$ ft	$5\frac{2}{3}$ ft

a. During which lunch periods did students purchase the least and the most number of sandwiches? **Least: Lunch D; most: Lunch C**

b. What was the total amount of sandwiches purchased? **$26\frac{1}{24}$**

6. Miguel's brother, Carlos, is $69\frac{1}{2}$ inches tall. Last year, Carlos was $63\frac{3}{4}$ inches tall. How much did he grow in the year? **$5\frac{3}{4}$ in.**

Estimate each sum or difference by rounding mixed numbers to whole numbers. Then find each sum or difference. Give your answers in lowest terms.

7. $3\frac{7}{8} + 2\frac{1}{4}$ **6; $6\frac{1}{8}$**

8. $3\frac{7}{8} - 2\frac{1}{4}$ **2; $1\frac{5}{8}$**

9. $6\frac{1}{3} - 5\frac{3}{4}$ **0; $\frac{7}{12}$**

10. $13\frac{3}{4} + 8\frac{19}{20}$ **23; $22\frac{7}{10}$**

11. $22\frac{7}{10} - 13\frac{3}{4}$ **9; $8\frac{19}{20}$**

12. $9\frac{1}{2} + 3\frac{7}{8}$ **14; $13\frac{3}{8}$**

Share & Summarize

Look back at Althea's and Jing's methods for subtracting mixed numbers.

1. For which types of exercises do you prefer Althea's method? Give an example.

2. For which types of exercises do you prefer Jing's method? Give an example.

1. Possible answer: I like Althea's method when the whole numbers are small enough that the fractions will not have very large numerators, for example, $4\frac{1}{5} - 2\frac{1}{2}$.

2. Possible answer: I prefer Jing's method when the whole numbers are large, for example, $36\frac{1}{2} - 24\frac{5}{8}$.

✅ *Develop & Understand: B*

Suggested Grouping: Individuals

▶ **Exercises 7–12** You may want to draw or use diagrams to model addition and subtraction. For example, a model for Exercise 7 would be:

$$= 6 + \frac{1}{8}$$
$$= 6\frac{1}{8}$$

Real-World Link

Stock prices are now quoted in decimals to the hundredth of a dollar, and the number of shares of stock is quoted in decimals to the thousandth of a share. For example, you could own 82.346 shares of stock worth $32.59 a share.

Share & Summarize

Have students share their reasons for choosing the type of problem in which to use each strategy. This can help other students solidify their understanding and expand their mathematical skills. You might also ask students if they have another method they prefer over these two.

Troubleshooting If students are having difficulty adding and subtracting mixed numbers, have them draw pictures or use fraction manipulatives to model some problems. Encourage them to write the equations and expressions that describe their models.

(On the Spot) *Assessment*

Watch for students who regroup the mixed number in Exercise 8. This is unnecessary. Remind students that they only need to regroup sometimes, just as with whole number subtraction. Ask students to explain how they can tell whether regrouping is necessary. Their responses should reflect that when the fraction being subtracted is greater than the fraction being subtracted from, regrouping is necessary.

Inquiry

Investigation

Suggested Grouping: Pairs

Materials and Preparation

Most of the keystrokes in this investigation are given for the Texas Instruments 34II calculator. You may need to revise these keystrokes if your students are using a different calculator.

In addition to calculators, each pair of students will need one copy of Lesson 4.1 Masters 5–8 and scissors. To help keep the difference between the two decks, you might copy each deck onto its own color. To conserve paper and save time, you may want to give half the class masters for one deck of cards and the other half masters for the other deck, have them cut out the cards, and then trade decks after they play the first game.

Learning the Basics This hands-on investigation introduces the fraction calculator and provides step-by-step instructions for using the calculator to add and subtract fractions.

Begin by reviewing calculator basics, especially if students have not used their calculators before. Point out the location of the fraction key, and allow students time to familiarize themselves with the location of other keys such as the operation keys. If the calculators in your class are not set so that students can simplify manually, you may have to walk students through the steps to put their calculators in this mode.

After **Exercise 1**, discuss the N/D → n/d notation and what the "Simp" abbreviation stands for on the key. This text has used the phrase *lowest terms*, but some texts use *simplify* to describe the same process.

For **Exercise 2**, some students may be able to simplify the fraction mentally, arriving at an estimate that is in fact the fraction in lowest terms. Encourage them to see that 180 and 210 are close to 200, so $\frac{180}{210}$ is close to $\frac{200}{200}$, or 1.

Inquiry

Investigation Use a Calculator

Materials

- calculator with fraction capabilities keys
- two decks of Fraction Match cards

In this lab, you will use a calculator to add and subtract fractions and mixed numbers.

Learning the Basics

To enter a fraction on your calculator:
- Enter the numerator.
- Press ÷ .
- Enter the denominator.

To enter a mixed number:
- Enter the whole-number part.
- Press UNIT .
- Enter the numerator of the fraction part.
- Press ÷ .
- Enter the denominator of the fraction part.

1. Use your calculator to find $\frac{1}{4} + 1\frac{2}{3}$. $1\frac{11}{12}$

If you enter a fraction that is not in lowest terms, or if a calculation results in a fraction that is not in lowest terms, the calculator may display something like N/D → n/d. Use the following steps to put the fraction in lowest terms.
- Press SIMP .
- Enter a common factor of the numerator and denominator.
- Press ENTER .

The calculator will divide the numerator and denominator by the factor you specify and display the result. If the fraction is still not in lowest terms, the calculator will continue to display N/D → n/d. In that case, repeat the above steps to divide by another common factor.

2. About 1; $\frac{6}{7}$; $\frac{6}{7}$ is about 1.

2. Estimate the value of $\frac{180}{210}$. Then use your calculator to help you write $\frac{180}{210}$ in lowest terms. Compare your answer to your estimate.

Use the following steps to change a fraction to a mixed number or to change a mixed number to a fraction.
- Press 2nd [A^b/$_c$ ◄► ^{d}/$_e$].
- Press ENTER .

3. Use your calculator to change $3\frac{5}{7}$ to a fraction and to change $\frac{43}{21}$ to a mixed number. $\frac{26}{7}$, $2\frac{1}{21}$

Reaching *All Learners*

ELL **English Language Learners** Students who are not proficient in English may have an even more difficult time using calculators than other students because the keys are labeled with abbreviations. Ask students to make note cards listing the calculator key abbreviation along with the English equivalent and a description of how the key is used. Allow them to use these note cards on tests where calculators are allowed.

Playing *Fraction Match*

Fraction Match is a memory game for two players. Here are the rules.

- Choose Deck 1 or Deck 2.
- Shuffle the cards. Place them face down in five rows of six cards each.

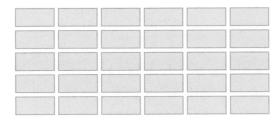

- The first player turns over two cards. If needed, he or she uses a calculator to determine whether the values on the cards are the same.
- If the cards have the same value, the player keeps them and takes another turn. If they have different values, the player turns them back over and his or her turn ends.
- Play continues until all the cards have been taken. The player with the most cards at the end of the game wins.

When you finish the game, play again with the other deck.

4. Possible answer:
Enter 2.
Press UNIT.
Enter 11.
Press ÷.
Enter 14.
Press −.
Enter 2.
Press ÷.
Enter 7.
Press ENTER.
Press SIMP.
Enter 7.
Press ENTER.

What Did You Learn?

4. Describe step by step how to use a calculator to find $2\frac{11}{14} - \frac{2}{7}$.

5. Design your own deck of *Fraction Match* cards. Your deck should have at least 16 cards. Test your deck by playing *Fraction Match* with a friend or classmate. Decks will vary.

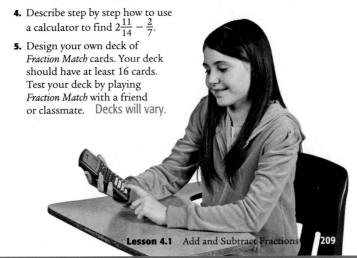

Lesson 4.1 Add and Subtract Fractions **209**

Teacher Tips Discuss how to change fractions to mixed numbers. Remind students that they should check any answers displayed to make sure that they are in the correct form. Remind them to use the buttons shown in the text to make these changes.

Playing *Fraction Match*

Provide students with two decks of *Fraction Match* cards and scissors. The game requires students to use memory skills as they practice using a fraction calculator. Students may add, subtract, write a number in lowest terms, or use any combination of these skills to determine if the value of two cards match.

Read the rules for the game with the class, clarifying as needed. Then allow students to play the game twice, one time with each deck.

What Did You Learn?

Exercise 5 Students can use lined or grid paper to make their decks for this exercise. If students are having difficulty making the deck or playing the game, have them make the deck with only eight cards, making sure that they have four sets of matching pairs. They can use either lined or grid paper to make their decks.

Discuss any problems students had making the deck after they have tested their decks. Most students will realize that they need to have a match for every card they make.

Investigation 1
Pages 198–201
Practice & Apply: 1–14
Connect & Extend: 32–35

Investigation 2
Pages 201–204
Practice & Apply: 15–24
Connect & Extend: 36–43, 48

Investigation 3
Pages 205–207
Practice & Apply: 25–31
Connect & Extend: 44–47, 49–53

Inquiry Investigation 4
Pages 208–209

Assign Anytime
Mixed Review: 54–68

▶ **Exercises 7–14** Students are given the option of using fraction pieces. Even if other manipulatives were used in class, you may want to give students copies of Lesson 4.1 Masters 1–2 to complete these exercises as homework.

▶ **Exercise 22** Suggest that students write each fraction in lowest terms and then look for a common denominator. This can help them see that using 13 as the common denominator makes the calculation easier: $\frac{4}{13} + \frac{3}{13} = \frac{7}{13}$.

▶ **Exercises 23 and 24** Encourage students to make manipulatives for creating the magic squares. Provide them with grids from Lesson 4.1 Master 4, have them write fractions in the grid, cut out the squares, and use them to make the magic square. Students' magic squares should be either like the possible answer or like a rotation or a reflection of that magic square for each exercise.

5. $\frac{9}{9}$, or 1

6. $\frac{12}{11}$, or $1\frac{1}{11}$

7. $\frac{3}{4}$, or $\frac{9}{12}$

8. $\frac{1}{6}$, or $\frac{2}{12}$

9. $\frac{4}{12}$, $\frac{2}{6}$, or $\frac{1}{3}$

10. $\frac{1}{12}$

11. $\frac{1}{3}$, $\frac{2}{6}$, or $\frac{4}{12}$

12. $\frac{9}{12}$, or $\frac{3}{4}$

13. $\frac{1}{3}$, $\frac{2}{6}$, or $\frac{4}{12}$

14. $\frac{1}{12}$

23. Possible magic square:

$\frac{3}{4}$	$\frac{1}{3}$	$\frac{11}{12}$
$\frac{5}{6}$	$\frac{2}{3}$	$\frac{1}{2}$
$\frac{5}{12}$	1	$\frac{7}{12}$

24. Possible magic square:

$\frac{7}{12}$	$\frac{1}{6}$	$\frac{3}{4}$
$\frac{2}{3}$	$\frac{1}{2}$	$\frac{1}{3}$
$\frac{1}{4}$	$\frac{5}{6}$	$\frac{5}{12}$

Solve each equation in your head.

1. $\frac{3}{4} - \frac{2}{4} = \dfrac{1}{4}$

2. $\frac{12}{17} - \frac{4}{17} = \dfrac{8}{17}$

3. $\dfrac{4}{8} - \frac{3}{8} = \frac{1}{8}$

4. $\frac{5}{12} - \dfrac{4}{12} = \frac{1}{12}$

5. $\underline{\hspace{1cm}} - \frac{8}{9} = \frac{1}{9}$

6. $\underline{\hspace{1cm}} - \frac{7}{11} = \frac{5}{11}$

Use your fraction pieces or another method to help fill in each blank.

7. $\frac{1}{4} + \underline{\hspace{1cm}} = 1$

8. $\frac{1}{2} + \frac{1}{3} + \underline{\hspace{1cm}} = 1$

9. $\frac{1}{12} + \frac{2}{6} + \underline{\hspace{1cm}} + \frac{1}{4} = 1$

10. $\frac{1}{6} + \frac{5}{12} + \underline{\hspace{1cm}} + \frac{1}{3} = 1$

11. $\frac{1}{2} + \frac{1}{3} + \underline{\hspace{1cm}} = 1\frac{1}{6}$

12. $\frac{2}{3} + \frac{11}{12} - \underline{\hspace{1cm}} = \frac{5}{6}$

13. $\frac{5}{6} + \frac{1}{3} + \frac{1}{2} + \underline{\hspace{1cm}} = 2$

14. $\frac{1}{6} + \frac{1}{2} + \underline{\hspace{1cm}} = \frac{3}{4}$

Use your fraction pieces or another method to write each sum or difference with a common denominator. Then find the sum or difference. Give your answers in lowest terms. If an answer is greater than 1, write it as a mixed number.

15. $\frac{5}{6} - \frac{1}{2}$ $\frac{5}{6} - \frac{3}{6} = \frac{1}{3}$

16. $\frac{11}{12} - \frac{3}{4}$ $\frac{11}{12} - \frac{9}{12} = \frac{1}{6}$

17. $\frac{7}{6} - \frac{1}{3}$ $\frac{7}{6} - \frac{2}{6} = \frac{5}{6}$

18. $\frac{13}{12} + \frac{3}{4}$ $\frac{13}{12} + \frac{9}{12} = 1\frac{5}{6}$

Find each sum or difference. Give your answers in lowest terms. If an answer is greater than 1, write it as a mixed number.

19. $\frac{3}{8} + \frac{2}{3}$ $1\frac{1}{24}$

20. $\frac{9}{22} - \frac{3}{10}$ $\frac{6}{55}$

21. $\frac{25}{32} + \frac{7}{24}$ $1\frac{7}{96}$

22. $\frac{8}{26} + \frac{9}{39}$ $\frac{7}{13}$

23. On a sheet of paper, create a magic square with a sum of 2 using the numbers $\frac{11}{12}, \frac{3}{4}, \frac{5}{6}, \frac{1}{2}, \frac{2}{3}, \frac{5}{12}, \frac{1}{3}, 1,$ and $\frac{7}{12}$.

24. On a sheet of paper, create a magic square with a sum of $1\frac{1}{2}$ using the numbers $\frac{1}{2}, \frac{1}{4}, \frac{2}{3}, \frac{1}{6}, \frac{5}{12}, \frac{5}{6}, \frac{1}{3}, \frac{3}{4},$ and $\frac{7}{12}$.

Estimate each sum or difference. Then find each sum or difference, showing each step of your work. Give your answers in lowest terms. If an answer is greater than 1, write it as a mixed number.

25. $2\frac{1}{2} - \frac{7}{9}$ $2; 1\frac{13}{18}$

26. $1\frac{8}{15} - \frac{3}{5}$ $1; \frac{14}{15}$

27. $10\frac{2}{5} - 4\frac{1}{3}$ $6; 6\frac{1}{15}$

28. $3\frac{5}{6} + \frac{6}{7}$ $5; 4\frac{29}{42}$

29. $3\frac{1}{4} + 1\frac{1}{3}$ $4; 4\frac{7}{12}$

30. $4\frac{1}{3} - 2\frac{3}{8}$ $2; 1\frac{23}{24}$

31. For the second year, a scout troop has participated in community efforts to clear litter from local roads. Last year, the scouts cleared $8\frac{3}{4}$ miles of roadways. So far this year, the scouts have cleared the following lengths of roadways.

$\frac{7}{8}$ mi $1\frac{1}{2}$ mi $1\frac{1}{4}$ mi $\frac{3}{4}$ mi

a. This year, what are the least and greatest lengths of roadways cleared by the scouts?   Least, $\frac{3}{4}$ mi; greatest, $1\frac{1}{2}$ mi

b. Since the beginning of last year, what is the total length of roadway cleared by the scouts? $13\frac{1}{8}$ mi

Connect & Extend   **32. Number Sense** Cover your whole square in as many different ways as you can using *four* different types of fraction pieces.

a. Write an equation for each combination you find.

b. Describe the strategy you used to find all the possible equations. See margin.

Give the rule for finding each term in the sequence from the previous term. Then use your rule to find the missing terms. Use the last term to help check your answers.

33. $0, \frac{1}{4}, \frac{2}{4}, \frac{3}{4}, \underline{\frac{4}{4}}, \underline{\frac{5}{4}}, \underline{\frac{6}{4}}, \underline{\frac{7}{4}}, \frac{8}{4}$ Add $\frac{1}{4}$

34. $0, \frac{2}{3}, \frac{4}{3}, \frac{6}{3}, \underline{\frac{8}{3}}, \underline{\frac{10}{3}}, \underline{\frac{12}{3}}, \underline{\frac{14}{3}}, \frac{16}{3}$ Add $\frac{2}{3}$

32a. There are three possible equations:
$$\frac{1}{2} + \frac{1}{4} + \frac{1}{6} + \frac{1}{12} = 1$$
$$\frac{1}{3} + \frac{1}{4} + \frac{1}{6} + \frac{3}{12} = 1$$
$$\frac{1}{3} + \frac{1}{4} + \frac{2}{6} + \frac{1}{12} = 1$$

35. $\frac{24}{4}, \frac{21}{4}, \frac{18}{4}, \frac{15}{4}, \underline{\frac{12}{4}}, \underline{\frac{9}{4}}, \underline{\frac{6}{4}}, \underline{\frac{3}{4}}, \frac{0}{4}$ Subtract $\frac{3}{4}$

Lesson 4.1   Add and Subtract Fractions   **211**

▶ **Exercise 27** Suggest that students rewrite the mixed numbers with a common denominator before deciding whether they need to regroup. Until the two fractions, $\frac{2}{5}$ and $\frac{1}{3}$, are rewritten with a common denominator, some students may not realize that regrouping is not necessary.

▶ **Exercise 32** Fraction pieces and a fraction mat are required. If you assign this exercise, be sure students have their pieces from class or copies of Lesson 4.1 Masters 1 and 2.

▶ **Exercises 33–35** Each sequence has fractions written with a common denominator. Students can use what they learned about patterns in fractions in Lesson 2.1 to help them find the missing terms.

Additional Answer

32b. Possible answer: I worked from the largest pieces to the smallest. I started with a $\frac{1}{2}$ piece and looked for combinations of three other types of pieces that would fill the square. Then I started with the $\frac{1}{3}$ pieces. When I got to the $\frac{1}{4}$ pieces, I knew I was done because there were not three different types of pieces to try. I had already found all combinations using $\frac{1}{2}$ and $\frac{1}{3}$.

▶ **Exercises 36–41** You may want to have students actually play the *Rolling Fractions* game in class to determine the rules and make the situations in these exercises more easily understood.

▶ **Exercises 36–39, 41** If students have difficulty visualizing the game board, have them sketch 4-by-6 grids and shade them for each exercise.

37. $\frac{1}{2}$ and $\frac{1}{12}$, or $\frac{1}{3}$ and $\frac{1}{4}$

38. Jahmal; Jahmal can win if he rolls $\frac{1}{12}$. Conor still needs to shade $\frac{3}{8}$, which will take at least two more turns.

40. Two, $\frac{1}{2}$ and $\frac{1}{2}$

Rolling Fractions is played with a number cube with faces labeled $\frac{1}{2}, \frac{1}{3}, \frac{1}{4}, \frac{1}{6}, \frac{1}{8}$, and $\frac{1}{12}$. Each player has a game card divided into 24 equal rectangles. Players take turns rolling the cube and shading that fraction of the card. For example, if a player rolls $\frac{1}{2}$, he would shade 12 of the 24 rectangles.

If the fraction rolled is greater than the unshaded fraction of the card, the player shades no rectangles for that turn. The first player to shade the card completely is the winner.

Rolling Fractions Game Card

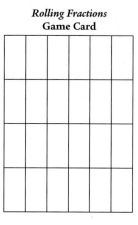

36. In her first two turns, Caroline rolled $\frac{1}{2}$ and $\frac{1}{6}$. To win the game on her next turn, which fraction would she need to roll? $\frac{1}{3}$

37. In his first two turns, Miguel rolled $\frac{1}{3}$ and $\frac{1}{12}$. To win the game in *two* more turns, which two fractions would he need to roll?

38. In their first three turns, Conor rolled $\frac{1}{8}, \frac{1}{6}$, and $\frac{1}{3}$, and Jahmal rolled $\frac{1}{12}, \frac{1}{2}$, and $\frac{1}{3}$. Who is more likely to win on his next roll? Explain why.

39. In her first two turns, Rosita rolled $\frac{1}{2}$ and $\frac{1}{3}$.
    a. To win on her next turn, which fraction would she need to roll? $\frac{1}{6}$
    b. To win in *two* more turns, which fractions would she need to roll? $\frac{1}{12}$ and $\frac{1}{12}$
    c. Which fractions would give Rosita a sum greater than 1 on her third turn? $\frac{1}{2}, \frac{1}{3}, \frac{1}{4}$

40. What is the fewest number of turns it could take to win this game? Which fractions would a player have to roll in that number of turns?

41. Luke rolled $\frac{1}{2}, \frac{1}{3}$, and $\frac{1}{8}$. He says he might as well quit because there is no way for him to win. Do you agree? Explain.
    Yes; He has filled in $\frac{23}{24}$ of his card, and there is no way to roll $\frac{1}{24}$.

42. Arrange the numbers $\frac{3}{4}, \frac{2}{3}, \frac{1}{4}, \frac{11}{12}, \frac{5}{12}, \frac{1}{3}, \frac{7}{12}, \frac{1}{2}$, and $\frac{5}{6}$ into a magic square. What is the sum for your magic square?
See margin.

43. Arrange the numbers $1, \frac{2}{3}, \frac{5}{6}, \frac{1}{3}, \frac{1}{2}, \frac{7}{6}, \frac{3}{2}, \frac{4}{3}$, and $\frac{5}{3}$ into a magic square. What is the sum for your magic square?
See margin.

44. Arrange 1, 2, 3, 4 in the boxes to create the least possible sum. Use each number exactly once.

$$\frac{\boxed{1}}{\boxed{3}} + \frac{\boxed{2}}{\boxed{4}} = \frac{5}{6}$$

45. Arrange 1, 2, 3, 4 in the boxes to create the least possible positive difference. Use each number exactly once.

$$\frac{\boxed{2}}{\boxed{4}} - \frac{\boxed{1}}{\boxed{3}} = \frac{1}{6}$$

46. Arrange 2, 3, 4 and 12 in the boxes to create the least possible sum. Use each number exactly once.

$$\frac{\boxed{2}}{\boxed{4}} + \frac{\boxed{3}}{\boxed{12}} = \frac{3}{4}$$

47. Arrange 2, 3, 4, and 12 in the boxes to create the least possible positive difference. Use each number exactly once.

$$\frac{\boxed{2}}{\boxed{4}} - \frac{\boxed{3}}{\boxed{12}} = \frac{1}{4}$$

▶ **Exercises 42 and 43** These exercises are more difficult than the previous magic square problems because the sum of every row, column, and diagonal is not given. You may want to allow students to work on one of these exercises in small groups in class. Encourage them to discuss how they could find a workable sum.

One way is to rewrite all the numbers using a common denominator, add the numerators, and divide by 3. The sum is the fraction with the division result in the numerator and the common denominator. This works because all three rows (or columns) must add to the same number.

▶ **Exercises 44–47 Extension** Have students look for any patterns in the fractions they used to create the least possible sum and the least possible positive difference. Students may note that the same fractions are used in both situations, and the two digits with the lesser values are the numerators. The greater numerator is paired with the greatest number in the denominator.

Math Link
Challenge students to write a magic square to help them review.

Additional Answers

42. Possible magic square $\left(\text{sum is } 1\frac{3}{4}\right)$:

$\frac{1}{3}$	$\frac{3}{4}$	$\frac{2}{3}$
$\frac{11}{12}$	$\frac{7}{12}$	$\frac{1}{4}$
$\frac{1}{2}$	$\frac{5}{12}$	$\frac{5}{6}$

43. Possible magic square (sum is 3):

$\frac{1}{2}$	$\frac{4}{3}$	$\frac{7}{6}$
$\frac{5}{3}$	1	$\frac{1}{3}$
$\frac{5}{6}$	$\frac{2}{3}$	$\frac{3}{2}$

▶ **Exercise 48** Point out that not all the factors of 24 needs to be used in the solution, but encourage students to use as many factors as they can when creating the magic square.

One simple way to approach this is to create a magic square using whole numbers, and then use those numbers as numerators in fractions with a denominator of 24. Rewrite the fractions using lowest terms.

▶ **Exercises 49–51** Students have to find and then extend patterns involving mixed numbers. These are similar to the skip counting exercises younger students do, and they are important in helping students build an intuitive feel for how fractions "work" as they move up and down by fractional amounts. Some students may want to make a sketch of a ruler, with the relevant fractional divisions, to help them find the missing numbers.

52a. $\frac{1}{16}$; There are 16 spaces in every inch.

52b. Start at $1\frac{1}{8}$ on the ruler and count 5 small divisions to the right. You end at the sum, $1\frac{7}{16}$.

52c. Start at $2\frac{1}{4}$ and move 5 small divisions to the left. You end at the difference, $1\frac{15}{16}$.

52d. No; there are no markings for 12ths.

52e. Yes; start at $\frac{3}{8}$, move right 1 in. to $1\frac{3}{8}$, and then count 7 sixteenths to $1\frac{13}{16}$ in.

48. **Challenge** Create a magic square with a sum of 1 in which the denominators of the fractions are factors of 24.   See margin.

Patterns Give the rule for finding each term in the sequence from the previous term. Then use your rule to find the missing terms. Use the last term to check your answers.

49. $1\frac{2}{5}, 2\frac{4}{5}, 4\frac{1}{5}, 5\frac{3}{5}, \underline{\hspace{1cm}}, 7, \underline{\hspace{1cm}}, 8\frac{2}{5}, \underline{\hspace{1cm}}, 9\frac{4}{5}, 11\frac{1}{5}, 12\frac{3}{5}$ Add $1\frac{2}{5}$

50. $3\frac{1}{2}, 6\frac{3}{4}, 10, 13\frac{1}{4}, \underline{\hspace{1cm}}, 16\frac{1}{2}, \underline{\hspace{1cm}}, 19\frac{3}{4}, 23, \underline{\hspace{1cm}}, 26\frac{1}{4}, 29\frac{1}{2}$ Add $3\frac{1}{4}$

51. $15, 14\frac{5}{8}, 14\frac{1}{4}, 13\frac{7}{8}, \underline{\hspace{1cm}}, 13\frac{1}{2}, \underline{\hspace{1cm}}, 13\frac{1}{8}, 12\frac{3}{4}, \underline{\hspace{1cm}}, 12\frac{3}{8}, 12$ Subtract $\frac{3}{8}$

52. **Measurement** Below is part of a ruler.

a. What fraction of an inch does the smallest division of this ruler represent? How do you know?

b. How could you use this ruler to find $1\frac{1}{8} + \frac{5}{16}$? Find the sum.

c. How could you use this ruler to find $2\frac{1}{4} - \frac{5}{16}$? Find the difference.

d. Could you use this ruler to find $2\frac{1}{2} - \frac{5}{12}$? Explain.

e. Could you use this ruler to find $\frac{3}{8} + 1\frac{7}{16}$? Explain.

53. **In Your Own Words** Explain why you do not add fractions by just adding the numerators and adding the denominators.   Different denominators indicate different sized pieces. To add fractions, add only the numerators of fractions with equal denominators.

Additional Answer

48. Possible magic square (sum is 1):

$\frac{3}{8}$	$\frac{13}{24}$	$\frac{1}{12}$
$\frac{1}{24}$	$\frac{1}{3}$	$\frac{5}{8}$
$\frac{7}{12}$	$\frac{1}{8}$	$\frac{7}{24}$

Mixed Review

Geometry   The measure of two angles of a triangle are given. Find the measure of the third angle.

54. 23° and 47°   110°

55. 60° and 60°   60°

56. 10° and 120°   50°

57. 94° and 20°   66°

Identify the property illustrated by each equation.

58. $5 + 7 = 7 + 5$ Commutative

59. $19 + (81 + 25) = (19 + 81) + 25$ Associative

60. $8(3 + 2) = 8 \cdot 3 + 8 \cdot 2$ Distributive

61. $a \cdot (b \cdot c) = (a \cdot b) \cdot c$ Associative

62. $x \cdot y = y \cdot x$ Commutative

Find each sum or difference without using a calculator.

63. $165.7 + 47.5$ 213.2

64. $3.179 - 0.238$ 2.941

65. $976,556 + 0.002$ 976,556.002

66. $87.78 + 94.76$ 182.54

67. $10.0101 + 1.101$ 11.1111

68. $9.02 - 7.34$ 1.68

Lesson 4.1   Add and Subtract Fractions   **215**

Quick Check

Informal Assessment Students should be able to:

✔ use fraction models

✔ find common denominators, add and subtract fractions, and write the answers in lowest terms

✔ use a calculator to add and subtract fractions

Quick Quiz

1. Explain how you would use fraction pieces to find the sum $\frac{2}{3} + \frac{1}{4}$. Then give the answer and write two related subtraction equations.
Place two $\frac{1}{3}$-pieces and one $\frac{1}{4}$-piece on the mat. Find identical fractions that cover the same space. $\frac{2}{3} + \frac{1}{4} = \frac{11}{12}$; $\frac{11}{12} - \frac{1}{4} = \frac{2}{3}$; $\frac{11}{12} - \frac{2}{3} = \frac{1}{4}$

2. Explain how to find a common denominator for each pair of fractions. Then find the sum or difference.

a. $\frac{1}{2} + \frac{2}{3}$ Possible method: Find the product of the two denominators: $2 \cdot 3$, or 6; $\frac{1}{2} + \frac{2}{3} = \frac{3}{6} + \frac{4}{6} = \frac{7}{6} = 1\frac{1}{6}$.

b. $\frac{5}{8} - \frac{3}{10}$ Possible method: Find the least common multiple of 8 and 10; $\frac{5}{8} - \frac{3}{10} = \frac{25}{40} - \frac{12}{40} = \frac{13}{40}$.

c. $\frac{3}{8} + \frac{7}{16}$ Possible method: Since 8 is a factor of 16, 16 is a common denominator; $\frac{3}{8} + \frac{7}{16} = \frac{6}{16} + \frac{7}{16} = \frac{13}{16}$.

3. Find each sum or difference.

a. $\frac{1}{4} + \frac{5}{12}$ $\frac{8}{12}$ or $\frac{2}{3}$

b. $\frac{2}{3} - \frac{1}{4}$ $\frac{5}{12}$

c. $2\frac{3}{10} - \frac{5}{8}$ $1\frac{27}{40}$

d. $1\frac{5}{8} + 2\frac{3}{10}$ $3\frac{37}{40}$

e. $22\frac{3}{8} - 20\frac{7}{16}$ $1\frac{15}{16}$

f. $12\frac{7}{16} + 1\frac{3}{8}$ $13\frac{13}{16}$

Multiply and Divide Fractions

Objectives

▶ To multiply fractions by whole numbers

▶ To model fraction multiplication

▶ To multiply and divide fractions

Overview

In this lesson, students first find fractional parts of whole numbers using realistic contexts.

They use this work to develop an understanding of how to multiply fractions and whole numbers. Using models, they extend their knowledge to multiplying fractions by fractions, including learning to use the conventional algorithm.

Students look at division with fractions in a similar way. They divide whole numbers by fractions by asking such questions as "How many half apples are there in five apples?" Eventually they learn that dividing by a fraction is the same as multiplying by the reciprocal of that fraction.

Advance Preparation

You may want to provide copies of Chapter 4 Master 1 to facilitate class discussion while presenting these topics, including multiplying and dividing fractions.

	Summary	Materials	On Your Own Exercises (pp. 233–241)	Assessment Opportunities
Investigation 1 (p. 216) *Pacing: 2 days*	Students multiply whole numbers by fractions.		Practice & Apply: 1–4 Connect & Extend: 40–51 Mixed Review: 73–82	• Share & Summarize (p. 219) • Troubleshooting (p. 217)
Investigation 2 (p. 219) *Pacing: 1 day*	Students use area models to multiply two fractions and explore the shortcut algorithm $\frac{a}{b} \cdot \frac{c}{d} = \frac{a \cdot c}{b \cdot d}$.	Chapter 4 Master 1 or grid, colored pencils (optional), rulers or straightedges (optional)	Practice & Apply: 5–12 Connect & Extend: 52–54 Mixed Review: 73–82	• On the Spot Assessment (pp. 220, 221) • Share & Summarize (p. 221) • Troubleshooting (pp. 219, 221)
Investigation 3 (p. 222) *Pacing: 1 day*	Students multiply mixed numbers.	Chapter 4 Master 1 or grid paper, rulers or straightedges (optional)	Practice & Apply: 13–18 Connect & Extend: 55–57 Mixed Review: 73–82	• On the Spot Assessment (pp. 222, 223) • Share & Summarize (p. 225) • Troubleshooting (p. 225)
Investigation 4 (p. 226) *Pacing: 1 day*	Students use models and the related multiplication equations to divide whole numbers by fractions.		Practice & Apply: 19–23 Connect & Extend: 58–60 Mixed Review: 73–82	• On the Spot Assessment (pp. 226, 227) • Share & Summarize (p. 229)
Investigation 5 (p. 229) *Pacing: 1 day*	Students divide two fractions.		Practice & Apply: 24–39 Connect & Extend: 61–72 Mixed Review: 73–82	• Share & Summarize (p. 232)

Leveled Lesson Resources

CRM *Available in:* **Chapter 4 Resource Masters**

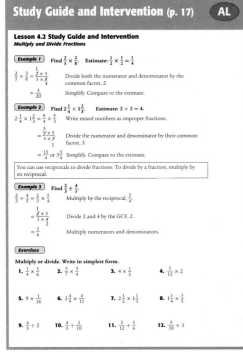

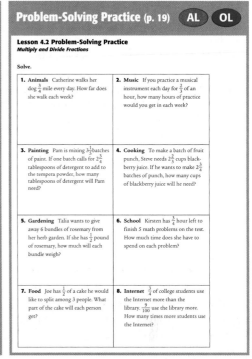

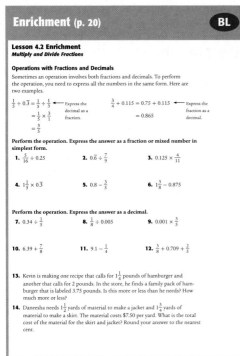

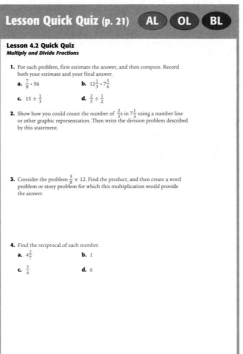

Additional Lesson Resources

Teacher Tech Tools
- TeacherWorks
- ExamView Assessment Suite
- Classroom Presentation Toolkit
- Advance Tracker

Student Tech Tools
- StudentWorks Plus
- Math Online eGlossary •
  Concepts in Motion

Other Print Products
- Investigation Notebook
  and Reflection Journal
- Quick Review Math Handbook

Lesson 4.2 Multiply and Divide Fractions   **216B**

Introduce

Multiply and Divide Fractions Briefly review the concepts of multiplication and division. Ask students when they might multiply to find a solution and when they might divide. Their answers may include the ideas that they can multiply when putting together equal-sized groups and divide when sharing equally. Point out that the same ideas apply to multiplying and dividing with fractions.

Explore

Suggested Grouping: Groups of 3 or 4

▶ **Prepare** Discuss the two situations presented in this activity. Encourage students to use problem-solving strategies to help answer these questions. Strategies may include repeated addition and drawing diagrams, or using fraction pieces to model the problem.

▶ **Play** Ask students to share and discuss strategies they will use. Another possible strategy for the lemonade problem is to think about how many $\frac{3}{4}$-cup portions are needed to equal a whole number and then find multiples of the whole number that are close to 20. For example, $\frac{3}{4} + \frac{3}{4} + \frac{3}{4} + \frac{3}{4} = 3$, so 3 cups of lemonade will serve 4 people, 6 cups will serve 8 people, and so on.

▶ **Report** Have students take turns discussing the strategies they found. Discuss as a class why the strategies are successful or not successful.

▶ **Score** Give each group credit for doing the exploration.

Investigation 1

On Your Own Exercises
Pages 233–241
Exercises 1–4, 40–51

Multiply Fractions This investigation introduces the idea of multiplying a fraction by a whole number in realistic contexts. Students will use their strategies from the Explore as they continue.

LESSON 4.2 — Multiply and Divide Fractions

In this lesson, you will learn how to multiply and divide with fractions. As you work the exercises, it may be helpful to think about what multiplication and division mean and about how these operations work with whole numbers.

① $20 \cdot \frac{3}{4} = 15$; To find how much lemonade is needed, you add $\frac{3}{4}$ twenty times. This is the same as finding $20 \cdot \frac{3}{4}$. $12 \cdot \frac{2}{3} = 8$; You can think of taking $\frac{2}{3}$ of 1 lb to get $\frac{2}{3}$ lb and then multiplying by 12 to get $\frac{2}{3}$ of all 12 lb.

Explore See teaching notes for sample strategies.

Work with your group to answer these questions. Try to find more than one way to answer each question.

• You want to serve lemonade to 20 people. Each glass holds $\frac{3}{4}$ cup. How many cups of lemonade do you need?   15

• You grew 12 pounds of peas. You give some away, keeping $\frac{2}{3}$ of the peas for yourself. How many pounds do you have left?   8

The questions you just answered can be represented with multiplication equations. Write a multiplication equation to represent each question. Explain why the equation fits the situation.   See ①.

Investigation 1 — Multiply Fractions and Whole Numbers

In this investigation, you will explore more exercises involving multiplication with fractions. As you work the exercises, you might try some of the strategies that you and your classmates used in Explore.

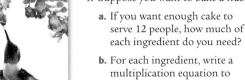

Real-World Link

The vanilla extract used in recipes is derived from the vanilla planifolia orchid. This plant is native to Mexico, where it is pollinated by bees and hummingbirds.

1a. $2\frac{1}{4}$ c sugar, $7\frac{1}{2}$ c flour, $1\frac{1}{2}$ tsp salt, $4\frac{1}{2}$ tsp vanilla, 6 eggs

1b. sugar: $3 \cdot \frac{3}{4} = \frac{9}{4}$ $= 2\frac{1}{4}$; flour: $3 \cdot 2\frac{1}{2} = \frac{15}{2} = 7\frac{1}{2}$; salt: $3 \cdot \frac{1}{2} = \frac{3}{2} = 1\frac{1}{2}$; vanilla: $3 \cdot 1\frac{1}{2} = \frac{9}{2} = 4\frac{1}{2}$; eggs: $3 \cdot 2 = 6$

3. Possible answer: I know that $\frac{1}{4}$ of 20 is 5, so $\frac{3}{4}$ of 20 is $3 \cdot 5$, or 15. I know that $\frac{1}{2}$ of 20 is 10, so $\frac{3}{2}$ of 20 is $3 \cdot 10$, or 30.

Develop & Understand: A

1. Suppose you want to bake a fraction cake.   See below.

   a. If you want enough cake to serve 12 people, how much of each ingredient do you need?

   b. For each ingredient, write a multiplication equation to represent the work you did in Part a.

   > **Fraction Cake**
   > $\frac{3}{4}$ cup sugar
   > $2\frac{1}{2}$ cups flour
   > $\frac{1}{2}$ teaspoon salt
   > $1\frac{1}{2}$ teaspoons vanilla
   > 2 eggs
   > Serves four people

2. Find each product using any method you like.

   a. $\frac{1}{4} \cdot 20$ 5   **b.** $20 \cdot \frac{1}{2}$ 10   **c.** $20 \cdot \frac{3}{4}$ 15   **d.** $\frac{3}{2} \cdot 20$ 30

3. Describe the strategies you used to find the products in Exercise 2.

Think & Discuss

Hannah and Jahmal have different strategies for multiplying a whole number by a fraction.

The following is Hannah's strategy.

I multiply the whole number by the numerator of the fraction. Then I divide the result by the denominator.

The following is Jahmal's strategy.

I do just the opposite. I divide the whole number by the denominator of the fraction. Then I multiply the result by the numerator.

Try both methods on Parts a–d of Exercise 2 above. Do they both work?   Yes

You will probably find that some multiplication expressions are easier to simplify with Hannah's method and others are easier with Jahmal's method. For each expression below, tell whose method you think would be easier to use.   Answers will vary.

$$7 \cdot \frac{5}{14} \qquad \frac{3}{4} \cdot 8 \qquad 10 \cdot \frac{7}{36} \qquad \frac{9}{10} \cdot 5$$

The methods described above also work for multiplying a fraction by a decimal. The exercises on page 218 provide an opportunity to practice Hannah's and Jahmal's methods.

Develop & Understand: A

Suggested Grouping: Pairs

▶ **Exercises 1 and 2** Suggest that students use any approach they wish to triple the amounts in the recipe in Exercise 1 and find the products in Exercise 2.

▶ **Exercise 3** Have students share their descriptions to reinforce the wide variety of strategies that students can use to solve these problems. Encourage all students who used different strategies to share their methods. Use this discussion to lead into the Think & Discuss.

Wrap-Up Invite students to share their descriptions from **Exercise 3** to reinforce the wide variety of strategies that students can use to solve these problems. Encourage all students who used different strategies to share their methods. Use this discussion to lead into Think & Discuss.

Think & Discuss

Read through Hannah's and Jahmal's strategies and have students try their methods. Discuss how students' strategies from the exercises compare with Hannah's and Jahmal's strategies.

Revisit that a fraction can be thought of as a division problem and vice versa. Ask students where the division operation is in the problem $\frac{1}{4} \cdot 20$.

Point out that Hannah's and Jahmal's methods can also be used to multiply a fraction and a decimal.

Troubleshooting Watch for students who multiply each ingredient of the fraction cake by 12 instead of 3 in **Exercise 1a**. If students do not understand why they should multiply by 3, have them use the make a table problem-solving strategy and make a table like the one below.

Number of Cakes	1	2	3
Number of Servings	4	8	12

Mathematical Background

Since division by a number is the same thing as multiplying by its reciprocal, the Commutative Property of Multiplication can be extended to include division, as long as the divisor remains the same. For example, $c \cdot a \div b = a \div b \cdot c$; note that in both cases, b is the divisor.

To show that these expressions are equivalent, convert the division to multiplication by a fraction before commuting:

$$c \cdot a \div b = c \cdot a \cdot \frac{1}{b}$$
$$= a \cdot \frac{1}{b} \cdot c$$
$$= a \div b \cdot c$$

Develop & Understand: B

Suggested Grouping: Pairs

▶ **Exercise 4** Encourage students to write their answers as mixed numbers, when possible.

▶ **Exercises 5 and 6** Point out that these exercises require multiplying a dollar amount by a fraction. Students need to be aware of the different units used in each problem (ounces and pounds in Exercise 5, and inches, feet, and yards in Exercise 6).

Students may use the strategies below.

- Write the money amounts as cents before multiplying. For example, in **Exercise 6a**, they may find that $\frac{2}{3}$ of $2 is $1.33.

- Find the unit cost and multiply that cost by the number of units. In **Exercise 6c**, students may find that one inch of fabric costs $0.056, so 8 inches would cost 8 times as much, or $0.44.

- Write the measure as a fraction and then multiply. In **Exercise 5b**, 8 ounces is $\frac{8}{16}$, or $\frac{1}{2}$ of a pound. Multiplying $\frac{1}{2}$ by $6 gives $3.

- Use number sense and the answers to prior problems. For example, the cost of 4 ounces in **Exercise 5c** should be half the cost of 8 ounces in **Exercise 5b**, and half of $3 is $1.50.

Wrap-Up Have students share their methods for solving Exercises 5b, 5c, 6b, and 6c.

Develop & Understand: C

Suggested Grouping: Pairs

▶ **Exercise 7** Suggest that students use patterns to complete the table.

▶ **Exercises 8 and 9** Suggest that students work backward from the products to the factors.

Analyze the Table Ask students to discuss any patterns they see in the tables for **Exercises 7–9**.

Develop & Understand: B

Use Hannah's or Jahmal's method, or one of your own, to solve these exercises. Show how you find your answers.
Solution methods will vary.

4. A cocoa recipe for one person calls for $\frac{3}{4}$ cup milk. Tell how much milk is needed to make the recipe for the following numbers of people.

   a. 3 people   **b.** 5 people   **c.** 6 people   **d.** 8 people

5. Fudge costs $6 per pound. Use the fact that 16 ounces equals 1 pound to help find the cost of each amount of fudge.

   a. $\frac{3}{4}$ pound   **b.** 8 ounces   **c.** 4 ounces   **d.** $1\frac{1}{2}$ pounds

6. At Fiona's Fabrics, plaid ribbon costs $2 per yard. Give the cost of each length of ribbon.

   a. $\frac{2}{3}$ yard   **b.** $1\frac{1}{2}$ feet   **c.** 8 inches   **d.** $1\frac{3}{4}$ yards

Develop & Understand: C

Complete each multiplication table.

Real-World Link

Milk chocolate was first created in Switzerland in 1876. The country consumes more than 20 pounds per person every year, more than anywhere else in the world.

4a. $2\frac{1}{4}$ c

4b. $3\frac{3}{4}$ c

4c. $4\frac{1}{2}$ c

4d. 6 c

5a. $4.50
5b. $3.00
5c. $1.50
5d. $9.00

6a. $1.33
6b. $1.00
6c. $0.44
6d. $3.50

7.

×	24	120	60	72
$\frac{1}{2}$	12	60	30	36
$\frac{2}{3}$	16	80	40	48
$\frac{1}{4}$	6	30	15	18
$\frac{3}{4}$	18	90	45	54

300

8.

×	180	?	60	120
$\frac{1}{5}$	36	60	12	24
$\frac{1}{2}$	90	150	30	60
$\frac{2}{3}$	120	200	40	80
$\frac{1}{4}$	45	75	15	30

96   144   24

9.

×	?	?	?	120
$\frac{3}{2}$	144	216	36	180
$\frac{2}{3}$?	64	96	16	80
$\frac{3}{8}$	36	54	9	45
$\frac{5}{6}$?	80	120	20	100

Reaching *All Learners*

OL **On Level** Students will need to use various strategies to complete the tables in **Exercises 8 and 9**.

- They must use problem-solving strategies to decide what information they can use to find some of the missing information and what steps to follow to complete the entire table.

- They must find the missing factor in some problems.

- They must multiply to find the products needed to complete the table.

1. **Possible answer:**
A recipe calls for $\frac{2}{3}$ c water. To double the recipe, how much water will you need? Solution: $2 \cdot \frac{2}{3} = \frac{4}{3} = 1\frac{1}{3}$. You need $1\frac{1}{3}$ c water.

Share & Summarize

1. Create a real-world situation that can be solved by multiplying a whole number and a fraction. Explain how to solve it.

2. What calculation do you need to do to find $\frac{3}{4}$ of 6 inches? What is $\frac{3}{4}$ of 6 inches? $\frac{3}{4} \cdot 6, 4\frac{1}{2}$ in.

Investigation 2 Model Fraction Multiplication

You can visualize the product of two whole numbers by drawing a rectangle with side lengths equal to the numbers. The area of the rectangle represents the product. This rectangle represents 4 · 6.

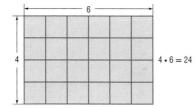

You can represent the product of a whole number and a fraction in the same way. The shaded portion of this diagram represents the product $\frac{1}{2} \cdot 6$.

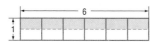

Think & Discuss

What is the area of each small rectangle in the above diagram? $\boxed{}$ $\frac{1}{2}$

How many small rectangles are shaded?   6

Use your answers to the previous questions to find the total shaded area. Explain why this area is equal to $\frac{1}{2} \cdot 6$. 3; Possible explanation: The shaded area is composed of 6 rectangles, each with area $\frac{1}{2}$, so the total area is $6 \cdot \frac{1}{2}$.

Lesson 4.2 Multiply and Divide Fractions   **219**

Troubleshooting

Encourage students who are having difficulty multiplying a whole number and a fraction to model each problem and write an equation for the model. For example, in Exercise 4a on page 218, students could use three $\frac{1}{4}$-fraction pieces to show $\frac{3}{4}$-cup milk. They can show three groups of these pieces to represent the number of cups needed to serve three people, and then rearrange the pieces into wholes and fractions to help them write the number in lowest terms.

Share & Summarize

Discuss these two exercises with the class. The exercises encourage students to consider *when* they may need to multiply a fraction by a whole number. The sample response given for **Exercise 1** represents the kind of problem that is probably easier for students to recognize as multiplication: when a fractional quantity has to be doubled or tripled.

Exercise 2 poses a different situation: finding a fractional part of a whole-number quantity. Be sure students recognize that phrases containing *of*, such as *three-fourths of 6*, mean to multiply.

Investigation 2

On Your Own Exercises
Pages 233–241
Exercises 5–12, 52–54

Model Fraction Multiplication This investigation introduces a visual area model for understanding multiplication of fractions. Students use this model to discover the algorithm $\frac{a}{b} \cdot \frac{c}{d} = \frac{a \cdot c}{b \cdot d}$.

Review the area, or rectangle, model for multiplying two whole numbers. Then point out that a similar model can be used to multiply when one or more of the factors are fractions. Discuss how the dashed line is used to show $\frac{1}{2}$ in the second diagram.

Think & Discuss

Use this activity to be sure that students can interpret the sketch that shows $\frac{1}{2} \cdot 6$ as a shaded portion of the 1 × 6 grid.

If students are not clear about the area of the small rectangles in the sketch, ask them how many equal-sized parts are in each 1 × 1 square. 2 Alternatively, you could ask them to describe the horizontal length of each rectangle and the number of equal parts in the vertical length of the square. They should see that the horizontal length is one unit and the vertical length is divided into 2 parts.

Develop & Understand: A

Suggested Grouping: Pairs

▶ **Exercise 1** Work through the exercise with the class if most students had trouble understanding the diagram in Think & Discuss on page 219.

▶ **Exercise 2** Students may experience some confusion about using the area model for multiplication because it differs from the way the model is used to show addition of fractions. The area model for multiplication is two-dimensional. The two fractions are displayed along two different sides of the square, and it is the *overlapped* area that gives the solution. For example, Exercise 2's diagram could be shown this way:

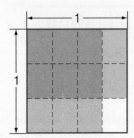

▶ **Exercises 3–5** Point out that students will need to draw and shade the grids themselves. Some students may need extra assistance to draw the diagrams. You may want to encourage students to use two different colored pencils so they can clearly see the double-shaded area.

▶ **Exercise 5** If necessary, remind students that an asterisk is another symbol used to show multiplication.

Teacher Tips If possible, have students use grid paper, or copies of Chapter 4 Master 1 to make their diagrams. This can help them focus on the ideas rather than the mechanics of drawing the diagrams.

Wrap-Up Have students describe the models they created for Exercises 3–5. Use students' answers to Exercise 6 to lead into Think & Discuss on page 221.

1a. $\frac{2}{3}$ and 6

2c. The shaded area is a rectangle with dimensions $\frac{2}{3}$ and $\frac{3}{4}$. Its area is the product of the dimensions, $\frac{2}{3} \cdot \frac{3}{4}$.

3. $\frac{1}{2} \cdot \frac{1}{3} = \frac{1}{6}$

4. $\frac{3}{5} \cdot \frac{3}{4} = \frac{9}{20}$

5. $\frac{1}{2} \cdot \frac{5}{6} = \frac{5}{12}$

Develop & Understand: A

1. Consider this diagram.

   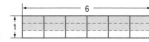

   a. The shaded region shows the product of what two numbers?

   b. What is the area of each small rectangle? How many small rectangles are shaded? $\frac{1}{3}$, 12

   c. Use your answers from Part b to find the total shaded area.　4

   d. Write a multiplication equation to represent the product of the numbers from Part a. $\frac{2}{3} \cdot 6 = 4$

2. You can use similar diagrams to represent the product of two fractions. The shaded portion of this diagram represents the product $\frac{2}{3} \cdot \frac{3}{4}$.

   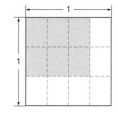

   a. What are the dimensions of the entire figure?　1 by 1

   b. Look at the entire shaded region. What is the height of this region? What is the width of this region? $\frac{2}{3}$, $\frac{3}{4}$

   c. Use your answers from Part b to explain why the area of the shaded region is $\frac{2}{3} \cdot \frac{3}{4}$.

   d. What is the area of each small rectangle? How many small rectangles are shaded? $\frac{1}{12}$, 6

   e. Use your answers from Part d to find $\frac{2}{3} \cdot \frac{3}{4}$.　$\frac{6}{12}$, or $\frac{1}{2}$

Draw a diagram like the one in Exercise 2 to represent each product. Then use your diagram to find the product. Give your answer as a multiplication equation, for example, $\frac{2}{3} \cdot \frac{3}{4} = \frac{6}{12}$.

3. $\frac{1}{2} \cdot \frac{1}{3}$

4. $\frac{3}{5} \cdot \frac{3}{4}$

5. $\frac{1}{2} \cdot \frac{5}{6}$

6. Look at your diagrams and equations from Exercises 3–5. Can you see a shortcut for multiplying two fractions *without* making a diagram? If so, use your shortcut to find $\frac{4}{7} \cdot \frac{2}{3}$. Then draw a diagram to see if your shortcut worked. Possible answer: Multiply the numerators to get the numerator of the product, and multiply the denominators to get the denominator of the product; $\frac{4}{7} \cdot \frac{2}{3} = \frac{8}{21}$.

On the Spot Assessment

Watch for students who count the lines they are drawing to divide the square rather than the spaces between the lines. For example, in Exercise 4, they need to divide a square into five parts horizontally and four parts vertically (or vice versa). Some students may mistakenly draw five horizontal lines and end up with sixths rather than fifths.

① Possible answer: For $\frac{1}{2} \cdot \frac{5}{6}$, the product of the denominators, 12, is the number of rectangles into which the square is divided; and the product of the numerators, 5, is the number of rectangles that are shaded. The shaded area is $\frac{5}{12}$, the product of the numerators over the product of the denominators.

Think & Discuss

You may have noticed the following shortcut for multiplying two fractions.

The product of two fractions is the product of the numerators over the product of the denominators.

Use one of your rectangle diagrams from Exercises 3–5 on page 220 to explain why this shortcut works. **See ①.**

✅ Develop & Understand: B

Use the shortcut described above to find each product. Express your answers in both the original form and in lowest terms.

7. $\frac{3}{5} \cdot \frac{1}{4}$ $\frac{3}{20}$

8. $\frac{1}{6} \cdot \frac{2}{3}$ $\frac{2}{18}, \frac{1}{9}$

9. $\frac{4}{5} \cdot \frac{5}{8}$ $\frac{20}{40}, \frac{1}{2}$

10. $\frac{2}{3} \cdot \frac{3}{7}$ $\frac{6}{21}, \frac{2}{7}$

11. $\frac{2}{3} \cdot \frac{1}{8}$ $\frac{2}{24}, \frac{1}{12}$

12. $\frac{2}{3} \cdot \frac{3}{8}$ $\frac{6}{24}, \frac{1}{4}$

13. Rob wants to create a small herb garden in his backyard. The space he marked off is a square, $\frac{7}{8}$ of a meter on each side. What will be the area of his herb garden? $\frac{49}{64}$ square meters

② Possible answer:

The area of the shaded region is $\frac{3}{4} \cdot \frac{1}{2}$. The product of $\frac{3}{4} \cdot \frac{1}{2}$ is $\frac{3}{8}$. Each rectangle is $\frac{1}{8}$ of the whole square and 3 rectangles are shaded.

Share & Summarize

Draw a diagram to represent the product of two fractions you have not yet multiplied together in this investigation. Explain how the diagram shows the product. **See ②.**

 Assessment

Watch for students who rewrite the factors with a common denominator and then multiply only the numerators and write the product over the common denominator. Remind them that they must multiply both the numerators and the denominators, and rewriting with common denominators is not necessary. Encourage students to use area models to check their answers.

Think & Discuss

By now, students are likely to recognize that the product of two fractions can be found by multiplying the numerators together, multiplying the denominators together, and writing the two products as a fraction. Take some time to allow students to tie this algorithm back into the drawings they have been making, especially if they did not make this connection in the prior exercise set.

You can also use the area model for multiplying two fractions to point out that the product of two factors less than one must be less than either factor. This observation can become a valuable reference point when estimating the product of two fractions or checking whether an answer is reasonable in the exercises on this page.

✅ Develop & Understand: B

Suggested Grouping: Individuals

▶ **Exercises 7–12** Emphasize that students should give their answers in two forms, the original form and the answer in lowest terms.

▶ **Exercise 13** Point out that a unit of measure is required in the answer.

Share & Summarize

Have students present their diagrams, with explanations, to the class. This question gives students a chance to demonstrate whether they understand the area model for multiplying fractions. You may want to collect all student responses for individual assessment.

Troubleshooting If students cannot use the shortcut algorithm to multiply, but they understand the area model, have them write out the steps for using the algorithm and refer to them when multiplying. For example, they might write:

1. Multiply the numerators and write the product on paper.

2. Draw a fraction bar below the product.

3. Multiply the denominators and write the product below the fraction bar.

Multiply with Fractions In this investigation, students learn how to multiply mixed numbers and how to simplify multiplication problems before multiplying. They also estimate products to check that their answers are reasonable.

Tell students that they can use their knowledge of multiplying fractions to multiply mixed numbers.

Example

The Example extends the use of the area model to include mixed numbers. Students who are comfortable with the model from Investigation 2 will have little trouble here. For those having difficulty, ask questions like these as you review the model:

How does the diagram show $1\frac{1}{2}$? The shaded area is a full unit at the top and half a unit on the bottom.

How can you tell from the model that $1\frac{1}{2} \cdot 2 = 3$? The shaded area has length 2 and width $1\frac{1}{2}$, and there are three full units shaded: two at the top, and two halves at the bottom.

Be sure students can explain the model before they draw similar diagrams in the exercises on this page.

✓ Develop & Understand: A

Suggested Grouping: Pairs

▶ **Exercises 1–4** Provide students with Chapter 4 Master 1, or grid paper, to use when making their diagrams.

▶ **Exercise 2** Suggest the use of an area diagram to demonstrate that Marcus' approach to multiplying mixed numbers (in Exercise 3) does not work.

▶ **Exercises 3 and 4** Discuss each exercise and give examples of why the shortcuts are correct or incorrect.

Investigation ③ Multiply with Fractions

In the last investigation, you found a shortcut for multiplying fractions. Now you will look at products involving mixed numbers.

Example

This diagram illustrates $1\frac{1}{2} \cdot 2$. Each shaded section is labeled with its area. The total area is $1 + 1 + \frac{1}{2} + \frac{1}{2} = 3$. So,
$$1\frac{1}{2} \cdot 2 = 3$$

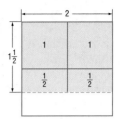

1. $1\frac{1}{2} \cdot \frac{1}{3} = \frac{1}{2}$
Possible diagram:

2. $1\frac{1}{2} \cdot 2\frac{1}{2} = 3\frac{3}{4}$
Possible diagram:

3. For Exercise 1, Marcus' method gives $\frac{1}{6}$. For Exercise 2, it gives $2\frac{1}{4}$. His method does not work.

✓ Develop & Understand: A

Draw a diagram to illustrate and find each product. Give your answer as a multiplication equation.

1. $1\frac{1}{2} \cdot \frac{1}{3}$

2. $1\frac{1}{2} \cdot 2\frac{1}{2}$

3. Marcus suggested this shortcut for multiplying mixed numbers.

   Multiply the whole number parts, multiply the fraction parts, and add the two results.

   Try Marcus' method to find the products in Exercises 1 and 2. Does it work?

4. Miguel suggested this shortcut for multiplying mixed numbers.

   Change the mixed numbers to fractions and multiply.

   Try Miguel's method on the products in Exercises 1 and 2. Does it work? For Exercise 1, Miguel's method gives $\frac{3}{2} \cdot \frac{1}{3} = \frac{3}{6} = \frac{1}{2}$. For Exercise 2, it gives $\frac{3}{2} \cdot \frac{5}{2} = \frac{15}{4} = 3\frac{3}{4}$. Miguel's method works.

ᴼⁿ ᵗʰᵉ Spot *Assessment*

To show Marcus' approach for Exercise 3 is incorrect, draw the correct and incorrect diagrams below to show the shaded areas are not the same.

The incorrect method: $2 \cdot 1$ and $\frac{1}{2} \cdot \frac{1}{2}$.

★ indicates multi-step problem

There are several calculations involved in multiplying two mixed numbers. It is a good idea to estimate the product before you multiply.

Think & Discuss

Consider $1\frac{1}{3} \cdot 5\frac{2}{3}$.

Before multiplying, make an estimate of the product. Explain how you found your answer.   See ①.

Now change both mixed numbers to fractions and multiply.   See ②.

How does your result compare to your estimate?
Comparisons will vary.

✓ Develop & Understand: B

In Exercises 5–10, complete Parts a and b.

a. Estimate the product.   Estimates will vary.

b. Find the product, showing all of your steps. Give your result as a mixed number. If your answer is far from your estimate, check your calculations.

5. $1\frac{3}{8} \cdot 2\frac{1}{2}$ $3\frac{7}{16}$
6. $3\frac{1}{3} \cdot \frac{8}{5}$ $5\frac{1}{3}$
7. $\frac{1}{4} \cdot 8\frac{3}{5}$ $2\frac{3}{20}$

8. $3\frac{1}{2} \cdot 1\frac{2}{3}$ $5\frac{5}{6}$
9. $9\frac{2}{3} \cdot 1\frac{1}{2}$ $14\frac{1}{2}$
10. $2\frac{1}{4} \cdot \frac{7}{8}$ $1\frac{31}{32}$

★11. Wei-Ling wants to hang wallpaper on two walls in her kitchen. One wall measures $11\frac{1}{2}$ feet by $8\frac{1}{2}$ feet, and the other measures $15\frac{2}{3}$ feet by $8\frac{1}{2}$ feet.

About how many square feet of wallpaper will she need? Estimate first and then calculate.   Estimates will vary; calculation: $230\frac{11}{12}$

Suppose one roll of wallpaper contains 55 square feet. How many rolls of wallpaper will Wei-Ling need?   5 rolls

① Possible answers:
• More than 5 (1 · 5) and less than 12 (2 · 6).
• Rounding the factors to the nearest whole numbers gives 1 · 6, so the product will be about 6.

② $1\frac{1}{3} \cdot 5\frac{2}{3} =$
$\frac{4}{3} \cdot \frac{17}{3} =$
$\frac{68}{9} = 7\frac{5}{9}$

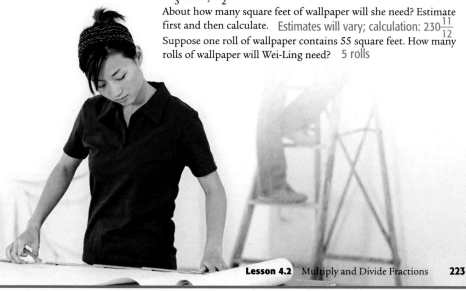

Lesson 4.2 Multiply and Divide Fractions **223**

On the Spot Assessment

Watch for students who try to use the same process to multiply mixed numbers as they do to add mixed numbers. These students may use Marcus' approach from the exercises on page 222. Remind them that this approach ignores some partial products, specifically the products of any whole numbers and fractions. Suggest that students write each mixed number as a fraction and then multiply.

Teacher Tips You may want to discuss why it is a good idea to estimate before multiplying.

Think & Discuss

As you discuss the sample problem, ask students to share their approaches to estimating the product of the two fractions. While students are most likely to estimate by rounding each mixed number to the nearest whole number, they may use another method to estimate the value either as a single value or as a range. Regardless of the method used to estimate, when students calculate the exact solution, those who estimate by multiplying only the whole-number portions of the mixed numbers may find that their estimates are a less than the actual product. Giving a range allows them to take into account the fractional parts more fully.

Point out the method suggested for calculating the actual product. You may want to reinforce that students can use any correct method, but that this is an efficient method. Encourage students to use any method for estimating.

✓ Develop & Understand: B

Suggested Grouping: Individuals

▶ **Exercises 5–11** Although estimating their answers first is an important step, many students tend to see it as optional and may want to omit it. One way to address this tendency is to give students a set amount of time to estimate the solution for all the problems. Then have them complete the problems and compare their final answers to their estimates.

Remind students to show all the steps they used to find each product. Encourage them to write their answers in lowest terms.

Additional Examples Use these examples if students are having difficulty multiplying mixed numbers.

Estimate each product, and then multiply to find the actual product. Estimates will vary.

1. $3\frac{1}{2} \cdot 2\frac{1}{4}$ $7\frac{7}{8}$
2. $8\frac{1}{2} \cdot 1\frac{1}{4}$ $10\frac{5}{8}$
3. $2\frac{1}{2} \cdot 3\frac{1}{2}$ $8\frac{3}{4}$

After you multiply fractions or mixed numbers, you often have to put the product in lowest terms. Sometimes, it is easier to simplify *before* you multiply. Check whether the numerator of each fraction shares a common factor with the denominator of the other fraction.

─**Example**

Find $\frac{1}{3} \cdot \frac{3}{4}$.

Notice that **3** is a factor of the denominator of $\frac{1}{3}$ and the numerator of $\frac{3}{4}$.

$$\frac{1}{3} \cdot \frac{3}{4} = \frac{1 \cdot 3}{3 \cdot 4}$$ Rewrite as the product of numerators over the product of denominators.

$$= \frac{3}{3} \cdot \frac{1}{4}$$ Group the common factors to form a fraction equal to 1.

$$= 1 \cdot \frac{1}{4}$$ Simplify.

$$= \frac{1}{4}$$

Find $\frac{2}{3} \cdot \frac{9}{16}$.

Notice that **2** is a factor of 2 and 16, and **3** is a factor of 3 and 9. As in the previous example, group these common factors to form a fraction equal to 1.

$$\frac{2}{3} \cdot \frac{9}{16} = \frac{2 \cdot 9}{3 \cdot 16}$$ Rewrite as the product of numerators over the product of denominators.

$$= \frac{2 \cdot 3 \cdot 3}{3 \cdot 2 \cdot 8}$$ Rewrite 9 as 3 · 3 and 16 as 2 · 8.

$$= \frac{2 \cdot 3}{2 \cdot 3} \cdot \frac{3}{8}$$ Group the common factors to form a fraction equal to 1

$$= 1 \cdot \frac{3}{8}$$ Simplify.

$$= \frac{3}{8}$$

24. $1\frac{4}{5}$ c stock, $\frac{4}{5}$ c carrots, $\frac{9}{10}$ c asparagus, 1 c peas, $1\frac{3}{5}$ lb pasta, $2\frac{2}{5}$ tbs oil, $1\frac{2}{5}$ c cheese

✓ Develop & Understand: C

In Exercises 12–17, find the product in two ways.
- Multiply the fractions. Write the product in lowest terms.
- Simplify before finding the product.

Show all of your steps. Students should show all steps for both methods.

12. $\frac{3}{5} \cdot \frac{15}{6}$ $1\frac{1}{2}$

13. $\frac{5}{6} \cdot \frac{3}{10}$ $\frac{1}{4}$

14. $\frac{1}{8} \cdot \frac{2}{3}$ $\frac{1}{12}$

15. $\frac{7}{12} \cdot \frac{3}{5}$ $\frac{7}{20}$

16. $\frac{3}{10} \cdot \frac{2}{3}$ $\frac{1}{5}$

17. $\frac{1}{2} \cdot 2\frac{4}{5}$ $1\frac{2}{5}$

Find each product.

18. $\frac{3}{8} \cdot \frac{16}{7}$ $\frac{6}{7}$

19. $\frac{2}{3} \cdot \frac{7}{8}$ $\frac{7}{12}$

20. $\frac{2}{5} \cdot \frac{5}{6}$ $\frac{1}{3}$

21. $\frac{4}{5} \cdot \frac{3}{4}$ $\frac{3}{5}$

22. $\frac{1}{5} \cdot 1\frac{1}{2}$ $\frac{3}{10}$

23. $\frac{4}{5} \cdot 5\frac{3}{16}$ $4\frac{3}{20}$

24. Mai wants to make enough fraction pasta for six servings. Rewrite the recipe for her.

> **Fraction Pasta**
> $1\frac{1}{2}$ cups vegetable stock
> $\frac{2}{3}$ cup diced carrots
> $\frac{3}{4}$ cup asparagus tips
> $\frac{5}{6}$ cup peas
> $1\frac{1}{3}$ pounds pasta
> 2 tablespoons olive oil
> $1\frac{1}{6}$ cups Parmesan cheese
> Makes five servings

1. Possible answer: Change the numbers to fractions, and find the product of the numerators over the product of the denominators. To determine whether the answer is reasonable, estimate the product by rounding the factors to the nearest whole numbers and multiplying.

Share & Summarize

1. Explain how to multiply two mixed numbers. Tell how you can use estimation to determine whether your answer is reasonable.

2. Explain how you could find the product $\frac{3}{4} \cdot \frac{8}{9}$ by simplifying before you multiply.   See ① in margin.

Reaching All Learners

BL Beyond Level Show students how they can use "helping numbers" to eliminate rewriting the fractions in the second step. For example, to find $\frac{2}{3} \cdot \frac{9}{16}$, students can remove the factors of 2 and 3. Then students can multiply the remaining values. The helping notation for $\frac{2}{3} \cdot \frac{9}{16}$ is shown below.

$$\frac{\overset{1}{\cancel{2}}}{\underset{1}{\cancel{8}}} \cdot \frac{\overset{3}{\cancel{9}}}{\underset{8}{\cancel{16}}}$$

✓ Develop & Understand: C

Suggested Grouping: Pairs

▶ **Exercises 12–14** Ask one student of each pair to do these exercises by simplifying before multiplying. Ask the other student to multiply and then write the product in lowest terms. Have them compare their work and then switch methods for **Exercises 15-17**.

▶ **Exercise 24** Students may use one of these strategies to do this exercise:

- Multiply each quantity by $\frac{6}{5}$.
- Multiply each quantity by $\frac{1}{5}$ and add the product to the quantity in the recipe.

If students use the second strategy, make sure they understand that multiplying by $\frac{6}{5}$ gives the same answer.

Share & Summarize

Ask students to share their strategies, being sure to ask other students if they thought about each question in a different way. Help students understand that there may be more than one way to simplify a multiplication problem and to estimate a product.

Troubleshooting Students who are having difficulty multiplying mixed numbers because they cannot write mixed numbers as fractions can use fraction pieces or draw diagrams to help them rewrite the numbers. Have them divide any wholes into the appropriate number of equal-sized pieces, count the number of pieces, and write that total over the number of pieces in one whole.

If students are having difficulty because of weak multiplication and division skills, allow them to use calculators to determine if they understand the process. If they do not, you can provide remedial instructions for multiplication and division of one- and two-digit numbers.

If students are having difficulty simplifying before multiplying, you can remind them that they can solve these problems by multiplying first and writing the results in lowest terms.

Additional Answer for Share & Summarize Exercise 2 is on page 287A.

Divide Whole Numbers by Fractions
Introduce division of whole numbers by fractions by reminding students that they know how to add, subtract, and multiply fractions. Tell them that they will learn how to divide with fractions by looking for patterns and using related facts.

Explore

Suggested Grouping: Groups of 3 or 4

▶ **Prepare** Help students understand the first situation by rewording it using whole numbers in place of the fractions and asking students to describe some ways to solve the problem. Point out that they can divide with fractions using some of the same strategies they used to divide with whole numbers.

Remind students that division is not commutative, so $5 \div 2$ is not the same as $2 \div 5$. Likewise, $5 \div \frac{1}{2}$ is not the same as $\frac{1}{2} \div 5$.

You may want to have students use manipulatives like unifix cubes.

▶ **Play** Ask students to share the strategies they will use, including the strategies in the cartoon. Refer to the cartoon as part of the discussion. Have students discuss which method they prefer for these problems, and then think of a different problem in which the less-preferred method works better.

Ask students to answer the following questions in their groups:

1. What does $10 \div 2$ mean? The number of groups of 2 in 10

2. What does $10 \div \frac{2}{3}$ mean? The number of groups of $\frac{2}{3}$ in 10

▶ **Report** Have a reporter from each group share their strategies and answers to questions with the class.

▶ **Score** Give each group credit for doing the activity.

Investigation (4) Divide Whole Numbers by Fractions

Real-World Link
Apples belong to the rose family. More than 7,500 varieties of apples are grown worldwide, including 2,500 varieties grown in the United States.

You know how to add, subtract, and multiply fractions. Now you will learn how to divide a whole number by a fraction.

Explore

Work with your group to answer the following questions. Try to find more than one way to answer each question.

- Suppose you have five apples to share with your friends. If you divide each apple in half, how many halves will you have to share? See ①.
- There are 10 cups of punch left in the punchbowl. Each glass holds $\frac{2}{3}$ of a cup. How many glasses can you fill? See ②.

The questions above can be represented by division equations. Write an equation to represent each question. Explain why the equation fits the situation. See ③.

Caroline and Marcus solved the second Explore question in different ways.

① 10; Possible strategy: I drew a picture of 5 apples, divided each into halves, and counted all the halves.

② 15; See the cartoon following the Explore for possible strategies.

③ $5 \div \frac{1}{2} = 10$; Possible explanation: You are finding how many $\frac{1}{2}$ apples are in 5 whole apples. $10 \div \frac{2}{3} = 15$; Possible explanation: You are finding how many $\frac{2}{3}$ cup servings are in 10 cups.

I thought, "How many $\frac{2}{3}$s are in 10?" I drew 10 rectangles and split them into thirds. Then I circled groups of $\frac{2}{3}$. I counted 15 groups.

I drew a number line from 0 to 10 and marked it off in thirds. Then I counted intervals of $\frac{2}{3}$. There were 15.

226 CHAPTER 4 Fraction and Decimal Operations

On the Spot Assessment

Watch for students who think that all quotients are less than the dividends. Point out that to divide fractions, they need to develop a more complex sense for determining the reasonableness of a quotient. Point out that when a whole number is divided by a fraction less than 1, the quotient is actually greater than the dividend.

✅ Develop & Understand: A

Use Caroline's or Marcus' method to find each quotient. Try each method at least once. Show your work. Methods will vary.

1. $5 \div \frac{1}{3}$ 15

2. $6 \div \frac{1}{6}$ 36

3. $4 \div \frac{2}{3}$ 6

4. $8 \div \frac{4}{5}$ 10

5. $3 \div \frac{3}{6}$ 6

6. $5 \div \frac{5}{6}$ 6

Every multiplication equation has two related division equations. Here are two examples.

Multiplication Equations	Related Division Equations	
$2 \cdot 10 = 20$	$20 \div 10 = 2$	$20 \div 2 = 10$
$\frac{1}{2} \cdot 40 = 20$	$20 \div 40 = \frac{1}{2}$	$20 \div \frac{1}{2} = 40$

You can use this idea to perform divisions involving fractions.

Example

Find $20 \div \frac{1}{4}$.

The *quotient* is the number that goes in the blank in this division equation.

$$20 \div \frac{1}{4} = \underline{\qquad}$$

You can find the quotient by thinking about the related multiplication equation.

$$\frac{1}{4} \cdot \underline{\qquad} = 20$$

Now just think, "One fourth of what number equals 20?" The answer is 80. So, $20 \div \frac{1}{4} = 80$.

✅ Develop & Understand: B

Fill in the blanks in each pair of related equations.

7. $15 \div \frac{1}{2} = \underline{30}$ $\frac{1}{2} \cdot \underline{30} = 15$

8. $20 \div \frac{2}{3} = \underline{30}$ $\frac{2}{3} \cdot \underline{30} = 20$

Lesson 4.2 Multiply and Divide Fractions   **227**

✅ Develop & Understand: A

Suggested Grouping: Pairs

▶ **Exercises 1–6** Ask students to use either Caroline's or Marcus' method on page 226.

▶ **Exercise 5** Ask some students to rework the problem using the simplified $\frac{1}{2}$ as the divisor. Ask them to predict whether the quotient will be the same.

Teacher Tips Review the relationship between multiplication and division, making sure students can write two related division problems for each multiplication problem. Explain that the **Example** will show how to use this relationship to find quotients.

Show students the strategy of solving a division problem by finding a missing factor.

Example

The strategy for solving a division problem introduced in this Example is to rewrite the problem as a multiplication problem with a missing factor. Students can solve the original problem by finding the missing factor. The strategy should be a familiar one for most students, who will need only a quick walk-through to apply what they know about solving missing-factor problems involving whole numbers to similar problems involving fractions.

✅ Develop & Understand: B

▶ **Exercises 7 and 8** Ask students to express the pair of related equations in words as is done in the Example.

On the Spot Assessment

Watch for students who draw their number lines incorrectly. Make sure students are clear that to divide a number line in thirds, for example, means three spaces between whole numbers, not three lines. To mark off a number line into thirds, they actually have to draw two lines between whole numbers. Encourage them to label each mark on their number lines to avoid making this error.

▶ **Exercises 9–14** Encourage students to express each division equation in words, as shown in the example on page 227: "One fourth of what number is 20?" Some students can answer this question mentally. Others will need a guess-check-and-improve strategy to find the missing number.

Wrap-Up Discuss how students used the related-equation strategy for Exercises 13 and 14. Since this method is a good one for solving some problems mentally and, more generally, can be a powerful strategy for any division problem, it is important that students understand and use it well. When you feel that students have a good understanding, have them work through the next set of exercises.

Teacher Tips Review the how to apply the guess-check-and-improve strategy for Exercises 7–12.

✓ Develop & Understand: C

Suggested Grouping: Small Groups

▶ **Exercises 15–17** In this exercise set, students continue dividing whole numbers by fractions, and then look for patterns in the results. Students develop a sense of the patterns that occur in dividing a whole number by a series of fractions with the same denominator, for instance, $\frac{1}{3}$, $\frac{2}{3}$, and $\frac{3}{3}$.

Analyze the Table Be sure students understand that each entry is found by dividing the row head by the column head. In each case, the dividend is a whole number and the divisor is a fraction.

9. $\frac{1}{5} \cdot$ ____ $= 20, 100$

10. $\frac{2}{3} \cdot$ ____ $= 14, 21$

11. $\frac{3}{5} \cdot$ ____ $= 15, 25$

12. $\frac{3}{4} \cdot$ ____ $= 12, 16$

13. $\frac{15}{2}$, or $7\frac{1}{2}$; Possible explanation: There are fifteen $\frac{1}{5}$s in 3, so there must be half as many $\frac{2}{5}$s in 3.

14. $\frac{28}{3}$, or $9\frac{1}{3}$; Possible explanation: There are twenty-eight $\frac{1}{4}$s in 7, so there must be $\frac{1}{3}$ as many $\frac{3}{4}$s in 7.

Find each quotient by writing and solving a related multiplication equation.

9. $20 \div \frac{1}{5} =$ ____

10. $14 \div \frac{2}{3} =$ ____

11. $15 \div \frac{3}{5} =$ ____

12. $12 \div \frac{3}{4} =$ ____

All the quotients you have found so far are whole numbers. Of course, this is not always the case. Find each quotient below using any method you like. Explain how you found your answer.

13. $3 \div \frac{2}{5} =$ ____

14. $7 \div \frac{3}{4} =$ ____

✓ Develop & Understand: C

Use any methods you like to complete each division table. Each entry is the result of dividing the first number in that row by the top number in that column. As you work, look for patterns that might help you complete the table without computing every quotient.

15.

÷	$\frac{1}{3}$	$\frac{2}{3}$	$\frac{3}{3}$
6	18	9	6
4	12	6	4
2	6	3	2

16.

÷	$\frac{1}{4}$	$\frac{2}{4}$	$\frac{3}{4}$	$\frac{4}{4}$
12	48	24	16	12
18	72	36	24	18
24	96	48	32	24

17.

÷	$\frac{1}{5}$	$\frac{2}{5}$	$\frac{3}{5}$	$\frac{4}{5}$	$\frac{5}{5}$
24	120	60	40	30	24
18	90	45	30	$22\frac{1}{2}$	18
9	45	$22\frac{1}{2}$	15	$11\frac{1}{4}$	9

Reaching All Learners

AL **Approaching Level** Remind students of the "fact families" they may have used when learning basic facts. For example,

$$3 \cdot 5 = 15, 5 \cdot 3 = 15, 15 \div 3 = 5, \text{ and } 15 \div 5 = 3.$$

Point out that the related multiplication and division problems in this investigation have the same relationship as the equations in fact families. The equations also follow the pattern of using the same three numbers: the product in the multiplication equations is the dividend in the division equations, while the factors in the multiplication equations are the quotient and divisors in the division equations.

18. Possible answer: As the fractions to divide by increase, the results decrease. As the whole numbers to be divided into increase, the results increase. The second entry in each row is the first entry divided by 2, the third entry is the first entry divided by 3, and so on.

18. What patterns did you notice as you completed each table?

19. Suppose you know that $16 \div \frac{1}{3} = 48$. Describe a quick way to find $16 \div \frac{2}{3}$. What is $16 \div \frac{2}{3}$? Divide 48 by 2 to get 24.

20. Suppose you know that $15 \div \frac{1}{4} = 60$. Describe a quick way to find $15 \div \frac{2}{4}$ and $15 \div \frac{3}{4}$. What are the results? Divide 60 by 2 to get 30. Divide 60 by 3 to get 20.

21. Use the fact that $15 \div \frac{1}{5} = 75$ to find each quotient.
  a. $15 \div \frac{2}{5}$ $37\frac{1}{2}$ **b.** $15 \div \frac{3}{5}$ 25 **c.** $15 \div \frac{4}{5}$ $18\frac{3}{4}$

Share & Summarize

1. Describe how to find $6 \div \frac{2}{3}$ by using a related multiplication equation.

2. Describe one other method for computing $6 \div \frac{2}{3}$.

Investigation 5 Divide Fractions by Fractions

Vocabulary
reciprocal

1. Possible answer: Find the missing factor in $\frac{2}{3} \cdot$ _____ $= 6$. Since $\frac{2}{3}$ of 9 is 6, the answer is 9.
2. Possible answers:
  • Draw a number line from 0 to 6, divided into thirds, and count off intervals of $\frac{2}{3}$.
  • Draw six rectangles divided into thirds, circle groups of $\frac{2}{3}$, and count the groups.

In the last investigation, you saw how to divide a whole number by a fraction. You can use the same methods to divide a fraction by a fraction.

Explore

Find $\frac{5}{8} \div \frac{1}{4}$ by using a diagram, a number line, or another model to figure out how many $\frac{1}{4}$s are in $\frac{5}{8}$. See ①.

Find $\frac{5}{8} \div \frac{1}{4}$ by writing a related multiplication equation. See ②.

Now try to use one of the methods above to find $\frac{2}{3} \div \frac{3}{5}$. (Warning: It is not easy.) If you find the answer, explain how you found it. See ③.

① Possible answer: The first rectangle is divided into eighths, and $\frac{5}{8}$ is shaded. The second diagram is divided into fourths. Comparing the diagrams shows that there are two and a half $\frac{1}{4}$s in $\frac{5}{8}$, so $\frac{5}{8} \div \frac{1}{4} = 2\frac{1}{2}$.

② Possible answer: $\frac{1}{4} \cdot$ _____ $= \frac{5}{8}, \frac{5}{2}$, or $2\frac{1}{2}$

③ Possible answer: $\frac{3}{5} \cdot$ _____ $= \frac{2}{3}$. Rewrite $\frac{2}{3}$ as $\frac{10}{15}$, producing $\frac{3}{5} \cdot \frac{?}{3} = \frac{10}{15}$. To find ?, solve $3 \cdot$ _____ $= 10$ to get $\frac{10}{3}$. This gives $\frac{\frac{10}{3}}{3}$. Multiplying the numerator and denominator by 3 gives $\frac{10}{9}$.

Lesson 4.2 Multiply and Divide Fractions **229**

Reaching All Learners

BL **Beyond Level** Challenge students to make a table like those in Exercises 15–17 on page 228 to show division by sixths.

▶ **Exercise 18** Point out that another pattern is that dividing a number by $\frac{1}{n}$ gives the same result as multiplying the number by n. For example:

$6 \div \frac{1}{3} = 18$ and $6 \cdot 3 = 18$

$12 \div \frac{1}{4} = 48$ and $12 \cdot 4 = 48$

▶ **Exercises 19–21** Point out that when a divisor is multiplied by a number, the quotient is divided by that same number.

Share & Summarize

For **Exercises 1 and 2**, ask students to share their descriptions. The goal is to help them realize that they can use their prior knowledge and visual aids to solve problems involving dividing whole numbers by fractions.

Investigation 5

On Your Own Exercises
Pages 233–241
Exercises 24–39, 61–72

Divide Fractions by Fractions Open the investigation by having students describe some of the methods they used to divide a whole number by a fraction. They may mention drawing pictures, using a number line, and solving related multiplication equations. Point out that they can use some of these methods to divide a fraction by a fraction.

Explore

Pose the first problem and allow students time to find the answer and share their strategies for solving. Then have students write a multiplication equation for the division problem, and ask them how they would find the answer using that method.

Next, point out that another method for solving $\frac{5}{8} \div \frac{1}{4}$ is to find $\frac{5}{8} \div \frac{2}{8}$, or how many $\frac{2}{8}$ are there in $\frac{5}{8}$? Since the equations are the same, $5 \div 2 = 2\frac{1}{2}$.

Teacher Tips Read the paragraph and discuss the facts at the top of the page with the class. Point out that students will learn how to use these facts to divide fractions.

When discussing Fact 2, you may want to present an example such as $\frac{2}{3} \cdot \frac{3}{3} = \frac{6}{9}$ and ask students why $\frac{2}{3}$ and $\frac{6}{9}$ are equivalent. They may say that the two fractions describe the same amount. For example, $\frac{2}{3}$ of a circle covers the same area as $\frac{6}{9}$ of the same circle. Then ask students why multiplying by $\frac{3}{3}$ did not change the value of the fraction. Students should know that $\frac{3}{3}$ equals 1, and that multiplying any number by one results in a product that is the same as the number multiplied.

(**Example**) ················

Using the first fact, the first part of the Example is easy to understand and do: write the division problem as a complex fraction. Note that this term is not used in the text, but if students are interested, you might mention that fractions with fractions in the numerator or denominator are called *complex fractions*.

Students might be less likely to see how the second fact applies. Work through the second part of the Example with them, explaining that the purpose of multiplying is to simplify the fraction and make it easier to work with. Stress that students should multiply by a common denominator so that each part of the fraction becomes a whole number.

You may want to work through another problem such as $\frac{1}{2} \div \frac{2}{3} = \frac{3}{4}$ with the class to reinforce the method. Then tell students that they can practice this method as they work through the next set of exercises.

·······························

Real-World Link

There are several variations of the dotted division symbol. Ask students if they can find them on the Internet.

·······························

Real-World Link
The ÷ symbol for division is called an *obelus*. The word comes from the Greek word *obelos,* meaning "spike." The word *obelisk* is a four-sided tapering pillar and has a similar origin.
····················

You may have found it difficult to use the methods you know to compute $\frac{2}{3} \div \frac{3}{5}$ in Explore. Luckily, there is an easier method for dividing fractions. To understand how it works, you will need to use two facts you learned earlier.

Fact 1: A division expression can be written in the form of a fraction. For example, $2 \div 3$ can be written $\frac{2}{3}$.

Fact 2: The value of a fraction does not change when its numerator and denominator are multiplied by the same number.

─**Example**

Find $\frac{3}{4} \div \frac{2}{3}$.

Start by using *Fact 1* to rewrite the division expression as a fraction.

$$\frac{\frac{3}{4}}{\frac{2}{3}}$$

This fraction looks complicated, but you can make it simpler by using *Fact 2*.

You want to multiply the numerator and denominator by a number that will change *both* the numerator and the denominator to whole numbers. Any common multiple of 4 and 3 will do, such as 12.

$$\frac{\frac{3}{4} \cdot \frac{12}{1}}{\frac{2}{3} \cdot \frac{12}{1}} = \frac{\frac{36}{4}}{\frac{24}{3}} = \frac{9}{8}$$

So, $\frac{3}{4} \div \frac{2}{3} = \frac{9}{8}$, or $1\frac{1}{8}$.

It is always a good idea to check the answer by multiplying.

$$\frac{2}{3} \cdot \frac{9}{8} = \frac{18}{24} = \frac{3}{4}$$

The answer is correct.

✓ Develop & Understand: A

Use the method described in the example to find each quotient. Show all your steps.

1. $\frac{7}{8} \div \frac{2}{3}$ $1\frac{5}{16}$

2. $\frac{5}{6} \div \frac{1}{4}$ $3\frac{1}{3}$

3. $5 \div \frac{3}{8}$ $13\frac{1}{3}$

4. $\frac{1}{4} \div \frac{3}{4}$ $\frac{1}{3}$

5. $\frac{2}{5} \div 4$ $\frac{1}{10}$

6. $1\frac{1}{3} \div \frac{4}{5}$ $1\frac{2}{3}$

Fill in each blank with *greater than, less than,* **or** *equal to.* **Give an example to illustrate each completed sentence.**

7. When you divide a fraction by a greater fraction, the quotient is ___less than___ 1. Possible example: $\frac{2}{3} \div \frac{7}{8} = \frac{16}{21}$

8. When you divide a fraction by a lesser fraction, the quotient is ___greater than___ 1. Possible example: $\frac{7}{8} \div \frac{2}{3} = \frac{21}{16} = 1\frac{5}{16}$

Many people use a shortcut when dividing with fractions. The patterns you find in Think & Discuss will help you understand the shortcut and why it works.

Think & Discuss

Find each product in your head. Describe any patterns you see in the expressions and the answers.

$$\frac{3}{4} \cdot \frac{4}{3} \qquad \frac{2}{15} \cdot \frac{15}{2} \qquad \text{See ①.}$$
$$\frac{5}{8} \cdot \frac{8}{5} \qquad \frac{25}{100} \cdot \frac{100}{25}$$

Now find these products. How are these expressions similar to those above?

$$\frac{1}{4} \cdot 4 \qquad \frac{1}{6} \cdot 6 \qquad \text{See ②.}$$
$$\frac{1}{20} \cdot 20 \qquad \frac{1}{100} \cdot 100$$

Two numbers with a product of 1 are **reciprocals** of one another. Every number except 0 has a reciprocal. You can find the reciprocal of a fraction by switching its numerator and denominator.

Math Link
A reciprocal is also called a multiplicative inverse. The inverse property of multiplication states the product of a number and its inverse is 1.

Lesson 4.2 Multiply and Divide Fractions   **231**

Reaching All Learners

OL **On Level** Encourage students to list the denominators for both fractions and then find multiples of those numbers to find a common denominator.

Suggest they use a longer fraction bar separating the fraction in the numerator and the fraction in the denominator than between the parts of the fractions making up the numerator and the denominator. For example, in Exercise 1, they would write $\dfrac{\frac{7}{8}}{\frac{2}{3}}$.

✓ Develop & Understand: A

Suggested Grouping: Pairs

▶ **Exercise 6** Encourage students to write their answers in lowest terms and as mixed numbers when possible. In Exercise 6, you may need to suggest that students write $1\frac{1}{3}$ as a fraction before they divide.

▶ **Exercises 7–8** Check answers as a class before having students complete these exercises.

Math Link
Point out that the reciprocal of a whole number is a number less than one, and the reciprocal of a number less than one is a number greater than one.

Think & Discuss

In this activity, students experiment with multiplying by reciprocals and discover that the product is always one. Since this simple concept is one of the most useful ideas for manipulating expressions involving fractions, it is worth taking time to help students become comfortable with it.

Stress the idea that the reciprocal of a whole number is one divided by that number. For example, the reciprocal of 4 is $\frac{1}{4}$. Similarly, it is important for students to recognize that the reciprocal of any fraction with a numerator of one is a whole number. For example, the reciprocal of $\frac{1}{7}$ is 7. While students are looking at these multiplication problems, you may wish to introduce the term *reciprocal* to define the relationship between any two numbers whose product is one. Point out that every number except zero has a reciprocal.

Teacher Notes Take time to help students become comfortable with the pattern in the factors that makes each product one.

Show students the shortcut above the example and then how to divide using the reciprocal of the denominator.

The explanation following the example provides a step-by-step description of why students can multiply by the reciprocal when dividing a fraction by a fraction. Take the time to go through the explanation in detail with the class.

✔ **Develop & Understand: B**

Suggested Grouping: Pairs

▶ **Exercises 9–11** Students may either multiply through the complex fraction by a common denominator or multiply by the reciprocal of the divisor. Encourage students to use the reciprocal method to solve at least one problem. With either method, each problem will require several steps, so some students may need help in organizing their work.

▶ **Exercises 12–17** Ask students to go back over the exercises in this problem set as well as those in on page 231 to look for examples where the dividend is greater than the divisor and vice versa. List the problems on the board in those two categories, and ask the class to observe whether the quotients in each category are greater than or less than one. Then ask the class if they can see a reason for the pattern they have found. Remind students of their original concept of division: $A \div B$ means, "How many B's are in A?" They should see that

- If B is less than A, there is more than one B in A.

- If B is the same as A, there is exactly one B in A.

- If B is greater than A, there is not even one B in A.

Share & Summarize

Discuss student answers to these exercises.

---

12. Less than 1, $\frac{4}{5}$

13. Greater than 1, $3\frac{1}{3}$

14. Less than 1, $\frac{4}{5}$

15. Less than 1, $\frac{2}{7}$

16. Greater than 1, $12\frac{1}{4}$

17. Greater than 1, 2

1. Possible answer:
   - Write the division expression as a fraction. Then multiply both the numerator and the denominator by a number that will make both equal to whole numbers.
   - Multiply the first fraction by the reciprocal of the second fraction.

The shortcut for dividing fractions follows.

To divide a fraction by a fraction, multiply the first fraction by the reciprocal of the second fraction.

Example

Find $\frac{5}{7} \div \frac{10}{12}$.

To find $\frac{5}{7} \div \frac{10}{12}$, multiply $\frac{5}{7}$ by the reciprocal of $\frac{10}{12}$.

$$\frac{5}{7} \div \frac{10}{12} = \frac{5}{7} \cdot \frac{12}{10} = \frac{60}{70} = \frac{6}{7}$$

To see why the shortcut works, rewrite the division expression as a fraction. Multiply *both* the numerator and denominator by the reciprocal of the denominator. The denominator becomes 1.

$$\frac{5}{7} \div \frac{10}{12} = \frac{\frac{5}{7}}{\frac{10}{12}} = \frac{\frac{5}{7} \cdot \frac{12}{10}}{\frac{10}{12} \cdot \frac{12}{10}} = \frac{\frac{5}{7} \cdot \frac{12}{10}}{1} = \frac{5}{7} \cdot \frac{12}{10}$$

So, $\frac{5}{7} \div \frac{10}{12} = \frac{5}{7} \cdot \frac{12}{10}$.

✔ **Develop & Understand: B**

Find each quotient using any method you like.

9. $\frac{3}{2} \div \frac{9}{6}$ 1

10. $\frac{2}{5} \div \frac{5}{2}$ $\frac{4}{25}$

11. $\frac{1}{8} \div \frac{1}{9}$ $1\frac{1}{8}$

Estimate whether each quotient will be greater than, less than, or equal to 1. Then find the quotient.

12. $\frac{3}{5} \div \frac{3}{4}$

13. $2 \div \frac{3}{5}$

14. $\frac{2}{3} \div \frac{5}{6}$

15. $1 \div 3\frac{1}{2}$

16. $3\frac{1}{2} \div \frac{2}{7}$

17. $4\frac{1}{2} \div 2\frac{1}{4}$

Share & Summarize

1. Describe two methods for dividing a fraction by a fraction.

2. Write two fraction division expressions, one with a quotient greater than 1 and the other with a quotient less than 1.
   Possible answer: $\frac{1}{2} \div \frac{1}{4}$ is greater than 1; $\frac{1}{4} \div \frac{1}{2}$ is less than 1.

Mathematical Background

The number zero does not have a reciprocal because division by zero is undefined. For example, 0 can be written as $\frac{0}{1}$. If 0 had a reciprocal, the number would be $\frac{1}{0}$, which is undefined.

Another way to look at this situation is that the product of two reciprocals is one. This is impossible when one of the numerators is zero; there is no number that can be multiplied by 0 to give a product of 1. If $\frac{0}{1}$ is multiplied by any number, the numerator will still be 0, and the value of the new fraction will always be 0, not 1.

Practice & Apply

Real-World Link

The first practical sewing machines were built in the mid 1800s and could sew only straight seams. Modern sewing machines utilize computer technology. For instance, scanners can take an image and reproduce it in an embroidered version on cloth.

....

3b. Possible answer: The answers increase by the same amount, $2\frac{1}{2}$, each time the fraction being multiplied increases by $\frac{1}{4}$.

4b. Possible answer: If you multiply the denominator of the fraction by the result, you always get 60. The result is 60 divided by the denominator of the fraction.

1. Caroline is sewing a costume with 42 small ribbons on it. Each ribbon is $\frac{1}{3}$ of a yard long. How many yards of ribbon does she need? 14

2. Caroline is sewing a costume from a pattern that calls for 4 yards of material. Because the costume is for a small child, she is reducing all the lengths to $\frac{2}{3}$ of the lengths given by the pattern. How many yards of material should she buy? $2\frac{2}{3}$

3. Consider this table of products.

   a. Copy the table. Write the result of each multiplication expression in the second column.

   b. What patterns do you see in the expressions and the results?

   c. What would be the next two expressions and results?

Problem	Result
$\frac{9}{4} \cdot 10$	$22\frac{1}{2}$
$\frac{10}{4} \cdot 10$	25

Expression	Result
$\frac{1}{4} \cdot 10$	$2\frac{1}{2}$
$\frac{2}{4} \cdot 10$	5
$\frac{3}{4} \cdot 10$	$7\frac{1}{2}$
$\frac{4}{4} \cdot 10$	10
$\frac{5}{4} \cdot 10$	$12\frac{1}{2}$
$\frac{6}{4} \cdot 10$	15
$\frac{7}{4} \cdot 10$	$17\frac{1}{2}$
$\frac{8}{4} \cdot 10$	20

4. Consider this table of products.

   a. Copy the table. Write the result of each multiplication expression in the second column.

   b. What relationships do you see between the fraction in each expression and the result?

   c. If you changed the expressions so the numerator of each fraction was 2 instead of 1, how would the products change? They would double.

Expression	Result
$\frac{1}{30} \cdot 60$	2
$\frac{1}{20} \cdot 60$	3
$\frac{1}{15} \cdot 60$	4
$\frac{1}{12} \cdot 60$	5
$\frac{1}{6} \cdot 60$	10
$\frac{1}{5} \cdot 60$	12
$\frac{1}{4} \cdot 60$	15
$\frac{1}{3} \cdot 60$	20
$\frac{1}{2} \cdot 60$	30

Investigation 1
Pages 216–219
Practice & Apply: 1–4
Connect & Extend: 40–51

Investigation 2
Pages 219–221
Practice & Apply: 5–12
Connect & Extend: 52–54

Investigation 3
Pages 222–225
Practice & Apply: 13–18
Connect & Extend: 55–57

Investigation 4
Pages 226–228
Practice & Apply: 19–23
Connect & Extend: 58–60

Investigation 5
Pages 229–232
Practice & Apply: 24–39
Connect & Extend: 61–72

Assign Anytime
Mixed Review: 73–82

▶ **Exercise 1** Some students may think of this exercise as converting 42 feet into yards. You may want to ask how converting between larger and smaller units of measure is related to multiplying by fractions.

▶ **Exercises 3 and 4** Encourage students to write about the patterns they find. Suggest that they try one of the following:

- Imagine describing the pattern to a friend on the phone clearly enough that the friend can understand the pattern and then create an example of it with a beginning starting number.

- Look for patterns among different elements of the exercises, including patterns relating a factor to the product or patterns relating growth in the factors to growth in the products.

- Imagine a real context for the numerical problem and use that context to describe the pattern or explain why the pattern makes sense.

▶ **Exercises 5 and 6** You may want to supply students with copies of Chapter 4 Master 1 or other grid paper to create their diagrams.

▶ **Exercises 7–12** You may want to ask students to estimate each product before they do the calculation. Estimation is emphasized more in the division sections of this lesson than in the multiplication sections, but it is a good idea to ask students to make initial estimates on a wide range of problems.

▶ **Exercises 14–17** Encourage students to write out each step as they solve these exercises.

5. Consider the product $\frac{3}{4} \cdot 8$.

   a. Draw a rectangle diagram to represent this product.

   b. What is the area of each small rectangle in your diagram? How many small rectangles are shaded? $\frac{1}{4}$, 24

   c. What does $\frac{3}{4} \cdot 8$ equal? 6

6. Consider the product $\frac{2}{3} \cdot \frac{4}{5}$.

   a. Draw a rectangle diagram to represent this product.

   b. What is the area of each small rectangle in your diagram? How many small rectangles are shaded? $\frac{1}{15}$, 8

   c. What does $\frac{2}{3} \cdot \frac{4}{5}$ equal? $\frac{8}{15}$

Find each product. Give your answers in lowest terms.

7. $\frac{7}{8} \cdot \frac{2}{5}$ $\frac{7}{20}$

8. $\frac{2}{3} \cdot \frac{7}{12}$ $\frac{7}{18}$

9. $\frac{6}{11} \cdot \frac{2}{3}$ $\frac{4}{11}$

10. $\frac{30}{50} \cdot \frac{15}{20}$ $\frac{9}{20}$

11. $\frac{4}{7} \cdot \frac{7}{9}$ $\frac{4}{9}$

12. $\frac{13}{15} \cdot \frac{5}{6}$ $\frac{13}{18}$

13. Copy and complete this multiplication table. Give each answer as both a fraction and a mixed number. The first answer is provided.

×	$1\frac{1}{2}$	$2\frac{2}{3}$	$3\frac{3}{4}$
$1\frac{1}{2}$	$\frac{9}{4} = 2\frac{1}{4}$	$\frac{24}{6} = 4$	$\frac{45}{8} = 5\frac{5}{8}$
$2\frac{1}{2}$	$\frac{15}{4} = 3\frac{3}{4}$	$\frac{40}{6} = 6\frac{2}{3}$	$\frac{75}{8} = 9\frac{3}{8}$
$3\frac{1}{2}$	$\frac{21}{4} = 5\frac{1}{4}$	$\frac{56}{6} = 9\frac{1}{3}$	$\frac{105}{8} = 13\frac{1}{8}$

Find each product by simplifying before you multiply.

14. $\frac{3}{4} \cdot \frac{8}{9}$ $\frac{2}{3}$

15. $\frac{2}{3} \cdot \frac{3}{8}$ $\frac{1}{4}$

16. $\frac{3}{5} \cdot \frac{4}{9}$ $\frac{4}{15}$

17. $\frac{2}{5} \cdot \frac{5}{9}$ $\frac{2}{9}$

18b. Possible answer: As you move across the rows, the answers increase by the same amount. As you move down the columns, each answer is $\frac{1}{2}$ of the answer above it.

20. $\frac{45}{2}$, or $22\frac{1}{2}$

22g. The answers in each pair are equal. This is because the left question is a division context and the right question is the related multiplication context. For example, Part a is $16 \div \frac{1}{4} = $ _____ and Part b is $\frac{1}{4} \cdot $ _____ $= 16$.

24. $\frac{3}{2}$, or $1\frac{1}{2}$

18. Consider the following multiplication table.

×	$\frac{2}{3}$	$1\frac{1}{3}$	2	$2\frac{2}{3}$	$3\frac{1}{3}$
$\frac{1}{2}$	$\frac{1}{3}$	$\frac{2}{3}$	1	$1\frac{1}{3}$	$1\frac{2}{3}$
$\frac{1}{4}$	$\frac{1}{6}$	$\frac{1}{3}$	$\frac{1}{2}$	$\frac{2}{3}$	$\frac{5}{6}$
$\frac{1}{8}$	$\frac{1}{12}$	$\frac{1}{6}$	$\frac{1}{4}$	$\frac{1}{3}$	$\frac{5}{12}$

a. Copy and complete the table. Give your answers in lowest terms. Express answers greater than 1 as mixed numbers.

b. What patterns and relationships do you see in the table?

Fill in each blank.

19. $\frac{2}{3} \cdot \underline{\ 30\ } = 20$ **20.** $\frac{2}{3} \cdot \underline{\ \ \ } = 15$ **21.** $\frac{2}{3} \cdot \underline{\ 15\ } = 10$

22. In Parts a–f, use any method you like to find the answer.

a. How many $\frac{1}{4}$s are in 16? 64   **b.** $\frac{1}{4}$ of what number is 16? 64

c. How many $\frac{2}{3}$s are in 16? 24   **d.** $\frac{2}{3}$ of what number is 16? 24

e. How many $\frac{4}{3}$s are in 16? 12   **f.** $\frac{4}{3}$ of what number is 16? 12

g. How are the answers to Parts a and b related? Parts c and d? Parts e and f? Explain why this makes sense.

23. Find the first quotient. Use your result to predict the second quotient. Check your answers by multiplying.

a. $14 \div \frac{1}{3}$ 42 $14 \div \frac{2}{3}$ 21

b. $5 \div \frac{5}{8}$ 8 $15 \div \frac{5}{8}$ 24

c. $6 \div \frac{1}{5}$ 30 $6 \div \frac{3}{5}$ 10

d. $6 \div \frac{3}{7}$ 14 $24 \div \frac{3}{7}$ 56

Fill in each blank.

24. $\frac{2}{3} \cdot \underline{\ \ } = 1$ **25.** $\underline{\ 8\ } \cdot \frac{1}{8} = 1$ **26.** $1\frac{1}{2} \cdot \frac{2}{3} = \underline{\ 1\ }$

27. $\underline{\frac{8}{9}} \cdot 1\frac{1}{8} = 1$ **28.** $\frac{5}{3} \cdot \underline{\frac{3}{5}} = 1$ **29.** $2\frac{1}{2} \cdot \frac{4}{5} = \underline{\ 2\ }$

▶ **Exercise 22** This exercise reinforces the connection between the English language descriptions of a problem and its symbolic representation, as well as the fact that multiplication is often, but not always, indicated by the word *of*. It also reinforces the connection between division and multiplication.

▶ **Exercise 23** Encourage students to show how they found the first quotient by drawing a picture, using a related multiplication problem, and so on.

▶ **Exercise 27** It is acceptable if students answer $\frac{1}{1\frac{1}{8}}$ instead of $\frac{8}{9}$.

▶ **Exercise 30** The relationship between the quotient $\frac{a}{b}$ and the quotient $\frac{b}{a}$ is introduced in this exercise. You may want to reiterate that division is not commutative, so the order of the numbers does matter. However, students should see that these two quotients are reciprocals of each other.

▶ **Exercises 40–45** These exercises preview division of fractions.

▶ **Exercises 46 and 47b** Students may not realize that these problems have multiple steps and cannot be solved by only multiplying the fraction and the whole number given.

For **Exercise 46**, you might ask students what fraction of the original price Rosita paid, as opposed to how much the price was reduced. They should be able to see that she paid $\frac{2}{3}$ of the original price. Then ask, what is the original price? That is, 8 is $\frac{2}{3}$ of what number? 12 Students should be able to see then that Rosita saved $4.

For **Exercise 47b**, the steps are a little more straightforward. You might ask, if the Toronto Zoo has $\frac{23}{70}$ fewer species than the St. Louis Zoo and the St. Louis Zoo has 700 species, how many fewer species does the Toronto Zoo have? 230 Again, students should be able to see that they need to calculate 700 − 230 to find the final answer.

30g. The answers are reciprocals of each other; one quotient is greater than 1 and the other is less than 1. Possible explanation: If you write the division expressions as fractions, the fractions are reciprocals of one another.

Real-World Link

The first modern zoo was the Imperial Managerie at the Schönbrunn Palace in Vienna, which opened to the public in 1765. The National Zoological Park in Washington, D.C., was the first zoo created to preserve endangered species.

. . . .

30. In Parts a–f, estimate whether the quotient will be greater than, less than, or equal to 1. Then find the quotient. Leave answers greater than 1 in fraction form.

a. $\frac{1}{3} \div \frac{2}{5}$ Less than 1, $\frac{5}{6}$ **b.** $\frac{2}{5} \div \frac{1}{3}$ Greater than 1, $\frac{6}{5}$

c. $\frac{7}{8} \div \frac{3}{4}$ Greater than 1, $\frac{7}{6}$ **d.** $\frac{3}{4} \div \frac{7}{8}$ Less than 1, $\frac{6}{7}$

e. $\frac{1}{5} \div \frac{1}{7}$ Greater than 1, $\frac{7}{5}$ **f.** $\frac{1}{7} \div \frac{1}{5}$ Less than 1, $\frac{5}{7}$

g. Look at the expressions and answers for Parts a–f. How are the answers to Parts a and b related? Parts c and d? Parts e and f? Explain why this makes sense.

Find each quotient. Give all answers in lowest terms. If an answer is greater than 1, write it as a mixed number.

31. $7\frac{1}{2} \div 1\frac{1}{2}$ 5   **32.** $3\frac{1}{3} \div \frac{3}{4}$ $4\frac{4}{9}$ **33.** $2\frac{2}{3} \div \frac{8}{5}$ $1\frac{2}{3}$

34. $\frac{9}{8} \div \frac{2}{3}$ $1\frac{11}{16}$ **35.** $\frac{8}{10} \div \frac{1}{100}$ 80   **36.** $5\frac{1}{3} \div 2\frac{2}{3}$ 2

37. $2\frac{1}{3} \div 3\frac{1}{3}$ $\frac{7}{10}$ **38.** $18 \div 4\frac{1}{2}$ 4   **39.** $7\frac{1}{2} \div 4\frac{1}{2}$ $1\frac{2}{3}$

Preview Find each missing factor.

40. $\frac{1}{3} \cdot \underline{180} = 60$ **41.** $\frac{2}{3} \cdot \underline{90} = 60$

42. $\frac{1}{5} \cdot \underline{300} = 60$ **43.** $\frac{2}{5} \cdot \underline{150} = 60$

44. $\frac{3}{5} \cdot \underline{100} = 60$ **45.** $\frac{4}{5} \cdot \underline{75} = 60$

46. Economics Rosita paid $8 for a CD marked "$\frac{1}{2}$ off." How much did she save? $8

47. Life Science The St. Louis Zoo has about 700 species of animals.

a. The Detroit Zoological Park has $\frac{2}{5}$ as many species as the St. Louis Zoo. About how many species does the Detroit park have? 280

b. The Toronto Zoo has $\frac{23}{70}$ *fewer* species than the St. Louis Zoo. About how many species does the Toronto Zoo have? 470

53. Possible answer: Multiplying the numerator and denominator by the same number is the same as multiplying by 1, which does not change the fraction's value.

Tell whether each statement is true or false.

48. $\frac{2}{3}$ of $300 = \frac{3}{4}$ of 200 False   **49.** $\frac{1}{3}$ of $150 = \frac{1}{2}$ of 100 True

50. $\frac{2}{3}$ of $300 = \frac{1}{2}$ of 400 True   **51.** $\frac{2}{3}$ of $100 = \frac{1}{3}$ of 200 True

52. Economics Last week, Sal's Shoe Emporium held its semiannual clearance sale. All winter boots were marked down to $\frac{4}{5}$ of the original price. This week, the sale prices of the remaining boots were cut in half. What fraction of the original price is the new sale price? $\frac{2}{5}$

53. Using what you have learned about multiplying fractions, explain why multiplying the numerator and denominator of a fraction by the same number does not change the fraction's value. Give examples if they help you to explain.

54. Measurement The Danson's horse ranch is a rectangular shape measuring $\frac{3}{5}$ mile by $\frac{4}{7}$ mile.

   a. What is the area of the ranch? $\frac{12}{35}$ sq mi

   b. There are 640 acres in 1 square mile. What is the area of the Danson's ranch in acres? $219\frac{3}{7}$, or about 219.4 acres

55. Measurement The left column of the table shows the ingredient list for a spice cake that serves 12 people. Complete the table to show the amount of each ingredient needed for the given numbers of people.

	12 People	10 People	8 People	6 People	4 People	2 People
Flour	$2\frac{1}{4}$ c	$1\frac{7}{8}$ c	$1\frac{1}{2}$ c	$1\frac{1}{8}$ c	$\frac{3}{4}$ c	$\frac{3}{8}$ c
Sugar	$1\frac{1}{3}$ c	$1\frac{1}{9}$ c	$\frac{8}{9}$ c	$\frac{2}{3}$ c	$\frac{4}{9}$ c	$\frac{2}{9}$ c
Salt	$\frac{3}{4}$ tsp	$\frac{5}{8}$ tsp	$\frac{1}{2}$ tsp	$\frac{3}{8}$ tsp	$\frac{1}{4}$ tsp	$\frac{1}{8}$ tsp
Butter	$1\frac{1}{2}$ sticks	$1\frac{1}{4}$ sticks	1 stick	$\frac{3}{4}$ stick	$\frac{1}{2}$ stick	$\frac{1}{4}$ stick
Ginger	$\frac{1}{2}$ tsp	$\frac{5}{12}$ tsp	$\frac{1}{3}$ tsp	$\frac{1}{4}$ tsp	$\frac{1}{6}$ tsp	$\frac{1}{12}$ tsp
Raisins	$\frac{2}{3}$ c	$\frac{5}{9}$ c	$\frac{4}{9}$ c	$\frac{1}{3}$ c	$\frac{2}{9}$ c	$\frac{1}{9}$ c

▶ **Exercises 48–51** Encourage students to rewrite each statement after they find the value of each side, and then determine whether the rewritten statement is true or false. For example, in Exercise 48, the statement could be rewritten as 200 = 150, which is obviously false.

Lesson 4.2 Multiply and Divide Fractions   **237**

► **Exercise 56** Ask students to share any strategies that they used in addition to guess-check-and-improve. Elicit the idea that a fraction whose numerator is greater than its denominator has a greater value than a fraction whose denominator is greater than its numerator. So, to get the greatest product, put the greatest available numbers into the numerators and the least available numbers into the denominators. To get the least product, do the opposite.

56a. $\frac{6}{1} \cdot \frac{5}{2} = 15$, or

$\frac{5}{1} \cdot \frac{6}{2} = 15$

56b. $\frac{1}{6} \cdot \frac{2}{5} = \frac{1}{15}$, or

$\frac{2}{6} \cdot \frac{1}{5} = \frac{1}{15}$

57c. Possible answer: To get the values in the second, third, and last rows, multiply the values in the first row by 3, 5, and 7, respectively. Or, add the number at the top of the column for each row down.

56. Number Sense In Parts a and b, use the numbers 1, 2, 3, 4, 5, and 6.

$$\frac{\square}{\square} \cdot \frac{\square}{\square}$$

a. Fill in each square with one of the given numbers to create the greatest possible product. Use each number only once.

b. Fill in each square with one of the given numbers to create the least possible product. Use each number only once.

c. Choose four different whole numbers. Repeat Parts a and b using your four numbers.   Answers will vary.

57. Consider this multiplication table.

×	$4\frac{1}{2}$	$2\frac{1}{4}$	$1\frac{1}{8}$	$\frac{9}{16}$	$\frac{9}{32}$
$\frac{1}{2}$	$2\frac{1}{4}$	$1\frac{1}{8}$	$\frac{9}{16}$	$\frac{9}{32}$	$\frac{9}{64}$
$1\frac{1}{2}$	$6\frac{3}{4}$	$3\frac{3}{8}$	$1\frac{11}{16}$	$\frac{27}{32}$	$\frac{27}{64}$
$2\frac{1}{2}$	$11\frac{1}{4}$	$5\frac{5}{8}$	$2\frac{13}{16}$	$1\frac{13}{32}$	$\frac{45}{64}$
$3\frac{1}{2}$	$15\frac{3}{4}$	$7\frac{7}{8}$	$3\frac{15}{16}$	$1\frac{31}{32}$	$\frac{63}{64}$

a. Copy the table. Use your knowledge of fraction multiplication and number patterns to help complete it. Try to do as few paper-and-pencil calculations as possible.

b. Describe the pattern in the table as you read across the rows from left to right.   Each value is $\frac{1}{2}$ the previous value.

c. Describe the pattern in the table as you read down the columns.

58b. Possible answer: I changed $\frac{1}{2}$ ft to $\frac{1}{6}$ yd and then found $6 \div \frac{1}{6} = 36$.

58d. Possible answer: I changed 6 yd to 18 ft and then found $18 \div \frac{2}{3} = 27$.

60b. Possible answer: I converted 3 gallons to cups: $3 \cdot 4 \cdot 4 = 48$. Then I found $48 \div \frac{3}{4}$ by writing $\frac{3}{4} \cdot \underline{\quad} = 48$ and finding the missing factor.

60d. Possible answer: I converted 3 gallons to ounces: $3 \cdot 4 \cdot 4 \cdot 8 = 384$. Then I found $384 \div 4 = 96$.

58. Rosita bought six yards of ribbon for a sewing project.

   a. She wants to cut the ribbon into pieces $\frac{1}{2}$ foot long. How many pieces can she cut from her six-yard ribbon?   36

   b. What calculations did you do to solve Part a?

   c. Rosita decides instead to cut pieces $\frac{2}{3}$ foot long. How many pieces can she cut?   27

   d. What calculations did you do to solve Part c?

59. Hannah made up riddles about the ages of some people in her family. See if you can solve them.

   ★ **a.** My brother Tim is $\frac{3}{4}$ my cousin Janice's age. Tim is 15 years old. How old is Janice?   20

   ★ **b.** To find my grandpa Henry's age, divide my aunt Carol's age by $\frac{4}{5}$ and then add 10. Aunt Carol is 40. How old is Grandpa Henry?   60

   c. Today is Uncle Mike's 42nd birthday. He is now $\frac{2}{3}$ of his father's age and $\frac{7}{3}$ of his daughter's age. How old are Uncle Mike's father and daughter?   63, 18

60. Measurement In this exercise, use the following facts.

   1 cup = 8 ounces   1 quart = 4 cups   1 gallon = 4 quarts

   a. Conor has 3 gallons of lemonade to serve at his party. If he pours $\frac{3}{4}$-cup servings, how many servings can he pour?   64

   b. What calculations did you do to solve Part a?

   c. If Conor pours 4-ounce servings instead, how many servings can he pour?   96

   d. What calculations did you do to solve Part c?

Lesson 4.2 Multiply and Divide Fractions   **239**

▶ **Exercise 58** Some students may convert all measures to inches and solve using whole numbers: 6 yd = 216 in., $\frac{1}{2}$ ft = 6 in., and $\frac{2}{3}$ ft = 8 in. This is an acceptable approach.

▶ **Exercise 59 Extension** Challenge students to write their own riddles.

▶ **Exercise 60** You may want to point out that 8 fluid ounces is a measure of capacity that equals one cup. This does not transfer to weight comparisons, and 8 fluid ounces do not usually weigh 8 ounces.

▶ **Exercises 68 and 69** Students need to use order of operations to evaluate each expression. You may want to review this convention before assigning the exercises.

61b. The quotients double. Possible explanation: This occurs because each time the number you are dividing by is half the previous number.

61c. For the first three rows, each quotient is half the quotient above. The same thing occurs for the last three rows. Possible explanation: This occurs because the number you are dividing into is half the previous number.

61. Consider this division table.

$\div$	$\frac{1}{2}$	$\frac{1}{4}$	$\frac{1}{8}$	$\frac{1}{16}$	$\frac{1}{32}$	$\frac{1}{64}$
$\frac{1}{2}$	1	2	4	8	16	32
$\frac{1}{4}$	$\frac{1}{2}$	1	2	4	8	16
$\frac{1}{8}$	$\frac{1}{4}$	$\frac{1}{2}$	1	2	4	8
$\frac{3}{2}$	3	6	12	24	48	96
$\frac{3}{4}$	$\frac{3}{2}$	3	6	12	24	48
$\frac{3}{8}$	$\frac{3}{4}$	$\frac{3}{2}$	3	6	12	24

a. Copy the table. Use your knowledge of fraction division and number patterns to help complete it. Try to do as few paper-and-pencil calculations as possible.

b. Describe the number pattern in the table as you read across the rows from left to right. Explain why this pattern occurs.

c. Describe the number pattern in the table as you read down the columns. Explain why this pattern occurs.

Tell whether each statement is true or false. If a statement is false, give the correct quotient.

62. $\frac{9}{12} \div \frac{1}{4} = 3$ True

63. $\frac{1}{4} \div \frac{9}{12} = \frac{2}{3}$ False, $\frac{1}{3}$

64. $3\frac{1}{2} \div \frac{7}{4} = 2$ True

65. $\frac{7}{4} \div 3\frac{1}{2} = \frac{1}{2}$ True

66. $\frac{10}{4} \div \frac{4}{10} = 1$ False, $6\frac{1}{4}$

67. $\frac{4}{10} \div \frac{10}{4} = 1$ False, $\frac{4}{25}$

Evaluate each expression.

68. $\frac{1}{2} \cdot \frac{3}{4} + \frac{1}{2} \div \frac{5}{6}$ $\frac{39}{40}$

69. $\left(\frac{3}{5} + \frac{7}{8}\right) \cdot \frac{1}{5} \div \frac{2}{15}$ $2\frac{17}{80}$

70a. $\frac{12}{2} \div \frac{4}{10} = 15,$
or $\frac{12}{4} \div \frac{2}{10} = 15$

70b. $\frac{2}{12} \div \frac{10}{4} = \frac{1}{15},$
or $\frac{4}{12} \div \frac{10}{2}$
$= \frac{1}{15}$

71. Possible answer: Since the two division expressions are "opposites," the quotients are reciprocals and the product of the quotients is 1.
$\frac{5}{6} \div \frac{4}{7} = \frac{35}{24},$
$\frac{4}{7} \div \frac{5}{6} = \frac{24}{35},$
$\frac{35}{24} \cdot \frac{24}{35} = 1$

Mixed Review

70. In Parts a and b, use the numbers 2, 4, 6, 8, 10, and 12.

  a. Fill in each blank with one of the given numbers to create the greatest possible quotient. Use each number only once.

  b. Fill in each blank with one of the given numbers to create the least possible quotient. Use each number only once.

  c. Choose four different whole numbers. Repeat Parts a and b using your four numbers.   Answers will vary.

71. Explain how you could solve the problem below without doing any calculations. Give the result, and check your answer by performing the calculations.

$$\left(\frac{5}{6} \div \frac{4}{7}\right) \cdot \left(\frac{4}{7} \div \frac{5}{6}\right)$$

72. In Your Own Words Which methods do you prefer for multiplying fractions? Which methods do you prefer for dividing fractions? Explain why you chose each method.   Answers will vary. Check students' work for explanations.

Write a rule for each relationship between p and q.

73.
p	2	3	4	5	6	7
q	4	6	8	10	12	14

Possible rule: $q = 2p$

74.
p	14	6	8.35	8	12	9
q	9	1	3.35	3	7	4

Possible rule: $q = p - 5$

75.
p	2	$\frac{2}{3}$	7	3	10	1
q	4	0	19	7	28	1

Possible rule: $q = 3p - 2$

76.
p	$\frac{1}{2}$	0	1	2	3	$3\frac{1}{2}$
q	2	1	3	5	7	8

Possible rule: $q = 2p + 1$

Write each expression as repeated multiplication. Then find the value of each expression.

77. 5^2 $5 \cdot 5$; 25

78. 10^2 $10 \cdot 10$; 100

79. 4^3 $4 \cdot 4 \cdot 4$; 64

80. 2^4 $2 \cdot 2 \cdot 2 \cdot 2$; 16

81. 5^4 $5 \cdot 5 \cdot 5 \cdot 5$; 625

82. 2^6 $2 \cdot 2 \cdot 2 \cdot 2 \cdot 2 \cdot 2$; 64

Lesson 4.2 Multiply and Divide Fractions   **241**

4. Find the reciprocal of each number.

  a. $4\frac{2}{7}$ $\frac{7}{30}$

  b. 1 1

  c. $\frac{3}{4}$ $\frac{4}{3}$ or $1\frac{1}{3}$

  d. 6 $\frac{1}{6}$

▶ **Exercise 70** This exercise is similar to Exercise 56. You may want to discuss them in a similar way. Ask students how their strategy for finding the greatest or least quotient is different from their strategy for finding the greatest or least product.

▶ **Exercise 71** Students who have completed Exercise 30 will find it much easier to solve this exercise. If students have difficulty, suggest they look over Exercise 30.

Quick Check

Informal Assessment Students should be able to:

✔ multiply fractions by whole numbers

✔ model fraction multiplication

✔ multiply and divide fractions

Quick Quiz

1. For each problem, first estimate the answer, and then compute. Record both your estimate and your final answer. Estimates will vary.

  a. $\frac{7}{8} \cdot 56$ 49

  b. $12\frac{1}{3} \cdot 7\frac{5}{6}$ $96\frac{11}{18}$

  c. $15 \div \frac{1}{3}$ 45

  d. $\frac{2}{5} \div 1\frac{1}{2}$ $\frac{4}{5}$

2. Show how you could count the number of $\frac{2}{3}$s in $7\frac{1}{3}$ using a number line or other graphic representation. Then write the division problem described by this statement. $7\frac{1}{3} \div \frac{2}{3} = 11$; Possible representation:

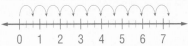

3. Consider the problem $\frac{3}{8} \cdot 12$. Find the product, and then create a word problem or story problem for which this multiplication would provide the answer. $4\frac{1}{2}$; Possible problem: Joe is making capes as costumes for the preschool play. Each cape requires $\frac{3}{8}$ yard of fabric. If Joe needs to make 12 capes in all, how many yards of fabric will he need?

LESSON 4.3

Multiply and Divide Decimals

Objectives

▶ To multiply whole numbers and decimals

▶ To multiply decimals as fractions

▶ To multiply and divide decimals

Overview

This lesson introduces multiplication and division with decimals. The mechanics of multiplication or division with whole numbers also apply here; however, students often have difficulty understanding where in the answer the decimal point should be. For example, they may not be sure about the size of the correct answer relative to the factors or dividend and divisor. In this lesson, students apply the formal and informal generalizations they developed about the results of multiplying and dividing fractions. Students will be using calculators throughout this lesson to solve multiplication and division problems, which they in turn examine for patterns.

Advance Preparation

You may want to provide copies of Lesson 4.3 Masters 1–2 to facilitate class discussion while presenting these topics, including multiplying and dividing decimals.

	Summary	Materials	On Your Own Exercises (pp. 257–264)	Assessment Opportunities
Investigation 1 (p. 242) *Pacing: 2 days*	Students estimate results of multiplying whole numbers by decimal numbers.		Practice & Apply: 1–8 Connect & Extend: 35, 36 Mixed Review: 42–54	• Share & Summarize (p. 245) • Troubleshooting (pp. 243, 245)
Investigation 2 (p. 245) *Pacing: 1 day*	Students discover the relationship between the number of decimal places in factors and their product.		Practice & Apply: 9–18 Connect & Extend: 37 Mixed Review: 42–54	• Share & Summarize (p. 247) • Troubleshooting (p. 247)
Investigation 3 (p. 248) *Pacing: 1 day*	Students work with real-world problems involving multiplying decimals.		Practice & Apply: 19–25 Connect & Extend: 38 Mixed Review: 42–54	• Share & Summarize (p. 250) • Troubleshooting (p. 250)
Investigation 4 (p. 251) *Pacing: 1 day*	Students learn to divide decimals.		Practice & Apply: 26–31 Connect & Extend: 39 Mixed Review: 42–54	• Share & Summarize (p. 254) • Troubleshooting (p. 254)
Investigation 5 (p. 254) *Pacing: 1 day*	Students consider real-world problems and determine when to multiply and when to divide.	card decks from Lesson 4.3 Masters 1–2 (optional)	Practice & Apply: 32–34 Connect & Extend: 40, 41 Mixed Review: 42–54	• Share & Summarize (p. 256) • Troubleshooting (p. 256)

Leveled Lesson Resources

CRM *Available in:* **Chapter 4 Resource Masters**

Also on
TeacherWorks™
Lesson 4.3

Study Guide and Intervention (p. 22) — AL

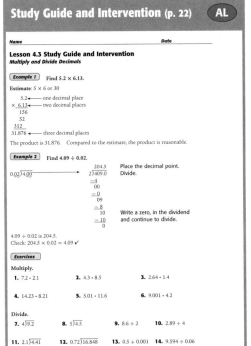

Skills Practice (p. 23) — AL OL

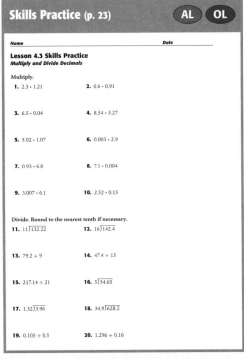

Problem-Solving Practice (p. 24) — AL OL

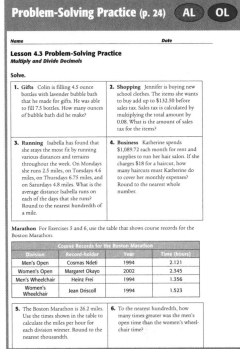

Enrichment (p. 25) — BL

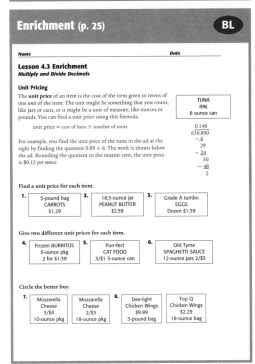

Lesson Quick Quiz (p. 26) — AL OL BL

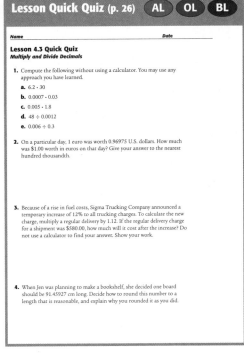

Lesson Masters 1–2 (pp. 27–28)

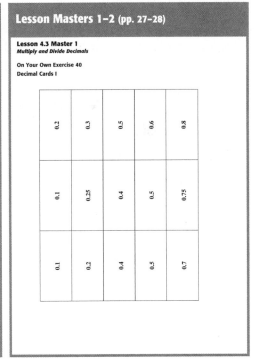

Additional Lesson Resources

Teacher Tech Tools
- TeacherWorks
- ExamView Assessment Suite
- Classroom Presentation Toolkit
- Advance Tracker

Student Tech Tools
- StudentWorks Plus
- Math Online eGlossary •
- Concepts in Motion

Other Print Products
- Investigation Notebook and Reflection Journal
- Quick Review Math Handbook

Introduce

Multiply and Divide Decimals Tell students that they will now learn to multiply and divide with decimal numbers. Point out that since they already know how to multiply and divide with fractions, and since decimals are just a different way of writing fractions, they already know about multiplying and dividing with decimals.

Think & Discuss

Ask several students for answers to each part of this exercise and put them on the board. Then have the class look at the responses together and try to identify a range of values for each part.

In particular, discuss the conditions on the last two parts, which both involve the product of 16 and another number being less than 16. Draw out the connection to multiplying by a fraction between 0 and 1: the product will always be less than the other factor, in this case 16. Be sure students realize that since the products in these two examples are less than 16, the missing factor must be a number between zero and one.

Investigation 1

On Your Own Exercises
Pages 257–264
Exercises 1–8, 35, 36

Estimate Products In this investigation, students begin working with the logic of multiplication to estimate products. They use what they know about multiplying fractions and whole numbers to explore problems involving multiplying a whole number by a decimal. In particular, they see that when you multiply a whole number by a decimal less than 1, the product is less than the whole number. This should fit in with students' previous work in multiplying whole numbers by fractions, where they observed the same pattern.

Multiply and Divide Decimals

Figuring out the tip on a restaurant bill, converting measurements from one unit to another, finding lengths for a scale model, and exchanging money for different currencies are just a few activities that involve multiplying and dividing with decimals.

In this lesson, you will learn how to multiply and divide decimals and to use estimation to determine whether your results are reasonable.

Think & Discuss

Fill in the blank with a whole number or a decimal so the product is: $16 \cdot \underline{\hspace{1cm}}$

- greater than 100.   Any number greater than 6.25

- greater than 32 but less than 100.   Any number greater than 2 and less than 6.25
- at least 17 but less than 32.   Any number greater than or equal to 1.0625 and less than 2
- equal to 16.   1

- greater than 8 but less than 16.   Any number greater than 0.5 or less than 1
- less than 8 but greater than 0.   Any positive number less than 0.5

Investigation 1 Multiply Whole Numbers and Decimals

Although you may not be able to calculate $172 \cdot 97$ in your head, you know the product is greater than both 172 and 97. In fact, when you multiply any two numbers greater than 1, the product must be greater than either of the numbers.

In the next exercises, you will explore what happens when one of the numbers is less than 1.

1e. Less; Each can cost less than a dollar, so the cost is less than (number of cans) · 1, or less than the number of cans.

2a. Possible answer: $5.60 is nearly half of the cost of the CD, and $\frac{1}{2}$ is 0.5, which is far greater than 0.04.

4. Possible answer: Each answer has the same digits as the original number but the decimal point is moved two places to the left.

1. Luke considered two brands of food for his cats. Kitty Kans cost $0.32 per can, and Purrfectly Delicious cost $0.37 per can. Find the cost of each of the following.

   a. 10 cans of Kitty Kans $3.20

   b. 10 cans of Purrfectly Delicious $3.70

   c. 12 cans of Kitty Kans $3.84

   d. 12 cans of Purrfectly Delicious $4.44

   e. Look at your answers to Parts a–d. In each case, was the cost more or less than the number of cans? Explain why this makes sense.

2. After buying cat food, Luke went to CD-Rama and bought a CD for $14.00 plus 4% sales tax. To calculate a 4% sales tax, multiply the cost of the purchase by 0.04.

   a. The cashier tried to charge Luke $19.60, $14.00 for the CD and $5.60 for sales tax. Without actually calculating the tax, how do you know that the cashier made a mistake?

   b. What is the correct amount of sales tax on Luke's $14 purchase? $0.56

3. Multiply each number by 0.01. If you see a shortcut for finding the answer without doing any calculations, use it.

   a. 1,776 17.76

   b. 28,000 280

   c. 29,520 295.2

   d. 365.1 3.651

4. If you used a shortcut for Exercise 3, explain what you did. If you did not use a shortcut, compare the four original numbers with the answers. What pattern do you see?

Lesson 4.3 Multiply and Divide Decimals **243**

Develop & Understand: A

Suggested Grouping: Individuals

▶ **Exercises 1–4** Students are asked to multiply whole numbers by decimals less than 1. The patterns and shortcuts they find will lead, in the next investigation, to a general rule for multiplying decimal numbers.

These problems are straightforward for students using calculators.

▶ **Exercise 2a** Discuss the estimation strategy presented in the sample answer. Also, discuss the importance of analyzing one's answer for reasonableness.

▶ **Exercise 2b** Have students multiply 14 by 1.04 and then discuss what this value represents.

Wrap-Up Discuss students' explanations of why the calculations do or do not make sense in Exercises 1e and 2a. Then discuss their answers to Exercise 4 so that everyone can see the pattern for multiplying by 0.01 without a calculator. You might ask students to extend their observations to suggest what pattern they could use when multiplying a number by 0.1 or 0.001.

Troubleshooting If students have difficulty with the explanations in Exercises 1e and 2a, suggest that they convert the decimal to a fraction or mixed number and then think again about the question.

Reaching All Learners

BL **Beyond Level** Challenge students to see if they can find the answers for Exercise 3 without using a calculator. They can use the calculator to check their results.

✓ Develop & Understand: B

Suggested Grouping: Individuals

▶ **Exercise 5** There may be some confusion about whether 0.45207 is a possible interpretation of Jahmal's calculator display. Some calculators show a 0 in the ones place for decimal numbers less than 1, while some do not. Either .45207 or 0.45207 should be accepted as a correct answer.

If a student suggests numbers such as 0.045207 or .0045207, point out that these initial zeros would have to be displayed on Jahmal's calculator.

▶ **Exercise 9** Let students use calculators to check their answers. Discuss the exercise with the class. Ask students how they made their estimates and how their estimates helped them determine where to place the decimal point.

Wrap-Up Discuss Exercise 9 with the class. Ask students how they made their estimates and how their estimates helped them determine where to place the decimal point.

Additional Answers
9a. Possible estimate:
$200 \times 2 = 400$; 365.4

9b. Possible estimate:
half of $30,000 = 15,000$; 14,357

9c. Possible estimate: $42 \times \frac{1}{10} = 4.2$; 4.62

9d. Possible estimate:
$9,000 \times 70 = 630,000$; 628,878.25

9e. Possible estimate:
$\frac{2}{10} \times 200 = 40$; 47.52

9f. Possible estimate: $71 \times \frac{1}{10} = 7.1$; 6.39

---

5. 45,207, 4520.7, 45.207; Some students may include 0.45207.

6. The product should be slightly greater than 5 · 9, or 45, so the result must be 45.207.

7. The product should be slightly more than 5 · 900, or 4,500, so the result must be 4,520.7.

8a. Less; 279 is being multiplied by a number less than 1.

8b. Yes; 279 is close to 300, and 0.41 is close to $\frac{40}{100}$.

8d. 114.39, because it must be close to the estimate, 120.

9. See margin.

You can multiply with decimals by first ignoring the decimal points and multiplying whole numbers. Then you can use your estimation skills to help determine where to put the decimal point in the answer.

✓ Develop & Understand: B

Jahmal's calculator is broken. It calculates correctly but no longer displays decimal points. The result 452.07 is displayed as 45207. Unfortunately, 4.5207 is displayed the same way.

5. List all other numbers that would be displayed as 45207.

6. Jahmal's calculator displays 45207 when he enters 5.023 · 9. Without using a calculator, estimate the product. Use your estimate to figure out where to place the decimal point in the result.

7. Jahmal's calculator also displays 45207 when 5 · 904.14 is entered. Use estimation to figure out the correct result of this calculation. Explain how you found your answer.

8. When Jahmal enters 279 · 0.41, his calculator displays 11439.

   a. Is the correct result greater than or less than 279? Explain.

   b. Jahmal estimated the result by multiplying 300 by $\frac{40}{100}$. Will this calculation give a good estimate of the actual answer? Explain.

   c. What estimate will Jahmal get for the product?   120

   d. What is the exact answer to 279 · 0.41? Explain how you know.

9. Below are some calculations that Jahmal entered and the results that his calculator displayed. Estimate each product. Explain how you made your estimate. Then give the actual product by placing the decimal point in the correct place in the display number.

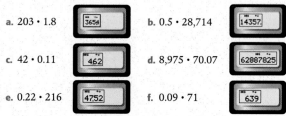

   a. 203 · 1.8 `3654`   b. 0.5 · 28,714 `14357`

   c. 42 · 0.11 `462`   d. 8,975 · 70.07 `62887825`

   e. 0.22 · 216 `4752`   f. 0.09 · 71 `639`

10. Look back at your results for Exercise 9. For each part, tell whether the product is greater than or less than the whole number. Explain why.   See margin.

11. Jahmal's calculator displayed a result as 007. What might be the actual result? Give all the possibilities.   See margin.

---

10. In Parts b, c, e, and f, the product is less than the whole number, because the decimal is less than 1. In Parts a and d, the product is greater than the whole number, because the decimal is greater than 1.

11. If the calculator displays an initial zero for numbers less than 1, it must be 0.07; otherwise, it must be 0.007.

1b. If the decimal is greater than 1, the product is greater than the whole number. Possible example: $40 \cdot 1.07 = 42.8$

Share & Summarize

1. Suppose you are multiplying a whole number by a decimal.

   a. When do you get a result less than the whole number? Give some examples. *If the decimal is less than 1, the product is less than the whole number. Possible example: $40 \cdot 0.7 = 28$*

   b. When do you get a result greater than the whole number? Give some examples.

2. Explain how using estimation is helpful when multiplying with decimals. *Possible answer: To multiply with decimals, you can ignore the decimal points and multiply whole numbers. Then you can use estimation to determine where to place the decimal point in the answer.*

Investigation 2 — Multiply Decimals as Fractions

One strategy for multiplying decimals is to write them as fractions, multiply the fractions, and then write the answer as a decimal. For example, this strategy is used to calculate $0.7 \cdot 0.02$.

$$0.7 \cdot 0.02 = \frac{7}{10} \cdot \frac{2}{100} = \frac{14}{1,000} = 0.014$$

Think & Discuss

Althea said the $\frac{2}{100}$ in the calculation above should have been written in lowest terms before multiplying. Rosita disagreed. She said it is easier to change the answer to a decimal if the fractions are not written in lowest terms before multiplying.

What do you think? Defend your answer. *See ①.*

① Possible answer: It is easier if you do not write the fractions in lowest terms. That way, the denominator of the result will be a power of 10 (10, 100, 1,000, and so on), and it will be easy to write it as a decimal.

Math Link
A decimal greater than 1 can be represented by a fraction or a mixed number. For example, 5.12 can be written as $\frac{512}{100}$ or $5\frac{12}{100}$.

Develop & Understand: A

Write the decimals as fractions and then multiply. Give each product as a decimal. Show all of your steps.

1. $0.6 \cdot 0.7$ $\frac{6}{10} \cdot \frac{7}{10} = \frac{42}{100} = 0.42$

2. $1.06 \cdot 0.07$ $\frac{106}{100} \cdot \frac{7}{100} = \frac{742}{10,000} = 0.0742$

3. $5.12 \cdot 0.2$ $\frac{512}{100} \cdot \frac{2}{10} = \frac{1,024}{1,000} = 1.024$

4. $0.002 \cdot 0.003$ $\frac{2}{1,000} \cdot \frac{3}{1,000} = \frac{6}{1,000,000} = 0.000006$

Lesson 4.3 Multiply and Divide Decimals **245**

Troubleshooting

If students have difficulty estimating with decimals less than one, suggest that they convert them to fractions and use what they know about multiplying whole numbers by fractions to make their estimates. This approach is used in Investigation 2.

Share & Summarize

For **Exercise 1**, invite students to give several examples for each part and to check their results, before asking the class to agree on a general answer to each question.

Investigation 2

On Your Own Exercises
Pages 257–264
Exercises 9–18, 37

Multiply Decimals as Fractions To introduce the investigation, you might write $0.7 \cdot 0.02$ on the board or overhead. Have students volunteer equivalent fractions for each of these numbers and either replace each with a fractional form or write the fraction below the appropriate decimal. Then have students multiply the fractions and convert the result into a decimal.

You may want to review the names of the decimal place values, possibly after Think & Discuss. You might also have students create a chart such as the following (or provide one) for reference:

Decimal	Fraction	Description in Words	Number of 0s in Denominator
0.3	$\frac{3}{10}$	3 tenths	1
0.03	$\frac{3}{100}$	3 hundredths	2
0.003	$\frac{3}{1,000}$	3 thousandths	3

Think & Discuss

In the discussion, be sure students understand why it is better not to simplify these fractional factors before multiplying.

Develop & Understand: A

Suggested Grouping: Individuals

▶ **Exercises 1–6** Point out that students should practice converting decimals to fractions and then multiplying the numbers as fractions before writing their answers as decimals.

Lesson 4.3 Multiply and Divide Decimals **245**

Suggested Grouping: Individuals

▶ **Exercise 5** Some students may have trouble finding the flaw in Jing's reasoning. If necessary, prompt them to multiply the fractions by hand, or use a calculator to multiply the numerators and then the denominators. When they see the result is $\frac{10,000}{1,000,000}$, they should be able to see that this fraction is not in lowest terms. Rewriting it in lowest terms removes several zeros in both the numerator and the denominator.

Think & Discuss

This activity follows up on the patterns students may have noticed in the exercises. It leads students to see the logic behind the familiar rule about placing the decimal point in the product when multiplying decimals: the number of decimal places to the right of the decimal point in the product is equal to the total number of decimal places to the right of the decimal points in the factors.

Work through these questions carefully and discuss students' questions or misconceptions. The paragraph at the top of page 247 states the rule as a quick reference for students.

Real-World Link

The early calculators could only add, subtract, multiply, and divide. Today's calculators can do most mathematical functions.

Real-World Link

The first battery-operated, hand-held calculators were introduced in 1970 and sold for about $400.

. . . .

5. 0.01; Conor did not make a mistake. $\frac{625}{1,000} \cdot \frac{16}{1,000} = \frac{10,000}{1,000,000}$, which is equivalent to $\frac{1}{100}$. Although this fraction has denominator 1,000,000, the product is equivalent to a fraction with denominator 100.

5. Conor calculated 0.625 · 0.016 on his calculator and got 0.01. Jing told him, "You must have made a mistake. When you write the expression with fractions, you get $\frac{625}{1,000} \cdot \frac{16}{1,000}$. When you multiply these fractions, you get a denominator of 1,000,000. Your answer is equal to $\frac{1}{100}$, which has a denominator of 100."

Find 0.625 · 0.016 using your calculator. Did Conor make a mistake? If so, explain it. If not, explain the mistake in Jing's reasoning.

6. In a particular state, the sales tax is 5%. To calculate the sales tax on an item, multiply the cost by 0.05. Assume the sales tax is always rounded up to the next whole cent.

   a. Calculate the sales tax on an $0.89 item. Show your steps.
   $0.89 \cdot 0.05 = \$0.0445$, which rounds up to $0.05.

   b. Find a price less than $1 so that the sales-tax calculation results in a whole number of cents without rounding. Possible answer: $0.20

Multiplying decimals is just like multiplying whole numbers, except you need to determine where to place the decimal point in the product. In the last investigation, you used estimation to locate the decimal point. The idea of writing decimals as fractions before multiplying leads to another method for multiplying decimals.

Think & Discuss

Write each number as a fraction.

   10.7 $\frac{107}{10}$ 2.43 $\frac{243}{100}$ 0.073 $\frac{73}{1,000}$ 13.0601 $\frac{130,601}{10,000}$

How does the number of digits to the right of the decimal point compare to the number of zeros in the denominator of the fraction? The number of digits after the decimal point equals the number of zeros in the denominator.
Find each product.

10 · 10,000	100 · 100	1,000,000 · 10,000
100,000	10,000	10,000,000,000

How is the number of zeros in each product related to the numbers of zeros in the numbers being multiplied? The number of zeros in each product is the sum of the numbers of zeros in the numbers being multiplied.
Now consider the product 0.76 · 0.041.

If you wrote 0.76 and 0.041 as fractions, how many zeros would be in each denominator? How many zeros would be in the denominator of the product? 2, 3, 5

Use the fact that 76 · 41 = 3,116 and your answers to the above questions to find the product 0.76 · 0.041. Explain how you found your answer. See ① in margin.

Additional Answers for Think & Discuss

① 0.03116; The product will have five 0s in the denominator, so in decimal form, the product will have five digits to the right of the decimal point. I started with 3116 and placed the decimal point to give five digits to the right.

7a. Calculate $1{,}123 \cdot 92 = 103{,}316$. Since there are four digits after the decimal point in 0.1123 and two digits after the decimal point in 0.92, place the decimal point in the product so there are six digits following it: 0.103316.

7b. $\dfrac{1{,}123}{10{,}000} \cdot \dfrac{92}{100} = \dfrac{103{,}316}{1{,}000{,}000} = 0.103316$

7c. Possible answer: It cannot be greater than 1 since both numbers are less than 1. And since 0.92 is close to 1, and 0.1123 is close to 0.1, or $\dfrac{1}{10}$, if you compute $1 \cdot \dfrac{1}{10}$, you get 0.1, so 0.0103316 is too small.

9. According to the rule, you multiply the whole numbers, $625 \cdot 16$, which gives 10,000. Then you place the decimal point so there are six digits to its right. This gives 0.010000, which is displayed as 0.01 on a calculator.

2. Possible answer: Ignoring decimal points and multiplying gives $25 \cdot 12 = 300$. Placing the decimal point so there are five digits to its right gives 0.00300, which is the same as 0.003.

The following rule was used to multiply decimals in Think & Discuss.

- Ignore the decimal points. Multiply the numbers as if they were whole numbers.
- Place the decimal point so that the number of digits to its right is equal to the total number of digits to the right of the decimal points in the numbers being multiplied.

✓ *Develop & Understand: B*

7. Consider the product $0.1123 \cdot 0.92$.

   a. Use the rule above to find the product. Explain each step.

   b. Check your answer to Part a by changing the numbers to fractions and multiplying.

   c. Without multiplying, how could you know that the correct answer could not be 1.03316 or 0.0103316?

8. Use the rule above to recalculate the answers to Exercises 1–4 on page 245. Do you get the same results you found by writing the decimals as fractions and then multiplying? *The results should be the same.*

9. Jing said, "The rule doesn't work for the product $0.625 \cdot 0.016$. When I find the product on my calculator, I get 0.01, which has only two digits to the right of the decimal point. According to the rule, there should be six digits to the right of the decimal point. What's going on?" Explain why this is happening.

Find each product without using a calculator.

10. $43.3 \cdot 2.05$
    88.765

11. $0.0005 \cdot 10.5$
    0.00525

12. $2.667 \cdot 0.11$
    0.29337

Share & *Summarize*

1. Explain how you can use fractions to determine where to place the decimal point in the product of two decimals. Give an example to illustrate your answer.

2. The total number of digits to the right of the decimal points in 0.25 and 0.012 is five. Explain why the product $0.25 \cdot 0.012$ has only three decimal places.

1. Possible answer: Write each decimal as a fraction. Each denominator has a 1 followed by 0s; the total number of 0s in both denominators is the number of digits to the right of the decimal point in the answer. For example, $0.035 \cdot 0.11 = \dfrac{35}{1{,}000} \cdot \dfrac{11}{100}$. Since there are five 0s in the denominators, there will be five decimal places in the result. Since $35 \cdot 11 = 385$, the answer is 0.00385.

Teacher Tips Review the rule for multiplying decimals using the number of digits to the right of the decimal point.

✓ *Develop & Understand: B*

Suggested Grouping: Individuals

▶ **Exercise 7b** Have students multiply fractional forms as a check to reinforce their understanding of why the counting method works.

▶ **Exercise 7c** Point out that it is easy to make keying errors when using a calculator. Even when using such a tool, students should estimate to determine whether the result displayed seems correct.

▶ **Exercise 9** This exercise revisits Exercise 5 on page 246. Students should realize that trailing zeros must be considered in the final answer.

Share & *Summarize*

Have students write their answers to **Exercise 1** on their own before discussing them as a class. You may want to collect their responses to assess how well they understand the underpinnings of the counting method.

Troubleshooting If students are still having difficulty understanding why a calculator displays 0.002 instead of 0.0020 for the product of 0.04 and 0.05, you can ask them to complete the chart below.

Teacher Tips Watch for students who make errors when multiplying decimals with a calculator. Suggest they estimate the answers first to help them identify keying errors.

Students should see that, when multiplying the whole numbers, they keep getting a result that is 10 times greater as they go from one calculation to the next. They should also see that the number of decimal places increases, so the results are all equal to 0.15.

Multiplication Problem	Product when Ignoring Decimals	Total Places to Right of Decimal Points	Final Product
$0.3 \cdot 0.5$	$3 \cdot 5 = 15$	2 decimal places	0.15
$0.30 \cdot 0.5$	$30 \cdot 5 = 150$	3 decimal places	0.150
$0.30 \cdot 0.50$	$30 \cdot 50 = 1{,}500$	4 decimal places	0.1500
$0.300 \cdot 0.50$	$300 \cdot 50 = 15{,}000$	5 decimal places	0.15000

On Your Own Exercises
Pages 257–264
Exercises 19–25, 38

Multiply Decimals in Real Life This investigation helps students further build their number sense about decimals by presenting them with multiplication problems in real-world contexts. They will see that although a multiplication problem may result in a decimal with several places to the right of the decimal point, sometimes such precision is not meaningful or measurable.

Think & Discuss

Use this activity to remind students that one way to check the correctness of a calculation is to make sure that the result makes sense.

Develop & Understand: A

Suggested Grouping: Pairs

▶ **Exercises 1 and 2** Encourage students to use common sense to decide whether a calculation with decimals is correct or whether a particular degree of precision makes sense.

If necessary, remind students that the formula for approximating height at age 12 from height at age 4 is given in the Think & Discuss.

Wrap-Up Discuss Exercise 2 with the class to help them understand why a height value of 148.125 cm is a correct calculation, but the precision is not meaningful. You might ask them how close to the actual value they think this prediction of someone's height 8 years in the future might be: Within a tenth of a centimeter? Within a centimeter? Within a few centimeters?

Investigation **3** Multiply Decimals in Real Life

Decimals are easy to understand and compare. They are easier to use than fractions when doing computations with calculators and computers. For these reasons, numerical information is often given in decimal form. In this lesson, you will explore some real situations involving calculations with decimals.

Think & Discuss

You can predict approximately how tall a four-year-old will be at age 12 by multiplying his or her height by 1.5.

Hannah's four-year-old brother, Jeremy, likes to play with her calculator. She let him press the buttons as she predicted his height at age 12. He is now 101.5 cm tall, so she told him to enter 1.5 · 101.5. The calculator's display read 1522.5.

Hannah realized right away that Jeremy had pressed the wrong keys. How did she know?   Possible answer: 101.5 · 1.5 is about 100 · 1.5, or 150. *Or,* 1,522.5 is more than 15 meters, which is way too tall.

Develop & Understand: A

1. On her fourth birthday, Shanise was exactly as tall as a meterstick. Predict her height at age 12.   150 cm, or 1.5 m

2. Ynez is a four-year-old who likes to use very precise numbers. She claims she is exactly 98.75 cm tall.

   2b. Possible answer: Yes; the calculation is an approximation. A person is not likely to grow by exactly 1.5 times his or her height.

   a. Use this value to predict Ynez's height at age 12. 148.125 cm
   b. Rosita says it does not make sense to use the exact decimal answer as a prediction for Ynez's height. Do you agree? Explain.

   c. What is a reasonable prediction for Ynez's height at age 12? Possible answer: 148 cm or 150 cm

Real-World Link
The practice of tipping began in the 18th century in British inns. Patrons gave waiters money before a meal with a note indicating the money was "to insure promptness." The word tip is an abbreviation of this message.

3. Possible answer: $85 is more than twice the food bill of $42, so it must be incorrect.

4c. 1¢; Possible explanation: Even though 3.57\frac{9}{10}$ is very close to $3.58, to consumers, it looks like $3.57 rather than $3.58. So they perceive the gas to be cheaper than it actually is.

The most common decimal calculations are probably those that involve money. You will now explore some situations involving money.

Develop & Understand: B

3. To figure out the cost of dinner at a restaurant, Mr. Rivera multiplies the total of the prices for the items by 1.25. The result includes the cost of the items ordered, the 5% sales tax, and a 20% tip.

Mr. Rivera and his friend went to dinner. The cost of the items that they ordered was $42. When Mr. Rivera tried to calculate the cost with tax and tip, he got $85. Without doing any calculations, explain why this result cannot be correct.

Since you cannot pay for something in units smaller than a penny, most prices are given in dollars and whole numbers of cents. Gasoline prices, however, are often given to tenths of a cent, which is thousandths of a dollar, and displayed in a form that combines decimals and fractions. For example, a price of $3.579 is given as 3.57\frac{9}{10}$. The fraction $\frac{9}{10}$ represents $\frac{9}{10}$ of a cent.

4. Imagine you are buying exactly 10 gallons of gas priced at 3.57\frac{9}{10}$ per gallon.

   a. Without using a calculator, figure out exactly how much the gas will cost. $35.79

   b. If the price were rounded to $3.58 per gallon, how much would you pay? $35.80

   c. How much difference is there in your answers to Parts a and b? Why do you think gas prices are not just rounded up to, for example, $3.58 per gallon?

5. Ms. Kenichi filled her sports utility vehicle with 38.4 gallons of gas. The gas cost 3.57\frac{9}{10}$ per gallon.

   a. Estimate the total cost for the gas. $140

   b. Now calculate the exact price, rounding off to the nearest penny at the end of your calculation. $137.43

Develop & Understand: B

Suggested Grouping: Individuals

▶ **Exercise 3** Discuss students' results for this exercise with the class. Have them share their results with a partner and reach a consensus about a common answer.

▶ **Exercise 4c** Students might have different speculations for the second question in this exercise. Accept any answer that seems reasonable. The sample answer given on this page is a common belief not just for gasoline prices, but prices of other goods as well, including groceries, automobiles, and electronic equipment.

As an extension, you could ask students to notice how gasoline prices are posted at their local station and bring that information to class.

▶ **Exercise 5a** Discuss students' estimation strategies. One strategy would be to use compatible numbers. 38.4 · 1.57$\frac{9}{10}$ is about 40 · 1.5, or 60.

Real-World Link
To leave a standard tip of 15%, find 10% of the bill and then add that to one-half of the 10% amount. For example, if the bill is $42.50, then 10% would be $42.50 · 0.10 = $4.25. Add $4.25 to $\frac{1}{2}$ of $4.25, or about $2.10. The 15% tip is $6.35.

Suggested Grouping: Pairs

▶ **Exercises 6–10** Depending on your class, you might let them find their own ways to work these exercises, or you might demonstrate some currency exchange problems with simpler numbers. For example, a dollar was equal to about 11 Mexican pesos in 2008. You can demonstrate converting a few different pesos values into dollars and a few different dollar values into pesos.

▶ **Exercises 6 and 7** Ask students to estimate their answers before they calculate.

▶ **Exercises 8 and 10** Have students suggest any shortcuts and strategies they used. Point out that rounding is necessary to give an answer to the nearest penny.

▶ **Exercise 10** Note that this exercise is different from all the others: students have to convert dollars to yen rather than yen to dollars.

Analyze the Table Ask students to look for the patterns in the tables for Exercise 8. Ask them how they would apply the pattern for another currency.

Share & Summarize

Have students share their estimation strategies.

Troubleshooting If students are still having difficulty estimating products of numbers with decimals, have them work the following additional examples.

Additional Examples

- Estimate the cost of 11.8 gallons of gasoline at $1.17 \frac{9}{10}$ per gallon.
  Possible answer: Since $12 \cdot \$1.20 = \$14.40$, the actual cost will be a little less than this, or about $14.00.

- Estimate the dollar equivalents for 500; 1,500; 2,500; and 5,000 yen.
  Possible answer:

  500 yen = 5 · 100 yen, or about $4.35

  1,500 yen = 3 · 500 yen, or about $13.05

  2,500 yen = 5 · 500 yen, or about $21.75

  5,000 yen = 2 · 2,500 yen, or about $43.50

The dollar is the unit of currency in the United States, but coins allow you to pay amounts less than a dollar. In Japan, there are no coins worth less than a yen, so you can pay only whole numbers of yen.

9. Possible answer: 3,000 yen are worth about $26.15, so 6,000 yen must be worth about $52.

10. Possible answer: 11,400; 10,000 yen are worth about $87.15; 1,000 yen are worth about $8.72; 300 yen are worth about $2.61. So 11,300 yen are worth about $98.48.

① Possible answer: 23,500 · 0.008715 is close to 20,000 · 0.01, which is about $200, not $21. Even if the exchange rate had changed, it would not have changed by that much.

When visiting other countries, travelers exchange the currency of their home country for the currency used in the country they are visiting. Converting from one unit of currency to another involves operations with decimals.

Develop & Understand: C

The unit of currency in Japan is the yen. On October 30, 2007, one yen was worth $0.008715, slightly less than one U.S. penny. In the following exercises, round your answers to the nearest cent.

6. On October 30, 2007, what was the value of 100 yen in U.S. dollars? $0.87

7. Dr. Kuno was traveling in Japan on October 30, 2007. On that day, she purchased a digital camera priced at 14,100 yen for her nephew. What was the equivalent price in U.S. dollars? $122.88

8. Copy and complete the table to show the dollar equivalents for the given numbers of yen.

Yen	Dollars
10	0.09
50	0.44
100	0.87
150	1.31
200	1.74
300	2.61
1,000	8.72
2,000	17.43
3,000	26.15
10,000	87.15
1,000,000	8,715.00

9. Use your table to help estimate the dollar equivalent of 6,000 yen. Explain how you made your estimate.

10. Use your table to help estimate the yen equivalent of $100. Explain how you made your estimate.

Share & Summarize

On her return from Japan, Dr. Kuno traded her yen for dollars. She handed the teller 23,500 yen. The teller gave her a $20 bill, a $1 bill, and some change. Use estimation to explain how you know the teller gave Dr. Kuno the incorrect amount. See ①.

In this investigation, you will divide decimals. First, you will examine patterns relating multiplication and division.

✓ Develop & Understand: A

Math Link
The ÷ symbol was used by editors of early manuscripts to indicate text to be cut. The symbol was used to indicate division as early as 1650.

1. Copy and complete this table.

3.912 • 0.1 =	0.3912	3.912 ÷ 0.1 =	39.12
3.912 • 0.01 =	0.03912	3.912 ÷ 0.01 =	391.2
3.912 • 0.001 =	0.003912	3.912 ÷ 0.001 =	3,912
4,125.9 • 0.1 =	412.59	4,125.9 ÷ 0.1 =	41,259
4,125.9 • 0.01 =	41.259	4,125.9 ÷ 0.01 =	412,590
4,125.9 • 0.001 =	4.1259	4,125.9 ÷ 0.001 =	4,125,900

2. Look for patterns in your completed table.

   a. What happens when a number is multiplied by 0.1, 0.01, and 0.001?

   b. What happens when a number is divided by 0.1, 0.01, and 0.001?

2a. Possible answer: The decimal point moves left 1, 2, and 3 places.

2b. Possible answer: The decimal point moves right 1, 2, and 3 places.

3. Copy and complete this table.

3.912 ÷ 10 =	0.3912	3.912 • 10 =	39.12
3.912 ÷ 100 =	0.03912	3.912 • 100 =	391.2
3.912 ÷ 1,000 =	0.003912	3.912 • 1,000 =	3,912
4,125.9 ÷ 10 =	412.59	4,125.9 • 10 =	41,259
4,125.9 ÷ 100 =	41.259	4,125.9 • 100 =	412,590
4,125.9 ÷ 1,000 = 4.1259		4,125.9 • 1,000 =	4,125,900

4. Compare your results for Exercises 1 and 3. Then complete these statements.

   a. Multiplying a number by 0.1 is the same as dividing it by __10__.

   b. Multiplying a number by 0.01 is the same as dividing it by __100__.

   c. Multiplying a number by 0.001 is the same as dividing it by __1,000__.

   d. Dividing a number by 0.1 is the same as multiplying it by __10__.

   e. Dividing a number by 0.01 is the same as multiplying it by __100__.

   f. Dividing a number by 0.001 is the same as multiplying it by __1,000__.

Lesson 4.3 Multiply and Divide Decimals **251**

On Your Own Exercises
Pages 257–264
Exercises 26–31, 39

Divide Decimals In this investigation, students use what they know about multiplying and dividing by powers of 10, including powers of 0.1, to develop intuition and strategies for dividing by decimals.

✓ Develop & Understand: A

Suggested Grouping: Pairs

▶ **Exercise 2** Discuss this exercise with the class. Ask students to explain not just *what* happens but *why*. For example, as you multiply 3.912 by a smaller and smaller decimal, you are finding a smaller and smaller fraction of the original number. So, the products get smaller. Since you are getting a tenth of the previous result each time, the decimal point moves to the left by one place.

For the division portion of the table, students may find it helpful to think of $A ÷ B$ as "How many B's are there in A?" If A stays the same while B gets smaller, there will be more B's in A, and so the quotient will increase.

▶ **Exercise 3** Ask students to apply the same contextual basis as Exercise 2.

▶ **Exercise 4** Take some time to discuss this exercise together. Once students have correctly filled in the blanks, ask if they see any relationship between each pair of numbers (0.1 and 10, 0.01 and 100, and so on). If they do not see the relationship, suggest that they write the decimals as fractions. Remind them of the term *reciprocal* if needed.

Analyze the Table Ask students to look for the patterns in the tables for Exercises 1 and 3. Ask students why the pattern exists.

Reaching All Learners

AL **Approaching Level** If students continue to have difficulty seeing the patterns here, ask them to use their calculators to solve problems in which they multiply (or divide) by a number and then multiply (or divide) by its reciprocal. For example,

$(17 • 0.1) • 10 =$ ___17___

$(17 ÷ 0.1) ÷ 10 =$ ___17___

$(14.659 • 0.01) • 100 =$ ___14.659___

$(14.659 ÷ 0.01) ÷ 100 =$ ___14.659___

This example introduces an approach to estimating quotients for problems in which a number is divided by a decimal.

As you go over the example, you may want to take a minute to review different notations for division; students are often confused about the placement of the dividend and the divisor when writing a division problem as a fraction. Be sure students understand which number becomes the denominator in each of the following. All of the following are the same:

$$\frac{0.0351}{0.074} \quad 0.0351 \div 0.074$$

$$0.0351/.074 \quad 0.074\overline{)0.035}$$

The estimation strategy used to approximate $\frac{351}{740}$ is to round the numerator and denominator so that when simplified, the fraction is equal to a benchmark fraction. $\frac{351}{740}$ is about $\frac{350}{700}$. Since 350 is half of 700, $\frac{350}{700} = \frac{1}{2}$ or 0.5.

✅ Develop & Understand: B

Suggested Grouping: Pairs

▶ **Exercises 5–7** Students will use the method in the example for this exercise set. Watch that students are not using their calculators until after they have tried the estimation method.

▶ **Exercise 5** Ask several students to explain their reasoning. Choosing whether to multiply or divide in different situations is the primary focus of the next investigation, and these problems are good introductions.

·······························

Real-World Link

The Universal Currency Converter Web page at www.xe.com/ucc has rates that are updated every minute.

·······························

5. Possible estimate:
$$\frac{25.27}{0.59} = \frac{2,527}{59} \approx \frac{2,500}{50}$$
or 50; 42.831

6. Possible estimate:
$$\frac{32.47}{81.5} = \frac{3,247}{8,150} \approx \frac{3,000}{8,000}$$
or $\frac{3}{8} = 0.375$; 0.398

7. Possible estimate:
$$\frac{0.4205}{0.07} = \frac{4,205}{700} \approx \frac{4,200}{700}$$
or 6; 6.007

·······························

Real-World Link

Currency exchange rates change continually. Internet sites provide currency conversion tools to convert between any two units of currency.

9a. $10 \div 0.008715$; Possible explanation: The number of yen should be much greater than the number of dollars. The first two calculations give results that are much too small.

Now you can probably divide by such decimals as 0.1, 0.01, and 0.001 mentally. For other decimal divisors, it is not easy to find an exact answer in your head. However, the next example shows a method for estimating the quotient of two decimals.

Example

Estimate $0.0351 \div 0.074$.

Think of the division expression as a fraction.

$$\frac{0.0351}{0.074}$$

Multiply both the numerator and denominator by 10,000 to get an equivalent fraction involving whole numbers.

$$\frac{0.0351 \cdot 10,000}{0.074 \cdot 10,000} = \frac{351}{740}$$

$\frac{351}{740}$ is close to $\frac{1}{2}$, or 0.5. So, $0.0351 \div 0.074$ is about 0.5.

✅ Develop & Understand: B

In Exercises 5–7, estimate each quotient. Then use your calculator to find the quotient to the nearest thousandth.

5. $25.27 \div 0.59$ 6. $32.47 \div 81.5$ 7. $0.4205 \div 0.07$

8. Find $10 \div 0.01$ without using a calculator.   1,000

9. Suppose one Japanese yen is worth 0.008715 U.S. dollar. You have $10 to exchange.

a. Which of the following calculations will determine how many yen you will receive? Explain your answer.

$$0.008715 \cdot 10 \qquad 0.008715 \div 10 \qquad 10 \div 0.008715$$

b. How many yen will you receive for $10?   About 1,147

c. Your answer to Part b should be fairly close to your answer for Exercise 8. Explain why.   Possible answer: Since 0.008715 is close to 0.01, $10 \div 0.008715$ is close to $10 \div 0.01$.

d. Caroline calculated that she could get about 22 yen in exchange for $20. Is Caroline's answer reasonable? Explain.   No. Possible explanation: There are more than 1,000 yen in $10, so there are more than 2,000 yen in $20.

When you do not have a calculator to divide decimals, you can use the method shown in the next example to change a decimal-division expression into a division expression involving whole numbers.

Example

Calculate $5.472 \div 1.44$.

Write the division expression as a fraction. Then multiply the numerator and denominator by $1,000$ to get a fraction with a whole-number numerator and denominator.

$$\frac{5.472}{1.44} = \frac{5.472 \cdot 1,000}{1.44 \cdot 1,000} = \frac{5,472}{1,440}$$

Now just divide the whole numbers.

$$
\begin{array}{r}
3.8 \\
1440{\overline{)5472}} \\
4320 \\
\hline
1152\,0 \\
1152\,0 \\
\hline
0
\end{array}
$$

So, $5.472 \div 1.44 = 3.8$.

✓ Develop & Understand: C

Solve these exercises without using a calculator.

For Exercises 10–12, find each quotient.

10. $10.5 \div 0.42$ 25   **11.** $37.5 \div 1.25$ 30   **12.** $0.00045 \div 0.06$
0.0075

13. There are 2.54 centimeters in 1 inch.

a. Estimate the number of inches in 25 cm.   10

b. Use your answer to Part a to estimate the number of inches in 100 cm.   40

c. Find the actual number of inches in 25 cm and in 100 cm.
9.84, 39.37

d. The average height of a 12-year-old girl in the United States is 153.5 cm. Convert this height to inches. Round to the nearest tenth of an inch.   60.4 in.

This example presents a method for dividing decimals without a calculator. Work through the problem with the class and discuss why the answer makes sense. If students are uncertain, or have limited skills dividing large whole numbers, you might work through some additional examples before assigning the exercises on this page.

Additional Examples
Find each quotient.

- $2.4 \div 0.04$ 60

- $52.5 \div 1.5$ 35

- $10,111.5 \div 52.5$ 192.6

✓ Develop & Understand: C

Suggested Grouping: Pairs or Individuals

For this exercise set, students work without calculators.

▶ **Exercise 13a–d** Discuss students estimation strategies in these exercises.

▶ **Exercise 13a** Point out that 25 cm is about 10 times 2.54 cm, and so there must be about 10 inches in 25 cm.

Students might also use a ruler to estimate that one inch is about 2.5 cm. 25 cm is thus $25 \div 2.5$ inches.

$$\frac{25}{2.5} = \frac{25 \cdot 10}{2.5 \cdot 10} = \frac{250}{25} \text{ or } 10.$$

▶ **Exercise 13d** The answer given assumes that students divide 153.5 by 2.54 to convert centimeters to inches.

Exercise 1 asks for the quick (decimal point shifting) method of multiplying and dividing by a power of 10. This focuses students on their understanding of the inverse relationship between dividing and multiplying. If students do not mention this relationship, ask them to describe a quick way to multiply a decimal by 100. Why is this the same as dividing by 0.01?

Exercise 2 involves conversion of measurement units. Discuss this situation and ask students to determine whose cat is heavier. In deciding whether Luke's cat (23 pounds) is 50.6 kg (23 · 2.2) or 10.45 kg (23 ÷ 2.2), students should realize that since there must be a greater number of pounds than kilograms in any measurement, they must divide by 2.2 to get the mass in kilograms.

Point out that measurement is covered in more detail in Chapter 7.

Investigation 5

On Your Own Exercises
Pages 257–264
Exercises 32–34, 40, 41

Multiply or Divide In this investigation, students reason about whether to multiply or divide in word problems. Pay special attention to students who had difficulties in Investigation 4.

As a warm-up activity, have the class practice several problems on the board in which a whole number is multiplied or divided by a decimal. Have students jot down whether they predict the answer will be greater than or less than the whole number, and then discuss their answers.

Think **&** Discuss

Give students a limited time to write individually which computation they think is correct for each problem and, most importantly, why. Allow time for several students to share their reasoning, as well as their estimation strategies, with the class.

Math Link

Mass measures the material an object contains. Weight measures the force with which it is attracted toward the planet. For practical purposes, the distinction is not important.

1. Possible answer: Move the decimal point two places to the right. This works because dividing by 0.01, or $\frac{1}{100}$, is the same as multiplying by the reciprocal of the fraction, which is 100. Multiplying a number by 100 moves the decimal point two places to the right.

① 15.95 ÷ 8; Possible explanation: You have to divide the total cost among 50 DVDs.

② 2.54 · 8.5; There are 2.54 cm in 1 inch, and we want to find out how many centimeters are in $8\frac{1}{2}$ in.

Share **&** Summarize

1. Describe a quick way to divide a number by 0.01. Use your knowledge of fraction division to explain why your method works.

2. Luke and Rosita are arguing about whose cat is heavier. Luke says his cat Tom is huge, almost 23 pounds. Rosita says her cat Spike is even heavier, close to 11 kilograms. There are about 2.2 pounds in 1 kilogram. Describe a calculation you could do to figure out whose cat is heavier. Possible answer: Multiply the weight of Rosita's cat by 2.2 to find its weight in pounds, or divide the weight of Luke's cat by 2.2 to find its mass in kilograms.

Investigation 5 Multiply or Divide

Your calculator multiplies and divides decimals accurately, as long as you do not make any mistakes when pressing the keys. However, it cannot tell you *whether* to multiply or divide. In this investigation, you will decide whether to multiply or divide in specific situations.

Think **&** Discuss

For each question, choose the correct calculation. Explain your selection. Although you do not have to do the calculation, you may want to make an estimate to check that the answer is reasonable.

- A package of fifty recordable DVDs costs $15.95. Which calculation could you do to find the cost per DVD? See ①.

$$15.95 \cdot 50 \text{ or } 15.95 \div 50$$

- There are 2.54 centimeters in one inch. A sheet of paper is $8\frac{1}{2}$ inches wide. Which calculation could you do to find the paper's width in centimeters? See ②.

$$2.54 \cdot 8.5 \text{ or } 2.54 \div 8.5$$

- Marcus is building a model-railroad layout in HO scale, in which 0.138 inch in the model represents one foot in the real world. He wants to include a model of the Sears Tower in Chicago, which is about 1,450 feet tall. Which calculation could he do to find the height of the model tower in inches? See ③.

$$1,450 \cdot 0.138 \text{ or } 1,450 \div 0.138$$

③ 1,450 · 0.138; The dimensions must be smaller on the model. Multiplying by 0.138 makes numbers smaller, while dividing by 0.138 make them larger.

Troubleshooting

If students are having difficulty with unit-conversion problems, ask them to complete the table below.

Kilograms	Pounds
0.5	1.1
1	2.2
5	11.0
10	22.0
25	55.0
50	110.0
100	220.0

In Exercises 1–4, you will need to think carefully about whether to multiply or divide to find each answer.

✅ Develop & Understand: A

Real-World Link
The euro is used by countries in the European Union's Eurozone. Having a common currency makes buying and selling products among these nations easier.

1. On January 1, 1999, the *euro* was introduced as the common currency of 11 European nations. Currency markets opened on January 4. On that day, one euro was worth 1.1874 U.S. dollars.

   a. On January 4, 1999, what was the value of 32 euros in U.S. dollars? Explain how you decided whether to multiply or divide.

   b. On January 4, 1999, what was the value of $32.64 in euros? Explain how you decided whether to multiply or divide.

2. A kilometer is equal to approximately 0.62 mile.

   a. Molly ran a 42-km race. Find how far she ran in miles. Explain how you decided whether to multiply or divide.

   b. The speed limit on Duncan Road is 55 miles per hour. Convert this speed to kilometers per hour. Round to the nearest whole number. Explain how you decided whether to multiply or divide. See margin.

✅ Develop & Understand: B

3. Miguel's father's car can travel an average of 18.4 miles on one gallon of gasoline. Gas at the local station costs $3.53\frac{9}{10}$ per gallon.

   a. Miguel's father filled the car with 12.8 gallons of gas. How much did he pay? **$45.30**

   b. Miguel's brother took the car to the gas station and handed the cashier two $20 bills. How much gas could he buy with $40? Round your answer to the nearest hundredth of a gallon. **11.30 gal**

   c. How far could Miguel's brother drive on the amount of gas he bought? Round your answer to the nearest mile. **208 mi**

   d. Over spring break, Miguel's family drove the car on a 500-mile trip. About how much gas was used? Round your answer to the nearest gallon. **27 gal**

1a. About $38.00; Possible explanation: If 1 euro is worth 1.1874, then 32 euros must be worth 32 times that amount.

1b. About 27.49 euros; Each 1.1874 dollars is worth 1 euro; you need to divide to find how many 1.1874s are in 32.64.

2a. 26.04; Possible explanation: Since 1 km is less than 1 mi, the answer must be less than 42 miles. Multiplying 42 by 0.62 gives a number less than 42, while dividing 42 by 0.62 gives a number greater than 42.

Additional Answer
2b. about 89 kph; Since 1 km is less than 1 mi, there must be more than 55 km in 55 mi. Dividing 55 by 0.62 gives a number greater than 55, while multiplying 55 by 0.62 gives a number less than 55.

Teacher Tips Remind students that a calculator can give them a precise answer to a computation, but it cannot tell them what computation to make.

✅ Develop & Understand: A

Suggested Grouping: Pairs

▶ **Exercise 2b** Tell students that since speed limits are usually given in round numbers, a speed limit of 55 mph will probably be posted as 90 kph.

✅ Develop & Understand: B

Suggested Grouping: Pairs

▶ **Exercise 3** More numbers are supplied than are needed to answer each part. Caution students to be careful about using the proper numbers. For example, in **Part a**, they need to multiply the amount of gas purchased by the cost; the average gas mileage is extraneous information for this part. In **Part c**, however, students must multiply 6.5 (the answer to **Part b**) by the average mileage.

Teacher Tips Suggest one of the following strategies for students having difficulty:

• For each part, answer the following:
   1 Choose which two numbers are relevant to answer this specific question.
   2 Decide whether you expect the answer to be a greater number or a lesser number.
   3 Use your answer to Part 2 to decide whether to multiply or divide.
   4 Use your calculator to do the calculation, and then check it for reasonableness.

• Make a table for each type of calculation. Sample for Exercise 3:

Gallons	Cost	Miles
1	$3.54	18.4
2	7.08	36.8
5	17.70	92
10	35.40	184
20	70.80	368

Real-World Link
The value of a euro may be given in ten-thousandths of a dollar.
For example, "1 euro = 1.4671 dollars."

▶ **Exercise 4c** Point out that there are practical limitations to how precise measurements can be. If students answer exactly 0.4 inches, you can accept this as correct, but you might have them look at rulers and ask if they can make a mark between two divisions on the ruler. For example, if the ruler is marked in sixteenths of an inch, you might ask if they can find $3\frac{1}{32}$ inch on the ruler. Students should see that although they cannot be sure to find exactly $3\frac{1}{32}$, they could get closer to this measure than the nearby divisions, 3 or $3\frac{1}{16}$.

Share & Summarize

Students are probably unfamiliar with hectares. You may want to give some concrete examples of areas measured in hectares, for example, the area of a football field (6,955 yd^2 or 0.582 hectare, including end zones) or a local park. The following equivalencies may help you with this task:

43,560 ft^2 = 4,840 yd^2 = 1 acre = 0.405 hectare

Students should be able to articulate that for any particular piece of land, the area of the land in hectares will always be a lesser number than the number giving the area in acres. Students should also realize that since both values refer to the same piece of land, they describe the same area in different units.

Troubleshooting The issues here are similar to those discussed in Investigation 4. If students continue to have difficulty, you may want to discuss On Your Own Exercises 32–34 on pages 260–261 in some detail.

4. Althea is building a model-railroad layout using the Z scale, the smallest scale for model railroads. In the Z scale, 0.055 inch on a model represents one foot in the real world.

   a. The caboose in Althea's model is one inch long. How long is the real caboose?   About 18.18 ft

   b. Althea is making model people for her layout. She wants to make a model of her favorite basketball player, who is 6 feet 9 inches tall. If she could make her model exactly to scale, how tall would it be?   0.37125 in.

   c. Althea is using an architect's ruler, which measures to the nearest tenth of an inch. Using this ruler, it is impossible for her to build her basketball-player model to the exact scale height that you calculated in Part b. How tall do you think she should make the model?   A bit less than 0.4 in.

Share & Summarize

In the United States, people measure land area in acres. People in many other countries use hectares, the metric unit for land area. There is approximately 0.405 hectare in one acre.

1. To convert 3.5 acres to hectares, do you multiply or divide 3.5 by 0.405? Explain how you know.

2. To convert 3.5 hectares to acres, do you multiply or divide 3.5 by 0.405? Explain how you know.

1. Multiply; Possible explanation: I can tell that to find the number of hectares in 3.5 acres, I have to multiply 3.5 by 0.405.
2. Divide; Possible explanation: I multiplied to convert acres to hectares, so I have to divide to convert in the other direction.

Practice & Apply

1. Dae Ho made a spreadsheet showing products of decimals and whole numbers. The toner in his printer is running low. When he printed his spreadsheet, the decimal points were nearly invisible. Copy the spreadsheet. Insert decimal points in the first and third columns to make the products correct.   Answers will vary.

Decimal	Whole Number	Product
4 8.3 9 8	3 0 6	1 4 8 0 9.7 8 8
3 6.4	9 6 7	3 5 1 9 8.8
1 7.0 6	6 9 8	1 1 9 0 7.8 8
1 6.7 9 3 5	5 3 4	8 9 6 7.7 2 9
7 5.0 7 2	9 7 6	7 3 2 7 0.2 7 2
9.3	1 6 0	1 4 8 8.0

2. **Economics** Gloria, Wilton, and Alex have a band that plays for dances and parties. Gloria does most of the song writing, and Wilton acts as the manager. The band divides their earnings as shown below.

   • Gloria gets 0.5 times the band's profit.

   • Wilton gets 0.3 times the band's profit.

   • Alex gets 0.2 times the band's profit.

   a. This month, the band earned $210. How much money should each member receive?   Gloria: $105; Wilton: $63; Alex: $42

   b. A few months later, the band members changed how they share their profit. Now, Gloria gets 0.42 times the profit, Wilton gets 0.3 times the profit, and Alex gets 0.28 times the profit. Alex said his share of $210 would now be $66. Explain why this estimate could not be correct. Calculate the correct amount.

   c. If the band makes $2,000 profit over the next several months, how much more will Wilton earn than Alex? Try finding the answer without calculating how much money Wilton earns.

2b. Possible answer: Since 0.28 is less than 0.3, Alex's share must be less than Wilton's share from Part a. The correct amount is $58.80.

2c. $40; Possible calculation: The difference in their shares is 0.02, so Wilton makes $2,000 • 0.02 more than Alex, or $40.

Measurement Use the fact that 1 m = 0.001 km to convert each distance to kilometers without using a calculator.

3. 283 m   0.283 km

4. 314,159 m   314.159 km

5. 2,000,000 m   2,000 km

6. 1,776 m   1.776 km

7. 7 m   0.007 km

8. 0.12 m   0.00012 km

Lesson 4.3   Multiply and Divide Decimals   **257**

Investigation 1
Pages 242–245
Practice & Apply: 1–8
Connect & Extend: 35, 36

Investigation 2
Pages 245–247
Practice & Apply: 9–18
Connect & Extend: 37

Investigation 3
Pages 248–250
Practice & Apply: 19–25
Connect & Extend: 38

Investigation 4
Pages 251–254
Practice & Apply: 26–31
Connect & Extend: 39

Investigation 5
Pages 254–256
Practice & Apply: 32–34
Connect & Extend: 40, 41

Assign Anytime
Mixed Review: 42–54

Teacher Tips Students will need calculators at home for most of these exercises.

▶ **Exercise 1** Each row has more than one possible solution. For example, the first row can be 4.8398 for the decimal and 1480.9788 for the product, which is different from the possible solution given. When you discuss these in class, ask for more than one solution to each.

Extension Ask students if they can find *all* the possible solutions to each problem.

▶ **Exercise 2c** This exercise challenges students to find their answer without calculating Wilton's share of the earnings. However, all correct answers should be counted as correct, regardless of how the students find their answers.

▶ **Exercises 3–8** Students should not use calculators for these exercises.

▶ **Exercises 9–12** You may want to check students' work to be sure they followed directions and wrote the decimals as fractions before multiplying. Also tell them not to use their calculators for these exercises.

▶ **Exercises 13–22** Students should not use calculators for these exercises.

▶ **Exercise 24 Extension** Have students bring in prices for their favorite snacks that can be purchased in bulk rather than prepackaged, including nuts as well as sweets. You can then have them answer similar questions about their snacks, including applicable sales tax for your state. If students do bring in prices for prepackaged snacks, have them save the prices so they can use them to find unit prices after they have completed Investigation 4 or Investigation 5.

Write the decimals as fractions and then multiply. Give the product as a decimal.   9–12. See below.

9. 0.17 · 0.003   **10.** 0.0005 · 0.8

11. 0.00012 · 12.34   **12.** 0.001 · 0.2 · 0.3

Find each product without using a calculator.

13. 0.023 · 17.51   0.40273   **14.** 0.15 · 1.75   0.2625

15. 0.34 · 0.0072   0.002448   **16.** 3.02 · 100.25   302.755

17. 0.079 · 0.970   0.07663   **18.** 0.0354 · 97.3   3.44442

Calculate each product mentally.

19. 0.0002 · 2.5   0.0005   **20.** 7 · 0.006   0.042

21. 0.03 · 0.05   0.0015   **22.** 0.4 · 0.0105   0.0042

23. Economics The unit of currency in Guatemala is the *quetzal*. On October 31, 2007, one quetzal was worth 0.1300 U.S. dollar.

   a. How much was a 100-quetzal note worth in U.S. dollars? $13.00

   b. On this same day, a small rug in a Guatemalan market was priced at 52 quetzals. Convert this amount to U.S. dollars and cents. $6.76

24. Economics At Sakai's Sweet Shop, gummy worms cost $.28 per ounce and chocolate-covered raisins cost $.37 per ounce.

   a. How much do six ounces of gummy worms cost? $1.68

   b. Use the fact that 16 ounces is equal to one pound to calculate the cost of a pound of chocolate-covered raisins. $5.92

   c. In the state where Sakai's is located, sales tax on candy is computed by multiplying the price by 0.1 and rounding up to the next penny. Without using a calculator, find the tax on six ounces of gummy worms. Also, find the tax on one pound of chocolate-covered raisins.   17¢, 60¢

Real-World Link
The quetzal is a bird that is found in the rain forests of Central America. Today the male quetzal appears on Guatemalan currency and on the Guatemalan flag.

9. $\dfrac{17}{100} \cdot \dfrac{3}{1,000} = \dfrac{51}{100,000} = 0.00051$

10. $\dfrac{5}{10,000} \cdot \dfrac{8}{10} = \dfrac{40}{100,000} = 0.0004$

11. $\dfrac{12}{100,000} \cdot \dfrac{1,234}{100} = \dfrac{14,808}{10,000,000} = 0.0014808$

12. $\dfrac{1}{1,000} \cdot \dfrac{2}{10} \cdot \dfrac{3}{10} = \dfrac{6}{100,000} = 0.00006$

25. **Economics** When she eats at a restaurant, Viviana likes to leave a 15% tip. She multiplies the price of the meal by 0.15. Franklin usually leaves a 20% tip. He multiplies the price by 0.20. They both round up to the nearest 5¢.

    a. How much tip would Viviana leave for a meal costing $24.85?
    $3.75
    b. How much tip would Franklin leave for a meal costing $24.85?
    $5.00
    c. The price $24.85 does not include tax. Viviana and Franklin live in a state where the meal tax is 6%, and fractions of a cent are rounded to the nearest penny. Figure out the tax on the $24.85 meal by multiplying by 0.06. $1.49

    d. Calculate the tips Viviana and Franklin would leave if they tipped based on the cost of the meal plus tax.   Viviana would leave $4.00. Franklin would leave $5.30.

26. **Measurement** In Investigation 3, you learned that you can multiply a four-year-old's height by 1.5 to predict his or her height at age 12. You can work backward to estimate what a 12-year-old's height might have been at age 4.

    a. Nicky is 127.5 cm tall at age 12. Estimate her height at age 4 to the nearest centimeter.   85 cm

    b. Javon is 152.4 cm tall at age 12. Estimate his height at age 4 to the nearest centimeter.   102 cm

27a. Possible answer: 700 ÷ 7.25 is close to 700 ÷ 7, which is 100. The train will be slightly less than 100 in. long.

Real-World Link
The HO scale is the most popular size for model railroads. Using this scale, models are $\frac{1}{87}$ the size of real trains.

27. **Measurement** To determine a length in inches on an HO-scale model of an object, divide the actual length in feet by 7.25. For example, a 15-foot-high building would have a height of about 2 inches in the model.

    a. Without using a calculator, estimate how long a model train would be if the real train is 700 feet long. Explain how you made your estimate.

    b. Calculate the length of the model train to the nearest quarter of an inch.   96.50 in.

    c. Estimate the length of the model train to the nearest foot. Is the length of the model shorter or longer than your estimate?
    8 ft, shorter

▶ **Exercise 27** Students should not use calculators for **Part a**. You may want to ask them to write how they made their estimates.

· ·

Real-World Link
Point out that the track for an HO scale train is 0.65 inch wide.

· ·

Lesson 4.3   Multiply and Divide Decimals   **259**

▶ **Exercise 28** There are several possible answers and strategies for **Part c**. Students could choose one person whose share they would like to raise, calculate that person's new share (the dollar amount, not the number to divide into the profit), and then figure out the new divisor. They can do this by finding the missing factor: new share · ? = 482.50. They also might divide 482.50 by the new share to get the number to divide into the profit.

A less likely way for students to approach this problem is to realize that dividing a number by 2.5 is the same as multiplying it by $\frac{1}{2.5}$. Also, if the total of all the shares is to equal 482.5, the sum of all four fractions must equal 1. (This would be a conceptual leap for most students.) Writing the reciprocal of the given numbers gives 0.4 for Rosita, 0.25 for Miguel, 0.16 for Luke, and 0.1 for Marcus, for a sum of 0.91. Increase one person's share by 0.09, and find the reciprocal to give a new number to divide into the profit. The easiest way is to increase Luke's share. Since 0.16 + 0.09 is 0.25, you would get his new share by dividing the profit by $\frac{1}{0.25}$, or 4.

▶ **Exercises 29–31** Students should not use calculators for these exercises. Do not remind students to follow order of operations until after they have attempted the exercises.

▶ **Exercise 32** Students will need to use the fact that there are 4 quarts in a gallon.

▶ **Exercise 33** To solve this exercise, students will find it helpful to recognize that for any given amount of money, the number of vatus will be more than 100 times the number of dollars.

Real-World Link
Vanuatu is a Y-shaped group of 83 islands in the Southwest Pacific.

28. Economics Last summer, Rosita, Miguel, Luke, and Marcus shared a paper route. At the end of the summer, they divided their $482.50 profit according to how much each had worked.

• To get Rosita's share, the profit was divided by 2.5.

• To get Miguel's share, the profit was divided by 4.0.

• To get Luke's share, the profit was divided by 6.25.

• To get Marcus' share, the profit was divided by 10.

a. Without using a calculator, estimate how much each friend earned. Explain how you made your estimates.   See below.

b. Now calculate the exact amount each friend received.   Rosita: $193; Miguel: $120.63; Luke: $77.20; Marcus: $48.25

c. Do their shares add to $482.50? If not, change one person's share so they *do* add to $482.50.   No; Possible change: Give Luke $120.62.

Evaluate each expression without using a calculator.

29. 0.1 · 17 + 15 · 0.001   1.715

30. 8.82 ÷ 0.63 ÷ 0.7   20

31. 2.75 − 0.05 · 10   2.25

32. Economics Sasha wants to buy a gallon of orange juice. He is considering two brands. Sunny Skies costs $.77 per quart, and Granger's Grove costs $2.99 per gallon. Sasha likes the taste of both brands. Which brand is a better deal? Explain.   Sunny Skies costs $3.08 per gallon, so Granger's Grove is a better deal.

33. Economics The unit of currency in Vanuatu is the *vatu*. In March 2003, there were 125.37 vatus to one U.S. dollar.

a. What is the value of 853.25 vatus in dollars? $6.81

b. What is the value of $853.25 in vatus? Round your answer to the nearest hundredth of a vatu.   106,971.95

c. In January 1988, there were 124.56 vatus to one U.S. dollar. Did the value of a vatu go up or down between January 1988 and March 2003? Justify your answer.   Down; in January 1988, there were more vatus to the dollar.

28a. Possible answer: Rosita received less than half, or about $200. To find Miguel's share, the total is divided in half twice, so he earned half of about $240, or about $120. Since 6 times 80 is 480, Luke earned about $80. Marcus received $482.50 divided by 10, or $48.25.

34a. VineFresh; Possible explanation: VineFresh costs $1.25 ÷ 0.947, or about $1.32, per liter, 3¢ less than Groovy Grape.

34. Measurement In this exercise, use the following facts.

1 quart = 0.947 liter   1 quart = 32 ounces

a. VineFresh grape juice is $1.25 a quart. Groovy Grape is $1.35 a liter. If you like both brands, which is the better buy? Explain.

b. How many quarts are in 0.5 liter? In 1 liter? In 1.5 liters? In 2.0 liters? Express your answers to the nearest hundredth.
0.53 qt, 1.06 qt, 1.58 qt, 2.11 qt

c. How many liters are in 10 ounces? In 12 ounces? In 20 ounces? In 2 quarts? Express your answers to the nearest thousandth.
0.296 L, 0.355 L, 0.592 L, 1.894 L

Connect & Extend

35. Number Sense Try to get as close to 262 as you can, without going over, by multiplying 210 by a number. You can use a calculator, but the only operation you may use is multiplication.

a. Should you multiply 210 by a number greater than 1 or less than 1?   Greater than 1

b. Get as close as you can to 262 by multiplying 210 by a number with only one decimal place. By what number did you multiply 210? What is the product?   1.2, 252

c. Get as close as you can to 262 by multiplying 210 by a number with two decimal places. By what number did you multiply 210? What is the product?   1.24, 260.4

d. Now get as close as you can using a number with three decimal places. Give the number by which you multiplied and the product.   1.247, 261.87

35e. Possible answer: 261.9999999 = 1.247619047 · 210; Use the fact that 0.1 times 210 is 21, 0.01 times 210 is 2.1, and so on, to figure out how much to increase the number by which you multiply 210.

e. Try multiplying 210 by numbers with up to nine decimal places to get as close to 262 as possible. Give each number by which you multiplied and the product. Describe any strategies you develop for choosing numbers to try.

36a. Possible answer: 10 ft · 12 ft · 9 ft = 1,080 ft^3

36. Measurement In this exercise, you will figure out how much water it would take to fill a room in your home.

a. Choose a room in your home that has a rectangular floor. Find the length, width, and height of the room to the nearest foot. If you do not have a yardstick or tape measure, just estimate. Multiply the three measurements to find the volume, or number of cubic feet, in the room.

b. A cubic foot holds 7.48 gallons of water. How many gallons will it take to fill the room?   Possible answer: 8,078.4 gal

c. Suppose 748 gallons of water cost $164. How much would it cost to fill the room? Explain how you found your answer.
See margin.

Lesson 4.3 Multiply and Divide Decimals   **261**

> ▶ **Exercise 34** Students should understand that for any volume, the number of quarts will be slightly greater than the number of liters. Therefore, to convert liters to quarts, they must divide by 0.947. To convert quarts to liters, they must multiply. For **Part c**, they will have to convert ounces to fractions of a quart before multiplying by 0.947.

> ▶ **Exercise 35** The strategy suggested in the sample answer for **Part e** will take some thought. To use it, a student would have to recognize that 210 is 52 away from 262. To get close to 52 by multiplying 210, consider that 0.1 · 210 is 21, so 0.2 · 210 is 42 and 0.3 · 210 is 63 (too much). Therefore, 1.2 gets the closest: 210 + 42, or 252. Now the student is 10 away; noting that 0.01 · 210 is 2.1, multiplying by 0.04 would give 8.4 and by 0.05 would give 10.5 (too much). Now the student has 1.24 for an answer, to give 252 + 8.4, or 160.4, which is 1.6 away. A guess-check-and-improve procedure is more straightforward and, for most students, probably faster for **Parts a–c**. Students using this method might give up before they reach the nine decimal places required for Part e. If so, you might prompt them to suggest ways to make their work easier using educated guesses. For example, they might start by using 5 for the new digit: once they have 1.247, try 1.2475. The result is too low, so they have four possibilities: 1.2476, 1.2477, 1.2478, and 1.2479. Trying 1.2477 or 1.2478 is more likely to reduce these possibilities faster than trying 1.2476 or 1.2479.

Additional Answer

36c. $1771.20; Possible explanations:

1,080 ft^3 · 7.48 $\frac{gal}{ft^3}$ is the same as 10.80 · 748. So, the cost would be 10.80 · $164 = $1,771.20.
Or, 8,078.4 ÷ 748 = 10.8, and 10.8 · $164 = $1,771.20.

▶ **Exercise 37a** Point out that students should first analyze the question and decide if they need to multiply or divide. Suggest that since one watt → 75 watts is a multiplication, 0.001 kilowatts → ? kilowatts should also be a multiplication.

. . . .

Real-World Link
Fluorescent light bulbs use 75% less energy and last 8–10 times longer than incandescent bulbs.

. . . .

Real-World Link
The common light bulb is an incandescent bulb, thin glass filled with a mixture of nitrogen and argon gas and a tungsten wire filament. Fluorescent and halogen bulbs are usually shaped like tubes or spotlights.

. . . .

38a. $\frac{1}{5}$, 0.2

37. **Physical Science** A light bulb's wattage indicates how much energy the bulb uses in one hour. For example, a 75-watt bulb uses 75 watt-hours of energy per hour. Electric companies charge by the kilowatt-hour.

   a. One watt-hour equals 0.001 kilowatt-hour. How many kilowatt-hours does a 75-watt bulb use in an hour? In 24 hours?
0.075, 1.8

   b. Suppose your electric company charges $0.21 per kilowatt-hour. How much would it cost to leave a 75-watt bulb on for 24 hours?
$0.38

★ **c.** Figure out how much it would cost to leave on all of the light bulbs in your home for 24 hours. You will need to count the bulbs and note the wattage of each bulb. Do not look directly at a light bulb. If it is not possible to find the wattage of some bulbs, assume each is a 75-watt bulb. Count only incandescent bulbs, not fluorescent or halogen bulbs.   Answers will vary.

38. **Economics** The imaginary country of Glock uses *utils* for its currency. One util has the same value as five U.S. dollars. In other words, there are $5 per util.

   a. What is the value of $1 in utils? That is, how many utils are there per dollar? Express your answer as both a fraction and a decimal.

   b. In Part a, you used the number of dollars per util to find the number of utils per dollar. What mathematical operation did you use to find your answer?   Division

   c. Use the same process to find the number of yen per dollar if one yen is worth $0.008715. Round your answer to the nearest whole yen.   About 115

   d. If you are given the value of one unit of a foreign currency in dollars, describe a rule you could use to find the value of $1 in that foreign currency.   Divide 1 by the amount the currency is worth in dollars.

   e. If a unit of foreign currency is worth more than a dollar, what can you say about how much $1 is worth in that currency?
It is worth less than 1 unit of the currency.

   f. If a unit of foreign currency is worth less than a dollar, what can you say about how much $1 is worth in that currency?
It is worth more than 1 unit of the currency.

Real-World Link

The Great Pyramid of Giza was built around 2560 B.C. The pyramid was constructed from about two million blocks of stone, each weighing more than 2 tons.

40b. Divide by 1.3; 88 · 1.3 is 88 plus about $\frac{1}{3}$ of 88, which is more than 100. $88 \div 0.6 =$ $88 \cdot \frac{10}{6} = \frac{880}{6}$, which is more than 100. 88 · 0.6 is a little less than 90 · 0.6, or 54, while 88 ÷ 1.3 is more than 88 ÷ 1.5, or 88 · $\frac{2}{3}$, which is about 60. My new score is 68.

39. **Architecture** Miguel built a scale model of the Great Pyramid of Giza as part of his history project. He used a scale factor of 0.009 for his model. This means he multiplied each length on the actual pyramid by 0.009 to find the length for his model.

Some of the measurements of Miguel's model are below. Find the measurements of the actual pyramid. Round your answers to the nearest meter.

a. Height of pyramid: 1.23 m   137 m

b. Length of each side of pyramid's base: 2.07 m   230 m

c. Height of king's chamber: 0.05 m   6 m

d. Length of king's chamber: 0.04 m   4 m

e. Width of king's chamber: 0.09 m   10 m

40. Imagine you are playing a game involving multiplying and dividing decimals. The goal is to score as close to 100 as possible without going over. Each player starts with ten points. The following are directions for what to do on each turn.

- Draw two cards with decimals on them.

- Using estimation, choose to multiply or divide your current score by one of the decimals.

- Once you have made your decision, compute your new score by doing the calculation and rounding to the nearest whole number. If the result is over 100, you lose.

- You may decide to stop at the end of any turn. If you do, your opponent gets one more turn to try to score closer to 100 than your score.

a. On one turn, you start with a score of 50 and draw 0.2 and 1.75. Tell what your new score will be if you do each of the following.

   i. divide by 0.2   250   **ii.** multiply by 0.2   10

   iii. divide by 1.75   29   **iv.** multiply by 1.75   88

★**b.** Suppose your score is 88, and you draw 1.3 and 0.6. Use estimation to figure out your best move. Then calculate your new score.

★**c.** Jahmal and Hannah are playing against each other. On his last turn, Jahmal's score was 57. He drew 0.8 and 1.8. On her last turn, Hannah's score was 89 and she drew 0.7 and 1.2. If each player made the best move, who has the greater score now? Explain.   Hannah; Jahmal's best move was 57 ÷ 0.8, for a score of 71. Hannah's best move was 89 ÷ 1.2, for 74.

Lesson 4.3   Multiply and Divide Decimals   **263**

▶ **Exercise 40 Extension** Students may find this game an enjoyable way to practice their multiplication and division estimation skills. You can create several 32-card decks by copying Lesson 4.3 Masters 1 and 2 onto heavy paper and cutting them. You can have students play the game in pairs or groups of four.

Quick Check

Informal Assessment Students should be able to:

✔ multiply whole numbers and decimals

✔ multiply decimals as fractions

✔ multiply and divide decimals

Quick Quiz

1. Compute the following without using a calculator. You may use any approach you have learned.

    a. $6.2 \cdot 30$ 186

    b. $0.0007 \cdot 0.03$ 0.000021

    c. $0.005 \cdot 1.8$ 0.009

    d. $48 \div 0.0012$ 40,000

    e. $0.006 \div 0.3$ 0.02

2. On a particular day, one euro was worth 0.96975 U.S. dollars. How much was $1.00 worth in euros on that day? Give your answer to the nearest hundred thousandth. 1.03119 euros

3. Because of a rise in fuel costs, Sigma Trucking Company announced a temporary increase of 12% for all trucking charges. To calculate the new charge, multiply a regular delivery by 1.12. If the regular delivery charge for a shipment was $580.00, how much will it cost after the increase? Do not use a calculator to find your answer. Show your work. $649.60

4. When Jen was planning to make a bookshelf, she decided one board should be 91.45927 cm long. Decide how to round this number to a length that is reasonable, and explain why you rounded it as you did.
Possible answer: This should be rounded to 91.5 cm, because carpenters' rulers cannot measure accurately any closer than the nearest tenth of a centimeter (millimeter).

Mixed Review

41. Answers will vary. Possible situations: Multiplication: Calculating the tip for a restaurant check; Division: Calculating the number of servings in a food quantity; For example, the number of $\frac{3}{4}$, or 0.75, cup servings in 8 cups of pasta.

41. In Your Own Words Describe a realistic situation in which you would have to multiply two decimal numbers. Then describe another situation in which you would have to divide by a decimal.

Geometry Identify each geometric figure.

42. a quadrilateral with four equal sides   Square or rhombus

43. a five-sided polygon   Pentagon

44. a polygon whose interior angles add to 180°   Triangle

45. two rays with the same endpoint   Angle

46. a six-sided polygon with six equal sides   Hexagon

47. a segment from the center of a circle to a point on the circle   Radius

48. Geometry Choose which of these terms describe each polygon, quadrilateral, pentagon, hexagon, concave, symmetric, regular. List all that apply.

  a.   **b.**   **c.**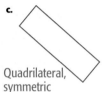

  Pentagon, concave   Hexagon, symmetric, regular   Quadrilateral, symmetric

Find each sum or difference.

49. $\frac{7}{10} - \frac{3}{15}$ $\frac{1}{2}$

50. $3\frac{4}{7} + 2\frac{18}{21}$ $6\frac{3}{7}$

51. $\frac{7}{8} - \frac{5}{12}$ $\frac{11}{24}$

52. $\frac{37}{13} - 2\frac{1}{2}$ $\frac{9}{26}$

53. $\frac{3}{8} + 10\frac{4}{5}$ $11\frac{7}{40}$

54. $\frac{1}{15} - \frac{1}{40}$ $\frac{1}{24}$

What Is Typical?

Objectives

▶ To find the mode, median, mean, and range of a data set

▶ To make line plots and use them to describe a data set

▶ To predict how changing a value in a data set impacts the mean and median

Overview

In this lesson, students use line plots and stem-and-leaf plots to display sets of data and practice differentiating between numerical and categorical data. They use range and measures of central tendency to analyze data sets displayed in tables and line plots. Mode and median (measures of central tendency) and range (a measure of dispersion) are introduced first. Mean is introduced in Investigation 3 since research has shown that many students develop a better conceptual understanding of mean when this concept is introduced after they have worked with median, mode, and range. Students then further develop their analytical skills by looking at how median, mean, and mode can be used to compare groups and how changing a value in a data set affects these measures.

Advance Preparation

You may want to provide copies of Lesson 4.4 Master 1 to facilitate class discussion while presenting these topics, including finding the measures of central tendency.

	Summary	Materials	On Your Own Exercises (pp. 276–284)	Assessment Opportunities
Investigation 1 (p. 265) *Pacing: 2 days*	Students make line plots. They find the mode, median, and range of data sets displayed in tables and line plots.	Lesson 4.4 Master 1 (optional)	Practice & Apply: 1, 2, Connect & Extend: 6, 8, 9 Mixed Review: 15–24	• On the Spot Assessment (p. 267) • Share & Summarize (p. 268) • Troubleshooting (pp. 267, 268)
Investigation 2 (p. 269) *Pacing: 1 day*	Students compute the mean.		Practice & Apply: 3, 4 Connect & Extend: 10, 11 Mixed Review: 15–24	• Share & Summarize (p. 271) • Troubleshooting (p. 271)
Investigation 3 (p. 272) *Pacing: 1 day*	Students compare mean and median as measures of typicality and decide which measure better describes a set of data.		Practice & Apply: 5–7 Connect & Extend: 12–14 Mixed Review: 15–24	• Share & Summarize (p. 275) • Troubleshooting (pp. 272, 275)

Leveled Lesson Resources

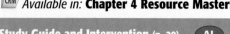

CRM *Available in:* **Chapter 4 Resource Masters**

Also on
TeacherWorks™
Lesson 4.4

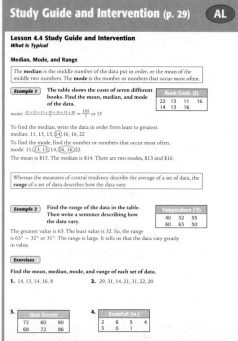

Study Guide and Intervention (p. 29) — AL

Lesson 4.4 Study Guide and Intervention
What Is Typical?

Median, Mode, and Range

The **median** is the middle number of the data put in order, or the mean of the middle two numbers. The **mode** is the number or numbers that occur most often.

Example 1 The table shows the costs of seven different books. Find the mean, median, and mode of the data.

Book Costs ($)			
22	13	11	16
14	13	16	

mean: $\frac{22+13+11+16+14+13+16}{7} = \frac{105}{7}$ or 15

To find the median, write the data in order from least to greatest.
median: 11, 13, 13, (14) 16, 16, 22
To find the mode, find the number or numbers that occur most often.
mode: 11,(13, 13) 14,(16, 16) 22
The mean is $15. The median is $14. There are two modes, $13 and $16.

Whereas the measures of central tendency describe the average of a set of data, the **range** of a set of data describes how the data vary.

Example 2 Find the range of the data in the table. Then write a sentence describing how the data vary.

Temperature (°F)		
40	32	55
60	63	50

The greatest value is 63. The least value is 32. So, the range is 63° − 32° or 31°. The range is large. It tells us that the data vary greatly in value.

Exercises

Find the mean, median, mode, and range of each set of data.

1. 14, 13, 14, 16, 8   **2.** 29, 31, 14, 21, 31, 22, 20

3.
Quiz Scores		
72	60	80
68	72	86

4.
Snowfall (in.)			
2	6	5	4
3	0	1	

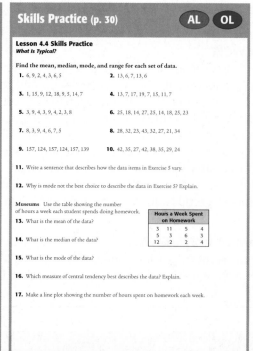

Skills Practice (p. 30) — AL OL

Lesson 4.4 Skills Practice
What Is Typical?

Find the mean, median, mode, and range for each set of data.

1. 6, 9, 2, 4, 3, 6, 5   **2.** 13, 6, 7, 13, 6

3. 1, 15, 9, 12, 18, 9, 5, 14, 7   **4.** 13, 7, 17, 19, 7, 15, 11, 7

5. 3, 9, 4, 3, 9, 4, 2, 3, 8   **6.** 25, 18, 14, 27, 25, 14, 18, 25, 23

7. 8, 3, 9, 4, 6, 7, 5   **8.** 28, 32, 23, 43, 32, 27, 21, 34

9. 157, 124, 157, 124, 157, 139   **10.** 42, 35, 27, 42, 38, 35, 29, 24

11. Write a sentence that describes how the data items in Exercise 5 vary.

12. Why is mode not the best choice to describe the data in Exercise 5? Explain.

Museums Use the table showing the number of hours a week each student spends doing homework.

Hours a Week Spent on Homework			
3	11	5	4
5	3	6	3
12	2	2	4

13. What is the mean of the data?

14. What is the median of the data?

15. What is the mode of the data?

16. Which measure of central tendency best describes the data? Explain.

17. Make a line plot showing the number of hours spent on homework each week.

Problem-Solving Practice (p. 31) — AL OL

Lesson 4.4 Problem-Solving Practice
What Is Typical?

Science For Exercises 1–3, use Table A. For Exercises 4–6, use Table B. Table A shows the number of days it took for some seeds to germinate after planting. Table B shows how tall the plants were after 60 days.

Table A

Number of Days for Seeds to Germinate				
15	20	30	15	16
9	21	21	15	

Table B

Height (in.) of Plants After 60 Days				
17	19	13	17	20
15	17	21	14	

1. Refer to Table A. You are doing some experiments with germinating seeds. You are preparing a report on your findings to a seed company. What are the mean, median, and mode of the data?

2. Use your answer from Exercise 1. Which measure of central tendency best describes the data? Explain.

3. What is the range of the seed germination data? Describe how the data vary.

4. What are the mean, median, and mode of the plant height data?

5. Refer to your answer in Exercise 4. Which measure of central tendency best describes the data? Explain.

6. What is the range of the plant height data? Describe how the data vary.

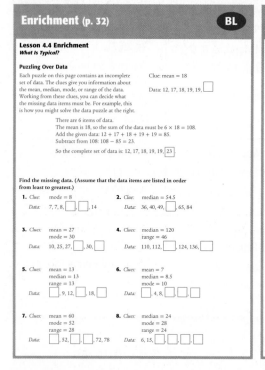

Enrichment (p. 32) — BL

Lesson 4.4 Enrichment
What Is Typical?

Puzzling Over Data

Each puzzle on this page contains an incomplete set of data. The clues give you information about the mean, median, mode, or range of the data. Working from these clues, you can decide what the missing data items must be. For example, this is how you might solve the data puzzle at the right.

Clue: mean = 18
Data: 12, 17, 18, 19, 19, ☐

There are 6 items of data.
The mean is 18, so the sum of the data must be 6 × 18 = 108.
Add the given data: 12 + 17 + 18 + 19 + 19 = 85.
Subtract from 108: 108 − 85 = 23.

So the complete set of data is: 12, 17, 18, 19, 19, 23.

Find the missing data. (Assume that the data items are listed in order from least to greatest.)

1. *Clue:* mode = 8
  Data: 7, 7, 8, ☐, ☐, 14

2. *Clue:* median = 54.5
  Data: 36, 40, 49, ☐, 65, 84

3. *Clues:* mean = 27
        mode = 30
  Data: 10, 25, 27, ☐, 30, ☐

4. *Clues:* median = 120
        range = 46
  Data: 110, 112, ☐, 124, 136, ☐

5. *Clues:* mean = 13
        median = 13
        range = 13
  Data: ☐, 9, 12, ☐, 18, ☐

6. *Clues:* mean = 7
        median = 8.5
        mode = 10
  Data: ☐, 4, 8, ☐, ☐, ☐

7. *Clues:* mean = 60
        mode = 52
        range = 28
  Data: ☐, 52, ☐, ☐, 72, 78

8. *Clues:* median = 24
        mode = 28
        range = 24
  Data: 6, 15, ☐, ☐, ☐, ☐

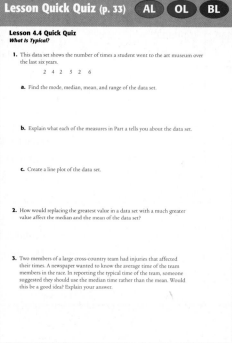

Lesson Quick Quiz (p. 33) — AL OL BL

Lesson 4.4 Quick Quiz
What Is Typical?

1. This data set shows the number of times a student went to the art museum over the last six years.

    2 4 2 5 2 6

  a. Find the mode, median, mean, and range of the data set.

  b. Explain what each of the measures in Part a tells you about the data set.

  c. Create a line plot of the data set.

2. How would replacing the greatest value in a data set with a much greater value affect the median and the mean of the data set?

3. Two members of a large cross-country team had injuries that affected their times. A newspaper wanted to know the average time of the team members in the race. In reporting the typical time of the team, someone suggested they should use the median time rather than the mean. Would this be a good idea? Explain your answer.

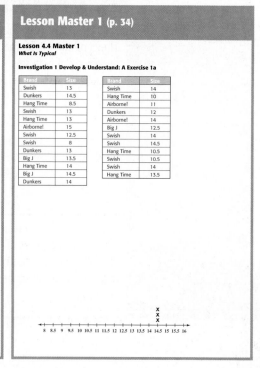

Lesson Master 1 (p. 34)

Lesson 4.4 Master 1
What Is Typical

Investigation 1 Develop & Understand: A Exercise 1a

Brand	Size
Swish	13
Dunkers	14.5
Hang Time	8.5
Swish	13
Hang Time	13
Airborne!	15
Swish	12.5
Swish	8
Dunkers	13
Big J	13.5
Hang Time	14
Big J	14.5
Dunkers	14

Brand	Size
Swish	14
Hang Time	10
Airborne!	11
Dunkers	12
Airborne!	14
Big J	12.5
Swish	14
Swish	14.5
Hang Time	10.5
Swish	10.5
Hang Time	14
Hang Time	13.5

8 8.5 9 9.5 10 10.5 11 11.5 12 12.5 13 13.5 14 14.5 15 15.5 16

Additional Lesson Resources

Teacher Tech Tools
• TeacherWorks
• ExamView Assessment Suite
• Classroom Presentation Toolkit
• Advance Tracker

Student Tech Tools
• StudentWorks Plus
Math Online ▶ eGlossary •
  Concepts in Motion

Other Print Products
• Investigation Notebook and Reflection Journal
• Quick Review Math Handbook

LESSON 4.4

What Is Typical?

To help people understand a set of data, it is useful to give them an idea of what is *typical*, or average, about the data. In this lesson, you will work with data sets involving fractions and decimals, and you will learn three ways to describe the typical value in a data set. You will also learn about a type of graph that is useful for showing the distribution of values in a set of data.

Think & Discuss

Have each student in your class estimate how many minutes he or she spent doing homework yesterday. Your teacher should record the data on the board. How would you describe to someone who is not in your class what is typical about your class' data? See margin.

Investigation 1 Mode and Median

Vocabulary

line plot

median

mode

range

The Jump Shot shoe store sells basketball shoes to college players. The tables show the brand and size of each pair the store sold one Saturday.

Brand	Size
Swish	13
Dunkers	14.5
Hang Time	8.5
Swish	13
Hang Time	13
Airborne!	15
Swish	12.5
Swish	8
Dunkers	13
Big J	13.5
Hang Time	14
Big J	14.5
Dunkers	14

Brand	Size
Swish	14
Hang Time	10
Airborne!	11
Dunkers	12
Airborne!	14
Big J	12.5
Swish	14
Swish	14.5
Hang Time	10.5
Swish	10.5
Swish	14
Hang Time	13.5

Lesson 4.4 What is Typical? **265**

Additional Answer for Think & Discuss

Answers will vary. Students may suggest reporting the value that occurs most often or adding the values and dividing by the number of values (finding the mean). Students may also suggest reporting the entire range or the part of the range in which most values occur (for example, most students spent between 30 and 40 minutes doing homework).

What Is Typical?

LESSON 4.4

Introduce

Typical Value Tell students that in this lesson they will consider ways to describe data, such as using the typical value.

Think & Discuss

Write the time students spent doing homework on the board or a transparency as each student reports his or her estimate. Be sure to have a student copy the list for your use as well. You could also save the transparency to display the results for students.

Ask volunteers to share their descriptions of the data. Some students may be familiar with some measures of central tendency and mention them at this time.

Investigation 1

On Your Own Exercises
Pages 276–284
Exercises 1, 2, 6, 8, 9

Mode and Median In this investigation, students find the mode, median, and range of various data sets. They analyze data from tables and line plots.

Have students look at the tables at the bottom of the page showing basketball shoe sales. Inform students that they will analyze these data in exercises on pages 266 and 267.

Analyze the Table Ask students if they can think of different ways to organize the data in the table.

Develop & Understand: A

Suggested Grouping: Pairs

▶ **Exercises 1–5** Introduce the terms *line plot, median, mode,* and *range* as they work through this problem set.

▶ **Exercise 1a** Provide students with copies of Lesson 4.4 Master 1 to complete the line plot. If you elect not to use the master, have rulers available for students to draw the number line.

Encourage students to confirm that all data have been recorded on their line plots by making sure that the number of values in the table is the same as the number of X's on the line plot.

Teacher Tips Suggest students use word association to help remember the definitions of mode and median. For example, students could think of the 'mo' sound in mode and most to remember that mode is the value that appears the most often. A median is also the name for the middle (often grassy) strip that separates lanes of traffic on a multilane highway; a median in data analysis is the middle number in an ordered set of data.

In the following exercises, you will learn ways to summarize the shoe store's data.

Develop & Understand: A

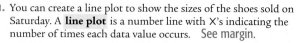

1. You can create a line plot to show the sizes of the shoes sold on Saturday. A **line plot** is a number line with X's indicating the number of times each data value occurs.   See margin.

   a. To make the line plot, copy the number line below. Mark an X above a shoe size each time it appears in the data set. For example, 14.5 appears three times, so put three X's above 14.5.

   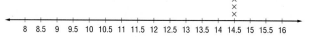

   b. Describe the shape of your line plot. Tell what the shape indicates about the distribution of shoe sizes.   See margin.

1b. Possible answer: There are a few scattered values on the left side of the plot, but most of the values are concentrated at the right side beween 12 and 15. This indicates that many more large sizes than small sizes were sold. Size 14 has the tallest stack of X's, so it was the most popular size. There is a gap between 8.5 and 10 and between 11 and 12, indicating that no shoes with sizes 9, 9.5, or 11.5 were sold. There are only two values of 13.5, although several shoes of the next smaller and next larger size were sold.

2. When you describe a data set, it is helpful to give the *minimum*, or least, and *maximum*, or greatest, values.

   a. Give the minimum and maximum shoe sizes in the data set.
   Minimum: 8; Maximum: 15

   b. How can you find the minimum and maximum values by looking at a line plot?   Find the least and greatest values with X's over them.

3. The **range** of a data set is the difference between the minimum and maximum values. Give the range of the shoe-size data.   7

4. The **mode** of a data set is the value that occurs most often. A data set may have no mode or several modes.

   a. Give the mode of the shoe-size data.   14

   b. How can you find the mode of a data set by looking at a line plot? Look for the tallest stack of X's.

5. The **median** is the middle value when all the values in a data set are ordered from least to greatest.

   a. List the shoe-size data in order from least to greatest and then find the median size. 8, 8.5, 10, 10.5, 10.5, 11, 12, 12.5, 12.5, 13, 13, 13, 13, 13.5, 13.5, 14, 14, 14, 14, 14, 14.5, 14.5, 14.5, 15; median: 13

   b. How can you find the median of a data set by looking at a line plot?   Possible answer: Start at one end and count the X's until you reach the middle value. In this data set, there are 25 values, so count until you get to the 13th X. The number this X is over is the median.

Additional Answer

1a.

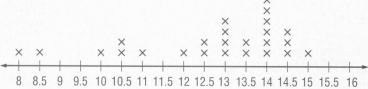

6. Suppose the store discovered five Saturday sales that were not recorded. Add 14.5, 14.5, 15, 14.5, and 16 to your line plot.

a. What is the range of the data now?   8

b. What is the mode now?   There are two modes, 14 and 14.5.

c. When a data set has an even number of values, there is no single middle value. In such cases, the median is the number halfway between the two middle values. Find the median of the new data set.   13.75

In Exercises 1–6, you looked at ways to summarize *numerical data*, that is, data that are numbers. You will now look at the brand-name data, which are not numbers. Non-numerical data are sometimes called *categorical data* because they can be thought of as names of *categories*, or groups.

✅ Develop & Understand: B

7. Is it possible to make a line plot to show the distribution of the brand-name data? Explain.   No; the data are not numbers, so you cannot plot them on a number line.

8. Can you find the range of the brand-name data? If so, find it. If not, explain why it is not possible to find the range.   No; there is no least or greatest value.

9. Do the brand-name data have a mode? If so, find it. If not, explain why it is not possible to find the mode.   Yes, Swish

10. Do the brand-name data have a median? If so, find it. If not, explain why it is not possible to find the median.

11. What are some other ways that you might summarize the brand-name data?

The mode and the median are two measures of the typical, or average, value of a data set. In some cases, one of these measures describes the data better than the other.

✅ Develop & Understand: C

12. Ms. Washington gave her class a ten-point quiz. Her students' scores follow.

$$7 \quad 9 \quad 10 \quad 5 \quad 5 \quad 8 \quad 6 \quad 10 \quad 6 \quad 7 \quad 10 \quad 2$$
$$7 \quad 5 \quad 8 \quad 8 \quad 4 \quad 9 \quad 10 \quad 4 \quad 10 \quad 7 \quad 6$$

a. Find the range, mode, and median of the quiz scores.   Range: 8; Mode: 10; Median: 7

b. Do you think the mode or the median is a better measure of what is typical in this data set? Explain.   Possible answer: The median; in this case, the mode is the highest score. Since the values in the data set are spread out between 2 and 10, the median of 7 gives a better idea of what is typical.

Lesson 4.4   What is Typical?   **267**

10. No; since the data are not numbers, they cannot be listed from least to greatest, so there is no middle value.

11. Possible answer: You could make a table or bar graph showing each brand name and the number of times it occurs. You could make a graph like a line plot but with brand names listed along the horizontal axis. You could list all the brands that were sold.

 On the Spot Assessment

Watch for students who do not find the correct median in **Exercises 12a** on this page, and **13a**, **and 14a** on page 268. Have them write the value in numerical order and cross off the greatest and least numbers, and continue the process until only one number remains. You might point out that when there is an even number of values in a data set, there will be two numbers left, and students should find the number halfway between them to determine the median.

▶ **Exercise 6b** Be sure students understand that the two values are both modes and that they should not find their average or median. You may want to mention that a data set can have more than two modes, and point out that when all the values in a data set appear the same number of times, the data set is considered to have no mode.

If students are concerned that the median in this exercise is not an actual shoe size, point out that the median is a mathematical concept that, in this case, reveals that half the shoes sold are in sizes greater than 13.75 and half the shoes sold are in sizes less than 13.75. It does not mean that any shoes sold are in that particular size.

✅ Develop & Understand: B

Suggested Grouping: Pairs

▶ **Exercise 7** If students are unfamiliar with the term *distribution*, take time to discuss how this term is used in the context of this exercise.

▶ **Exercises 7–11** Remind students to use the data from the table on page 265 as they work through the exercise set. Students look at ways to analyze categorical data in these exercises.

Wrap-Up Point out that this data cannot be shown with a line plot and do not have a range or a median.

✅ Develop & Understand: C

Suggested Grouping: Pairs

▶ **Exercises 12–16** Point out that students need to decide whether to use the mode or the median to describe the data in these exercises. They also are given facts about the data and asked make a data set that fits the description.

Troubleshooting Watch for students who think that a line plot can show the categorical data in **Exercise 7** if the brand names are placed along a horizontal axis and an X is placed above the brand name each time it is mentioned. Point out that while data can be shown in this way, the graph would not have the characteristics of a line plot.

▶ **Exercises 13–16** Discuss students' answers and reasoning for **Exercises 13b, and 14b**. If time permits, have students share and compare their data sets from **Exercise 16**.

Share & Summarize

Have students work in pairs to review the vocabulary from this investigation and compare two different ways to display data. When discussing **Exercise 3**, be sure students realize they are considering categorical data.

Troubleshooting If students are having difficulty understanding and finding median and mode, try this class activity:

Have each student write the number of siblings he or she has on a card. Then ask students to line up in order from those having the fewest siblings to those having the most siblings. Once students are in order, either have them count off from either end to find the median value or have the students at either end of the line sit down, leaving two new students as the "ends." Repeat the process until one or two students remain standing. One student standing represents the median value. Two students standing indicate that the median is halfway between the two values represented.

Additional Answers

14b. Possible answer: The median; since half of the values are above the median and half are below, I think the median gives a good picture of the overall performance. Since only one of the 13 throws is shorter than the mode, I do not think the mode reflects what is typical.

15b. Possible answer: The median; part of the week had minimal precipitation, and part of the week had significantly more precipitation.

16a. Possible answer: Many values are bunched at the beginning of the range. Half of the values are less than 57 but greater than 50.5. The other half of the values are between 57 and 99.5.

16b. Possible answer: 50.5, 51, 51, 53, 55, 55, 55, 57, 60, 65, 65, 72, 83, 90, 99.5

Real-World Link
The sport of javelin throwing evolved from ancient spear-throwing contests introduced as part of the pentathlon in the Olympics in 708 B.C.
· ·

13b. Possible answer: The modes; all but one person has 0 pets or 4 pets, so the modes give a very good indication of what is typical.

15a. Range: $7\frac{1}{2}$;
Mode: $\frac{1}{10}$;
Median: 3

13. Hannah asked nine of her classmates how many pets they have. The results follow.

0 4 1 0 0 4 4 0 4

a. Find the range, mode, and median of these data.   Range: 4;
Modes: 0 and 4; Median: 1
b. Do you think the mode or the median is a better measure of what is typical in this data set? Explain.   See bottom left.

14. During one afternoon practice, an athlete threw a javelin 13 times. The distances are listed here.

257.3   210.5   210   255.2   210   220.8
275.7   253   210   253.6   250.1   252.4   200

a. Find the range, mode, and median of the data.   Range: 75.7;
Mode: 210; Median: 250.1
b. If you had to use only one type of average, the mode or the median, to summarize this athlete's performance, which would you choose? Give reasons for your choice.   See margin.

15. During one week in January, the following precipitation amounts were reported. Data were reported in inches.

M	T	W	Th	F	S	S
0	$\frac{1}{10}$	$7\frac{1}{2}$	3	$6\frac{1}{4}$	$\frac{1}{10}$	5

a. Find the range, mode, and median of the data.

b. Which would you choose to represent the week's precipitation, the mode or the median?   See margin.

16. When you are given summary information about a set of data, you can sometimes get an overall picture of how the values are distributed. Suppose you know the following facts about a data set.
  • It has 15 values.   16a, b. See margin.
  • The minimum value is 50.5, and the maximum value is 99.5.
  • The mode is 55.
  • The median is 57.

a. What do you know about how the data values are distributed?

b. Create a data set that fits this description.

Share & Summarize   See margin.

1. Describe what the range, mode, and median tell you about a set of numerical data.

2. Which measure, the range, the mode, or the median, can be used to describe a set of categorical data? Explain.

Share & Summarize

1. The range indicates the difference between the least and greatest values. The mode tells you the value that occurs most often. The median tells you the middle value.

2. The mode; since categorical data are not ordered, they do not have a range or a middle value. However, there may be a value that occurs most often.

Investigation ② The Meaning of *Mean*

Vocabulary
mean

The median and the mode are two ways to describe what is typical, or average, about a set of data. These values are sometimes referred to as *measures of central tendency,* or simply *measures of center,* because they give an idea of where the data values are centered. In this investigation, you will explore a third measure of center, the *mean.*

Real-World Link
Strawberries were originally known as "strewberries" because they appeared to be strewn among the leaves of the strawberry plant.

. . . .

1. 6; Possible explanations: I found the total number of quarts and divided by 6. *Or,* I redistributed the quarts from the larger piles to the smaller piles until all the piles had the same number.

✅ Develop & Understand: A

1. Althea's scouting troop went strawberry picking. They decided to divide the strawberries they picked equally, so each girl would take home the same amount. The illustration shows how many quarts each girl picked.

Deepah   Althea   Mai   Tia   Ling   Randi

How many quarts did each girl take home? How did you find your answer?

2. Another group of friends went strawberry picking. They divided their berries equally. How many quarts did each friend receive?   8.5

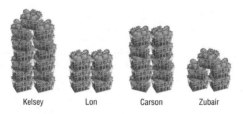

Kelsey   Lon   Carson   Zubair

3. A group of ten friends picked the following numbers of quarts of strawberries.

    5   10   4   5   7   9   9   6   8   7

Suppose the friends divided the strawberries equally. How many quarts did each friend get?   7

On Your Own Exercises
Pages 276–284
Exercises 3, 4, 10, 11

The Meaning of *Mean* In this investigation, students find the mean for various sets of data, beginning with a pictorial exercise using whole numbers and progressing to calculating means that may contain decimals. They explore how changing the values or the number of values in a data set affects the measures of central tendency. They also create data sets that meet given parameters.

You may want to let students use calculators when finding the mean of a data set, even though most students will be able to do the necessary calculations mentally or using paper and pencil.

Tell students that mode and median are two measures of central tendency. Explain that they will learn about a third measure, the mean, in this investigation.

✅ Develop & Understand: A

Suggested Grouping: Pairs

▶ **Exercises 1–3** Discuss whether this plan for dividing the berries is fair. Some may think that it is not fair since a person may not get to keep all of the strawberries he or she picked. Others may think it is fair because it accounts for physical differences like a sore back.

▶ **Exercise 3** Have students discuss how they found their answers and be sure they understand the mathematical basis for finding the answer. Some students may draw pictures or make a model to help them understand the exercise. The definition for finding a mean is on page 270.

Teacher Tips Introduce the term *mean,* relating it to the redistribution, or sharing, of strawberries in the exercises on page 271. Emphasize that the mean is computed by adding the values and dividing the sum by the number of values. You may want to provide students with another example. If so, have them find the mean for this data set: 2, 4, 6, 8. 5

Stress that the word *average* often refers to the mean when used in everyday language but that, mathematically, the term can refer to any of the measures of central tendency. This can be a difficult distinction for students to make.

✅ Develop & Understand: B

Suggested Grouping: Pairs

▶ **Exercise 4b** Students should see that *adding* new data at the high end of the range results in a new data set with a greater median and a greater mean than the median and mean of the original data set. You may want to point out that students can use their prior calculations to find the new mean by adding the values to the prior sum and then dividing the new sum by the new number of values.

▶ **Exercise 4c** Point out that *substituting* values at the high end of the range will not affect the median but does increase the mean.

▶ **Exercise 5** Students are asked to determine what value is added to a data set when they know all the other values in the data set and either the mean or the median. They should find the exact value of a missing data item when given the mean but not when given the median.

Wrap-Up Have students generalize about how adding a greater value to a data set affects the mean and the median. Then discuss their answers to **Exercises 5a and 5b**. Have students predict the effect of a value substituted at the low end of the range. They should see that the median would remain the same but the mean would decrease.

4d. The medians are the same. The mean in Part c is greater. The median is the middle value when the numbers are listed in order. In both Part b and Part c, two numbers are added to the end of the list; the size of the numbers does not affect which number is in the middle of the list. The mean is calculated by adding the numbers and dividing by 12. The greater the numbers added, the greater the total and therefore the greater the mean.

5a. Yes; Possible explanation: The sum of the 11 numbers is 80. To get a mean of 10, the total divided by 12 must be 10. Since $120 \div 12 = 10$, the total must be 120, so the 12th person must have read 40 books.

In each situation in Exercises 1–3, you redistributed the quarts to give each person the same number. The result was the *mean* of the number of quarts picked. The **mean** of a set of values is the number you get by evenly distributing the total among the members of the data set. You can compute the mean by adding the values and dividing the total by the number of values.

The mean is another measure of the typical, or average, value of a data set. In everyday language, the word *average* is often used for *mean.* However, it is important to remember that the mean, median, and mode are *all* types of averages.

✅ Develop & Understand: B

4. The astronomy club is selling calendars to raise money to purchase a telescope. The ten club members sold the following numbers of calendars.

   3 5 7 10 5 3 4 6 9 8

   a. Find the mean, median, and mode of the numbers of calendars the club members sold.   Mean: 6; Median: 5.5; Modes: 3 and 5

   b. Suppose two very motivated students join the club. One sells 20 calendars and the other sells 22. Find the new mean, median, and mode.   Mean: 8.5; Median: 6.5; Modes: 3 and 5

   c. In Part b, suppose that instead of 22 calendars, the 12th club member had sold 100 calendars. What would be the new mean, median, and mode?   Mean: 15; Median: 6.5; Modes: 3 and 5

   d. How does the median in Part c compare to the median in Part b? How do the two means compare? Explain why your answers make sense.

5. Luke asked 12 students in his class how many books they had read, other than school books, in the past six months. The following responses were given by 11 of the students.

   3 5 7 10 5 3 4 6 9 8 20

   a. Suppose you know that the mean number of books read by the 12 students is 10. Is it possible to find the number of books the 12th student read? If so, explain how. If not, explain why not.

   b. Suppose you know that the median number of books read by the 12 students is 5.5. Is it possible to find the number of books the 12th student read? If so, explain how. If not, explain why not. No; any value of 5 or less would give a median of 5.5.

Develop & Understand: C

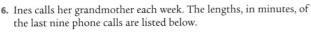

6. Ines calls her grandmother each week. The lengths, in minutes, of the last nine phone calls are listed below.

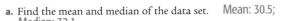

22.7   23.9   25.5   28   32.1   32.1   35   37.4   37.8

a. Find the mean and median of the data set.   Mean: 30.5; Median: 32.1

b. Add two values to the data set so the median remains the same but the mean decreases. Give the new mean.   Possible answer: 15, 45.5; mean: 30.45

c. Start with the original data set. Add two values to the set so the median remains the same but the mean increases. Give the new mean.   Possible answer: 20.4, 65.1; mean: 32.72

d. Start with the original data set. Add two values to the set so the mean remains the same but the median changes. Give the new median.   Possible answer: 30.5, 30.5; median: 30.5

For each description below, create a data set with ten values.

7. The minimum is 45, the maximum is 55, and the median and mean are both 50.   Possible answer: 45, 46, 47, 48, 49, 51, 52, 53, 54, 55

8. The minimum is 10, the maximum is 90, and the median and mean are both 50.   Possible answer: 10, 20, 30, 40, 50, 50, 60, 70, 80, 90

9. The range is 85, the mean is 50, and the median is 40.
Possible answer: 10, 15, 20, 25, 40, 40, 80, 85, 90, 95

10. The range is 55, the mean is 40, and the median is 50.
Possible answer: 10, 15, 20, 25, 50, 50, 50, 55, 60, 65

Share & Summarize

1. Jing said that the students in her class have an average of three pets each.

a. If Jing is referring to the mode, explain what her statement means.   More students have 3 pets than any other number.

b. If Jing is referring to the median, explain what her statement means.

c. If Jing is referring to the mean, explain what her statement means.

2. Suppose you have a data set for which the mean and median are the same. If you add a value to the set that is much greater than the other values in the set, would you expect the median or the mean to change more? Explain.   See margin.

1b. Half of the students have 3 or more pets and half have 3 or fewer.

1c. Possible answer: If you took all the pets and distributed them evenly among the students, each student would get 3 pets.

Additional Answer for Share & Summarize

2. The mean; the median is the middle number in an ordered list (or the value halfway between the two middle numbers). When you add a number to the end of the list, it does not matter how large the number is, the median may change slightly. However, adding a number much greater than the others would cause a big change in the sum of the data values, so it would also cause a big change in the mean.

 Develop & Understand: C

Suggested Grouping: Pairs

▶ **Exercises 6–10** All but the first problems have many possible answers. To emphasize this fact, you could have volunteers write their solutions on the board and have the rest of the class check the solutions. When it is clear that there are many correct solutions, challenge the class to explain why this is true.

Share & Summarize

For **Exercise 1**, ask students to explain what each measure tells about a data set. This is a chance to check students' understanding of the differences between the mode, the median, and mean.

Exercise 2 may be too abstract for some students. Encourage them to create a data set to check their answers.

Troubleshooting If students have difficulty finding the mean of a data set, have them use the make a model problem-solving strategy by using manipulatives such cubes or counters to model the situation. For example, they could use counters to show each number in the set. Then they could either move the counters from one stack to another until all the piles are equal, or they could put all the counters in one pile and distribute them into equal stacks so that the number of stacks is the same as the number of pieces of data. Of course, this works best when the mean is a whole number. They can also use the problem-solving strategy of drawing and using a picture as was done on page 269.

On Your Own Exercises
Pages 276–284
Exercises 5–7, 12

Mean or Median? In this investigation, students look at measures of central tendency and determine what facts can be ascertained from a data set. They explore the impact of outliers on each of the measures. They also consider how different measures can be used to influence decision making.

Introduce students to the title of the investigation, and read the opening paragraph out loud.

Teacher Tips In this problem set, students look at how large an outlier can have a greater impact on the mean than on the median or the mode of a data set. They also consider which measure to use to describe a data set.

✅ Develop & Understand: A

Suggested Grouping: Small Groups

▶ **Exercise 1** Have students focus on conclusions that can be derived about the two data sets when given their medians.

▶ **Exercise 1b** Point out that *must* means the action will always happen, not that the action may or may not happen. Thus, by definition, this statement is definitely false because the shortest student can be in either class.

▶ **Exercise 2** Emphasize that the exercise involves conclusions that can be drawn about the two data sets when given their means.

Troubleshooting Students who think that the statement in Exercise 1b can be true or false may be misinterpreting the word *must*. Point out that must means the action will always happen, not that the action may or may not happen. Thus, by definition, this statement is definitely false because the shortest student can be in either class.

Investigation 3 Mean or Median?

Vocabulary

outlier

This investigation will help you better understand what the mean and median reveal about a set of data.

✅ Develop & Understand: A

1. Lee and Arturo collected the heights of the students in their math classes. They found that the median height of students in Arturo's class is greater than the median height of students in Lee's class.

   Tell whether each statement below is *definitely true*, is *definitely false*, or *could be true or false* depending on the data. In each case, explain why your answer is correct. (Hint: It may help to create data sets for two small classes with three or four students each.)
   1a–c. See margin.
   a. The tallest person is in Arturo's class.

   b. Lee's class must have the shortest person.

   c. If you line up the students in each class from shortest to tallest, each person in Arturo's class will be taller than the corresponding person in Lee's class. Assume the classes have the same number of students.

   d. If you line up the students in each class from shortest to tallest, the middle person in Arturo's class would be taller than the middle person in Lee's class. Assume the classes have the same odd number of students. Definitely true; this is the definition of *median*.

2. Marta and Grace collected height data for their math classes. They found that Marta's class has a greater mean height than Grace's class.

   Tell whether each statement below is definitely true, is definitely false, or could be true or false depending on the data. In each case, explain how you know your answer is correct.

   a. The tallest person is in Marta's class. See margin.

   b. Grace's class must have the shortest person.

   c. If you line up the students in each class from shortest to tallest, each person in Marta's class will be taller than the corresponding person in Grace's class. Assume the classes have the same number of students. See margin.

   d. If you line up the students in each class from shortest to tallest, the middle person in Marta's class would be taller than the middle person in Grace's class. Assume the classes have the same odd number of students. See margin.

2b. Definitely false; Possible explanation: Marta's class could have heights 55, 65, 65, 65 and Grace's class could have heights 57, 57, 57, 57. Marta's class would have the greater mean and the shortest person.

Additional Answers

1a. could be true or false; possible explanation: The median is simply the middle value. It tells you nothing about the greatest value. Consider these two cases, for heights in inches:

Case 1: Arturo's class: 50, 51, 52;
         Lee's class: 48, 50, 58

Case 2: Arturo's class: 50, 51, 58;
         Lee's class: 48, 50, 52

In both cases, Arturo's class has the greater median. In Case 1, Lee's class has the tallest person. In Case 2, Arturo's class has the tallest person

Additional Answers for Develop & Understand: A Exercises 1b, 1c, 2a, 2c, and 2d are continued on page 287A.

Books, news reports, and advertisements often mention average values.

You have learned about three types of average. They are the mode, the median, and the mean. The average reported in a particular situation depends on many factors. Sometimes, one measure is "more typical" than the others. Other times, a measure is selected to give a particular impression or to support a particular opinion.

✅ Develop & Understand: B

Career Connections is a small company that helps college graduates find jobs. The company is creating a brochure to attract new clients and would like to include the average starting salary of recent clients. Career Connections has asked Data, Inc. to help it determine which type of average to use.

Listed below are the starting salaries of the clients that Career Connections has helped in the past three months.

$30,000	$25,000	$60,000	$40,000	$25,000
$50,000	$70,000	$50,000	$25,000	$60,000
$25,000	$1,000,000	$60,000	$25,000	$40,000
$50,000	$25,000	$50,000	$25,000	$25,000

3. You know how to compute three types of averages, which are the mode, the median, and the mean.

   a. Find the mode, median, and mean for these data. Mode: $25,000; Median: $40,000; Mean: $88,000

   b. Which average do you think best describes a typical value in this data set? Explain. Possible answer: The median; most of the data cluster around the median. The mode is the lowest salary. Since there are many greater values, it does not seem very typical. The very high salary of $1,000,000 makes the mean much higher than most of the other values.

Lesson 4.4 What is Typical? **273**

▶ **Exercise 4** You may want to reiterate that the outlier in this problem is much greater than the other values, but an outlier can also be a value that is much less than the other values in a data set.

Wrap-Up Discuss students' conclusions from Exercise 5. The variety of possible answers and the reasoning behind students' choices can help others broaden their thinking. Use the experience to point out that different points of view can be supported by the same set of data.

✅ *Develop & Understand: C*

Suggested Grouping: Pairs

▶ **Exercises 6 and 7** In this exercise set, student analysts must use their knowledge of statistics to support two opposing contentions. Some students may question whether the Wolves' player actually played in the game in which she scored 0 points. If they think she did not play, they may choose to disregard this score when finding the measures of central tendency to support their arguments.

Wrap-Up Have students share their arguments for each exercise. The problem is to determine which is "best." You might extend the discussion to include the attributes that make up an MVP (most valuable player) and how people's differing opinions influence the measures used to identify and select an MVP.

Real-World Link
The first women's intercollegiate basketball game was played in 1896 in San Francisco. The game pitted Stanford University against the University of California at Berkeley. Stanford won the game by a score of 2 to 1. Male spectators were not allowed at the game.

. . . .

6. Possible answer: The mean points per game for the Wolves' player is more than 4 points greater (Wolves: 30.9; Eagles: 26.7). The Wolves' player also has the greatest number of points scored in a single game.

274   CHAPTER 4 Fraction and Decimal Operations

4. One of the salaries, $1,000,000, is much greater than the rest. A value that is much greater than or much less than most of the other values in a data set is called an **outlier**. A Data, Inc. analyst suggested that this outlier should not be included when determining the average salary.

   a. Remove $1,000,000 from the data set. Recompute the mode, median, and mean.   Mode: $25,000; Median: $40,000; Mean: $40,000

   b. How does removing the outlier affect the three measures of center?   The mode and the median stay the same, but the mean drops by $48,000.

5. Write a brief letter to Career Connections telling the company what value you recommend it reports as the average starting salary of its clients. Give reasons for your choice. Consider all the averages you have computed for the salary data, both including and not including the $1,000,000 salary.   See margin.

In the following exercises, you will use a single set of data to support two very different points of view.

✅ *Develop & Understand: C*

The Hillsdale School District will hold its annual girls' basketball banquet. The head of athletics will present an award to the best scorer in the two high schools. The points per game scored by each school's best offensive player are shown below.

Points per game for Westside Wolves' best offensive player:

$$30, 61, 10, 0, 28, 48, 55, 12, 23, 55, 6, 25,$$
$$39, 18, 55, 31, 30$$

Points per game for Eastside Eagles' best offensive player:

$$22, 35, 12, 37, 19, 36, 39, 13, 13, 36, 11,$$
$$37, 13, 38, 21, 37, 35$$

Each coach wants to be able to argue that her player deserves the award. Both coaches have come to Data, Inc. for help.

6. Use your knowledge of statistics to argue that the Westside Wolves' player deserves the award.

7. Use your knowledge of statistics to argue that the Eastside Eagles' player deserves the award.   Possible answer: The median points per game for the Eagles' player is 5 points greater than the median points per game for the Wolves' player (Eagles: 35; Wolves: 30). The Eagles' player is also more consistent; most of her scores are clumped around the median.

Additional Answer
5. Possible answers:
   - I recommend reporting the median because it seems "most typical" and is not influenced by the outlier.
   - I recommend reporting $40,000, the mean when the outlier is removed. This value seems to summarize the data quite well, and since it ignores the $1,000,000 value, it will not mislead potential clients.
   - I recommend reporting $88,000, the mean with the outlier. Since this is the greatest measure of center, it will give the best impression to potential clients.

8a. Possible answer: 2, 3, 4, 5, 10, 10, 10, 10; median: 7.5; mean: 6.75

8b. Possible answer: 2, 3, 4, 5, 6, 11, 12, 13; median: 5.5; mean: 7

8c. Possible answer: 7, 8, 9, 10, 10, 11, 12, 13; median: 10; mean: 10

8d. Possible answer: 10, 10, 10, 10, 12, 20, 20, 20; median: 11; mean: 14

8e. Possible answer: 1, 2, 3, 10, 12, 12, 12, 12; median: 11; mean: 8

1. Possible answer: A few very large or small incomes can pull the mean up or down, resulting in a misleading "typical" income. The median is influenced very little by such values.

The next exercise set will help you better understand what the mean and median tell you about the distribution of a data set.

✓ Develop & Understand: D

8. Create a data set with eight values from 1 to 20 that fits each description. Give the median and mean of each data set you create.

   a. The median is greater than the mean.

   b. The mean is greater than the median.

   c. The mean and median are equal.

   d. The mean is 3 more than the median.

   e. The median is 3 more than the mean.

9. The data set 1, 2, 3, 4, 5 has a mean of 3. Change two values so the new data set has a mean of 4.   Possible answer: 1, 2, 3, 6, 8

Share & *Summarize*

1. Reports of the typical income of a city, state, or country often use the median rather than the mean. Why do you think this is so?

2. What might cause the mean of a data set to be much greater than the median?   See below.

3. What might cause the median of a data set to be much greater than the mean?   See below.

4. What might cause the median of a data set to be equal to the mean?   Possible answer: The data values might be fairly evenly distributed and have no outliers.

2. Possible answer: There might be some outliers that are much greater than the other values. It is also possible that the values below the median are fairly close to the median while the values above the median are not as close to the median.

3. Possible answer: There might be some outliers that are much less than the other values. It is also possible that the values above the median are fairly close to the median while the values below the median are not as close to the median.

✓ Develop & Understand: D

Suggested Grouping: Individuals

▶ **Exercise 8** If time is limited, you may want to have three or four students work on each part of this exercise and share their measures with the class. This will allow students to see that there are many ways to create a data set with certain criteria.

▶ **Exercise 9** Have students who finish early change a single value of the data set so that the mean changes from 3 to 4, from 3 to 5, and then from 3 to 6. Ask them to look for and describe the pattern in the increases and explain why the pattern occurs.

Share & *Summarize*

Students' ability to describe these data sets in abstract terms is an indication of their mastery of the concepts of the measures of central tendency. For example, some students may conclude that when the mean is higher than the median, the data set may have some very large outliers.

Troubleshooting If students have difficulty working in the abstract, have them refer to data sets from prior exercise sets or create data sets with a few values that meet the conditions in each question. For example, if the median and mean are the same, students can change one value in the set to see the effect on the measures.

Reaching All Learners

BL **Beyond Level** For early finishers have students change a single value of the data set in Exercise 9 so that the mean changes from 3 to 4, from 3 to 5, and then from 3 to 6. Ask them to look for and describe the pattern in the increases and explain why the pattern occurs.

The values change by 5, 10, and 15 respectively. The pattern is that for each increase of 5 in the sum of the data values, the mean increases by 1. This is true because there are five data values, so the sum is divided by 5. If the sum increases by 5, the mean will increase by 1.

Investigation 1
Pages 265–268
Practice & Apply: 1, 2, 6,
Connect & Extend: 8, 9

Investigation 2
Pages 269–271
Practice & Apply 3, 4
Connect & Extend: 10, 11

Investigation 3
Pages 272–275
Practice & Apply: 5–7
Connect & Extend: 12–14

Assign Anytime
Mixed Review: 15–24

▶ **Exercise 1** Students will need to recognize that **Parts a-c** use numerical data, while **Parts d and e** use categorical data, although they are not asked to identify these classifications.

▶ **Exercise 2** The data set has an even number of values, so you might want to have students explain how they found the median. Some students may simply state that the two middle values are 3, so the median must also be 3. Others may give a more detailed explanation, such as $\frac{3+3}{2} = 3$.

Practice & Apply

1. The table shows the style and size of all the hats sold at the Put a Lid on It! hat shop last Thursday.

Style	Size	Style	Size	Style	Size
Cap	$6\frac{5}{8}$	Cap	$7\frac{1}{4}$	Fedora	$7\frac{1}{4}$
Beret	$7\frac{3}{8}$	Beret	$6\frac{7}{8}$	Chef's hat	$7\frac{1}{8}$
Fedora	$7\frac{1}{4}$	Panama hat	$7\frac{5}{8}$	Beret	7
Sombrero	7	Fedora	$6\frac{7}{8}$	Derby	$7\frac{1}{8}$
Cap	$7\frac{1}{4}$	Cap	$7\frac{1}{4}$	Beret	$7\frac{1}{8}$
Cap	$7\frac{3}{8}$	Sombrero	$7\frac{1}{2}$	Top hat	$7\frac{3}{4}$
Fedora	$7\frac{3}{8}$	Fedora	$7\frac{1}{2}$	Panama hat	$7\frac{3}{8}$

   a. Make a line plot of the hat-size data.   See margin.

   b. Describe the shape of your line plot. Tell what the shape indicates about the distribution of the hat sizes sold.   See margin.

1c. Range: $1\frac{1}{8}$; Mode: $7\frac{1}{4}$; Median: $7\frac{1}{4}$

   c. Find the range, mode, and median of the hat-size data.

   d. Find the mode of the hat-style data.   Cap and fedora

1e. No; the data cannot be ordered, so there can be no least value, greatest value, or middle value.

   e. Is it possible to find the median and range of the hat-style data? If so, find them. If not, explain why it is not possible.

2. This list shows the number of hits Jing got in each softball game this season.

   0 3 2 7 4 2 3 0 4 0 6 5 5 2 4 0

   a. Find the mode and median of these data.   Mode: 0; Median: 3

2b. Possible answer: The median; the mode is 0, the smallest value, and in most games Jing did get two or more hits. The median, 3, gives a much better idea of the typical number of hits.

   b. Do you think the mode or the median is a better measure of what is typical in this data set? Explain.

3. Create a data set with 13 values that has a minimum value of 3, a maximum value of 13, a mode of 4, and a median of 8.
Possible answer: 3, 4, 4, 4, 4, 5, 8, 9 ,9, 10, 10, 12, 13

Additional Answers

1a.

					×				
					×	×			
		×	×	×	×	×	×		
×		×	×	×	×	×	×	×	×
$6\frac{5}{8}$	$6\frac{3}{4}$	$6\frac{7}{8}$	7	$7\frac{1}{8}$	$7\frac{1}{4}$	$7\frac{3}{8}$	$7\frac{1}{2}$	$7\frac{5}{8}$	$7\frac{3}{4}$

1b. Possible answer: Going from left to right, the stacks of X's get taller until reaching their highest point at $7\frac{1}{4}$ and then get shorter again. There is a gap at $6\frac{3}{4}$. The shape indicates that a couple of small sizes and a couple of large sizes were sold, but most of the sizes were somewhere in the middle, with $7\frac{1}{4}$ being the most popular.

4. A scientist in a science fiction story finds the mass of alien creatures from four areas of the planet Xenon.

Area of Xenon	Mass (kilograms)
Alpha	6, 21, 12, 36, 15, 12, 27, 12
Beta	18, 36, 36, 27, 21, 48, 36, 33, 21
Gamma	12, 18, 12, 21, 18, 12, 21, 12
Delta	30, 36, 30, 39, 36, 39, 36

a. Find the range, mean, median, and mode of the masses for each area of Xenon. Round to the nearest tenth.   See below.

b. The scientist realizes he made a mistake. One of the 39 kilogram creatures in the Delta area actually has a mass of 93 kilograms. Compute the new mean and median for the Delta area.
Mean: 42.9; Median: 36

c. Compare the original Delta mean and median to the mean and median you computed in Part b. Which average changed more? Explain why this makes sense.   See margin.

d. The scientist realized that one value for the Alpha area is missing from the table. He does not remember what the value is, but he remembers that the complete data set has a mean of 19. What value is missing?   30

5. Listed below are the number of unusual birds spotted by each member of a bird-watching club on a weekend excursion.

$$4 \quad 4 \quad 6 \quad 10 \quad 11 \quad 11 \quad 11 \quad 14 \quad 19$$

a. Find the mean and median of the data.   Mean: 10; Median: 11

b. Add two values to the data set so the median remains the same but the mean increases. Give the new mean.   Possible answer: 4, 40; mean: 12.18

c. Add two values to the original data set so the median decreases but the mean remains the same. Give the new median.
Possible answer: 10, 10; median: 10

d. Add two values to the original data set so both the mean and median stay the same.   Possible answer: 5, 15

4a.

Area	Range	Mean	Median	Mode
Alpha	30	17.6	13.5	12
Beta	30	30.7	33	36
Gamma	9	15.8	15	12
Delta	9	35.1	36	36

Exercise 4c Remind students than in mathematics, both the mean and the median are considered averages.

Additional Answer

4c.   The mean; this makes sense because the new total is much greater than the original total, but you are dividing by the same number of values. The median didn't change because 39 and 93 are in the same position when the numbers are listed in order, so the middle value does not change.

▶ **Exercise 6** You might remind students that 0 is an outlier in the data set since it is much less than the other scores.

▶ **Exercise 7** Some students may consider the grading scale when choosing which way to calculate the final grade and decide that the median is the best option. If 70 to 80 is a C on the grading scale, either option would give Elsa a C as long as she receives a score of at least 30 and less than 80. If her score is 80 or above, both the mean and the median will be at least 80 but less than 90, so she will receive a B. If her score is less than 30, she would receive a C if she selects the median but a D if she selects the mean.

6d. Possible answer: 82.83̄ (the mean with the 0 dropped); this score takes into account both the high and low scores and gives a good idea about what is average.

7b. The median; no matter how Elsa does on her last test, she will get a grade of at least 79.

Real-World Link
The first public swimming pool in the United States was built in Brookline, Massachusetts, in 1887. There are now more than 200,000 public swimming pools in the United States.
. . . .

6. Lonnie tutors students in algebra. The following are the scores his students received on their most recent algebra tests.

0   60   78   79   90   95   95

a. Lonnie claims that the students he tutored received an average score of 95 on their tests. Which measure of center is he using? Do you think 95 is a good measure of what is typical about these tests scores? Explain.   See margin.

b. Find the mean and median of the test scores.   Mean: 71; Median: 79

c. Lonnie said the score of 0 should not be counted when finding the average because the student did not show up for the test. Delete the 0, and find the new mean and median.   Mean: 82.8̄3̄ Median: 84.5

d. Which of the averages computed in Parts b and c do you think best represents the typical test scores for the students Lonnie tutored?

7. Elsa received the scores of 81, 79, 90, and 70 on her first four math tests this semester. There is one more test left. Elsa's teacher has told her she may choose to use her mean or her median test score as her final grade, but she must decide *before* she takes the final test.

a. Calculate Elsa's current mean and median test scores.   Mean: 80; Median: 80

b. If Elsa is not confident she will do well on the final test, should she choose the mean or the median? Explain.

c. If Elsa is confident she will do well on the final test, should she choose the mean or the median? Explain.   See margin.

278   CHAPTER 4   Fraction and Decimal Operations

Additional Answers

6a.   the mode; no; Possible explanation: 95 is the highest score. Since some of the test scores were much lower, and one of the scores was zero, reporting 95 as the average does not reflect how low some of the scores were.

7c.   the mean; even if Elsa gets 100, her median score will be only 81. If she chooses the mean, a score of 85 or above will give her a final grade of 81 or higher.

8. Alano and Kate are swimming instructors at the local recreation center. One day, both instructors asked their students to swim as many laps as they could. The results are shown in the table.

   a. Find the range, mean, median, and mode for all 12 swimmers.
      Range: 11; Mean: 7.625; Median: 7; Mode: 7

Student	Instructor	Laps Swum
Lucinda	Kate	7
Jay	Alano	15
Guto	Kate	9
Carson	Alano	11
Ebony	Kate	6
Darius	Kate	7
Curtis	Alano	9
Carmen	Alano	4.5
Avi	Kate	8
Theo	Kate	7
Gil	Alano	4
Louis	Alano	4

8b. Kate's students: range: 3; mean: 7.$\overline{3}$; median: 7; mode: 7 Alano's students: range: 11; mean: 7.91$\overline{6}$; median: 6.75; mode: 4

9b. An X over a number indicates that one person in the class has a family of that size. So, the single X over the 8 indicates that only one family, Zeke's, has eight people.

   b. Find the range, mean, median, and mode for each instructor's students.

   c. Alano said his students were stronger swimmers. Kate argued that her students were stronger. Use your knowledge of statistics to write two arguments, one to support Alano's position and one to support Kate's position.   See margin.

Connect & Extend

9. **Data Analysis** Zeke's class made a line plot showing the number of people in each student's family.

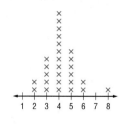

   a. What is the total number of people in all of the students' families?   113

   b. Zeke said, "The plot can't be right! My family has 8 people. If I have the largest family, why is the stack of X's over the 8 the shortest one on the graph?" Answer Zeke's question.

Lesson 4.4   What is Typical?   **279**

▶ **Exercise 9a** Students use data from a line plot to calculate the total number of people in 27 families. As they analyze the data, they may see that more can be learned from a graph of a data set than may be apparent at first glance. Watch for students who count the number of families (27) instead of the total number of people.

▶ **Exercise 9b** Point out that the focus is on the distinction between the size of a data item and its frequency. Students commonly confuse these two concepts.

Additional Answer

8c. Possible answer: Argument for Kate: Kate's group has a greater median than Alana's does. It also has a smaller range, so Kate's group is more consistent, with most scores clumping near the median

Argument for Alana: Alana's group has a greater mean. It also includes the two strongest swimmers. The strongest swimmer swam 15 laps, 6 more than Kate's strongest swimmer.

▶ **Exercise 10** Students should recognize that both the mode and the median could be used as a measure of typicality. Sometimes one measure may provide users with a better understanding of what is happening in a data set. In this exercise, there are a number of arguments to support that Group 1 did better and a number to support that Group 2 did better.

The sample answers give the mean for each data set.

▶ **Exercises 11 and 12** Encourage students to either refer to their work from the exercise sets or create a data set to check that their observations are accurate.

▶ **Exercise 12** Students construct data sets to fit median, mode, and range criteria in this exercise.

Additional Answers

10b. Possible answer: Group 2 did better. Three in Group 2 jumped more than 100 times, while only one in Group 1 jumped more than 100 times. The median value for Group 2 is 68, so more than half of them jumped 68 or more times. The median for Group 1 is 21, so half of them jumped 21 times or fewer. The mean for Group 2 is 65.6 while that for Group 1 is only 43.7. The range for Group 2 is 147 while the range for Group 1 is 299. This indicates that Group 2 was much more consistent.

11. The mode will be a whole number; the median and mean may not be. The mode is a value in the data set, so it will be a whole number. If the data set has an even number of values, the median will be halfway between the two middle values, so it is possible that it will not be a whole number (for example, if the two middle values are 10 and 13, the median will be 11.5). If the number of values does not divide evenly into the total of the values, the mean will not be a whole number.

12c. It must be much less than the other values. That would make the mean go down by a lot and the median by a little or not at all.

Real-World Link

Double Dutch jump roping involves skipping two ropes as they are swung in opposite directions. Since 1973, the American Double Dutch League has held an annual rope-jumping competition.

· · · · · · · · · · · · · · · · · · · ·

10a. Possible answer: Group 1 had the best jumper. This person jumped 300 times, 149 times more than the best jumper in Group 2. The mode for Group 1 is 26 while the mode for Group 2 is only 4. Clearly, Group 1 did better.

12a. Possible answer: About half of the numbers are at the mean or above and about half are at the mean or below.

12b. It must be much greater than the other values. That would make the mean go up by a lot and the median by a little or not at all.

10. Sports The students in Consuela's gym class recorded how many times they could jump rope without missing. The results are shown in the table.

	Group 1			Group 2	
Name	**Gender**	**Jumps**	**Name**	**Gender**	**Jumps**
Jorge	male	1	Lucas	male	4
Felise	female	1	Colin	male	4
Lana	female	5	Olivia	female	4
Sean	male	7	Trent	male	23
Matt	male	8	Lawana	female	35
David	male	11	Tyrone	male	48
Aaron	male	16	Francisca	female	68
Kara	female	26	Enola	female	83
Brandon	male	26	Shari	female	89
Enrique	male	26	Kiran	male	96
Emma	female	40	Meela	female	110
Nicholas	male	50	Consuela	female	138
Shondra	female	95	Tariq	male	151
Selena	female	300			

a. Group 1 claims it did better. Use what you have learned about statistics, along with any other information you think is useful, to write an argument Group 1 could use to support its claim.

b. Group 2 says it did better. Use what you have learned about statistics, along with any other information you think is useful, to write an argument Group 2 could use to support its claim. See margin.

11. If you have a data set that includes only whole numbers, which measures of center, mode, median, or mean, will *definitely be* whole numbers? Which measures of center *may* or *may not be* whole numbers? Explain your answers. See margin.

12. Suppose a data set has a mean and a median that are equal.

a. What must be true about the distribution of the data values?

b. Suppose one value is added to the set, and the new mean is much greater than the median. What must be true about the new value? Explain.

c. Now suppose you start with a new data set in which the mean and median are equal. You add one value to the set, and the new median is much greater than the mean. What must be true about the new value? See margin.

13a, c, d. See margin.

13. Emelia asked her friends to rate three movies on a scale from 1 to 5, with 5 being terrific and 1 being terrible.

Movie Ratings

Friend	Star Wars	The Sound of Music	The Wizard of Oz
Adam	2	1	4
Ashley	5	1	5
Corey	2	4	3
Emelia	4	4	2
Eric	4	4	4
Hector	3	5	5
Ilene	2	5	3
Jay	3	2	1
Jose	5	1	5
Kareem	3	3	2
Kara	2	5	3
Lawana	4	5	4
Letonya	3	5	4
Lynn	1	2	2
Mark	4	3	3
Maria	3	2	1
Marcos	3	1	1
Peter	1	1	2

Real-World Link

It is difficult to think of *The Wizard of Oz* without picturing Dorothy's ruby slippers. However, in the book on which the movie was based, Dorothy wore silver shoes, not ruby slippers.

a. For each movie, make a line plot of the friends' ratings.

b. Compute the mean and median rating for each movie. The mean and median are both 3 for all three movies.

c. Do you think reporting the means and medians is a good way to summarize the ratings for the three movies? Explain.

d. How would you summarize these data if you wanted to emphasize the differences in the ratings among the three movies? Explain why you would summarize the data this way.

14. In Your Own Words How are mean, median, and mode alike? How are they different?. Possible answer: All three are measures of center and are sometimes referred to as "average." The mean is found by adding values and dividing by the number of values. The mode is the value occuring most often, and the median is the middle value when data are listed from least to greatest.

Lesson 4.4   What is Typical?   **281**

▶ **Exercise 13c** Have several students give examples of data sets that support their answer.

Additional Answers

13a.   ***Star Wars***

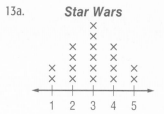

The Sound of Music

The Wizard of Oz

13c. No; although the distributions of ratings for the three movies are quite different, the means and medians are the same. Reporting those averages does not indicate the differences.

13d. Possible answer: I would give the mode. *The Sound of Music* has two modes, 1 and 5, which indicates that some students really loved it while others didn't like it at all. *The Wizard of Oz* has three modes, 2, 3, and 4, indicating that the ratings were fairly spread out. *Star Wars* has one mode, 3, which indicates that most students thought it was a pretty good movie.

Quick Check

Informal Assessment Students should be able to:

✔ find the mode, median, mean, and range of a data set

✔ make line plots and use them to describe a data set

✔ predict how change a value in a data set impacts the mean and median

Quick Quiz

1. This data set shows the number of times a student went to the art museum over the last six years. 2 4 2 5 2 6

  a. Find the mode, median, mean, and range of the data set. mode: 2; median: 3; mean: 3.5; range: 4

  b. Explain what each of the measures in Part a tells you about the data set. Possible answer: The mode tells the most typical number of visits per year. The median is the middle value of the data set, so there are the same number of visits greater than 3 as there are less than 3. The mean tells how many visits there would be if all the visits were spread out over the six years. The range tells the difference between the greatest and least numbers of visits.

  c. Create a line plot of the data set.

Number of Yearly Visits

2. How would replacing the greatest value in a data set with a much greater value affect the median and the mean of the data set? The median would not change (assuming the data set had more than two values), but the mean would increase.

3. Two members of a large cross-country team had injuries that affected their times. A newspaper wanted to know the average time of the team members in the race. In reporting the typical time of the team, someone suggested they should use the median time rather than the mean. Would this be a good idea? Explain your answer.

Mixed Review

Simplify each expression.

15. $\frac{1}{3} \div \frac{2}{3}$ $\frac{1}{2}$

16. $\frac{7}{5} \div \frac{5}{7}$ $\frac{49}{25}$

17. $\frac{7}{5} \div \frac{7}{5}$ 1

18. $\frac{1}{8} \div \frac{1}{4}$ $\frac{1}{2}$

Find three fractions equivalent to each given fraction.

19. $\frac{7}{9}$

20. $\frac{12}{54}$

19–22. Answers will vary.

21. $\frac{6}{13}$

22. $\frac{14}{5}$

23. Order these fractions from least to greatest.

$\frac{1}{3}$ $\frac{12}{30}$ $\frac{9}{28}$ $\frac{11}{30}$ $\frac{12}{29}$ $\frac{9}{28}, \frac{1}{3}, \frac{11}{30}, \frac{12}{30}, \frac{12}{29}$

24. Hannah and Rosita each wrote rules for the number of toothpicks in each stage of this sequence.

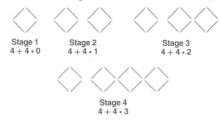

Stage 1   Stage 2   Stage 3   Stage 4

24b. Possible explanation: Stage 1 has 4 toothpicks, stage 2 has 4 toothpicks plus 1 group of 4, stage 3 has 4 toothpicks plus 2 groups of 4, stage 4 has 4 toothpicks plus 3 groups of 4, and so on. So, stage n has 4 plus $n - 1$ groups of 4, or $4 + 4 \cdot (n - 1)$ toothpicks.

Both girls used t to represent the number of toothpicks and n to represent the stage number. Use words or diagrams to explain why each rule is correct.

  a. Hannah's rule: $t = 2 \cdot n + 2 \cdot n$

  b. Rosita's rule: $t = 4 + 4 \cdot (n - 1)$

24a. Possible explanation: Each stage can be split into two halves. The number of toothpicks in each half is equal to 2 times the stage number. So, stage n has $2 \cdot n + 2 \cdot n$ toothpicks.

Stage 1
$4 + 4 \cdot 0$

Stage 2
$4 + 4 \cdot 1$

Stage 3
$4 + 4 \cdot 2$

Stage 4
$4 + 4 \cdot 3$

3. Possible answer: Yes, it would be a good idea. Since there are many members in the race, the slow times would influence the mean but not the median. The median would give a truer picture of the team's capabilities.

Review & Self-Assessment

Chapter Summary

In this chapter, you learned how to do calculations with fractions and decimals. You used fraction pieces to add and subtract fractions with different denominators. You found that by rewriting the fractions with a common denominator, you could add and subtract without fraction pieces.

You then used what you know about multiplying whole numbers to figure out how to multiply a whole number by a fraction. You used rectangle diagrams to discover a method for multiplying two fractions.

You learned how to divide a whole number by a fraction by using a model and by writing a related multiplication problem. Then you learned two methods for dividing two fractions.

You also turned your attention to operations with decimals. You learned that you could use estimation, along with what you already know about multiplying and dividing whole numbers, to multiply and divide decimals.

Finally, you were also introduced to some statistics used to summarize a data set. The *range* of a data set is the difference between the minimum and maximum values. The *mode* is the value that occurs most often. The *median* is the middle value. The *mean* is the value found by dividing the sum of the data values equally among the data items. The mean, median, and mode are all measures of what is typical, or average, about a set of data.

Vocabulary

- line plot
- mean
- median
- mode
- outlier
- range
- reciprocal

Strategies and Applications

The questions in this section will help you review and apply the important ideas and strategies developed in this chapter.

Adding and subtracting fractions and mixed numbers

1. Explain the steps you would follow to add two fractions with different denominators. Give an example to illustrate your steps.

2. Describe two methods for subtracting one mixed number from another. Use one of the methods to find $7\frac{1}{3} - 4\frac{5}{6}$. Show your work. See margin.

Multiplying fractions and mixed numbers

3. Find $\frac{2}{3} \cdot \frac{4}{5}$ by making a rectangle diagram. Show how this method of finding the product is related to finding the product of the numerators over the product of the denominators. See margin.

4. Describe how you would multiply two mixed numbers. Give an example to illustrate your method. See margin.

1. Possible answer: First, I would rewrite the sum so the fractions have the same denominator. I could do this by multiplying the numerator and denominator of each fraction by the denominator of the other fraction. Then I would add the numerators and write the sum over the common denominator. For example, $\frac{1}{3} + \frac{3}{8}$ $= \frac{1 \cdot 8}{3 \cdot 8} + \frac{3 \cdot 3}{8 \cdot 3} = \frac{8}{24}$ $+ \frac{9}{24} = \frac{17}{24}$.

3. $\frac{2}{3} \cdot \frac{4}{5}$ is the area of the shaded portion. The number of small rectangles is 15, the product of the denominators. The number of shaded rectangles is 8, the product of the numerators. So, the total area is $\frac{\text{product of numerators}}{\text{product of denominators}} = \frac{8}{15}$

4. Possible answer: Change both mixed numbers to fractions and multiply. For example, $2\frac{2}{3} \cdot 3\frac{1}{2} = \frac{8}{3} \cdot \frac{7}{2} = \frac{56}{6} = 9\frac{1}{3}$.

Review & Self-Assessment

Chapter Summary
This summary helps students recall the major topics of the chapter.

Vocabulary
Students should be able to explain each of the terms listed in the vocabulary section.

▶ **Exercise 1** Remind students that if they create an example before writing the steps they used to add the fractions, they can use the example as a guide to make sure they remember all the steps.

▶ **Exercise 2** Make sure students see the differences between the two methods for subtracting mixed numbers. If they confuse the steps of the two methods, their answers will be incorrect and they may have problems with future mixed number processes.

▶ **Exercises 3-6** When multiplying and dividing fractions and mixed numbers, encourage students to show all their work. Remind them that leaving out a step can cause errors in their work, and showing their work helps them check to be sure they did not skip any steps.

Additional Answers

2. Rewrite the mixed numbers as fractions and subtract, or subtract the whole parts and the fraction parts separately. If you subtract the parts separately, you may find that the fraction part of the second fraction is greater than the fraction part of the first fraction. If so, you can "borrow" 1 from the whole-number part of the first fraction and give it to the fraction part.

$$7\frac{1}{3} - 4\frac{5}{6} = 6\frac{4}{3} - 4\frac{5}{6}$$
$$= (6 - 4) + \left(\frac{4}{3} - \frac{5}{6}\right)$$
$$= 2 + \left(\frac{8}{6} - \frac{5}{6}\right)$$
$$= 2\frac{3}{6}$$
$$= 2\frac{1}{2}$$

▶ **Exercises 7–9** When asking students to explain problems without the aid of the calculator or a solved problem, it may help to discuss the problem. Have students tell what they think the problem is asking them to do, and how think they should do it. Help them orally organize their thoughts.

▶ **Exercise 10** It is hard for many students to understand why a foreign currency would not be equal to the American dollar. Explain to them that a dollar is worth more than a Moroccan dirham, but that we can calculate the value of each so that we can shop in each other's countries.

▶ **Exercises 11–20** Make sure students remember to find like denominators before adding or subtracting fractions. Remind them that the processes for multiplication and division are different; make sure they can distinguish between the processes for each operation.

Additional Answers

5. Possible answer: Draw a diagram to figure out how many times the fraction goes into the whole number. To find

   $4 \div \frac{2}{3}$, draw four rectangles divided into thirds and circle groups of two. There are six groups, so

   $4 \div \frac{2}{3} = 6$.

   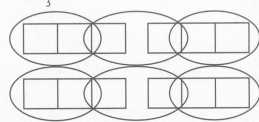

   Or, just multiply the whole number by the reciprocal of the fraction,

   $4 \div \frac{2}{3} = 4 \cdot \frac{3}{2} = \frac{12}{2} = 6$.

8. Possible answer: Ignore the decimal point. Multiply the whole numbers, $9,475 \cdot 12 = 113,700$. To locate the decimal point, add the decimal places in the numbers you are multiplying. $3 + 4 = 7$. Place the decimal point so there are 7 digits to its right, 0.0113700, or 0.01137.

9. Possible answer: Write the division exercise as a fraction. Then multiply the numerator

6. Possible answer: Write the division problem as a fraction, $\dfrac{\frac{5}{6}}{\frac{4}{9}}$. Then multiply the numerator and denominator by a common multiple of 6 and 9, $\dfrac{\frac{5}{6} \cdot 18}{\frac{4}{9} \cdot 18}$

   $= \frac{15}{8} = 1\frac{7}{8}$.

10a–c. See margin.

Real-World Link
Morocco is located on the westernmost tip of north Africa. Although the climate in most of the country is quite warm, parts of the mountains enjoy snow for most of the year.

Dividing fractions and mixed numbers

5. Describe two ways to divide a whole number by a fraction. Illustrate both methods by finding $4 \div \frac{2}{3}$.   See margin.

6. Use $\frac{5}{6} \div \frac{4}{9}$ to illustrate a method for dividing fractions.

7. Without dividing, how can you tell whether a quotient will be greater than 1? Less than 1?   See below.

Multiplying and dividing decimals

8. Describe how to multiply $9.475 \cdot 0.0012$ without using a calculator. Be sure to explain how to decide where to put the decimal point. See margin.

9. Describe how you can use what you know about dividing whole numbers to divide two decimals without using a calculator. Illustrate your method by finding $15.665 \div 0.65$.   See margin.

10. Suppose one U.S. dollar is equivalent to 10.3678 Moroccan dirham.

    a. To convert $100 to dirham, what calculation would you do? Explain how you know this calculation is correct.

    b. To convert 100 dirham to dollars, what calculation would you do? Explain how you know this calculation is correct.

    c. Caroline said that $750 is equal to about 7.5 dirham. Is Caroline's estimate reasonable? Explain.

Demonstrating Skills

Find each sum or difference. Give your answers in lowest terms. If an answer is greater than 1, write it as a mixed number.

11. $\frac{4}{5} + \frac{1}{10}$ $\frac{9}{10}$

12. $\frac{3}{7} + \frac{5}{9}$ $\frac{62}{63}$

13. $\frac{13}{15} + \frac{1}{3}$ $1\frac{1}{5}$

14. $\frac{5}{8} - \frac{1}{12}$ $\frac{13}{24}$

15. $\frac{11}{24} - \frac{3}{9}$ $\frac{1}{8}$

16. $\frac{4}{5} - \frac{9}{25}$ $\frac{11}{25}$

17. $3\frac{1}{3} + 2\frac{3}{5}$ $5\frac{14}{15}$

18. $1\frac{3}{8} - \frac{3}{4}$ $\frac{5}{8}$

19. $5\frac{1}{7} - \frac{11}{3}$ $1\frac{10}{21}$

20. $6\frac{4}{9} - 2\frac{5}{6}$ $3\frac{11}{18}$

7. If the number you are dividing into is greater than the number you are dividing by, the quotient will be greater than 1. If the number you are dividing into is less than the number you are dividing by, the quotient will be less than 1.

and denominator by a number that will "clear" the decimals. Then just divide the whole numbers. $15.665 \div 0.65$

$= \frac{15.665}{0.65}$

$= \frac{15.665 \cdot 1,000}{0.65 \cdot 1,000}$

$= \frac{15,665}{650} = 15,665$

$\div 650 = 24.1$.

10a. Multiply 10.3678 by 100. Possible explanation: We know how much $1 is worth, and $100 would be worth 100 times as much.

10b. Divide 100 by 10.3678. Possible explanation: We know $1 is worth about 10 dirham, so 100 dirham would be worth about $10. From that, I can tell I need to divide 100 by 10.3678 to get the actual amount.

10c. No; Possible explanation: $1 equals about 10 dirham, so $750 would equal about $750 \cdot 10$, or 7,500, dirham.

Find each product. Give your answers in lowest terms. If an answer is greater than 1, write it as a mixed number.

21. $5 \cdot \frac{3}{10}$ $1\frac{1}{2}$

22. $3\frac{1}{2} \cdot 6$ 21

23. $\frac{2}{3} \cdot 12$ 8

24. $\frac{5}{8} \cdot 14$ $8\frac{3}{4}$

25. $1\frac{2}{3} \cdot \frac{7}{8}$ $1\frac{11}{24}$

26. $\frac{6}{11} \cdot \frac{5}{3}$ $\frac{10}{11}$

27. $\frac{123}{12} \cdot \frac{12}{123}$ 1

28. $\frac{1}{3} \cdot \frac{75}{100}$ $\frac{1}{4}$

29. $\frac{9}{14} \cdot \frac{16}{21}$ $\frac{24}{49}$

30. $\frac{18}{35} \cdot \frac{14}{17}$ $\frac{36}{85}$

Find each quotient. Give your answers in lowest terms. If an answer is greater than 1, write it as a mixed number.

31. $4 \div \frac{1}{8}$ 32

32. $7 \div \frac{1}{5}$ 35

33. $45 \div \frac{3}{5}$ 75

34. $20 \div \frac{2}{3}$ 30

35. $\frac{15}{21} \div \frac{5}{7}$ 1

36. $\frac{7}{9} \div \frac{14}{27}$ $1\frac{1}{2}$

37. $3\frac{2}{7} \div 2\frac{3}{7}$ $1\frac{6}{17}$

38. $8\frac{1}{3} \div 1\frac{5}{9}$ $5\frac{5}{14}$

39. $\frac{3}{7} \div \frac{3}{7}$ 1

40. $\frac{343}{425} \div \frac{343}{425}$ 1

Use the fact that 652 • 25 = 16,300 to find each product without using a calculator.

41. $65.2 \cdot 2.5$ 163

42. $0.625 \cdot 25$ 16.3

43. $6.52 \cdot 0.00025$ 0.00163

44. $6.52 \cdot 2,500$ $16,300$

45. $0.00652 \cdot 0.25$ 0.00163

46. $65.2 \cdot 0.25$ 16.3

▶ **Exercises 21–40** Remind students to read each problem carefully, to determine the operation required and to identify the fractions and whole numbers used in each operation. For students who have difficulty using whole numbers in these problems, have them circle all the whole numbers they see before working the problems.

▶ **Exercises 41–46** These problems help assess a student's understanding of the decimal system. Point out to students that all the numbers are the same except the zeros, and that they need to pay close attention to decimal placement.

▶ **Exercises 47–56** When multiplying and dividing decimals, help students organize their work by turning a piece of notebook paper sideways to create columns. Students can keep the columns of numbers separate and prevent making confusing mistakes due to carelessness.

▶ **Exercises 57–59** Make sure English Language Learners fully understand the meanings of and differences in the terms *mean, median,* and *mode.*

Find each product or quotient.

47. 0.25 · 400   100

48. 64 ÷ 0.8   80

49. 32.07 · 0.001   0.03207

50. 32.07 ÷ 0.001   32,070

51. 7.75 · 12.4   96.1

52. 0.009 · 1.2   0.0108

53. 0.144 ÷ 0.6   0.24

54. 87.003 · 5.5   478.5165

55. 21 ÷ 0.0025   8,400

56. 19 ÷ 0.00038   50,000

57. Kristin determined the ages of all the children playing at a fast food play area. Here are her results.

2   2   3   4   2   3   2   5   3   2   8

a. Find the range, mode, and median of these data.   6; 2; 3

b. Which average best describes the data? Explain your choice
Mode, most of the children were 2 years old.

58. The students in Mrs. Foley's class are counting the number of pretzels they get in a small bag. Here are the numbers of pretzels.

10   11   12   10   9   13   12   11

a. Find the mean and median of the data set.   11; 11

b. Add two values to the data set so that the median remains the same, but the mean decreases. What is the new mean?
Sample: 11 and 8; 10.7

c. Start with the original set of data. Add two values to the set so the median remains the same, but the mean increases. What is the new mean?   Sample: 11 and 15; 11.4

59. Students at Central High School are donating money to a charity. The administration wants to know which average should be used to show how much the students donated.

Listed below are the amounts donated by individual students.

10	5	12	2	6	3	11
8	9	11	2	5	5	6
7	1	3	3	7	8	9
20	5	2	3	7	10	2

59a. Modes: 2, 3, 5
Median: 6
Mean: 6.5

a. Find the mode, median, and mean for these data.

b. Which average best describes a typical value in this set of data?
Mean

Test-Taking Practice

SHORT RESPONSE

Show your work:

Mean:
$$= \frac{35 + 28 + 54 + 29 + 47 + 35 + 42}{7}$$
$$= \frac{270}{7} = 38.57$$
Median: 28, 29, 35, 35, 42, 47, 54 The median is 35.
Mode: The mode is 35.

Answer:
Mean: 38.57, Median: 35, Mode: 35

1 The data set shows the amounts Mya earned working on different days. Find the mean, median, and mode of the amounts.

$35, \$28, \$54, \$29, \$47, \$35, \$42

Show your work.

Answer _____

MULTIPLE CHOICE

2 Lea needs $2\frac{2}{3}$ cups of flour for one recipe and $3\frac{1}{4}$ cups of flour for a second recipe. How much flour does Lea need for both recipes?

A $5\frac{1}{4}$

B $5\frac{3}{7}$

C $5\frac{11}{12}$

D $6\frac{11}{12}$

3 Shannon rode her bicycle $\frac{5}{6}$ mile Friday afternoon and $3\frac{1}{6}$ miles Saturday afternoon. How much farther did she ride her bicycle Saturday than Friday?

F $2\frac{1}{3}$ miles

G $2\frac{2}{3}$ miles

H $3\frac{1}{3}$ miles

J $3\frac{2}{3}$ miles

4 Find the product of 7.3 and 0.6.

A 4.38

B 7.9

C $12.1\overline{6}$

D 43.8

5 Lauren cut a $\frac{2}{3}$-yard piece of material into $\frac{1}{6}$-yard pieces. How many pieces did she cut?

F 2

G 3

H 4

J 6

Lesson 4.2, Share & Summarize (p. 225)

① Possible answer:

$\frac{3}{4} \cdot \frac{8}{9} = \frac{3 \cdot 8}{4 \cdot 9}$ Rewrite as the product of numerators over the product of denominators.

$= \frac{3 \cdot 2 \cdot 4}{4 \cdot 3 \cdot 3}$ Rewrite 8 as 2 · 4 and 9 as 3 · 3.

$= \frac{3 \cdot 4}{3 \cdot 4} \cdot \frac{2}{3}$ Group the common factors to form a fraction equal to 1.

$= 1 \cdot \frac{2}{3}$

$= \frac{2}{3}$ Simplify.

Lesson 4.4, Develop & Understand: A (p. 272)

1b. Definitely false; possible explanation: Arturo's class could have heights 57, 60, 64 and Lee's class could have heights 58, 59, 61. Arturo's class would have the greater median and the shortest person.

1c. Could be true or false; Possible explanation: Consider these two cases:

• Case 1: Arturo's class: 50, 55, 60; Lee's class: 51, 52, 62
• Case 2: Arturo's class: 50, 55, 60; Lee's class: 48, 52, 59

In Case 1, the median of Arturo's class is greater, and the shortest and tallest students are shorter than the shortest and tallest students in Lee's class. In Case 2, Arturo's class has the greater median, and each person in Lee's class is shorter than the corresponding person in Arturo's class.

2a. Could be true or false; Possible explanation: Suppose the heights for Marta's class are 58, 58, 60, 60 and the heights for Grace's class are 56, 56, 56, 62. Marta's class has a greater mean (59 vs. 57.5), but Grace's class has the tallest person. If the heights for Marta's and Grace's classes are 60, 61, 62, 63 and 58, 59, 60, 61, respectively, then Marta's class has both the greater mean and the tallest person.

2c. Could be true or false; Possible explanation: Suppose Marta's class has heights 50, 55, 60 and Grace's class has heights 45, 52, 62. Then the mean of Marta's class is greater, but the tallest student in his class is shorter than the tallest student in Grace's class. On the other hand, if Grace's class has heights 45, 52, 59, then each person in Grace's class is shorter than the corresponding person in Marta's class.

2d. Could be true or false; Possible explanation: Marta's class could have heights 56, 56, 56, 70, 70 and Grace's could have heights 56, 56, 56, 56, 56. The middle student in Marta's class is not taller than the middle student in Grace's class. If the heights for Marta's and Grace's classes are 60, 61, 62 and 58, 59, 60, respectively, then Marta's class has both the greater mean and the tallest middle person.

Notes

Rate, Ratio, and Proportion

Chapter Overview

In this chapter, students look at ways to compare data using ratios, proportions, and percentages. They are also introduced to similarity and congruency. Throughout the chapter, they solve problems in a variety of contexts. Students begin by writing ratios and using ratio tables to find equal ratios. They build on this knowledge when they write and solve proportions. The Inquiry Investigation provides preparation for later courses when students use proportions to solve real-world problems. The last lesson is an introduction to similarity and congruence. Students find the ratio of corresponding sides and identify similar polygons.

The **Big** Picture

Links to the Past	Chapter **5**	Links to the Future
Grade 5 Benchmark fractions such as $\frac{1}{2}$ and $\frac{1}{4}$. **Grade 4** Writing fractions and ratios.	**Lesson 5.1** (p. 290) Ratios and Rates	**Course 2, Chapter 8** Linear Relationships (pp. 366–433)
Grade 5 Using fraction models.	**Lesson 5.2** (p. 308) Proportions	**Course 2, Chapter 10** Proportional Reasoning and Percents (pp. 492–555) **Course 3, Chapter 3** Percents and Proportions (pp. 110–143)
Grade 5 Finding corresponding angles and sides for figures that are the same shape.	**Lesson 5.3** (p. 321) Similarity and Congruence	**Course 2, Chapter 10** Proportional Reasoning and Percents (pp. 492–555) **Course 3, Chapter 6** Transformational Geometry (pp. 258–309)

Mathematical Background

Ratio and proportion are two basic ideas that permeate all of mathematics and its applications. Basically, ratios are a way of *comparing* two quantities or magnitudes. This chapter explores these ideas in a wide variety of contexts, starting with basic applications such as: "If 3 apples cost $1, how much do 12 apples cost?" It continues by looking at applications of ratio and proportion to change-of-units problems, percentage problems, and the theory of similar figures in geometry.

Ratios and Equivalent Ratios In practice, ratios are used in several different kinds of situations. Ratios can compare:

• *part* of a group to the *whole* group

For example: the ratio of girls in a school to all the students in the school

• *part* of a group to another *part* of the same group

For example: the ratio of students taking French to the students taking German

• *two different groups*

For example: the ratio of teachers to students in the school

A special case of part-to-part ratios is when the two parts have no common members and together comprise the whole group; for example, the ratio of boys in a school to the girls in the school. In cases like this, we can think about all kinds of different ratios, including boys to total students ($b{:}s$) girls to total students ($g{:}s$) boys to girls ($b{:}g$) girls to boys ($g{:}b$) where s = total number of students; b = number of boys; g = number of girls. Since $b + g = s$, if you know any one of the four ratios above, you can calculate the other 3 without any further information. For example, if $\frac{b}{g} = \frac{3}{4}$, then you know that $\frac{b}{g} = \frac{b}{b+g} = \frac{3}{7}$

For ratios to be equivalent, you have to *multiply* the two parts of a ratio by the same number, not *add* the same number, just as you would do with fractions.

Proportions Equivalent ratios form a proportion. For example, $\frac{2}{3} = \frac{16}{24}$. One of the most important and useful applications of ratio and proportion is

in geometry. For over 2,000 years, people have used these basic ideas of ratio and proportion to calculate inaccessible distances and lengths, such as the distance across a river, the height of a mountain, the circumference of the earth, and the distances from the Earth to the Moon and to the Sun.

The basic idea is that corresponding sides of similar figures are proportional. Students can use their knowledge of similarity to build their understanding of proportion.

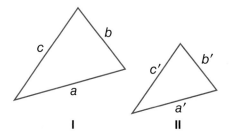

Then you have the basic proportion
$$\frac{a}{a'} = \frac{b}{b'} = \frac{c}{c'}$$
When you know the length of one side of triangle I and the lengths of two sides of triangle II, one of which corresponds to the known side in triangle I, you can use the proportion above to calculate the length of one of the unknown sides of triangle I.

Additional Reading
The concept that unit rates are useful to students in solving problems involving proportions is explained in *Ratio and Proportion: Connecting Content and Children's Thinking*. Students will apply these concepts as they do this chapter.

Planning Guide
Lesson Resources

	Lesson 5.1 Pacing: 4 days	**Lesson 5.2** Pacing: 3 days	**Lesson 5.3** Pacing: 4 days
Lesson Title	**Ratios and Rates** (p. 290)	**Proportions** (p. 308)	**Similarity and Congruence** (p. 321)
Lesson Objectives	• To recognize and express ratios in different situations • To recognize equivalent ratios • To compare ratios by converting to common units • To solve problems involving unit rates	• To recognize proportions as pairs of equivalent ratios • To use equivalent ratios to find the missing part of a proportion • To set up and use proportions to solve problems	• To identify congruent figures, angles, and segments by matching or measuring • To identify corresponding sides and angles of similar or congruent polygons • To identify equivalent ratios • To test for similarity by identifying corresponding sides with equivalent ratios and equl corresponding angles
Materials			Lesson 5.3 Masters 1–8, ruler, protractor, fasteners, metric ruler, *linkage strips
Quick Review Math Handbook	**Lesson 2.1** Fractions and Equivalent Fractions; Lesson 5.5 Ratio and Proportion	**Lesson 5.5** Ratio and Proportion	**Lesson 6.2** Naming and Classifying Polygons and Polyhedrons
Print Resources	CRM Study Guide and Intervention (p. 3) CRM Skills Practice (p. 4) CRM Problem-Solving Practice (p. 5) CRM Enrichment (p. 6) • Investigation Notebook and Reflection Journal • Differentiation Handbook	CRM Study Guide and Intervention (p. 8) CRM Skills Practice (p. 9) CRM Problem-Solving Practice (p. 10) CRM Enrichment (p. 11) • Investigation Notebook and Reflection Journal • Differentiation Handbook	CRM Study Guide and Intervention (p. 13) CRM Skills Practice (p. 14) CRM Problem-Solving Practice (p. 15) CRM Enrichment (p. 16) • Investigation Notebook and Reflection Journal • Differentiation Handbook
Technology Resources	TeacherWorks Plus Classroom Presentation Toolkit ExamView Assessment Suite StudentWorks Plus Math Online Brain Pops • Concepts in Motion	TeacherWorks Plus Classroom Presentation Toolkit ExamView Assessment Suite StudentWorks Plus Math Online Brain Pops • Concepts in Motion	TeacherWorks Plus Classroom Presentation Toolkit ExamView Assessment Suite StudentWorks Plus Math Online Brain Pops • Concepts in Motion

*Included in the Impact Mathematics Manipulative Kit

Assessment Resources

MARS Assessment: Teaching with Purpose

Lawn Mowing

In *Lawn Mowing,* students use both practical problem solving and proportional reasoning skills to solve problems involving ratios. Students find the square yards in a given area and compare the time it takes to complete the task of grass cutting.

Targeting the Task

- **Diagnostic**—Use Exercises 1–4 in the *Lawn Mowing* assessment to determine student's understanding of how to use proportional reasoning skills and solve practical problems involving ratios. For those students who do not have this understanding, completing this unit is needed.

- **Formative**—Exercises 1–4 can be administered individually according to the lessons.

- **Summative**—Administer the complete *Lawn Mowers* performance-based assessment.

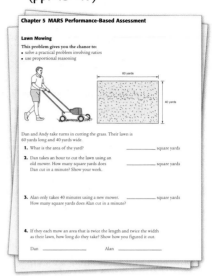

CRM **Chapter 5 MARS Assessment**
(pp. 45–47)

Assessment Planning Guide

Assessments are available for investigations, lessons, and chapters.

 **ExamView**
Assessment Suite

Customize and create multiple versions of tests and quizzes.

	Student Edition	Teacher Edition	Other Resources
Diagnostic			**CRM** Chapter 5 Pretest (p. 28) **Math Online** Online Chapter Quiz
Formative	Share & Summarize (pp. 294, 296, 299, 301, 311, 313, 325, 326, 331, 334)	Troubleshooting (pp. 294, 310, 326, 331, 334) On the Spot Assessment (pp. 291, 298, 328, 329) Quick Check (pp. 307, 320, 339) Quick Quiz (pp. 307, 320, 340)	
Summative	Review & Self-Assessment (pp. 341–345)		**CRM** Chapter 5 Test Forms: A and B (pp. 30–39) **CRM** Standardized Test Practice (p. 43) **CRM** Semester Test Forms: A and B (pp. 48–59)
Performance-Based	In Your Own Words (pp. 320, 338)		**CRM** MARS Performance-Based Assessment (p. 45) **CRM** Chapter Performance Assessment (p. 40) **CRM** Semester Performance Assessment (p. 60)

Differentiated Instruction

Reaching All Learners

Below are suggestions on differentiating the materials presented in this chapter. Additional modifications should be considered.

Approaching Level — AL

Lessons 5.3: Similarity and Congruency For students who need extra practice working with similarity and congruency, provide several pairs of larger cutout shapes. Have students decide whether they think each pair of shapes is similar and/or congruent. Then have them measure each side on both shapes and mark their measurements. Read the rules for similarity and congruency together, and then ask students to tell which figures are similar and which are congruent. Discuss how their first answers compared to the answers they found by measuring. Have students draw pairs of shapes and trade with a partner to find similarity and congruence on their own. Monitor for understanding.

Beyond Level — BL

Lesson 5.2: Investigation 3 Students who are comfortable solving the tile problem can create a larger model of the floor. Have pairs or small groups use the dimensions of the shape in Exercise 4 and set up proportions to make the floor about the size of their desktop. Then have them draw the shape on posterboard and outline the tile placement they found to be most economical. Remind students to label the dimensions of different tile sizes and the lengths of the sides of the room. Allow groups to present their drawings to the class. Discuss their models and how the larger drawings look the same as or different from the smaller drawing they used in solving the problem.

On Level — OL

Lesson 5.2: Proportions Have students work in pairs or small groups to create a word problem involving proportions. Tell them to write the problem, read it out loud to each other, and solve it to ensure the problem is written correctly. Once they have finished designing and checking the problem, have students create a drawing to go along with it. Encourage them to make it visually pleasing because others will see their work. Check to see that their problems and drawings are correct. Then have them present their problems to the class and allow the other students to solve the problems. Display the problems around the classroom and have students refer to them when they need extra practice.

English Language Learners — ELL

Lesson 5.3: Similarity and Congruency Students who are not yet proficient in English may need help distinguishing *similarity* from *congruency*. Use larger cutouts of various pairs of shapes to demonstrate each term. Have students measure and mark each side of each shape with its measurement. Then have them lay the two shapes on top of each other to compare their shapes and sizes. Have them put congruent shapes in one pile and similar shapes in another pile. Then have students tell you in their own words the meaning for similarity and the meaning for congruence. Clarify any errors in thought so that they understand how the terms are different.

KEY

AL Approaching Level   OL On Level   BL Beyond Level   ELL English Language Learners

Intervention Planning Guide

CRM Assess students' prerequisite skills and knowledge using the
Chapter Pretest found in the Chapter 5 Resource Masters, p. 28.

Intensive Intervention two or more years below grade level	**Strategic Intervention** below grade level	**On Level**	**Beyond Level**
If students miss 75% of the exercises: **Then** use *Math Triumphs,* an intensive intervention	**If** students miss 50% of the exercises: **Then** choose a resource:	**If** students miss 25% of the exercises: **Then** choose a resource:	**If** students miss 0%–10% of the exercises: **Then** choose a resource:
Math Triumphs, Grade 6 • Chapter 7: Ratios, Rates, and Unit Rates	CRM Study Guide and Intervention (pp. 3, 8, 13) • Investigation Notebook and Reflection Journal • Differentiation Handbook Math Online Brain Pops • Concepts in Motion	CRM Skills Practice (pp. 4, 9, 14) CRM Problem-Solving Practice (pp. 5, 10, 15) • Investigation Notebook and Reflection Journal	CRM Enrichment (pp. 6, 11, 16) • Differentiation Handbook

Literature Connections
Recommended Outside Reading for Students
Nonfiction

Jones, Teri Crawford. *Homework Survival Guide: Math.* Troll Communications, L.L.C., 1998.

This book includes facts about and practice in topics such as ratio, proportion, and percent. Other topics such as integers, place value, the four basic math operations, and fractions and decimals also are included, as well as graphs and charting data.

Fiction

Balmond, Cecil. *Number 9: The Search for the Sigma Code.* Prestel USA, 1998.

This novel explores number patterns as its narrator, the young boy Enjil, tries to solve a mathematical puzzle. Numbers are connected to geometry in topics including decimal expansions of fractions, Pascal's triangle, magic squares, primes, symmetry, and the golden ratio.

Mc Graw Hill **Professional Development**

Targeted professional development has been articulated throughout the *IMPACT Mathematics* series. The **McGraw-Hill Professional Development Video Library** provides short videos that support the mathematics standards. Log on to www.glencoe.com.

Model Lessons   Instructional Strategies

CHAPTER 5

Rate, Ratio, and Proportion

Real-Life Math

Gearing Up Ask students how many of them own or have used bicycles with multiple gears. Then ask why they think this type of bicycle is so popular. Direct their attention to the gear illustration on page 288. Then have them read the paragraph before and the paragraph after the illustration. Write the definition of gear ratio on the board: gear ratio =

$$\frac{\text{number of teeth on front chain ring}}{\text{number of teeth on rear chain cog}}$$

Show how the ratio can be set up when the front chain ring has 54 teeth and the rear cog has 27 teeth. Point out that the ratio can also be written as $\frac{2}{1}$, meaning that for each rotation of the pedals, the rear cog turns twice. Discuss the ratios when the chain is moved to a rear chain cog with 11 teeth. Tell students that a ratio is one way to compare data. They will learn other ways, such as proportions and percents, in the upcoming lessons.

Think About It You would want the bicycle to be in a gear with a high gear ratio because the back tire will rotate more times for each rotation of the pedals, which will take you farther with less pedaling.

CHAPTER 5

Rate, Ratio, and Proportion

Contents in Brief

Real-Life Math

Gearing Up Understanding *gear ratios* can help you ride your bike more efficiently.

A bike chain goes around a front chain ring, which is connected to the pedal, and a rear chain cog, which turns the back wheel. Changing gears moves the chain to a different rear cog or a different front ring.

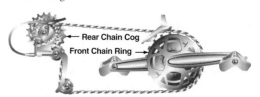

Rear Chain Cog
Front Chain Ring

The gear ratio for a particular gear tells you how many times the rear wheel rotates each time you rotate the pedals once. You find the gear ratio by counting teeth.

$$\text{gear ratio} = \frac{\text{number of teeth on front chain ring}}{\text{number of teeth on rear chain cog}}$$

For example, if the chain is on a front ring with 54 teeth and a rear cog with 27 teeth, the gear ratio is $\frac{54}{27}$, or $\frac{2}{1}$. This means that the back wheel rotates twice every time the pedals rotate once.

Think About It If you want to travel as far as possible with the least amount of pedaling, would you want to be in a gear with a high gear ratio or a low gear ratio?

Math Online
Take the **Chapter Readiness Quiz** at glencoe.com.

288

Chapter Resources

CRM Chapter 5 Resource Masters

CRM English/Spanish Family Letter (pp. 1, 2)

CRM Lesson Masters (pp. 18–27)

CRM Chapter 5 Pretest (pp. 28–29)

CRM Chapter 5 Tests (pp. 30–42)

Math Online ▷ Online Readiness Quiz • eGlossary

Dear Family,

Chapter 5 is about ratio and proportion.

Key Concept–Ratios
The class will begin with the idea of mixing different strengths of dye to explore ratios. Using this model makes the idea of ratio and proportion easy to understand. For example, Mixture A will be darker because the ratio of dye to water is 3:1. It is only 2:1 in Mixture B.

Mixture A   Mixture B

The class will also learn how to scale ratios. To make a larger batch of Mixture A, keep the ratio the same but increase the number of cans. This can be done by multiplying both parts of the ratio by the same number.

Students will use proportions to find missing quantities and to estimate large quantities that would be difficult to count. For example, the total number of people affected by a flu epidemic can be etimated by counting the number in a small sample and using the proportion to estimate the total.

Chapter Vocabulary

congruent	equivalent ratios
corresponding angles	ratio
corresponding sides	similar
counterexample	unit rate

Home Activities
- Encourage your student to point out different instances where ratios are used in his or her life, such as finding the cost of five cans of beans if two cans cost 70 cents.

Family Letter

Another version of the Family Letter, available in English and Spanish, is found in the Chapter 5 Resource Masters. You may want to send a copy of this letter home with your students.

Key Concept–Ratios Introduce students to ratios by asking them what the ratio of boys to girls is for the class. How many other ratios can they put together relating to the number of boys and girls in the class? Ask them why it may be important to know these ratios.

Home Activities
- Have your student look at food ads in the newspaper. What ratios can he or she find?

- Have your student think of various ratios that are used to describe sports statistics.

Key Vocabulary

English (Spanish) *Introduce the most important terms from Chapter 5.*

congruent (congruente) Line segments that have the same length or angles that have the same measure. (p. 321)

corresponding angles (ángulos correspondientes) Angles of congruent figures that have the same measure. (p. 328)

corresponding sides (lados correspondientes) Sides of congruent figures that have the same measure. (p. 328)

counterexample (contraejemplo) In testing a conjecture, an example for which the conjecture is not true. (p. 324)

equivalent ratios (razónes equivalentes) Ratios that can be represented by equivalent fractions. (p. 327)

ratio (razón) A comparison of two numbers by division. For example, the ratio of 2 to 3 can be stated as $\frac{2}{3}$. (p. 291)

similar (figuras semejantes) Figures that have the same shape but may have different sizes. (p. 321)

unit rate (tasa unitaria) A rate that describes how many units of the first type of quantity are equal to one unit of the other type of quantity. Example: 50 miles in 1 hour. (p. 300)

Ratios and Rates

Objectives

▶ To recognize and express ratios in different situations

▶ To recognize equivalent ratios

▶ To compare ratios by converting to common units

▶ To solve problems involving unit rates

Overview

This lesson begins with students' intuitive understanding of ratio, then builds to include ratio notation, equivalent ratios, and ratio tables. Throughout the lesson, students work with the seemingly concrete situation of mixing water and dye to make different concentrations of dye mixture. Although students never actually mix the dye, these thought experiments offer a memorable model for thinking about ratio. The lesson ends with problems involving a special case of ratio: rates and unit rates.

Advance Preparation

You may want to use containers of water and food coloring to demonstrate how the color of a dye mixture is affected by the quantities of the components.

	Summary	Materials	On Your Own Exercises (pp. 302–307)	Assessment Opportunities
Investigation 1 (p. 291) *Pacing: 1 day*	This investigation draws on students' informal understanding of ratio and introduces the conventional ways of writing ratios.		Practice & Apply: 1, 2 Connect & Extend: 24 Mixed Review: 30–42	• On the Spot Assessment (p. 291) • Share & Summarize (p. 294) • Troubleshooting (p. 294)
Investigation 2 (p. 294) *Pacing: 1 day*	Students work with mixtures of dye to compare ratios and explore the idea of equivalent ratios.		Practice & Apply: 3–8 Connect & Extend: 25, 26 Mixed Review: 30–42	• Share & Summarize (p. 296)
Investigation 3 (p. 297) *Pacing: 1 day*	Students use ratio tables to show equivalent ratios.		Practice & Apply: 9–13 Connect & Extend: 27 Mixed Review: 30–42	• On the Spot Assessment (p. 298) • Share & Summarize (p. 299)
Investigation 4 (p. 299) *Pacing: 1 day*	Students solve problems involving unit rates and finding common units for comparison.		Practice & Apply: 14–23 Connect & Extend: 28, 29 Mixed Review: 30–42	• Share & Summarize (p. 301)

Leveled Lesson Resources

CRM *Available in:* **Chapter 5 Resource Masters**

Also on
TeacherWorks™
Lesson 5.1

Study Guide and Intervention (p. 3) `AL`

Lesson 5.1 Study Guide and Intervention
Ratios and Rates

A **ratio** is a comparison of two numbers by division. A common way to express a ratio is as a fraction in simplest form. Ratios can also be written in other ways. For example, the ratio $\frac{2}{3}$ can be written as 2 to 3, two to three, or 2:3.

Example 1 Write the ratio that compares the number of circles to the number of triangles.

circles → $\frac{4}{5}$ The fraction is in lowest terms.
triangles →

So, the ratio of circles to triangles is $\frac{4}{5}$, 4 to 5, or 4:5.
For every 4 circles, there are 5 triangles.

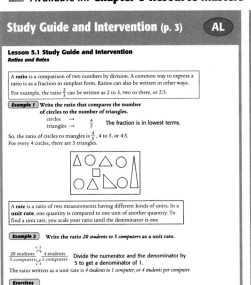

A **rate** is a ratio of two measurements having different kinds of units. In a **unit rate**, one quantity is compared to one unit of another quantity. To find a unit rate, you scale your ratio until the denominator is one.

Example 2 Write the ratio *20 students to 5 computers* as a unit rate.

$\frac{20 \text{ students}}{5 \text{ computers}} = \frac{4 \text{ students}}{1 \text{ computers}}$ Divide the numerator and the denominator by 5 to get a denominator of 1.

The ratio written as a unit rate is *4 students to 1 computer*, or *4 students per computer*.

Exercises

Write each ratio as a fraction in simplest form.
1. 2 guppies out of 6 fish
2. 12 puppies to 15 kittens
3. 5 boys out of 10 students

Write each ratio as a unit rate.
4. 6 eggs for 3 people
5. $12 for 4 pounds
6. 40 pages in 8 days

Skills Practice (p. 4) `AL` `OL`

Lesson 5.1 Skills Practice
Ratios and Rates

Write each ratio as a fraction in simplest form.
1. 3 sailboats to 6 motorboats
2. 4 tulips to 9 daffodils
3. 5 baseballs to 25 softballs
4. 2 days out of 8 days
5. 6 poodles out of 18 dogs
6. 10 yellow eggs out of 12 colored eggs
7. 12 sheets of paper out of 28
8. 18 hours out of 24 hours
9. 16 elms out of 20 trees
10. 15 trumpets to 9 trombones
11. 5 ducks to 30 geese
12. 14 lions to 10 tigers
13. 6 sodas out of 16 drinks
14. 20 blue jays out of 35 birds

Write each ratio as a unit rate.
15. 14 hours in 2 weeks
16. 36 pieces of candy for 6 children
17. 8 teaspoons for 4 cups
18. 8 tomatoes for $2
19. $28 for 4 hours
20. 150 miles in 3 hours
21. $18 for 3 CDs
22. 48 logs on 6 trucks

23. Write the ratio *21 wins to 9 losses* as a fraction in simplest form.

24. Write the ratio *$12 dollars for 3 tickets* as a unit rate.

The ratios in Exercises 25-28 are equivalent. Find the missing number.
25. 8 juice boxes out of 12 drinks ____ juice boxes out of 24 drinks
26. 6 ants out of 9 insects ____ ants out of 45 insects
27. 4 red markers out of 5 markers 16 red markers out of ____ markers
28. 11 daisies to 12 sunflowers 33 daisies to ____ sunflowers

---

Problem-Solving Practice (p. 5) `AL` `OL`

Lesson 5.1 Problem-Solving Practice
Ratios and Rates

Solve.

1. **Football** In the NFL 2007–2008 regular season, the New England Patriots won 16 games and the New York Giants won 10 games. What is the ratio of wins for the Patriots to wins for the Giants?

2. **Gardening** Rod has 10 rosebushes, 2 of which produce yellow roses. Write the ratio 2 yellow rosebushes out of 10 rosebushes in simplest form.

3. **Tennis** Nancy and Lisa played 20 sets of tennis. Nancy won 12 of them. Write the ratio of Nancy's wins to the total number of sets in simplest form.

4. **Ages** Oscar is 16 years old and his sister Julia is 12 years old. What will be the ratio of Oscar's age to Julia's age in 2 years? Write as a fraction in simplest form.

5. **Movies** Four friends paid a total of $32 for movie tickets. What is the ratio $32 for 4 people written as a unit rate?

6. **Working** At a warehouse, the employees can unload 18 trucks in 6 hours. What is the unit rate for unloading trucks?

7. **Animals** A reindeer can run 96 miles in 3 hours. At this rate, how far can a reindeer run in 1 hour? Explain.

8. **Shopping** Jenny wants to buy cereal that comes in large and small boxes. The 32-ounce box costs $4.16, and the 14-ounce box costs $2.38. Which box is less expensive per ounce? Explain.

Enrichment (p. 6) `BL`

Lesson 5.1 Enrichment
Ratios and Rates

Ratios and Rectangles

1. Use a centimeter ruler to measure the width and the length of each rectangle. Then express the ratio of the width to the length as a fraction in simplest form.

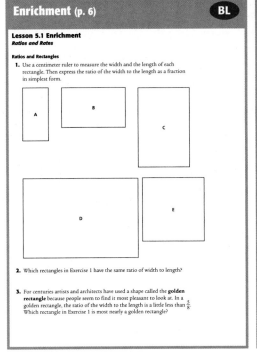

2. Which rectangles in Exercise 1 have the same ratio of width to length?

3. For centuries artists and architects have used a shape called the **golden rectangle** because people seem to find it most pleasant to look at. In a golden rectangle, the ratio of the width to the length is a little less than $\frac{5}{8}$. Which rectangle in Exercise 1 is most nearly a golden rectangle?

Lesson Quick Quiz (p. 7) `AL` `OL` `BL`

Lesson 5.1 Quick Quiz
Ratios and Rates

1. Write at least one ratio that represents the following situations:
   a. 1 scoop of drink mix for every 2 cups of water
   b. 5 school days in the week
   c. 7 white piano keys for every 5 black keys

2. Sort these ratios into three sets of equivalent ratios. Write each set in a ratio table. You will not use all the ratios in your tables, but there should be at least four ratios in each table.

2:10	3:8	1:4	3:12
6:16	2:3	1:5	1:3
4:20	9:24	15:40	3:15
2:8	5:25	2:5	12:32
4:16	5:10	5:20	2:5

3. For each choice, tell the unit rate and decide which choice is the better buy.
   a. pairs of socks: 3 for $10.00 or 5 for $12.50
   b. CDs: $15.95 each or $48.00 for 3
   c. packages of gum: 2 for $1.00 or a dozen for $5.00

Additional Lesson Resources

Teacher Tech Tools
- TeacherWorks
- ExamView Assessment Suite
- Classroom Presentation Toolkit
- Advance Tracker

Student Tech Tools
- StudentWorks Plus
- `Math Online` eGlossary •
  Concepts in Motion

Other Print Products
- Investigation Notebook and Reflection Journal
- Quick Review Math Handbook

Introduce

Comparison Statements Begin with a discussion of the data contained on nutrition labels. Then ask students to compare the nutrition labels for Original Crunchers and Lite Crunchers. Suggest that they look at the total carbohydrate content first. The easy comparison is that Lite Crunchers are higher in total carbohydrates than Original Crunchers, but encourage students to be more specific.

Record students' comparisons in the chart below. Perhaps you will get different kinds of statements—those involving differences (subtraction), rates or ratios. Categorize students' comparisons in this way as you write them on the board. The chart below is one way to organize their responses. If necessary, draw examples from the text to supplement the list.

Have students read the comparisons in the book and determine how each was created. Then have them explain their ideas to the class. For example, students might say that the first difference statement compares protein and carbohydrates. The number of grams of protein was subtracted from the number of grams of carbohydrate. When students are comfortable with the labels and making comparisons from them, move right into the Explore activity.

Ratios and Rates

LESSON 5.1

TastySnacks, Inc. is introducing Lite Crunchers, a reduced-fat version of its best-selling Crunchers popcorn.

The tables list nutrition information for both products.

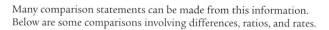

Original Crunchers Serving size: 35 g	
Total Fat	6 g
Saturated fat	5 g
Cholesterol	0 mg
Sodium	200 mg
Total Carbohydrate	15 g
Dietary fiber	1 g
Sugars	0 g
Protein	2 g

Lite Crunchers Serving size: 35 g	
Total Fat	3 g
Saturated fat	2 g
Cholesterol	0 mg
Sodium	160 mg
Total Carbohydrate	25 g
Dietary fiber	2 g
Sugars	0 g
Protein	3 g

Many comparison statements can be made from this information. Below are some comparisons involving differences, ratios, and rates.

Difference Comparisons

- A serving of Lite Crunchers has 22 more grams of carbohydrate than grams of protein.
- Original Crunchers has 40 more milligrams of sodium per serving than Lite Crunchers.

Rate Comparisons

- Lite Crunchers contains 3 g of protein per serving.
- Original Crunchers contains 200 mg of sodium per serving.

Ratio Comparisons

- The ratio of saturated fat grams to total fat grams in Original Crunchers is 5 to 6.
- The ratio of fiber grams in Lite Crunchers to fiber grams in Original Crunchers is 2:1.

Differences	Rates	Ratios	Percentages

Investigation 1 Ratios

Vocabulary

ratio

A **ratio** is a way to compare two numbers. When one segment is twice as long as another, the ratio of the length of the longer segment to the length of the shorter segment is "two to one."

One way to write "two to one" is 2:1. That means that for every two units of length on the longer segment, there is one unit of length on the shorter segment.

Ratios may be written in several ways. Three ways to express the ratio "two to one" are 2 to 1, 2:1, $\frac{2}{1}$.

✅ Develop & Understand: A

1. Consider this keyboard.

1a. $\frac{14}{10}$, or $\frac{7}{5}$

1c. $\frac{10}{24}$, or $\frac{5}{12}$

   a. What is the ratio of white keys to black keys on the keyboard?

   b. This pattern of keys is repeated on larger keyboards. How many black keys would you expect to find on a keyboard with 42 white keys?   30

   c. What is the ratio of black keys to *all* keys on this keyboard?

   d. How many black keys would you expect to find on a keyboard with 72 keys in all?   30

 Assessment

Watch for students who reverse the numbers in the ratio. For example, in Exercise 1a, these students will say the ratio of white keys to black ones is 5:7 rather than 7:5. If that happens, remind the students that the order of the numbers in a ratio matters. A quick memory aid is, "The numbers in the ratio must appear in the same order as the words." So, the ratio of white to black keys is 7:5, while the ratio of black to white keys is 5:7.

Investigation 1

On Your Own Exercises
Pages 302–307
Exercises 1, 2, 24

Ratios While ratio is generally considered to be a topic that many students find difficult, most middle school students have a good deal of informal (and perhaps some formal) experience with the underlying ideas. This investigation draws on students' informal and intuitive understanding of ratio and introduces conventional ways of writing ratios.

As part of the discussion, you might point out the different ways to write ratios shown in the left margin of the text: 4 to 1, 4:1, and $\frac{4}{1}$.

Tell students that they will use what they know about ratios to complete the next exercise set.

✅ Develop & Understand: A

Suggested Grouping: Pairs

▶ **Exercise 1** The relevant information is presented in pictures of black and white piano keys. The quantities involved are discrete, so the basic ratios can be obtained simply by counting. Students can count the 14 white and 10 black keys, so the ratio of white to black keys is 14:10. The same ratio can also be expressed as 7:5. Considering 7:5 the basis of a pattern, the third repetition of the pattern would result in the ratio: 21 (white) to 15 (black), and so on, for successive repetitions.

▶ Exercise 3b This exercise gives the relevant information as a picture of a concrete situation: spherical and cube-shaped beads. Students may use one of these strategies to solve this exercise:

- Use the mathematical idea presented on page 291 and think $r = 2:3$; so for every two spherical beads, there are three cube-shaped beads. Since Mercedes has 20 spherical beads, it means that there are 10 groups of spherical beads. So, there must be 10 corresponding groups of three cube-shaped beads. This means that there must be 30 cube-shaped beads.

- Write the ratios in the form $\frac{2}{3}$, then find an equivalent ratio: $\frac{2}{3} \cdot \frac{10}{40} = \frac{20}{30}$

- Look for a pattern and record their results in a table.

- Draw a picture or diagram.

Discuss with the class strategies that students used to solve Problem 4b.

Teacher Tips Make Exercise 3 more hands-on by having students reproduce the necklaces with real beads and then answering the questions for their necklaces.

---

2. The square tiles on Efrain's kitchen floor are laid in this pattern.

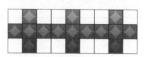

2a. $\frac{12}{15}$, or $\frac{4}{5}$

a. What is the ratio of white tiles to purple tiles in this pattern?

b. The entire kitchen floor contains 1,000 purple tiles. How many white tiles does it have?   800

c. What is the ratio of white tiles to all tiles in this pattern? $\frac{12}{27}$, or $\frac{4}{9}$

d. A floor with this pattern has 2,880 tiles in all. How many white tiles does it have?   1,280

3. Mercedes made this bead necklace at summer camp.

a. What is the ratio of spherical beads to cube-shaped beads on the necklace? $\frac{8}{12}$, or $\frac{2}{3}$

b. Mercedes wants to make a longer necklace with beads in the same pattern. She plans to use 20 spherical beads. How many cube-shaped beads will she need?   30

c. What is the ratio of cube-shaped beads to all of the beads on this necklace? $\frac{12}{20}$, or $\frac{3}{5}$

d. Mercedes wants to make a bracelet in the same pattern. She uses ten beads in all. How many cube-shaped beads will she need?   6

Mathematical Background

Exercises 1 and 2 illustrate this important mathematical idea: If you are given any two of the three quantities, a, b, or r, you can determine the third. In each exercise there are two sets, A and B, in which

A consists of a things;

B consists of b things; and

r represents a ratio of A to B

The relationship can be shown in these examples. If $a = 5$ and $b = 7$, then r is 5:7 or $\frac{5}{7}$. If the ratio of $A:B = r = 5:3$, and $b = 12$, then $a = 20$.

4a. 0.75, 2.4; Possible explanation: On each card the bottom number is 3 times the top number; $3 \cdot 0.25 = 0.75$ and $7.2 \div 3 = 2.4$.

4c. Possible answer:

4. The two numbers on each card in this set are in the same ratio.

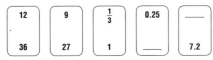

a. Find the missing numbers. Explain how you found your answers.

b. What ratio expresses the relationship between the top number and the bottom number on each card? $\frac{12}{36}$, or $\frac{1}{3}$

c. Draw three more cards that belong in this set.

5. The two numbers on each card in this set are in the same ratio.

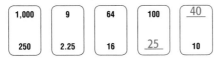

a. Fill in the missing numbers.

b. Draw three more cards that belong in this set. Possible answer:

Develop & Understand: B

The lists show the ten most popular first names in the United States given to children born during the 2000s.

Boys	Girls
1. Jacob	1. Emily
2. Michael	2. Madison
3. Joshua	3. Emma
4. Matthew	4. Hannah
5. Andrew	5. Abigail
6. Christopher	6. Olivia
7. Daniel	7. Ashley
8. Joseph	8. Samantha
9. Ethan	9. Alexis
10. Nicholas	10. Sarah

Source: Social Security Administration

6. What is the ratio of names that start with *J* to names that do not? 3:17

7. What is the ratio of students in your class with one of these first names to students whose names are not on these lists? Answers will vary.

8. What is the ratio of students in your class whose first *or* middle names are on these lists to the total number of students? Answers will vary.

▶ **Exercises 4 and 5** These exercises are more abstract and general than the preceding exercises. Some problems involve non-integers. Suggest that students look for a pattern when solving these problems. In Exercise 4, the bottom number on every card is three times the top number. In Exercise 5, the top number is always four times the bottom number.

Wrap-Up Have students share their answers and strategies for solving Exercises 3–5. Be sure students have a workable strategy for finding equivalent ratios.

Teacher Tips For the next set of exercises, students work with ratios created from lists of the most popular names for boys and girls in the United States, as well as from data drawn from the class. Most students find these name problems engaging, even though they have no practical value. Encourage students to ask imaginative questions about topics such as the frequencies of final letters, the number of syllables in the names, or the total length of a name.

Develop & Understand: B

Suggested Grouping: Individuals

▶ **Exercises 6–8** You may want to have a class roster or list of students' given names to display on an overhead projector to facilitate answering these exercises. Be aware that some students may not want their first or middle names to be known. You can accommodate their wishes by either excluding their names from the roster or you can substitute the names they are known by for their given name in the roster.

Wrap-Up Briefly discuss Exercise 9. Having students share their many comparisons may help classmates recognize the large number of comparisons possible.

Share & Summarize

Have students work individually and then discuss answers as a class. While students will come up with mostly ratios involving color in **Exercise 1**, many others can be found such as the ratio of corner patches to outside border patches or the ratio of patches in a vertical column to patches in a horizontal row. You may want to encourage students to come up with other ratios involving geometric concepts.

Exercise 2 is a kind of inverse to the preceding exercises where students were given two sets of objects and asked to find the ratio. In this exercise, students are given a ratio and asked to find two sets of objects that are in the given ratio. Inverse problems can be created in many mathematical situations and are often a good way of checking whether students have a deep understanding of the concepts. You might invent similar problems as assessment tools in other situations.

Investigation ②

On Your Own Exercises
Pages 302–307
Exercises 3–8, 25, 26

Compare and Scale Ratios In this investigation, students look at mixtures of dye to compare ratios and learn about equivalent ratios. A nice feature of the dye model is that students can determine the strengths of various water-dye mixtures without mixing any real water and real dye. It is sufficient for students to conduct thought experiments. They can be powerful tools for solving a variety of problems in mathematics and science. Tell students that they will use what they have learned about comparisons and ratios to solve problems.

9a. Possible answer: The ratio of names that start with C to all names is 1 to 20. The ratio of girls' names that start with S to all girls' names is 2 to 10.

9b. Possible answer: The ratio of boys' names with three vowels, including *y*, to all boys' names is 1 to 2. The ratio of boys' names with two vowels to all boys' names is also 1 to 2.

1. Possible answer: The ratio of red squares to all squares is 1 to 4. The ratio of white squares to all squares is 1 to 3. The ratio of white squares to red squares is 4 to 3. The ratio of pink squares to red squares is 5 to 3. The ratio of border squares to inside squares is 1 to 1.

9. Now you will use the lists to make some other ratio comparisons.

   a. Write two ratio statements based on the information on these lists. For example, one possible statement is "The ratio of girls' names that have only the letter *a* as a vowel to all the girls' names is 3 to 10."

   b. Try to write two different comparisons that involve the same ratio.

Share & Summarize

1. Work with a partner to write at least five ratio statements about this quilt with white, red, and pink squares.

2. Write a ratio statement about the quilt that involves each given ratio.   Possible answers:

   a. 1:4   The ratio of red squares to all squares is 1:4.

   b. 1:3   The ratio of white squares to all squares is 1:3.

   c. 3:5   The ratio of red squares to pink squares is 3:5.

Investigation ② Compare and Scale Ratios

You have practiced writing ratios to express comparisons between quantities. Reasoning about ratios will help you solve the exercises in this investigation.

Troubleshooting

Since this investigation is a review of ratio concepts students have seen before, they should feel comfortable with the idea of expressing a situation as a ratio. If they are having difficulty, provide them with problems where they are given a ratio and the number for one of the quantities and asked to find the other quantity. If necessary, have them model the situations using colored blocks. Students should be able to solve these problems with ease before they continue on to the next section.

✅ Develop & Understand: A

Researchers at First-Rate Rags are developing a shade of green for a new line of shirts. They are experimenting with various shades by mixing containers of blue and yellow dye.

1. Below are two mixtures the researchers tested. Each blue can represents a container of blue dye. Each yellow can represents a container of yellow dye. All containers contain the same amount of liquid. Which mixture is darker green? Explain how you decided.
Mixture A; see teaching notes for possible strategies.

In Exercises 2–4, tell which mixture is darker green.

2.

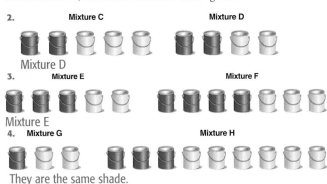

Mixture D
3.   **Mixture E**   **Mixture F**

Mixture E
4.   **Mixture G**   **Mixture H**

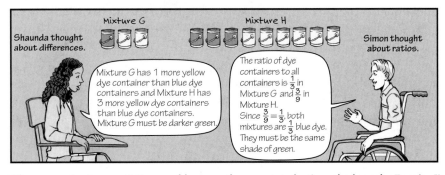

They are the same shade.

Think & Discuss

Shaunda and Simon found different answers for Exercise 4.

Whose reasoning is correct? How would you use the correct student's method to solve Exercise 5?
Simon's; The ratio of dye containers to all containers is $\frac{1}{3}$ for Mixture A and $\frac{1}{3}$ for Mixture B. Since $\frac{1}{3} = \frac{1}{3}$, they are the same shade of green.

Lesson 5.1 Ratios and Rates   **295**

Reaching *All Learners*

OL **On Level** If students do not accept Simon's argument, you might present this scenario. Mixture G consists of a total of 3 buckets of liquid, while Mixture H consists of a total of 9; there is exactly 3 times as much Mixture H as Mixture G. If you make three batches of Mixture G and pour them into one big container, you get: BWW BWW BWW = BBB WWW WWW

This more concrete argument shows that if you triple the amount of dye, you must also triple the amount of water to keep the strength of the mixture the same.

✅ Develop & Understand: B

Suggested Grouping: Pairs

▶ **Exercises 5–7** Students are asked to determine a ratio for a mixture and set up ratios equivalent to that ratio. Notice that the name of a particular dye-water mixture is really a generic name for the ratio used to make the mixture, independent of the particular numerical representation of that ratio. For example, Grassy Green is the name of the ratio that can be represented as one of many equivalent ratios. If students look at the ratio of blue dye to water, they might consider Grassy Green to be one of these ratios: 3:1, 6:2, 9:3, and so on. If they consider the ratio of blue dye to total containers, they could consider one of these ratios: 3:4, 6:8, 9:12, and so on. Students may use other equivalent ratios to determine the batches.

▶ **Exercise 8** This exercise deals with ordering ratios. Ordering the dye mixtures from darkest to lightest is analogous to ordering the corresponding ratios. Some students may order the mixture by using the drawings and logical reasoning. Others may order the ratios in the same way they have ordered fractions.

Share & Summarize

Exercise 1 asks students to describe strategies for determining which of the two dye mixtures is the darkest. The answers involve ordering the corresponding ratios. Your students may think of the problem in one of these ways:

Part-to-whole: Look at the ratio of dye containers to all containers: the greater that ratio, the bluer the mixture will be. Alternatively, you can look at the ratio of water to all containers, noting that the smaller this ratio is, the bluer the mixture will be.

Part-to-part: Look at the ratio of dye to water containers: the greater that ratio, the bluer the mixture. Alternatively, you can look at the ratio of water to dye, noticing that the smaller that ratio is, the bluer the mixture will be.

Exercise 2 revisits equivalent ratios. The problem is concrete because students draw the set of containers of dye and water. Then they are asked to demonstrate understanding by explaining why their answers are correct.

7. Answers will vary;
2 out of 5 containers should be blue.
8. Grassy Green, Grazing Green, Turtle Green; Possible explanation: Grassy Green is $\frac{3}{4}$ blue, Grazing Green is $\frac{2}{3}$ blue, and Turtle Green is $\frac{2}{5}$ blue; $\frac{3}{4} > \frac{2}{3} > \frac{2}{5}$.

1. Possible answer: Express the ratios of blue containers to all containers as fractions and compare the fractions; the greater fraction corresponds to the darker mixture. The ratio of blue containers to all containers for Mixture X is $\frac{4}{7}$ and for Mixture Y is $\frac{3}{5}$. Since $\frac{3}{5} > \frac{4}{7}$, Mixture Y is darker.

✅ Develop & Understand: B

The researchers at First-Rate Rags have found some shades that they like. Now they want to make larger batches of dye.

5. The researchers call this mixture Grassy Green. Draw a picture to show how Grassy Green can be created using 12 containers in all.

6. This mixture is called Grazing Green. Draw a set of containers that could be used to create a larger batch of Grazing Green. **Answers will vary; 2 out of 3 containers should be blue.**

7. This mixture is called Turtle Green. Draw a set of containers that could be used to create a larger batch of Turtle Green.

8. Order the three mixtures above from darkest to lightest. Use ratios to explain your ordering.

Share & Summarize

1. Describe a strategy for determining which of two shades of green is darker. Use your strategy to determine which mixture is darker.

Mixture X   **Mixture Y**

2. Draw a set of containers that would create a larger batch of dye the same shade as Mixture X. Explain how you know the shade would be the same. **Answers will vary; 4 out of 7 containers should be blue. Possible explanation: The ratio of blue containers to all containers is $\frac{4}{7}$ for both mixtures, so the shades are the same.**

Reaching All Learners

AL **Approaching Level** Some students may benefit from actually mixing colors, either food coloring or paint, with water in order to see the varying intensities. Have eyedroppers or measuring spoons available and jars or other clear containers so that they can see the resulting mixtures. Challenge them to complete either or both of these activities.

1. Make mixtures in a specific set of ratios, such as $\frac{1}{2}$, $\frac{2}{3}$, $\frac{3}{4}$, $\frac{4}{5}$, and $\frac{5}{6}$. Paint a spot of each mixture on paper, and label each spot with the correct ratio.

2. Use mixtures to prove that a set of ratios are equivalent.

Investigation ③ Ratio Tables

In the last investigation, you figured out how to make larger batches of dye that would be the same shade as a given mixture. There are many ways to think about exercises like these.

The mixture at the right is Grazing Green. Jin Lee, Zach, and Maya tried to make a batch of Grazing Green using nine containers.

Jin Lee: I'll draw copies of the 3 containers until I have 9 in all. First, I draw the mixture, that's 3 containers. Then I draw it again to get 6 containers. I draw it once more to get 9 containers, and I'm done.

Zach: The original mixture has 1 more container of blue than yellow. The new mixture must also have 1 more container of blue than yellow. So, I'll draw 9 containers, 5 blue and 4 yellow.

Maya: In the original mixture, $\frac{2}{3}$ of the containers are blue. If I use 9 containers, $\frac{2}{3}$ of them must be blue. $\frac{2}{3}$ of 9 is 6, so 6 containers must be blue and 3 must be yellow.

① No, Zach's reasoning is incorrect. Possible explanation: The mixtures must have the same ratio of blue to yellow to be the same shade. Adding 1 blue and 1 yellow container changes the ratio. For every yellow container added, 2 blue containers must be added.

Think & Discuss

Did all the students reason correctly? Explain any mistakes that they made. See ①.

Did any of the students use reasoning similar to your own? Answers will vary.

When Jin Lee answered the question above, she made copies of the original mixture until she had the correct number of containers. Jin Lee could have used a ratio table to record her work. A *ratio table*, a tool for recording many equal ratios, can help you think about how to find equal ratios.

This ratio table shows Jin Lee's thinking.

Blue Containers	2	4	6
Total Containers	3	6	9

All columns of a ratio table contain numbers in the same ratio. The equivalent ratios in this table are $\frac{2}{3}$, $\frac{4}{6}$, and $\frac{6}{9}$.

Math Link

The terms *rate* and *ratio* come from a Latin word that means "to calculate."

Reaching All Learners

BL **Beyond Level** The dye problems in the text are all discrete; that is they all involve only whole numbers of buckets of water and dye. As an extension activity, you may want to have the students investigate what happens if partial amounts, such as a half bucket of water, are added to the mixture. This leads to using equivalent ratios involving fractions such as $\frac{1}{2} : 2 = 1 : 4 = \frac{1}{4} : 1$.

On Your Own Exercises
Pages 302–307
Exercises 9–13, 27

Ratio Tables Investigation 3 gives another dye problem involving equivalent ratios. Have students use ratio tables to record equal ratios.

Think & Discuss

Discuss the cartoon with the whole class. The reasoning in each frame is as follows:

- Jin Lee's method is concrete. She replicates the ratio of dye to water 3 times.

- Zach's reasoning is that the difference between the number of containers of dye and those of water should always be one. This is additive and incorrect. He argues that adding equal amounts of water and dye will keep the concentration of dye constant.

- Maya's reasoning is correct, and more abstract. She calculates the fraction of dye in the liquid.

Most students will realize that Zach's reasoning is incorrect and be able to explain why. If there are students who find his argument persuasive, it is worth going over why it is wrong, since this incorrect reasoning can also be applied to other situations. You may want to use this example: Su is twice as old as John. Does this mean that Su will still be twice as old as John in five years? No. Consider this example: suppose Su is 10 years old and John is 5 years old. In five years, Su will be 15 and John will be 10. The ratio of their ages now is 2:1, but in 5 years, it will be 3:2.

This counterexample shows that you cannot add the same amount to both components of a ratio.

Teacher Tips Introduce *ratio tables* as a way to organize results about equivalent ratios. Ratio tables are another way to record Jin Lee's thinking. They can be used in lieu of drawing pictures.

Develop & Understand: A

Suggested Grouping: Pairs

▶ **Exercises 1 and 2** As the students work through these problems, they should rely less on drawings of the situations and start working with just the numbers or quantities involved. Students are sometimes asked to fill in the top number, sometimes the bottom number of a ratio table. Watch for students who reverse the entries in the two rows.

Exercise 2 introduces two new ideas: ratios involving decimals and variables.

▶ **Exercises 3 and 4** Leave the dye model behind. These problems can be thought of as rate problems (quantity per person). They foreshadow the discussion in Investigation 4 about comparison shopping.

Develop & Understand: A

1. Complete this ratio table to show the number of blue containers and the total number of containers for various batches of this shade.

Blue	1	3	4	8	25	37	200
Total	2	6	8	16	50	74	400

2. The ratio table in Exercise 1 compares the number of blue containers to the total number of containers. Complete the next ratio table to compare the number of blue containers to the number of yellow containers in this mixture.

Blue	2	3	6	10	30	90	n
Yellow	1	1.5	3	5	15	45	$0.5n$

3. The school band is holding a car wash to raise money for new uniforms. Ms. Chang, the band director, wants to order pizza for everyone. After the car wash last year, 20 people ate eight pizzas.

   a. Complete this ratio table based on last year's information.
   Possible answers are shown for the last two columns.

People	5	10	15	20	25	30
Pizzas	2	4	6	8	10	12

   b. How many people will two pizzas feed? 5

   c. Ms. Chang is planning to feed 25 people. How many pizzas will she need? 10

4. Jayvyn and Rosario are planning a party. They want to figure out how many pints of juice to buy. At Toya's party the month before, 16 people drank 12 pints of juice. Jayvyn and Rosario want the same ratio of juice to people at their party.

   a. Complete this ratio table based on the information about Toya's party.
   Possible answers are shown for the first two columns.

People	4	8	12	16	20	24
Pints	3	6	9	12	15	18

Spot Assessment

Watch for students who have difficulty completing the last column of the table in Exercise 2. Make sure these students have filled all the other columns in the table. Then you might ask this: The table tells us that for two containers of blue, we need one container of clear; for three containers of blue, we need 1.5 containers of clear; and so on. What is the general rule that relates the number of clear containers to the number of blue containers? Hopefully, students will see that the number of clear containers is one-half the number of blue containers.

4c. Yes; Possible explanation: You can multiply 3 pints and 4 people from the table by 7 to get 21 pints and 28 people.

1. Possible answer: The ratio of blue containers to all containers is $\frac{2}{6}$, which is equal to $\frac{3}{9}$. So, the mixture would contain 3 blue containers and 6 yellow containers.

b. How many people will 1.5 pints of juice serve?   2

c. Jayvyn said that if they extend the table, it will show that 21 pints are needed to serve 28 people. Is Jayvyn correct? How do you know?

Share & Summarize

This mixture is called Sea Green.

1. Describe how you could find a mixture of Sea Green that uses 9 containers in all.

2. Make a ratio table to show the number of blue containers and the total number of containers that you would need to make different-sized batches of Sea Green.   Possible table:

Blue	1	2	3	4	5	6	7
Total	3	6	9	12	15	18	21

Investigation ④ Comparison Shopping

Vocabulary

unit rate

1. Ben's; Possible explanation: The price per bagel at Bagel Barn is $3 \div 6 = 50¢$. The price per bagel at Ben's is $1 \div 3 \approx 33¢$.

In the blue-dye exercises, you can *compare* ratios to find the darkest mixture, and you can *scale* ratios to make larger and smaller batches of a given shade. Comparing and scaling ratios and rates is useful in many real-life situations.

In this investigation, you will see how these skills can help you get the most for your money.

✓ Develop & Understand: A

1. Alexi is inviting several friends to camp in her backyard. She wants to serve bagels for breakfast. She knows that Bagel Barn charges $3 for half a dozen bagels, and Ben's Bagels charges $1 for three bagels. At which store will Alexi get more for her money? Explain how you found your answer.

2. Alexi is considering serving muffins instead of bagels. Mollie's Muffins charges $6.25 per dozen. The East Side Bakery advertises "Two muffins for 99¢." Where will Alexi get more for her money? Explain.   East Side; Possible explanation: East Side sells 2 muffins for less than $1, so each item is less than 50¢. Mollie's sells 12 muffins for more than $6, which means they are more than 50¢ apiece.

Lesson 5.1 Ratios and Rates   **299**

Share & Summarize

Both exercises are in the context of the dye model. In **Exercise 1**, the ratio pictured, 2:6, is not given in simplest terms. Students who write equivalent ratios may first write the ratio in simplest terms, then write an equivalent ratio with 9 as the bottom number: $\frac{2}{6} = \frac{1}{3} = \frac{3}{9}$. Students may also think of the mixture as a group, then double the number of groups to solve. Others might recognize that there are twice as many clear containers as containers of dye. Therefore, if there are three containers of blue dye, there would be six clear containers. Since 6 + 3 is 9, a mixture of three blue containers and six clear containers would have the same shade as the original mixture.

Investigation ④

On Your Own Exercises
Pages 302–307
Exercises 14–23, 28, 29

Comparison Shopping This investigation connects the ideas of ratio and rate. Discuss the opening paragraphs and point out that students compared and scaled ratios in the prior investigation.

✓ Develop & Understand: A

Suggested Grouping: Individuals

▶ **Exercises 1 and 2** These problems ask students to compare prices for baked goods that are given in different units. They are straightforward, and students should have little difficulty. Use the Think & Discuss questions on page 300 to go over students' answers.

Think & Discuss

Simon and Shaunda present two somewhat different ways of thinking about converting to common units. Simon uses one bagel as the common unit while Shaunda goes to a half-dozen. Be sure students understand that any common unit is fine and that choosing the unit is usually a matter of preference or ease of computation.

Here is how Simon thought about solving Exercise 1.

Shaunda thought about scaling ratios.

Think & Discuss

Did you solve the bagel exercise using a method similar to either Simon's or Shaunda's?   Answers will vary.

Solve Exercise 2 using Simon's or Shaunda's method. Use a different method from the one you used to solve it the first time.
Answers will vary.

Simon's method involves finding *unit rates*. In a **unit rate**, one quantity is compared to one unit of another quantity. Simon found the prices for one bagel and compared them. Here are some other examples of unit rates.

$1.99 per lb	65 miles per hour	$15 for each CD
24 students per teacher	3 tsp in a tbsp	4 quarts in 1 gallon

Unit rates that involve prices, such as 50¢ per bagel and $1.99 per pound, are sometimes called *unit prices*. Supermarket shelves often have tags displaying unit prices. These tags can help consumers make more informed decisions about their purchases.

✓ Develop & Understand: B

3. The rate to Hong Kong; the rate to Honolulu is $0.37 per minute, and the rate to Hong Kong is $0.42 per minute.

4. FreshStuff; FreshStuff: $0.88 per mango; FruitMart: $0.92 per mango

5. Package C; Package A: $3.33 per CD; Package B: $2.59 per CD; Package C: $1.87 per CD; Package D: $2.00 per CD

6. Big Kicks has the best price. Big Kicks sells 20 balls for $110; Sport Town sells 20 balls for $128; Soccer Warehouse sells 20 balls for $115.

✓ Develop & Understand: B

Use unit rates to help you answer Exercises 3–5.

3. Camisha has a long-distance plan that charges the same amount for each minute of a call. The rate depends on where she calls. A 12-minute call to Honolulu costs $4.44. A 17-minute call to Hong Kong costs $7.14. Is the rate to Honolulu or the rate to Hong Kong higher? Explain how you found your answer.

4. At FreshStuff Produce, Antoine paid $3.52 for four mangoes. Manuela bought six mangoes at FruitMart for $5.52. Which store offers the better price for mangoes? Explain how you found your answer.

5. Blank CDs are sold in four packages at Xavier's Music Store.

   Which package costs the least per CD? Explain how you found your answer.

CDs For Sale!

Package A:	3 for	$9.99
Package B:	5 for	$12.95
Package C:	8 for	$14.95
Package D:	10 for	$19.95

6. Coach Thomas found several ads for soccer balls in the sports section of the local paper. Use the technique of scaling ratios to find which store offers the best buy. Explain how you made your decision.

Big Kicks 10 balls only $55

Sport Town 5 balls $32

SOCCER Warehouse 20 balls $115

Share & Summarize

1. Explain how unit prices can help you make wise purchasing decisions. Give an example to explain your thinking.
   See margin.

2. Suppose a package of eight pencils costs 92¢. A package of 12 costs $1.45. Which method would you prefer to use to find which package costs the least per pencil? Explain.
   Possible answer: Finding unit prices; this would be easier than trying to find the numbers for scaling the two ratios.

Additional Answer
Share & Summarize

1. Possible answer: If you have prices for several sizes or amounts, finding unit rates expresses everything as an amount per unit. This makes it easier to make comparisons. For example, suppose a 16-oz carton of juice costs $1.28 and a 48-oz carton costs $3.32. Rewriting these as unit prices, the 16-oz carton costs 8¢ per ounce and the 48-oz carton costs about 7¢ per ounce. The larger carton offers more juice for the money.

✓ Develop & Understand: B

Suggested Grouping: Individuals

▶ **Exercises 3–5** To give students exposure to using estimates while shopping, you might ask them to make quick estimates to determine the better buys in these exercises *before* having them find the actual answers. Have them record their estimates. Then discuss how sure they are of their estimates and why. After students have made the actual computations, have them go back and see how good their initial guesses were.

Point out that students should solve the exercises using unit prices. Students divide decimals to solve these problems, so you may want them to use their calculators.

▶ **Exercise 6** Tell students to solve this problem by using scaling ratios. Encourage students to find a handy common unit other than one. One obvious common unit is 20 balls, since 20 is the least common multiple of 5, 10, and 20. The overlay answer on the opposite page uses this approach.

Share & Summarize

Students are asked to verbalize the advantages of unit pricing in **Exercise 1**. This kind of discussion might be interesting in communities in which unit pricing labels in stores is not commonplace. If your community does have unit pricing, you might ask students to bring some real supermarket examples to class for discussion: What is a "good" unit to use when comparing these items? For example, would it be easier to compare the items using pounds, ounces, or quarts as the units? Answers may vary.
How many decimal places should unit prices include? Answers may vary.
What factors besides price comparison might enter into a wise buying decision? Possible answers: storage problems, quality, personal preference

In **Exercise 2**, students decide whether they would choose to find unit prices, to scale ratios, or to use another method to solve a problem. You can extend the problem by having students solve the problem. The answer is that the package of eight pencils has a lower cost.

Investigation 1
Pages 291–294
Practice & Apply: 1, 2
Connect & Extend: 24

Investigation 2
Pages 294–296
Practice & Apply: 3–8
Connect & Extend: 25, 26

Investigation 3
Pages 297–299
Practice & Apply: 9–13
Connect & Extend: 27

Investigation 4
Pages 299–301
Practice & Apply: 14–23
Connect & Extend: 28, 29

Assign Anytime
Mixed Review: 30–42

▶ **Exercises 1b** Students are asked to think about how the same data presented in different ways can leave the reader with different impressions. This can provide the basis for an interesting class discussion.

Real-World Link
Mention that the native Alaskan name for Mt. McKinley is Denali. There has been some discussion of returning to the native Alaskan name for the mountain itself.

Additional Answer
1a. Possible explanations:
  i. Half of 10,470 is 5,235, and the number of successful climbers is higher.

  ii. successful climbers: 5,271; unsuccessful climbers: 10,470 − 5,271 = 5,199

  iii. 5,271 − 5,199 = 72

  iv. $\dfrac{\text{total}}{\text{successful}} = \dfrac{10,470}{5,271} \cdot \dfrac{2}{1} = \dfrac{10,470}{5,235}$

  v. Half of 10,470 is 5,235, and the number of unsuccessful climbers is 5,199, so slightly less than 50%.

Practice & Apply

Real-World Link
The highest mountain on the North American Continent, Mount McKinley, was named for William McKinley, the 25th U.S. president (1897–1901).

. . . .

1b. Answers will vary. Many students may think statements i and iv sound the most hopeful.

2a. Possible answers: Text to total space, ads to total space, headlines to pictures, headlines and pictures combined to total space

2b. Possible answers: Pictures to total space, headlines to text, headlines to ads

2c. Possible answers: Pictures to text, pictures to ads, all but pictures to total space

1. Mount McKinley is located in Denali National Park, Alaska. Between 1980 and 1992, 10,470 climbers attempted to reach its summit, a height of 20,320 feet. Of these climbers, 5,271 were successful. The five comparisons below are based on this information.

  i. More than half the people who attempted to reach the summit were successful.

  ii. The ratio of climbers who successfully reached the summit to those who failed is 5,271 to 5,199.

  iii. Of the climbers who attempted to reach the summit, 72 more succeeded than failed.

  iv. The ratio of the total number of climbers to the number of successful climbers is about 2 to 1.

  a. Explain why each statement is true.   See margin.

  b. Suppose that Expert Expeditions arranges group climbing trips on Mount McKinley. Its guides help less-experienced climbers reach the summit. The company is designing an advertising brochure and would like to include one of the above statements. Which do you think should be used? Explain your reasoning.

2. Eduardo is laying out the pages of a newspaper. He divides one of the pages into 24 sections and decides which sections will be devoted to headlines, to text, to pictures, and to advertisements.

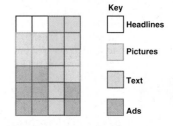

Key
■ Headlines
■ Pictures
■ Text
■ Ads

Describe something in the layout that has each given ratio.

  a. 1 to 3

  b. 1:4

  c. 3:4

---

3. Mixture A; $\frac{3}{5} > \frac{2}{4}$

3. First-Rate Rags wants to create a new shade of green using blue and yellow dye. They create two mixtures to compare. Decide whether Mixture A or Mixture B is a darker shade of green. Explain why.

Mixture A   Mixture B

▶ **Exercises 5–8** Students must choose the *lighter* shade in these exercises. Remind them to read the directions carefully.

4. First-Rate Rags has finally agreed on a shade of green for its shirts. A sample of the dye is shown below.

How many containers of blue dye and yellow dye are needed for a batch of green dye that has a total of 75 containers?
45 blue, 30 yellow

For each pair of mixtures, decide which is a *lighter* shade of green. Then draw or describe a larger batch that will make the same shade as the lighter mixture's shade.

5.   Mixture A   Mixture B

Mixture A; Answers will vary, but the blue:yellow ratio should be 3:4.

6.   Mixture C   Mixture D

Mixture D; Answers will vary, but the blue:yellow ratio should be 2:5.

7.   Mixture E   Mixture F

Mixture F; Answers will vary, but the blue:yellow ratio should be 2:1.

8.   Mixture G   Mixture H

Mixture H; Answers will vary, but the blue:yellow ratio should be 4:3.

Lesson 5.1 Ratios and Rates   **303**

▶ **Exercise 9** If students use decimals rather than fractions, have them round their answers to the nearest hundredth.

▶ **Exercises 11–13** Here, students work with abstract ratio tables that are not tied to any concrete situations. Sharing students' explanations with the class may help those who are less comfortable working with ratios at the abstract level.

Complete the ratio table for each mixture.

9.

Blue	1	3	6	10	50	100	n
Yellow	1.67	5	10	16.67	83.33	166.67	$1.67n$

10.

Blue	1	2	5	10	50	100	n
Total	2	4	10	20	100	200	$2n$

In Exercises 11–13, is the given table a ratio table? If so, tell the ratio. If not, explain why not.

11.

3	6	9	12	15
5	10	15	20	25

Yes, $\frac{3}{5}$

12.

1	4	7	10	13
2	5	8	11	14

No; the ratios of each pair of numbers are not equivalent.

13.

3	30	300	3,000	30,000
9	90	900	9,000	90,000

Yes, $\frac{1}{3}$

In Exercises 14–17, tell whether the given rate is a unit rate or a non-unit rate.

14. 25 heartbeats in 20 seconds Non-unit rate

15. 72 heartbeats per minute Unit rate

16. 30 mph Unit rate

17. 200 miles per five-hour period Non-unit rate

18. To serve seven people, Natasha needed two pizzas. What was the per-person rate?   0.29 pizza per person

19. At basketball camp, Belicia made 13 baskets for every 25 shots attempted. What was Belicia's success rate per attempt?
0.52 basket per attempt

20. Jogging burns about 500 calories every five miles. What is the rate of calorie consumption per mile?   100 calories per mile

In Exercises 21–23, determine the unit price for each offer. Then tell which offer is best.

21. Two pens for $3, ten pens for $16, or five pens for $7
$1.50, $1.60, $1.40 per pen; 5 for $7 has the best unit price.

22. Five lb of potatoes for $2.99, ten lb of potatoes for $4.99, or 15 lb of potatoes for $6.99 $0.60, $0.50, $0.47 per pound; 15 lb for $6.99 has the best unit price.

23. Three toy racing cars for $7, five toy racing cars for $11, two toy racing cars for $4.50 $2.33, $2.20, $2.25 per car; 5 for $11 has the best unit price.

Connect & Extend

24. Architecture In ancient Greece, artists and architects believed there was a particular rectangular shape that looked very pleasing to the eye. For rectangles of this shape, the ratio of the long side to the short side is roughly 1.6:1. This ratio is very close to what is known as the *Golden Ratio*.

  a. Try drawing three or four rectangles of different sizes that look like the most "ideal" rectangles to you. For each rectangle, measure the side lengths and find the ratio of the long side to the short side.   Rectangles and ratios will vary.

  b. Which of your rectangles has the ratio closest to the Golden Ratio?   Answers will vary.

Real-World Link
The famous Greek temple, the Parthenon, made entirely of white marble in the fifth century B.C., was built according to the Golden Ratio.

▶ **Exercises 21–23** Students compare various rates by first finding a unit rate. It is easy to decide which is the better buy by multiplying mentally to get other common units for comparison. Finding the exact cost or the unit rate is not as simple as multiplying. You might ask students to talk about how they would use scaling to decide which is the better buy.

▶ **Exercise 24** This exercise is largely an exploration for students. Many people, when asked to pick their ideal rectangle, will pick one whose side lengths have a ratio close to the Golden Ratio.

▶ **Exercise 24 Extension** There is vast literature about the Golden Ratio and the associated Golden Rectangle. Encourage your students to search out this literature for examples of the Golden Rectangle in nature and in human artifacts.

▶ **Exercise 26** Remind students about what it means to write a ratio in simplest terms. This term was not formally introduced in the lesson.

Additional Answers

25b. Possible answers: If 3 out of 4 containers are blue, there are fewer total containers, but still three containers are blue, so a greater amount of the mixture is blue. *Or,* the original mixture is $\frac{3}{5}$ blue, and $\frac{3}{5} < \frac{2}{3}$, so 2 blue out of 3 total is darker.

26b. 62.5 mph; Possible explanation: 100 km is 1.25 times farther than 80 km. So, Susan would have to go 1.25 times faster than 50 mph to drive 100 km in 1 hr. $50(1.25) = 62.5$.

25. Consider this mixture.

25a. There are two possibilities: 3 blue and 1 yellow, or 2 blue and 1 yellow.

a. Draw a mixture that is darker green than this one but uses fewer containers. Do not make *all* the containers blue.

b. Explain why you think your mixture is darker.   See margin.

26. Measurement Trevor always forgets how to convert miles to kilometers and back again. However, he remembers that his car's speedometer shows both miles and kilometers. Trevor knows that traveling 50 miles per hour is the same as traveling 80 kilometers per hour. In one hour, he would travel 50 miles, or 80 kilometers.

a. From this information, find the ratio of miles to kilometers in simplest terms.   5:8

b. To cover 100 km in an hour, how fast would Trevor have to go in miles per hour? Explain how you found your answer. See margin.

27. Denay's class sold posters to raise money. Denay wanted to create a ratio table to find how much money her class would make for different numbers of posters sold. She knew that $25 would be raised for every 60 posters sold.

27a. Possible answer: Set up the table with one row for the number of posters and the other for dollars earned. Simplify 25:60 to 5:12. Fill in the top row by counting by 5s and the bottom row by counting by 12s.

a. Describe how Denay can use that one piece of information to make a ratio table. Assume the relationship is proportional.

b. How much money would Denay's class make for selling 105 posters? $43.75

c. Could Denay's class raise exactly $31? If so, how many posters would need to be sold? If not, why not?   No; there is no whole number of posters n that gives a ratio of $\frac{n}{31}$ equal to $\frac{25}{60}$. Each poster raises $41\frac{2}{3}$¢, so 74 posters would raise $30.83 and 75 would raise $31.25.

28a. She can use division to figure out the cost per ounce. Almonds are $0.30 per ounce, cashews are $0.50 per ounce, filberts are $0.27 per ounce, peanuts are $0.125 per ounce.

28b. The greater amount gave her more for her money; almonds.

29. Possible answer: He can calculate the price for 12 oz: four 3-oz tubes is $5.96, and three 4-oz tubes is $5.91, so the 4-oz size is a slightly better buy.

28. Nora wants to make a batch of mixed nuts for a party that she is planning. The local health food store sells nuts by weight, so Nora can measure out exactly how much she wants. The table shows the cost of each type of nut.

Cost of Nuts

Nut	Amount	Price
Almonds	16 oz	$4.80
Cashews	16 oz	$8.00
Filberts	16 oz	$4.32
Peanuts	16 oz	$2.00

a. Nora wants to know how much 1 ounce of each type of nut will cost. How can she figure this out? How much does 1 ounce of each type of nut cost?

b. Nora paid the same for the almonds as the cashews but bought different amounts of each. How can you decide which nut gave her more for her money? Which nut is that?

c. Nora wants to buy 10 ounces of almonds, 6 ounces of cashews, 20 ounces of filberts, and 30 ounces of peanuts for her party. What will be the total cost of her peanut purchase, not including tax? $15.15

29. Jack is in the grocery store comparing two sizes of his favorite toothpaste. He can buy three ounces for $1.49 or four ounces for $1.97. Without calculating unit prices, how can Jack decide whether one size is a better buy than the other?

Mixed Review

30. Which of the following are factors of 36?

① ② ③ ④ 5 ⑥ 7 8
⑨ 10 11 ⑫ 13 14 24 ㊱

Fill in each ◯ with <, >, or = to make a true statement.

31. $\frac{6}{5} \ominus 1.2$

32. $0.37 \oslash \frac{7}{20}$

33. $\frac{13}{18} \oslash \frac{7}{10}$

34. $1.5 \oslash \frac{25}{19}$

35. $0.0375 \ominus \frac{3}{80}$

36. $\frac{23}{24} \oslash \frac{24}{25}$

Measurement Fill in the blanks.

37. 356 cm = __3.56__ m

38. 356 cm = __3,560__ mm

39. 44 m = __44,000__ mm

40. 5 mm = __0.005__ m

41. 5 mm = __0.5__ cm

42. 89,000 mm = __89__ m

Lesson 5.1   Ratios and Rates   **307**

3. For each choice, tell the unit rate and decide which choice is the better buy.

a. pairs of socks: 3 for $10.00 or 5 for $12.50 $3.33 each; $2.50 each; 5 for $12.50 is the better buy.

b. CDs: $15.95 each or $48.00 for 3 $15.95 each; $16.00 each; $15.95 is the better buy.

c. packages of gum: 2 for $1.00 or a dozen for $5.00 $0.50 each; approximately $0.42 each; a dozen for $5.00 is the better buy.

Quick Quiz continued at the left.

Quick Check

Informal Assessment Students should be able to:

✔ recognize and express ratios in different situations

✔ recognize equivalent ratios

✔ compare ratios by converting to common units

✔ solve problems involving unit rates

Quick Quiz

1. Write at least one ratio that represents the following situations:

a. 1 scoop of drink mix for every 2 cups of water Possible answers: 1:2 (mix to water); 2:1 (water to mix)

b. 5 school days in the week Possible answers: 5:7 (school days to total days); 5:2 (school days to weekend days); 7:5 (total days to school days); 2:5 (weekend days to school days)

c. Seven white piano keys for every five black keys Possible answers: 7:5 (white to black); 5:7 (black to white); 7:12 (white to total); 5:12 (black to total)

2. Sort these ratios into three sets of equivalent ratios. Write each set in a ratio table. You will not use all the ratios in your tables, but there should be at least four ratios in each table. 2:10, 3:8, 1:4, 3:12, 6:16, 2:3, 1:5, 1:3, 4:20, 9:24, 15:40, 3:15, 2:8, 5:25, 2:5, 12:32, 4:16, 5:10, 5:20, 2:5

1	2	3	4	5
5	10	15	20	25

3	6	9	12	15
8	16	24	32	40

1	2	3	4	5
4	8	12	16	20

Lesson 5.1   Ratios and Rates   **307**

Proptions

Objectives

▶ To recognize proportions as pairs of equivalent ratios

▶ To use equivalent ratios to find the missing part of a proportion

▶ To set up and use proportions to solve problems

Overview

In this lesson, students are formally introduced to proportions and to setting up *proportions* to solve real-world problems. The lesson begins by introducing the term *proportion* for sets of equivalent ratios, a concept that students began working with in Lesson 5.1. They use equivalent ratios to solve simple problems.

Advance Preparation

You may want to provide students with examples of proportional shapes and objects to facilitate class discussion while presenting new topics, including equivalent ratios and proportions.

	Summary	Materials	On Your Own Exercises (pp. 316–320)	Assessment Opportunities
Investigation 1 (p. 309) *Pacing: 1 day*	Students learn that proportions are pairs of equivalent ratios.		Practice & Apply: 1–3 Connect & Extend: 10, 11 Mixed Review: 18–27	• Share & Summarize (p. 311) • Troubleshooting (p. 310)
Investigation 2 (p. 312) *Pacing: 1 day*	Students use equivalent ratios to solve problems.		Practice & Apply: 4–9 Connect & Extend: 12–17 Mixed Review: 18–27	• Share & Summarize (p. 313)
Inquiry Investigation 3 (p. 314) *Pacing: 1 day*	Students set up and solve proportions.		Mixed Review: 18–27	

Leveled Lesson Resources

CRM *Available in:* **Chapter 5 Resource Masters**

Study Guide and Intervention (p. 8) **AL**

Lesson 5.2 Study Guide and Intervention
Proportions

In a proportional relationship, all pairs of corresponding values are in the same ratio. You can create a table to find the missing value.

Example 1 Peter rented mountain bikes at BigDrop Mountain.

He paid $32 for 4 hours of riding. He used the mountain bike for 7 hours. The rental cost is proportional to time. What will be his rental charge?

Create a table. 4 hours will cost $32

Cost in dollars	8	16	32	x	x
Time in hours	1	2	4	x	7

Complete the table to find the answer.

Cost in dollars	8	16	32	48	56
Time in hours	1	2	4	6	7

The rental cost is $56 for 7 hours.

Calculating the unit rate can also be used to solve a proportion.

Example 2 A bathroom measuring 5 feet by 7 feet is being tiled with a 6 in. × 6 in. tile. How many tiles are needed to cover the floor?

Convert square inches to square feet. $\frac{6in. \times 6in.}{12in. \times 12in.} = 0.25ft^2$ Unit rate. $\frac{0.25ft^2}{1tile}$

Set up a proportion. $\frac{0.25ft^2}{1tile} = \frac{35ft^2}{x}$ Solve. $\frac{0.25ft^2}{1tile} \times \frac{140}{140} = \frac{35ft^2}{140tiles}$

It will take 140 tiles to cover the floor.

Exercises

Create a table to find the answer.

1. A grocery store charges $2 per pound of trail mix. Antoine was charged $7 for the trail mix he bought. How many pounds of trail mix did he buy?

2. Brooke paid $16 to rent roller blades for 4 hours. She used the skates for 6 hours. The rental cost is proportional to time. What will be her rental charge?

Use the unit rate to solve the proportion.

3. A catalog sells reading award certificates for $1.25 each. Mr. Heath has $30 to spend on the certificates. How many certificates can he order?

4. The price of Crunchy Muncheroo Cereal is $3.60 for a 20-ounce box. The price is proportional to the number of ounces in the box. What is the price of a 32-ounce box?

Skills Practice (p. 9) **AL OL**

Lesson 5.2 Skills Practice
Proportions

The tables below represent a proportional relationship. Complete the table to find the missing value.

1.
Miles Driven	25	50	150	
Gallons of Gas	1	2	6	10

2.
Miles Driven	50	150	250	
Hours Driving	1	3	5	8

3.
Cost in dollars	12	36	60	
Time in hours	1	3	5	7

4.
Dollars	1	2	4	10
Yen	106	212	424	

5.
Ounces Red Paint	3	9	24	
Ounces Yellow Paint	1	3	8	12

6.
Students	17	34	68	
Teacher	1	2	4	9

Create a table using the given ratio to find the missing value.

7. 5 dinners cost $35
   What is the cost of 18 dinners?

8. 6 tickets cost $1.50
   What is the cost of 15 tickets?

9. 50 minutes for $4.00
   How many minutes with $6.00?

10. 16 girls to 24 boys
    How many girls if there are 30 boys?

Calculate the unit rate to solve the proportion.

11. $1.75 per ceramic tile
    How many tiles can be purchased for $42?

12. 240 miles driven on 8 gallons of gas
    How many gallons of gas are needed to drive 720 miles?

13. 20 ounces of drink for $1.40
    How much does 50 ounces of drink cost?

Problem-Solving Practice (p. 10) **AL OL**

Lesson 5.2 Problem-Solving Practice
Proportions

Create a table or find the unit rate to answer the word problems.

1. **School** The ratio of boys to girls in history class is 4 to 5. How many girls are in the class if there are 12 boys in the class?

2. **Factories** A factory can produce 6 motorcycles in 9 hours. How many hours will it take to produce 16 motorcycles?

3. **Reading** James reads at a rate of 4 pages every 6 minutes. How long will it take him to read 32 pages if he reads at the same rate?

4. **Cooking** A recipe that will make 3 pies calls for 7 cups of flour. How many cups of flour are needed to make 12 pies?

5. **Typing** Sara can type a 75 word paragraph in 4 minutes. How long will it take to type an essay that is 600 words long?

6. **Food** Two slices of Dan's Famous Pizza have 230 calories. How many calories are in 5 slices of the same pizza?

7. **Fundraising** Hector's school sold 18 discount cards and raised $54 for a new sign outside the school. How many discount cards must be sold to raise the $900 needed for the sign?

8. **Shipping** A shipping company charged $20 to ship a package that weighed 50 pounds. How much will it cost to ship a package that weighs 75 pounds?

Enrichment (p. 11) **BL**

Lesson 5.2 Enrichment
Proportions

Ada

Did you know that a woman wrote the first description of a computer programming language? She was the daughter of a famous English lord and was born in 1815. She had a deep understanding of mathematics and was fascinated by calculating machines. Her interests led her to create the first algorithm. In 1843, she translated a French version of a lecture by Charles Babbage. In her notes to the translation, she outlined the fundamental concepts of computer programming. She died in 1852. In 1979, the U.S. Department of Defense named the computer language *Ada* after her.

To find out this woman's full name, complete the table to find the number represented by each letter. The rows in the table are in proportion to each other.

1.
Row 1	7	14	21	28
Row 2	A			40

2.
Row 1	5	15	B	
Row 2	4	36	48	

3.
Row 1	1	2		C
Row 2	3		12	15

4.
Row 1	5	10	35	
Row 2	D	27	63	

5.
Row 1	2	E	12	
Row 2	5	20	30	40

6.
Row 1	1	2	L	4
Row 2			18	27

7.
Row 1	6	12	24	48
Row 2	N	14		

8.
Row 1	9	18	O	
Row 2	11		44	55

9.
Row 1	R	2		5
Row 2	4	8	12	

10.
Row 1	5		25	50
Row 2	V	12	30	

11.
Row 1	7	14	Y	
Row 2	4		28	36

Now look for each solution below. Write the corresponding letter on the line above the solution. If you have calculated correctly, the letters will spell her name.

$\overline{10}$ $\overline{9}$ $\overline{10}$ $\overline{45}$ $\overline{49}$ $\overline{1}$ $\overline{36}$ $\overline{7}$

$\overline{3}$ $\overline{36}$ $\overline{6}$ $\overline{3}$ $\overline{10}$ $\overline{5}$ $\overline{8}$

Lesson Quick Quiz (p. 12) **AL OL BL**

Lesson 5.2 Quick Quiz
Proportions

1. In each ratio table, the top numbers are proportional to the bottom numbers. Add another ratio to each table.

a.
2	20	1	10
3	30	1.5	15

b.
1	20	3	2
2.5	50	7.5	5

2. Ms. Walker divided her class into groups of 8. She gave 40 markers to each group. How many markers will she need for 24 students?

3. Consider two similar rectangles. One measures 2 cm by 5 cm. The width of the other rectangle is 10 cm. What is its length?

4. Juanita can exchange $10.00 U.S. for $8.50 Canadian. How much will she receive if she exchanges $25.00 U.S.? (Assume there is no transaction fee.)

5. A 12 in. × 12 in. square tile costs $1.25. Naomi is going to tile a floor that measures 10 feet by 14 feet. Set up proportions to determine the number of tiles needed to cover the floor and the total cost of the tiles.

6. A 18 in. × 18 in. square tile costs $1.89. Jasper is going to tile a floor that measures 9 feet by 30 feet. Set up proportions to determine the number of tiles needed to cover the floor and the total cost of the tiles.

7. A store is having a sale on 12 in. × 12 in. tiles and 18 in. × 18 in. tiles. The 12 in. × 12 in. tiles are $1.90 and the 18 in. × 18 in. tiles are $2.85. A room measures 12 feet by 18 feet. Set up a proportion to determine which is the better buy and how much money is saved.

Additional Lesson Resources

Teacher Tech Tools
- TeacherWorks
- ExamView Assessment Suite
- Classroom Presentation Toolkit
- Advance Tracker

Student Tech Tools
- StudentWorks Plus
- **Math Online** eGlossary •
  Concepts in Motion

Other Print Products
- Investigation Notebook and Reflection Journal
- Quick Review Math Handbook

Introduce

Proportions This lesson opens with a concrete illustration of the following important mathematical fact: If a quantity *y* is proportional to quantity *x*, then the graph of *y* as a function of *x* is a straight line through the origin. The converse is also true: if the graph of *y* as a function of *x* is a straight line through the origin, then quantity *y* is proportional to quantity *x*. Read through the introductory paragraphs, reviewing the term *proportional*. Then pose the questions raised in the Think & Discuss.

Analyze the Table Ask students to describe any patterns they see in the table. How are these patterns related to the graph of the table?

Think & Discuss

The objective of this section to show that the graph of the relationship between calendars sold and dollars raised is a line beginning at the origin. Then, once students know the ratio of calendars sold to dollars earned, they can calculate the amount of dollars needed for a different number of calendars.

① Possible answer: (10, 30), (20, 60); 10:30, 20:60; The ratios are equivalent.

② The table and graph indicate that for every calendar sold, $3 is raised. The ratios show 1:3.

③ Possible answer: You know that one calendar is worth $3. You can multiply 215 by 3 to get $645 earned.

LESSON 5.2

Proportions

The sixth graders at Summerville Middle School are selling calendars to raise money for a class trip. The amount of money raised is *proportional* to the number of calendars sold. *Proportional* means that as one variable doubles the other doubles, as one variable triples the other triples, and so on.

Dollars raised	0	15	30	45
Calendars sold	0	5	10	15

A graph could also be used to represent the same data from the table.

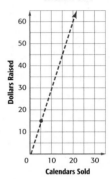

Calendar Sale

Think & Discuss

The point (5, 15) is on the graph. What does this tell you about the calendar sale?   If 5 calendars are sold, $15 is raised.

Identify two more points on the graph. Find the ratio of dollars raised to calendars sold for all three points. How do the ratios compare?   See ①.

What do the table and the graph tell you about the calendar sale? How does it relate to the ratios you found?   See ②.

Now that you know the ratio of calendars sold to dollars earned, how can you calculate the amount of dollars raised if 215 calendars were sold?   See ③.

Mathematical Background

If the variables *y* and *x* are proportional, then for any corresponding values of *x* and *y*, the ratio $\frac{y}{x}$ in simplest terms is a constant.

Moreover, this constant of proportionality is equal to the slope of the line. The term *constant of proportionality* is not used in the text, but it is a useful term you may want to use informally on occasion.

In Think & Discuss, you may have found that the ratio of dollars raised to calendars sold is the same for any values you choose. For example, (5, 15) and (10, 30) are both on the graph.

$$\frac{15}{5} = \frac{30}{10}$$

Math Link
Two ratios are equivalent ratios if they represent the same relationship.

This gives you another way to think about proportional relationships. A *proportional relationship* is a relationship in which all pairs of corresponding values have the same ratio.

We already know that when one ratio is set equal to another ratio, they are proportional.

$$\frac{1}{2} = \frac{3}{6}$$

$\frac{1}{2}$ and $\frac{3}{6}$ are proportional, just like $\frac{15}{5}$ and $\frac{30}{10}$ are proportional.

There are several ways you can test for proportionality, or equality.

You can compare the cross products.

$$\frac{3}{6} = \frac{4}{8}$$

Multiply the numerator of the first fraction with the denominator of the second fraction.

$$\frac{3}{6} \diagdown \frac{4}{8} = 3 \cdot 8 = 24$$

Now multiply the numerator of the second fraction with the denominator of the first fraction.

$$\frac{3}{6} \diagup \frac{4}{8} = 4 \cdot 6 = 24$$

Using cross products, you can ask yourself if three times eight is equal to four times six. Since it does, we can state that these two fractions are proportional.

Another way to test for proportionality is to reduce each fraction to lowest terms.

$$\frac{9}{27} = \frac{18}{54}$$

Since both $\frac{9}{27}$ and $\frac{18}{54}$ reduce to $\frac{1}{3}$, we can state that these two fractions are proportional, or equal.

Proportional Relationships Read the introductory paragraphs with students and introduce the term *proportional relationship*, a relationship in which all pairs of corresponding values have the same ratio.

Have students interpret the proportions on this page by explaining them to a partner.

Develop & Understand: A

Suggested Grouping: Pairs

This problem set places the mathematical ideas explored in Lesson 5.1 in different contexts. Students use ratios and proportional relationships to solve geometry, mixture, and other word problems.

▶ **Exercise 1** This exercise relates proportionality to similarity.

▶ **Exercise 3** Students may use one of these strategies:

- Consider the numbers on each card as ratios and find equivalent ratios.

- Find patterns in the cards shown, and then continue the pattern. For example, the top numbers increase by 0.5 and the bottom numbers increase by one in each successive card.

- Consider the numbers on the cards to be coordinates and then graph them on a coordinate grid. While it is unlikely that any student will approach the problem in this manner, it is a possible way to solve the problem.

▶ **Exercise 4** Santo's mistake is a rerun of Zach's mistake in Lesson 5.1, which is to add fixed amounts to each part of the ratio rather than multiply each part by the same factor.

Troubleshooting If students are having difficulty understanding the meaning of *proportional*, you may want to discuss Exercise 5. This problem requires students to describe a pattern and continue it to maintain a proportional relationship. Watch for students who use additive strategies for continuing a proportional pattern. You may want to have these students use tiles to construct the pattern. If necessary, have them make several models of the figure in Stage 1. Then have them attach two models, three models, and so on, while counting the tiles in each and writing ratios to show the proportional relationships.

1. Yes; Possible explanation: $\frac{15}{30} = \frac{22}{44} = \frac{23}{46}$; all ratios of corresponding side lengths are equivalent.

2. $\frac{35}{10}$, or $\frac{7}{2}$; $\frac{45}{20}$ or $\frac{9}{4}$, $\frac{50}{25}$ or $\frac{2}{1}$; no; Possible explanation: when reduced $\frac{7}{2} \neq \frac{9}{4} \neq \frac{2}{1}$

3. Possible answer: 3:6; The ratio of the top number to the bottom number is 1:2.

Math Link

To be a pattern, the arrangement of tiles must change in a predictable way from stage to stage.

4a. Possible answer: 1 blue tile is added to the center row, and 2 purple tiles are added to the border.

4b. No; the ratios of blue tiles to purple tiles for the four stages are $\frac{1}{8}$, $\frac{2}{10}$, $\frac{3}{12}$, and $\frac{4}{14}$, which are not equal.

Develop & Understand: A

1. Consider these triangles.

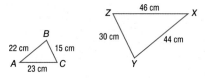

Are the side lengths of triangle *ABC* proportional to those of triangle *XYZ*? Explain how you know.

2. For each rectangle, find the ratio of the length to the width. Is the relationship between the lengths and widths of these rectangles proportional? Explain.

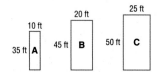

3. On the cards below, the top numbers are proportional to the bottom numbers. Find another card that belongs in this set. Explain how you know your card belongs.

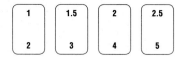

4. Santos created this tile pattern.

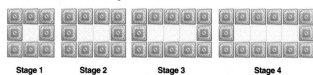

| Stage 1 | Stage 2 | Stage 3 | Stage 4 |

a. Describe how the pattern of blue and purple tiles changes from one stage to the next.

b. For the stages shown, is the number of blue tiles proportional to the number of purple tiles? Explain.

c. Starting with stage 1, draw the next two stages for a tile pattern in which the number of blue tiles is proportional to the number of purple tiles.
   Possible pattern:

   Stage 2   Stage 3

Mathematical Background

The general mathematical principle underlying Exercises 4 and 5 is that, in order to preserve a ratio *a:b*, any additions must also be in the ratio of *a:b*. In Exercise 4, the initial ratio of dye to water is 2:1. To preserve this ratio, any dye and water added to the mixture must also be in the same ratio, 2:1. So, when Jeff starts adding one dye and one water (a 1:1 ratio) to a 2:1 mixture, the initial dye to water ratio will not stay the same. The same analysis works for Exercise 5.

5. No; Possible explanation: The ratios of blue containers to yellow containers for the mixtures are 2:1, 3:2, and 4:3, which are not equal.

5. Jeff says, "I started with Mixture A. I created Mixture B by adding one blue container and one yellow container to Mixture A. Then I made Mixture C by adding one blue container and one yellow container to Mixture B. Since I added the same amount of blue and the same amount of yellow each time, the number of blue containers is proportional to the number of yellow containers."

Is Jeff correct? Explain.

Mixture A

Mixture B

Mixture C

1. Possible answer: Check that all pairs of values are in the same ratio. Or reduce the ratios to lowest terms to see if they are equal.

Share & Summarize

1. Describe at least two ways to determine whether a relationship is proportional.

2. Describe two quantities in your daily life that are proportional to each other.   Possible answer: The number of hours I babysit and the number of dollars I earn

3. Describe two quantities in your daily life that are not proportional to each other.   Possible answer: The number of books I read and the amount of food I eat

Share & Summarize

In **Exercises 2 and 3**, students are asked to relate proportionality to their lives. Since not all things in the everyday world are precise, some of the students' examples may be correct only over a limited range. That does not mean such answers are wrong, but you may want to have a class discussion about the limitations inherent in some of the student answers.

Equal Ratios Remind students about the proportional relationships they explored in the last investigation. Point out that in a proportional relationship, all corresponding values are in the same ratio. Tell students they will use proportional relationships to solve problems.

✅ Develop & Understand: A

Suggested Grouping: Pairs

▶ **Exercise 1** The numbers in this exercise are not easy to work with, so whether students solve this problem by using unit rates, scaling ratios up, or using an equation, it is unlikely many of them will be able to do the requisite arithmetic in their heads.

Wrap-Up Discuss students' answers and in particular how they arrived at them. Then move into the Example.

(**Example**) ·······························

The strategies modeled in the cartoon are:
- Find and compare unit rates. This method has the advantage because it is a standard way of solving all rate problems of this kind. Moreover, once the unit rate has been calculated, the ratio can be used to find other relationships.

- Scaling to find equivalent ratios. Students can scale up from $\frac{18}{6}$ to a ratio whose numerator is 63.00 which seems easier said than done because you need to figure out how many times three goes into 63.00.

- Finding the pattern in a table. Using a table has a great advantage because it organizes the work for you. After you have set up a table, you can analyze the pattern in the table to see that the number of calendars sold is 21.

Relate the methods shown in the cartoon to the methods your students used. If no one used a table, go through this method together as a class. Depending on your class, you may find it more worthwhile to do Exercise 4 as a class.

Investigation 2 Equal Ratios

You know that in a proportional relationship, all pairs of corresponding values are in the same ratio. You may find it helpful to think about this idea as you solve the next set of exercises.

✅ Develop & Understand: A

1. When the sixth grade calendar sale began, Mr. Diaz bought the first six calendars. From his purchase, the class raised $18.00. By the end of the first day of the sale, $63.00 was raised. How many calendars had been sold by the end of the first day?   21

Example

Luis, Kate, and Darnell each thought about Exercise 1 in a different way, but all three found the same answer.

2. Complete each student's method and find the number of calendars sold the first day. Find the same answer with each method.   21

3. The first ratio is $\frac{3}{18}$. The second ratio is $\frac{9}{x}$. You can multiply the numerator and denominator by 3 • $\frac{3 \cdot 3}{18 \cdot 3} = \frac{9}{54}$. So, $x = 54$

3. The rectangles below have lengths and widths that are proportional. How can you find the value of x? What is the value of x?

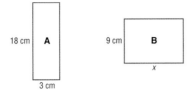

18 cm | A

3 cm

9 cm | B

x

4. Susan rented skis at Budget Mountain. She paid $20 for 4 hours and she used the skis for 6 hours. The rental cost is proportional to time. What will be her rental charge? See below.

5. First-Rate Rags wants to make a large batch of the shade of dye below. The final batch must have 136 containers in all (blue and yellow). How many containers of blue dye will be needed?
See margin.

6. Kyle and his parents went to Algeria during his summer break. Before they left, Kyle exchanged some money for Algerian dinar. In exchange for $12 U.S., he received 804 Algerian dinar. He returned with 201 Algerian dinar. If the exchange rate is still the same, how many dollars will Kyle receive for his dinar? See margin.

Share & Summarize

Choose one of the exercises from 3–6. Solve it using a different method. Explain each step clearly enough that someone from another class could understand what you did.
Answers will vary.

4. The rental cost is $30.00 for 6 hours

Cost in dollars	5	10	20	30
Time in hours	1	2	4	6

Suggested Grouping: Pairs or Individuals

▶ **Exercise 4** Point out that this exercise involves money, so the answer has to be rounded to the nearest cent.

▶ **Exercise 5** To solve this exercise by scaling up, students must figure out what number to multiply 8 by to get 136. In general, scaling from the ratio $a{:}b$ to the ratio $x{:}c$ (where x is unknown), leads to a missing factor problem: $b \times$ *what number* $= c$. The missing factor is always $c \div b$. Once a student knows how to solve the problem, the calculator makes doing it routine.

Share & Summarize

Here students are asked to solve one of the exercises using a different method than the one they originally used. Students may be reluctant to redo a problem they have already done. Point out that some methods are easier to use on one kind of problem than on another. Consider this example:

Ponytail holders have a sales price of 4 for $7. Melinda has $56 and wants to buy as many as she can to give as gifts. How many ponytail holders can she buy? It is easy to solve this problem by using guess-check-and improve, but it is not so easy to find the unit rate to solve the problem.

Additional Answers

5. 51; The ratio of blue containers to all containers is $\frac{3}{8}$, so we need to find an equivalent ratio in the form "something to 136." Multiplying both parts of the ratio by 17 gives $\frac{3 \cdot 17}{8 \cdot 17} = \frac{51}{136}$.

6. $3.00; Possible explanation: You can create a table to show that $12 is equal to 804 dinar. You can use multiplication and/or division to help you fill in the table.

Dollars	1	2	3	12
Dinars	67	134	201	804

Reaching *All Learners*

BL **Beyond Level** Have students choose a country and look up the conversion rates for a U.S. dollar and that country's currency in the newspaper. Encourage them to track the exchange rate over a period of time. You might even ask them to think about why the "price" of foreign currencies might go up or down with respect to the dollar. Point out that in some respects currencies are just like any other product. Their prices go up or down as a function of supply and demand.

Inquiry
Investigation ③

Suggested Grouping: Pairs

Materials and Preparation
Show students examples of tiles, blueprints, and other materials related to the area or design of a room.

Introduce
Solve Proportions In this investigation, students will practice using proportions to solve a problem. The interior design problem is one that most people will deal with in some form in real life, so it can easily be made relevant to students. Throughout the investigation, ask students to tell what might happen if they solve the problems incorrectly. Remind them that having too little or too much in materials can be costly.

Try It Out
▶ **Exercise 1** Make sure students can convert from inches to feet. Show a square divided into a 12 × 12 square inch tile to demonstrate the number of square inches that are in one tile. Make sure they see the reasoning for dividing by 144 (12 × 12).

▶ **Exercise 2** Remind students that one method used to find the value of a variable in a proportion is to multiply one ratio in the proportion by an equivalent form of one. To find an equivalent form of one, students can divide the larger numerator (or denominator) by the smaller numerator (or denominator). The quotient becomes the numerator and denominator of the equivalent form of one. For example, to find the value of x in the proportion $\frac{2.25}{1} = \frac{180}{x}$, since $\frac{180}{2.25} = 80$, multiply $\frac{2.25}{1} \cdot \frac{80}{80}$ to get $\frac{180}{80} = \frac{180}{x}$. Then since the numerators are equal, the denominators are equal, or $x = 80$.

Inquiry
Investigation ③ Solve Proportions

Proportional situations are one of the most common mathematical occurrences in life. Interior designers and landscape designers, for example, use the idea of proportions when creating a new design. In this investigation, you will be an interior designer responsible for ordering materials for a project. You will need to calculate the cost of those materials. Your client would like to spend as little money as possible on the materials.

Your client has decided to tile the floor of a rectangular room that measures 12 feet by 15 feet. The square tiles that your client likes come in three different sizes.

Tile Dimensions (inches)	Cost per Tile (dollars)
12 × 12	$1.45
18 × 18	$3.45
24 × 24	$5.65

1. Because the tiles are different sizes, you will need to know the number of each tile size needed to cover the floor. You know that there are 12 inches in one foot. Determine the number of square feet each tile will cover. Copy and complete the table.

Tile Dimensions	Convert Square Inches to Square Feet
12 inches × 12 inches	12 in. = 1 ft 12 in. × 12 in. = 1 ft × 1 ft or 1 ft^2
18 inches × 18 inches	$\frac{18 \text{ in.} \times 18 \text{ in.}}{12 \text{ in.} \times 12 \text{ in.}} = 2.25 \text{ ft}^2$
24 inches × 24 inches	$\frac{24 \text{ in.} \times 24 \text{ in.}}{12 \text{ in.} \times 12 \text{ in.}} = 4 \text{ ft}^2$

1. The 12 × 12 tile cover 1 square foot, the 18 × 18 tile cover 2.25 square feet; the 24 × 24 tile cover 4 square feet

2. $\frac{1 \text{ ft}^2}{1 \text{ tile}} = \frac{180 \text{ ft}^2}{x \text{ tiles}}$

$\frac{2.25 \text{ ft}^2}{1 \text{ tile}} = \frac{180 \text{ ft}^2}{x \text{ tiles}}$

$\frac{4 \text{ ft}^2}{1 \text{ tile}} = \frac{180 \text{ ft}^2}{x \text{ tiles}}$

$\frac{1 \text{ ft}^2}{1 \text{ tile}} \times \frac{180}{180} = \frac{180 \text{ ft}^2}{180 \text{ tiles}}$

$\frac{2.25 \text{ ft}^2}{1 \text{ tile}} \times \frac{80}{80} = \frac{180 \text{ ft}^2}{80 \text{ tiles}}$

$\frac{4 \text{ ft}^2}{1 \text{ tile}} \cdot \frac{45}{45} = \frac{180 \text{ ft}^2}{45 \text{ tiiles}}$

Try It Out

2. The floor measures 12 feet by 15 feet. How many of each size tile is needed to cover the floor? Set up and solve proportions to determine the number of each size tile needed to cover the floor.

The total area is 12 feet × 15 feet = 180 sq. ft. The 12 in. × 12 in. tiles cover 1 sq. ft each, which means you need 180 tiles. The 18 in. × 18 in. cover 2.25 sq. ft each, which means you need 80 tiles. The 24 in. × 24 in. tiles cover 4 sq. ft each, which means you need 45 tiles.

314 CHAPTER 5 Rate, Ratio, and Proportion

Reaching All Learners

ELL English Language Learners may need help understanding *square feet*. Draw a small square and a large square on the board and mark their measurements. Have students tell which covers more area. Demonstrate finding the area in each of the squares, and show how the amount is larger in the larger square.

3. $\dfrac{\$1.45}{1 \text{ tile}} = \dfrac{x}{180 \text{ tiles}}$

$\dfrac{\$3.45}{1 \text{ tile}} = \dfrac{x}{80 \text{ tiles}}$

$\dfrac{\$5.65}{1 \text{ tile}} = \dfrac{x}{45 \text{ tiles}}$

$\dfrac{\$1.45}{1 \text{ tile}} \times \dfrac{180}{180} = \dfrac{x}{180 \text{ tiles}}$

$\dfrac{\$3.45}{1 \text{ tile}} \times \dfrac{80}{80} = \dfrac{x}{80 \text{ tiles}}$

$\dfrac{\$5.65}{1 \text{ tile}} \times \dfrac{45}{45} = \dfrac{x}{45 \text{ tiles}}$

$\dfrac{\$1.45}{1 \text{ tile}} \times \dfrac{180}{180} = \dfrac{\$261}{180 \text{ tiles}}$

$\dfrac{\$3.45}{1 \text{ tile}} \times \dfrac{80}{80} = \dfrac{\$276}{80 \text{ tiles}}$

$\dfrac{\$5.65}{1 \text{ tile}} \times \dfrac{45}{45} = \dfrac{\$254.25}{45 \text{ tiles}}$

4. You would want to use as many of the most economical tiles (24 × 24 tiles) as can fit in the room, which is 41 tiles. To fill the remaining space, you would need 16 12 × 12 tiles.
41 · $5.65 = $231.65;
16 · $1.45 = $23.20;
$231.65 + $23.20 = $254.85

Try It Again

3. Now you know the number of each tile that you will need if you used only one size. Set up and solve proportions to determine the total cost of the project if you use only one size tile for the entire project.

4. Now consider a situation where the room is not rectangular. Your customer does not want you to cut tiles, so you must use whole tiles. Given the following shape of the room, what would be the most economical approach?

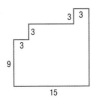

What Have You Learned?

Discuss with a classmate what you have learned about using proportions in everyday situations. Talk about professions with which you are familiar or about a profession you hope to have when you are older. Discuss how you think proportions might be used.

- How might proportions save a life in the medical profession?
- How would a hair stylist use proportions?
See ① in margin.

Lesson 5.2   Proportions   **315**

On the Spot Assessment

Monitor for signs of understanding of proportions. Students who cannot set up an equation to solve for proportions may need more instruction on the basic concepts. Students who get the wrong dollar amounts for each size tile may need help organizing their work so that they can sort the amounts after finding proportions.

Try It Again

▶ **Exercise 3** Watch to see that students multiply by an equivalent form of one. Make sure they write the fraction as a number over itself, and not one over that number.

▶ **Exercise 4** This exercise requires students to work through several steps. The first step is to determine the best way to tile a room that is not rectangular without cutting tiles. Have pairs create a larger version of the drawing using the given measurements. Then have them draw lines to show possible tile layouts. Remind them that finding the most economical approach means using the least expensive tiles.

What Have You Learned?

Use student suggestions to make a list on chart paper of everyday uses for proportions. Then discuss each suggestion. Have students choose one and write two sentences telling why proportions are important in that instance.

Additional Answers

① Student response might center around cost ratios in various professions. Those who work in the medical professions are responsible for administering medications in accurate proportions. A mistake made in the dosage of medication could be a life and death situation. A hair stylist may use proportions when mixing solutions to color treat or perm the hair of a client.

Investigation 1
Pages 309–311
Practice & Apply: 1–3
Connect & Extend: 10, 11

Investigation 2
Pages 312–313
Practice & Apply: 4–6
Connect & Extend: 12–15

Inquiry Investigation
Pages 314–315
Practice & Apply: 7–9
Connect & Extend: 16, 17

Assign Anytime
Mixed Review 18–27

▶ **Exercise 3** Be sure students understand that they find the ratio for each mix, then determine if the two ratios are proportional.

Practice & Apply

1. Yes; the ratios of the entries in each column are the same. The number of miles is 60 times the number of gallons; the ratio of gallons to miles is 1:60.

2. Yes; the ratio of blue containers to all containers in Mixture A is $\frac{4}{6}$ and in Mixture B is $\frac{6}{9}$. These ratios are equivalent, so the number of blue dye containers is proportional to the total number of containers.

3a. No; in Mountain Trail Mix, it is $\frac{7}{20}$, in Hiker's Trail Mix, it is $\frac{5}{15}$.

3b. Yes; in Mountain Trail Mix, it is $\frac{8}{20}$, or $\frac{2}{5}$; in Hiker's Trail Mix, it is $\frac{6}{15}$, or $\frac{2}{5}$.

1. **Ecology** One of the new energy-efficient cars will travel many miles on a gallon of fuel by using a combination of electricity and gasoline. The table shows estimates of how far the car will travel on various amounts of fuel.

Gallons of Fuel	0.5	1	1.5	2	2.5	3
Miles	30	60	90	120	150	180

Are the miles traveled proportional to the gallons of fuel? How do you know? If so, describe how they are related and write the ratio.

2. Is the number of blue dye containers in these two mixtures proportional to the total number of containers? Explain how you know.

Mixture A

Mixture B

3. The Summerville Co-op sells two types of trail mix. Here are the ingredients.

Mountain Trail Mix	Hiker's Trail Mix
8 oz toasted oats	6 oz toasted oats
7 oz nuts	5 oz nuts
5 oz raisins	4 oz raisins

a. Is the amount of nuts in each mix proportional to the total ounces of mix? Why or why not?

b. Is the amount of toasted oats in each mix proportional to the total ounces of mix? Why or why not?

4. Set up a proportion for the following situation. Choose any method to solve it.

Elena's grandmother wants to sell a gold ring that she no longer wears. The jeweler offered her $388 per ounce for her gold. This came to $97 for the ring. How much does the ring weigh?

Dollars	388	291	194	97
Ounce	1	0.75	0.5	0.25

The ring weighs 0.25 oz.

5. $\frac{3}{4}$ c oats, $2\frac{1}{4}$ c flour,
$\frac{1}{4}$ c syrup, $\frac{3}{4}$ T oil,
$\frac{15}{16}$ c water, $2\frac{1}{4}$ T yeast,
$\frac{3}{4}$ t salt

5. Mirna is following this recipe for maple oatmeal bread.

Just as she is preparing to mix the ingredients, she realizes her brother used most of the maple syrup for his breakfast. Mirna has only $\frac{1}{4}$ cup of syrup. She decides to make a smaller batch of bread. How much of each ingredient should she use?

Maple Oatmeal Bread
1 cup quick-cooking oats
3 cups bread flour
$\frac{1}{3}$ cup maple syrup
1 tablespoon cooking oil
$1\frac{1}{4}$ cups water
3 tablespoons yeast
1 teaspoon salt

6. Many schools have a recommended student-teacher ratio. At South High, the ratio is 17:1. Next year, South High expects enrollment to increase by 136 students. How many new teachers will need to be hired to maintain this student-teacher ratio?   8

7. A farmer wants to cut down three pine trees to use for a fence he is building. To decide which trees to cut, he wants to estimate their heights. He holds a 9-inch stick perpendicular to and touching the ground. He measures its shadow to be about 6 inches. He wants to cut down trees that are about 40 feet tall. How long are the tree shadows for which he should look?   26 ft to 27 ft

8. A surveyor needs to find the distance across a lake. She makes several measurements and prepares this drawing. The ratio of *AC:CE* is equal to the ratio of *AB:DE*. What is the distance across the lake?
About 167 ft

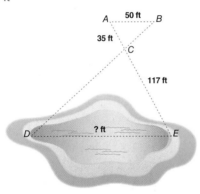

▶ **Exercise 6** Some students may think this exercise is impossible to solve since they are only given the student: teacher ratio but not the actual number of students (or teachers) in the school. However, the important thing to note is that to preserve the 17:1 ratio, as you add more students, you have to add more teachers in the same 17:1 ratio.

▶ **Exercise 8** Encourage students who have difficulty organizing the data to first draw a picture of the situation.

Lesson 5.2 Proportions   **317**

► Exercise 9 The thumb method is a very handy way of estimating how far away a distant object is if you have a good idea of its height. It can also be used to estimate heights of distant objects if you know how far you are from the object. Encourage students to try it out for themselves, reminding them that their answers are estimates rather than precise measurements.

► Exercise 9b Students may solve this exercise by setting up different proportions that compare the lengths within the triangles, such as

$$\frac{\text{lighthouse height}}{\text{distance of lighthouse}} = \frac{\text{thumb length}}{\text{distance from thumb to eye}}.$$

► Exercise 11 Many students will multiply each ingredient by the same number to write the new recipe. You may want to discuss how the quantities are proportional to relate it to the lesson.

Additional Answers

9a. One triangle has his eye, the top of his thumb, and the base of his thumb as vertices. The other has his eye, the top of the lighthouse, and the base of the lighthouse as vertices.

10. Possible answer: Their ages are not proportional because the father is always Christine's age + 25, and proportional relationships are related by multiplication. Or, if you graph the ages of daughter and father, the graph does not pass through the origin.

Connect & Extend

9. Captain Hornblower is out at sea and spots a lighthouse in the distance. He wants to know how far he is from the lighthouse.

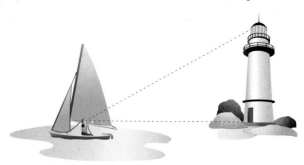

He holds up his thumb at arm's length. Then he brings his hand closer to his eye, until his thumb just covers the image of the lighthouse. His thumb is about 2.5 inches long. He measures the distance from his eye to the base of his thumb and finds that it is about 19 inches. His charts indicate that the lighthouse is Otter Point Lighthouse, which is 70 feet tall.

a. Make a sketch of this situation.   See margin.

b. The ratio of the height of his thumb to the height of the lighthouse is equal to the ratio of the distance from his eye to the base of his thumb to the distance from the boat to the lighthouse. Find the distance from the boat to the lighthouse. 532 ft

10. Ravi was born on his father's 25th birthday. On the day Ravi turned 25, his father turned 50, and they threw a big party. Then Ravi wondered, "Dad's twice as old as I am. Does that mean our ages are proportional?" Answer Ravi's question.   See margin.

11. This recipe makes one and a half dozen peanut butter cookies. Write a new recipe that will make more cookies and has ingredients in the proper proportions.

Possible recipe: 1 c peanut butter, 2 c flour, 1 c butter, $\frac{3}{2}$ c brown sugar, $\frac{1}{2}$ c white sugar, 4 egg whites, 1 tsp baking soda, $\frac{2}{3}$ tsp salt

Peanut Butter Cookies
$\frac{1}{2}$ cup peanut butter
1 cup flour
$\frac{1}{2}$ cup butter
$\frac{3}{4}$ cup brown sugar
$\frac{1}{4}$ cup white sugar
2 egg whites
$\frac{1}{2}$ tsp baking soda
$\frac{1}{3}$ tsp salt

12. No proportional relationships; Possible explanation: for white and red, and white and purple, the number of white tiles does not change, but the numbers of red and purple tiles both change. For red and purple, the ratios for each stage are 1:4, 2:6, and 3:8, which are not equivalent.

13. No proportional relationships; Possible explanation: for red and white, the ratios are 1:4, 2:6, and 3:8, which are not equivalent. For purple and white, they are 4:4, 7:6, and 10:8, which are not equivalent. For red and purple, they are 1:4, 2:7, and 3:10, which are not equivalent.

Decide whether the numbers of tiles of any two colors are proportional to each other. Consider three ratios, red:purple, purple:white, and red:white, for each stage of the tile patterns. Explain your answers.

12.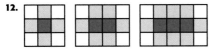

13.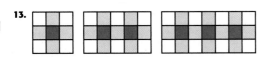

14.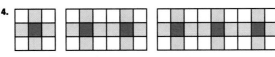

14, 15. See margin.

15.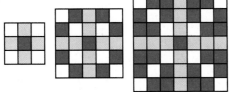

16. Felix made the following conjecture.

   Take any fraction. Add two to the numerator and the denominator. The new fraction will never be in the same ratio as the original.

   What do you think of his conjecture? Use examples or counter examples in your explanation.   Felix is correct. If you have $\frac{1}{2}$ as a fraction and add two to the numerator and the denominator, you will have $\frac{3}{4}$. $\frac{1}{2}$ is not the same ratio as $\frac{3}{4}$.

14. All relationships are proportional. Possible explanation: The pattern is made by adding Stage 1 each time, so the tiles remain in proportion. At each stage, red:purple = 1:4, purple:white = 4:4, and red:white = 1:4.

15. The relationship between white and purple is proportional but the others are not. Possible explanation: The ratio purple:white is equivalent to 1:1 for each stage. For red:white (and red:purple) the ratios are 1:4, 9:8, and 25:12, which are not equivalent.

▶ **Exercises 22–28** Remind students to work the multiplication of the numbers first, and then to find the correct place for the decimal in the product.

Quick Check

Informal Assessment Students should be able to:

✓ recognize proportions as pairs of equivalent ratios

✓ use equivalent ratios to find the missing part of a proportion

✓ set up and use proportions to solve problems

Quick Quiz

1. In each ratio table, the top numbers are proportional to the bottom numbers. Add another ratio to each table.

2	20	1	10
3	30	1.5	15

a. Possible answers: 4:6, 6:9, and 8:12

1	20	3	2
2.5	50	7.5	5

b. Possible answers: 4:10, 6:15, and 5:12.5

2. Ms. Walker divided her class into groups of 8. She gave 40 markers to each group. How many markers will she need for 24 students? 120

3. Consider two similar rectangles. One measures 2 cm by 5 cm. The width of the other rectangle is 10 cm. What is its length? 25 cm

4. Juanita can exchange $10.00 U.S. for $8.50 Canadian. How much will she receive if she exchanges $25.00 U.S.? (Assume there is no transaction fee.) $21.25 Canadian

5. A 12 in. × 12 in. square tile costs $1.25. Naomi is going to tile a floor that measures 10 feet by 14 feet. Set up proportions to determine the number of tiles needed to cover the floor and the total cost of the tiles. 140 tiles; $175

Mixed Review

17. In Your Own Words An architect has agreed to visit a sixth grade class to talk about how architects use scale drawings in their work. She is not sure all the students will know what it means when she talks about shapes being "in proportion." Write some advice telling her how to explain what this means.
Answers will vary. Sample answer: Explain to the class that proportional means that as one variable doubles the other doubles, as one variable triples the other triples, and so on.

Number Sense Name a fraction between the given fractions.

18. $\frac{1}{3}$ and $\frac{1}{2}$ Possible answer: $\frac{5}{12}$

19. $\frac{1}{4}$ and $\frac{4}{15}$ Possible answer: $\frac{31}{120}$

20. $\frac{13}{16}$ and $\frac{11}{12}$ Possible answer: $\frac{5}{6}$

21. Here are the first three stages of a sequence.

21b.

21c.

Stage 15

Stage 1   Stage 2   Stage 3

a. Describe the pattern in this sequence.   See below.

b. Draw the next two stages in the sequence.

c. Draw stage 15. Explain how you know you are correct.

The first four stages of the pattern repeat over and over. So, they will repeat three times in stages 1 through 12, and then start again with stage 13. So, stage 13 is the same as stage 1, stage 14 is the same as stage 2, and stage 15 is the same

Find each product without using a calculator.

22. 44 · 781   34,364

23. 4.4 · 0.781   3.4364

24. 440 · 781,000   343,640,000

25. 0.44 · 7.81   3.4364

26. 0.044 · 0.0781   0.0034364

27. 440 · 78.1   34,364

21a. Possible answer: Reading across and then down the rows in each stage, the squares follow the pattern yellow, spotted, blue, checked, yellow, spotted, blue, checked, and so on. Start a new stage from where you left off in the previous stage. For example, if the last stage ends in a spotted square, the new stage should start with a blue square. Color the remaining squares in the stage according to the pattern.

6. An 18 in. × 18 in. square tile costs $1.89. Jasper is going to tile a floor that measures 9 feet by 30 feet. Set up proportions to determine the number of tiles needed to cover the floor and the total cost of the tiles. 120 tiles; $226.80

7. A store is having a sale on 12 in. × 12 in. tiles and 18 in. × 18 in. tiles. The 12 in. × 12 in. tiles are $1.90 and the 18 in. × 18 in. tiles are $2.85. A room measures 12 feet by 18 feet. Set up a proportion to determine which is the better buy and how much money is saved. 18 in. × 18 in. square tile; $136.80 savings

Similarity and Congruence

Objectives

▶ To identify congruent figures, angles, and segments by matching or measuring

▶ To identify corresponding sides and angles of similar or congruent polygons

▶ To identify equivalent ratios

▶ To test for similarity by identifying corresponding sides with equivalent ratios and equal corresponding angles

Overview

This lesson starts with the general notion of "sameness," that is, that two rectangles are the same because they belong, in a general sense, to the class of rectangles. Students then discover that members of any class of geometric figures can further be categorized by the congruence and similarity relations. Students learn that congruent figures belong to the same class and have the same size *and* shape while similar figures belong to the same class and have the same shape.

Advance Preparation

You may want to provide students with rulers, protractors, scissors, and so on, and Lesson 5.3 Masters 1-8 to facilitate class discussion while presenting new topics, including similar and congruent polygons.

	Summary	Materials	On Your Own Exercises (pp. 335–340)	Assessment Opportunities
Investigation 1 (p. 322) *Pacing: 1 day*	Students explore several methods for testing for congruence.	Lesson 5.3 Masters 1–7 ruler, protractors	Practice & Apply: 1–4 Connect & Extend: 18–21 Mixed Review: 28–37	• Share & Summarize (p. 325)
Investigation 2 (p. 325) *Pacing: 1 day*	Students investigate several polygons to see if two polygons are similar when their sides are in a constant ratio.	Lesson 5.3 Master 8 or linkage strips, fasteners, metric rulers	Practice & Apply: 5–6 Connect & Extend: 22 Mixed Review: 28–37	• Share & Summarize (p. 326) • Troubleshooting (p. 326)
Investigation 3 (p. 327) *Pacing: 1 day*	Students learn about equivalent ratios, match corresponding parts, and discover that corresponding sides in a constant ratio do not in general guarantee similarity.	ruler, protractor, metric ruler	Practice & Apply: 7–13 Connect & Extend: 23–24 Mixed Review: 28–37	• On the Spot Assessment (pp. 328, 329) • Share & Summarize (p. 331) • Troubleshooting (p. 331)
Investigation 4 (p. 332) *Pacing: 1 day*	Students match angles and ratios of corresponding sides to determine if polygons are similar.	ruler, protractors	Practice & Apply: 14–17 Connect & Extend: 25–27 Mixed Review: 28–37	• Share & Summarize (p. 334) • Troubleshooting (p. 334)

Leveled Lesson Resources

CRM Available in: **Chapter 5 Resource Masters**

Also on TeacherWorks™
Lesson 5.3

Study Guide and Intervention (p. 13) AL

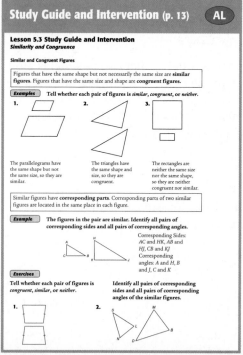

Lesson 5.3 Study Guide and Intervention
Similarity and Congruence

Similar and Congruent Figures

Figures that have the same shape but not necessarily the same size are **similar figures**. Figures that have the same size and shape are **congruent figures**.

Examples Tell whether each pair of figures is *similar, congruent,* or *neither*.

The parallelograms have the same shape but not the same size, so they are similar.

The triangles have the same shape and size, so they are congruent.

The rectangles are neither the same size nor the same shape, so they are neither congruent nor similar.

Similar figures have **corresponding parts**. Corresponding parts of two similar figures are located in the same place in each figure.

Example The figures in the pair are similar. Identify all pairs of corresponding sides and all pairs of corresponding angles.

Corresponding Sides:
AC and HK, AB and HJ, CB and KJ
Corresponding angles: A and H, B and J, C and K

Exercises

Tell whether each pair of figures is *congruent, similar,* or *neither*.

Identify all pairs of corresponding sides and all pairs of corresponding angles of the similar figures.

Skills Practice (p. 14) AL OL

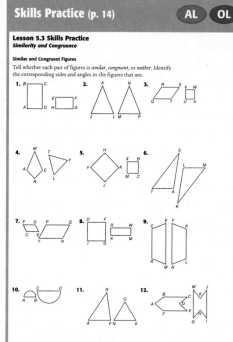

Lesson 5.3 Skills Practice
Similarity and Congruence

Similar and Congruent Figures

Tell whether each pair of figures is *similar, congruent,* or *neither*. Identify the corresponding sides and angles in the figures that are.

Problem-Solving Practice (p. 15) AL OL

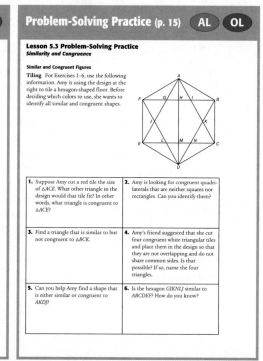

Lesson 5.3 Problem-Solving Practice
Similarity and Congruence

Similar and Congruent Figures

Tiling For Exercises 1–6, use the following information. Amy is using the design at the right to tile a hexagon-shaped floor. Before deciding which colors to use, she wants to identify all similar and congruent shapes.

1. Suppose Amy cut a red tile the size of △ACE. What other triangle in the design would that tile fit? In other words, what triangle is congruent to △ACE?

2. Amy is looking for congruent quadrilaterals that are neither squares nor rectangles. Can you identify them?

3. Find a triangle that is similar to but not congruent to △BCK.

4. Amy's friend suggested that she cut four congruent white triangular tiles and place them in the design so that they are not overlapping and do not share common sides. Is that possible? If so, name the four triangles.

5. Can you help Amy find a shape that is either similar or congruent to △AKDJ?

6. Is the hexagon GIKNLJ similar to ABCDEF? How do you know?

Enrichment (p. 16) BL

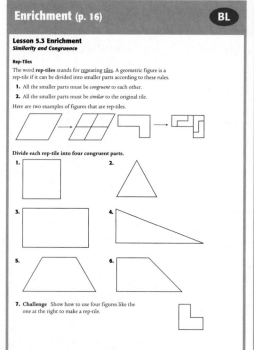

Lesson 5.3 Enrichment
Similarity and Congruence

Rep-Tiles

The word **rep-tiles** stands for *rep*eating *tiles*. A geometric figure is a rep-tile if it can be divided into smaller parts according to these rules.

1. All the smaller parts must be *congruent* to each other.

2. All the smaller parts must be *similar* to the original tile.

Here are two examples of figures that are rep-tiles.

Divide each rep-tile into four congruent parts.

7. Challenge Show how to use four figures like the one at the right to make a rep-tile.

Lesson Quick Quiz (p. 17) AL OL BL

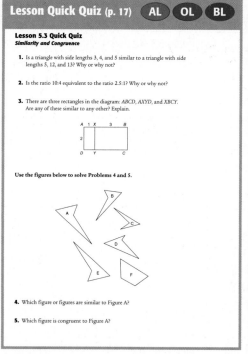

Lesson 5.3 Quick Quiz
Similarity and Congruence

1. Is a triangle with side lengths 3, 4, and 5 similar to a triangle with side lengths 5, 12, and 13? Why or why not?

2. Is the ratio 10:4 equivalent to the ratio 2.5:1? Why or why not?

3. There are three rectangles in the diagram: *ABCD, AXYD,* and *XBCY.* Are any of these similar to any other? Explain.

Use the figures below to solve Problems 4 and 5.

4. Which figure or figures are similar to Figure A?

5. Which figure is congruent to Figure A?

Lesson Masters 1–10 (pp. 18–27)

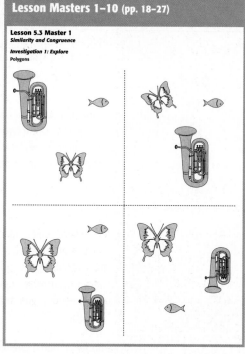

Lesson 5.3 Master 1
Similarity and Congruence

Investigation 1: Explore
Polygons

Additional Lesson Resources

Teacher Tech Tools
- TeacherWorks
- ExamView Assessment Suite
- Classroom Presentation Toolkit
- Advance Tracker

Student Tech Tools
- StudentWorks Plus
- Math Online eGlossary •
- Concepts in Motion

Other Print Products
- Investigation Notebook and Reflection Journal
- Quick Review Math Handbook

LESSON 5.3

Similarity and Congruence

Vocabulary

congruent

similar

What does it mean to say that two figures are the same?

These figures are "the same" because they are members of the same *class of objects*. They are both rectangles.

Some figures have more in common than just being the same *type* of figure. One of the figures below is an enlargement of the other. They have the same *shape* but are different *sizes*. Two figures that have the same *shape* are **similar**.

The most obvious way in which two figures can be "the same" is for them to be identical. Figures that are the same size *and* the same shape are **congruent**. The figures below are congruent.

These rectangles are also congruent.

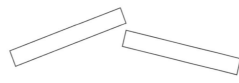

Notice that similarity and congruence do not depend on how the objects are positioned. They can be flipped and rotated from each other.

Introduce

Similarity and Congruence Introduce the lesson by providing some examples of *congruent* and *similar* figures—the overhead is a good tool for this. Be sure that students realize that it does not matter if the figures are in different positions as long as the size and shape requirements for congruency and similarity are met.

Teacher Tips Have student pairs practice drawing similar and congruent figures. Each student draws five figures and trades them with his or her partner. The partners then draw figures that are similar and figures that are congruent.

Provide students with copies of Lesson 5.3 Masters 1-7, Explore Polygons I–VII. Once students understand the directions, the activity is self-guiding. Students may use one of these ways to test for congruence:

- Take measurements to tell if two figures are the same; but, because these are complicated figures, they may not be sure what to measure.

- Test for congruence by laying figures on top of one another and checking to see if they align. This ignores the possibility of small variations in the figure but is not a bad test for congruence.

Investigation 1

On Your Own Exercises
Pages 335–340
Exercises 1–4, 18–21

Variables and Expressions In this investigation, students using their informal tests for congruence to decide if two figures are congruent. They build from here to develop their understanding as they refine and formalize tests for congruence.

✅ Develop & Understand: A

Suggested Grouping: Pairs

▶ **Exercise 1** Some students may object to using congruence to refer to segments that are of equal length, arguing that segments are not figures or that each segment is defined by its length. These students may find it clearer to think of the matching concept as it applies to congruency. Ask them which may have come first, the idea of matching or measuring. A carpenter will often match rather than measure to make a cut. It is reasonable to argue that measuring a length is the process of matching a fixed segment to a ruler segment that is moveable. In both cases, two segments of the same length must be congruent.

▶ **Exercise 4** Students who rely on visualization, not measurement or matching, may think that the figures are congruent. Encourage them to think of, and use, other ways to test for congruence.

Your teacher will give you a sheet of paper with drawings of three figures. One or two other students in your class have figures that are congruent to yours. Find these students.

How did you determine which of the other students' figures were congruent to yours?   Possible answers: We laid the figures on top of one another. We measured lengths of sides and angles.

Investigation 1   Congruent Figures and Angles

Vocabulary

counterexample

Materials

- ruler
- protractor

To find who had figures congruent to yours, you needed to invent a way to tell whether two figures are congruent. Now you will use your test for congruence on more figures and on angles.

✅ Develop & Understand: A

Decide whether figures A and B are congruent. If they are not congruent, explain why not.

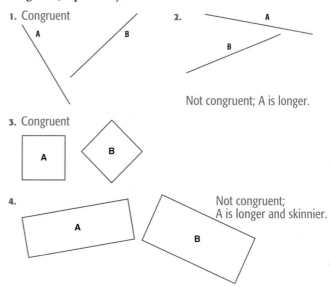

1. Congruent

2. Not congruent; A is longer.

3. Congruent

4. Not congruent; A is longer and skinnier.

Decide whether figures A and B are congruent. If they are not congruent, explain why not.

5. Congruent

6. Congruent

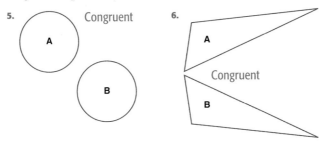

You just compared several pairs of figures. One important geometrical object is the angle, which is a part of many figures. What do you think congruent *angles* look like?

① Answers will vary. Congruent angles have the same measure; the lengths of the rays that define the angles do not affect congruency.

Think & Discuss

The angles in each pair below are congruent.   See ①.

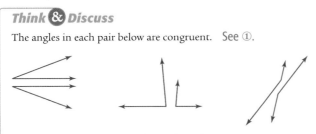

What do you think it means for angles to be congruent?

✓ Develop & Understand: B

Decide whether the angles in each pair are congruent. If they are not congruent, explain why not.

7.   Not congruent; ∠a is larger (69°) than ∠b (54°).

8.   Congruent

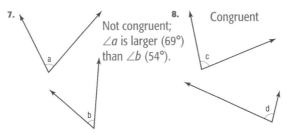

Lesson 5.3   Similarity and Congruence   **323**

Wrap-Up Be sure to discuss the answer to Exercise 6. It is important for students to realize that two triangles (or other figures) are congruent even if they are mirror images of each other.

Think & Discuss

Discuss the question in the book. Then discuss why it makes sense for congruent angles to have the same measure, independent of the length of the rays. You can demonstrate this concept on the board: Draw an angle. Then, on the same angle, just extend the sides. Ask students if you have changed the measure of the angle and, if so, how. Then ask the measurement with a protractor would be different. If necessary, measure the angles to show that they are the same.

You may need to spend some time reviewing how to measure angles with a protractor.

✓ Develop & Understand: B

Suggested Grouping: Individuals

▶ **Exercises 7 and 8** This problem set emphasizes that measuring the length of the rays in each angle is irrelevant in determining whether two angles are congruent. Understanding congruent angles will help students refine their tests for congruence. You may want to provide students with tracing paper to extend rays or segments or discuss other ways to use a protractor when the rays are too short to measure. One way is to use a straightedge to extend the ray, then measure.

Wrap-Up Discuss Exercise 8. Be sure that students realize that angles can be congruent regardless of the length of the rays.

Reaching All Learners

AL **Approaching Level** Students' experiences with angles vary greatly. Some students may have no sense of what it means to turn through an angle of 90°, 180°, or 360°. Engage these students in estimation exercises that involve angle measure. Show them a directional compass and ask them to face an object and turn slowly until they face it again.

Then ask these questions:

Through how many degrees have they turned?
How many 90° turns does this represent?
How many 60° turns?

Develop & Understand: C

Suggested Grouping: Pairs

▶ **Exercises 9–12** This exercise set presents some possible tests for congruence and asks students to confirm or reject them. Students may use one of these methods to determine if the tests prove congruence.

- Some students may be able to decide whether a proposed test works without measuring the figures. They may rely on known mathematical facts to support their answers. For example, in Exercise 10, students may know that the test works because by definition, the four sides of a square have the same length and each of the four angles measures 90°. Therefore, if the length of one side of one square equals the length of one side in another square, the squares would be congruent because they are the same size and the same shape.

- Other students may need to draw the shapes and match or measure the figures to support their answers.

Wrap-Up Allow some time for discussion of answers and counterexamples. Before moving on, have volunteers explain the informal tests they have been using to test for congruence such as matching or measuring. It might be helpful to list ideas on the board.

Share & Summarize

Students will have to measure some angles that are defined by segments too short to fit the protractor. Some students will not think of extending the sides of the figure, perhaps indicating that they think that length is relevant to defining the angle. If students have experience thinking of angles in terms of compass headings, they are already using the relative directions of the sides of an angle to define its size rather than the length of its sides.

One way to test whether two figures are congruent is to try fitting one exactly on top of the other. Sometimes it is not easy to cut out or trace figures. It is helpful to have other tests for congruency.

Develop & Understand: C

Each exercise below suggests a way to test for the congruence of two figures. Decide whether each test is good enough to be *sure* the figures are congruent. Assume you can make *exact* measurements.

If a test is not good enough, give a **counterexample**, an example for which the test would not work.

9. For two line segments, measure their lengths. The line segments are congruent if the lengths are equal.   Test works

10. For two squares, measure the length of one side of each square. The squares are congruent if the side lengths are equal.   Test works

11. For two angles, measure each angle with a protractor. They are congruent if the angles have equal measures.   Test works

12. For two rectangles, find their perimeters. The rectangles are congruent if the perimeters are equal.

12. Test does not work. Possible counter-example: 2 + 2 + 3 + 3 and 1 + 1 + 4 + 4 have equal perimeters but are not congruent.

1. Q and N are congruent; Possible explanation: Their side lengths and angles match.

2. ∠j and ∠l are congruent; Possible explanation: The angles have the same measure.

Share & Summarize

Decide which figures in each set are congruent. Explain how you know.

1.

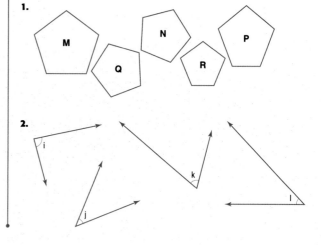

2.

Investigation ② Similar Figures

Math Link
Figures are similar if they have the exact same shape. They may be different sizes.

①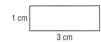
11 cm
12 cm

3. Note: Students should draw to actual size.

1.1 cm [ ]   1 cm [ ]
1.2 cm   2 cm

You now have several techniques for identifying *congruent* figures. How can you tell whether two figures are *similar*?

✓ Develop & Understand: A

Work with a partner. To begin, draw a rectangle with sides 1 cm and 3 cm long. You will need only one rectangle for the two of you.

1 cm [   ]
         3 cm

1. One partner should draw a new rectangle whose sides are 7 times the length of the original rectangle's sides. The other partner should draw a new rectangle in which each side is 7 cm longer than those of the original rectangle. Label the side lengths of both new rectangles.   See below.

2. With your partner, decide which of the new rectangles looks similar to the original rectangle.   The one with sides 7 times as long

In Exercises 1 and 2, you modified a figure in two ways to create *larger* figures. Now you will compare two ways for modifying a figure to create *smaller* figures.

✓ Develop & Understand: B

Work with a partner. Begin by drawing a rectangle with sides 11 cm and 12 cm long.   See ①.

3. Now, one partner should draw a new rectangle whose sides are one-tenth the length of the original rectangle's sides. The other partner should draw a new rectangle in which each side is 10 cm shorter than those of the original rectangle. Label the side lengths of both new rectangles.

4. With your partner, decide which of the new rectangles looks similar to the original rectangle.   The one with sides one-tenth as long

1. Note: Students should draw to actual size.

7 cm [   ]   8 cm [   ]
        21 cm   10 cm

Lesson 5.3 Similarity and Congruence   **325**

Investigation ②

On Your Own Exercises
Pages 335–340
Exercises 5, 6, 22

Similar Figures This investigation introduces similarity by having students enlarge rectangles. They then use the same techniques to reduce the size of the rectangles and to make similar triangles. Introduce the investigation by having a student give the meaning of *similar*. Tell them that they will first look at how to draw similar rectangles.

✓ Develop & Understand: A

Suggested Grouping: Pairs

▶ **Exercises 1 and 2** This problem set distinguishes between enlarging by multiplication and enlarging by addition. Students' intuition often mistakenly leads them to think that adding the same amount to each side of a figure produces a good enlargement, or a similar figure.

Wrap-Up Discuss in class which two rectangles are similar. Ask students if the rectangle created by addition represents an enlargement they might get from enlarging a photograph to poster size. Have them explain why or why not.

✓ Develop & Understand: B

Suggested Grouping: Pairs

▶ **Exercises 3 and 4** In these exercises, students look at similarity in the context of size reduction by subtraction versus division.

Mathematical Background

Although this should not affect students' conclusions in this investigation, it is worthwhile to note that in some cases, enlargement by addition *looks* as though it produces similar figures. This is true especially when the amount added is small enough so that the distortion is not immediately obvious. You may want to provide students with an example such as a 2.5 cm by 3.0 cm rectangle. Have them draw new rectangles, one whose sides are 2 times the length of the original rectangle and the other whose sides are 2 centimeters longer than the sides of the original figure.

ⓥ Develop & Understand: C

Suggested Grouping: Pairs

▶ **Exercises 5 and 6** You may wish to make copies of Lesson 5.3 Master 8, Linkage Strips, for students to use as they create triangles whose sides and angles are easy to match. This exercise applies the principles of previous exercises in a concrete and easy-to-manipulate environment. Students discover that applying a scale factor to the sides of a triangle will produce a smaller, similar triangle. Depending on the availability of supplies, you can have students use paper clips or pipe cleaners in place of brass fasteners.

Share & Summarize

It is important to recognize that multiplication and division can be applied to the sides of a rectangle or triangle to produce a figure similar to the original, but addition and subtraction cannot.

Troubleshooting Some students may be ready to generalize, deciding that the similarity of any two figures can be determined by testing corresponding sides for the same scale factor. If so, this misconception will be cleared up in Investigation 3.

You have used two types of modifications to create rectangles larger and smaller than a given rectangle. You will now try these modifications on a triangle.

ⓥ Develop & Understand: C

Work with a partner. You each need a set of linkage strips and three fasteners. To find lengths on the linkage strips, count the gaps between holes. Each gap is one unit.

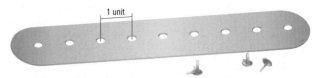

Separately, you and your partner should use your three linkage strips to construct a right triangle with legs 6 units and 8 units and hypotenuse 10 units. Trace the inside of your triangle on a sheet of paper. See ①.

① [triangle with sides 6, 10, 8]

5a. [triangle with sides 3, 5, 4]

5b. [triangle with sides 4, 8, 6]

5. One partner should follow the instructions in Part a, and the other should follow the instructions in Part b.

    a. Construct a triangle whose side lengths are half those of the first triangle. That is, the lengths should be 3, 4, and 5 units. Trace the inside of the triangle on your paper.

    b. Construct a triangle whose side lengths are each 2 units less than those of the first triangle. That is, the lengths should be 4, 6, and 8 units. Trace the inside of the triangle on your paper.

6. With your partner, decide which modification produces a triangle that looks similar to the original triangle.   Halving segment lengths

Share & Summarize

You have modified rectangles and triangles in two ways to create larger and smaller figures.

- In one method, you multiplied or divided each side length by some number.
- In the other method, you added a number to or subtracted a number from each side length.

Which method produced figures that looked similar to the original?
Multiplying or dividing each side length by some positive number

Investigation 3 Ratios of Corresponding Sides

Vocabulary

corresponding angles

corresponding sides

equivalent ratios

Materials

• ruler

• protractor

• metric ruler

Now that you have had some practice thinking about different types of comparisons, turn your attention to ratios of corresponding sides.

It is possible to use different ratios to describe the same relationship.

Example

Maya and Simon think about the ratios of the side lengths in triangles differently.

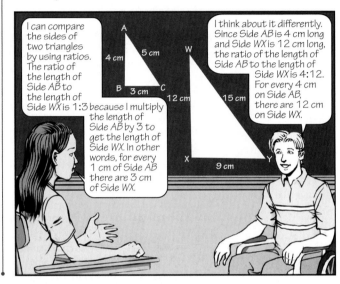

Two ratios are **equivalent ratios** if they represent the same relationship. Maya pointed out that the ratio 1:3 means that for every 1 cm of length on one segment, there are 3 cm of length on the other. Simon said the ratio 4:12 means that for every 4 cm of length on one segment, there are 12 cm of length on the other.

The length of the first segment is multiplied by 3 to get the length of the second segment. Therefore, 1:3 and 4:12 are equivalent ratios.

In the last lesson, we referred to equivalent ratios as proportional.

Lesson 5.3 Similarity and Congruence   **327**

Ratios of Corresponding Sides In this investigation, students use ratios to describe a relationship. They name corresponding parts of similar figures and learn that while the ratios of the lengths of corresponding sides are equivalent for similar figures, equivalent ratios are not sufficient proof that two figures are similar. Read the introductory paragraphs in the text as a class. Then ask students how they can prove that the ratio of Segment m to Segment k is 2:1. Students may suggest that they measure each segment with a ruler and see that one number is twice the other number, measure using some other unit, such as the length of line l; or fold Segment m and match that length to the length of Segment k.

Then introduce the several ways of writing ratios: $\frac{2}{1}$, 2:1, 2 to 1.

Example

Have the class read the cartoon. Point out that a ratio can be looked at in several ways. Maya and Simon have described two of these ways. Encourage a discussion of Maya's and Simon's ideas, and ask students to share any of their own, different ways of thinking about ratios.

Teacher Tips Discuss equivalent ratios and emphasize that the ratios represent the same relationship. You may want to have students give examples of other ratios that are equivalent to 1:3, such as 2:6 and 3:9.

✅ Develop & Understand: A

Suggested Grouping: Pairs

▶ **Exercise 1** You may want to have students use rulers to measure the segments in this exercise. They could also use other units of measure, or estimate the ratio using two integers.

Wrap-Up Discuss Exercise 6 as a class to reinforce the idea that students need to specify what relationship a ratio describes.

Teacher Tips Discuss the terms *corresponding sides* and *corresponding angles* as they relate to the figures at the bottom of page 328. It is difficult to put the definition of corresponding parts into words, but students will understand the definition after seeing some examples. You may want to ask students to identify other corresponding parts of triangles *ABC* and *DEF*.

1. Possible answer: 1:2, 2:4, 4:8
2. Yes; they both represent multiplying by 4.
3. No; the first represents multiplying by 2.5 and the second represents multiplying by 3.
4. No; the first represents multiplying by $\frac{5}{3}$ and the second represents multiplying by $\frac{3}{5}$.
5. Yes; they both represent multiplying by 3.
6. The students need to specify which segments they are using. The ratios 2:3 and 3:2 are not equivalent, but the ratio from the short segment to the long segment is 2:3, and the ratio from the long segment to the short segment is 3:2.

✅ Develop & Understand: A

1. Name at least two ratios equivalent to the ratio of the length of Segment *MN* to the length of Segment *OP*.

Decide whether the ratios in each pair are equivalent. Explain how you know.

2. 1:4 and 2:8

3. $\frac{2}{5}$ and $\frac{3}{9}$

4. 3:5 and 5:3

5. $\frac{1}{3}$:1 and 1:3

6. Brock and Dina were analyzing a pair of line segments. "The lengths are in the ratio 2:3," Brock said. "No," Dina replied, "the ratio is 3:2." Their teacher smiled. "You're both right. But to be clear, you need to give more information about your ratios."

   What did their teacher mean? Are 2:3 and 3:2 equivalent? How could Brock and Dina both be correct?

In Investigation 2, you created rectangles and triangles that were similar to other rectangles and triangles. For each shape, you used a part of the original figure to create the *corresponding part* of the new figure.

Corresponding parts of two similar figures are located in the same place in each figure. For example, Triangles *ABC* and *DEF* are similar. Sides *AB* and *DE* are **corresponding sides**, and ∠*B* and ∠*E* are **corresponding angles**.

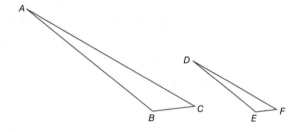

On the Spot *Assessment*

Watch for students who think that the ratios in Exercise 4 are equivalent because they involve the same numbers. Remind them that although these two ratios may be used to describe the same relationship, two ratios *A:B* and *C:D* are considered to be equivalent only when the number you multiply *A* by to get *B* is the same number you multiply *C* by to get *D*. A discussion of Exercise 6 will further reinforce this fact.

When you created similar rectangles and triangles, the ratios of the lengths of each pair of *corresponding sides* were equivalent. This is true for all similar figures. The ratios of the lengths of each pair of corresponding sides must be equivalent.

✓ Develop & Understand: B

The figures in each pair are similar. Identify all pairs of corresponding sides and all pairs of corresponding angles.

7.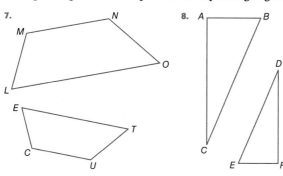

8.

9.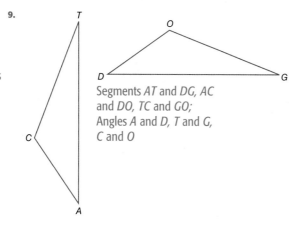

Real-World Link
The concept of similar triangles can be used to estimate dimensions of lakes, heights of pyramids, and distances between planets.

. . . .

7. Segments *LM* and *EC*, *MN* and *CU*, *NO* and *UT*, *LO* and *ET*; Angles *M* and *C*, *N* and *U*, *O* and *T*, *L* and *E*

8. Segments *CA* and *DF*, *AB* and *FE*, *CB* and *DE*; Angles *A* and *F*, *C* and *D*, *B* and *E*

Segments *AT* and *DG*, *AC* and *DO*, *TC* and *GO*; Angles *A* and *D*, *T* and *G*, *C* and *O*

 Assessment

Watch for students who confuse corresponding parts because of the orientations of the figures in Exercises 7–9. You may want these students to either redraw the figures or, when possible, turn one of their textbooks so that both figures have the same orientation and are thus easier to compare.

Teacher Tips Point out that a convention frequently used to match corresponding parts of congruent and similar figures is to designate the order of the vertices so the sides and angles match. For example, △*ABC* is similar to △*XYZ* as shown below.

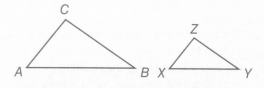

Angle *A* is similar to angle *X*, angle *B* is similar to angle *Y*, angle *C* is similar to angle *Z*.

The sides that are in the same ratio are easy to pair up: *AB* matches *XY*, *BC* matches *YZ*, and *AC* matches *XZ*. This can be shown symbolically as:

A̅B̅C is similar to X̅Y̅Z

The dotted, solid, and curved lines indicate the paired sides, whose ratios *AB:XY*, *BC:YZ*, and *AC:XZ* are all equivalent.

✓ Develop & Understand: B

Suggested Grouping: Pairs

▶ **Exercises 7–9** In this problem set, students practice matching corresponding parts of similar figures. The triangles in Exercise 9 are congruent and similar. You may want to discuss this relationship further using the examples below.

Additional Examples Have students use linkage strips and fasteners to draw two similar triangles that have a scale factor of three. Have them label the triangles *CBA* and *FGH*, being careful to label the triangles so that the vertices are not labeled in alphabetical order. Then have students mark the corresponding sides and angles. Then ask students to sketch and label two similar triangles *XAB* and *CDR* that have a scale factor of one. Make sure students understand that these triangles are also congruent. Have them state which sides and angles are corresponding parts and therefore congruent.

Teacher Tips Before students begin the next exercise set, remind them that the ratios for all pairs of corresponding sides of similar figures are equivalent. Tell them that they will now explore whether or not knowing that the ratios of corresponding sides are equivalent proves that the figures are similar.

In this exercise set, students begin building a more formal test for similarity than the informal strategies they used in Investigation 2. The issue in this problem set is to discover whether polygons whose corresponding sides have a constant ratio are always similar. Students compare quadrilaterals to reach their conclusions. In the next investigation, students continue to build their understanding of similarity by discovering that corresponding angles must also be equal.

✅ *Develop & Understand: C*

Suggested Grouping: Pairs

▶ **Exercise 10** Tell students to measure the quadrilaterals to the nearest tenth of a centimeter, or millimeter. Students will see that the figures are not similar because they do not have the same shape. Remind them that they are checking to see if ratios of each pair of corresponding sides suggest that two polygons are similar.

✅ *Develop & Understand: C*

If figures are similar, each pair of corresponding sides must have the same ratio. But if ratios of corresponding sides are the same, does that mean the figures *must* be similar? You will explore this question now.

10. Here are two quadrilaterals.

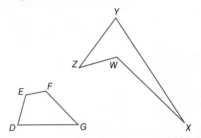

a. Copy and complete the table for quadrilateral *DEFG*.

Description	Side	Length (cm)
longest side	DG	2.4
second-longest side	FG	1.8
third-longest side	DE	1.2
shortest side	EF	0.8

b. Now complete the table for quadrilateral *WXYZ*.

Description	Side	Length (cm)
longest side	XY	4.8
second-longest side	WX	3.6
third-longest side	YZ	2.4
shortest side	ZW	1.6

c. Find the ratio of the longest side in quadrilateral *WXYZ* to the longest side in quadrilateral *DEFG*. Find the ratios of the remaining three pairs of sides in the same way. All ratios are 2:1.

- second longest to second longest
- third longest to third longest
- shortest to shortest

d. What do you notice about the ratios in Part c? Are quadrilaterals *WXYZ* and *DEFG* similar? Explain your answer. The ratios are the same, but the quadrilaterals are not similar because they are not the same shape.

11c. The ratios are the same; yes; the two figures look close to the same shape and corresponding side lengths are in the same ratio. However, we cannot say for sure that the figures have the same shape.

12a. No; only the rectangle, quadrilateral Z, is similar to rectangle A.

12b. The angle measures

12c. Some information about the angles is needed. (Note: Students may not be sure exactly what that information is.)

Math Link

Alaska, the largest U.S. state, has an area of 656,400 square miles. Rhode Island, the smallest, has an area of 1,545 square miles. The ratio of their areas is 1,545:656,400, or about 1:425. This means 425 Rhode Islands could fit inside Alaska!

11. Here is a third quadrilateral.

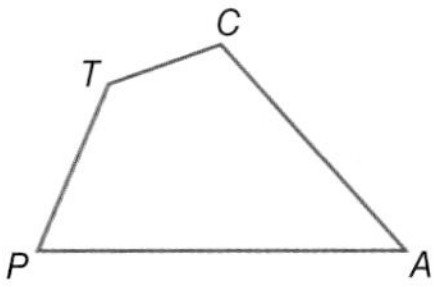

a. Complete the table for quadrilateral *CAPT*.

Description	Side	Length (cm)
longest side	*AP*	3.6
second-longest side	*CA*	2.7
third-longest side	*TP*	1.8
shortest side	*TC*	1.2

b. Find the ratio of the longest side in quadrilateral *CAPT* to the longest side in quadrilateral *DEFG*. Find the ratios of the remaining three sides in the same way. All ratios are 3:2.

c. What do you notice about the ratios you found in Part b? Could quadrilateral *CAPT* be similar to quadrilateral *DEFG*? Explain.

12. The corresponding side lengths of quadrilateral *Y* and quadrilateral *Z* and rectangle *A* are 1:2.

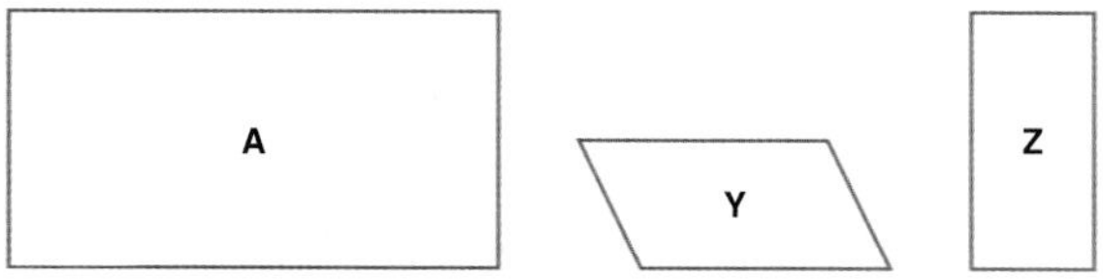

a. Are quadrilaterals *Y* and *Z* both similar to rectangle *A*? Explain.

b. How is quadrilateral *Y* different from quadrilateral *Z*?

c. What information, other than corresponding side lengths having the same ratio, might help you decide whether two polygons are similar?

Share & Summarize
See margin.

1. Describe *equivalent ratios* in your own words.

2. Is the fact that corresponding sides are in the same ratio enough to guarantee that two polygons are similar? Explain your answer.

Additional Answers
Share & Summarize

1. Possible answer: Two ratios are equivalent if you can multiply both parts of one ratio by the same number to get the other ratio.

2. No; we have seen polygons of different shapes (one convex and one concave, for example) with sides in the same ratio, so they are not similar. We need information about the angles.

▶ **Exercise 11** Point out that this exercise provides the basis for learning that corresponding angles in similar figures are congruent, a concept formally introduced in Investigation 4. It is important that students recognize that more information about the angles is needed to determine the similarity of two figures. They do not need to be specific about the type of information needed at this point.

Wrap-Up Discuss students' answers to Exercises 10d, 11c, and 12c.

Share & Summarize

For **Exercise 2**, have students give examples of figures that have proportional sides but are not similar. It is important that they realize that, in general, corresponding sides in a common ratio is *not* enough to guarantee similarity.

Be sure this discussion includes the students' answers for Exercise 12c on page 332, when students predicted the information that would be necessary to show similarity. Some students may conjecture that the angles must have a special relationship, and some may even guess that corresponding angles are equal. The discovery of the importance of angles in determining similarity is assumed in the opening text of Investigation 4, where these ideas will be further developed.

Troubleshooting If students have difficulty understanding why corresponding sides in the same ratio do not prove that two polygons are similar, have them focus on the shape of the figures. If they still seem unsure, try showing different examples on the overhead. Use linkage strips or a transparency to construct two quadrilaterals that meet the ratio test and the angle test. Verify with students that these meet the test. Project one quadrilateral onto the board and have a student trace its image. Then use the overhead to vary the size of the second quadrilateral until its image projects on top of the tracing on the board.

On Your Own Exercises
Pages 335–340
Exercises 14–17, 25–27

Identifying Similar Polygons In this investigation, students determine similarity by looking for corresponding sides with the same common ratio and congruent corresponding angles. Then they look at ways to determine if nonlinear figures are similar. Before starting the problem sets, review the findings from Investigation 3: that corresponding sides in a *common ratio* do not guarantee similarity. Ask students what else is needed to guarantee similarity. If someone does not suggest it, tell students that you must also have congruent corresponding angles. Tell students that this is an important fact that they will use in the remainder of the chapter.

Teacher Tips In the next exercise set, students determine if pairs of polygons are similar and explain their answers. Remind students to give specific mathematical explanations for their answers and point out that it is not sufficient to say that the figures are not the same shape. Students need to explain why they know the figures are not the same shape.

✅ Develop & Understand: A

Suggested Grouping: Pairs

▶ **Exercises 3 and 5** Point out that in these exercises students determine similarity of polygons with more than four sides.

Investigation 4 Identifying Similar Polygons

Materials

- ruler
- protractor

In Investigation 3, you found that when two figures are similar the ratio of their corresponding side lengths is always the same. Another way of saying this is that the lengths of corresponding sides share a *common ratio.*

You also discovered that *angles* are important in deciding whether two figures are similar. However, you might not have found the relationship between corresponding angles. In fact, *for two polygons to be similar, corresponding angles must be congruent.* You will not prove this fact here, but you will use it throughout the rest of this chapter.

To test whether two polygons are similar, you need to check only that corresponding side lengths share a common ratio and that corresponding angles are congruent. Two angles are congruent if they have the same measure.

✅ Develop & Understand: A

Determine whether the figures in each pair are similar. If they are not similar, explain how you know.

1. Not similar; Possible explanations: Corresponding angles are not congruent. *Or,* corresponding side lengths do not share a common ratio.

1.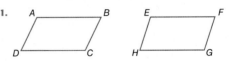

2. Similar

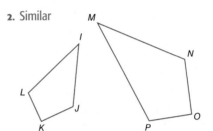

3. Not similar; corresponding side lengths do not share a common ratio.

3.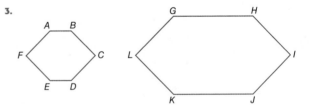

Determine whether the figures in each pair are similar. If they are not similar, explain how you know.

4.

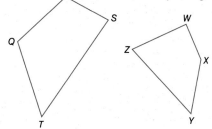

Not similar; corresponding angles are not congruent.

5. Similar

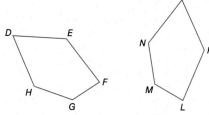

If two figures do not have line segments and angles to measure, how can you decide whether they are similar? One method is to check important corresponding segments and angles, even if they are not drawn. For example, on these two spirals, you might measure the widest and tallest spans of the figures, shown by the dashed segments, and check whether they share a common ratio.

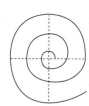 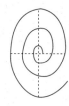

Just checking these two segments will not tell you for *sure* that the figures are similar, but it will give you an idea whether they *could* be. If the ratios are not equivalent, you will know for certain the figures are not similar.

Wrap-Up Discuss which pairs of polygons are similar, which are not, and take special note of the pair of congruent figures in Exercise 5. Emphasize that congruent figures are similar figures whose side lengths are in a constant ratio of 1:1.

Teacher Tips As a class, read and discuss the ideas about determining whether shapes without sides or angles are similar after the exercise set on page 333. Have students share their ideas about how to test for similarity in cases such as these. Reinforce that these methods do not prove that the figures are similar, only either that they *could be* similar or that they are *not* similar. Students will test their ideas in the following exercise set.

Suggested Grouping: Pairs

▶ **Exercise 6** Point out that most students will have an intuitive sense that these, and in fact all, circles are similar. Some students may have a hard time deciding why this is true. You may want to use one of these methods to illustrate the idea for these students:

- One way to illustrate the idea is to take two circles, one larger than the other and use pins, thumbtacks, or paper brads to attach them at their centers. This makes it easy to compare the radii. If one radius of the big circle is twice as long as the one radius of the small circle, then all the other radii of the two circles will have the same relationship.

- Another way to think about it is to think about the distance you are from a circular-shaped object. If you have a circle, you cannot tell if it is a small circle that is close to you or a big circle that is far away. For example, ask students whether they can tell how close they are to a full Moon simply by looking at it. Then ask them how they think the Moon would look if they were closer to it, and how it would look if it were as far away as the Sun. Point out that the Sun may look a little smaller than the Moon, but that it is actually much larger.

- One other idea is to relate the circle to other figures. Just as a square is completely determined by a single measurement (its side), a circle is completely determined by a single measurement (its radius). So all circles, as well as all squares, cubes, and spheres, are similar.

Wrap-Up Have students share their answers and explanations for the three problems.

Share & Summarize

Have students prepare their figures on an acetate sheet so that you can project the most challenging. Then have volunteers make the measurements and explain why the figures are or are not similar to the one shown in the text.

Develop & Understand: B

Work with a partner. Try to figure out whether each pair of figures is or could be similar. Explain your decisions.

6. Similar; all diameters share the same ratio.
7. Not similar; Possible explanation: First figure is about 3 times as wide as it is tall; second figure is about 2 times as tall as it is wide.
8. Similar; Possible explanations: Corresponding measurements share a common ratio. *Or,* the figures match when put on top of one another.

6.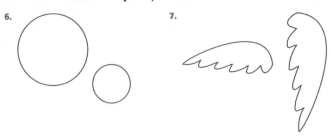

7.

8.

Share & Summarize

Challenge your partner by drawing two pentagons, one that is similar to this pentagon and another that is not. Exchange drawings with your partner.

Try to figure out which of your partner's pentagons is similar to the original, and explain how you decided. Verify with your partner that you each have correctly identified the similar pentagon.

Drawings and explanations will vary.

Troubleshooting

Some students may have trouble creating a figure similar to a given figure. These students may need some scaffolding-type questions to help them determine the angle measures and some possible side lengths. The point is for them to try to build in the right characteristics: sides in the same ratio (e.g., half as long or three times as long as the original) and equal corresponding angles.

Practice & *Apply*

1. Look at the triangles below. Make no measurements.

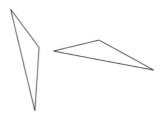

a. Just by looking, guess whether the triangles are congruent.
Answers will vary.
b. Check your guess by finding a way to determine whether the triangles are congruent. Are they congruent? How do you know?
Yes; Possible explanation: They fit on top of each other exactly.

2. Look at the triangles below. Make no measurements.

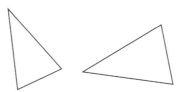

a. Just by looking, guess whether the triangles are congruent.
Answers will vary.
b. Check your guess by finding a way to determine whether the triangles are congruent. Are they congruent? How do you know?
No; Possible explanation: They do not fit on top of each other exactly.

3. Examine these rectangles.

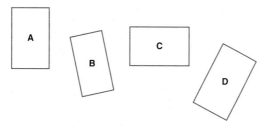

a. Just by looking, guess which rectangle is congruent to rectangle A.   Answers will vary.

b. Find a way to determine whether your selection is correct. Which rectangle *is* congruent to rectangle A? How do you know?
C; Possible explanations: The length and width of A are equal to those of C. *Or,* if you trace the figures and lay A and C on top of each other, you see they are identical.

Investigation 1
Pages 322–324
Practice & Apply: 1–4
Connect & Extend: 18–21

Investigation 2
Pages 325–326
Practice & Apply: 5–6
Connect & Extend: 22

Investigation 3
Pages 327–331
Practice & Apply: 7–13
Connect & Extend: 23–25

Investigation 4
Pages 332–334
Practice & Apply: 14–17
Connect & Extend: 25–27

Assign Anytime
Mixed Review: 28–37

▶ **Exercises 1–3** Students are asked to make a guess about congruence or similarity, then check their guesses. This is an important activity that encourages and develops spatial reasoning and reinforces the idea that you cannot always tell whether two figures are similar or congruent just by looking—often you need to use some kind of test for congruence or similarity.

▶ **Exercise 4** Students determine the congruency of figures that are not polygons for the first time.

▶ **Exercise 5c** It is important that all students realize that they cannot reduce the size of a rectangle by subtraction and still produce a similar figure.

▶ **Exercise 6** Students get a preview of a situation where addition and subtraction can be used to enlarge and reduce similar figures. This works because the figure is a square and all squares are similar to one another.

Additional Answer

6d. They both make squares similar to the original. All squares are similar, so although the square in Part C is not defined to have sides that share a common ratio, the sides are in fact all half as long as the original square's sides.

4. Examine the figures below.

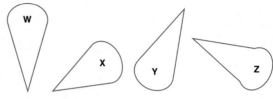

4b. Y; If you trace W and Y and lay them on top of each other, you see they are identical.

a. Just by looking, guess which figure is congruent to figure W. Answers will vary.

b. Find a way to determine whether your selection is correct. Which figure *is* congruent to figure W? How do you know?

5. Rectangle R is 4.5 cm by 15 cm.

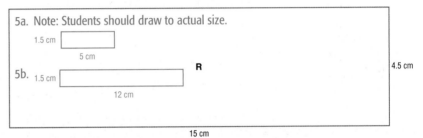

5a. Note: Students should draw to actual size.

1.5 cm

5 cm

5b. 1.5 cm

12 cm

R

4.5 cm

15 cm

a. Draw and label a rectangle with sides one-third as long as those of rectangle R.

b. Draw and label a rectangle with sides three centimeter shorter than those of rectangle R.

c. Which of your rectangles is similar to rectangle R?

5c. The rectangle in Part a, whose sides are one-third those of the original.

6a. Note: Students should draw to actual size.

6 cm

6 cm

6b. 2 cm

2 cm

6c. 3 cm

3 cm

6. In Investigation 2, you explored two ways to modify rectangles and triangles. One method produces similar figures. The other does not. In this exercise, you will examine whether either of the methods will produce a similar figure when the original is a square.

a. Draw a square that is 6 cm on a side. This is your *original* square.

b. Make a new square with sides one-third as long as the sides of your original square.

c. Make a new square with sides three centimeters shorter than those of your original square.

d. Which of the methods in Parts b and c creates a square that is similar to your original? Explain.   See margin.

Real-World Link

Of the approximately
301 million people in the
United States in 2007, an
estimated 31 million were
born in another country. This
is a ratio of 31:301, or about
1 in 10.

. . . .

9. Equivalent; they
both represent
multiplying by $\frac{4}{3}$.

10. Equivalent; they
both represent
multiplying by $\frac{b}{a}$.

11. Possible answers:
4:6, 20:30, 2x:3x

12. Possible answers:
$\frac{3}{5}$, $\frac{60}{100}$, $\frac{3n}{5n}$

13. Possible answers:
1:1, 3:3, b:b

14. Segments *LM* and
QS, *MN* and *SR*, *NL*
and *RQ*; Angles *M*
and *S*, *N* and *R*, *L*
and *Q*

15. Segments *MA* and
PY, *AT* and *YL*, *TH*
and *LO*, *HM* and
OP; Angles *A* and *Y*,
T and *L*, *H* and *O*,
M and *P*

Decide whether the ratios in each pair are equivalent. Explain how you decided.　7, 8.　See margin.

7. 1:3 and 9:11

8. $\frac{1}{2}$ and $\frac{2}{3}$

9. 3:4 and 6:8

10. *a:b* and 2*a*:2*b*

Name two ratios that are equivalent to each given ratio.

11. 2:3

12. $\frac{6}{10}$

13. 50:50

Exercises 14 and 15 show a pair of similar figures. Identify all pairs of corresponding sides and angles.

14.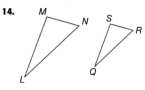

15.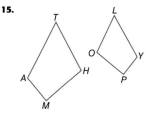

16. Examine these triangles.

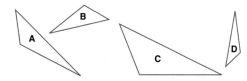

　a. Just by looking, guess which triangle is similar to triangle A.
　　Answers will vary.
　b. Make some measurements to help determine whether your
　　selection is correct. Which triangle *is* similar to triangle A?　D

17. Examine these quadrilaterals.

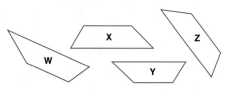

　a. Just by looking, guess which is similar to quadrilateral Z.
　　Answers will vary.
　b. Make some measurements to help determine whether your
　　selection is correct. Which quadrilateral *is* similar to
　　quadrilateral Z?　X

Lesson 5.3　Similarity and Congruence　　**337**

▶ **Exercise 10** Students are exposed to ratios
containing variables for the first time, and
they must determine their equivalency.
Suggest that students having difficulty
solving this exercise substitute numbers
for the variables.

Additional Answers

7. Not equivalent; the first represents
multiplying by three and the second
represents multiplying by $\frac{11}{9}$.

8. Not equivalent; the first represents
multiplying by two and the second
represents multiplying by 1.5.

▶ **Exercise 19** Some students may test for more information than they need, such as the measures of the angles of the equilateral triangle in addition to the measures of its sides. For now, this is okay; however, you may want to discuss the minimum number of equal matching parts that ensure congruence in each case.

▶ **Exercise 22** Students will need a safety compass to complete this exercise. Students who have never used a compass will need some basic instruction on its use. You may wish to have students work in pairs on this exercise. You may want to provide them with Lesson 5.3 Master 9 to help with the constructions.

Additional Answers

20a. Possible answers: Measure the length, width, and depth of each cereal box; corresponding measurements should be equal. *Or*, open the boxes up into nets (along the same lines); if the nets are congruent, the boxes are congruent.

20b. Possible answers: Measure the diameter and height of each soup can; corresponding measurements should be equal. Or, place cans side by side to check that heights are equal, and then place one can on top of the other to check that bases are congruent.

18. Possible answer: Measure the radii, or diameters; they should be equal.

19. Possible answer: Measure the length of a side of each triangle; they should be equal.

21. Possible answer: Two similar pentagons could be congruent. They would have to be the same size, same shape, and have the same angles. If two pentagons are congruent, they would have to be similar.

Connect & Extend For each pair of figures, explain what you would measure to test for congruence and what you would look for in your measurements.

18. two circles

19. two equilateral triangles

20. One way to determine whether two-dimensional figures are congruent is to lay them on top of each other. This test will not work with three-dimensional figures.   See margin.

  a. How could you determine whether two cereal boxes are congruent?

  b. How could you determine whether two cylindrical soup cans are congruent?

21. **In Your Own Words** If two pentagons are similar, are they congruent? Explain why or why not. If two pentagons are congruent, are they similar? Explain why or why not.

22. **Challenge** The word *bisect* means to divide into two equal parts. The steps below show how to bisect ∠JKL using a compass and a straightedge.

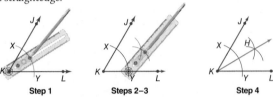

| Step 1 | Steps 2–3 | Step 4 |

Step 1. Place the compass at point *K* and draw an arc that intersects both sides of the angle. Label the intersections *X* and *Y*.

Steps 2–3. With the compass at point *X*, draw an arc in the interior of ∠JKL. Using this setting, place the compass at point *Y* and draw another arc.

Step 4. Label the intersection of these arcs *H*. Then draw $\overrightarrow{KH}$. $\overrightarrow{KH}$ is the *bisector* of ∠JKL.

  a. Describe what is true about ∠JKH and ∠HKL.
  The angles are congruent.
  b. Draw several angles and then bisect them using the above steps.
  See students' work.

23. Maps are designed to be similar to the layout of a city's streets. This map shows a section of London.

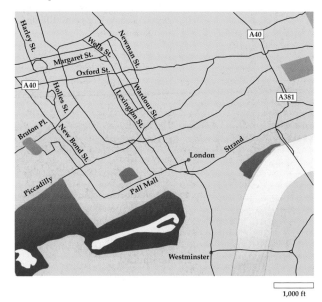

1,000 ft

a. The scale of the map is given at the right. How many inches on the map are the same as 1,000 feet in London? Measure to the nearest $\frac{1}{16}$ inch. $\frac{10}{16}$ in.

b. What is the distance on the map along Oxford St. between Holles St. and Newman St.? $\frac{22}{16}$ in., or $1\frac{3}{8}$ in.

c. What is the real distance (in feet) along Oxford St. between Holles St. and Newman St.?   About 2,200 ft

d. What is the distance on the map along New Bond St. between Bruton Pl. and Piccadilly? $\frac{3}{4}$ in., or $\frac{12}{16}$ in.

e. What is the real distance along New Bond St. between Bruton Pl. and Piccadilly?   About 1,200 ft

24. You have two polygons that you know are similar.

a. What would you measure to determine whether the two similar polygons are also congruent?

b. What would you need to know about your measurements to be sure the polygons are congruent? Explain.

24a. The lengths of one pair of corresponding sides

24b. If the lengths are equal, the ratio of lengths is 1:1. Since the polygons are similar, the ratio of lengths of other corresponding sides must also be 1:1, so the polygons must be congruent.

Lesson 5.3 Similarity and Congruence   **339**

▶ **Exercise 23** Students gain practical experience using ratios by finding distances on a map.

▶ **Exercises 26a and 26b** Students generalize their answer from Exercise 5 on page 328, where they looked at the similarity of two circles. Then they determine the similarity for three-dimensional figures. Some students may struggle before realizing that no test is required in either of these cases.

▶ **Exercise 27b** Some students may not immediately see that no shortcut is needed to test squares for similarity.

Quick Check
Informal Assessment Students should be able to:

✔ identify congruent figures, angles, and segments by matching or measuring

✔ identify corresponding sides and angles of similar or congruent polygons

✔ identify equivalent ratios

✔ test for similarity by identifying corresponding sides with equivalent ratios and equal corresponding angles

Quick Quiz

See Lesson 5.3 Master 10 for a copy of this quiz.

1. Is a triangle with side lengths 3, 4, and 5 similar to a triangle with side lengths 5, 12, and 13? Why or why not? No. The ratios of sides are not equal; for example, the ratio of the shorter sides is $\frac{3}{5}$. This is not the same as the ratio of the longer sides: $\frac{5}{13}$.

2. Is the ratio 10:4 equivalent to the ratio 2.5:1? Why or why not? Yes, the first number in both ratios are 2.5 times the second number.

3. There are three rectangles in the diagram: *BADC*, *AXYD*, and *XBCY*. Are any of these similar to any other? Explain.

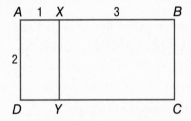

Rectangle *AXYD* is similar to rectangle *ABCD* with Segment *AX* corresponding to Segment *AD*. The two rectangles are similar because they each have congruent corresponding angles and the corresponding sides are in a common ratio of 2:1.

Use the figures below to solve Exercises 4 and 5.

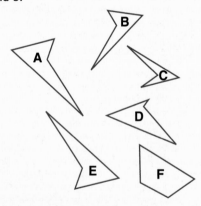

4. Which figure or figures are similar to Figure A? Figure E and Figure B

5. Which figure is congruent to Figure A? Figure E

---

25. He is not correct. Any pair of similar rectangles in which side lengths are in a ratio of 1:2 will also have the perimeter with a ratio of 1:2.

Math Link

Ratios can be written in several ways.
- one to two
- 1 to 2
- 1:2
- $\frac{1}{2}$

26c. Possible answer: Measure their diameters and heights. The ratio of the heights should be the same as the ratio of the diameters.

Mixed Review

---

25. Preview Delsin proposed a conjecture. "If you are given two similar rectangles with side lengths that share a common ratio of 1 to 2, the ratio of the perimeters are also 1 to 2. That is, the perimeter of the larger rectangle is twice the perimeter of the smaller rectangle."

Is Delsin correct? If he is, explain how you know. If he is not, give a counterexample for which the conjecture is not true.

26. In Investigation 1, you examined rules for testing two figures to determine whether they are congruent. For each pair of figures in this exercise, describe a test that you could use to tell whether they are similar.

a. two circles
You do not need to do anything. All circles are similar.
b. two cubes
You do not need to do anything. All cubes are similar.
c. two cylinders

27. In Investigation 4 on page 332, you discovered that *similar polygons* have corresponding sides that share a common ratio and corresponding angles that are congruent. For some special polygons, you can find easier tests for similarity. For each pair of special polygons below, find a shortcut for testing whether they are similar.

a. two rectangles Possible answer: Right angles are always congruent, so just test the side lengths.
b. two squares
You do not need to do anything. All squares are similar.

Use the fact that $783 \cdot 25 = 19,575$ to find each product without using a calculator.

28. $7.83 \cdot 25$ 195.75 **29.** $78.3 \cdot 2.5$ 195.75 **30.** $7,830 \cdot 250$
1,957,500

Use the fact that $7,848 \div 12 = 654$ to find each quotient without using a calculator.

31. $7,848 \div 0.12$ **32.** $7.848 \div 12$ 0.654 **33.** $78.48 \div 1.2$ 65.4
65,400

Measurement Convert each measurement to meters.

34. 32 cm 0.32 m **35.** 32 mm 0.032 m **36.** 32,000 cm 320 m

37. Statistics Monica asked her homeroom classmates which cafeteria lunch was their favorite. She recorded her findings in a table. Make a bar graph to display Monica's results. See margin.

Lunch	Number of Students
Pizza	10
Veggie lasagna	4
Macaroni and cheese	5
Hamburger	7
Tuna casserole	2
Never buy lunch	2

37. Possible answer:

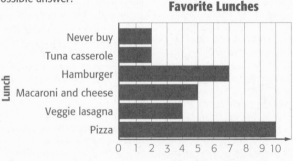

Favorite Lunches

Review & Self-Assessment

Chapter Summary

Comparisons can take many forms, including differences, rates, ratios, and percentages. In this chapter, you learned to compare ratios using equivalent ratios and *unit rates*. You also used percentages as a common scale for comparisons.

In this chapter, you examined two ways in which figures can be considered the same, *congruence* and *similarity*.

You looked at characteristics of congruent and similar figures. For example, congruent figures must be exactly the same shape and size. Similar figures can be different sizes but must be the same shape.

In congruent figures, *corresponding sides* and *corresponding angles* must be congruent. In similar figures, corresponding sides must have lengths that share a common *ratio*. Corresponding angles must be congruent.

You discovered tests that allow you to decide whether two triangles are similar or congruent without finding the measurements of both the angles *and* the sides.

Vocabulary

- congruent
- corresponding angles
- corresponding sides
- counterexample
- ratio
- similar
- unit rate

Strategies and Applications

The questions in this section will help you review and apply the important ideas and strategies developed in this chapter.

Comparing and scaling ratios and rates

1. The Quick Shop grocery store sells four brands of yogurt.

Brand	Meyer's	Quick Shop	Rockyfarm	Shannon
Price	2 for $1.50	3 for $2	$.75 each	$.80 each
Size	8 oz	6 oz	6 oz	8 oz

a. For each brand, find the ratio of price to ounces.

b. For each brand, find the unit price.

c. Use the unit rates to list the brands from least expensive to most expensive.

d. Explain how you could use the ratios in Part a instead of the unit rates to list the brands by how expensive they are. Possible answer: Write each ratio as a decimal and compare them.

1a. Meyer's: 1.5:16; Quick Shop: 2:18; Rockyfarm: 0.75:6; Shannon: 0.8:8

1b. Meyer's: $0.094 per oz; Quick Shop: $0.111 per oz; Rockyfarm: $0.125 per oz; Shannon: $0.10 per oz

1c. Meyer's, Shannon, Quick Shop, Rockyfarm

Review & Self-Assessment

Chapter Summary
This summary helps students recall the major topics of the chapter.

Vocabulary
Students should be able to explain each of the terms listed in the vocabulary section.

▶ **Exercise 1** When finding the ratio of price to ounces for each brand, remind students that two brands show the price for two instead of one. Make sure they adjust the price to find the correct ratio.

▶ **Exercise 2** When setting up proportions for making different amounts of the drink, make sure students correctly multiply the fraction for peach juice.

▶ **Exercise 3** Tell students that, to make the crane look the same when it is larger, each dimension must be enlarged by the same proportion. The wingspan and the height must be enlarged by the same amount, or the picture will be wrong.

▶ **Exercises 4–6** Have students jot down the rules they can remember for similarity and congruence. Tell them to use their notes as they answer each question.

2e. Possible answer: The ratio of tea to drink is 3:3.5, which is equivalent to 6:7. That means it takes 6 quarts of tea to make 7 quarts of drink; the remaining quart is peach juice.

2. Every summer, Joe makes his famous peach cooler. To make the drink, he mixes three quarts of tea with $\frac{1}{2}$ quart of peach juice.

   a. Find the ratio of tea to peach juice in Joe's peach cooler.   3:0.5

   b. Find the ratio of tea to peach cooler, that is, to the final drink.
   3:3.5

   c. If Joe has only two quarts of tea, how much peach juice should he add? $\frac{1}{3}$ qt

   d. For a party, Joe wants to make seven quarts of peach cooler. How much tea and peach juice does he need? 6 qt tea, 1 qt peach juice

   e. Explain how you found your answer for Part d.

3. The sandhill crane has a wingspan of approximately six feet, and is about four feet tall. If you were to draw a proportional picture of the crane with a wingspan of nine inches, what would be the height of the crane in your drawing? $\frac{1}{2}$ foot or 6 inches

Understanding congruence and similarity

4. Consider the difference between similarity and congruence.

   a. Can similar figures also be congruent? Do similar figures *have* to be congruent?   Yes, no

   b. Can congruent figures also be similar? Do congruent figures *have* to be similar?   Yes, yes

5. Explain how you can tell whether two angles are congruent.
   They will have the same measure.

6. Suppose you know that two triangles are similar.

   a. What do you know about their side lengths?
   Corresponding side lengths have the same ratio.
   b. What do you know about their angles?
   Corresponding angles are congruent.

Demonstrating Skills

7. Examine the tile pattern. Write the ratio of white tiles to purple tiles.   16 : 33

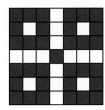

8. Suppose you want to tile a large area using this pattern. Make a ratio table of possible numbers of purple and white tiles that you could use.   See margin.

Find the value of the variable in each proportion.

9. $\frac{12}{5} = \frac{x}{15}$ 36

10. $\frac{2}{y} = \frac{4}{7}$ 3.5

11. $\frac{92}{36} = \frac{23}{w}$ 9

12. $\frac{a}{4} = \frac{15}{60}$ 1

Testing figures for congruence and similarity

13. Consider the tests you know for congruent and similar triangles.

    a. Describe a congruence test involving only the sides of triangles.

    b. Describe a similarity test involving only the sides of triangles.

    c. Describe a similarity test involving only the angles of triangles.

    d. Compare the three tests you described.

14. How can you tell whether two polygons are similar? How can you tell whether two polygons are congruent?   See margin.

Demonstrating Skills

Tell whether the figures in each pair are congruent, similar, or neither.

15.

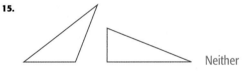

Neither

13a. If all corresponding sides of two triangles are congruent, the triangles are congruent.

13b. If all corresponding sides of two triangles are in the same ratio, the triangles are similar.

13c. If all corresponding angles in two triangles are congruent, the triangles are similar.

13d. Possible answer: Each test uses three pieces of information. For each, you have to compare corresponding parts. If the sides are congruent, the triangles are congruent. But if the angles are congruent, the triangles are similar but not necessarily congruent.

▶ **Exercises 7–8** Remind students that each color tile can be used in any of the ratios; have them work with a partner to compare the different colors and to form the ratio table.

▶ **Exercises 9–12** These exercises are posed without providing a context. All these problems use variables so students can work on their algebraic skills. Remind students that the variable must be in the numerator before they can find its value. Monitor to see that they cross-multiply correctly.

▶ **Exercises 13–14** Have students draw two triangles and test them for similarity and congruence using the tests they described.

▶ **Exercises 15–17** Watch for students who have trouble distinguishing whether pairs of figures are congruent, similar, or neither due to the orientation of the figures. Remind students to look closely at pairs of shapes that are turned at different angles. Have them mark sides that are the same as they look for similarity.

Additional Answers
8. Possible table:

Purple	33	66	99	132	165	198
White	16	32	48	64	80	96

14. For two polygons to be similar, corresponding angles must be congruent and corresponding sides must share a common ratio. For two polygons to be congruent, corresponding angles and corresponding sides must be congruent.

▶ **Exercises 18–22** Watch for students who have trouble distinguishing whether pairs of figures are congruent, similar, or neither due to the orientation of the figures.

Tell whether the figures in each pair are congruent, similar, or neither.

16.

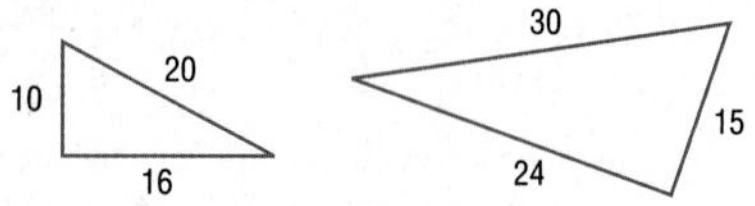

Similar

17.

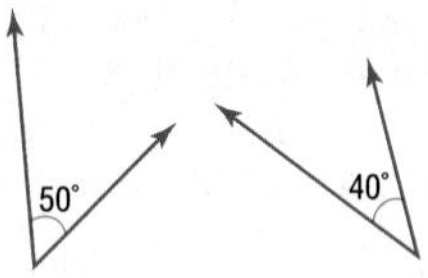

Neither

18.

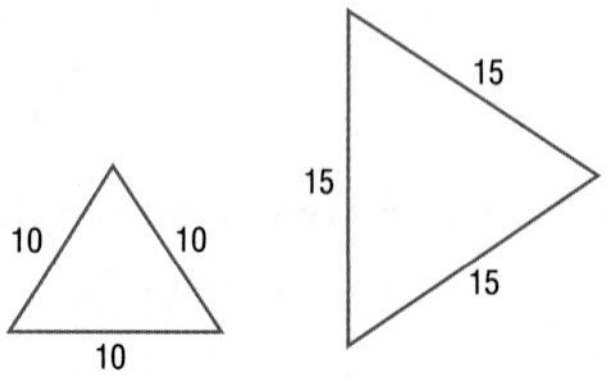

Similar

19.

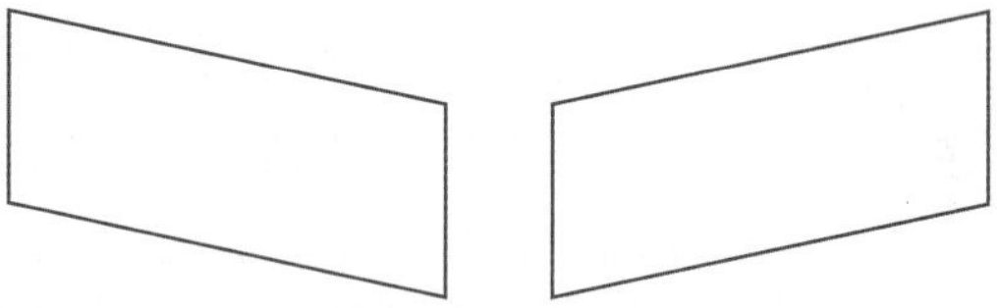

Congruent

20.

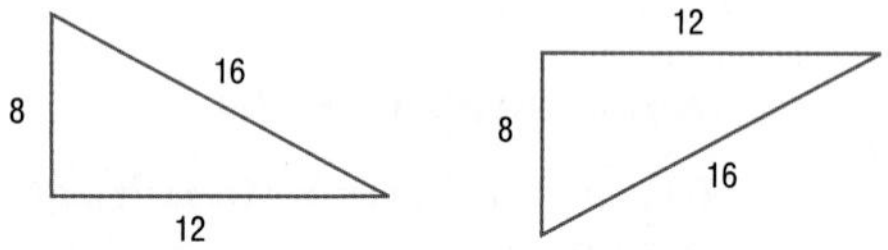

Congruent

21.

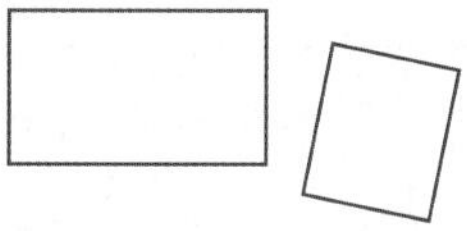

Neither

22.

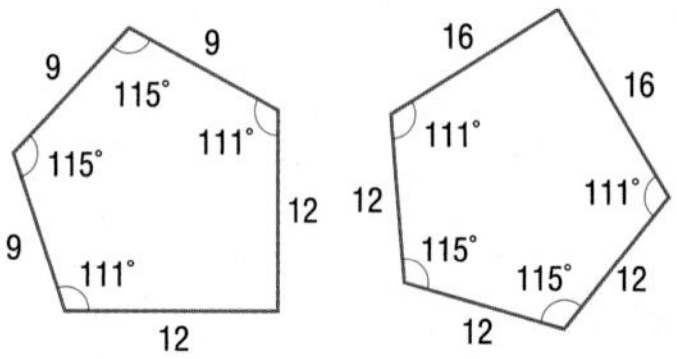

Similar

Test-Taking Practice

1 The table below shows the amount that different people paid for gasoline. Use proportions to find the unit price that each person paid. Who received the best buy? Round to the nearest cent.

Name	Amount Paid	Gallons of Gas
Dave	$35.76	12
Amelia	$41.44	14
Roman	$27.45	9

Show your work:

$\frac{35.76}{12} = \frac{d}{1}$

$35.76 = 12d$

$d = 2.98$

$\frac{41.44}{14} = \frac{r}{1}$

$41.44 = 14r$

$r = 2.96$

$\frac{27.45}{9} = \frac{n}{1}$

$27.45 = 9n$

$n = 3.05$

Dave: $2.98/gal,
Amelia: $2.96/gal,
Roman: $3.05/gal.

Answer: Dave $2.98/gal, Amelia $2.96/gal, Roman $3.05/gal. Amelia received the better deal.

Show your work.

Answer _____

MULTIPLE CHOICE

2 Which of the following is <u>not</u> proportional to $\frac{36}{60}$?

A $\frac{27}{45}$

B $\frac{3}{5}$

C $\frac{12}{25}$

D $\frac{9}{15}$

3 Triangle *ABC* is similar to triangle *DEF.*

What is the missing measure *x*?

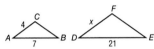

E 7

F 10

G 12

H 16

4 Which of the following is a fraction between $\frac{1}{3}$ and $\frac{1}{4}$?

A $\frac{1}{2}$

B $\frac{3}{10}$

C $\frac{1}{5}$

D $\frac{2}{20}$

5 Which of the following fractions is proportional to $\frac{16}{54}$?

E $\frac{32}{54}$

F $\frac{4}{9}$

G $\frac{18}{56}$

H $\frac{8}{27}$

6

Percents

Chapter Overview

In this chapter, students learn how to use percents to represent parts of a whole. They convert among percents, fractions, and decimals. They also find percents of quantities, and use percents to compare parts of different–sized wholes.

Students apply percents to situations such as finding sale prices for items with a percent discount. They also solve problems that involve finding the percent of a whole that are represented by a part and the size of a whole when a given percent represents a given part.

The **Big** Picture

Links to the Past	**Chapter 6**	**Links to the Future**
Course 1, Chapter 2 Converting among fractions and decimals. Comparing fractions and decimals. **Grade 5** Using fractions and decimals to represent part of a whole.	**Lesson 6.1** (p. 348) Use Percents	**Course 2, Chapter 10** Proportional Reasoning and Percents (pp. 492–555) **Course 3, Chapter 3** Percents and Proportions (pp. 110–143)
Grade 4 Understanding simple percents (25%, 50%, 100%).	**Lesson 6.2** (p. 368) Percent of a Quantity	**Course 2, Chapter 6** Data and Probability (pp. 260–317) **Course 3, Chapter 3** Percents and Proportions (pp. 110–143)
Course 1, Chapter 4 Multiplying and dividing with fractions.	**Lesson 6.3** (p. 380) Percents and Wholes	**Course 2, Chapter 10** Proportional Reasoning and Percents (pp. 492–555)

Mathematical Background

Percents appear in many areas of our everyday lives, such as interest rates, weather reports, test grades, taxes, and sales discounts. Everyone needs to understand and be able to work with percents.

The word percent comes from the Latin per centum, or "out of 100." So, for example, 15 percent is just another way of saying "15 out of 100" or "15 hundredths." The percent sign, %, is just a modification of $\frac{}{100}$: 15% is a fast way of writing $\frac{15}{100}$.

One reason percents are so handy is that they are all based on a common scale of 100. Since all percents involve the same denominator, they are very easy to compare. For example, suppose you are trying to compare the number of students trying out for sports teams in two schools: In School A, 247 out of 1,351 students are on teams, while in School B, there are 114 out of 598 students on teams. Comparing $\frac{247}{1,351}$ versus $\frac{114}{598}$ is not easy. Converting these fractions to percents gives about 18% for School A and about 19% for School B. This shows you right away that interest in sports in the two schools is just about the same, or approximately one out of five students in each school participates on a sports team.

Not every fraction can be written as an exact, whole number percent, however. For example, you can write $\frac{1}{4}$ exactly as 25%, but writing $\frac{1}{7}$ as an exact percent is more difficult. The best one can do is $14\frac{2}{7}\%$. If an exact number is needed, $\frac{1}{7}$ is more practical.

For everyday purposes, a "feel" for the sizes of various percents is helpful to save one from unnecessary calculations. When a person sees 50%, he or she should know intuitively that 50% is $\frac{1}{2}$.

You can describe many real-world situations by sentences of the form "a is x% of b." If you know any two of the three quantities in such a statement, you can always figure out the value of the third. This fact used to be referred to as the "three kinds of percent problems," and being able to solve the three kinds of percent problems continues to be very important.

What is 23% of 47?   What percent of 50 is 40?   7 is 30% of what number?

Understanding Percents Students learn that percents can be used as an alternative to fractions that have a denominator of 100. They build on what they know about converting between fractions and decimals to include converting to and from percents. They also develop an understanding of why percents are a convenient way of representing and comparing different kinds of data. Students model percents by using 100–grids, circle graphs, and number lines. They also see that percents can help them make comparisons in many types of real–life situations.

Part–Whole Percents In part–whole situations, the percent can never exceed 100%, since 100% is "all." For example, it makes no sense to say 120% of the class went on the field trip. The sports cliché is to give 110% percent, which is impossible mathematically (but figuratively means to push oneself beyond one's usual performance level). However, percents greater than 100 do come up in other types of situations, and students need to become comfortable with these as well. For example, it makes perfectly good sense to say, "The price of butter today is 130% of what it was in 1995." Or, "On average, doctors make 300% of what nurses make."

Additional Reading

According to Kroll and Mitler in *Research Ideas for the Classroom: Middle Grades Mathematics*, students will be more effective problem solvers if they are able to move flexibly among steps as they do problems. Students should be able to explain their steps as they do real life percent problems.

Planning Guide
Lesson Resources

	Pacing: 5 days	**Pacing:** 3 days	**Pacing:** 4 days
	Lesson 6.1	**Lesson 6.2**	**Lesson 6.3**
Lesson Title	**Use Percents** (p. 348)	**Percent of a Quantity** (p. 368)	**Percents and Wholes** (p. 380)
Lesson Objectives	• To recognize that a percent is a comparison of a quantity to 100 • To recognize that equivalent fractions, decimals, and percents are different representations of the same value • To convert among fractions, decimals, and percents • To develop a sense of the relative amounts that various percents represent	• To calculate a percent of a quantity • To use benchmarks to estimate a percent of a quantity	• To calculate the percent of a given whole that a given part is • To find the whole quantity when told what percent of the whole a given part represents
Materials	sheet of 100–grids, transparent 100–grid, supermarket receipts	sheet of 100–grids, slips of paper numbered 1–20, paper bag	page from a telephone book, trash can or bucket, 6 sheets of paper, score sheets
Quick Review Math Handbook	**Lesson 2.7** Meaning of Percent **Lesson 2.9** Fraction, Decimal, and Percent Relationship	**Lesson 2.8** Using and Finding Percents	**Lesson 2.8** Using and Finding Percents
Print Resources	CRM Study Guide and Intervention (p. 4) CRM Skills Practice (p. 5) CRM Problem-Solving Practice (p. 6) CRM Enrichment (p. 7) • Investigation Notebook and Reflection Journal • Differentiation Handbook	CRM Study Guide and Intervention (p. 10) CRM Skills Practice (p. 11) CRM Problem-Solving Practice (p. 12) CRM Enrichment (p. 13) • Investigation Notebook and Reflection Journal • Differentiation Handbook	CRM Study Guide and Intervention (p. 15) CRM Skills Practice (p. 16) CRM Problem-Solving Practice (p. 17) CRM Enrichment (p. 18) • Investigation Notebook and Reflection Journal • Differentiation Handbook
Technology Resources	TeacherWorks Plus Classroom Presentation Toolkit ExamView Assessment Suite StudentWorks Plus Math Online Brain Pops • Concepts in Motion	TeacherWorks Plus Classroom Presentation Toolkit ExamView Assessment Suite StudentWorks Plus Math Online Brain Pops • Concepts in Motion	TeacherWorks Plus Classroom Presentation Toolkit ExamView Assessment Suite StudentWorks Plus Math Online Brain Pops • Concepts in Motion

*Included in the Impact Mathematics Manipulative Kit

Assessment Resources

MARS Assessment: Teaching with Purpose

Basketball

In *Basketball*, students interpret the results of a survey of 5th grade boys who were asked to name their favorite sport. Students also use percentages to compare the number of boys who chose each sport.

Targeting the Task

- **Diagnostic**—Use Exercises 1–5 in the *Basketball* assessment to determine students' understanding of how to interpret surveys and use percents. For those students who do not have this understanding, completing this unit is needed.

- **Formative**—Exercises 1–5 can be administered individually according to the lessons.

- **Summative**—Administer the complete *Basketball* performance-based assessment.

CRM Chapter 6 MARS Assessment (pp. 42–44)

> **Chapter 6 MARS Performance-Based Assessment**
>
> **Basketball**
>
> **This problem gives you the chance to:**
> - interpret the results of a survey
> - use percents
>
> Marvin asked all the boys at a Grade 5 basketball tournament, "What is your favorite sport?"
>
> The table shows the results of Marvin's survey.
>
> | Sport | Number of boys |
> | --- | --- |
> | Baseball | 19 |
> | Basketball | 60 |
> | Football | 19 |
> | Ice Hockey | 12 |
> | Soccer | 7 |
> | Other | 3 |
>
> 1. How many boys are in Marvin's survey? _____
>
> 2. What number is the mode? _____
>
> 3. What percentage of boys chose basketball? _____
>
> 4. What percentage of boys chose ice hockey? _____
>
> 5. Marvin says, "My survey shows that basketball is the most popular sport in the United States."
>
>   Give two reasons why Marvin's conclusion may not be correct.
>   _____
>   _____
>   _____

Assessment Planning Guide

Assessments are available for investigations, lessons, and chapters.

ExamView® Assessment Suite Customize and create multiple versions of tests and quizzes.

	Student Edition	Teacher Edition	Other Resources
Diagnostic			CRM Chapter 6 Pretest (p. 23) Math Online Online Chapter Quiz
Formative	Share & Summarize (pp. 351, 354, 357, 361, 371, 375, 384, 387)	Troubleshooting (pp. 351, 357, 359, 360, 370, 371, 375, 382, 384) On the Spot Assessment (pp. 353, 374, 380, 383, 387) Quick Check (pp. 367, 379, 392) Quick Quiz (pp. 367, 379, 392)	
Summative	Review & Self-Assessment (pp. 393–395)		CRM Chapter 6 Test: Forms A and B (pp. 27–36) CRM Standardized Test Practice (p. 39)
Performance-Based	In Your Own Words (pp. 366, 378, 391)		CRM MARS Performance-Based Assessment (p. 41) CRM Chapter Performance Assessment (p. 37)

Differentiated Instruction

Reaching All Learners

Below are suggestions on differentiating the materials presented in this chapter. Additional modifications should be considered.

Approaching Level   **AL**

Lesson 6.1: 10x10 Grid Students who have trouble understanding and/or using percents may still need some sort of visual aid to make the concept more concrete. Provide a laminated 10 x 10 grid that students can use with markers and wipe clean. Show students how to use the grid by coloring in the correct number of squares. Point out that one row or column is ten squares, so students can shade faster. Remind students that working with percents means working with parts of a whole. Allow them to use it the grid when doing exercises involving percents, but require them to show their answers in written form as well, so that they can gradually develop confidence and be able to work without the grid.

Beyond Level   **BL**

Lesson 6.1: Surveys Have students who understand percents work with a partner to create a survey for the class. Allow them to take the survey, and then have them give their results in the form of percents. For example, students may find the percent of students in the class who prefer iced tea to soda. Instruct students to create a small poster displaying the results of their survey. On the poster, make sure they show the steps for showing at least one survey finding as a percent. Then, have pairs present their findings and discuss whether the results they found were the results they expected. In discussion, use percents to describe each finding.

On Level   **OL**

Lesson 6.3: Word Problems Students can use percents and wholes to create their own word problems. Have groups work together to create a word problem involving percents and wholes. Make sure they phrase the question in the problem as, "What percent of _____ is _____?" Remind students that in order to solve a word problem, there must be sufficient information available to set up the problem. Have them decide on a topic, decide what information is necessary, and then write the problem. Tell them to write the problems neatly and to take up one whole piece of paper. Solve the problems as a class, and display them for others to see and solve.

English Language Learners   **ELL**

Lesson 6.3: Reading Percents Students who are learning the English language may need extra help understanding the importance of word order when using percents. They may have difficulty distinguishing "What percent of 140 is 12?" from "What is 12 percent of 140?" Solve several problems and make sure students can find the whole number first. Then concentrate on helping students determine the remaining fact to find. Point out that 12 percent of 140 is not the same as 12 out of 140. Give examples of each type of problem. Write and illustrate at least one of each type of problem on a piece of paper, and have students refer to the paper when they have difficulty.

KEY

AL Approaching Level **OL** On Level **BL** Beyond Level **ELL** English Language Learners

Intervention Planning Guide

CRM Assess students' prerequisite skills and knowledge using the **Chapter 6 Pretest** found in the Chapter 6 Resource Masters, p. 23.

Intensive Intervention two or more years below grade level	Strategic Intervention below grade level	On Level	Beyond Level
If students miss 75% of the exercises:	**If** students miss 50% of the exercises:	**If** students miss 25% of the exercises:	**If** students miss 0%–10% of the exercises:
Then use *Math Triumphs,* an intensive intervention	**Then** choose a resource:	**Then** choose a resource:	**Then** choose a resource:
Math Triumphs, Grade 6 • Chapter 3: Decimals • Chapter 7: Ratios, Rates, and Unit Rates	CRM Study Guide and Intervention (pp. 4, 10, 15) • Investigation Notebook and Reflection Journal • Differentiation Handbook **Math Online** Brain Pops • Concepts in Motion	CRM Skills Practice (pp. 5, 11, 16) CRM Problem-Solving Practice (p. 6, 12, 17) • Investigation Notebook and Reflection Journal	CRM Enrichment (pp. 7, 13, 18) • Differentiation Handbook

Literature Connections
Recommended Outside Reading for Students
Nonfiction
Elam, Kimberly. *Geometry of Design: Studies in Proportion and Composition.* Princeton Architectural Press, 2001.
  This book examines the relationship between mathematics and beauty by showing how artists and designers have used proportions in their work. This book includes common ratios and proportions.

Fiction
Sundby, Scott. *Cut Down to Size at High Noon.*
Charlesbridge Publishing, 2000.
  This is a funny, Wild West adventure about two barbers who sculpture haircuts to scale in a showdown. This book gives a different look at scale drawings.

McGraw Hill Professional Development

Targeted professional development has been articulated throughout the *IMPACT Mathematics* series. The **McGraw-Hill Professional Development Video Library** provides short videos that support the mathematics standards. Log on to **www.glencoe.com**.

Model Lessons   Instructional Strategies

Real-Life Math

Survey Says! Have students read the section titled, "Survey Says!" Ask them if they have ever heard results of polls or surveys that claim to give the views of a group of people. You might have a recent example from a newspaper or magazine to show them. Point out that percents are often used to report these claims.

Tell students that to understand what surveys are telling us, they often have to understand what a percent is. Then let them know that they are going to be learning about percents in this chapter.

Think About It Discuss students' ideas, and point out those that would provide reliable predictions. Give students an example of a sample that would not provide reliable predictions, such as surveying students at two or three tables during one lunch period.

CHAPTER
6

Percents

Contents in Brief

Real-Life Math

Survey Says! Results of surveys are often reported as percents. For example, a retail association recently reported that 72%, a little less than $\frac{3}{4}$, of Americans give Mother's Day gifts. Of course, the association did not survey every American. People who conduct surveys often use a method called *sampling*. This method involves surveying a part of a population, called a *sample*, and using the results to make predictions about the entire population.

Think About It For survey predictions to be reliable, the sample should include all the different types of people in the population. How would you design a survey to find out the favorite lunch in your school?

Math Online
Take the **Chapter Readiness Quiz** at glencoe.com.

346

Chapter Resources

CRM Chapter 6 Resource Masters

CRM English/Spanish Family Letter (pp. 1 and 2)

CRM Lesson Masters (pp. 3, 9, 20–22)

CRM Chapter 6 Pretest (pp. 23–26)

CRM Chapter 6 Tests (pp. 27–38)

Math Online Online Readiness Quiz • eGlossary

Dear Family,

Look in any magazine or newspaper, and you are likely to see numbers written as percents. Listen to any sporting event, and you will probably hear statistics reported using percents.

Key Concept—Percents

The word *percent* means *for each 100*. So, a percent like 50% is the same as the fraction $\frac{50}{100}$ (or $\frac{1}{2}$), or the decimal 0.50 (or 0.5). Fractions, decimals, and percents can be used interchangeably to represent parts of a whole quantity.

Often, the word *percent* is used in connection with the *percent of* some quantity. No matter what the quantity, 100% of a quantity always means all of it, and 50% always means half of it.

The amount indicated by a certain percent changes as the size of the quantity changes. For example, 50% of 10 dogs is 5 dogs, but 50% of 100 dogs is 50 dogs.

Chapter Vocabulary

percent   rational numbers

Home Activities

- Calculate the tip when you eat at a restaurant.
- Calculate the price of an item that is on sale for 25% off.
- Compare interest rates on credit cards.
- Discuss the relationship between percents, fractions, and decimals.

347

Family Letter

Another version of the Family Letter, available in English and Spanish, is found in the Chapter 6 Resource Masters. You may want to send a copy of this letter home with your students.

Key Concept—Percents Introduce students to percents by having them separate groups of 100 counters as models so that they show 25%, 50%, 75%, and 90% of the whole. Have them brainstorm how to determine how many counters should be in each pile.

Ask students to repeat the activity with 20 counters. How will they determine how many counters should be in each pile?

Ask students to conjecture if two percents can be added.

Home Activities

- Have students calculate the sales tax on groceries. Is there more then one tax rate used?

- Each day, have your student cut out a different rectangular strip of paper 10 inches long and then remove a percent of the paper. Use the percents 50%, 25%, 75%, and 80%. What are the lengths of paper that remain?

- Comparison shop between items that have different prices with different percents off the regular prices.

Key Vocabulary

English (Spanish) *Introduce the most important terms from Chapter 6.*

percent (por ciento, porcentaje) *Percent* means "out of 100." A percent represents a number as a part out of 100 and is written with a percent sign. For example, 39% means 39 out of 100, or $\frac{39}{100}$, or 0.39. (p. 349)

rational number (el número racional) Numbers that can be written as the ratio of two whole numbers. Fractions, percents, decimals, or repeating decimals are all rational numbers. (p. 358)

Use Percents

Overview

In this lesson, students learn that percents can be used as an alternative to fractions that have a denominator of 100. They build on what they know about converting between fractions and decimals to include converting to and from percents. They also develop an understanding of why percents are a particularly convenient way of representing and comparing different kinds of data.

Students model percents by using 100–grids and number lines. They also see that percents can help them make comparisons in many types of real–life situations. Finally, students also use percents and fractions to compare and order rational numbers.

Advance Preparation

You may want to provide pennies or other coins and 100-grids to facilitate class discussion while presenting new topics, including equivalent fractions, decimals, and percents.

Objectives

▶ To recognize that a percent is a comparison of a quantity to 100

▶ To recognize that equivalent fractions, decimals, and percents are different representations of the same value

▶ To convert among fractions, decimals, and percents

▶ To develop a sense of the relative amounts that various percents represent

	Summary	Materials	On Your Own Exercises (pp. 362–367)	Assessment Opportunities
Investigation 1 (p. 349) *Pacing: 2 days*	Students write percents, decimals, and fractions for shaded parts of 100–grids. They also estimate what percent of a square is shaded.	Chapter 6 Master 1, transparencies of Chapter 6 Master 1, 100 pennies and other coins, supermarket receipts	Practice & Apply: 1–19 Connect & Extend: 37, 38 Mixed Review: 43–50	• Share & Summarize (p. 351) • Troubleshooting (p. 351)
Investigation 2 (p. 352) *Pacing: 1 day*	Students use fractions and percents to compare different–sized groups.		Practice & Apply: 20, 22 Connect & Extend: 39, 40 Mixed Review: 43–50	• On the Spot Assessment (p. 353) • Share & Summarize (p. 354)
Investigation 3 (p. 354) *Pacing: 1 day*	Students focus on equivalent fractions, decimals, and percents. They use number lines to record equivalent ways of writing the same number.	Lesson 6.1 Master 1	Practice & Apply: 23–29 Connect & Extend: 41, 42 Mixed Review: 43–50	• On the Spot Assessment (p. 356) • Share & Summarize (p. 357) • Troubleshooting (p. 357)
Investigation 4 (p. 357) *Pacing: 1 day*	Students use benchmarks to estimate the size of a number and then use number lines to compare and order them.		Practice & Apply: 30–36 Connect & Extend: Mixed Review: 43–50	• Share & Summarize (p. 361) • Troubleshooting (pp. 359, 360)

Leveled Lesson Resources

CRM *Available in:* **Chapter 6 Resource Masters**

Also on
TeacherWorks™
Lesson 6.1

Study Guide and Intervention (p. 4) — AL

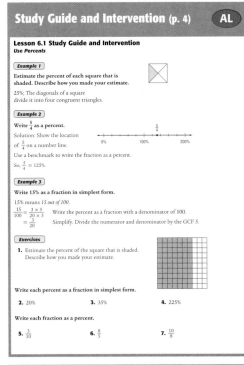

Lesson 6.1 Study Guide and Intervention
Use Percents

Example 1

Estimate the percent of each square that is shaded. Describe how you made your estimate.

25%; The diagonals of a square divide it into four congruent triangles.

Example 2

Write $\frac{5}{4}$ as a percent.

Solution: Show the location of $\frac{5}{4}$ on a number line.

Use a benchmark to write the fraction as a percent.

So, $\frac{5}{4} = 125\%$.

Example 3

Write 15% as a fraction in simplest form.

15% means *15 out of 100.*

$\frac{15}{100} = \frac{3 \times 5}{20 \times 5}$ Write the percent as a fraction with a denominator of 100.

$= \frac{3}{20}$ Simplify. Divide the numerator and denominator by the GCF 5.

Exercises

1. Estimate the percent of the square that is shaded. Describe how you made your estimate.

Write each percent as a fraction in simplest form.

2. 20%   3. 35%   4. 225%

Write each fraction as a percent.

5. $\frac{3}{10}$ 6. $\frac{8}{5}$ 7. $\frac{10}{8}$

Skills Practice (p. 5) — AL OL

Lesson 6.1 Skills Practice
Use Percents

Write each percent as a fraction in simplest form.

1. 40%   2. 30%   3. 55%

4. 75%   5. 140%   6. 175%

7. 24%   8. 68%   9. 44%

Write each fraction as a percent.

10. $\frac{4}{5}$ 11. $\frac{3}{20}$ 12. $\frac{7}{10}$

13. $\frac{3}{5}$ 14. $\frac{3}{2}$ 15. $\frac{5}{4}$

16. $\frac{6}{5}$ 17. $\frac{9}{20}$ 18. $\frac{13}{20}$

19. Which of these numbers are greater than one fourth? Which are less than one fourth?

0.249   25.2% $\frac{5}{24}$ 24.7% $\frac{11}{40}$

20. Suppose 8 out of 20 sixth graders and 9 out of 30 seventh graders like macaroni and cheese. Will comparing the numbers of students in each class who like macaroni and cheese tell you whether it is more popular in sixth or seventh grade? Explain.

Problem-Solving Practice (p. 6) — AL OL

Lesson 6.1 Problem-Solving Practice
Use Percents
Solve

1. **Toys** The Titanic Toy Company has a 4% return rate on its products. Write this percent as a fraction in simplest form.

2. **Music** There are 4 trombones out of 25 instruments in the Landers town band. What percent of the instruments are trombones?

3. **Shopping** Alicia's favorite clothing store is having a 30% off sale. What fraction represents the 30% off sale?

4. **Food** At Ben's Burger Palace, 45% of the customers order large soft drinks. What fraction of the customers order large soft drinks?

5. **Basketball** In the 2001-2002 NBA season, Shaquille O'Neal of the Los Angeles Lakers made 60% of his field goals. What fraction of his field goals did Shaquille make?

6. **School** In Janie's class, 7 out of 25 students have blue eyes. What percent of the class has blue eyes?

7. **Tests** Michael answered $\frac{17}{20}$ questions correctly on his test. What percent of the questions did Michael answer correctly?

8. **Restaurants** On Saturday afternoon, $\frac{41}{50}$ telephone calls taken at The Overlook restaurant were for dinner reservations. What percent of the telephone calls were for dinner reservations?

Enrichment (p. 7) — BL

Lesson 6.1 Enrichment
Use Percents

Percent and the Hundred Chart

The chart at the right shows all the whole numbers from 1 through 100.

This page challenges you to connect percents to what you know about number theory, factors, multiples, and so on. Whenever you can, use a pattern in the chart to make your work easier.

For example, the multiples of 5 make up two columns of the chart, the fifth column and the tenth. So, 20 out of 100 numbers, or 20% of the numbers, are multiples of 5.

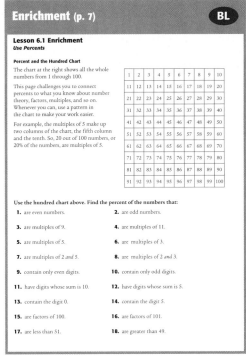

Use the hundred chart above. Find the percent of the numbers that:

1. are even numbers.
2. are odd numbers.
3. are multiples of 9.
4. are multiples of 11.
5. are multiples of 5.
6. are multiples of 3.
7. are multiples of 2 *and* 5.
8. are multiples of 2 *and* 3.
9. contain only even digits.
10. contain only odd digits.
11. have digits whose sum is 10.
12. have digits whose sum is 5.
13. contain the digit 0.
14. contain the digit 5.
15. are factors of 100.
16. are factors of 101.
17. are less than 51.
18. are greater than 49.

Lesson Quick Quiz (p. 8) — AL OL BL

Lesson 6.1 Quick Quiz
Use Percents

1. Write a percent for each fraction.
   a. $\frac{36}{100}$ b. $\frac{27}{50}$
   c. $\frac{9}{100}$ d. $\frac{118}{100}$

2. Write a decimal and a fraction or mixed number for each percent.
   a. 48%   b. 60%
   c. 110%   d. 240%

3. Of the 120 fifth graders at Carson Middle School, 42 marched in the Thanksgiving Day parade. Of the 102 sixth graders, 38 marched in the parade. Which of the grades was better represented in the parade? Use percents to explain your answer.

4. Which of the numbers is closest to three fourths?
   0.748 $\frac{55}{72}$ 75.1%   0.754 $\frac{19}{26}$

5. Order the numbers from least to greatest.
   $\frac{41}{100}$ 40.1% $\frac{2}{5}$ 39.9% $\frac{33}{80}$

Lesson Master (p. 9)

Lesson 6.1 Master 1
Use Percents

Investigation 3: Develop & Understand: B

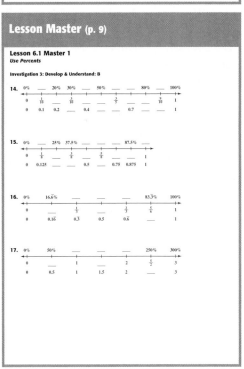

14.
15.
16.
17.

Additional Lesson Resources

Teacher Tech Tools	**Student Tech Tools**	**Other Print Products**
• TeacherWorks	• StudentWorks Plus	• Investigation Notebook and Reflection Journal
• ExamView Assessment Suite	**Math Online** eGlossary •	• Quick Review Math Handbook
• Classroom Presentation Toolkit	Concepts in Motion	
• Advance Tracker		

Introduce

Percents This lesson introduces percents through what students have learned about fractions and decimals. Many students may find percents difficult at first, so it will help to consider a number of examples to illustrate how often they encounter percents in everyday life.

Ask some questions using "benchmark" percents that students can easily relate to fractions:

- If 50% of the students in a class voted to go on a field trip, what fraction of the class voted to go on the field trip? $\frac{1}{2}$

- If 25% of the students in your school said that yellow is their favorite color, what fraction of the students said yellow is their favorite color? $\frac{1}{4}$

- Suppose 75% of the juice in a can of mixed juice is orange juice. What fraction of the juice is orange juice? $\frac{3}{4}$

Think & Discuss

Discuss each question with the class, possibly extending each question to have students do some additional thinking about percents. For example, after the first question, have students consider what percent of its shots a basketball team would need to make to be considered good or excellent. After the second question, discuss how high the percent chance of rain would have to be for someone to decide to carry an umbrella or to postpone plans for a picnic. For the third question, ask students how much money Rosita would need to buy two CDs at the sale price.

Conclude the discussion by asking students to describe other real-life situations they have encountered where percents are used to describe or compare fractions.

Use Percents

You see and hear percents used all of the time.

You may not understand exactly what percents are, but you are probably familiar with them from your everyday experiences. For example, you know that 95% is a good test score while 45% is not.

Think & Discuss

Use what you know about percents to answer these questions.

- In the last game, the Kane High School basketball team made 10% of its shots. Do you think the team played well? Explain. Possible answer: No; 10% is only 1 out of every 10 shots.
- Nate is going camping this weekend. The weather report for the area to which he is traveling claims a 90% chance of rain. Do you think Nate should bring his rain gear? Explain. See ①.

- The latest Digit Heads CD normally costs $16. But this week, it is on sale for 25% off. Rosita has $15. Do you think she has enough money to buy the CD? Explain.
  Yes; 25% is $\frac{1}{4}$, and $\frac{1}{4}$ of 16 is 4, so the CD's price is $16 − $4, or $12.

In this lesson, you will explore what percents are and how they can be used to make comparisons.

① Possible answer: Yes; 90% is close to 100%. Since a 100% chance of rain means that rain is certain, a 90% chance means that rain is very likely.

Investigation 1 Understand Percents

Vocabulary
percent

Materials
- sheet of 100-grids
- transparent 100-grid
- supermarket receipts

Real-World Link
Of the 10,000 to 15,000 cheetahs alive today, about 10% live in captivity. In the wild, a cheetah lives about 7 years. The average life span in captivity is about 70% longer.

Like a fraction or a decimal, a percent can be used to represent a part of a whole. The word **percent** means "out of 100." For example, 28% means 28 out of 100, or $\frac{28}{100}$, or 0.28.

Think & Discuss

Each *100-grid* below contains 100 squares. Express the part of each grid that is shaded as a fraction, a decimal, and a percent.

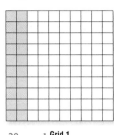

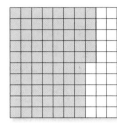

$\frac{20}{100}$, or $\frac{1}{5}$; 0.2; 20% **Grid 1**

$\frac{75}{100}$, or $\frac{3}{4}$; 0.75; 75% **Grid 2**

Develop & Understand: A

Shade the given percent of a 100-grid. Then express the part of the area that is shaded as a fraction and as a decimal. 1–6. See margin.

1. 10%	**2.** 25%
3. 1%	**4.** 15%
5. 50%	**6.** 110%

For each square in Exercises 7–12, estimate the percent of the area that is shaded.

7. Estimates will vary. Actual percent is 50%.

8. Estimates will vary. Actual percent is 25%.

Lesson 6.1 Use Percents **349**

Additional Answers

1. $\frac{10}{100}$, or $\frac{1}{10}$; 0.1

2. $\frac{25}{100}$, or $\frac{1}{4}$; 0.25

Additional Answers for Develop & Understand: A Exercises 3–6 are continued on page 395A.

On Your Own Exercises
Pages 362–367
Exercises 1–19, 37, 38

Understand Percents This investigation begins by focusing on the fact that percent means "out of 100." Students use shaded regions on 100-grids to consider equivalent fractions, decimals, and percents. They next consider a number of situations involving parts of a whole and use what they know about equivalent fractions and decimals to convert fractions and decimals to percents.

Define percent as "out of 100." You might have students read the introductory text, including the example of 28%. Provide them with copies of Chapter 6 Master 1, 100-grids.

Think & Discuss

Quickly discuss the examples in this activity. Students are familiar with the use of shaded regions on 100-grids to represent fractions and decimals, so they should be able to write those representations easily.

The fractions represented by these models can be written in simplest form to get small numerators and denominators. However, it is important that students first write fractions with denominators of 100 to ensure that they are clear what percent of the regions are shaded.

Develop & Understand: A

Suggested Grouping: Pairs

▶ **Exercises 1–6** Students should shade regions on 100-grids to show given percents. Each answer should include a fraction with a denominator of 100, but encourage students to write the fractions in simplest form.

▶ **Exercise 6** Point out that this exercise uses a percent that is greater than 100%, so students will need to use two 100-grids to show the percent. There are eight on Chapter 6 Master 1, so tell students to leave the sixth one blank. Discuss the fact that 110% can be rewritten as $\frac{110}{100}$ and as the mixed number $1\frac{1}{10}$. Use the discussion to observe that $1\frac{1}{10}$ means $1 + \frac{1}{10}$ and that 110% can be thought of as 100% + 10%.

350   CHAPTER 6 Percents

► **Exercise 13** Suggest that compare different regions and use earlier estimates in later exercises. For example, the shaded region in Exercise 8 appears to be about half the size of the shaded region in Exercise 7. Since 50% seems a reasonable estimate for Exercise 7, 25% is a reasonable estimate for Exercise 8. The estimate for Exercise 9 should be greater than 25%, since the shaded region seems to be greater than that in Exercise 8.

► **Exercise 14** Provide students with a transparency of a 100-grid to overlay the square so they can be sure their answers are accurate. You can copy Chapter 6 Master 1 onto transparencies and cut out the grids, one per student. For each of the shaded regions, students can include a fraction written in lowest terms, but a fraction with a denominator of 100 must be part of the answer.

Wrap-Up Review students' answers to Exercises 7–12 on pages 353 and 354, and then discuss Exercise 13. Point out that students can write fractions as percents by finding an equivalent fraction with a denominator of 100. Tell them that sometimes this is not easy to do, and it may be better to write the fraction as a decimal first.

Think **&** *Discuss*

Pose these questions to the class and let them suggest answers. Prompt them for explanations, if necessary.

The last three fractions may confuse students, since there is no way to multiply numerator and denominator by the same whole number to get a denominator of 100. You may need to remind them that every fraction can be converted to a decimal by dividing the numerator by the denominator.

You may want to discuss how to handle the calculations for $\frac{11}{15}$, since the decimal is nonterminating.

9. Estimates will vary.
   Actual percent is 30%.
10. Estimates will vary.
    Actual percent is 10%.
11. Estimates will vary.
    Actual percent is 82%.
12. Estimates will vary.
    Actual percent is 80%.
13. Possible answer: In Exercises 7 and 10, I used my fingers as a "ruler" and estimated how much of a side of the square the shaded section took. In Exercises 8 and 9, I thought about how many of the shaded areas would fill the whole square. In Exercises 11 and 12, I estimated the percent of the area that was unshaded and subtracted that amount from 100%.
14. 7. 50%; $\frac{50}{100}$, or $\frac{1}{2}$; 0.5; 8. 25%; $\frac{25}{100}$, or $\frac{1}{4}$; 0.25; 9. 30%; $\frac{30}{100}$, or $\frac{3}{10}$; 0.3; 10. 10%; $\frac{10}{100}$, or $\frac{1}{10}$; 0.1; 11. 82%; $\frac{82}{100}$, or $\frac{41}{50}$; 0.82; 12. 80%; $\frac{80}{100}$, or $\frac{4}{5}$; 0.8

9.    10.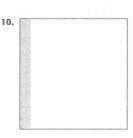

11.    12.

13. Describe the strategies that you used to estimate the percents of the areas that were shaded.

14. Now place a 100-grid over each square in Exercises 7–12. Express the exact portion that is shaded as a percent, a fraction, and a decimal.

You have seen that a percent is a way of writing a fraction with a denominator of 100. You can change a fraction to a percent by first finding an equivalent fraction with a denominator of 100. However, in many cases, it is easier to find a decimal first.

Think **&** *Discuss*

Write each fraction or decimal as a percent. Explain how you found your answers.   See ① in margin.

$\frac{13}{20}$ $\frac{3}{5}$ $\frac{73}{50}$ 0.13   0.9   0.072

Write each fraction as a percent. Explain how you found your answers.   See ② in margin.

$\frac{5}{8}$ $\frac{11}{15}$ $\frac{87}{150}$

Additional Answers for Think & Discuss

① 65%, 60%, 146%, 13%, 90%, 7.2%; Possible explanation: I rewrote the fractions as equivalent fractions with denominator 100; the numerator was then the percent. For the decimals, I used what I know about place value.

$0.13 = \frac{13}{100} = 13\%$,

$0.9 = \frac{19}{100} = 90\%$,

$0.072 = \frac{72}{1,000} = \frac{7.2}{100}$

$= 7.2\%$

② 62.5%, 73.$\overline{3}$%, 58%; Possible explanation: I divided to find an equivalent decimal and then used what I know about place value to write a percent.

18. Possible answer: We will find the total number of prices on the receipts and the number that end in 9 or 5. We will divide the number that end in 9 or 5 by the total number to find a decimal and then a percent to represent the portion of the prices that end in 9 or 5.

In Exercises 1–14, you used percents to represent part of an area. You can also use a percent to represent part of a collection or a group. Finding a percent is easy when the group is made up of 100 items. In other cases, you can apply what you know about fractions and decimals to find a percent.

 Develop & Understand: B   15–17. See margin.

15. Of the 25 students in Ms. Sunseri's homeroom, 11 are in band or choir. Express the part of the class in band or choir as a fraction, a decimal, and a percent. Explain how you found your answers.

16. Of the 78 All-Star Baseball Games played between 1933 and 2007, 40 were won by the National League. Express the portion of games won by the National League as a fraction, a decimal, and a percent. Round the decimal to the nearest hundredth and the percent to the nearest whole percent. Explain how you found your answers.

17. Last winter, Reynaldo worked by shoveling driveways. He hoped to earn $200 so he could buy a new bike. At the end of the winter, he had earned $280. Express the portion of the bike's cost that Reynaldo earned as a fraction, a decimal, and a percent. Explain how you found your answers.

Develop & Understand: C

In October 1989, *Harper's* magazine printed this fact.

Percent of supermarket prices that end in 9 or 5: 80%

More than 15 years have passed since this statistic was printed. In this exercise set, you will analyze some data to see whether it is still true.

18. With your group, devise a plan for testing whether the statistic is true today. Describe your plan.

19. Carry out your plan. Describe what you discovered.
Answers will vary.

20. Compare your results with those of other groups in your class. Describe how the findings of other groups are similar to or different from your findings.   Answers will vary.

21. Do you think the statistic is still true? If not, what percent do you think better describes the portion of today's supermarket prices that end in 9 or 5?   Answers will vary.

Share & Summarize

Tell what the word *percent* means. Explain how to use a percent to represent part of a whole. Give an example to illustrate your explanation.   See margin.

Real-World Link
The first price scanner was introduced at a supermarket convention in 1974. The first product ever purchased using a checkout scanner was a pack of chewing gum.

Lesson 6.1   Use Percents   **351**

Additional Answers

15. $\frac{11}{25}$, 0.44, 44%; Possible explanation: I wrote 11 out of 25 as the fraction $\frac{11}{25}$. $\frac{11}{25}$ is equivalent to $\frac{44}{100}$, which is equivalent to both 0.44 and 44%.

16. $\frac{40}{78}$, 0.51, 51%; Possible explanation: I wrote 40 out of 78 as the fraction $\frac{40}{78}$ and divided to get the decimal 0.51. Since 0.51 means $\frac{51}{100}$, the percent is 51%.

17. $\frac{280}{200}$, or $\frac{7}{5}$; 1.4; 140%; Possible explanation: I wrote 280 out of 200 as the fraction $\frac{280}{200}$. By rewriting this as $\frac{140}{100}$, it is easy to get the decimal equivalent 1.4 and the percent equivalent 140%.

Additional Answer for Share & Summarize is on page 395A.

Develop & Understand: B

Suggested Grouping: Pairs

▶ **Exercise 16** Make sure students round the decimal correctly.

Develop & Understand: C

Suggested Grouping: Small Groups

▶ **Exercise 18** Students should agree on a plan for collecting data on supermarket prices. They can use prices from receipts (or copies of receipts) that you provide, receipts that they bring from home, or prices from newspaper ads. Before students decide on a plan, ask them to consider how to treat prices for multiples of the same item. For example, if a sales receipt shows that three quarts of milk were purchased and the receipt lists the price of a quart of milk three times, it would not be a good idea to use that price three times. If a receipt shows the price of a three-can pack of cat food, the price for the pack may be better than the price per can. You may want to have students clear their plans with you before they attempt to implement them in Exercise 19. Ideally, not all groups will be using identical data.

▶ **Exercise 20** Have each group present its results to the entire class. Each presentation could include a brief description of the plan from Exercise 18 and any calculations performed in Exercise 19.

▶ **Exercise 21** Let students do this exercise with their groups, or let the class discuss it.

Share & Summarize

Discuss students' examples as a class, and use the examples to gauge how well they understand the basic meaning of percent.

Troubleshooting You can ask students to express the percents illustrated in their Share & Summarize examples in different ways to ascertain whether they can name equivalent decimals and fractions.

On Your Own Exercises
Pages 362–367
Exercises 20–22, 39, 40

Parts of Different Wholes In this investigation, students explore how percents can be used to compare parts of different wholes. Such comparisons are often made when similar types of data are collected from two different groups of people within a population. The exercise sets in this investigation can help students see that percents are often much easier to use than fractions for making comparisons.

Think & Discuss

Discuss these questions with the class. Students do not need to perform calculations; rather, they should focus on the kinds of comparisons that are fair and reasonable and realize that the two groups are very different in size.

Investigation ② Parts of Different Wholes

A survey was conducted at Pioneer Middle School. Data were gathered from 160 sixth-grade students. The students were asked to respond to the following question.

Which is your favorite sport to watch? Choose one.

football   soccer   basketball   baseball   ice hockey   other   none

Below is a table of the results.

① Possible answer: No; most sports will receive more votes in Pioneer Middle School just because there are more students. In the Pioneer survey, 16 votes is only $\frac{1}{10}$ of the people surveyed. In our class, it is more than half of the students.

② Possible answer: Both would work because they express the portion of the total votes each sport received. Since each result is expressed as part of a whole, you can compare them even though the wholes are different.

③ Possible answer: Comparing percents; it is easier than finding a common numerator or denominator to compare fractions.

Sport	Number of Votes	Fraction of Total Votes
Football	12	$\frac{12}{160}$
Soccer	22	$\frac{22}{160}$
Basketball	40	$\frac{40}{160}$
Baseball	28	$\frac{28}{160}$
Ice Hockey	14	$\frac{14}{160}$
Other	28	$\frac{28}{160}$
None	16	$\frac{16}{160}$

Think & Discuss

Suppose you want to compare the popularity of a particular sport among sixth graders at Pioneer Middle School with its popularity among students in your class.

- Would comparing the numbers of votes the sport received tell you whether it was more popular at Pioneer or in your class? Explain.   See ①.

- Would comparing the fraction of votes each sport received tell you whether it was more popular at Pioneer or in your class? What about comparing percents? Explain.   See ②.

- Do you think comparing numbers of votes, fractions, or percents would be best for comparing popularity? Explain. See ③.

Real-World Link
Rugby is the second most-played team sport in the world. Only soccer is more popular.

1. Football: 8%; soccer: 14%; basketball: 25%; baseball: 18%; ice hockey: 9%; other: 18%; none: 10%
4. No; Possible explanation: Europe received more votes in the Period 2 class, but the percent of votes it received is 10% in both classes.

✅ Develop & Understand: A

1. Calculate the percent of the votes each sport received at Pioneer Middle School. Round your answers to the nearest whole percent.

2. Do the percents add to 100%? If so, why? If not, why not?
   No because of rounding

3. Write a paragraph for a newspaper article comparing the Pioneer Middle School data with the data from your class. Answers will vary.

In Exercises 1–3, you found that percents allow you to compare parts of different groups, even if the groups are of very different sizes. The next two exercise sets will give you more practice with this idea.

✅ Develop & Understand: B

Mrs. Torres asked her first and second period classes a question.

Which continent would you most like to visit?

The results for the two classes are listed below.

Continent	Period 1 Votes	Period 2 Votes
Europe	2	3
Antarctica	0	1
Asia	3	8
Australia	10	5
South America	1	2
Africa	4	11

4. Ajay is in the Period 2 class. He said Europe was a more popular choice in his class than in the Period 1 class. Is he correct? Explain.

5. Luisa is in the Period 1 class. She said Australia was twice as popular in her class as in the Period 2 class. Is she correct? Explain. See below.

6. Nolan is in the Period 2 class. He said that in his class, Asia was four times as popular as South America. Is he correct? Explain. See below.

7. Write two true statements similar to those made by Ajay, Luisa, and Nolan comparing the data in the table. Answers will vary.

5. No; Possible explanation: Although Australia received twice as many votes in the Period 1 class, the percent of votes it received is more than twice the percent received in the Period 2 class, 50% versus 17%.

6. Yes; Possible explanation: We are comparing categories within the same class, so we can just compare the numbers. Asia received four times as many votes as South America.

Lesson 6.1 Use Percents **353**

On the Spot Assessment

If students do not understand the answers to Exercises 4–6, ask them to copy the table on page 357 into their notes and then add two other columns. The heading for each new column should be "Percent". Have students then show the calculations to find the percent of each class that voted for each continent.

✅ Develop & Understand: A

Suggested Grouping: Pairs

▶ **Exercises 1–3** In this exercise set, students calculate percents of votes received from data displayed on page 356

▶ **Exercise 1** Check whether students understand how to convert fractions to decimals and percents.

Wrap-Up You might have a volunteer from each group read their articles from Exercise 3 to the class to be sure students understand both the percent calculations and the comparison process.

Real-World Link
Ask students what sports are most popular at your school.

✅ Develop & Understand: B

Suggested Grouping: Individuals

▶ **Exercises 4–7** Point out that students will get more practice in using percents to compare data about two groups of different sizes.

▶ **Exercises 4–6** Emphasize that the number of votes should not be compared directly when the groups are of different sizes. It is more reasonable to compare the relative percents for the different categories of votes. A direct comparison of the votes for two groups is completely fair only if the groups are the same size.

Analyze the Table Explain the table as showing "raw data," or the number of votes for each continent that each class gave. The actual data must then be interpreted as a percent so the percents can be compared.

Suggested Grouping: Individuals

▶ **Exercises 8 and 9** Point out that students should see two possible ways to measure the participation in an event.

▶ **Exercise 10** Emphasize that students focus on the fairest way to compare participation when the groups in question are of different sizes.

Share & Summarize

You can use this question to achieve closure on why fractions and percents are often better than raw data for making fair comparisons. You can also use the question to remind students that percents are often much easier to compare than fractions.

Teacher Tips Discuss why fractions and percents are often better for comparison than raw data.

Investigation 3

On Your Own Exercises
Pages 362–367
Exercises 23–29, 41, 42

Percents, Fractions, and Decimals This investigation is designed to build facility in converting among percents, decimals, and fractions. Students use number lines to develop number sense as they practice equivalent ways of writing numbers. They also examine a real-life application that uses fractions and percents to make comparisons.

Introduce the investigation by letting students know that they will work with changing numbers among the three forms (fraction, decimal, and percent). Ask them to think as they work about whether one form seems easier to understand in different situations.

8. Possible answer: 200 students participated in the event, while only 150 West students participated.

9. Possible answer: 46% of West's students participated, while only 40% of East's students participated.

Real-World Link
Hockey pucks are constructed of rubber and measure 3 inches in diameter.

10. Possible answer: West; comparing numbers of students is unfair because West has fewer students. It is fairer to look at the percent of the student population that participated.

Develop & Understand: C

Marathon City held a walkathon to raise money for charity. Of the 500 students at East Middle School, 200 participated in the walkathon. At West Middle School, 150 of the 325 students participated. The sponsors of the walkathon plan to give an award to the middle school with the greater participation.

8. What argument might the principal at East present to the sponsors to convince them to give the award to her school?

9. What argument might the principal at West make to convince the sponsors to give the award to his school?

10. Which school do you think deserves the award? Defend your choice.

Share & Summarize

Suppose Ms. Wright's class has fewer students than your class. They would like to compare their results for the sports survey with the results from your class.

- Celia suggests comparing the number of votes each sport received.
- Ian thinks it would be better to compare the fraction of the votes each sport received.
- Oscar says it is best to compare percents.

Which type of comparison do you think is best? Defend your answer. Oscar's comparsion would give the most accurate information

Investigation 3 Percents, Fractions, and Decimals

Percents, fractions, and decimals can all be used to represent parts of a whole. However, in some situations, one form may be easier or more convenient.

For example, you have seen that it is often easier to compare percents than to compare fractions. To be a good problem-solver, you need to become comfortable changing numbers from one form to another.

✓ Develop & Understand: A

In Exercises 1–3, write each given fraction or mixed number as a decimal and a percent. Write each given percent as a decimal and a fraction or mixed number in lowest terms.

1. The head of the cafeteria staff took a survey to find out what students wanted for lunch.

   1a. $0.77, \frac{77}{100}$

   a. He found that 77% of the students wanted pizza every day.

   b. He was surprised to find that $\frac{2}{5}$ of students would like to have a salad bar available, in case they did not want what was served for lunch. 0.4, 40%

   c. He found that $\frac{11}{20}$ of students favored french fries while 45% preferred mashed potatoes. 0.55, 55%; 0.45, $\frac{9}{20}$

2. Mt. Everest, with an estimated elevation of 29,028 feet, is the highest mountain in Asia and in the world.

   a. Mt. Aconcagua is the highest mountain in South America. It is approximately 78% of the height of Mt. Everest. 0.78, $\frac{39}{50}$

   b. Mt. McKinley is the highest mountain in North America. It is approximately 70% of the height of Mt. Everest. 0.70, $\frac{7}{10}$

   c. Mt. Kilimanjaro is the highest peak in Africa. It is approximately $\frac{2}{3}$ of the height of Mt. Everest. $0.\overline{6}, 66.\overline{6}$%

3. The Ob-Irtysh, with a length of approximately 3,460 miles, is the longest river in Asia and the fourth longest river in the world.

   a. The Mississippi–Missouri–Red Rock River is the longest river in North America and the third longest in the world. It is about $1\frac{2}{25}$ as long as the Ob-Irtysh. 1.08, 108%

   b. The Amazon is the longest river in South America and the second longest in the world. It is about 113% as long as the Ob-Irtysh. 1.13, $1\frac{13}{100}$

You have been thinking about percents as parts of wholes. Like fractions and decimals, you can also think of percents simply as numbers.

In the next exercise set, you will label points on a number line with fractions, decimals, and percents. As you work, you will become familiar with some common percents that are often used as benchmarks.

Real-World Link
One of the greatest challenges for mountain climbers is the "seven summits," climbing the highest mountain on each of the seven continents. Mt. Kiliminjaro in Tanzania is the highest mountain in Africa.

Reaching All Learners

BL **Beyond Level** You may want students to use the height of Mt. Everest to calculate the heights of the other three mountains and the length of the Ob-Irtysh to calculate the lengths of the other two rivers.

Teacher Tips In this exercise set, students get additional experience with writing numbers as equivalent fractions, decimals, and percents.

✓ Develop & Understand: A

Suggested Grouping: Individuals

▶ **Exercise 2** Percents are given that relate the heights of three mountains to the height of Mt. Everest. You may want to point out that while the estimated height of Mt. Everest is mentioned in the exercise, that number is not needed to answer any part of the exercise.

▶ **Exercise 3** Students may find percents greater than 100% confusing. You may want to point out in **Part b** that the length of the Amazon is the length of the Ob-Irtysh (100%) plus 13% more. The actual length of the Ob-Irtysh is not needed to answer the exercise.

Real-World Link
Ask students if they can research and list the "seven summits."

Wrap-Up Review students' answers to the exercises. You may want to have volunteers explain how they found their answers. You may also want to pose a few additional conversion problems so that any confusion can be addressed.

Additional Examples
One-digit percents:

$4\% = \frac{4}{100} = 0.04$

(Watch for students writing 0.4.)

Decimal percents:

$24.5\% = \frac{24.5}{100} = \frac{245}{1,000} = 0.245$

$3.8\% = \frac{3.8}{100} = \frac{38}{1,000} = 0.038$

(Watch for students writing 0.38.)

In this exercise set, students label points on a number line with equivalent percents, fractions, and decimals. The emphasis is on benchmark fractions, decimals, and percents.

The number lines in Exercises 4–7 have been reproduced on Lesson 6.1 Master 1; you may want to give a copy to each student or each pair of students.

Math Link

Ask students to name benchmark fractions they know.

✏ Develop & Understand: B

Suggested Grouping: Pairs

▶ **Exercises 4–7** Remind students that they should use benchmark percents for these exercises. Give each student or pair of students a copy of Lesson 6.1 Master 1 to use.

▶ **Exercises 8 and 9** Point out that students should give percent equivalents of fractions with nonterminating decimal representations. Suggest that students first convert the fraction to a decimal, using the note for Exercise 8. Help students see that $33.\overline{3}\%$ is equal to $33\% + 0.\overline{3}\%$, or $33\% + \frac{1}{3}\%$.

✐ Develop & Understand: B

Copy each number line. Fill in the blanks so that each tick mark is labeled with a percent, a fraction, and a decimal. Write all fractions in lowest terms.

4.

0%	10%	20%	30%	40%	50%	60%	70%	80%	90%	100%
0	$\frac{1}{10}$	$\frac{1}{5}$	$\frac{3}{10}$	$\frac{2}{5}$	$\frac{1}{2}$	$\frac{3}{5}$	$\frac{7}{10}$	$\frac{4}{5}$	$\frac{9}{10}$	1
0	0.1	0.2	0.3	0.4	0.5	0.6	0.7	0.8	0.9	1

Math Link

Benchmarks are familiar values that you can use to approximate other values.

5.

0%	12.5%	25%	37.5%	50%	62.5%	75%	87.5%	100%
0	$\frac{1}{8}$	$\frac{1}{4}$	$\frac{3}{8}$	$\frac{1}{2}$	$\frac{5}{8}$	$\frac{3}{4}$	$\frac{7}{8}$	1
0	0.125	0.25	0.375	0.5	0.625	0.75	0.875	1

6.

0%	16.$\overline{6}$%	33.$\overline{3}$%	50%	66.$\overline{6}$%	83.$\overline{3}$%	100%
0	$\frac{1}{6}$	$\frac{1}{3}$	$\frac{1}{2}$	$\frac{2}{3}$	$\frac{5}{6}$	1
0	0.1$\overline{6}$	0.$\overline{3}$	0.5	0.$\overline{6}$	0.8$\overline{3}$	1

7.

0%	50%	100%	150%	200%	250%	300%
0	$\frac{1}{2}$	1	$\frac{3}{2}$	2	$\frac{5}{2}$	3
0	0.5	1	1.5	2	2.5	3

8. Possible answer: $\frac{1}{3} = 0.\overline{3}$, and multiplying by 100 to change this to a percent gives $33.\overline{3}\%$. Since $0.\overline{3} = \frac{1}{3}$, this is equivalent to $33\frac{1}{3}\%$.

8. The percent equivalent for $\frac{1}{3}$ is often written as $33\frac{1}{3}\%$. Explain why this makes sense.

9. What fraction is equivalent to $66\frac{2}{3}\%$? $\frac{2}{3}$

⊙ₛₚₒₜ *Assessment*

In Exercise 6, some students may have difficulty with the repeating decimals and the corresponding percents. It may help to write $0.1\overline{6}$ as $0.16666\ldots$ and move the decimal point two places to the right to obtain $16.666\ldots\%$. Then rewrite this as $16.\overline{6}\%$. Check that students have a conceptual understanding of why the "moving the decimal point" procedure is valid.

Develop & Understand: C

Sunscreens block harmful ultraviolet (UV) rays produced by the sun. Each sunscreen has a Sun Protection Factor (SPF) that tells you how many minutes you can stay in the sun before you receive one minute of burning UV rays. For example, if you apply sunscreen with SPF 15, you get one minute of UV rays for every 15 minutes you stay in the sun.

To solve Exercises 10–12, you will need to apply what you know about converting between fractions and percents.

10. A sunscreen with SPF 15 blocks $\frac{14}{15}$ of the sun's UV rays. What percent of UV rays does the sunscreen block? $93.\overline{3}$ %

11. Suppose a sunscreen blocks 75% of the sun's UV rays.

   a. What fraction of UV rays does this sunscreen block? Give your answer in lowest terms. $\frac{3}{4}$

   b. Use your answer from Part a to calculate this sunscreen's SPF. Explain how you found your answer.

12. A label on a sunscreen with SPF 30 claims the sunscreen blocks about 97% of harmful UV rays. Assuming the SPF factor is accurate, is this claim true? Explain.

Share & Summarize

1. How do you change a percent to a fraction?

2. How do you change a percent to a decimal?

3. How do you change a decimal to a percent?

4. How do you change a fraction to a percent? Possible answer: Divide the numerator by the denominator to get a decimal, move the decimal point two places to the right, and add a percent symbol.

Investigation 4

Compare and Order Rational Numbers

Vocabulary
rational numbers

In Investigation 3, you used number lines to show the fraction, decimal, and percent forms of various benchmark numbers. Number lines can be helpful when you want to use a benchmark to estimate the size of a number, compare the value of two numbers, or order several different numbers by value.

Lesson 6.1 Use Percents **357**

Develop & Understand: C

Suggested Grouping: Pairs or Individuals

▶ **Exercises 10–12** Point out that students relate the SPF number of a sunscreen product to the percent of UV rays that it blocks. This may be one of those "simple but tricky" problems for many students.

Teacher Tips To discuss what the SPF number means. Ask:

• Does a higher SPF number mean that the sunscreen lets in more or less UV radiation? Less

• Does a higher SPF number mean that the sunscreen blocks more or less UV radiation? More

• If a sunscreen lets in half of the UV radiation and blocks the other half, what would its SPF be? Explain. 2; it would block one out of every two minutes' worth of UV rays

Share & Summarize

These questions are straightforward and offer a good assessment of students' understanding of converting among fractions, decimals, and percents. Have students work individually and then share their answers with the class.

Investigation 4

On Your Own Exercises
Pages 362–367
Exercises 30–36

Compare and Order Rational Numbers
In this investigation, students will use benchmarks and number lines to compare and order fractions, decimals, and percents. Remind students that benchmarks are numbers that are easy to work with and remember, such as 50%. Number lines are used to compare the numbers because they make it easier to see the answer quickly.

Troubleshooting

Investigation 3 focused on the procedural skills of converting among fractions, decimals, and percents. If students are able to complete these procedures but have trouble articulating what they are doing, you might give them some concrete problems. For example, for Exercise 1 of Share & Summarize, ask them to change 34% to a fraction and explain what they are doing as they work. They can do this orally or in writing.

Suggested Grouping: Groups of 3 or 4

Finding the best ways to label a number line can be difficult for some students. Deciding which units to use and making sure most of the numbers land on tick marks is difficult. Remind students that in many problems like these, trial and error works.

Encourage them to try marking the number line in the way they think will work. If the numbers fall between tick marks, they will know to try a more exact unit. Have them label the number lines in groups so they can share their opinions and see what works best.

✓ Develop & Understand: A

Suggested Grouping: Individuals

▶ **Exercises 1 and 2** Students have already determined which numbers are less or greater than $\frac{1}{2}$. Remind them that *closest to* and *farthest from* can be either greater or less than the number. It is the distance from the number that matters, not whether it is to the left or right.

▶ **Exercise 3** This problem leads students to see that the degree of accuracy is important. Guide them to see that in most cases, *about half* provides enough information to solve a problem. However, in some instances, it is important to know exactly how close to $\frac{1}{2}$ a number gets. Point out that students should read problems carefully to know how accurate they need to be.

✓ Develop & Understand: B

Suggested Grouping: Individuals

▶ **Exercises 4 and 5** Students will not all use the same benchmarks. More advanced students may choose benchmarks closer to the given numbers. Others may choose the same benchmarks for every problem, such as fourths or tenths. Watch to see that all students are choosing benchmarks that are logical.

▶ **Exercise 5** When dealing with such small numbers, make sure students are writing the numbers correctly. It is easy to place a decimal in the wrong place when plotting on the number line or when dividing a fraction to get a decimal.

Math Link

All of the numbers with which you have worked to this point are called **rational numbers**. Rational numbers can be written as the ratio of two whole numbers. Fractions, percents, decimals, or repeating decimals are all rational numbers.

① Greater than one half: $\frac{11}{20}$, 0.593, 50.1%. Less than one half: 48%, 0.49, $\frac{7}{15}$

② Sample answer: Since the numbers are all close together, it makes sense to label the line in hundredths. That way, everything except 50.1% will be on a tick mark instead of between marks. The numbers all seem to be close to one half. So if the line went from three-tenths to seven-tenths, it would probably include everything.

Explore

• Which of these numbers are greater than one half? Which are less than one half?

$$0.593 \qquad \frac{11}{20} \qquad 50.1\% \qquad \frac{7}{15} \qquad 48\% \qquad 0.49 \qquad \text{See ①.}$$

Draw a number line. Place the numbers in order on the number line.

• What is a convenient way to label the number line so that these numbers can be placed on it? What should be the units on the number line? What value will be the left most value? The right most value? See ②.

• What strategies can you use to figure out where to place the numbers? See ③ in margin.

✓ Develop & Understand: A

Use the number line from Explore for Exercises 1–3.

1. Which number, 0.593, $\frac{11}{20}$, 50.1%, $\frac{7}{15}$, 48%, 0.49, is closest to one half? 50.1%

2. Which is furthest from one half? 0.593

3. Is 50% a good approximation for each of the numbers? See margin.

You can often estimate a fraction, decimal, or percent by comparing it to a *benchmark*, a number whose fraction, decimal, and percent representations you know. Benchmarks can also help you decide which of two numbers is greater. For example, because you know that $\frac{11}{20}$ is more than $\frac{1}{2}$ and 48% is less than $\frac{1}{2}$, you can tell that $\frac{11}{20}$ must be more than 48%.

✓ Develop & Understand: B

For each pair of numbers, use a benchmark to decide which number is greater. Show the location of the benchmark and the approximate location of the other numbers on a number line.

4. Which is greater, 32% or $\frac{4}{9}$? $\frac{4}{9}$

5. Which is greater, 0.6% or $\frac{1}{98}$? $\frac{1}{98}$

Additional Answers

③ Sample answer: For the decimals, look at the tenths place to see how many tenths; or if there are hundredths, it goes between one mark and the next. For percents, look at the tens place. That tells you how many tenths in decimal or fraction form, or convert the percent to a decimal and then decide where it goes. $\frac{7}{15}$ is easiest to convert to a decimal by long division: 7 divided by 15 is $0.4\overline{6}$.

3. It depends on how accurate you want to be. "About half" is often as accurate as you need. 0.593 is closer to 60%, so that might be a better approximation. 50.1% is quite close to 50%, and percents are often used without more accuracy than that in real life.

For Exercises 6–8, use benchmarks and a number line to order sets of three numbers from least to greatest.

6. $\frac{3}{8}$, 0.21, 52%   The order is 0.21, $\frac{3}{8}$, 52%.

7. 0.3, $\frac{5}{6}$, 96%   The order is 0.3, $\frac{5}{6}$, 96%.

8. $\frac{3}{4}$, 0.22, 100%   The order is 0.22, $\frac{3}{4}$, 100%.

9. Identify a fraction between $\frac{2}{3}$ and $\frac{5}{6}$.   Check students' work.
   Possible answer: $\frac{7}{9}$.

10. Identify a decimal between 57% and 71%.   Check students' work.
    Possible answer: 0.64.

11. Identify a percent between $\frac{1}{3}$ and $\frac{2}{5}$.   Check students' work.
    Possible answer: 38%.

Mark the approximate location of each fraction on the number line. For those percents which are not whole numbers, use the closest benchmark to estimate the value of the fraction as a percent.

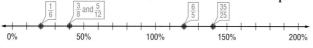

12. $\frac{6}{5}$ <u>120%</u>

13. $\frac{3}{8}$ <u>40%</u>

14. $\frac{5}{12}$ <u>40%</u>

15. $\frac{35}{25}$ <u>140%</u>

16. $\frac{1}{6}$ <u>20%</u>

17. Which of the percents in Exercises 12–16 are exact?
    120% is exactly $\frac{6}{5}$; $\frac{35}{25}$ is exactly 140%

▶ **Exercise 6** When ordering three numbers, it may help students to think of a strategy. For example, they may always want to start by placing the percents and decimals, if that is easiest for them. Then they can use division to find a decimal for placing the fraction.

▶ **Exercise 7** Students are probably comfortable enough with percents to know that 96% is almost at the one whole mark on the number line. Encourage them to place numbers that they recognize on the number line first.

▶ **Exercises 9–11** These exercises allow for many possible answers. You will need to check to see that students find numbers within the given benchmarks. For fractions, students may need assistance finding the appropriate denominator for an amount within the given boundaries.

Troubleshooting Students who have trouble with comparing and ordering close numbers may need to be reminded to use hundredths for tick marks on their number lines. If they are using tenths, several numbers may fall between the same two tick marks, making it hard to compare the numbers. Using hundredths will ensure that most of the numbers will fall on a tick mark.

Real-World Link

Do an informal survey of the class to find out what percent of students drink fat-free, 1%, 2%, and whole milk.

Reaching *All Learners*

AL **Approaching Level** Students who have trouble with comparing and ordering different forms of a number may need a visual way to recognize benchmarks in any form. Help them create a study guide by drawing a number line and marking it with several common benchmarks (fourths, halves, tenths, etc.). Label all three forms of each benchmark with the same color to help students associate the numbers. Use a different color for each benchmark.

Suggested Grouping: *Pairs*

Students will enjoy guessing numbers. While they play, monitor to be sure they understand the concept. Make sure they are crossing off the appropriate sections of their number lines, and that they are getting closer to the number each time.

Teacher Tips Be sure students understand that approximations are not exact, but they are important. In many exercises, it may not be necessary to find an exact number, but it will be important that the approximation be as close as possible to the exact number. Encourage them to aim to get as close as possible when finding an estimate.

—**Explore**

Play *Guess My Number* with a partner. You will need two copies of a number line marked in tenths that goes from 0 to 2.

Step 1. Each player secretly writes a rational number between 0 and 2. The number can be written as a fraction, a decimal, or a percent.

If it *is* a decimal, it should have no more than 3 digits to the right of the decimal point. If it *is* a percent, it should have no more than 1 digit to the right of the decimal point. If it *is* a fraction, the denominator should be either between 1 and 10, or a multiple of 10.

Step 2. One player asks the other a yes/no question about the secret rational number. Three types of questions are allowed.

a. Is your number a fraction/decimal/percent?

b. Is your number greater/less than _____?

c. Is your number exactly _____?

The second player answers the question. Using this information, the first player crosses off any part of the number line where the number cannot lie.

Step 3. Now it is the second player's turn to ask the first player a question about that player's secret number. The players continue taking turns until one player guesses the other's number exactly.

✓ Develop & Understand: C

Miguel made up a rational number puzzle.

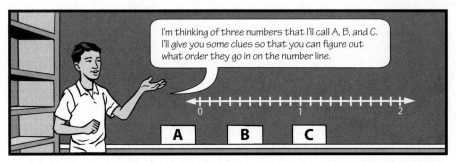

Use the number line to help you solve Miguel's puzzle.

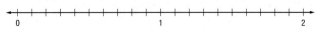

Troubleshooting

Students who have trouble finding the greatest number in a set of three may have trouble converting numbers to the same format. If they cannot convert all the numbers to the same format, they may do better with a number line. It may also help to draw a greater than symbol on the right and a less than symbol on the left side of the number line.

Clue 1 A is greater than 0.05 and less than 0.82.

B is greater than $\frac{1}{5}$ and less than $\frac{8}{5}$.

C is greater than 83% and less than 200%.

18. What can you tell about the relationship between A, B, and C?
A is less than C, but I cannot tell about B.

Clue 2 A > $\frac{1}{5}$ and A < $\frac{4}{5}$.

B > 50% and B < 145%

C > 1.50 and C < 1.85

19. Given clue 2, now what can you tell about the order of A, B, and C?

19. C is greater than B, but I still do *not* know which order A and B go.

Clue 3 A is greater than 0.25 and less than 0.4.

B is greater than $\frac{9}{10}$ and less than $\frac{7}{5}$.

C is greater than 159% and less than 180%.

20. Given clue 3, now what can you tell about the order of A, B, and C? A is the least, B is in the middle, C is the greatest.

21. What values could A be?
It is between 0.25 and 0.4.

22. What values could B be?
It is between 0.9 and 1.4.

23. What values could C be?
It is between 159% and 180%.

25a. Sample response: $\frac{1}{4}$

25b. Sample response: 1

25c. Sample response: 160%

24. Could A, B, or C be $\frac{3}{10}$? Yes, A could, but not B or C.

25. Give one value that each of the secret numbers could have. Mark each of your choices on the number line. Check students' number lines.

① You can convert everything into one format and compare. You can also place them on a number line to show relative sizes of numbers. With or without a number line, you can also compare two numbers to a benchmark.

Share & Summarize

1. Which quantity is greatest: 45%, $\frac{14}{25}$, or 0.532? $\frac{14}{25}$ is greatest.

2. What strategies can you use to compare fractions, percents, and decimals? See ①.

Lesson 6.1 Use Percents   361

✅ *Develop & Understand: C*

Suggested Grouping: Pairs

▶ **Exercises 18–25** In these exercises, students will show their understanding of ordering rational numbers by placing them on a number line. You may want to have students copy the number line onto a separate piece of paper so that they will have space for taking notes and so that they can organize their thoughts as they add information to the problem.

Share & Summarize

It may be helpful to have pairs do the exercises. Have partners discuss the strategies they use to compare fractions, percents, and decimals. Then have them share their answers with the class.

Investigation 1
Pages 349–351
Practice & Apply: 1–19
Connect & Extend: 37, 38

Investigation 2
Pages 352–354
Practice & Apply: 20, 21
Connect & Extend: 39, 40

Investigation 3
Pages 354–357
Practice & Apply: 22–29
Connect & Extend: 41, 42

Investigation 4
Pages 357–361
Practice & Apply: 30–36
Connect & Extend: 43

Assign Anytime
Mixed Review: 43–50

▶ **Exercises 1–4** Students will need 100-grids for these exercises. Each student should have a copy of Chapter 6 Master 1.

▶ **Exercise 7** Students who have difficulty seeing that each shaded corner is a quarter of the large square may find it helpful to trace the figure and draw in the diagonals of the unshaded square.

Additional Answers

1. Possible answer: $\frac{37}{100}$, 0.37

2. Possible answer: $\frac{72}{100}$, or $\frac{18}{25}$; 0.72

3. Possible answer: $\frac{4}{100}$, or $\frac{1}{25}$; 0.04

Practice & Apply

1–4. See margin.
5. Possible answer: 70%; the middle section takes up about half the area; each shaded section takes up about $\frac{1}{10}$ of the area. So, the shaded area is 50% + 10% + 10% = 70% of the total area.
6. Possible answer: 40%; if the square was divided into five strips, two of them would be shaded.
7. Possible answer: 50%; the four shaded corners fit exactly inside the unshaded section, so the corners must take up half the total area.
8. Possible answer: 75%; three copies of the unshaded section would fill the square, so the unshaded section is 25% of the total area. The shaded section must be 75% of the total area.

Shade the given percent of a 100-grid. Then express the shaded portion as a fraction and a decimal.

1. 37%   **2.** 72%   **3.** 4%   **4.** 125%

Estimate the percent of each square that is shaded. Describe how you made your estimate.

5.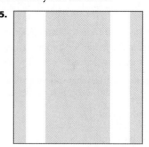
6.
7.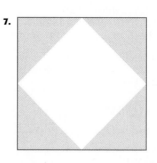
8.

Write each fraction or decimal as a percent. Round to the nearest tenth of a percent.

9. $\frac{4}{5}$ 80%   **10.** 0.32 32%   **11.** 0.036 3.6%   **12.** $\frac{3}{71}$ 4.2%

13. 1 100%   **14.** $\frac{19}{20}$ 95%   **15.** 2.7 270%   **16.** 0.004 0.4%

17. Seven of the 20 people at Sondra's birthday party are in her math class. Express the portion of the guests who are in her math class as a fraction, a decimal, and a percent. Explain how you found your answers. $\frac{7}{20}$, 0.35, 35%; Possible explanation: I wrote 7 out of 20 as the fraction $\frac{7}{20}$ and then wrote the equivalent fraction $\frac{35}{100}$. From this, I could see that the decimal is 0.35 and the percent is 35%.

4. $\frac{125}{100}$, or $1\frac{1}{4}$; 1.25

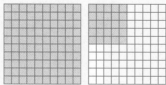

Real-World Link

In 2005, the United States recycled about 30% of its garbage, more than triple the percent recycled 30 years ago.

19. $\frac{12}{9}$, or $1\frac{1}{3}$; 1.3; 133%; Possible explanation: I wrote 12 out of 9 as the fraction $\frac{12}{9}$ and divided to get the decimal $1.\overline{3}$, which is about 133%.

Real-World Link

The ancient Chinese and Leonardo da Vinci are both credited with conceiving the idea of a parachute. The first recorded parachute jump was made in France in 1797 by Andre Jacques Garnerin who jumped from a hot air balloon.

18. **Social Studies** Of the 232 million tons of garbage generated in the United States every year, about 87 million tons are paper products. Express the portion of U.S. garbage that is paper as a fraction, a decimal, and a percent. Explain how you found your answers. See below.

19. Last season, Brian set a goal of hitting 9 home runs. When the season was over, he had hit 12 home runs. Express the portion of his goal Brian reached as a fraction, a decimal, and a percent. Round to the nearest whole percent. Explain how you found your answers.

20. A sports magazine asked 3,600 of its subscribers this question.

Which of these sports do you think is most dangerous? Choose one.

☐ football   ☐ ice hockey   ☐ skiing
☐ sky diving   ☐ rock climbing   ☐ other

Ms. Johnson's math students decided to conduct the same survey in their class. The table shows the results of the magazine's survey and Ms. Johnson's class survey.

Sport	Fraction of Votes in Magazine Survey	Fraction of Votes in Ms. Johnson's Class
Football	$\frac{524}{3,600}$	$\frac{3}{25}$
Ice Hockey	$\frac{320}{3,600}$	$\frac{0}{25}$
Skiing	$\frac{870}{3,600}$	$\frac{8}{25}$
Skydiving	$\frac{607}{3,600}$	$\frac{11}{25}$
Rock Climbing	$\frac{959}{3,600}$	$\frac{2}{25}$
Other	$\frac{320}{3,600}$	$\frac{1}{25}$

a. Find the percent of votes each sport received in the magazine survey. Round to the nearest percent. See margin.

b. Find the percent of votes each sport received in Ms. Johnson's class. Round to the nearest percent. Football: 12%; ice hockey: 0%; skiing: 32%; sky diving: 44%; rock climbing: 8%; other 4%

c. Write a short newspaper article comparing the results of the magazine survey with the results of the survey conducted in Ms. Johnson's class. See margin.

18. $\frac{87}{232}$, or $\frac{3}{8}$; 0.375; 37.5%; Possible explanation: I wrote 87 out of 232 as the fraction $\frac{87}{232}$ and divided to get the decimal 0.375. Since $0.375 = \frac{375}{1000} = \frac{37.5}{100}$, the equivalent percent is 37.5%.

Lesson 6.1 Use Percents   **363**

▶ **Exercise 19** Suggest that students note before they make any calculations that the percent for this exercise will be greater than 100%.

▶ **Exercise 20a** You may wish to allow calculators for changing the fractions to decimals.

▶ **Exercise 20c** Students should note that they could write equivalent fractions with a denominator of 100 by multiplying each numerator and denominator by 4. They can then use the meaning of percent to write the corresponding percent.

Real-World Link

Ask students if garbage is recycled in their community. How could they find out the percent increase in recycling in the last 10 years?

Additional Answers

20a. Football: 15%; ice hockey: 9%; Skiing: 24%; sky diving: 17%; Rock climbing: 27%; other 9%

20c. Possible answer: Ms. Johnson's class and readers of a popular sports magazine have very different opinions about what the most dangerous sport is. While 9% of people responding to the magazine survey think ice hockey is the most dangerous sport, not a single student in Ms. Johnson's class voted it most dangerous. In Ms. Johnson's class, 44% of students think skydiving is the most dangerous sport, while only 17% of the magazine readers voted it most dangerous. The choice of rock climbing was more than three times as popular among respondents to the magazine survey as it was among Ms. Johnson's students.

▶ **Exercise 22** You may want to discuss students' ideas about which granola company would be more truthful in saying their product has less fat. There are arguments for both sides. By eating the specified serving of Harvest Granola, a consumer ingests less fat than by eating the specified serving of Healthy Crunch. If a consumer wants a serving of a particular size regardless of the brand, however, he or she would ingest less fat by choosing Healthy Crunch. Being able to consider such information is an important part of being an informed consumer.

· ·

Real-World Link

In 2005, it was estimated that the number of cable television subscribers was 54%.

· ·

Additional Answers

21a. No; Possible explanation: Although more students voted for drama in Period 5, it was actually a more popular choice in Period 1. Drama received about 27% of the votes in Period 5 compared to 32% in Period 1.

21b. Yes; Possible explanation: Comedy received seven votes, and suspense received only three. Since we are comparing within the same class, we can just compare the numbers.

21c. No; Possible explanation: Although animation received the same number of votes in both classes, it received a greater percent of the votes in Period 1.

21d. Possible answer: Action was twice as popular as suspense in the Period 5 class. Comedy was more than twice as popular in Period 1 as in Period 5.

22a. Possible answer: Harvest has 1.5 fewer grams of fat per serving than Crunch.

Real-World Link

Cable-television signals are received from antennas and satellites by cable companies. The signals are then sent out to customers along coaxial and fiber-optic cables.

· ·

21. Mr. Gordon asked his first and fifth period classes to vote for their favorite type of movie. The results are below.

Movie Type	Period 1 Votes	Period 5 Votes
Action	3	6
Suspense	0	3
Drama	8	9
Comedy	11	7
Animation	2	2
Other	1	6

21a–d. See margin.

   a. Chloe is in Period 5. She said drama was a more popular choice in her class than in the Period 1 class. Is she correct? Explain.

   b. Meliah is in Period 5. She said comedy was more than twice as popular as suspense in her class. Is she correct? Explain.

   c. Ricky is in Period 1. He said animation was just as popular in Period 5 as it was in his class. Is he correct? Explain.

   d. Write two true statements comparing the data in the table.

22. Nutrition Harvest Granola has 6.5 grams of fat per 38-gram serving. Crunch Granola has 8 grams of fat per 50-gram serving.

   a. The makers of Harvest Granola claim that their product has less fat than Crunch Granola. How can they defend their claim?

   b. The makers of Crunch claim that their granola has less fat than Harvest. How can they defend their claim?   Possible answer: Harvest is about 17% fat while Crunch is only 16% fat.

For Exercises 23–26, write each given percent as a decimal and a fraction in lowest terms. Write each given fraction as a decimal and a percent.

23. Social Studies About 7% of Americans are under age 5, and about 13% are over age 65. $0.07, \frac{7}{100}; 0.13, \frac{13}{100}$

24. About $\frac{2}{3}$ of U.S. households with televisions subscribe to a cable-television service. $0.\overline{6}, 66.\overline{6}\%$

25. In 1820, almost 72% of U.S. workers were farmers. By 1994, only $\frac{1}{40}$ of U.S. workers were employed in farming. $0.72, \frac{18}{25}; 0.025, 2.5\%$

26. The number of students in band is about 115% of the number in orchestra and about $\frac{5}{4}$ of the number in choir.
$1.15, \frac{23}{20},$ or $1\frac{3}{20}; 1.25, 125\%$

27. Copy and complete the table so the numbers in each row are equivalent.

Fraction	Decimal	Percent
$\frac{1}{2}$	0.5	50%
$\frac{39}{500}$	0.078	7.8%
$\frac{26}{5}$, or $5\frac{1}{5}$	5.2	520%
$\frac{7}{16}$	0.4375	43.75%
$\frac{37}{100}$	0.37	37%

Use information from Develop and Understand: C on pages 360 and 361 to solve Exercises 28 and 29.

28. Science What percent of the sun's UV rays are blocked with SPF 25 sunscreen? 96%

29. A sunscreen blocks 95% of the sun's UV rays. What is the SPF of the sunscreen? 20

30. 0.08, $\frac{2}{18}$, 18%; 0.1, or 10%, is a good benchmark.

31. The order is 31%, 0.355, $\frac{3}{6}$. $\frac{1}{3}$ would be a good benchmark.

32. The order is 84%, 0.845, $\frac{6}{7}$. $\frac{7}{8}$ would be a good benchmark.

Use a benchmark to order the numbers from least to greatest in each set.

30. 18%, $\frac{2}{18}$, 0.08   **31.** 31%, 0.355, $\frac{3}{6}$ **32.** 84%, 0.845, $\frac{6}{7}$,

Use the closest benchmark to estimate the value of the fraction as a percent. Mark the approximate location of each fraction on the number line. Put a star next to any answers that are exact.

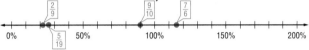

33. $\frac{9}{10}$ _____ 90%*   **34.** $\frac{5}{19}$ _____ 30%

35. $\frac{7}{6}$ _____ 120%   **36.** $\frac{2}{9}$ _____ 20%

Connect & Extend

37. Every January, Framingham Middle School holds its annual Winter Event. An article in the school paper reported that 45% of seventh graders voted that this year's event should be an ice-skating party. The president of the seventh grade class said that $\frac{9}{20}$ of seventh graders voted for ice skating. Could both reports be correct? Explain. Yes, $\frac{9}{20} = \frac{45}{100} = 45\%$

▶ **Exercises 28 and 29** You may suggest that students refer to the exercises on page 361 when they do these exercises.

▶ **Exercises 30–32** You may want to remind students to make a quick mental judgment of the numbers in order to choose a benchmark. For example, $\frac{3}{6}$ is equivalent to $\frac{1}{2}$, so the student can know exactly where to plot the location for $\frac{3}{6}$.

▶ **Exercises 33–36** Students will need a number line marked in tenths, from 0 to 200%. Before they start, ask them to glance over all the problems in the set and tell how far they think the number line should reach. They should notice that $\frac{7}{6}$ is an improper fraction and will be located to the right of 100%.

▶ **Exercise 38** Students will need a 100-grid for this exercise. They should be able to use the copy of Chapter 6 Master 1 from Exercises 1–4, if you assigned those exercises.

Students may enjoy presenting their proposals to the class. Have them explain how they know that their plans comply with the guidelines.

▶ **Exercise 40** Urge students to read **Part a** carefully. They should divide 8 by the number of students in each grade and change the resulting decimals to percents.

You may want to have a class discussion of the answers that students propose for **Parts b and c**.

▶ **Exercise 42** Help students organize their work. This problem requires a lot of thought and students may be frustrated if they do not take notes as they read. Show them how to make notes on a separate piece of paper, listing the names in order but allowing plenty of space for changes.

40b. Possible answer: Grade 6: 8 students; Grade 7: 16 students; Grade 8: 12 students; In this plan, 5% of each grade is represented.

38. Imagine that you are in charge of planning a town park. The park will be shaped like a square. The community council has given you these guidelines.

- At least 12% of the park must be a picnic area.
- Between 15% and 30% of the park should be a play area with a sandbox and playground equipment.
- A goldfish pond should occupy no more than 10% of the park.

On a 100-grid, sketch a plan for your park. You may include any features you want as long as the park satisfies the council's guidelines. Label the features of your park, including the picnic area, play area, and goldfish pond. Tell what percent of the park each feature will occupy.   Answers will vary.

39. Economics Suni needs a new winter coat. The Winter Warehouse advertises that everything in the store is 75% of the retail price. Coats Galore advertises that of all its coats are on sale for $\frac{7}{10}$ of the retail price. If the stores carry the same brands at the same prices, where will Suni find better prices? Explain.
Coats Galore; $\frac{7}{10} = 70\%$, which is less than 75%.

40. At Valley Middle School, the sixth grade has 160 students, the seventh grade has 320 students, and the eighth grade has 240 students. The student congress is traditionally made up of eight representatives from each grade.

a. For each grade, find the percent of students in the congress. Give your answers to the nearest tenth of a percent.
5%, 2.5%, 3.3%

b. Tom is in the seventh grade class. He believes that since his class has more students, it should have more representatives. He suggests that each grade be represented by the same *percent* of its students.

Devise a plan for setting up the student congress this way. Tell how many representatives each grade should elect and the percent of each grade that is represented.

c. Which plan do you think is more fair, the original plan or the plan you devised in Part b? Defend your answer.   Answers will vary.

41. Possible answer: The percentages can be found for each group individually. Then the percentages can be used to compare the two groups.

41. In Your Own Words Give an example to illustrate how percents can be used to compare data for two groups of different sizes.

42a. Cora: 126%,
Juanita: 86%,
Jase: 0.49, John: $\frac{5}{16}$,
Chandra: 0.13,
Stuart: $\frac{12}{9}$

43. Mean: 79; median: 73; mode 99; mean or median

44. Mean: 65; median: 85; mode: none; median

45. Mean: 75.5; median: 77; mode: none; mean or median

42. Six students agreed to sell tickets for a raffle. After two weeks, they met to report how sales were going. Some of them had sold more tickets than they had promised. Others had sold fewer. Each of them reported the percent of the target number of tickets they had sold. Some of them expressed the percent as a fraction or a decimal.

Students: Cora, Juanita, Jase, John, Chandra, Stuart

Percent reported: $\frac{5}{16}$, 86%, 0.13, $\frac{12}{9}$, 126%, 0.49

a. Use the clues to match the students to the percent they sold.

    Clues: A. Cora sold more than 100% of the target number.

            B. Juanita sold a greater percent of the target number than Jase did.

            C. Jase sold a greater percent of the target number than John did.

            D. Chandra's percent was the closest to $\frac{1}{8}$.

            E. Stuart's percent was greatest.

b. On a line labeled in increments of 10%, place each student's reported percent. You may need to approximate. See below.

c. Which numbers were you able to place exactly?
None, They are all approximations.

d. If you had a line labeled in increments of 1%, which numbers would you be able to place exactly? All except $\frac{5}{16}$ and $\frac{12}{9}$

Mixed Review

48. Possible answer: Each term is half of the preceding term; $\frac{3}{16}, \frac{3}{32}, \frac{3}{64}$.

49. Possible answer: Every other letter of the alphabet; k, m, o.

50. Possible answer: Start with 1, add 1, then 2, then 3, and so on; 22, 29, 37.

Statistics Find the mean, median, and mode of each set of test scores. Then tell which measure you think best represents the data.

43. 85, 99, 73, 64, 99, 80, 69, 72, 70

44. 0, 90, 93, 6, 85, 97, 84

45. 52, 94, 73, 81, 65, 88

Write a rule that fits all the input/output pairs in each table.

46.

Input	1	2	4	6	10	11
Output	4	7	13	19	31	34

Output = 3 · input + 1

47.

Input	2	4	6	3	7	5
Output	3	11	19	7	23	15

Output = 4 · input − 5

Describe the pattern in each sequence. Use the pattern to find the next three terms.

48. 12, 6, 3, $\frac{3}{2}$, $\frac{3}{4}$, $\frac{3}{8}$, …   **49.** a, c, e, g, i, …   **50.** 1, 2, 4, 7, 11, 16, …

42b.

Lesson 6.1 Use Percents   **367**

Percent of a Quantity

Objectives

▶ To calculate a percent of a quantity

▶ To use benchmarks to estimate a percent of a quantity

Overview

In this lesson, students learn how to find a percent of a quantity. They consider different methods of calculating a percent of a quantity, and use benchmark fractions and percents to help them estimate a percent of a quantity. They also apply these ideas to real-world contexts.

Advance Preparation

You may want to provide counters, paper bags, and slips of paper numbered from 1–20 and 100-grids (Chapter 6 Master 1) to facilitate class discussion while presenting new topics, including modeling and calculating percents.

	Summary	Materials	On Your Own Exercises (pp. 376–379)	Assessment Opportunities
Investigation 1 (p. 369) *Pacing: 2 days*	Students practice finding 1% of a quantity and using that information to calculate another percent of the same quantity.	Chapter 6 Master 1, 100 counters (optional)	Practice & Apply: 1–7 Connect & Extend: 23–25 Mixed Review: 29–41	• Share & Summarize (p. 371) • Troubleshooting (pp. 370, 371)
Investigation 2 (p. 372) *Pacing: 1 day*	Students use benchmarks to estimate a percent of a quantity and calculate percents in real–world contexts.	paper bags, slips of paper numbered 1–20	Practice & Apply: 8–22 Connect & Extend: 26–28 Mixed Review: 29–41	• On the Spot Assessment (p. 374) • Share & Summarize (p. 375) • Troubleshooting (p. 375)

Leveled Lesson Resources

Also on
TeacherWorks™
Lesson 6.2

Study Guide and Intervention (p. 10) [AL]

Lesson 6.2 Study Guide and Intervention
A Percent of a Quantity

Example 1 Find 70% of 40.

Method 1 Write the percent as a fraction.

$70\% = \frac{70}{100}$ or $\frac{7}{10}$

$\frac{7}{10}$ of 40 $= \frac{7}{10} \times 40$ or 28

So, 70% of 40 is 28.
Use a model to check the answer. The model comfirms that 70% of 40 is 28.

Method 2 Write the percent as a decimal.

$70\% = \frac{7}{100}$ or 0.7

0.7 of 40 $= 0.7 \times 40$ or 28

Example 2 Find 120% of 25.

Method 1 Write the percent as a fraction.

$120\% = \frac{120}{100}$ or $\frac{6}{5}$

$\frac{6}{5}$ of 25 $= \frac{6}{5} \times 25$ or 30

So, 120% of 25 is 30.

Method 2 Write the percent as a decimal.

$120\% = \frac{120}{100}$ or 1.2

1.2 of 25 $= 1.2 \times 25$ or 30

Exercises

Find the percent of each number.

1. 10% of 120 2. 60% of 25 3. 75% of 24
4. 90% of 40 5. 120% of 20 6. 150% of 2
7. 15% of 40 8. 30% of 70 9. 150% of 6
10. 165% of 20 11. 8% of 15 12. 6% of 6

Skills Practice (p. 11) [AL] [OL]

Lesson 6.2 Skills Practice
A Percent of a Quantity

Find the percent of each number.

1. 25% of 16 2. 50% of 70 3. 10% of 30
4. 60% of 40 5. 75% of 20 6. 20% of 90
7. 30% of 110 8. 50% of 140 9. 25% of 80
10. 4% of 100 11. 75% of 36 12. 90% of 120
13. 125% of 40 14. 8% of 25 15. 150% of 22
16. 110% of 50 17. 125% of 60 18. 40% of 5
19. 15% of 40 20. 5% of 14 21. 20% of 29
22. 130% of 80 23. 4.5% of 60 24. 35% of 34
25. 14.5% of 60 26. 14% of 30 27. 24% of 15
28. 140% of 30 29. 6% of 55 30. 160% of 22

Problem-Solving Practice (p. 12) [AL] [OL]

Lesson 6.2 Problem-Solving Practice
A Percent of a Quantity

Solve

1. **School** There are 520 students at Northridge High School. 80% of these students take the bus. How many students take the bus?

2. **Age** Theresa is 60% as old as her sister Mala, who is 20 years old. How old is Theresa?

3. **Tipping** Charlie wants to leave a 15% tip for a meal that costs $40. How much should Charlie leave for a tip?

4. **Sales tax** Charmaine wants to buy a shirt for $15. If the sales tax is 4% of $15, how much will she pay in sales tax?

5. **Football** In the 2007–2008 regular season, the New York Giants won 62.5% of their games. There were 16 regular season games. How many games did the Giants win?

6. **Baseball** During the 2007 World Series, Manny Ramirez of the Bosten Red Sox had a batting average of .250, or 25%. He was at bat 16 times. How many hits did he get?

7. **Books** Wide Eyed Books is advertising that every book is on sale for 80% of its original price. What is the sale price of a book that originally cost $35?

8. **Shopping** A DVD player that normally costs $160 is on sale for 70% of its normal price. What is the sale price of the DVD player?

Enrichment (p. 13) [BL]

Lesson 6.2 Enrichment
A Percent of a Quantity

Estimating Sales Tax

Many states charge a *sales tax* on purchases. To be sure that you have enough money, you should be able to estimate the amount of sales tax and the total cost of an item. For example, this is how you can estimate the total cost of the purchase shown at the right.

$10.95
sales tax rate: 6.75%

First, round the price and the rate.

$10.95 → $11

6.75% → 7%

Multiply the rounded numbers.

11 dollars
× 7¢ per dollar
77¢ ≈ 80

7% means 7¢ per 100¢

So, the total cost is close to $11 + 80¢, or $11.80.

Estimate the total cost of each purchase.

1. $6.98 sales tax rate: 5%
2. $11.97 sales tax rate: 5.75%
3. $19.88 sales tax rate: 4.255%
4. $29.95 sales tax rate: $6\frac{1}{2}\%$
5. $79.00 sales tax rate: $8\frac{1}{4}\%$
6. $117.99 sales tax rate: 6.25%

Will $50 be enough money to make such purchase?

7. $48.95 sales tax rate: 3%
8. $46.99 sales tax rate: 4.75%
9. $46.99 sales tax rate: $8\frac{1}{4}\%$

10. **Challenge** The price marked on a cassette tape is $8.99. With the sales tax, the total cost of the tape is $9.37. Estimate the sales tax rate.

Lesson Quick Quiz (p. 14) [AL] [OL] [BL]

Lesson 6.2 Quick Quiz
A Percent of a Quantity

1. Find each result using any method you like.

   a. 12% of 50 b. 6% of 137

   c. 84% of 220 d. 115% of 82

2. Use benchmarks to estimate each result. Then find the exact value.

   a. 24% of 120

   b. 66% of 48

   c. 151% of 1,800

3. A shirt is on sale for 15% off the original price of $27. What is the sale price of the shirt?

4. How much would you pay for a CD that usually sells for $12.50 if it is on sale for 30% off?

Additional Lesson Resources

Teacher Tech Tools
- TeacherWorks
- ExamView Assessment Suite
- Classroom Presentation Toolkit
- Advance Tracker

Student Tech Tools
- StudentWorks Plus
- **Math Online** eGlossary •
- Concepts in Motion

Other Print Products
- Investigation Notebook and Reflection Journal
- Quick Review Math Handbook

Introduce

Percent of a Quantity To introduce the lesson, you might ask students if they recall hearing any statements like those in the text (13% of Americans are age 65 or over, and so on). You may want to make a transparency of some recent newspaper articles with examples of percent statements and display them. Ask, or point out: How much is 100% or 50% of a quantity?

Think & Discuss

You can use the Think & Discuss questions to remind students that percent means "out of 100." You may need to suggest that students convert the percents to fractions. Then you can ask, for example, what is $\frac{1}{2}$ of 500, instead of what is 50% of 500. You can also use the activity to review benchmark fractions and percents.

Two of the questions ask students to find 1% of a number. If necessary, point out that 1% is $\frac{1}{100}$ times 100%, or $\frac{1}{100}$ of the whole. To find 1%, then, students can simply move the decimal point two places to the left.

Percent of a Quantity

You often read and hear statements that mention the "percent of" a particular quantity.

73% of Voters Favor New Park

70% of U.S. Schools Have Internet Access

13% of Americans Are Age 65 or Over

No matter what the quantity, 100% is all of it, and 50% is half of it. The specific amount a given percent represents depends on the quantity. For example, 50% of 10 tree frogs is 5 tree frogs, while 50% of 100 tree frogs is 50 tree frogs.

Think & Discuss

Use what you know about fractions and percents to answer each of these questions.

- What is 100% of 500? 500 • What is 50% of 500? 250
- What is 25% of 500? 125 • What is 1% of 500? 5
- What is 100% of 40? 40 • What is 50% of 40? 20
- What is 25% of 40? 10 • What is 1% of 40? 0.4

Investigation ① Model Percents

Materials
- sheet of 100-grids

Imagine that this 100-grid represents a value of 200 and that this value is divided evenly among the 100 small squares.

2a. 75

Value: 300

2b. 30

Value: 300

2c. 51

Value: 300

2d. 225

Value: 300

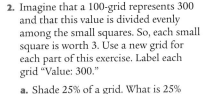
Value: 200

Think & Discuss

What is the value of each small square in the grid? What percent of 200 does each small square represent?   **2, 1%**

What percent of 200 do 10 small squares represent? What is the value of 10 small squares?   **10%, 20**

How could you use the grid to find 20% of 200?   **Possible answer: 20% is 20 squares. Each square has value 2, so 20% of 200 is 20 · 2 = 40.**

✓ Develop & Understand: A

1. Refer to the grid above.
   a. What is 15% of 200?   30   b. What is 50% of 200?   100

2. Imagine that a 100-grid represents 300 and that this value is divided evenly among the small squares. So, each small square is worth 3. Use a new grid for each part of this exercise. Label each grid "Value: 300."

   a. Shade 25% of a grid. What is 25% of 300?
   b. Shade 10% of a grid. What is 10% of 300?
   c. Shade 17% of a grid. What is 17% of 300?
   d. Shade 75% of a grid. What is 75% of 300?
   e. Shade 120% of a grid. What is 120% of 300?   See margin.

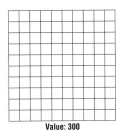
Value: 300

Lesson 6.2   A Percent of a Quantity   **369**

Additional Answer
2e. Possible answer: 360

Value: 300

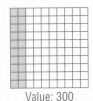
Value: 300

100-grid Have students look at the 100-grid, and tell them it represents a total value of 200 instead of 100.

Think & Discuss

When you discuss these questions, be sure students understand that if 1% of the value of the grid is 2, then 10% of the value is 10 times that amount, or 20. Students should then have little difficulty seeing that 20% of the value of the grid can be found by multiplying 2 by 20.

Teacher Tips Provide students with two copies of Chapter 6 Master 1, 100-grids. When doing the exercises, you may want students to label one small square with its value, as well as the whole grid.

Some teachers use a spice box crate to show each portion as a number on the grid. This distinguishes the value of the grid from the value of each small square.

✓ Develop & Understand: A

Suggested Grouping: Individuals

▶ **Exercise 1** Suggest that students use the grid at the top of the page. Refer to the Think & Discuss activity to prompt students, if necessary, or use a transparent 100-grid on the overhead to demonstrate

▶ **Exercise 2** Tell students to label each grid "300." You may want to suggest that they write "3" in one of the squares to indicate that each square has a value of 3. Again, if necessary, refer to the Think & Discuss activity to help students see that they can multiply the percent number by 3 (1% of 300) to find the percents. For example, in **Part a**, 25% of 300 is 25 times 1% of 300 (that is, 25 times 3).

▶ **Exercise 3** Students may benefit from a class discussion of why each square represents $\frac{1}{2}$ or 0.5. You might ask:

- If the grid represents a value of 50, how much would one row represent? Why?

- So one row represents 5. If you want to split the row into five groups, how many squares would be in each group?

- What value would two squares represent?

- Students should easily see that each individual square represents a value of $\frac{1}{2}$.

▶ **Exercise 4** Point out that no whole number of small squares has a value exactly equal to 1. However, students should be able to use reasoning similar to that above to find that the value of an individual square is 0.24. Encourage them to check their results by multiplying 0.24 by 100 (the total number of small squares) to get 24, the given value for the whole grid.

Wrap-Up Discuss Exercise 5 with the class. You may need to provide some guidance for students who have difficulty verbalizing the generalization that grows out of the earlier problems in the set. Ask those students to demonstrate using a specific example, such as finding 40% of 500, and have them explain what they do at each step. You can use their words to show them how to generalize. For example, if a student says, "I divide 500 by 100 to get the value of one square," you can say, "So if you're finding a percent of a number, you first divide the number by 100. What percent of the number does that result represent?" 1%

Troubleshooting Some students may make careless computational errors when they calculate percents of quantities, especially with problems like Exercise 4. Encourage students to check that they moved the decimal point correctly when rewriting percents as decimals. They should also check their multiplication.

3a–4b. Possible answers:

3a. $\frac{1}{2}$, or 0.5

Value: 50

3b. 5

Value: 50

3c. 25

Value: 50

4a. 0.24

Value: 24

4b. 2.4

Value: 24

3. Imagine that a 100-grid has value 50 and that this value is divided evenly among the small squares. Use a new grid for each part of this exercise. Label each grid "Value: 50."

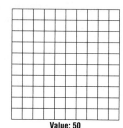

Value: 50

a. Shade 1% of a grid. What is 1% of 50?

b. Shade 10% of a grid. What is 10% of 50?

c. Shade 50% of a grid. What is 50% of 50?

4. Imagine that a 100-grid has value 24 and that this value is divided evenly among the small squares. Use a new grid for each part of this exercise. Label each grid "Value: 24."

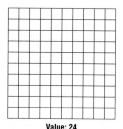

Value: 24

a. Shade 1% of a grid. What is 1% of 24?

b. Shade 10% of a grid. What is 10% of 24?

c. Shade 80% of a grid. What is 80% of 24?   See margin.

5. Look back at your work in Exercises 1–4. Describe a shortcut for finding a percent of a number without using a grid. Give an example to show how it works.   Possible answer: Find 1% of the number by dividing it by 100 or by moving the decimal point two places to the left. Then multiply the result by the number in the percent you are trying to find. For example, to find 40% of 500, first find 1% of 500, which is 5, and then multiply the result by 40. So, 40% of 500 is 40 · 5, or 200.

Additional Answer
4c. Possible answer: 19.2

Value: 24

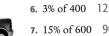

✅ *Develop & Understand: B*

Find each result without using a grid.

6. 3% of 400   12

7. 15% of 600   90

8. 44% of 50   22

9. 12% of 250   30

10. In a recent year, about 8,000,000 new cars were sold in the United States. About 16% of these cars were luxury cars.

    a. About how many new luxury cars were sold?   1,280,000

    b. About 10% of the new luxury cars sold were green. How many green luxury cars were sold?   About 128,000

11. You know that 10% of 360 is 36.

    a. Use this fact to find 20% of 360 and 40% of 360. Explain the calculations that you did.

    b. Use the fact that 10% of 360 is 36 to find 5% of 360 and 15% of 360. Explain your calculations.

11a. 72, 144; Possible explanation: I multiplied 36 by 2 to find 20% and by 4 to find 40%.

11b. 18, 54; Possible explanation: To find 5%, I found half of 10%. To find 15%, I added 10% plus half of 10%: 36 + 18 = 54.

12. \$6; Possible explanation: 10% of 40 is 4. 15% is 10% plus half of 10%, or \$4 + \$2 = \$6.

12. The Palmer family went out for dinner. The total cost for the meal was \$40. Calculate a 15% tip in your head. Explain what you did.

Share & *Summarize*

Describe two methods for finding 15% of 400.   Possible answer: Find 1% of 400, which is 4, and then multiply by 15 to get 60. Or find 10% of 400, which is 40, and then add half of 10%, which is 20.

Reaching All Learners

AL Approaching The size of the number (8 million) in Exercise 10 might be intimidating to some students. If they have trouble, you might ask them to imagine that the number was only 800. Then ask how their answers would be different if the number was 8,000, then 80,000.

 ## *Develop & Understand: B*

Suggested Grouping: Individuals or Pairs

▶ **Exercises 6–9** Students have opportunities to calculate a percent of a quantity by using the general strategy from Exercise 5 on page 374. They should not need to refer to 100-grids at this point, but you may want to let students having particular difficulty check their answers with a grid.

▶ **Exercise 10b** Most students are likely to find the answer by calculating 10% of the answer to **Part a**. Point out that 10% of any whole number or decimal can be found by moving the decimal point one place to the left.

▶ **Exercises 11 and 12** Point out that benchmark percents can be used to calculate a variety of other percents mentally.

Share & *Summarize*

Discuss students' methods. Some may find it difficult to provide an immediate description of two methods for finding 15% of 400. They may find it easier to demonstrate the calculations and then write verbal descriptions of their steps. Ask if their methods would work with numbers other than 400.

Troubleshooting Students should be able to find percents of quantities at this point. If they understand only one method, and they cannot see alternates such as the second method in the sample answer for the Share & Summarize, it is not necessary to belabor the point. As long as they understand one method, they can succeed with the rest of the chapter.

Calculate Percents In this investigation, students learn a method that allows them to calculate quickly any percent of any number: change the percent to a decimal and multiply the other number by the decimal. They practice using benchmark percents and fractions to estimate a percent of a number and use their estimates to check the reasonableness of exact results. They apply these skills to calculate prices of items that are being sold at a discount.

Example

Use Conor's calculations and explanation to remind students of their work finding percents of quantities in Investigation 1. Then have students read Rosita's method, and discuss Conor's explanation of it.

Point out that students should estimate an answer before calculating to be sure their answer is reasonable. When calculating with percents, it is easy for students to place the decimal in the wrong place. Estimating the answer will make that error obvious.

✓ Develop & Understand: A

Suggested Grouping: Individuals

▶ **Exercises 1–4** You may want to have a brief discussion of how students got their estimates.

▶ **Exercise 4** Use this exercise to gain insight into how sophisticated students are in their estimation procedures. For example, some students may round 72% up to 75% and 1,100 up to 1,200 to obtain an estimate of $\frac{3}{4} \cdot 1,200$, or 900. However, rounding 72% up to 75% and 1,100 down to 1,000 gives an estimate of $\frac{3}{4} \cdot 1,000$, or 750, which is closer than 900 to the exact value.

▶ **Exercises 5–10** Suggest that students estimate each result before or after calculating the exact answer.

Investigation ② Calculate Percents with a Shortcut

Materials

- slips of paper numbered 1–20
- paper bag

In the last investigation, you used a grid to help find a given percent of a number. You probably discovered a shortcut or two for finding a percent of a number without using a grid. The example shows how Conor and Rosita thought about finding 23% of 800.

Example

In Exercises 1–11, you will practice Rosita's method. Estimate each answer by using benchmark fractions and percents. This will check whether your answer is reasonable.

For example, 23% of 800 is a little less than 25%, or $\frac{1}{4}$, of 800. So, the result should be a little less than 200. Conor and Rosita's answer of 184 is reasonable.

✓ Develop & Understand: A

1. Estimates will vary; the exact value is 36.
2. Estimates will vary; the exact value is 180.
3. Estimates will vary; the exact value is 54.
4. Estimates will vary; the exact value is 792.

Estimate each result using benchmarks. Then find the exact value using Rosita's shortcut.

1. 30% of 120	**2.** 45% of 400
3. 9% of 600	**4.** 72% of 1,100

Find each result using any method you like.

5. 3% of 45 1.35	**6.** 15% of 64 9.6
7. 44% of 125 55	**8.** 2% of 15.4 0.308
9. 125% of 40 50	**10.** 12.5% of 80 10

11. In 2006, there were 124,521,886 households in the United States.

    a. About 64% of U.S. households had at least one computer. How many U.S. households had a computer?   79,694,007

    b. About 57% of U.S. households had access to the Internet. How many U.S. households had Internet access?   70,977,475

When stores have sales, they often advertise that items are a certain "percent off." In the rest of this investigation, you will practice calculating the sale price when a percent discount is taken.

✅ Develop & Understand: B

A department store is having its annual storewide sale.

12. All athletic shoes are on sale for 20% off the original price. Caroline bought a pair of cross-trainers with an original price of $80. What was the sale price for this pair of shoes? Explain how you found your answer. $64; Possible explanation: I found 20% of $80 and subtracted the result, $16, from $80.

13. All fall jackets are on sale for 35% off the original price. Miguel bought a jacket originally priced at $60. How much did he pay? Explain how you found your answer. $39; Possible explanation: I found 65% of $60, which is 0.65 · $60 = $39.

14. A CD player, originally priced at $120, is on sale for 25% off. What is the sale price? $90

Caroline and Miguel have different ways of calculating the sale price for the items that they bought.

As you work on Exercises 15–17, try both of their methods to see which you prefer.

▶ **Exercise 11** You may want to tell students to round their answers to the nearest thousand. For **Part b**, students should find 41.5% of the number of households in the United States, not 41.5% of the answer from **Part a**. Point out the phrase "of U.S. households" if necessary. You may also want to remind students that Internet access is not limited to people who have computers; there are other ways to access it, including cell phones and devices designed solely for Internet access.

Real-World Link

If the number of Internet users grows at the same rate of 6,667%, how many users would you expect in 2010? Is this a reasonable number?

✅ Develop & Understand: B

Suggested Grouping: Pairs

▶ **Exercises 12–14** You may want to have students apply what they have learned about calculating a percent of a number to solve problems about items that are on sale. Let students take a few minutes to find their own ways to answer these questions, which are straightforward.

Wrap-Up In a class discussion, have students describe how they would find the sale price of an item. Use the discussion as a lead-in to the cartoon. Have students read the cartoon, and ask them to relate Caroline's and Miguel's methods to their own work in Exercises 12–14. If only one of the methods was suggested by students, you might ask them to identify that method.

✅ Develop & Understand: C

Suggested Grouping: Individuals

▶ **Exercises 15–17** Encourage students to try each method from the cartoon on page 377 at least once. You may even want to suggest that students use both methods for each problem, using the results of one as a check on the other.

▶ **Exercise 17** Point out that students need to calculate one sale price and compare it to the given sale price at the other store.

Teacher Tips For the next set of exercises, each pair of students will need a paper bag that contains 20 slips of paper (of approximately equal size) numbered 1–20.

✅ Develop & Understand: D

Suggested Grouping: Pairs

▶ **Exercise 18** You may want to start this exercise with the whole class. For this exercise, students apply the act it out problem-solving strategy. Discuss how to fill in the numbers for the columns "First Number" and "Second Number." For each row of the table, students draw two numbers from the paper bag and record the numbers drawn in these columns. (It actually makes no difference which number they put in which column.) After students record the numbers in the table, they should put the slips back into the bag. Encourage students to remix the number slips after each replacement.

▶ **Exercise 19** Ask students to complete the table one row at a time. Most students will round sale-price results to the nearest cent, but you may need to suggest it.

✅ Develop & Understand: C

15. At K.C. Nickel's back-to-school sale, everything is 40% off the price marked on the tag. Find the sale price of each item.

a. $37.10 $22.26

b.   SALE $970 $582

Real-World Link

The average U.S. resident receives 20 greeting cards each year, a third of which are birthday cards.

16. At Celebrate! card store, birthday cards are on sale for 25% off. What is the sale price for a card originally marked $1.60? $1.20

17. Zears and GameHut both usually charge $75 for Quasar-Z, a hand-held electronic game. This week, Quasar-Z is on sale for $60 at GameHut and is 25% off at Zears. At which store is the game less expensive? Explain.   Zears; the price at Zears is 0.75 · $75, or $56.25, which is less than the GameHut price.

✅ Develop & Understand: D

The If the Shoe Fits shoe store is having a "Draw a Discount" sale. For the sale, the numbers 1 through 20 are put in a box. Each customer draws two numbers and adds them. The result is the percent the customer will save on his or her purchase.

18. To test how the sale works, pretend to be five customers. The price of each customer's purchase is given in the table. Place slips of paper numbered 1 through 20 in a bag. For each customer, draw two slips of paper, record the numbers, and return the two slips to the bag.   Answers will vary.

Customer	Original Price	First Number	Second Number	Percent Off	Sale Price
1	$37.00				
2	20.50				
3	12.98				
4	45.79				
5	79.99				

19. Complete the table by finding the percent off and the sale price for each customer's purchase.   Answers will vary.

On the Spot Assessment

Keep an eye out for students who correctly use the "percent off" information to calculate how much less than the original price an item will cost, but forget to subtract the result from the original price. Help them to see that they have calculated how much lower the price will be, and then ask how they can use that information to find the final price of the item.

20. What is the total amount the five customers paid for their purchases? Answers will vary.

21. Now figure out the price each customer would have paid if, instead of the "Draw a Discount" sale, the store had offered 20% off all purchases.

Real-World Link
People in Canada and the United States spend approximately $35 billion per year on shoes, averaging five pairs per person.

Customer	Original Price	Percent Off	Sale Price
1	$37.00	20%	$29.60
2	20.50	20%	16.40
3	12.98	20%	10.38
4	45.79	20%	36.63
5	79.99	20%	63.99

22. What is the total amount the five customers would have paid during a 20% off sale? How does this compare to the total for the "Draw a Discount" sale? $157.00; Comparisons will vary.

23. If you were the store manager, which type of sale would you hold? Explain. Answers will vary.

Share & Summarize

1. Describe a method for calculating a given percent of a number. Demonstrate your method by finding 67% of 320.

2. Write an exercise about a "percent off" sale. Explain how to solve it. Possible answer: A mountain bike with an original price of $250 is marked 25% off. What is the sale price for the bike? Solution: The sale price is 25% off, so you pay 75%. So, the sale price is 75% of 250 = 0.75 · 250 = $187.50.

1. Possible explanation: I change the percent to a decimal by moving the decimal point two places to the left. Then I multiply the result by the quantity I am finding the percent of. So, 67% of 320 is 0.67 · 320 = 214.4.

Lesson 6.2   A Percent of a Quantity   375

▶ **Exercise 21** In this exercise, students fill in a second table, this time assuming that a flat 20% is taken off the original price of each item. Point out that the original prices for the items in this table are the same as those in the first table. When students calculate the sale prices for the second table, they should again round to the nearest cent.

▶ **Exercise 22** After students have completed this exercise, you may wish to have a class discussion to allow pairs of students to share their results for Exercises 20 and 22 with the rest of the class. This can serve as a check, but also give more evidence for students to consider as they answer Exercise 23.

▶ **Exercise 23** Point out that students should think about the results for Exercises 20 and 22 and decide which type of sale will make more money for the store.

Share & Summarize

For **Exercise 1**, let students work individually, and then have volunteers present their answers to the class. Suggest that students having trouble articulating their method complete the example first, and then describe (in general terms if possible) what they did.

For **Exercise 2**, watch for students who have trouble remembering that the amount taken off at a "percent off" sale must be subtracted from the original price to determine the sale price.

Troubleshooting If there are students who are still having difficulty finding a percent of a number, have them show how they would do a specific problem so you can see the stage or stages at which they are having difficulty. Provide practice as needed for students who make simple errors when they change percents to decimals.

Reaching All Learners

OL **On Level** If time permits, you may wish to allow interested students to do an extended analysis of the situation. Have students consider just one price, say $50, and consider all the possibilities for the "Draw a Discount" approach. Students will probably assume each draw is equally likely, so it is important to have them consider each of the two draws separately. For example, drawing 3 and then 14 should be considered different from drawing 14 and then 3.

Investigation 1
Pages 369–371
Practice & Apply: 1–7
Connect & Extend: 23–25

Investigation 2
Pages 372–375
Practice & Apply: 8–22
Connect & Extend: 26–28

Assign Anytime
Mixed Review: 29–41

▶ **Exercise 1** Suggest that students copy the 100-grid, or supply them with a copy of Chapter 6 Master 1, so they can actually shade in the squares as needed.

▶ **Exercise 6** In **Part a**, students may think that they must write $313 billion in standard form before they do the calculations. If you observe students doing this, explain how it is possible to do the calculation without resorting to a number with nine zeros.

▶ **Exercise 7** When you discuss the exercise in class, you may want to ask students to describe the strategies they used for the mental calculations.

Real-World Link
Do an informal survey to find what percent of students ate at a fast-food restaurant in the last week.

On Your Own Exercises
Lesson 6.2

Practice  **Apply**

1. Imagine that a 100-grid has value 150 and that this value is divided evenly among the small squares.

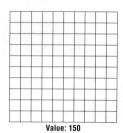

Value: 150

  a. What is the value of 25 small squares? 37.5

  b. What is the value of 1% of the grid? 1.5

  c. What is the value of $\frac{1}{10}$ of the grid? 15

  d. What is 40% of 150? 60

  e. What is 17% of 150? 25.5

  f. What is 150% of 150? 225

Find each result without using a grid.

2. 22% of 700 154   **3.** 90% of 120 108

4. 30% of 15 4.5   **5.** 65% of 210 136.5

Real-World Link
There are more than 300,000 fast-food restaurants in the United States.

6. In a recent year, Americans spent about 313 billion dollars on food prepared away from home. Of this total, almost 48% was spent on fast food.

  a. About how much money did Americans spend on fast food? Round your answer to the nearest billion dollars. $150 billion

  b. Of the total dollars spent on fast food, about 64% was spent on takeout food. About how many fast-food dollars were spent on takeout food? $96 billion

7. Economics Mrs. Diaz took her mother out for dinner. The total for the items they ordered was $20.

  a. Mentally calculate the 5% sales tax on the order. $1

  b. Mrs. Diaz wants to leave a 20% tip on the food cost plus the sales tax. Mentally calculate how much the tip should be. $4.20

8. Estimates will vary;
   the exact value
   is 60.

9. Estimates will vary;
   the exact value
   is 54.

10. Estimates will vary;
    the exact value
    is 39.

11. Estimates will vary;
    the exact value
    is 45.6.

Estimate each result using benchmarks. Then find the exact value.

8. 75% of 80   **9.** 60% of 90

10. 65% of 60   **11.** 57% of 80

Find each result using any method you like.

12. 19% of 43   8.17   **13.** 45% of 234   105.3   **14.** 67% of 250   167.5

15. 112% of 70   78.4   **16.** 0.55% of 100   0.55   **17.** 72% of 3.7   2.664

18. Nutrition If a 64-ounce carton of fruit juice contains 10% real fruit juice, how many ounces of fruit juice does the carton contain?   6.4 oz

19. A hockey arena has a seating capacity of 30,275. Of these seats, about 31% are taken by season ticket holders. About how many seats are taken by season ticket holders?   9,385

20. Of the 2,000 students at Franklin High School, 28% are freshmen. How many Franklin students are freshmen?   560

21. Economics At Sparks electronic store, all CD players are reduced to 66% of the original price.

   a. What is the sale price for a CD player that originally cost $90?
   $59.40
   b. How much money would you save on a $90 CD player? What "percent off" is this? $30.60, 34%

22. The Fountain of Youth health products store is going out of business. To help clear out the remaining merchandise, the store is having a "Save Your Age" sale. Each customer saves the percent equal to his or her age on each purchase.

   a. Andrew bought a case of all-natural soda originally priced at $18. Andrew is 12 years old. How much did he pay for the case of soda? $15.84

   b. Andrew's father bought some soap and shampoo originally priced at $24. He is 36 years old. How much did he pay for the items?
   $15.36
   c. Andrew's grandmother is 63 years old. She bought a juicer originally priced at $57. How much did she pay? $21.09

▶ **Exercises 8–11** You may want to have students explain how they found their estimates.

▶ **Exercise 21** Students need to read this exercise carefully. Some students may think that the "percent off" is 66%.

▶ **Exercise 22** Emphasize that for each customer, the "percent off" is found by writing the person's age followed by a percent sign.

Lesson 6.2 A Percent of Quantity   **377**

▶ **Exercise 24** Students will need 100-grids (Chapter 6 Master 1) for this exercise. For **Part a**, check that students understand how to find the value of a small square and how to calculate the number of small squares needed to represent $880. You may want to have a volunteer explain to the class how to solve **Part b**.

▶ **Exercise 25** All students may benefit from a class discussion of this exercise. It is quite possible students have heard people say such things as, "I'm 1,000% certain that what I said is correct." Point out that, in this case, the percent is simply an exaggeration.

▶ **Exercise 26** When you discuss this exercise, help students understand the meaning of the terms percent increase and percent decrease. You may want to refer to Exercise 25 to help make the point that a store can make a price more than 100% of its original price but would not decrease the price by 100% or more.

Additional Answers

24a. Possible answer: Use a 100-grid to represent the whole $2,000. Each square represents $20. To make $880, shade 44 squares. The 56 unshaded squares represent the amount they still have to raise. So, they still have 56% left to raise.

44%　　56%

Value: $2000

---

23. In Your Own Words Describe the difference between finding a "percent of" a given price and the "percent off" a given price. Give examples to show how to do each calculation.

Connect & Extend

23. Sample answer: There is no difference between the "percent of" and the "percent off" a number. 50% of 200 is 100. 50% off $200 is $100 off. To do the calculation, you change the percent to a decimal by moving the decimal point two places to the left. Then multiply the result by the quantity you are finding "the percent of."

25a. No; 100% means that it is certain to rain, so the chance of rain cannot be greater than 100%.

25b. Yes; for example, if their goal was $100 and they raised $130, they would have raised 130% of their goal.

25c. No; 100% is all of the drink, so it is impossible for more than 100% of the drink to be fruit juice.

25e. Yes; this is the same as doubling the price and then adding 20% more.

24. You can use 100-grids to model real-world situations involving percents. In Parts a and b, show how you could use a 100-grid to model and solve the exercise.　See margin.

　a. Students in the sixth grade have raised $880 of the $2,000 they need for a class trip. What percent of the $2,000 do they still need to raise?

　b. Challenge This year, tickets to the dance cost $15. This is 125% of last year's cost. How much did tickets cost last year?

25. This exercise will give you practice thinking about percents greater than 100%.

　a. Could there be a 125% chance of rain tomorrow? Explain.

　b. Could a fundraiser bring in 130% of its goal? Explain.

　c. Could a drink be 110% fruit juice?

　d. Could a candidate get 115% of the votes in an election?　See margin.

　e. Could prices in a store increase by 120%?

26. Economics You have learned two ways to compute the sale price when a percent discount is taken. You can use similar methods to solve exercises involving a percent increase.

　a. Last year, Irene bought an antique radio for $28. Since then, the radio's value has increased by 25%. By how many dollars did the value increase? What is the new value of the radio?　$7, $35

　b. In Part a, you computed the value of the radio in two steps. You calculated the number of dollars the value increased, then you added the increase to the original value.

　　How could you calculate the value in one step? Explain why your method works. Show that it gives the same answer that you found in Part a.
　　See margin.

24b. Possible answer: Let one whole grid, 100%, represent last year's price. Since this year's price is 125% of last year's, represent this year's price by shading one whole grid and 25 squares of another. The 125 shaded squares represent $15, so each square represents $15 ÷ 125, or $.12. So, 100 squares represent $12. Last year's price was $12.

Last Year's Price　　Last Year's Price

25d. No; 100% of the votes is all the votes, and a candidate could not get more than all the votes that were cast.

26b. Find 125% of $28 by multiplying $28 by 1.25. This works because if the value increases by 25%, the new value is 125% of the original value: $1.25 \cdot \$28 = \$35$.

27. Which is greater, 300% of 8 or 250% of 10? 250% of 10

28b. Method 1:
($32 − $15) • 0.75
= $12.75;
Method 2:
$32 • 0.75 − $15
= $9

28c. Possible answer:
Method 2; the buyer
should receive the
full discount even
if using a gift
certificate.

28. Tinley's department store is having a 25% off sale. Victor has a $15 Tinley's gift certificate that he wants to use toward a chess set with an original price of $32. He is unsure which method the sales clerk will use to calculate the amount owed.

• Method 1: Subtract $15 from the price and take 25% off the resulting price.

• Method 2: Take 25% off the original price and then subtract $15.

a. Do you think both methods will give the same result? If not, predict which method will give a lower price.   Answers will vary.

b. For each method, calculate the amount Victor would have to pay. Show your work.

c. Which method do you think stores actually use? Why?

Mixed Review   **Find the next three terms or stages in each sequence.**

29. 99, 98, 96, 93, 89, 84, ...   78, 71, 63

30. 729, 243, 81, 27, 9, ... $3, 1, \frac{1}{3}$

31. 1, 1, 2, 6, 24, 120, 720, ...   5,040; 40,320; 362,880

32. ❀, ✭, ❀, ✭, ✭, ❀, ✭, ✭, ✭, ❀, ✭, ✭, ...   ✭, ✭, ❀

33. Of the 80 acres on Ms. Cole's farm, 28 acres are devoted to growing corn. What percent of the farm's area is devoted to corn? 35%

34. Of the animals on Ms. Cole's farm, 12.5% are goats. If Ms. Cole has 7 goats, what is the total number of animals on her farm?   56

35. At the farmer's market, Ms. Cole sold 60% of the 42 pounds of tomatoes she picked last week. How many pounds of tomatoes did she sell at the market?   25.2 lb

Measurement Fill in the blanks.

36. 429 cm = __4.29__ m

37. 862 cm = __8,620__ mm

38. 16 m = _____ mm   16,000

39. 1 mm = __0.001__ m

40. 7 mm = __0.7__ cm

41. 47,000 mm = __47__ m

Lesson 6.2 A Percent of Quantity   **379**

▶ **Exercise 28** In **Part c**, you may find it necessary to discuss why Method 1 would not give the customer the full value of the gift certificate.

▶ **Exercises 36–41** Remind students that when they are converting from a larger unit to a smaller unit, they multiply, and when they convert from a smaller to a larger unit, they divide.

Quick Check

Informal Assessment Students should be able to:

✔ calculate a percent of a quantity

✔ use benchmarks to estimate a percent of a quantity

Quick Quiz

1. Find each result using any method you like.
a. 12% of 50 6
b. 6% of 137 8.22
c. 84% of 220 184.8
d. 115% of 82 94.3

2. Use benchmarks to estimate each result. Then find the exact value.
a. 24% of 120 30; 28.8
b. 66% of 48 32; 31.68
c. 151% of 1,800 2,700; 2,718

3. A shirt is on sale for 15% off the original price of $27. What is the sale price of the shirt? $22.95

4. How much would you pay for a CD that usually sells for $12.50 if it is on sale for 30% off? $8.75

Percents and Wholes

Objectives

▶ To calculate the percent of a given whole that a given part is

▶ To find the whole quantity when told what percent of the whole a given part represents

Overview

In this lesson, students examine how they can find a percent when they are given the whole quantity and a part of the quantity. They also consider how to find the whole quantity if they are given a part and what percent of the whole quantity it represents. They then use these new ideas and skills in situations that involve games and real-world applications.

Advance Preparation

You may want to provide pages from a phone book, a trash can or bucket and Lesson 6.3 Masters 1–3 to facilitate class discussion while presenting new topics, including relating percents to wholes.

	Summary	Materials	On Your Own Exercises (pp. 390–392)	Assessment Opportunities
Investigation 1 (p. 381) _Pacing: 1 day_	Students practice finding what percent one quantity is of another.	pages from a telephone book, Lesson 6.3 Masters 1 and 3 (optional)	Practice & Apply: 1–10 Connect & Extend: 20–24 Mixed Review: 29–41	• On the Spot Assessment (pp. 380, 383) • Share & Summarize (p. 384) • Troubleshooting (pp. 382, 384)
Investigation 2 (p. 384) _Pacing: 1 day_	Students develop skill in finding a whole quantity when told what percent of the whole a given part represents.		Practice & Apply: 11–19 Connect & Extend: 25–28 Mixed Review: 29–41	• On the Spot Assessment (p. 387) • Share & Summarize (p. 387)
Inquiry Investigation 3 (p. 388) _Pacing: 1 day_	Students use percents to study how variations in individual rounds of a game affect the cumulative score.	trash cans or buckets, Lesson 6.3 Master 2	Mixed Review: 29–41	

Leveled Lesson Resources

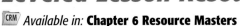

CRM *Available in:* **Chapter 6 Resource Masters**

Also on
TeacherWorks™
Lesson 6.3

Study Guide and Intervention (p. 15) AL

Lesson 6.3 Study Guide and Intervention
Percents and Wholes

Example 1 _____ % of 40 is 8

$8 \div 40 =$ _____ %   Rewrite the sentence as a division sentence.

$0.20 =$ _____   Divide to find the answer. Express the answer in hundredths.

$0.20 \cdot 100 = 20\%$ Change the answer to a percent.

So, 20% of 40 is 8.

Example 2 55% of _____ = 99

$0.55 \cdot$ _____ = 99   Rewrite the sentence as a multiplication sentence.

$99 \div 0.55 =$ _____   Write the equivalent division problem.

$99 \div 0.55 =$ _____   Divide to find the answer.

So, 55% of 180 = 99

Exercises

Fill in each blank. Show your work.

1. _____% of 18 = 9   **2.** _____% of 50 = 7   **3.** _____% of 75 = 7.5

4. _____% of 120 = 90   **5.** _____% of 80 = 16   **6.** _____% of 78 = 62.4

7. 45% of _____ = 27   **8.** 30% of _____ = 12   **9.** 60% of _____ = 84

10. 71% of _____ = 142   **11.** 95% of _____ = 114   **12.** 76% of _____ = 38

Skills Practice (p. 16) AL OL

Lesson 6.3 Skills Practice
Percents and Wholes

Find the percent. Fill in each blank. Show your work.

1. _____ % of 24 is 6   **2.** _____ % of 110 is 11

3. _____ % of 144 is 18   **4.** _____ % of 80 is 40

5. _____ % of 63 is 21   **6.** _____ % of 100 is 44

7. _____ % of 192 is 12   **8.** _____ % of 800 is 200

9. _____ % of 3.4 is 1.7   **10.** _____ % of 1 is 0.2

11. _____ % of 180 is 108   **12.** _____ % of 60 is 33

Find each number. Fill in each blank. Show your work.

13. 35% of _____ is 24.5   **14.** 18% of _____ is 7.2

15. 60% of _____ is 30   **16.** 22% of _____ is 19.8

17. 45% of _____ is 39.6   **18.** 15% of _____ is 9.3

19. 45% of _____ is 25.2   **20.** 30% of _____ is 16.2

21. 60% of _____ is 120   **22.** 150% of _____ is 45

23. 125% of _____ is 100   **24.** 100% of _____ is 63

Problem-Solving Practice (p. 17) AL OL

Lesson 6.3 Problem-Solving Practice
Percents and Wholes
Solve

1. Summer Vacation Rosalinda drove 500 miles during her summer vacation. If she drove 200 miles on the first day, what percent of the total miles did she drive on the first day?

2. Statehood Of the fifty states which make up the United States of America, thirteen are considered to be part of the original colonies. What percent of the total number of states do the original thirteen colonies represent?

3. Baseball There are 5 professional baseball teams in the American League Central Division. If 2 of those teams are located west of the Mississippi River, what percent of the teams are located east of the river?

4. Shopping Millie bought a chair for her living room. The chair was originally priced at $112. What percent of the original price did she pay if she paid $78.40?

5. Photography 40% of Hector's photo collection are pictures of landscapes. He has 36 landscape photos. How many photos does he have in his collection?

6. Collectables Yue Yan collects porcelain dolls. Six of the dolls were given to her by her mother. These dolls represent 25% of her total collection. How many dolls are in her collection?

7. Body and Water Lyle's doctor told him that 63 pounds of his total body weight is water. If the water represents 70% of his total weight, how much does he weigh?

8. Alaska and Texas The size of Texas is approximately 270,000 square miles. This area represents approximately 41% of the size of Alaska. Approximately how many square miles make up Alaska?

Enrichment (p. 18) BL

Lesson 6.3 Enrichment
Percents and Wholes

It is customary to tip people for services provided. For instance, if you go to a restaurant for dinner it is normal to give the waiter 15% to 20% of the total bill as a reward for his or her service. Similarly one would tip one's hairstylist or barber. The table below shows the customary tips given to four different service providers.

Service	Suggested Tip
Restaurant Waiter	15% – 20% of the total bill
Hairstylist or Barber	10% – 20% of the total bill
Manicurist	15% of the total bill
Massage Therapist	10% – 20% of the total bill

1. If a barber charges $15 for a haircut, what is the smallest tip you should give the barber? What is the largest tip?

2. If you had a massage costing $50, what dollar amount would represent the smallest suggested tip?

3. If you went out for dinner and the bill was $75, what dollar amount would represent the largest suggested tip?

4. Your friend told you that she just had her hair styled and left an $18 tip which represented 20% of the cost of the cut. How much did the stylist charge your friend for her services?

5. While having dinner, your waitress told you that she always gives 10% of her tip to the bus person who helps her clean off the table after the customer leaves. If your dinner bill was $120 dollars and you left a 20% tip, how much did your waitress give the bus person?

6. Would $10 be too small of a tip to leave your stylist if she charged you $30 for her services? Explain.

Lesson Quick Quiz (p. 19) AL OL BL

Lesson 6.3 Quick Quiz
Percents and Wholes

Fill in the blanks. Round each answer to the nearest whole percent.

1. _____% of 35 = 14   **2.** _____% of 500 = 340

3. _____% of 75 = 25   **4.** _____% of 44 = 68.2

Find each missing whole.

5. 60% of _____ = 48   **6.** 75% of _____ = 96

7. $33\frac{1}{3}$% of _____ = 210   **8.** 130% of _____ = 91

Lesson Masters 1–3 (pp. 20–22)

Lesson 6.3 Master 1
Percents and Wholes
Investigation 1: Develop & Understand: A

Digit	Tally	Number of Tallies	Fraction of Tallies	Estimated Percent	Exact Percent
0					
1					
2					
3					
4					
5					
6					
7					
8					
9					

Additional Lesson Resources

Teacher Tech Tools
- TeacherWorks
- ExamView Assessment Suite
- Classroom Presentation Toolkit
- Advance Tracker

Student Tech Tools
- StudentWorks Plus
- **Math Online** eGlossary •
- Concepts in Motion

Other Print Products
- Investigation Notebook and Reflection Journal
- Quick Review Math Handbook

LESSON 6.3 Percents and Wholes

Introduce

Percents and Wholes Begin the lesson by having students read the mathematical sentences at the top of the page, or write them on the board. Point out how the sentences are of the form

a percent of the whole = the part

Emphasize the three quantities in each: percent, whole, and part. Tell students that in this lesson, they will learn how to use two of the three quantities to find the third.

Explore ....

Suggested Grouping: Individuals

▶ **Prepare** Ask students to draw a three by three grid like the one shown in the text or provide students with Lesson 6.3 Master 3. Then ask them to choose nine numbers from the list and write them on the grid. This should be done quickly.

▶ **Play** Call out a percent. Have students look for an equivalent decimal or fraction on the grid. If they find one, they should circle it. If there are two, they can circle both of them.

▶ **Report** If three numbers in a row, horizontally, vertically, or diagonally, are circled, then have students call out "Bingo!"

▶ **Score** The first student who gets bingo wins.

Teacher Tips The decimals in the instructions for the game are the quickest way to tell what percents you can call out. For example, one of the decimals is 0.125, so you can move the decimal point two places to the right and call out, "12 and 5 tenths percent." The percents for the repeating decimals might be a little tricky for some students. For $0.1\overline{6}$ you might call out, "16 and 6 tenths percent, with a bar over the last 6," and simultaneously write "$16.\overline{6}\%$" on the board.

LESSON 6.3

Percents and Wholes

Think about these mathematical sentences.

$$44\% \text{ of } 125 = 55 \qquad 15\% \text{ of } 200 = 30$$

Both sentences are in this form.

a percent of the whole = the part

In the last lesson, you were given a percent and the whole. You found the part. This is like filling in the blank in sentences like these.

$$44\% \text{ of } 125 = \underline{\qquad} \qquad 15\% \text{ of } 200 = \underline{\qquad}$$

In this lesson, you will fill in the blanks in sentences like these.

$$\underline{\qquad}\% \text{ of } 125 = 55 \qquad 15\% \text{ of } \underline{\qquad} = 30$$

As you work, you will find it helpful to use benchmark fractions, decimals, and percents. The *Percent Bingo* game below will help refresh your memory about equivalent fractions, decimals, and percents.

Explore ....

Choose nine of the numbers listed below. Write one in each square of a grid like the one at the right.

$$\frac{1}{8} \quad \frac{1}{4} \quad \frac{1}{2} \quad \frac{1}{3} \quad \frac{1}{5} \quad \frac{1}{6}$$

$$\frac{2}{3} \quad \frac{2}{5} \quad \frac{3}{4} \quad 1 \quad \frac{1}{10} \quad \frac{5}{8}$$

0.125   0.25   0.5 $0.\overline{3}$ 0.2 $0.1\overline{6}$

$0.\overline{6}$ 0.4   0.75   0.1   0.625

When your teacher calls out a percent, look for an equivalent decimal or fraction on your grid. If you find one, circle it. If your grid contains both a fraction and a decimal equal to the given percent, circle both.

If you circle three numbers in a row, call out "Bingo!" Rows can be horizontal, vertical, or diagonal. The first student who gets bingo wins.

 Assessment

You may want to walk around the room and glance at students' grids as you call out the percents. Noticing what numbers they have used in their grids may provide some useful information about whether students feel more comfortable with fractions or decimals.

Investigation 1 Find the Percent

Materials
- page from a telephone book

The question "What percent of 75 is 20?" gives you the part, 20, and the whole, 75, and asks you to find the percent. Answering this question is like filling in the blank in the sentence below.

$$\underline{\hspace{1.5cm}}\% \text{ of } 75 = 20$$

You already solved several exercises like this in Lesson 6.1.

Example

In a sports survey, 14 out of 160 students said they like watching ice hockey best. What percent of the students is this? In other words, what percent of 160 is 14?

In this case, the part is 14 and the whole is 160. To find the percent, write "14 out of 160" as a fraction. Then change the fraction to a percent.

$$14 \text{ out of } 160 = \frac{14}{160} = 0.0875 = 8.75\%$$

Estimating with benchmarks can help you make sure your answer is reasonable. The fraction $\frac{16}{160}$ is equivalent to $\frac{1}{10}$. Since $\frac{14}{160}$ is a little less than $\frac{16}{160}$, or $\frac{1}{10}$, the percent should be a little less than 10%. Therefore, 8.75% is reasonable.

On Your Own Exercises
Pages 390–392
Exercises 1–10, 20–24

Find the Percent Most basic percent problems involve three pieces of information: a percent, a whole quantity, and a part of the whole quantity. Usually two of the pieces of information are given, and the problem involves finding the third. In this investigation, students practice finding the percent given the whole and a part of the whole.

You might start the investigation by reading the introductory text, or move straight to the Example. In either case, remind students that they have worked problems like this in Lesson 6.1.

Example

As you discuss this example with the class, remind them that fractions, decimals, and percents are equivalent ways of writing the same number. Emphasize that "14 out of 160" means the same as $\frac{14}{160}$, and remind students that fractions can be written as decimals by dividing the numerator by the denominator.

When you discuss how to estimate a percent for $\frac{14}{160}$ by using benchmarks, check that students understand that, in this case, the benchmark is $\frac{1}{10}$. Remind them that a benchmark is a commonly used fraction or decimal that is easy to use in calculations.

Teacher Tips For this problem set, you will need to provide each group of students with a torn-out or photocopied page from a telephone book. You may also want to provide copies of Lesson 6.3 Master 1, which reproduces the table.

✅ *Develop & Understand: A*

Suggested Grouping: Small Groups

▶ **Exercise 1** Students are asked to make some predictions, and it is worth the time to discuss this problem before students complete the exercise set. You might ask:

Do you expect that the ten possible digits will appear approximately an equal number of times?

If so, what percent of the tallies do you expect for each digit?

If not, which digits do you predict will have higher frequencies, and why?

Troubleshooting If converting from a fraction to a percent is difficult for students, you may need to review work from the beginning of the chapter:

- If the fraction has a denominator that is a factor of 100, then it can be converted mentally to an equivalent fraction with 100 as the denominator. The numerator of the equivalent fraction can then be used to write the percent. For example, $\frac{1}{25}$ can easily be converted to $\frac{4}{100}$, or 4%.

- For other fractions, divide the numerator by the denominator and move the decimal point in the quotient to obtain the percent.

Wrap-Up If time allows, put all of the groups' data together on the board or overhead and see whether the result is similar to the predictions students made in Exercise 1.

✅ *Develop & Understand: A* 1–9. Answers will vary.

1. Your teacher will give you a page from a telephone book. Quickly scan the last four digits of the phone numbers on your page. Which digit do you think appears most often?

2. Starting with a phone number near the top of the page, analyze 30 phone numbers in a row. Use a table like the one below to keep a tally of the last four digits. For example, if one of the numbers you choose ends 2329, make two tally marks next to the 2, one next to the 3, and one next to the 9.

Digit	Tally	Number of Tallies	Fraction of Tallies	Estimated Percent	Exact Percent
0					
1					
2					
3					
4					
5					
6					
7					
8					
9					

3. Count the number of tally marks for each digit. Record the results in your table. You should have a total of 120 tally marks.

4. Find the fraction of the 120 tally marks each digit received. Record the results.

5. Use benchmarks to estimate the percent of the 120 tally marks each digit received. Record your results.

6. Calculate the exact percent of the 120 tally marks each digit received. Record your results.

7. Choose one of the digits. Explain how you found the estimated percent and the exact percent for that digit.

8. Which digit occurred most often? For what percent of the 120 digits does this digit account?

9. Which digit occurred least often? For what percent of the 120 digits does this digit account?

Reaching All Learners

ELL **English Language Learners**
Be sure all students understand what *tally* means. You may need to demonstrate. For example, you might invite student participation as you tally the different vowels that appear in the wording of Exercise 1.

Exercises 10–13 will give you more practice finding percents when you know the part and the whole.

✅ Develop & Understand: B

For Exercises 10–13, first write a fraction and then calculate the percent. Round your answers to the nearest whole percent.

10. What percent of numerals from 1 through 40 are formed at least partially with curved lines? Assume the digits are written like the digits below.

$$0 \quad 1 \quad 2 \quad 3 \quad 4 \quad 5 \quad 6 \quad 7 \quad 8 \quad 9 \quad \frac{34}{40}, 85\%$$

11. Consider the whole numbers from 1 through 80.

   a. What percent of these numbers have two digits? $\frac{71}{80}, 89\%$

   b. What percent are multiples of 9? $\frac{8}{80},$ or $\frac{1}{10}; 10\%$

   c. What percent are even and prime? $\frac{1}{80}, 1\%$

   d. What percent are greater than 9? $\frac{71}{80}, 89\%$

   e. What percent are factors of 36? $\frac{9}{80}, 11\%$

12. Now think about the whole numbers from 1 through 26.

   a. What percent contain only even digits? $\frac{8}{26}, 31\%$

   b. What percent contain only odd digits? $\frac{10}{26}, 38\%$

   c. What percent contain one even digit and one odd digit? $\frac{8}{26}, 31\%$

13. Consider the whole numbers from 1 through 52.

   a. What percent are common multiples of 2 and 3? $\frac{8}{52}, 15\%$

   b. What percent are common factors of 24 and 42? $\frac{4}{52}, 8\%$

Real-World Link

Early phone operators knew the names of customers in their area, and users just gave them the name of the person they wanted to call.

Teacher Tips Point out that in this exercise set, students get more practice writing fractions for parts of a whole and converting fractions to percents. They also have an opportunity to review several important concepts from earlier chapters: even numbers, odd numbers, prime numbers, factors, multiples, common factors, and common multiples.

✅ Develop & Understand: B

Suggested Grouping: Pairs

▶ **Exercise 10** If necessary, help students decide which numerals should be included.

▶ **Exercises 11–13** Point out that these exercises are about common multiples, factors, and primes. Students should have had these concepts in previous grades, but review them as necessary. Students will revisit these concepts in Course 2.

▶ **Exercise 13b** Watch for students who incorrectly answer $\frac{3}{52}$, or 6%. Ask what the common factors are; they most likely have forgotten that one is a common factor of the two numbers.

Real-World Link

Point out that early phone numbers did not use area codes like those used today.

 Assessment

If students are taking too long on Exercise 10, you may wish to ask them to consider which digits are not formed with any curved lines. 1, 4, and 7 Then ask which of the numbers from 1 through 40 can be made from these digits. 1, 4, 7, 11, 14, and 17 You might then ask what that means about whether curved lines are used for the remaining 34 numbers. They must all have at least one curved line in at least one digit.

Teacher Tips Before students start on the problems, you may want to check to be sure that students understand that answering a question such as "What percent is 45 of 65?" is equivalent to finding the number needed to complete the equation "_____% of 65 = 45."

✔ Develop & Understand: C

Suggested Grouping: Individuals

▶ **Exercises 14–19** Encourage students to use estimation to check that their answers are reasonable.

▶ **Exercise 20** Students may be able to estimate the percent visually, although such estimates may vary more from one student to another than estimates obtained by calculation. Be sure students explain how they found their answers.

Share & Summarize

Have students answer this question on their own. Then you might have several volunteers read their answers to the class.

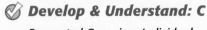

On Your Own Exercises
Pages 390–392
Exercises 11–19, 25–28

Find the Whole Students should be using informal methods to solve the exercises in this investigation. Solving equations will be taught in Chapter 9. Remind students of the two basic kinds of percent problems they have worked with so far. Write the following on the board:

_____% of 80 = 20
percent   **whole part**

15% of 34 = _____
percent   **whole part**

Point out that in the first case, the whole and the part are known, and the percent needs to be found. In the second case, the percent and the whole are known, and the part needs to be found.

Then present the problem at the bottom of the page. Ask which quantity is missing: the percent, the whole, or the part? The whole Let students know they will learn how to solve this kind of problem.

★ indicates multi-step problem

✔ Develop & Understand: C

Math Link
The area of a rectangle is its length times its width.

Fill in the blanks. Round each answer to the nearest whole percent.

14. __69__ % of 65 = 45   15. __74__ % of 23 = 17

16. __50__ % of 9 = 4.5   17. __81__ % of 93 = 75

18. __133__ % of 45 = 60   19. __200__ % of 250 = 500

20. 60%; The perimeter of the small rectangle is 3 cm + 3 cm + 2.4 cm + 2.4 cm = 10.8 cm. The perimeter of the large rectangle is 5 cm + 5 cm + 4 cm + 4 cm = 18 cm. To find the percent, write $\frac{10.8}{18}$ as a percent. $\frac{10.8}{18}$ = 0.6 = 60%.

★20. What percent of the perimeter of the large rectangle is the perimeter of the small rectangle? Explain how you found your answer.

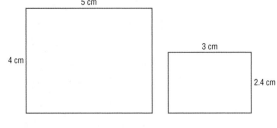

Share & Summarize

Describe a method for finding a percent when you are given the part and the whole. Demonstrate your method by finding what percent 25 is of 60.   Possible answer: Write a fraction with the part as the numerator and the whole as a denominator, divide to find an equivalent decimal, and change the decimal to a percent. $\frac{25}{60}$ = 0.41$\overline{6}$, or about 41.7%.

Investigation 2   Find the Whole

The question "50% of what number is 8?" gives you the percent, 50%, and the part, 8, and asks you to find the whole. Answering this question is like filling in the blank in the sentence below.

50% of _____ = 8

To find the whole in this exercise, try using what you know about fraction equivalents for percents.

Troubleshooting

If students are still having difficulty calculating percents, use their answers to the Share & Summarize to assess where what they do not understand.

If students are having difficulty estimating percents, you may want to ask what they do first to solve a problem such as "_____% of 60 is 25." Ask students to share their estimation strategies. For example, "Thirty would be half of 60, or 50%. Twenty-five is a little less than 30, so it should be a little less than 50% of 60."

① 16; Possible explanation: Since $50\% = \frac{1}{2}$, this is the same as $\frac{1}{2}$ of ___ = 8. The answer is 16.

Math Link
$33\frac{1}{3}\% = \frac{1}{3}$

② 50; Possible explanation: Since $20\% = \frac{1}{5}$, this is the same as $\frac{1}{5}$ of ___ = 10. Since $\frac{1}{5}$ of 50 = 10, the answer is 50.

9. Punchbowl: $40; cup and saucer: $3; table: $48; folding chair: $16; sound system: $1,000; Possible explanation: Since 25% is $\frac{1}{4}$, I multiplied each rental cost by 4 to get the purchase price.

Think & Discuss

Find each missing whole. Explain how you found your answer.

50% of ___ = 8   20% of ___ = 10
See ①.   See ②.

Develop & Understand: A

In Exercises 1-6, find the missing whole.

1. 50% of __46__ = 23
2. 100% of __65__ = 65
3. 25% of __12__ = 3
4. 10% of __70__ = 7
5. 25% of __80__ = 20
6. 150% of __6__ = 9
7. $33\frac{1}{3}\%$ of what number is 30? 90
8. 75% of what number is 30? 40

9. It's a Party! caterers rents equipment for parties. The cost to rent an item for one week is 25% of the price the caterers paid to purchase the item. The rental costs are listed in the table. Find the purchase price of each item. Explain how you found your answers.

Item	Rental Cost
Punchbowl	$10.00
Cup and saucer	0.75
Table	12.00
Folding chair	4.00
Sound system	250.00

Lesson 6.3 Percents and Wholes   **385**

Think & Discuss

Write the equations in the Think & Discuss on the board with the words percent, whole, and part under the appropriate number or blank. Ask students for suggestions on how to solve the two equations. Accept responses that give the correct answer, even if the method is vague or intuitive.

Develop & Understand: A

Suggested Grouping: Individuals

▶ **Exercises 1–6** These problems are presented in equation form. The last two problems are posed in question form. Point out that all the problems involve percents that are equivalent to benchmark fractions. Emphasize that students should have a good sense of what the answers should be without a formal algorithm or procedure. This also allows most students to do these problems mentally, although there is nothing wrong with using pencil and paper.

▶ **Exercise 6** Help students with this exercise if necessary, because it deals with a percent over 100%.

▶ **Exercise 9** This exercise asks students to find the purchase price of each of a set of items that rent for 25% of the purchase price. The rental costs are given. Once students convert the percent to the benchmark fraction $\frac{1}{4}$, they should have little trouble seeing that the purchase prices can be found by multiplying the rental costs by 4.

Reaching All Learners

AL **Approaching Level** Some students may have difficulty with Exercise 6. Ask them to think about 100-grids. Ask how much the shaded area should represent (9) and then prompt them to consider what this means a whole should represent. Have them use the make a drawing problem-solving strategy by making a drawing and splitting the fully shaded square in half. Then ask:

How many halves are shaded? 3 If all the shaded area represents 9, how much is each half? 3 So how much does one whole represent? 6

Teacher Tips Point out that the exercises on page 385 involved percents that were easy to work with. Write the problem of the example, 55% of _____ = 20, on the board. You might ask if any benchmark fractions are equivalent to 55%. When students realize that none is equivalent, tell them they can still solve this problem using skills they already have.

(Example)

Discuss the example thoroughly to ensure that students focus on how the multiplication and division problems are related. Use the problem in the example to motivate a more formal approach to finding the percent of a number.

✅ Develop & Understand: B

Suggested Grouping: Individuals

▶ **Exercise 12** Point out that the whole will be less than the part because the percent is greater than 100%.

▶ **Exercises 13 and 14** Ask students who are having difficulty with these exercises how they would write these two problems using a blank, as in Exercises 10–12.

Familiar percents whose fraction equivalents are easy to work with appeared in Exercises 1–8. For more complicated exercises, you can use what you know about the relationship between multiplication and division.

┌ Example

Find the missing whole.

$$55\% \text{ of } \underline{\qquad} = 20$$

First, make an estimate. Since 55% is close to 50%, or $\frac{1}{2}$, the missing number must be close to 40.

To find the exact answer, rewrite the sentence as a multiplication equation.

$$0.55 \cdot \underline{\qquad} = 20$$

You know that this multiplication equation is equivalent to the division equation below.

$$20 \div 0.55 = \underline{\qquad}$$

Now you can just divide to find the answer.

$$20 \div 0.55 = 36.\overline{36}$$

So, the missing whole is $36.\overline{36}$, or about 36.

✅ Develop & Understand: B

In Exercises 10–12, first estimate the missing whole. Then calculate the exact value.

10. 40% of _____ = 70   About 140; 175

11. 12% of _____ = 3   About 30; 25

12. 124% of _____ = 93   About 80; 75

13. 90% of what number is 99.9?   111

14. 4% of what number is 30?   750

✅ *Develop & Understand: C*

Tammy's Food Emporium is having a sale.

15. Spices are on sale for 35% of the original price.

    a. A jar of cinnamon costs $3 on sale. What was the original price?
    $8.57
    b. Salt is on sale for $0.20 per pound. What was the original price?
    $0.57 per pound
    c. Pepper costs $4 per package. What was the original price?
    $11.43 per package

16. Fruit is on sale for 45% of the original price.

    a. Apples are on sale for $4.00 per bag. What was the original price?
    $8.89 per bag
    b. Dried apricots cost $2.50 per bag. What was the original price?
    $5.56 per bag

17. Snacks are to be marked down to 75% of the original price. Tammy might have marked some incorrectly. For each item, tell whether the sale price is correct. If not, give the correct price.

a. Correct

b. Correct

c. Incorrect $0.56

d. Incorrect $1.31

Share & Summarize

Describe a method for finding the whole when you are given the part and the percent. Demonstrate your method by answering this question, "54 is 6% of what number?" See margin.

 **Assessment**

Watch for students who mistake "35% of" for "35% off." You might ask these students to read the problem more carefully; if they do not see their mistake, ask if the 35% gives the new price or the amount the customer saves because of the sale.

▶ **Exercises 15 and 16** Ask that students to take turns rewriting the problems in two forms before solving. For example, in Exercise 15a, one student might rewrite the problem as the question, "35% of what original price is $3?" The other student can then write the problem as the equation "35% of _____ = $3."

▶ **Exercise 17** See if students noticed that the correctness of the sale price marked on the package can be decided without solving a "missing whole" problem. It is sufficient to find 75% of the original price to see whether it equals the sale price marked on the package. If it does, nothing more need be done. If it does not, then the calculated value of 75% of the original price gives the required additional information for the answer.

Share & Summarize

Have students write answers individually, and then discuss their responses as a class. Students who have difficulty formulating general statements of rules may find it helpful to solve the example first, and then describe what they did. You might have them write the word percent above the percent in their example and the word part above the number for the part. In their description of what they did to solve the problem, they can replace the particular numbers in the explanation with the corresponding words percent and part to construct the general statement.

Additional Answer for Share & Summarize
Possible answer: First write the problem in the form *percent of whole =_____ part*, with a blank for the whole. For example, 6% of _____ = 54. Then write the problem as a multiplication problem: 0.06 · _____ = 54. Then write the equivalent division problem and compute the answer with a calculator: 54 ÷ 0.06 = _____; since 54 ÷ 0.06 = 900, the answer is 900.

Inquiry
Investigation 3

Suggested Grouping: Pairs

In this investigation, you will play a game in which scores are recorded as percents. You will explore how your score for each turn affects your cumulative score for the game.

Materials
For this activity, you will need to provide each pair of students with a trash can or bucket and three copies of Lesson 6.3 Master 2. They will also each need six pieces of paper crumpled into balls.

The Game
Read and discuss with the class the procedure for playing the game and for recording the turn score and cumulative score. To be sure they understand, you may want to have them consider what should be recorded in the example scoresheet if Player 1 made 3 of 6 shots in Turn 3. Have them find the turn score and cumulative score for the example and give help to any pairs who miscalculated.

Try It Out
Exercise 3 may be difficult for some students. They will get another chance to find a pattern in Exercise 4, so an answer is not essential here. However, if enough pairs of students are unclear about how to understand the behavior of the cumulative scores, you may want to address the matter in a class discussion. Otherwise, you may help individual pairs of students resolve their difficulties.

Try It Again
Exercise 4 takes the prediction from Exercise 3 further and asks not only whether a score on one turn will make the cumulative score rise, but also asks for the general effect that a new score has on the cumulative score. Students may need help seeing that the effect of a new score on the cumulative score must be considered in relation to the previous cumulative score rather than to the previous turn's score.

Inquiry
Investigation 3 Play *Percent Ball*

Materials
- trash can or bucket
- 6 sheets of paper
- score sheets

2. No; there are many more possibilities for the cumulative scores, and not all cumulative scores will be a multiple of $\frac{1}{6}$.

3. Answers will vary. Some students may see that if the turn score is greater than the cumulative score for the previous turn, the cumulative score will rise.

4. If my turn score is greater than my cumulative score for the previous turn, my cumulative score will go up. If my turn score is less than my cumulative score for the previous turn, my cumulative score will go down. If my turn score is equal to my cumulative score for the previous turn, my cumulative score will stay the same.

In this investigation, you will play a game. You will explore how your score for each turn affects your cumulative score for the game.

Play this game with a partner. Crumple each sheet of paper into a ball. On your turn, take the following steps.

- Try to toss six paper balls into a trash can from about 5 feet away.
- Record your *turn score* as a number out of 6 and as a percent. Round to the nearest whole percent.
- Record your *cumulative score* for the game so far. For example, if you made 4 shots on the first turn and 2 on the second, you have made 6 shots out of 12. So, record $\frac{6}{12}$ and 50%.

Player 1's Score Sheet

	Turn Score		Cumulative Score	
Turn 1	$\frac{4}{6}$	67%	$\frac{4}{6}$	67%
Turn 2	$\frac{2}{6}$	33%	$\frac{6}{12}$	50%

After 10 turns, the highest cumulative score wins.

Try It Out

1. Look at the turn score percents for you and your partner. What pattern do you see? (Hint: Are there certain scores that occur over and over?) Explain why the pattern makes sense. See below.

2. Look at the cumulative score percents. Do you see the same pattern? Explain why or why not.

3. Look at the turns for which your cumulative score increased. Can you see a pattern that could help you predict whether your score for a particular turn will make your cumulative score rise? If so, describe it.

Try It Again

Play again. After each turn, predict whether your cumulative score will go up, down, or stay the same. Play until your prediction method works every time.

4. How can you predict, based on your turn score, whether your cumulative score will go up, go down, or stay the same?

1. The scores are all 17%, 33%, 50%, 67%, 83%, or 100%. This makes sense because every score must be equivalent to $\frac{1}{6}, \frac{2}{6}, \frac{3}{6}, \frac{4}{6}, \frac{5}{6},$ or $\frac{6}{6}$.

6. The first situation; Possible explanation: In the first situation, the score changes from $\frac{6}{12}$ to $\frac{7}{18}$. In the second, it changes from $\frac{27}{54}$ to $\frac{28}{60}$. $\frac{7}{18}$ is $\frac{1}{9}$ away from 50%, while $\frac{28}{60}$ is only $\frac{1}{30}$ away.

Take It Further

Play a new version of the game in which the object is to make your cumulative score alternate between going up and going down. As you play the game, record a D next to a cumulative score if it went down from the previous turn and a U if it went up. Here is how to determine the winner.

- A player earns one point each time his or her score changes from D to U or from U to D.
- Subtract one point for every turn score of 0 out of 6.
- The player with the greatest point total wins.

For this scoresheet, the cumulative score changes between U and D three times, but the player got 0 out of 6 once. So, the final score is $3 - 1 = 2$.

	Turn Score		Cumulative Score	
Turn 1	$\frac{2}{6}$	33%	$\frac{2}{6}$	33%
Turn 2	$\frac{4}{6}$	67%	$\frac{6}{12}$	50% U
Turn 3	$\frac{0}{6}$	0%	$\frac{6}{18}$	33% D
Turn 4	$\frac{5}{6}$	83%	$\frac{11}{24}$	46% U
Turn 5	$\frac{2}{6}$	33%	$\frac{13}{30}$	43% D
Turn 6	$\frac{1}{6}$	17%	$\frac{14}{36}$	39% D

What Did You Learn?

5. Suppose you are playing the game with the original rules. In your first six turns, you have made 27 shots. What is the fewest number of shots you must make on your seventh turn to make your cumulative score rise?   5

★6. In which situation below does making 1 out of 6 cause a greater change in your cumulative score? Why?

- After two turns, you have a cumulative score of 50%. On your third turn, you make 1 out of 6 shots.
- After nine turns, you have a cumulative score of 50%. On your tenth turn, you make 1 out of 6 shots.

Lesson 6.3 Percents and Wholes   **389**

Take It Further

There are no questions that specifically address the results of this variation on the original game. Students should use what they discovered about the cumulative score in Exercises 3 and 4 as part of their strategy with this variation. If time permits, you may want to invite discussion of any observations they have about how to raise or lower a cumulative score.

What Did You Learn?

▶ **Exercise 5** Ask students to explain how they arrived at their answers.

▶ **Exercise 6** You may find it helpful to have a class discussion to help students understand that with more and more trials, each new turn score has a relatively smaller effect on the cumulative score.

On Your Own Exercises
Lesson 6.3

★ indicates multi-step problem

Investigation 1
Pages 381–384
Practice & Apply: 1–10
Connect & Extend: 20–24

Investigation 2
Pages 384–387
Practice & Apply: 11–19
Connect & Extend: 25–28

Investigation 3
Pages 388–389

Assign Anytime
Mixed Review: 29–41

▶ **Exercise 2** Students should take care to read **Part c** carefully. It does not ask what percent of the pets are birds and what percent are cats. It asks about the legs of the pets.

▶ **Exercises 3–8** You may want to ask students how they could check their answers for these exercises.

▶ **Exercise 17** Students may find it easier to answer this exercise if they first rewrite it as a fill-in-the-blank problem, like Exercises 3–8 and 11–16.

Practice & *Apply*

1. Consider the whole numbers from 1 to 64. In Parts a–c, round your answer to the nearest tenth of a percent.

   a. What percent of the numbers are greater than 56?   12.5%

   b. What percent have an even tens digit?   39.1%

   c. What percent are multiples of 6?   15.6%

2. Ivan has three dogs, two cats, three parakeets, and eight fish. In Parts a–c, round your answer to the nearest tenth of a percent.

   ★**a.** What percent of his pets have four legs? What percent have no legs? 31.3%, 50%

   b. What percent of Ivan's pets have beaks? What percent have fins? 18.8%, 50%

   ★**c.** What percent of the total number of pet legs belong to birds? What percent belong to cats? 23.1%, 30.8%

Fill in the blanks. Round each answer to the nearest whole percent.

3. $\underline{20}$ % of 15 = 3   4. $\underline{14}$ % of 120 = 17

5. $\underline{49}$ % of 41 = 20   6. $\underline{61}$ % of 132 = 80

7. $\underline{133}$ % of 45 = 60   8. $\underline{15}$ % of 16 = 2.4

9. Of the 27 girls on the varsity soccer team, 18 are seniors. What percent of the players are seniors?   66.7%

10. Last year, 235 seniors out of 346 in the graduating class went on to college. What percent went to college?   67.9%

Find each missing whole.

11. 50% of $\underline{684}$ = 342   12. 100% of $\underline{9}$ = 9   13. 25% of $\underline{20}$ = 5

Estimate each missing whole. Then find the value to the nearest hundredth.

14. 12% of ___ = 7   15. 28% of ___ = 20   16. 98% of ___ = 85
About 70, 58.33   About 80, 71.43   About 85, 86.73

17. **Economics** Jodi and her friends went out to lunch. They left a $5 tip, which was 20% of the bill. How much was the bill? $25

18. Life Science Scientists have named about 920,000 insect species. This is about 85% of all known animal species. How many known animal species are there?   About 1,082,353

19. About 2,600 bird species live in the rain forest. This is about $33\frac{1}{3}$% of the world's bird species. About how many bird species are there?
7,800

20. In Your Own Words Write an exercise that requires finding the whole when you know the part and the percent of the whole that part is. Then explain how to solve it.

Connect & Extend

20. Answers will vary. Possible answer: A sweater cost $30 on sale. The sweater's price reflected a 25% savings. What was the original price? Saving 25% is the same as paying 75%. This is the same as $\frac{3}{4}$ of ____ = 30. Since $\frac{3}{4}$ of 40 is 30, the answer is $40.

21. An aquarium with an original price of $95 is on sale for $80.

  a. What *percent of* the original price is the sale price? Explain how you found your answer.   See margin.

  b. What *percent off* the original price is the sale price? Explain how you found your answer.   See margin.

22. Preview The students in Mr. Turner's class were asked how many siblings they had. The results are shown in this plot. An X over a number indicates one student with that number of siblings. For example, the three X's over the 4 indicate that three students have four siblings.

Number of Siblings

22a. 23; I counted the X's.

  a. How many students are in the class? Explain how you know.

  b. What percent of the students are only children?   17%

  c. What percent of the students have more than five siblings?   4%

  d. What percent of the students have fewer than three siblings?   74%

  e. What percent of the students are from a three-child family?   26%

▶ **Exercise 21** Be sure students are making the proper distinction between percent of and percent off.

▶ **Exercise 22** Students learning English may need an explanation of the terms "only children" and "siblings."

Additional Answers

21a. About 84%; Possible explanation: I needed to find what percent 80 is of 95, so I wrote the fraction $\frac{80}{95}$ and converted it to a percent.

21b. About 16%; Possible explanation: I subtracted 84% from 100%.

★ indicates multi-step problem

▶ **Exercises 23–25** Students may benefit from a class discussion of these exercises. Sketching diagrams or writing equations that have blanks for the unknown quantities may be helpful for some students.

. . . .

Real-World Link
Ask students if they know about the Tour de France and Lance Armstrong. Do they have any information to share?

. . . .

Quick Check

Informal Assessment Students should be able to:

✔ calculate the percent of a given whole that a given part is

✔ find the whole quantity when told what percent of the whole a given part represents

Quick Quiz

Fill in the blanks. Round each answer to the nearest whole percent.

1. __40%__ of 35 = 14

2. __68%__ of 500 = 340

3. __$33\frac{1}{3}$%__ of 75 = 25

4. __155%__ of 44 = 68.2

Find each missing whole.

5. 60% of __80__ = 48

6. 75% of __128__ = 96

7. $33\frac{1}{3}$% of __630__ = 210

8. 130% of __70__ = 91

Real-World Link
American Lance Armstrong won the 2,287-mile Tour de France between the years 1999–2005. Just three years before his first victory, Armstrong was diagnosed with cancer and given a 50% chance of survival.

. . . .

Mixed Review

In Exercises 23–25, solve if possible. If it is not possible, tell what additional information you would need to solve it.

23. The Tour de France bicycle race has been won by a French cyclist 36 times. What percent of the races have been won by a French cyclist? Need to know how many times the race took place

24. Of the new trucks and vans sold in the United States in a recent year, 22.5% were white and 11.5% were black. How many of the trucks and vans were black or white? Need to know the total number of trucks and vans sold

25. Nutrition A serving of asparagus contains 2 grams of protein. What percent of the asparagus' weight is protein? Need to know the number of grams in a serving

26. Renee is a lifeguard at the local pool. She thinks there may be more than 40 swimmers, the maximum number allowed. She starts to count, but Emilio says, "Just count the swimmers with red bathing suits. I've already figured out that 20% of the people in the pool have red bathing suits." Renee counts 8 people wearing red bathing suits. How many people are in the pool? 40

27. Economics The label on a bottle of shampoo states, "20% More Than Our Regular Size!" The bottle contains 18 ounces of shampoo. How many ounces are in a regular-sized bottle? Explain how you found your answer. See margin.

28. Geometry Isabella's family has a plot in the community garden that measures 9 feet by 12 feet.

★ **a.** A section measuring 6 feet by 2 feet is devoted to tomatoes. What percent of the garden's area is planted in tomatoes? About 11%

b. The green bean section has 75% of the area of the tomato section. What is the area of the green bean section? 9 sq ft

c. The green bean section is 90% of the area of the squash section. What is the area of the squash section? 10 sq ft

Number Sense Fill in each ◯ with >, <, or =.

29. $33\frac{1}{3}$ ◯ $\frac{1}{3}$ **30.** $\frac{7}{8}$ ◯ 85%

31. 0.398 ◯ $\frac{2}{5}$ **32.** −5 ◯ −1

33. $0.\overline{5}$ ◯ $\frac{5}{9}$ **34.** $\frac{31}{40}$ ◯ 75%

35. $\frac{347}{899}$ ◯ $\frac{347}{900}$ **36.** $\frac{6}{7}$ ◯ $\frac{7}{8}$

37. 80% ◯ $\frac{45}{60}$ **38.** 0.01 ◯ 0.1%

Additional Answer
27. 15 oz; Possible explanation: 18 oz is 120% of the amount in the original size, so I need to fill in the blank in this sentence: 120% of _____ = 18. The answer is 18 ÷ 1.2 = 15.

Review & Self-Assessment

Vocabulary

- percent
- rational numbers

Chapter Summary

In this chapter, you learned that, like a fraction or a decimal, a percent can be used to represent a part of a whole. You used the fact that percent means "out of 100" to convert fractions and decimals to percents and to convert percents to fractions and decimals.

You saw that percents are useful for comparing parts of different groups, even when the groups are of very different sizes. Then you learned how to find a given percent of a quantity and to compute a sale price when a percent discount is taken. Finally, you solved situations that involved finding the percent when you know the part and the whole and finding the whole when you know the part and the percent that part represents.

Strategies and Applications

The questions in this section will help you review and apply the important ideas and strategies developed in this chapter.

Converting among fractions, decimals, and percents

1. Explain how to convert a decimal to a percent and how to convert a fraction to a percent. Give examples to illustrate your methods. See margin.

2. Explain how to convert a percent to a fraction and to a decimal. Give examples to illustrate your methods. Possible answer: Use the fact that percent means "out of 100." So, $72\% = \frac{72}{100}$, or 0.72.

Using a percent to represent part of a whole

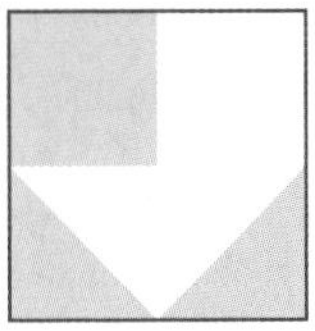

3. Estimate the percent of the square that is shaded. Explain how you made your estimate.

4. Of the 20 students in Dulce's ballet class, 17 took part in the spring recital. What percent of the students participated in the recital? Explain how you found your answer.

5. The school band held a carnival to raise $750 for new uniforms. When the carnival was over, the band had raised $825. What percent of its goal was reached? Explain how you found your answer.

Using percents to compare groups of different sizes

6. This summer, the 96 fifth graders and 72 sixth graders at Camp Maple Leaf were asked this question.

Which is your favorite camp activity? Choose one.

- ☐ *swimming*
- ☐ *hiking*
- ☐ *arts and crafts*
- ☐ *volleyball*
- ☐ *canoeing*
- ☐ *other*

Margin answers (left page):

3. 50%; Possible explanation: The shaded square in the top-left corner looks like about $\frac{1}{4}$, or 25%, of the square. It looks like the two triangles could be arranged to exactly cover the shaded square.

4. 85%; I wrote 17 out of 20 as the fraction $\frac{17}{20}$ and then found an equivalent fraction with a denominator of 100, $\frac{85}{100}$.

5. 110%; I wrote 825 out of 750 as the fraction $\frac{825}{750}$ and divided to get 1.1, which is equivalent to 110%.

Chapter Summary
This summary helps students recall the major topics of the chapter.

Vocabulary
Students should be able to explain each of the terms listed in the vocabulary section.

▶ **Exercises 1 and 2** Writing the steps of a math process reinforces a skill for students. However, many students get nervous at the thought of a writing assignment in math. Have them work a problem to use as a guide when writing; all they have to do is list the steps they used.

▶ **Exercises 3–5** Remind students to be careful to note the important numbers in each of these problems. For example, in Exercise 4, make sure they are finding what percent of 20 is 17, and not 17% of 20.

Additional Answer

1. Possible answer: To convert a decimal to a percent, use what you know about place value and the fact that percent means "out of 100." For example, $0.6 = \frac{6}{10} = \frac{60}{100}$, so $0.6 = 60\%$. To convert a fraction to a percent, change the fraction to an equivalent fraction with a denominator of 100, or divide to find an equivalent decimal and then change the decimal to a percent. For example, $\frac{13}{20} = \frac{65}{100} = 65\%$ and $\frac{145}{125} = 1.16 = \frac{116}{100} = 116\%$.

▶ **Exercise 6** Although all parts of this exercise can be answered by comparing fractions, encourage students to use percents. If there are students who want to use fractions to check their answers, they will probably agree that percents greatly facilitate the comparisons.

Make sure students understand the concept of *three times as popular*, etc, and that they are using the numbers correctly.

▶ **Exercises 7 and 8** In describing a method, remind students to list all the steps for using the method. Also, make sure they are choosing the correct method for each problem.

▶ **Exercise 8** Be on the lookout for students who correctly calculate 20% of $15.99 but forget to subtract the result from $15.99. Encourage them to look at 20% off as 80% of the cost so that they only have to do one calculation.

▶ **Exercise 10** A fill-in-the-blank problem should be accepted, but you may want to encourage students to be creative and think of a situation for their problem. Writing a problem alone can be daunting; allow Approaching–Level learners to work with a partner.

▶ **Exercises 11–18** Have students review the steps for changing a fraction or decimal to a percent in their minds before beginning these problems. Encourage them to work one in the margin of their paper as a guide for the others.

Additional Answers

6a. No; Possible explanation: Although arts and crafts received three times the number of votes among fifth graders as among sixth graders, it received less than three times the percent of votes (about 19% versus about 8%).

6b. Yes; although volleyball received a greater number of votes from fifth graders, it received a smaller percent of the votes (about 15% versus about 17%).

The results are given in the table.   6a–d. See margin.

Activity	Fifth-Grade Votes	Sixth-Grade Votes
Swimming	34	24
Hiking	5	10
Arts and crafts	18	6
Volleyball	14	12
Canoeing	21	16
Other	4	4

a. Coty said arts and crafts is three times as popular among fifth graders as among sixth graders. Is he correct? Explain.

b. Maya said volleyball is more popular among sixth graders than among fifth graders. Is she correct? Explain.

c. Dante said that, among sixth graders, swimming is four times as popular as arts and crafts. Is he correct? Explain.

d. Kylie said the choice "other" was equally popular among the two grades. Is she correct? Explain.

Calculating a percent of a whole

7. Describe a method for computing a given percent of a quantity. Demonstrate your method by finding 72% of 450 and 125% of 18.

8. A CD originally priced at $15.99 is on sale for 20% off. Calculate the sale price. Explain the method that you used.

Finding the whole from the part and the percent

9. Last year, Eliza's hourly wage was 75% of her hourly wage this year. She made $12 per hour last year. How much does she make this year? Explain how you found your answer.

10. Write an equation that requires finding the whole when you know the percent and the part. Explain how to solve your equation. See margin.

Demonstrating Skills

Convert each fraction or decimal to a percent.

7. Possible answer: Change the percent to a decimal and then multiply the quantity by the decimal. 72% of $450 = 0.72 \cdot 450 = 324$, and 125% of $18 = 1.25 \cdot 18 = 22.5$

8. $12.79; Possible explanation: Since you save 20%, you pay 80%, so calculate 80% of $15.99. 80% of $15.99 = 0.80 \cdot 15.99 = $12.79.

9. $16; Possible explanation: I needed to answer the question "75% of what number is 12?" This is the same as "$\frac{3}{4}$ of what is 12?" Since $\frac{3}{4}$ of 16 is 12, the answer is 16.

11. 0.56 56%
12. $\frac{7}{8}$ 87.5%
13. 0.3 30%
14. $\frac{90}{125}$ 72%
15. 7.25 725%
16. $\frac{67}{20}$ 335%
17. $\frac{2}{3}$ 66.$\overline{6}$%
18. 0.008 0.8%

6c. Yes; since we are comparing within the same group, we can just compare numbers of votes. Arts and crafts received 6 votes and swimming received 24, four times as many.

6d. No; Possible explanation: Although "other" received the same number of votes in each grade, it received a smaller percent of the fifth grade vote.

10. Possible answer: There are 12 students on the basketball team. This is 60% of the number on the soccer team. How many students are on the soccer team? Solution: To solve the problem, you must fill in the blank in this equation: 60% of _____ = 12. This is the same as the multiplication equation $0.60 \cdot$ _____ = 12. To find the answer, solve the related division problem: $12 \div 0.6 =$ _____. Dividing gives 20, so 20 students are on the soccer team.

Convert each percent to a decimal and a fraction or mixed number in lowest terms.

19. $33\frac{1}{3}\%$ $0.\overline{3}, \frac{1}{3}$ **20.** 99% $0.99, \frac{99}{100}$ **21.** 25% $0.25, \frac{1}{4}$

22. 7.6% $0.076, \frac{19}{250}$ **23.** 0.4% $0.004, \frac{1}{250}$ **24.** 325% $3.25, 3\frac{1}{4}$

Fill in the blanks.

25. __40__ % of 25 = 10

26. 34% of 650 = __221__

27. 10% of __53__ = 5.3

28. __150__ % of 54 = 81

29. What is 83% of 320?   265.6

30. What percent of 65 is 26?   40%

31. A tricycle originally priced at $76 is on sale for 20% off. What is the sale price? $60.80

For each pair of numbers, use a benchmark to decide which number is larger.

32. 33% or $\frac{1}{3}$ $\frac{1}{3}$ **33.** 45% or $\frac{4}{9}$ 45%   **34.** 0.5% or $\frac{1}{4}\%$ 0.5%

35. 25% or $\frac{1}{4}$ Equal   **36.** 0.21 or $\frac{3}{10}$ $\frac{3}{10}$ **37.** .01 or $\frac{1}{9}$ $\frac{1}{9}$

Use a number line to compare the sets of three numbers from least to greatest.

38. $\frac{2}{5}$, 0.5, 45% $\frac{2}{5}$, 45%, 0.5   **39.** $\frac{1}{9}$, $\frac{1}{3}$, 22% $\frac{1}{9}$, 22%, $\frac{1}{3}$

40. Identify a decimal between 23% and 34%.   Sample: 0.30

41. Identify a percent between $\frac{1}{2}$ and $\frac{8}{11}$.   Sample: 60%

Test-Taking Practice

SHORT RESPONSE

1 Derek is buying a shirt that originally cost $25. If the shirt is on sale at 30% off, how much will Derek save?

Show your work.

Answer _____

Show your work:
$\frac{part}{base} = \frac{percent}{100}$;
$\frac{x}{25} = \frac{30}{100}$;
Divide 30 and 100 by 4 to get an equivalent fraction.
$\frac{x}{25} = \frac{7.5}{25}$; $x = 7.5$;
7.5 represents how much Derek will save.

Answer: $7.50

MULTIPLE CHOICE

2 Amber made $\frac{6}{8}$ of her free-throws in the last basketball game. What percent of free-throws did Amber make?

A 25%

B 68%

C 75%

D 86%

3 There are 16 sixth graders who want to stay inside for recess. This is 32% of the sixth graders. How many sixth graders are in this school?

F 20

G 45

H 48

J 50

▶ **Exercises 19–24** Watch for errors in decimal placement on these problems, especially for numbers like 7.6% and 0.4%. Decimal errors can make the rest of the problem incorrect and confusing for students.

▶ **Exercises 25–30** It is very important that students can properly use words to distinguish values in these problems. Finding "10% of 53," for example, is completely different from "10 is what percent of 53?" Use chart paper to create a chart for students to use as a reference when solving these problems.

▶ **Exercises 32–37** Remind students of the importance of choosing benchmarks that are easy to use and near the values of the given numbers. For students who have difficulty, help them use number lines to find appropriate benchmarks.

▶ **Exercises 38 and 39** Monitor students to see that they are correctly plotting the given numbers on their number lines. If they are having difficulty with placement, have them label benchmarks along the number line with all three forms of the benchmark numbers (decimal, fraction, and percent).

▶ **Exercises 40 and 41** These problems require students to find a number between two benchmarks. Make sure students remember which end of the number line is greater, and that they correctly label the two given benchmarks.

Lesson 6.1, Develop & Understand: A (p. 349)

3. $\frac{1}{100}$, 0.01

4. $\frac{15}{100}$, or $\frac{3}{20}$; 0.15

5. $\frac{50}{100}$, or $\frac{1}{2}$; 0.5

6. $\frac{110}{100}$, $\frac{11}{10}$, or $1\frac{1}{10}$; 1.1

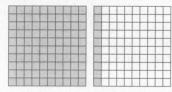

Lesson 6.1, Share & Summarize (p. 351)

Possible Answer: Percent means "out of 100." To express as part of a whole as a percent, first write it as a fraction in the form $\frac{part}{whole}$. If you can rewrite the fraction with a denominator of 100, the numerator will be the percent. If not, divide the numerator by the denominator to get a decimal. Then move the decimal point two places to the right to get the percent.

Notes

Area, Volume, and Capacity

Chapter Overview

Students were introduced to some basic ideas of measurement in Chapter 1, including how to measure, draw, and classify angles as well as the measures (and the sum of the measures) of the interior angles of any polygon and the perimeter of polygons and circles. In this chapter, students will learn how to measure other aspects of polygons, including the area. They will also find the surface area and volume of three-dimensional figures by using formulas, and in the final lesson, students will measure the capacity of a three-dimensional figure by using metric units or customary units.

The Big Picture

Links to the Past	Chapter 7	Links to the Future
Grade 5 Exploring relationships between squaring a number and finding its square root.	**Lesson 7.1** Squares	**Course 2, Chapter 7** Real Numbers (pp. 318–365) **Course 3, Chapter 8** Quadratic and Inverse Relationships (pp. 372–463)
Grade 5 Reviewing area concepts and units of area; developing and applying formulas for the area of rectangles, triangles, parallelograms, and circles.	**Lesson 7.2** Calculate Area	**Course 2, Chapter 5** Geometry in Three Dimensions (pp. 210–259)
Grade 5 Find the area of rectangles, triangles, parallelograms, and circles.	**Lesson 7.3** Surface Area and Volume	**Course 2, Chapter 5** Geometry in Three Dimensions (pp. 210–259)
Grade 5 Practicing measurement skills.	**Lesson 7.4** Capacity	**Course 2, Chapter 5** Geometry in Three Dimensions (pp. 210–259)

Mathematical Background

Chapter 7 gives students an opportunity to explore basic concepts of area, volume, and capacity. Area and volume are important not only in geometry but also in innumerable real-world applications of geometry. Students are already acquainted with some basic ideas about measuring angles, line segments, and perimeter from Chapter 1. In this chapter, they will explore area by counting unit squares and then develop the area formulas for rectangles, parallelograms, triangles, trapezoids, and circles. They will then extend these formulas for two-dimensional figures to formulas for finding the surface area and volume of three-dimensional figures.

Area of Polygons In this chapter, students will study the areas of two-dimensional figures. For simple figures such as squares, rectangles, parallelograms, and triangles, they will develop methods and formulas for calculating area. To find the area of a geometric figure, you count the squares that fit in the figure. Students learn quickly that it is not always convenient to count squares, so they develop shortcuts, or formulas to find the area.

The simple formula for finding the area of a rectangle, based on the number of squares in the rectangle and a multiplication model is Area = length times width. If the length of the rectangle is called the "base" and the height of the rectangle is called the "width," a simple formula for the area of a parallelogram is Area = base times height. From there, the formula for the area of a triangle can be derived because it can be shown that a triangle is always one-half of a parallelogram. Hence, the formula for the area of a triangle is Area = one-half base times height.

Similarly, the area of a trapezoid is shown to be the area of two triangles.

So, each of these formulas depends on the initial knowledge that the area of a rectangle is the number of squares that fits along the length of the rectangle times the number of squares that fits along the width of the rectangle.

Volume of Prisms Once students are able to find the area of a geometric figure by finding the number of unit squares, then area concepts can be extended to three-dimensional objects. The volume of a three-dimensional object is the number of unit cubes that are contained within the object. Since it is often inconvenient to count the cubes, formulas are also used to find the volume.

To find the volume of a figure, refer to its length l, width w, and height h as its *dimensions*. Then a rectangular prism can be seen as a stack of rectangles h units tall. So the volume of a rectangular prism is the same as the area of rectangles stacked h units tall, or Volume = length times width times height.

The other volume formulas can also be derived in the same way. For example, a triangular prism can be thought of as a stack of triangles h units tall. So the volume a triangular prism is the area of the triangle (called the base) times the height of the triangular prism.

You can summarize the formulas for the volume of any prism by saying the volume of a prism is the area of the base of the prism times its height.

Additional Reading

According to the "The van Hiele Model of Thinking in Geometry among Adolescents," which appeared in *Journal for Research in Mathematics Education,* students need to be able to distinguish between common and mathematical usage in geometry vocabulary. Much of the vocabulary in this chapter will be new. Ask students to focus on the difference in common versus mathematical usage.

Planning Guide
Lesson Resources

	Lesson 7.1 Pacing: 3 days	Lesson 7.2 Pacing: 4 days	Lesson 7.3 Pacing: 4 days	Lesson 7.4 Pacing: 2 days
Lesson Title	**Squares** (p. 398)	**Calculate Areas** (p. 409)	**Surface Area and Volume** (p. 434)	**Capacity** (p. 449)
Lesson Objectives	• To find areas by counting unit squares • To find the formula for the area of a rectangle	• To derive and apply a formula for the areas of parallelograms, triangles, trapezoids, circles, and circle sectors	• To find the volume of a block structure • To find the surface area of a rectangular prism • To find the volume of a rectangular prism	• To find the capacity of a figure in metric units • To find the capacity of a figure in customary units
Materials	Lesson 7.1 Master 1, scissors, metric rulers, *1-inch tiles, Chapter 7 Masters 1 and 2, pages from a newspaper	Chapter 7 Masters 2–5, Lesson 7.2 Masters 1–3, metric rulers, protractors, scissors, tape	Chapter 7 Masters 2, 5, 6, Lesson 7.3 Masters 1-4, *blocks, grid paper or dot paper, paper polygons, tape	1-liter or 2-liter bottles, scissors, tape, string, half-gallon milk or juice carton, Chapter 7 Master 6, drinking glasses, water bottles, small and medium container, measuring cups, funnel, water
Quick Review Math Handbook	**Lesson 3.1** Powers and Exponents	**Lesson 6.5** Area **Lesson 6.8** Circles	**Lesson 6.6** Surface Area **Lesson 6.7** Volume	**Lesson 7.3** Area, Volume, and Capacity
Print Resources	CRM Study Guide and Intervention (p. 9) CRM Skills Practice (p. 10) CRM Problem-Solving Practice (p. 11) CRM Enrichment (p. 12) • Investigation Notebook and Reflection Journal • Differentiation Handbook	CRM Study Guide and Intervention (p. 15) CRM Skills Practice (p. 16) CRM Problem-Solving Practice (p. 17) CRM Enrichment (p. 18) • Investigation Notebook and Reflection Journal • Differentiation Handbook	CRM Study Guide and Intervention (p. 23) CRM Skills Practice (p. 24) CRM Problem-Solving Practice (p. 25) CRM Enrichment (p. 26) • Investigation Notebook and Reflection Journal • Differentiation Handbook	CRM Study Guide and Intervention (p. 32) CRM Skills Practice (p. 33) CRM Problem-Solving Practice (p. 34) CRM Enrichment (p. 35) • Investigation Notebook and Reflection Journal • Differentiation Handbook
Technology Resources	TeacherWorks Plus Classroom Presentation Toolkit ExamView Assessment Suite StudentWorks Plus Math Online Brain Pops • Concepts in Motion	TeacherWorks Plus Classroom Presentation Toolkit ExamView Assessment Suite StudentWorks Plus Math Online Brain Pops • Concepts in Motion	TeacherWorks Plus Classroom Presentation Toolkit ExamView Assessment Suite StudentWorks Plus Math Online Brain Pops • Concepts in Motion	TeacherWorks Plus Classroom Presentation Toolkit ExamView Assessment Suite StudentWorks Plus Math Online Brain Pops • Concepts in Motion

*Included in the Impact Mathematics Manipulative Kit

Assessment Resources

MARS Assessment: Teaching with Purpose

Leaky Faucet

In *Leaky Faucet,* students use numbers and quantity in a real-life situation. Students estimate the number of times a kitchen faucet drips in a week and how much water is wasted in a year.

Targeting the Task

- **Diagnostic**—Use Exercises 1–2 in the *Leaky Faucet* assessment to determine students' understanding of how to use numbers and quantity in a real-life situation to solve a problem. For those students who do not have this understanding, completing this unit is needed.

- **Formative**—Exercises 1–2 can be administered individually according to the lessons.

- **Summative**—Administer the complete *Leaky Faucet* performance-based assessment.

CRM Chapter 7 MARS Assessment (pp. 49–51)

> Name _____ Date _____
>
> **Chapter 7 MARS Performance-Based Assessment**
>
> **Leaky Faucet**
> **This problem gives you the chance to:**
> • use number and quantity in a real-life situation
>
> Jan estimates that the faucet in her kitchen drips at a rate of 1 drop every 2 seconds.
>
> 1. Estimate how many times the faucet drips in a **week**. _____
>   Show your calculations.
>
> Jan estimates that approximately 575 drops fill a 100-milliliter bottle.
>
> 2. Estimate how much water her leaky faucet wastes _____ liters
>   in a **year**. Show how you figured it out.

Assessment Planning Guide

Assessments are available for investigations, lessons, and chapters.

ExamView® Assessment Suite Customize and create multiple versions of tests and quizzes.

	Student Edition	Teacher Edition	Other Resources
Diagnostic			CRM Chapter 7 Pretest (p. 37) Math Online Online Chapter Quiz
Formative	Share & Summarize (pp. 402, 404, 412, 416, 419, 421, 424, 437, 440, 453, 456)	Troubleshooting (pp. 402, 410, 412, 419, 421, 424, 437, 439, 442, 453, 455) On the Spot Assessment (pp. 400, 401, 412, 415, 417, 424, 453) Quick Check (pp. 408, 433, 448, 461) Quick Quiz (pp. 408, 433, 448, 461)	
Summative	Review & Self-Assessment (pp. 462-465)		CRM Chapter 7 Test: Forms A and B (pp. 39–44) CRM Standardized Test Practice (pp. 47–48)
Performance-Based	In Your Own Words (pp. 408, 431, 445, 461)		CRM MARS Performance-Based Assessment (p. 49) CRM Chapter Performance Assessment (p. 45)

Differentiated Instruction

Reaching All Learners

Below are suggestions on differentiating the materials presented in this chapter.
Additional modifications should be considered.

Approaching Level **AL**

Lesson 7.1: Square Units For students who have difficulty finding area in square units for some figures, provide graph paper and have students draw several figures that are not squares or rectangles. Then have them work in pairs to shade each square inside the figures. When all the complete squares are shaded, have students use another color to shade the parts of squares that are left. Then have pairs work together to count all the whole squares and all the pieces of squares. Remind them to add the two totals together to find the area of the figure, and to use square units. Check students' work to be sure they correctly shaded the shapes and that they counted correctly to find the area.

Beyond Level **BL**

Lesson 7.3: Polyhedra Have students who quickly grasp the concepts of area and volume of polygons practice with polyhedra. Have them reread the process for constructing polyhedra with triangles on pages 441-442. Then instruct pairs to choose a different shape and create a polyhedron using that shape and the instructions. Remind them that other prisms may come together differently than the triangles, so they will have to look at the examples on page 441 as a guide for the number of faces and edges. Provide paper and tape for students to use. When they are finished, check to see that they have correctly created a polyhedron, and discuss the proper name for it. Display each polyhedron for others to see.

On Level **OL**

Lesson 7.4: Customary Units Have students suggest items they buy in packages that have capacity labeled on the packaging. Use their suggestions to create a list on chart paper. Divide students into pairs and have them estimate the amount they think each item would hold. Remind them to use reasonable units. Assign each student in the class one object from the list. Have students find the capacity labeled on their assigned objects at home. When the students return, record their findings on the chart. Discuss how the actual capacity of each item compared to the estimates students had made. Point out that most items of relatively the same size used the same units.

English Language Learners **ELL**

Lesson 7.4: Metric System Have groups create a poster illustrating the units of the metric system. Remind them to include a table that shows all the prefixes and their meanings. If possible, have them also show the equivalent for each term in their own language. Then have them challenge one another with examples to convert from one unit to the next. Make sure they understand that each unit is proportional to the base unit by a power of 10. Have groups display and explain their posters to the class, and tell how to pronounce each of the words in their own native language. Point out that the prefixes still refer to the same measurements and amounts, and that the metric system is used in many other countries.

KEY

AL Approaching Level **OL** On Level **BL** Beyond Level **ELL** English Language Learners

Intervention Planning Guide

CRM Assess students' prerequisite skills and knowledge using the **Chapter Pretest** found in the Chapter 7 Resource Masters, p. 37.

Intensive Intervention two or more years below grade level	**Strategic Intervention** below grade level	**On Level**	**Beyond Level**
If students miss 75% of the exercises: **Then** use *Math Triumphs,* an intensive intervention	**If** students miss 50% of the exercises: **Then** choose a resource:	**If** students miss 25% of the exercises: **Then** choose a resource:	**If** students miss 0%–10% of the exercises: **Then** choose a resource:
Math Triumphs, Grade 6 • Chapter 10: Formulas	CRM Study Guide and Intervention (pp. 9, 15, 23, 32) • Investigation Notebook and Reflection Journal • Differentiation Handbook Math Online Brain Pops • Concepts in Motion	CRM Skills Practice (pp. 10, 16, 24, 33) CRM Problem-Solving Practice (pp. 11, 17, 25, 34) • Investigation Notebook and Reflection Journal	CRM Enrichment (pp. 12, 18, 26, 35) • Differentiation Handbook

Literature Connections
Recommended Outside Reading for Students
Nonfiction

Emberly, Ed. *Ed Emberley's Drawing Book of Animals.* Little Brown and Company, 1994.

Students use polygons and other shapes to draw various types of animals. Art and math converge in this step-by-step book that shows students, budding artists and sketchers alike, how to succeed at drawing animals.

Herz-Fischler, Roger. *The Shape of the Great Pyramid.* Winfred Laurier University Press, 2000.

Fiction

Neuschwander, Cindy. *Sir Cumference and the First Round Table: A Math Adventure.* Charlesbridge Publishing, Inc, 1997.

Sir Cumference has to determine the best shape for his table. He enlists his wife and son, Radius, to help.

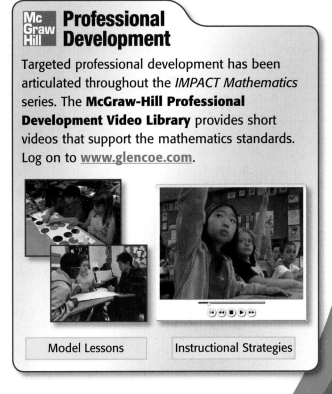

McGraw Hill **Professional Development**

Targeted professional development has been articulated throughout the *IMPACT Mathematics* series. The **McGraw-Hill Professional Development Video Library** provides short videos that support the mathematics standards. Log on to www.glencoe.com.

Model Lessons   Instructional Strategies

Olympic Proportions Ideas of geometry and measurement are evident in the world around us. One place where measurement takes center stage is at the Olympics. The 2004 Summer Olympic Games held in Athens, Greece, featured 28 sports. The size of the fields or courts on which the Olympians competed and the equipment they used are very important in their sports.

Have students look over the table on this page. Ask them if they know (and then explain) the difference between perimeter and area as they study the dimensions of different types of fields.

Think About It Students will need to measure the length and width of the classroom in meters. Have them find the perimeter and area of the classroom and compare their results to the perimeter and area of the gymnastics floor.

CHAPTER

7

Area, Volume, and Capacity

Contents in Brief

Area, Volume, and Capacity

Real-Life Math

Olympic Proportions The Olympic Games feature sports that are played on rectangular courts, fields, mats, and pools. The table below lists some dimensions, perimeter, and area.

Sport	Length (meters)	Width (meters)	Perimeter (meters)	Area (square meters)
Football (soccer) field	100	70	340	7,000
Field hockey field	91.4	55	292.8	5,027
Swimming pool	50	25	150	1,250
Handball court	40	20	120	800
Water polo pool	30	20	100	600
Volleyball court	18	9	54	162
Badminton court (singles)	13.4	5.18	37.16	69.41
Gymnastics floor	12	12	48	144

Think About It How do the dimensions of your classroom compare to the dimensions of the gymnastics floor?

Math Online
Take the **Chapter Readiness Quiz** at glencoe.com.

Chapter Resources

CRM Chapter 7 Resource Masters

CRM English/Spanish Family Letter (pp. 1 and 2)

CRM Lesson Masters (pp. 3–8, 14, 20–22, 28–31)

CRM Chapter 7 Pretest (pp. 37 and 38)

CRM Chapter 7 Tests (pp. 39–46)

Math Online Online Readiness Quiz • eGlossary

Dear Family,

The next chapter is about calculating area, surface area, volume, and capacity.

Key Concept—Area

Area is measured in square units. For example, a square centimeter is the area inside a square with sides one centimeter long.

1 square centimeter

The area of a shape is the number of square units that fit inside it.

Area = 7 square centimeters

Finding the area of a shape by counting squares can be tedious. Fortunately, there are shortcuts for some shapes. Some formulas that students will learn in this chapter are listed to the right.

Area of a Rectangle	$A = l \cdot w$
Area of a Parallelogram	$A = b \cdot h$
Area of a Triangle	$A = \frac{1}{2} \cdot b \cdot h$
Area of a Circle	$A = \pi \cdot r^2$

Chapter Vocabulary

arc	circle sector	rectangular prism
area	parallelogram	surface area
capacity	perfect square	trapezoid
central angle	prism	volume

Home Activities

- Ask your student for examples of area in his or her daily life.
- Help your student figure out if it is more cost effective to order a circular pizza with a 10-inch diameter for $8, or to order a rectangular pizza that is 16 inches by 10 inches for $14.

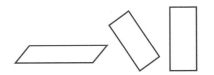

397

Family Letter

Another version of the Family Letter, available in English and Spanish, is found in the Chapter 7 Resource Masters. You may want to send a copy of this letter home with your students.

Key Concept—Area Introduce students to area of geometric figures by describing it as the number of unit squares that fit into the figures. Point out that formulas are shortcuts for counting the number of unit squares.

Home Activities

- Each day have your students find the area of a different geometric figure in your home by measuring its dimensions and then by using a formula for those dimensions.

- Have your students do a floor plan of their dream home. How will they find the total area of the floor?

Key Vocabulary

English (Spanish) *Introduce the most important terms from Chapter 7.*

area (área) The amount of space inside a two-dimensional shape. (p. 398)

capacity (capacidad) The amount of dry or liquid material a container can hold. (p. 449)

parallelogram (paralelogramo) A quadrilateral with opposite sides that are the same length. Each of the figures below is a parallelogram. (p. 410)

perfect square (cuadrado perfecto) A number that is the square of another number. Example: 0, 1, 4, 9, … , and so on. (p. 404)

rectangular prism (prisma rectangular) A three-dimensional figure with six faces that are rectangles. (p. 435)

surface area (área de superficie) The area of the exterior surface of an object, measured in square units. (p. 434)

LESSON 7.1

Squares

Overview

In this lesson, students examine basic area concepts. They count unit squares to find areas of simple polygons, and use their observations to arrive at the formula $A = L \cdot W$. Next, students examine the concept of the square of a number and relate it to areas of squares. They examine the concept of a perfect square and see how it can be interpreted geometrically in terms of area.

Advance Preparation

You may want to provide Lesson 7.1 Master 1 to facilitate class discussion while presenting new topics, including finding the area of rectangle by counting unit squares.

Objectives

▶ To find areas by counting unit squares

▶ To find the formula for the area of a rectangle

	Summary	Materials	On Your Own Exercises (pp. 405–408)	Assessment Opportunities
Investigation 1 (p. 399) *Pacing: 2 days*	Students use observations about areas of figures made from unit squares to arrive at a formula for the area of a rectangle.	Lesson 7.1 Master 1, scissors and metric rulers, * 1-inch tiles (12 per group), Chapter 7 Masters 1 and 2, pages from a newspaper	Practice & Apply: 1–8, 10 Connect & Extend: 21–23 Mixed Review: 29–41	• On the Spot Assessment (pp. 400, 401) • Share & Summarize (p. 402) • Troubleshooting (p. 402)
Investigation 2 (p. 402) *Pacing: 1 day*	Students examine squares of numbers and the concept of a perfect square and relate these to areas of squares.	Chapter 7 Master 1, * 1-inch tiles	Practice & Apply: 9, 11–20 Connect & Extend: 24–28 Mixed Review: 29–41	• Share & Summarize (p. 404)

*Included in the Impact Mathematics Manipulative Kit

Leveled Lesson Resources

CRM *Available in:* **Chapter 7 Resource Masters**

Study Guide and Intervention (p. 9)   AL

Lesson 7.1 Study Guide and Intervention
Squares

Area of Rectangles and Squares

The **area** of a figure is the number of square units needed to cover a surface. You can use a formula to find the area of a rectangle. The formula for finding the area of a rectangle is $A = l \times w$. In this formula, A represents area, *l* represents the length of the rectangle, and *w* represents the width of the rectangle.

Example 1   Find the area of a rectangle with length 8 feet and width 7 feet.

$A = l \times w$ Area of a rectangle
$A = 8 \times 7$ Replace *l* with 8 and *w* with 7.
$A = 56$
The area is 56 square feet.

Example 2   Find the area of a square with sides that are 11 inches in length.

$A = l \times w$ Area of a square
$A = 11 \times 11$ Substitute 11 for both *l* and *w*
$A = 121$
The area is 121 square inches.

Exercises

Find the area of each rectangle.

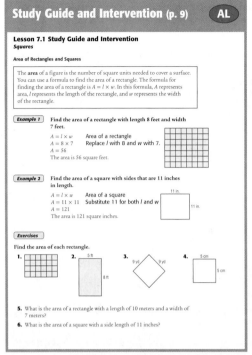

5. What is the area of a rectangle with a length of 10 meters and a width of 7 meters?

6. What is the area of a square with a side length of 11 inches?

Skills Practice (p. 10)   AL OL

Lesson 7.1 Skills Practice
Squares

Area of Rectangles and Squares

Complete each problem.

1. Give the formula for finding the area of a rectangle.

2. Draw and label a rectangle that has an area of 18 square units.

3. Give the dimensions of another rectangle that has the same area as the one in Exercise 2.

4. Find the area of a rectangle with a length of 3 miles and a width of 7 miles.

5. Find the area of a square with a side length of 15 centimeters

Find the area of each rectangle.

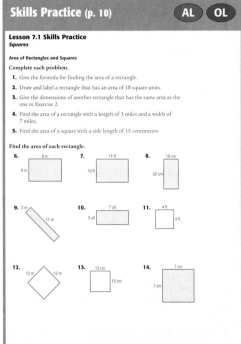

Problem-Solving Practice (p. 11)   AL OL

Lesson 7.1 Problem-Solving Practice
Squares

Area of Rectangles and Squares

Floor Plans For Exercises 1–6, use the diagram that shows the floor plan for a house. Show your work.

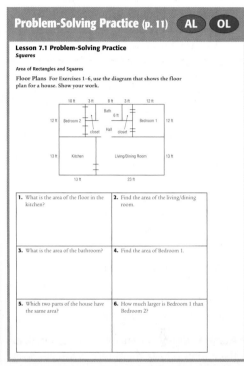

1. What is the area of the floor in the kitchen?

2. Find the area of the living/dining room.

3. What is the area of the bathroom?

4. Find the area of Bedroom 1.

5. Which two parts of the house have the same area?

6. How much larger is Bedroom 1 than Bedroom 2?

Enrichment (p. 12)   BL

Lesson 7.1 Enrichment
Squares

Area of Composite Figures

A **composite figure** is made up, or composed, of other figures. For example, the L-shaped figure at the right is composed of two rectangles. To find the area of the L-shape, find the area of each rectangle, then add.

Area of A   Area of B
$A = l \times w$ $A = l \times w$
$A = 10 \times 6$ $A = 20 \times 8$
$A = 60$ $A = 160$

So the area of the L-shaped figure is 60 ft² + 160 ft², or 220 ft².

Find the area of each composite figure.

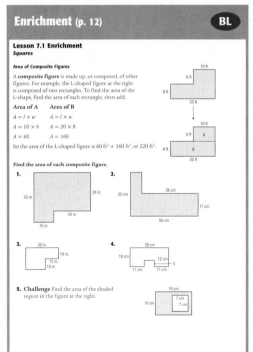

5. Challenge Find the area of the shaded region in the figure at the right.

Lesson Quick Quiz (p. 13)   AL OL BL

Lesson 7.1 Quick Quiz
Squares

1. Find the area of the following shape:

2. Find the area of a rectangle that is 24.3 cm long and 12 cm wide.

3. Find the length of a rectangle that has a width of 18 in. and an area of 558 in.²

4. Write the area of the square shown below.

5. Find the area of a square with a side length of 12 cm.

6. A rectangle has an area of 36 square inches. Write two possible sets of length and width that will equal the given area.

7. A square has a side length of 8 cm. Write the length and width of a rectangle that will equal the area of the square.

8. Samantha has 50 square tiles that each has an area of 1 cm². The tiles will be arranged to make a large square. What is the side length of the largest square that can be created with the tiles?

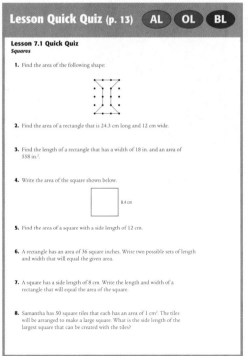

Lesson Master 1 (p. 14)

Lesson 7.1 Master 1
Squares

Investigation 1 Explore

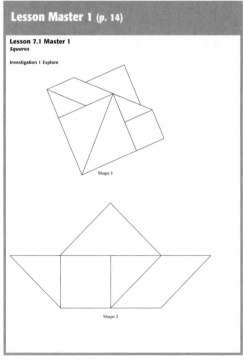

Additional Lesson Resources

Teacher Tech Tools
- TeacherWorks
- ExamView Assessment Suite
- Classroom Presentation Toolkit
- Advance Tracker

Student Tech Tools
- StudentWorks Plus
- **Math Online** eGlossary •
  Concepts in Motion

Other Print Products
- Investigation Notebook
  and Reflection Journal
- Quick Review Math Handbook

LESSON 7.1 Squares

Introduce

Squares Begin this lesson by reminding students that the perimeter of a figure tells us how far it is around the figure. Tell students that they will now use *area* to tell how much space is inside the figure.

Explore ....

Suggested Grouping: Pairs

▶ **Prepare** Provide each pair of students with a copy of Lesson 7.1 Master 1 and a pair of scissors. Tell the students that in this lesson they will use squares to get a numerical measure of the amount of space inside a two-dimensional figure.

▶ **Play** Have pairs of students cut apart the two shapes in the master and rearrange the pieces to make two squares. Have them discuss the answers to the questions.

▶ **Record** When students are finished making the squares, have them record the answers to the questions. Discuss the questions with the class.

▶ **Score** Give students credit for doing the activity.

....

Real-World Link

Ask students if shape 2 is a tangram. Can they make other shapes from the pieces?

....

LESSON 7.1

Squares

Vocabulary

area

Materials

• copies of the two shapes
• scissors

....

Real-World Link

Shape 1 is made with tangram pieces. A *tangram* is a Chinese puzzle consisting of a square cut into five triangles, a square, and a parallelogram that can be put together to form various shapes.

You know that the perimeter of a two-dimensional shape is the distance around the shape. The **area** of a two-dimensional shape is the amount of space inside the shape.

Explore ....

Consider these shapes.

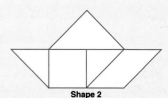

Shape 1   Shape 2

Which shape do you think is larger? That is, which shape do you think has the greater area?   Answers will vary.

Cut out shape 1 along the lines. Rearrange the pieces to make a square. Do the same for shape 2.   See ① in margin.

Of the two squares you made, which has the greater area? How can you tell?   See ② in margin.

Do the original shapes have the same areas as the squares? Why or why not?   Yes, because they are made of exactly the same pieces.

When determining which shape has the greater area, is it easier to compare the original shapes or the squares? Why? Possible answer: The squares are easier to compare because they are the same shape.

Squares are the basic unit used for measuring areas. In this lesson, you will look closely at areas of squares and at a special operation associated with the areas of squares.

Additional Answers

① Square for Shape 1   Square for Shape 2

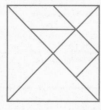 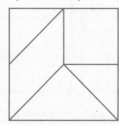

② The square for shape 2; Possible explanations: You could put the square for shape 1 on top of it, and it would fit inside. Or, the sides of the square for shape 2 are longer.

Investigation 1 — Count Square Units

Materials

- 1-inch tiles
- 1-inch dot paper
- page from a newspaper
- metric ruler

1. Possible answer:

Area = 8 sq in.

Area = 5 sq in.

2. Possible answer:

Perimeter = 14 in.

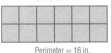

Perimeter = 16 in.

3a. 18 in., 10 sq in.

3b. Possible answer:
The new perimeter is 14 in. The area is the same.

3c. Possible answer:
The new perimeter is 22 in. The area is the same.

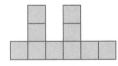

Area is measured in *square units*, such as square inches and square centimeters. A *square inch* is the area inside a square with sides 1 inch long. A *square centimeter* is the area inside a square with sides 1 centimeter long.

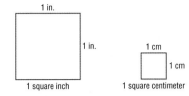

1 in.

1 in.

1 square inch

1 cm

1 cm

1 square centimeter

The area of a shape is the number of square units that fit inside it.

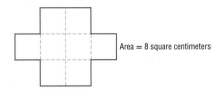

Area = 8 square centimeters

✓ Develop & Understand: A

1. Use your tiles to create two rectangles with perimeters of 12 inches but different areas. Sketch your rectangles. Label them with their areas.

2. Now create two rectangles with areas of 12 square inches but different perimeters. Sketch your rectangles. Label them with their perimeters.

3. Now use your tiles to create this shape.

   a. Find the perimeter and area of the shape. Do not forget to give the units.

   b. Move one tile to create a shape with a smaller perimeter. Sketch the new shape. Give its perimeter. How does the new shape's area compare to the original area?

   c. Reconstruct the original shape. Move one tile to create a shape with a greater perimeter. Sketch the new shape. Give its perimeter. How does the new area compare to the original area?

   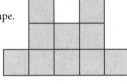

4. Use your tiles to create two new shapes so that the shape with the smaller area has the greater perimeter. Sketch your shapes. Label them with their perimeters and areas.   See margin.

Lesson 7.1 Squares   **399**

Additional Answer

4. Possible answer:

Perimeter = 10 in.
Area = 6 sq in.

Perimeter = 12 in.
Area = 5 sq in.

On Your Own Exercises
Pages 405–408
Exercises 1–8, 10, 21–23

Count Square Units In this investigation, students use tiles to explore the relationship between perimeter and area. They discover that two shapes with equal perimeters do not necessarily have equal areas. Likewise, shapes with equal areas do not necessarily have equal perimeters. Students will find areas of figures made from square tiles and areas of figures drawn on dot paper. They will use their results as evidence for the formula $A = L \cdot W$, which relates the area A of a rectangle to the length L and width W of the rectangle.

Provide students with twelve 1-inch tiles for their work on the exercises, along with 1-inch dot paper (Chapter 7 Master 1), a page from a newspaper, and a metric ruler.

✓ Develop & Understand: A

Suggested Grouping: Pairs

Exercise 1 Three rectangles are possible, and some students may mention this in their answers. Note that a 2 × 4 rectangle and a 4 × 2 rectangle are counted only once.

Exercise 2 There are only three rectangles that have an area of 12 square inches. They all have different perimeters.

Exercise 3 You may wish to mention that shapes in which two squares have only a corner point in common are not allowed.

Wrap-Up Discuss students' answers for these exercises with the class. Ask volunteers to summarize what they have learned from the exercises about how area and perimeter are related. One conclusion is that knowing the perimeter of a rectangle does not let you predict its area. Likewise, knowing the area of a rectangle does not let you predict its perimeter.

Teacher Tips In the exercise set on this
page, students first consider areas of
figures drawn on dot paper. They consider
some figures that are not rectangles. In the
final problems, they examine rectangles
that do not lend themselves well to being
drawn on dot paper. Students discover that
they can find the area of any rectangle by
simply multiplying the length by the width.
Chapter 7 Master 1 (Inch Dot Paper) is
available for students to use with this
exercise set.

✅ Develop & Understand: B

Suggested Grouping: Small Groups

▶ **Exercise 6** Students can connect dots
horizontally and vertically to show 4 unit
squares. This allows them to think of the
hexagon as being composed of 2 unit
squares and 4 half-squares.

▶ **Exercise 7** Students can think of the
triangle as half of a 2 × 4 rectangle.

▶ **Exercise 12** Students should recognize that
the sides of the square must be drawn
diagonally.

▶ **Exercises 13–16** Students might recall
models they have used to illustrate
multiplication of whole numbers and to
show multiplication with fractions.

▶ **Exercise 17** Students should have little
difficulty coming up with the generalization
for this exercise.

✅ Develop & Understand: B

The shapes in Exercises 5–8 are drawn on dot grids. Find the area of each
figure. Consider the horizontal or vertical distance between two dots to be
1 unit.

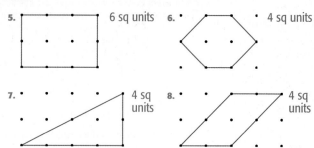

5. 6 sq units **6.** 4 sq units

7. 4 sq units **8.** 4 sq units

In Exercises 9–12, draw the shape by connecting dots on a sheet of
1-inch dot paper.

9. a square with area 4 square inches

10. a rectangle with area 2 square inches

11. a shape with an area of at least 15 square inches and a perimeter of
no more than 25 inches

12. Challenge a square with an area of 2 square inches

9.

10.

11. Possible shape:

12.

Find the area of each shape.

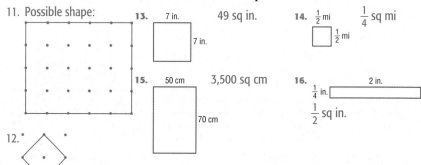

13. 7 in. 49 sq in. 7 in.

14. $\frac{1}{2}$ mi $\frac{1}{4}$ sq mi $\frac{1}{2}$ mi

15. 50 cm 3,500 sq cm 70 cm

16. 2 in. $\frac{1}{4}$ in. $\frac{1}{2}$ sq in.

17. If you know the length and width of a rectangle, how can you find
the rectangle's area without counting squares? Multiply the
length by the width.

On the Spot Assessment

If students have difficulty
distinguishing the shapes drawn on
dot paper in Exercises 5–8, ask
them to redraw the figures on
blank paper and then add the units.

Finding the area of a shape by counting squares is not always easy or convenient. Fortunately, there are shortcuts for some shapes.

To find the area of a rectangle, just multiply the length by the width.

Area of a Rectangle
$A = L \cdot W$

In this formula, A represents the area of a rectangle, and L and W represent the length and width.

Think & Discuss

On dot or grid paper, draw a rectangle with side lengths 5 units and $7\frac{1}{2}$ units.   See ①.

①

Use the formula above to find the area of your rectangle. Check that your answer is correct by counting the squares. $37\frac{1}{2}$ sq units

✓ Develop & Understand: C   Answers will vary.

18. On your newspaper page, draw rectangles around the major items, such as photographs and art, advertisements, articles, and headlines.

    a. Measure the sides of each rectangle to the nearest tenth of a centimeter.

    b. Calculate the area of each rectangle.

    c. Calculate the area of the entire page.

19. What percent of your newspaper page is used for the following items?

    a. photographs and art

    b. advertisements

    c. articles

    d. headlines

Real-World Link
The first successful daily newspaper in the United States was the *Pennsylvania Packet & General Advertiser,* which was first printed on September 21, 1784.

Investigation 2

On Your Own Exercises
Pages 405–408
Exercises 9, 11–20, 24–28

Perfect Squares In this investigation, students examine the operation of squaring. They interpret the square of a number greater than zero geometrically. They also learn about numbers that are perfect squares. Remind students that writing a number with an exponent means that the number is to be multiplied by itself. The exponent indicates the number of times the other number is to be used as a factor. Tell students that an expression such as 5^2 can be read as "5 squared."

Think & Discuss

Students should not need much time to answer the questions in this Think & Discuss. If there is any hesitation about what square they should draw on their 1-centimeter dot paper (Chapter 7 Master 2) ask students how they would write 5 squared as a product. Briefly discuss their answers to the questions.

Teacher Tips Ask students to use their calculators to evaluate 5^2 by using the square key. Be sure to use the word "squared" when you read the expressions. Call students' attention to the last paragraph on page 402.

---

1. Possible answer: the length of a pencil, the space on my desk

2. No; the first shape has the greater area but the smaller perimeter.

Perimeter = 10 in.
Area = 6 sq in.

Perimeter = 12 in.
Area = 5 sq in.

① $5^2 = 25$

Share & Summarize

1. Give an example of something you would measure in inches. Then give an example of something you would measure in square inches.

2. If one shape has a greater area than another, must it also have a greater perimeter? Explain or illustrate your answer.   See below.

3. Describe two ways to find the area of a rectangle.   Count the number of unit squares inside the rectangle, or multiply the length by the width.

Investigation 2 Perfect Squares

Vocabulary

perfect square

Materials

- 1-inch dot paper
- 1-inch tiles

Recall that an exponent tells you how many times a number is multiplied by itself. You can write the product of a number times itself using the exponent 2.

$$5 \cdot 5 = 5^2$$

Multiplying a number by itself is called *squaring* the number. The expression 5^2 can be read "5 squared."

Think & Discuss

Evaluate 5^2. Then, on a sheet of dot paper, draw a square with an area equal to that many square units.   See ①.

How long is each side of the square?   5 units

Why do you think 5^2 is read "5 squared"?   Because 5^2 is the area of a square with side length 5

You can use the x^2 key on your calculator to square a number. To calculate 5^2, press these keys.

$$[5] \; \boxed{x^2} \; \boxed{\text{ENTER}}$$

The exponent 2 is often used to abbreviate square units of measurement. For example, *square inch* can be abbreviated in^2 and *square centimeter* can be abbreviated cm^2.

✅ Develop & Understand: A

Fill in the blank to find the area of each square. The first one is done for you.

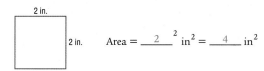

2 in.

2 in.   Area = $\underline{\quad 2 \quad}^2$ in^2 = $\underline{\quad 4 \quad}$ in^2

1.   13 ft

13 ft   Area = $\underline{\quad 13 \quad}^2$ ft^2 = $\underline{\quad 169 \quad}$ ft^2

2.   1.25 cm

1.25 cm   Area = $\underline{\quad 1.25 \quad}^2$ cm^2 = $\underline{\quad 1.5625 \quad}$ cm^2

3. $\frac{7}{4}$ in.

$\frac{7}{4}$ in.   Area = $\underline{\quad \frac{7}{4} \quad}^2$ in^2 = $\underline{\quad \frac{49}{16} \quad}$ in^2

4. Write a formula for finding the area A of a square if you know the side length s. Use an exponent in your formula. $A = s^2$

Find the area of a square with the given side length.

5. 1 in. 1 in^2 **6.** $\frac{1}{3}$ in. $\frac{1}{9}$ in^2 **7.** 19 cm 361 cm^2

Find the side length of a square with the given area.

8. 144 ft^2 12 ft   **9.** 10,000 in^2 100 in.   **10.** 53.29 cm^2 7.3 cm

In Exercises 11–15, you will look at the squares that can be made with square tiles.

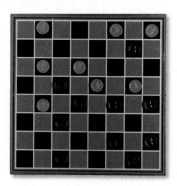

✅ Develop & Understand: A

Suggested Grouping: Individuals

Exercises 1–3 These exercises focus on the geometric meaning of the square of a number. For Exercise 3, suggest that students write the number for the first blank in parentheses to avoid the appearance that only one of the numbers in the fraction is being squared.

Exercises 5–7 Encourage students to use an exponent when they abbreviate the area units.

Exercise 10 Students can reason that since $7^2 = 49$ and $8^2 = 64$, the answer will be a decimal between 7 and 8. Since a number is being multiplied by itself to give a product that ends in the digit 9, the number should be 7.3 or 7.7. Calculation shows that 7.3 is the correct number.

Develop & Understand: B

Suggested Grouping: Pairs

Students will need 1-inch dot paper (Chapter 7 Master 1) for these exercises.

▶ **Exercise 11** Point out that a table is an excellent way to show all the possibilities.

▶ **Exercise 12** Students can think about their answer for Exercise 11. Since 20 square units was not among the areas listed, there is no way to use tiles to make a square with an area of 20 square units. Be sure students understand that this is *not* the same as saying that there is no square with area 20 square units, only that there is no such square made up entirely of *unit* (whole) tiles.

▶ **Exercise 14** Some students may try the diagram shown in the answer and reject it because they think that the sides are 2 units long. It is true that each side joins two grid dots and has a single dot in the center, but this does not mean that the sides are 2 units long. The *vertical* and *horizontal* distances between neighboring dots represent 1 unit of length. The diagonal distance between neighboring dots is greater.

Develop & Understand: C

Suggested Grouping: Pairs

▶ **Exercise 16** Students will come up with perfect squares greater than 1,000. When you discuss this problem, you might ask where these numbers begin to occur. Since $30^2 = 900$, $31^2 = 961$, and $32^2 = 1,024$, students can see that the perfect squares greater than 1,000 are the squares of whole numbers greater than or equal to 32.

▶ **Exercises 18–21** Discuss the strategies that students use. One strategy is to find a number whose square is less than the given number and one whose square is greater than the given number.

▶ **Exercise 22** One approach is to list the first few perfect squares starting with 1:1, 4, 9, 16, 25, 36,… . Then scan the list for two numbers in the list that have a sum that is also in the list.

Share & Summarize

Ask volunteers to share their answers with the class. As you discuss them, ask for examples that illustrate each correct answer.

---

12. No; Possible explanation: A 4 · 4 square has 16 tiles, and a 5 · 5 square has 25 tiles. There are no whole numbers between 4 and 5, so there are no squares with between 16 and 25 tiles.

14.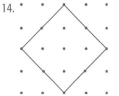

15. Possible answer: If the number of tiles is equal to a whole number times itself, you can make a square with them.

19. No; Possible explanation: You cannot multiply a whole number by itself and get a decimal.

20. No; $110^2 = 12,100$ and $111^2 = 12,321$, so there is no whole number that can be squared to give 12,225.

21. Yes; $184,041 = 429^2$

1. The square of a number is the area of a square whose side lengths are that number.

2. Yes; any number can be multiplied by itself.

Develop & Understand: B

11. Find every square that can be made from 100 tiles or fewer. Give the side length and area of each square. See margin.

12. Is it possible to make a square with 20 tiles? If so, explain how. If not, explain why not.

13. Is it possible to make a square with 625 tiles? If so, explain how. If not, explain why not. Yes; make a square with side length 25.

14. **Challenge** Hakan tried to make a square with area 8 in^2 using tiles. After several tries, he said, "I don't think I can make this square using my tiles. But I know I can make it on dot paper."

On dot paper, draw a square with area 8 in^2.

15. How can you tell whether a given number of tiles can be made into a square without actually making the square?

A number is a **perfect square** if it is equal to a whole number multiplied by itself. In other words, a perfect square is the result of *squaring* a whole number.

Whole Number Squared	1^2	2^2	3^2	4^2	5^2
Perfect Square	1	4	9	16	25

In Exercises 11–15, the perfect squares were the numbers of tiles that could be formed into squares.

Develop & Understand: C

16. Find three perfect squares greater than 1,000.
    Possible answer: 1,024; 1,600; 5,625

17. Is 50 a perfect square? Why or why not? See margin.

Tell whether each number is a perfect square. Explain how you know.

18. 3,249   19. 9,196.81   20. 12,225   21. 184,041
Yes; $3,249 = 57^2$

22. Find two perfect squares whose sum is also a perfect square.
    Possible answer: $9 + 16 = 25$

23. Find two perfect squares whose sum is not a perfect square.
    Possible answer: $16 + 4 = 20$, which is not a perfect square

Share & Summarize

1. How is the idea of squaring a number related to the area of a square?

2. Can *any* number be squared? Why or why not?

3. Can *any* number be a perfect square? Why or why not?
   No; only numbers that are the squares of whole numbers are perfect squares.

Additional Answers

11.

Side length (in.)	1	2	3	4	5	6	7	8	9	10
Area (in.^{2})	1	4	9	16	25	36	49	64	81	100

17. No; Possible explanation: $7^2 = 49$ and $8^2 = 64$, so you cannot square a whole number and get 50.

Practice & Apply

1. On dot paper or grid paper, draw a rectangle with an area of 20 square units, whole-number side lengths, and the greatest possible perimeter. What is the perimeter of your rectangle? See margin.

2.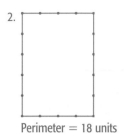

   Perimeter = 18 units

2. On dot paper or grid paper, draw a rectangle with an area of 20 square units, whole-number side lengths, and the least possible perimeter. What is the perimeter of your rectangle?

These shapes are drawn on centimeter dot grids. Find the area of each shape.

3. 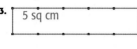 5 sq cm

4. 3.5 sq cm

5. 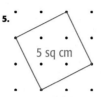 5 sq cm

6. Find the area of a rectangle with length 7.5 feet and width 5.7 feet. 42.75 sq ft

7. Find the length of a rectangle with width 11 centimeters and the given area.

   a. 165 square centimeters 15 cm

   b. 60.5 square centimeters 5.5 cm

8. Find the length of a rectangle with area 484 square inches and the given width.

   a. 10 inches 48.4 in.

   b. 22 inches 22 in.

9. A square garden has an area 289 square feet. How long is each side of the garden? 17 ft

10. If one rectangle has a greater perimeter than another, must it also have a greater area? Explain your answer. No; Possible explanation: A 10 · 1 rectangle has perimeter 22 and area 10. A 4 · 4 rectangle has perimeter 16 and area 16. So, the rectangle with the greater perimeter has the smaller area.

Investigation 1
Pages 399–402
Practice & Apply: 1–8, 10
Connect & Extend: 21–23

Investigation 2
Pages 402–404
Practice & Apply: 9, 11–20
Connect & Extend: 24–28

Assign Anytime
Mixed Review: 29–41

▶ **Exercise 1** Students can list all possible ways of writing 20 as a product of two whole numbers: 1 · 20, 2 · 10, 4 · 5 (with products such as 1 · 20 and 20 · 1 counted as the same). They can use the factors as the dimensions and calculate the perimeter of each rectangle to find the dimensions that give the greatest perimeter.

▶ **Exercise 5** If students need a hint, suggest that they connect the four inside dots to show a 1 × 1 square, and then connect each vertex of the inside square to the nearest vertex of the large square.

Additional Answer

1.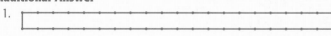

   Perimeter: 42 units

▶ **Exercise 22** This exercise uses the idea that of all rectangles that have a given perimeter, the square having that perimeter has the greatest area.

· ·

Real-World Link
Ask students why they think the length of a soccer field varies.

· ·

Additional Answers

16. no; Possible explanation: The factor pairs of 40 are 1 · 40, 2 · 20, 4 · 10, and 5 · 8. None of the pairs is a whole number squared.

18. No; Possible explanation: The factor pairs of 125 are 1 · 125 and 5 · 25. Neither of the pairs is a whole number squared.

Real-World Link
The length of a soccer field can vary from 100 yards to 130 yards. The width can vary from 50 yards to 100 yards. So, the least possible area is 100 · 50, or 5,000, square yards. The greatest possible area is 130 · 100, or 13,000, square yards.

· · · · · · · · · · · · · · · · · · ·

Square each number.

11. 14   196

12. 21.5   462.25

13. $\frac{9}{10}$ $\frac{81}{100}$

14. 0.3   0.09

15. List five perfect squares between 100 and 500.
Possible answer: 121, 144, 169, 196, 225

Tell whether each number is a perfect square. Explain how you know.

16. 40   See margin.

17. 81   Yes, $81 = 9^2$

18. 125   See margin.

19. 256   Yes, 16^2

20. If a square has area 30.25 square feet, how long is each side?   5.5 ft

21. Ms. Dixon built this tile patio around a square fountain. The tiles measure 1 foot on each side. The patio is constructed of white, light green, dark green, and blue tiles.

    a. What is the total perimeter of the patio? Add the inner and outer perimeters.   40 ft

    b. What is the area of the patio?   60 sq ft

    c. Express the portion of the patio that each color makes up as a fraction and as a percent.   See below.

22. Daniel wants to build a fenced-in play area for his rabbit. He has 30 feet of fencing. Give the dimensions and area of the largest rectangular play area that he can fence.
7.5 ft · 7.5 ft, 56.25 sq ft

21c. Dark green: $\frac{1}{3}$, $33.\overline{3}\%$;
White: $\frac{1}{3}$, $33.\overline{3}\%$;
Blue: $\frac{1}{6}$, $16.\overline{6}\%$;
Light Green: $\frac{1}{6}$, $16.\overline{6}\%$

23. Each of these rectangles has whole-number side lengths and an area of 25 square units.

Below is the only rectangle with whole-number side lengths and an area of 5 square units.

a. How many different rectangles are there with whole-number side lengths and an area of 36 square units? Give the dimensions of each rectangle.

b. Consider every whole-number area from 2 square units to 30 square units. For which of these areas is there only one rectangle with whole-number side lengths?   2, 3, 5, 7, 11, 13, 17, 19, 23, 29

c. What do the areas you found in Part b have in common?
They are prime numbers.

d. For which area from 2 square units to 30 square units can you make the greatest number of rectangles with whole-number side lengths? Give the dimensions of each rectangle you can make with this area.

24. Katia squared a number. The result was the same as the number with which she started. What number might she have squared? Give all of the possibilities.   0 or 1

25. Rashid squared a number. The result was 10 times the number with which he started. What was his starting number?   10

26. Meera squared a number. The result was less than the number with which she started. Give two possible starting numbers for Meera.
Possible answer: 0.3, 0.99

27. In this exercise, you will explore what happens to the area of a square when you double its side lengths.

a. Draw and label four squares of different sizes. Calculate the areas.
Answers will vary.

b. For each square you drew, draw a square with sides twice as long. Calculate the areas of the four new squares.   The areas should be 4 times the areas in Part a.

c. When you doubled the side lengths of your squares, did the areas double as well? If not, how did the areas change? Why do you think this happened?

d. If you double the side lengths of a rectangle that is not a square, do you think the same pattern would hold? Why or why not?

e. If you triple the side lengths of a square, what do you think will happen to the area? Test your hypothesis on two or three squares.
The area will be multiplied by 9.

23a. 5 rectangles:
$1 \cdot 36, 2 \cdot 18,$
$3 \cdot 12, 4 \cdot 9, 6 \cdot 6$

23d. 24 sq units: $1 \cdot 24,$
$2 \cdot 12, 3 \cdot 8, 4 \cdot 6$ or
30 sq units: $1 \cdot 30,$
$2 \cdot 15, 3 \cdot 10, 5 \cdot 6$

27c. No, the areas were multiplied by 4. Possible explanation: Since you multiply each side length by 2, and multiply the side lengths to get the area, the original area gets multiplied by 2 twice, which is the same as being multiplied by 4.

27d. Yes; you are still multiplying the length by 2 and the width by 2, so you are multiplying the area by 4.

▶ **Exercise 23b** Some students may need a hint to get started. You might try the following questions: Can each of the whole-number areas from 2 square units to 30 square units be obtained by using a rectangle of width 1 unit? Yes If that is the only rectangle possible for a certain area, what does that tell you about the factors of that area number? There are only two factors, 1 and the number itself.

▶ **Exercise 26** If students have difficulty with this exercise, you may want to suggest that students use the guess-check-and-improve strategy.

▶ **Exercise 27** Providing grid paper for this exercise will make it much easier for students to draw the squares and rectangles and make comparisons.

Lesson 7.1 Squares   **407**

Quick Check

Informal Assessment Students should be able to:

✔ find areas by counting unit squares

✔ find the formula for the area of a rectangle

Quick Quiz

1. Find the area of the following shape:

6 square units

2. Find the area of a rectangle that is 24.3 cm long and 12 cm wide. 291.6 cm^2

3. Find the length of a rectangle that has a width of 18 in. and an area of 558 in^2. 31 in.

4. Write the area of the square shown below. $A = (8.4 \text{ cm})^2$; 70.56 cm^2

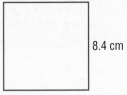

8.4 cm

5. Find the area of a square with a side length of 12 cm. 144 cm^2

6. A rectangle has an area of 36 square inches. Write two possible sets of length and width that will equal the given area. Any length and width whose product is 36. Sample answer: length = 12 in., width = 3 in.

7. A square has a side length of 8 cm. Write the length and width of a rectangle that will equal the area of the square. Any length and width whose product is 64. Sample answer: length = 32 cm, width = 2 cm

8. Samantha has 50 square tiles that each has an area of 1 cm^2. The tiles will be arranged to make a large square. What is the side length of the largest square that can be created with the tiles? 7 cm

28. In Your Own Words Explain how squaring whole numbers is different for numbers greater than 1 than for numbers less than 1.

Mixed Review

28. Sample answer: Squaring a number greater than 1 results in a number that is greater than the original number. Squaring a positive number that is less than 1 results in a number that is less than the original number.

Find each product or quotient.

29. $\frac{3}{4} \cdot \frac{4}{3}$ 1

30. $\frac{3}{4} \div \frac{4}{3}$ $\frac{9}{16}$

31. $\frac{12}{21} \cdot \frac{7}{16}$ $\frac{1}{4}$

32. $\frac{27}{32} \cdot \frac{24}{45}$ $\frac{9}{20}$

33. $2\frac{2}{5} \cdot \frac{1}{3}$ $\frac{4}{5}$

34. $3\frac{5}{8} \div \frac{1}{4}$ $14\frac{1}{2}$

35. $1\frac{3}{8} \cdot 4\frac{1}{2}$ $6\frac{3}{16}$

36. $4\frac{4}{7} \div 1\frac{1}{2}$ $3\frac{1}{21}$

37. $5 \div \frac{1}{9}$ 45

Evaluate each expression.

38. $0.6 \cdot 0.6$ 0.36

39. $0.3 \cdot 0.3$ 0.09

40. $0.02 \cdot 0.02$ 0.0004

41. The 180 sixth-grade girls at Wright Middle School were asked to name their favorite activity in gym class. The results are shown in the table.

Favorite Gym Activity

Activity	Percent of Girls
Softball	15
Track	8
Gymnastics	4
Basketball	28
Soccer	23
Volleyball	22

a. Which activity is most popular? About how many girls chose that activity? Basketball, 50

b. Which activity is least popular? About how many girls chose that activity? Gymnastics, 7

c. What is the difference in the *percent* of girls who chose volleyball and the percent who chose track? What is the difference in the *number* of girls who chose these sports? 14%, about 25

Calculate Areas

Overview

The lesson begins by having students estimate the area of their hand drawn on grid paper by counting grid squares. Students learn that formulas can be developed to find areas of many geometric figures. They cut apart parallelograms and reassemble the parts to make rectangles. Students see that two identical triangles can be put together to form a parallelogram. This leads to a formula for the areas of a triangle and trapezoid. Finally, students estimate areas of circles drawn on grids and use their results to arrive at a formula for the area of a circle and of a circle sector.

Advance Preparation

You may want to provide students with Lesson 7.2 Masters 1-3 to facilitate class discussion.

	Summary	Materials	On Your Own Exercises (pp. 425–433)	Assessment Opportunities
Investigation 1 (p. 410) *Pacing: 2 days*	Students develop a formula for the area of a parallelogram.	Chapter 7 Masters 3 and 4, Lesson 7.2 Master 1, metric rulers and protractors, scissors and tape	Practice & Apply: 1–5, 10 Connect & Extend: 25–28 Mixed Review: 42–48	• On the Spot Assessment (p. 412) • Share & Summarize (p. 412) • Troubleshooting (pp. 410, 412)
Investigation 2 (p. 413) *Pacing: 1 day*	Students develop a formula for the area of a triangle.	Chapter 7 Master 2, Lesson 7.2 Masters 2 and 3, metric rulers and protractors, scissors and tape	Practice & Apply: 6–9 Connect & Extend: 29–31 Mixed Review: 42–48	• On the Spot Assessment (p. 415) • Share & Summarize (p. 416)
Investigation 3 (p. 416) *Pacing: 1 day*	Students develop a formula for the area of a trapezoid.		Practice & Apply: 15–20 Connect & Extend: 35, 36 Mixed Review: 42–48	• On the Spot Assessment (p. 417) • Share & Summarize (p. 419) • Troubleshooting (p. 419)
Investigation 4 (p. 419) *Pacing: 1 day*	Students estimate areas of circles and use the formula for the area of a circle.	Chapter 7 Master 5	Practice & Apply: 11-14 Connect & Extend: 32–34 Mixed Review: 42–48	• Share & Summarize (p. 421) • Troubleshooting (p. 421)
Investigation 5 (p. 422) *Pacing: 1 day*	Students find the area of a circle sector by finding a fraction of a circle.		Practice & Apply: 21–24 Connect & Extend: 37–41 Mixed Review: 42–48	• On the Spot Assessment (p. 424) • Share & Summarize (p. 424) • Troubleshooting (p. 424)

Leveled Lesson Resources

Also on
TeacherWorks™
Lesson 7.2

Study Guide and Intervention (p. 15) AL

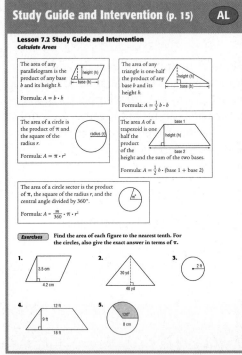

Skills Practice (p. 16) AL OL

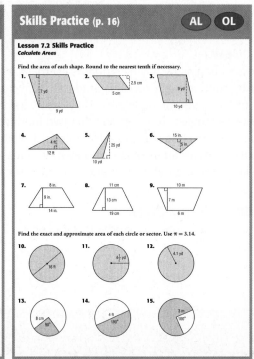

Problem-Solving Practice (p. 17) AL OL

Lesson 7.2 Problem-Solving Practice
Calculate Areas

For Exercises 1–8, round to the nearest tenth if necessary.

1. **Sunflowers** Norman is a sunflower farmer. His farm is in the shape of a parallelogram with a height measuring 3 kilometers and a base measuring 4.2 kilometers. What is the area of Norman's farm?

2. **Volleyball** Ella and Veronica are in charge of making a banner for the volleyball game this Saturday. How much poster paper will they need for a parallelogram-shaped banner with height $3\frac{1}{2}$ feet and base 6 feet?

3. **Carpeting** Courtney wants to carpet part of her bedroom that is shaped like a right triangle with base 4 meters and height 5.2 meters. How much carpet will she need?

4. **Lawn** Mrs. Giuntini's lawn is triangle-shaped with a base of 25 feet and a height of 10 feet. What is the area of Mrs. Guintini's lawn? Explain how you found your answer.

5. **Barn** The front of Mr. Enzo's barn is shaped like a trapezoid. The base of the barn measures 30 feet and the roof measures 20 feet. The height of the barn measures 15 feet. What is the area of the front of the barn?

6. **Quilting** Emma is making a quilt using trapezoid-shaped pieces of fabric. The bases of the fabric measure 4 inches and 6 inches. The fabric has a height of 3 inches. How many pieces will she need to cover an area of 600 square inches?

7. **Tables** A carpenter is making a template for a circular table. The table has a radius of 3 feet. What is the area of the template for the table? Use π = 3.14.

8. **Manufacturing** A company makes open cylinders out of cardboard. The base of the cylinder is a circle with an 8 inch diameter. What is the area of the base? Use π = 3.14.

Enrichment (p. 18) BL

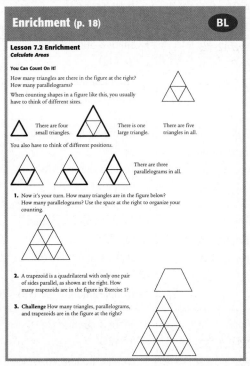

Lesson Quick Quiz (p. 19) AL OL BL

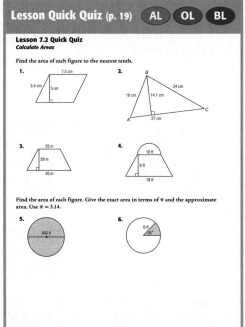

Lesson Masters 1–3 (pp. 20–22)

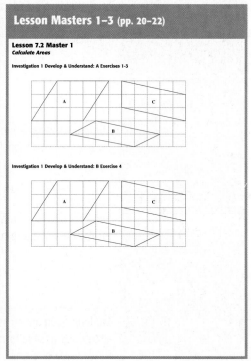

Additional Lesson Resources

Teacher Tech Tools
- TeacherWorks
- ExamView Assessment Suite
- Classroom Presentation Toolkit
- Advance Tracker

Student Tech Tools
- StudentWorks Plus
- Math Online > eGlossary •
  Concepts in Motion

Other Print Products
- Investigation Notebook and Reflection Journal
- Quick Review Math Handbook

Calculate Areas

In the last lesson, you learned that the area of a shape is the number of square units that fit inside it.

Materials

- 1-inch grid paper
- $\frac{1}{2}$-inch grid paper

① Possible answer: The $\frac{1}{2}$-inch grid estimate; with this grid, more whole squares fit inside the tracing, and less of the area is made up of partial squares. With partial squares, you have to approximate, so the less area that is made up of partial squares, the more accurate the area estimate will be.

Explore

Place one hand on a sheet of 1-inch grid paper with your fingers held together. Trace around your hand.

- Estimate the area of your hand tracing in square inches by counting grid squares.   Estimates will vary.

Now trace your hand onto a sheet of $\frac{1}{2}$-inch grid paper.

- Estimate the number of squares inside the tracing.   Estimates will vary.
- On $\frac{1}{2}$-inch grid paper, each small square has side length $\frac{1}{2}$-inch. What is the area of each small square in square inches? $\frac{1}{4}$ in^2
- Use the previous two answers to estimate the area of your hand in square inches.   Estimates will vary.

Which estimate do you think is more accurate, the estimate based on the 1-inch grid or the estimate based on the $\frac{1}{2}$-inch grid? Why?   See ①.

When you want to estimate the area of an odd shape such as your hand, counting grid squares is a fairly good method. Although, it does take time. For many other shapes, you can use formulas to find the area quickly. You already know formulas for areas of squares and rectangles. In this lesson, you will explore formulas for areas of parallelograms, triangles, and circles.

Real-World Link

The area of the palm of your hand is about 1% of the area of your skin. Doctors use this approximation to estimate the percent of a person's skin that is affected by a burn or other problem. It is known as the "rule of palms."

Reaching All Learners

BL **Beyond Level** If you have some students want a challenge, have them trace the same hand they used earlier but with the fingers spread out. Have them count the grid squares inside the tracing and compare the area of their hand with the area they found previously. Discuss the following questions.

- Which area was harder to find (count)? Why?
- Are the two areas the same? Why or why not?
- What factors lead to the difference in areas?

Introduce

Calculate Areas Remind students that the area of a two-dimensional shape is the number of square units that fits inside it. Tell them that in this lesson they will see how to estimate areas of irregular shapes with curved sides. Explain that they will then find formulas for areas of several geometric shapes that are not squares or rectangles. Then move on to the Explore.

Explore

Suggested Grouping: Pairs

▶ **Prepare** Conduct this Explore with the entire class. Each student will need a sheet of 1-inch grid paper (Chapter 7 Master 3) and $\frac{1}{2}$-inch grid paper (Chapter 7 Master 4). You may want to trace your own hand on a transparency of Chapter 7 Master 3. You can project the transparency to discuss with the class how to get started on the Explore.

▶ **Play** Tell students that they should draw a straight line at the bottom of the hand to show where the hand stops. Tell them that they will be counting the grid squares inside the tracing. Students will easily see that if they count only whole squares entirely inside the hand outline, they will probably get a rough estimate of the area. To get a better estimate, they will need to use fractions for squares that are partially inside the outline.

▶ **Record** After students have had time to estimate the area of their hands by using both the 1-inch and $\frac{1}{2}$-inch grids, discuss the results. Be sure students understand why the estimate with $\frac{1}{2}$-inch grid paper requires that the number of squares be multiplied by $\frac{1}{4}$ to get the area in square inches.

▶ **Score** Discuss students' findings on both the 1-inch and $\frac{1}{2}$-inch grid paper. Ask them which grid was easier to use to estimate the area of their hand and why.

Areas of Parallelograms Have students read the opening paragraph in the investigation. Discuss the definition of the term *parallelogram* as well the terms *base* and *height of a parallelogram*. Students should accept the fact that if the opposite sides of a quadrilateral are parallel, then the quadrilateral is a parallelogram. This means that if the opposite sides are parallel, then the opposite sides will also be equal. You may want to use Lesson 7.2 Master 1 for Exercise 1 of this investigation.

✔ Develop & Understand: A

Suggested Grouping: Pairs

▶ **Exercise 1** Point out that there are different ways to find the area of Parallelogram A.

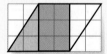 

- On the left, the triangle with gray shading is half of a 3 × 2 rectangle. So its area is $\frac{1}{2} \cdot 6$, or 3 cm². Likewise, the triangle on the right with gray shading has an area of 3 cm². The part with green shading is a rectangle made up of 6 squares. The total area of the shaded region is 3 + 6 + 3, or 12 cm².

- The approach on the right has students imagine cutting off the gray triangle on the left and moving it to the right side to obtain the figure shown. Pieces of the original parallelogram have been rearranged to form a rectangle. None of the original area has been lost. So, the area of the parallelogram is 4 · 3, or 12 cm².

Wrap-Up Discuss the results for Exercise 3. Ask for which type of parallelogram it is possible to find the area by multiplying the lengths of two sides. Rectangles

---

Investigation 1 **Areas of Parallelograms**

Vocabulary

base of a
  parallelogram
height of a
  parallelogram
parallelogram

Materials

- copies of the parallelograms
- metric ruler
- scissors
- tape
- protractor

1. Parallelogram A: 12 cm²; Parallelogram B: 7 cm²; Parallelogram C: 10 cm²; See the teaching notes for possible strategies.
2. Parallelogram A: 4.0 cm and 3.6 cm; Parallelogram B: 5.1 cm and 2.2 cm; Parallelogram C: 5.1 cm and 2.0 cm

A **parallelogram** is a quadrilateral with opposite sides that are the same length. The term *parallelogram* refers to the fact that the opposite sides are *parallel*. That is, no matter how far they are extended, they will never meet.

In this investigation, you will use what you know about finding areas of rectangles to develop a formula for the area of a parallelogram.

✔ Develop & Understand: A

1. Find the area of each parallelogram below. Explain the method that you used.

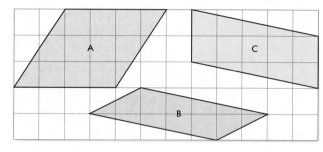

2. Measure the lengths of the sides of each parallelogram to the nearest tenth of a centimeter.

3. Is the area of a parallelogram equal to the product of the lengths of its sides? No

The **base of a parallelogram** can be any of its sides. The **height of a parallelogram** is the distance from the side opposite the base to the base. The height is always measured along a segment perpendicular to the base or to the line containing the base.

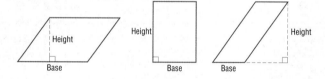

Troubleshooting

If students have difficulty finding the area of Parallelogram B, point out that in the small triangle, with gray shading, is half of a 1 × 2 rectangle, so its area is 1 cm². The large triangle, with green shading, is half of a 1 × 5 rectangle, so its area is 2.5 cm². The bottom part of the parallelogram can be treated the same way. The area of the parallelogram is therefore 1 + 2.5 + 2.5 + 1, or 7 cm².

In Exercises 4–8, you will explore how the base and height of a parallelogram are related to its area.

✅ Develop & Understand: B

4. Complete Parts a–c for each parallelogram in Exercise 1.

   a. Choose a side of the parallelogram as the base. Draw a segment perpendicular to the base that extends to the side opposite the base. The segment should be completely inside the parallelogram. For parallelogram A, you might draw the segment shown using the pink dashed line. **See students' work.**

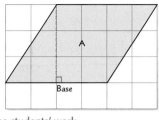

4b. Possible answer: See the table. (Note: For each parallelogram, there are two possible sides that can be chosen as the base, so students may not get the values shown.)

4c. Possible answer: See the table. (Note: The length and width values should match the base and height values.)

   b. Find the lengths of the base and the height. The height is the length of the segment you drew in Part a. Record these measurements in a table like the one below.

	Parallelogram		Rectangle	
	Base	**Height**	**Length**	**Width**
A	4 cm	3 cm	4 cm	3 cm
B	5.1 cm	1.4 cm	5.1 cm	1.4 cm
C	2 cm	5 cm	5 cm	2 cm

   c. Divide the parallelogram into two pieces by cutting along the segment you drew in Part a. Then reassemble the pieces to form a rectangle. Record the length and width of the rectangle in your table.

5. How do the base and height of each parallelogram compare with the length and width of the rectangle formed from the parallelogram? The length and width are the same as the base and height.

6. How does the area of each parallelogram compare with the area of the rectangle formed from the parallelogram? The areas are equal.

7. How can you find the area of a parallelogram if you know the length of a base and the corresponding height? Use what you have discovered to explain why your method works. **See margin.**

8. Find the area of this parallelogram without forming it into a rectangle. Explain each step of your work. **See margin.**

Additional Answers

7. Multiply the length of the base by the height. This works because you can form the parallelogram into a rectangle with length and width equal to the base and height of the parallelogram. The area of the rectangle is the length times the width, which is the same as the base times the height. Since the parallelogram's area is equal to the rectangle's area, the area of the parallelogram is also equal to the base times the height.

8. About 6 cm^2; Possible explanation: I chose a side to be the base and then used a protractor to help draw a segment from the opposite side perpendicular to the base. I measured the base and the height and multiplied these two measurements to get the area.

✅ Develop & Understand: B

Suggested Grouping: Pairs

▶ **Exercises 4a and 4c** The segment perpendicular to the base will correspond to the height of the parallelogram. In Exercise 4c, students will cut along this segment and separate the parallelogram into the two pieces that will form a rectangle. Getting this rectangle requires that the segment drawn in Exercise 4a lies completely inside the parallelogram. For Parallelograms A and C, suggest students use segments that are parts of grid lines. For parallelogram B, students must use one of the long sides of the parallelogram as the base. Otherwise, the segment for the height will not lie entirely inside the parallelogram. To get accurate results, students should use their protractors to draw the segment for the height.

▶ **Exercise 4c** Students cut out each parallelogram, cut along the heights, and reassemble the pieces of the parallelogram to make a rectangle. They can use a piece of tape to hold the pieces together. (Note: Although the length and width values should match the base and height values, their order may be interchanged. In the given answers, base equals length and height equals length for Parallelogram C.)

▶ **Exercise 5** The rectangles students made for Exercise 4 should make it clear that the base and height of each parallelogram are the same as the length and width of the corresponding rectangle. It is important that students understand this.

▶ **Exercise 6** Students should recall that the area of each parallelogram is the amount of space *inside* the parallelogram. None of this space is lost in making the rectangles. Exercise 6 does not ask the student to state the area of either figure, only to recognize that reassembling the cut-apart parallelogram does not change the total area.

▶ **Exercise 7** Point out that students will synthesize the results of Exercises 4–6. The result will tell them how to find the area of any parallelogram if they know the length of the base and the corresponding height.

▶ **Exercise 8** Suggest that students measure the lengths and heights in centimeters.

✓ Develop & Understand: C

Suggested Grouping: Pairs

▶ **Exercises 9–12** Point out that students will calculate the areas of parallelograms using a formula. They will also find the length of the base of a parallelogram, given the area and height of the parallelogram.

▶ **Exercises 9–11** Students are given the side lengths and one height of a parallelogram. The segment that is drawn perpendicular to a side of the parallelogram gives the height of the parallelogram and indicates which side is used as the base.

▶ **Exercise 12** Students can find the value of b by solving the equation $b \cdot 2.45 = 12.93$. Be sure they understand why this is the equation to use rather than $b \cdot 2.98 = 12.93$. To solve the equation, students can use related multiplication and division equations.

Share & Summarize

Call on volunteers to read their answers to the class. Discuss the answers. Pay special attention to whether the answers indicate a clear understanding of what is meant by the base and height of a parallelogram. You may want to put some diagrams on the board that students can refer to during the discussion.

Troubleshooting If students seem to have trouble determining how to identify the base and height of some parallelograms, you may want to give them a few more parallelograms to measure, and have them check their findings with a partner.

You can find the area of a parallelogram by multiplying the length of the base by the height. This can be stated using a formula.

Area of a Parallelogram
$A = b \cdot h$

In this formula, A represents the area, b represents the base, and h represents the height.

✓ Develop & Understand: C

Find the area of each parallelogram to the nearest hundredth of a square unit.

9. 1.32 in^2

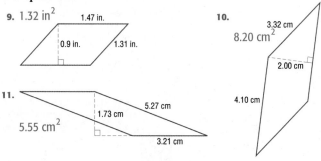

10.

11.

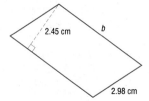

12. The area of the parallelogram below is 12.93 cm^2. Find the value of b to the nearest hundredth.   5.28 cm

Share & Summarize

How is finding the area of a parallelogram similar to finding the area of a rectangle? How is it different?   See ①.

① Possible answer: In both cases, you multiply two measurements. For a rectangle, the measurements are both side lengths. For the parallelogram, one of the measurements (the length of the base) is a side length, but the other may not be. The height is the length of a segment from the side opposite the base to the base, perpendicular to the base. In both cases, the two segments whose lengths are multiplied are perpendicular.

On the Spot Assessment

Some students may multiply the wrong measures to find the area of the parallelograms in Exercises 9–11. Use questions to help them understand which segment in each diagram indicates the height of the parallelogram. Ask them to show you the sides to which this segment is perpendicular. Then ask them the length of each of these sides. Finally, have them multiply this length by the height to find the area.

Investigation 2 — Areas of Triangles

Vocabulary
base of a triangle

height of a triangle

Materials
- copies of the triangle
- 3 copies of the triangle dot paper
- copies of the triangles
- scissors
- tape
- protractor
- ruler

① Triangle A: 6 cm²;
Triangle B: 8 cm²;
Triangle C: 3 cm²;
See the teaching notes for possible strategies.

You have looked at areas of rectangles and parallelograms. Now you will turn your attention to triangles.

✅ Develop & Understand: A

Find the area of each triangle. Explain the method that you used. See ①.

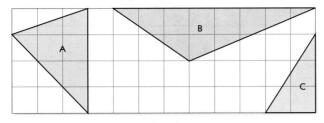

The **base of a triangle** can be any of its sides. The **height of a triangle** is the distance from the base to the vertex opposite the base. The height is always measured along a segment perpendicular to the base or the line containing the base.

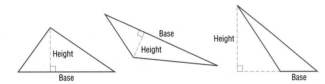

You may have used a variety of methods for finding the areas of the triangles. You will now see how you can find the area of a triangle by relating it to a parallelogram.

Cut out two copies of each triangle like those shown above.

1. Complete Parts a–d for each triangle.

   a. Make as many different parallelograms as you can by putting together the two copies of the triangle. Do not tape them together. Make a sketch of each parallelogram. See margin.

   b. How does the area of the triangle compare to the area of each parallelogram? The area of the triangle is half the area of each parallelogram.

Additional Answer

1a. For each triangle, you can make three different parallelograms. Here are the three parallelograms for Triangle B:

On Your Own Exercises
Pages 425–433
Exercises 6–9, 29–31

Areas of Triangles Point out that in this investigation, students will apply what they have learned about the area of a parallelogram to develop a formula for the area of a triangle. After developing the formula, they apply it and explore some consequences.

✅ Develop & Understand: A

Suggested Grouping: Pairs

▶ **Exercise 1** The triangles for this exercise set and the next can be found on Lesson 7.2 Master 2. Each pair of students will need two copies of this master.

Students can find the areas of these triangles by using ideas similar to those used for parallelograms drawn on grids. They will explore ways to join two copies of a triangle to make a parallelogram.

Point out that Triangle A can be thought of as two triangles, each of which is half of a rectangle. Triangle B can be thought of in the same way. Triangle C is already half of a rectangle.

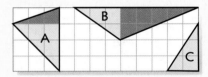

Urge students to be careful when they cut out the triangles. This will make it possible for them to get a good fit when the copies are put together.

1c. Answers will depend on the parallelogram students chose and the side they designated as the base.

c. Tape the two copies of the triangle together to form one of the parallelograms you sketched in Part a. Choose one side of the parallelogram as the base. Draw a segment perpendicular to the base extending to the opposite side.

d. Do the base and height of the parallelogram correspond to a base and height of the triangle? **Yes**

2. Think about what you learned in Exercise 1 about the relationship between triangles and parallelograms. How can you find the area of a triangle if you know the length of a base and the corresponding height? **Possible answer: Multiply the base times the height and divide the result by 2.**

Find the area of each triangle to the nearest hundredth.

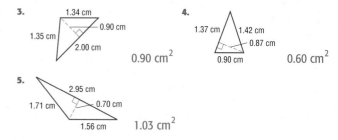

3. 1.34 cm, 0.90 cm, 1.35 cm, 2.00 cm **0.90 cm^2**

4. 1.37 cm, 1.42 cm, 0.87 cm, 0.90 cm **0.60 cm^2**

5. 2.95 cm, 0.70 cm, 1.71 cm, 1.56 cm **1.03 cm^2**

In Exercises 1–5, you probably discovered that the area of a triangle is half the length of the base times the height. You can state this using a formula.

Area of a Triangle
$A = \frac{1}{2} \cdot b \cdot h$
In this formula, A represents the area, b represents the base, and h represents the height.

Real-World Link
Triangles are rigid shapes. If you build a triangle out of a strong material, it will not collapse or change shape when you press on its sides or vertices. Because of this property, triangles are used frequently as supports for buildings, bridges, and other structures.

Mathematical Background

Students may look at the triangle in Exercise 5 and wonder if there is another way to find the area. Point out that an obtuse triangle always has one height (to the longest side) that is inside the triangle and two heights that are outside the triangle. Extend the sides and draw the other heights for Example 5, if necessary, so students understand this concept. Emphasize that every triangle has three heights because any side can be a base.

Develop & Understand: B

Three students found the area of this triangle. Seth used the 4.5-centimeter side as the base, Margo used the 4.2-centimeter side, and Yori used the 3.8-centimeter side.

6. Assuming the students did the calculations correctly, do you think they found the same area or different areas? Explain.

7. Complete Parts a–c to find the area using the 4.5-cm side as the base.

   a. Draw a segment perpendicular to the base from the vertex opposite the base. Use your protractor to make sure the base and the segment form a right angle.

   b. Measure the height to the nearest tenth of a centimeter.
   Possible answer: 3.4 cm

   c. Use the base and height measurements to calculate the area of the triangle.   7.7 cm^2

8. Repeat Parts a–c of Exercise 7 using the 4.2-cm side as the base.

9. Repeat Parts a–c of Exercise 7 using the 3.8-cm side as the base.

10. Compare your results for Exercises 7, 8, and 9. Did the area you calculated depend on the base you used? Explain.

Develop & Understand: C

△ABD and △ABE were created by shearing △ABC. *Shearing* a triangle means "sliding" one of its vertices along a line parallel to the opposite side. In this case, △ABC was sheared by sliding vertex C to vertex D and then to vertex E.

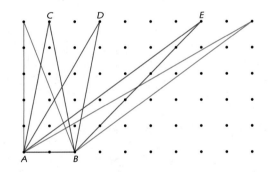

Answers (left margin)

6. Answers will vary. The areas will be the same no matter which side is used as the base.

7a.

8a.

8b. Possible answer: 3.6 cm

8c. Possible answer: 7.6 cm^2

9a.

9b. Possible answer: 4.0 cm

9c. Possible answer: 7.6 cm^2

10. No; in all three cases, I found an area of a little more than 7.6 cm^2. The small differences are probably due to measuring error.

Develop & Understand: B

Suggested Grouping: Pairs

▶ **Exercises 6–10** In this exercise set, students confirm that the area formula for triangles gives the same number of square units no matter which side is chosen as the base. Each pair of students will need three copies of Lesson 7.2 Master 3.

▶ **Exercise 7a** Demonstrate how to draw the segment for the height accurately. Explain that the bottom line of the protractor (the line through the center point of the protractor) should be exactly on top of the base of the triangle (in this case, the side that measures 12 cm). Slide the protractor along this line until the opposite vertex (the top vertex of the triangle) is on the 90° mark. The center point of the triangle will be at a certain point of the base when this occurs. Mark this point. Then draw the segment from this point to the opposite vertex. Tell students to use the square corner symbol to show which segments are perpendicular.

Another method for locating the correct point on the base is to use a square corner of a sheet of paper. If students use this method, they can use their protractors to check that the base and the segment for the height are perpendicular.

▶ **Exercises 7b and 7c** If students have trouble drawing the perpendicular segments when the base is not horizontal, tell them to turn the triangle to get the base in a horizontal position. When they have drawn the segment for the height, they should use the square corner symbol to show which segments are perpendicular.

Teacher Tips You can demonstrate how to "get a triangle in a horizontal position" by cutting out a large triangle and resting it on a chalkboard or whiteboard ledge.

On the Spot Assessment

If students' answers for Exercises 7–9 differ markedly from the sample answer, examine their work to see whether the students had difficulty drawing the segments for the heights. You may need to demonstrate the proper procedure again.

Develop & Understand: C

Suggested Grouping: Pairs

▶ **Exercises 11–14** In this exercise set, students see that shearing a triangle does not change the area of the triangle but generally does change the perimeter. Discuss the introductory paragraph to be sure students understand what is meant by *shearing a triangle*.

▶ **Exercise 12** Have students copy the triangles in the diagram on their sheet of 1-centimeter dot paper (Chapter 7 Master 2). They should label the triangles in the copy the same way as in the original.

Share & Summarize

Have volunteers read their answers to the class. Encourage them to put diagrams on the board whenever they think they will be helpful in explanations.

Investigation 3

On Your Own Exercises
Pages 425–433
Exercises 15–20, 35, 36

Areas of Trapezoids In this investigation, students learn to identify trapezoids and their characteristics. They will use their knowledge of polygons to determine whether a shape is a trapezoid and how to use bases and height to find its area. Students will also learn to distinguish trapezoids from parallelograms.

Think & Discuss

Draw a Venn diagram on the board to compare the characteristics and definitions of trapezoids and parallelograms. Fill in each section using students' answers to each of these questions. Use drawings of each polygon to illustrate each detail in the Venn diagram.

Additional Answers

11. Possible answer: All share side *AB*, and all have vertices in the top row of dots. If side *AB* is considered the base, then all three triangles have the same base and height. △*ABE* is longer and skinnier than △*ABD*, which is longer and skinnier than △*ABC*. △*ABC* has two sides of the same length. In the other triangles, all three sides have a different length.

14. Yes; as the vertex moves farther from point *C*, the nonhorizontal sides get longer and longer, so the perimeter increases.

11. How are △*ABC*, △*ABD*, and △*ABE* alike? How are they different? See margin.
12. Draw two more triangles by shearing △*ABC*. See the figure for a possible answer.
13. Does shearing △*ABC* change its area? Explain. No; the base and height stay the same, so the area is the same as well.
14. Does shearing △*ABC* change its perimeter? Explain.

Share & Summarize

Describe how finding the area of a triangle is related to finding the area of a parallelogram. See ①.

Investigation 3 Areas of Trapezoids

Vocabulary
trapezoid
bases of a trapezoid
height of a trapezoid

① Possible answer: The area of a triangle is half the area of a parallelogram formed by two copies of the triangle. When you form such a parallelogram, the parallelogram's base and height correspond to the triangle's base and height. Since the area of the parallelogram is the base times the height, the area of a triangle is half the base times the height.

In this investigation, you will explore the area of a special quadrilateral, a **trapezoid**.

These figures are trapezoids.

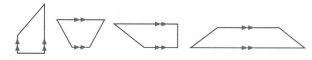

These figures are not trapezoids.

What do you notice about the figures that are trapezoids and the figures that are not trapezoids? How are they different? See ② in margin.
Can you state the definition of a trapezoid by examining the figures above? See ③ in margin.

You may have noticed that a trapezoid has one pair of parallel sides, called the **bases of a trapezoid**. The **height of a trapezoid** is the length of a perpendicular segment between the bases.

Think & Discuss See ④–⑦ in margin.

Can the bases of a trapezoid be different lengths? The same length?

Can the non-base side of a trapezoid be the same length? Draw an example or explain why not.

How many heights can you draw in a trapezoid?

② Sample answer: The figures that are trapezoids have one set of parallel lines. The figures that are trapezoids have 4 sides. The figures that are not trapezoids have two sets of parallel lines, and the triangle has no parallel lines. The amount of parallel lines makes them different from each other.

③ Sample answer: You can define a trapezoid as a figure with one set of parallel lines.

④ Yes. See figure in definition above.

⑤ No, because then the other pair of sides would be parallel; it would be a parallelogram.

⑥ Yes.

⑦ You can draw two equal heights.

✅ Develop & Understand: A

1. Use the trapezoids below for Parts a–c.

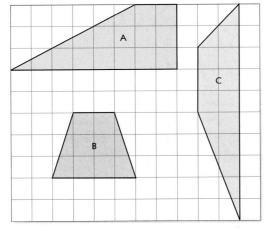

a. Trace each trapezoid twice on a sheet of paper. Cut out the trapezoids. Check students' work.

b. Label the top of each trapezoid "base 1" and the bottom "base 2". Check students' work.

c. Place the two matching trapezoids together to form a parallelogram. Check students' work.

2. In Investigation 1, you learned the formula for the area of a parallelogram. Find the area of this parallelogram in terms of base 1, base 2, and its height, h.

3. If the area of the parallelogram is the same as the area of two of the original trapezoids, what would be the formula for the area of the trapezoid?

In Exercise 1, you discovered that you can find the area of a trapezoid by adding the lengths of the two bases, multiplying by the height, and dividing by 2. This can be stated using a formula.

Area of a Trapezoid
$A = \frac{1}{2}h\,(\text{base 1} + \text{base 2})$

In this formula, A represents the area, h represents the height of the trapezoid, and base 1 and base 2 represent the two bases.

Math Link

Mathematicians sometimes use a different definition for a trapezoid. "A trapezoid is a quadrilateral that has *at least* one pair of parallel sides." Using this definition, what would be the difference between a trapezoid and a parallelogram? See ①.

① According to this definition, a trapezoid could be a parallelogram if it had two pairs of parallel sides.

2. The formula for the area of a parallelogram is $A = b \cdot h$, there are two base 1s and two base 2s that are added together to make this formula.

3. If the area of two trapezoids are the same as the area for one parallelogram. You could divide the formula for the area of a parallelogram in half to get $A = \frac{1}{2}h$ (base 1 + base 2)

Math Link

The lengths of the two bases in a trapezoid, base 1 and base 2, can also be written using the subscripts, b_1 and b_2. You may see the formula for the area of a trapezoid written as $A = \frac{1}{2}h\,(b_1 + b_2)$.

Math Link

Discuss how *at least* is different from *exactly* in the two definitions of a trapezoid. Draw a trapezoid and a parallelogram on the board and have students explain how using *at least* instead of *exactly* could affect the way they identify trapezoids and parallelograms.

Teacher Tips Go over the formula for a trapezoid with students. They should clearly be able to look at a diagram of a trapezoid, point to each of the dimensions, and know how to substitute values into the formula.

✅ Develop & Understand: A

Suggested Grouping: Individuals

▶ **Exercises 1–3** Discuss with students why the two methods for finding the area of a trapezoid gives the same area. Have them explain why each particular method worked.

Math Link

Have students label the bases of a trapezoid with base 1 and base 2. Then have them work together to find the area of the trapezoid. Discuss how labeling the bases helps clarify the formula given with subscripts b_1 and b_2 in this side note.

On the Spot Assessment

Monitor for understanding as students identify trapezoids. Students who can identify trapezoids but cannot distinguish between trapezoids and parallelograms need more practice learning the characteristics of each. Students who cannot identify trapezoids as compared to any other polygons need more practice understanding the characteristics of polygons.

Develop & Understand: B

Suggested Grouping: Pairs

▶ **Exercise 4** Check to see that students correctly found the area of the trapezoids. Discuss how students can use more than one method to find the area of a trapezoid. Remind them that the answer remains the same even though they found it in another way.

Develop & Understand: C

Suggested Grouping: Whole Group

▶ **Exercise 6** Discuss with students why Quincy's method formed a parallelogram. Help students divide the trapezoids to create the parallelogram and the triangle. Make sure they understand how to determine where to place the line. Have them explain why making a parallelogram helps confirm the formula for the area of a trapezoid.

▶ **Exercises 7–9** Have student pairs check their answers for these exercises.

▶ **Exercises 10–12** Monitor students as they find the area of the trapezoids. Make sure they use the appropriate formula and can apply it properly. Remind students that they can use any of the methods they have learned to find the area of each trapezoid. Encourage partners to each try a different method, and then compare answers.

Teacher Tips Teaching students to find the areas of trapezoids and other polygons can be confusing. It is important to make the process as concrete as possible by using visual aids.

Wrap-Up Help students put together two copies of the trapezoids to create the parallelogram using Quincy's method. If they have difficulty understand how the trapezoid formula applies, do additional examples.

Develop & Understand: B

Find the area of each trapezoid.

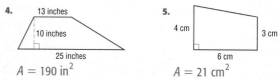

4. 13 inches / 10 inches / 25 inches $A = 190$ in^2

5. 4 cm / 3 cm / 6 cm $A = 21$ cm^2

Develop & Understand: C

Quincy found another way to develop the formula for the area of a trapezoid. Here are his instructions.

Step 1. Find the midpoints of the two non-base sides. Connect them with a line segment.

Step 2. Cut along this line segment.

Step 3. Rotate the upper half of the trapezoid clockwise so that the two congruent half-sides meet.

Step 4. The new quadrilateral is a parallelogram.

6. Perform Quincy's instructions on a copy of one of the trapezoids you made in Exercise 1. Before you cut along the line, label the bases as base 1 and base 2.   See students' work

7. How does the height of this parallelogram compare to the height of the original trapezoid?

    7. Height of the parallelogram is half the height of the original trapezoid

8. How does the base of this parallelogram compare to the two bases of the original trapezoid?   Base of the parallelogram is the sum of the two bases

9. What formula did Quincy use for the area of this parallelogram, if base 1 and base 2 are the bases of the original trapezoid and h is the height of the original trapezoid?

    9. Area of trapezoid = $\frac{1}{2}$ the height times the sum of base 1 and base 2

Find each missing length or area for the trapezoids below.

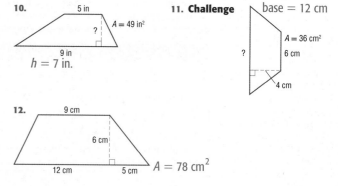

10. 5 in / ? / $A = 49$ in^2 / 9 in / $h = 7$ in.

11. **Challenge** base = 12 cm / $A = 36$ cm^2 / 6 cm / ? / 4 cm

12. 9 cm / 6 cm / 12 cm / 5 cm / $A = 78$ cm^2

Reaching *All Learners*

ELL **English Language Learners** Review the meanings of basic terms for this lesson with students. Make sure they fully understand and can use the terms *length, height, base, same,* and *different*. Create a poster of a trapezoid and label it using each of these terms. Allow students to refer to it as needed.

13.

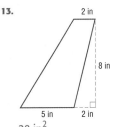

28 in^2

① Sample answer:
The area of a
parallelogram is
base · height. The
area of a trapezoid
is like doing the
same thing with the
average of the two
bases (add the bases
together and divide
by 2, then multiply
that by the height).

14. A trapezoid and a parallelogram each have the same area and the
same height. Can the base of the parallelogram be equal to one of
the bases of the trapezoid? Why or why not?   No. If they were
the same, then the trapezoid would have a second base with
no length.

Share & Summarize

How is finding the area of a trapezoid similar to finding the area of
a parallelogram? How is it different?   See ①.

Investigation 4 **Areas of Circles**

Finding the area of a figure with curved sides often requires counting
grid squares or using another estimation method. However, there is a
surprisingly simple formula for calculating the area of a circle.

✔ Develop & Understand: A

These circles are drawn on 1-centimeter grid paper.

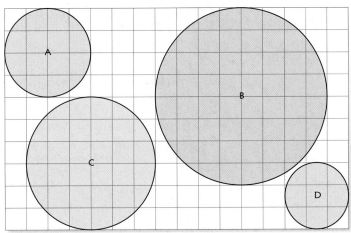

Share & Summarize

Discuss how finding the area of a
parallelogram is similar to finding the area
of a trapezoid. Ask students why finding the
average of the bases for a trapezoid makes
the trapezoid formula similar to the
parallelogram formula. Discuss methods for
finding the area of each and compare them.

Investigation 4

On Your Own Exercises
Pages 425–433
Exercises 11–14, 32–34

Area of Circles In this investigation,
students approximate areas of circles drawn
on a grid. They complete a table that will
help them see how the area of a circle and
the radius of the circle are related. They
learn a formula for the area of a circle. They
then apply the formula to solve
mathematical and real-world problems. If
you wish, you can provide students with
Chapter 7 Master 5, Centimeter Grid Paper.

Troubleshooting

For students who have difficulty
finding the area of a trapezoid,
draw several trapezoids on the
board and label the measurements
of each. Then have pairs choose a
method for finding area. Check
each step of students' work, and
correct as needed.

Suggested Grouping: *Pairs*

▶ **Exercises 1–3** In this exercise set, students investigate how the area and the radius of a circle are related.

▶ **Exercise 2** Encourage students to estimate the area of each circle as accurately as they can. More accurate estimates will give better results for the last column of the table.

Analyze the Table Students may not get the same answers for the radius entries in this table. Have them discuss their answers with a partner and agree on a common radius. This should make the answers to the other columns the same.

▶ **Exercise 5** Students are asked to look for a pattern and recall a similar pattern. Suggest that students look back to how to do patterns in Chapter 3.

▶ **Exercise 6a** There are various ways to see that Cesar's estimate is not reasonable. The sample answer points out that his estimate is out of line with the pattern in the table students completed on page 420. Here is another way to reason about this problem. Suppose you draw a quarter circle of radius 10 cm centered at the lower-right corner of the grid on this page. The quarter circle will pass through the point at the upper-right corner of the grid and will cross the bottom side of the grid at the point 10 cm to the left of the bottom-right corner. If you connect these points, you get a triangle that lies entirely inside the quarter circle. By the formula for the area of a triangle, the area of this triangle is 50 cm^2, which is already greater than Cesar's estimate.

Wrap-Up Discuss the results from This exercise set. Pay special attention to the table and to the answer to Exercise 5.

Teacher Tips Read with the class the information following the exercise set. Discuss the formula for the area of a circle to be sure students understand the formula. Ask volunteers to demonstrate how to find the area of circle using the formula in the formula box.

Math Link

Point out that π has been calculated to millions of decimal places by a computer, and a pattern has never been found.

---

1. Copy the table. Find the radius of each circle. Record your results in the "Radius" column.

Circle	Radius, r (cm)	Estimated Area, A (cm^2)	$A \div r$	$A \div r^2$
A	2	12	6	3
B	4	48	12	3
C	3	28	9.3	3.1
D	1.5	7	4.7	3.1

2. Estimate the area of each circle by counting grid squares. Record your estimates in your table. **See table.**

3. For each circle, divide the area by the radius. Record the results. **See table.**

4. For each circle, divide the area by the radius squared. Record the results. **See table.**

5. Possible answer: The $A \div r^2$ values show a pattern that all the results are around 3.

6a. Possible answer: $A \div r^2$ should be about 3, but for Cesar's measurements, $A \div r^2$ is only about 0.4.

· · · · · · · · · · · · · · ·

Math Link

π is a decimal number with digits that never end or repeat. It can be approximated as 3.14.

· · · · · · · · · · · · · · ·

5. Look at the last two columns of the table. Do the values in either column show an obvious pattern? If so, does it remind you of other patterns you have seen?

6. Cesar estimated that the area of a circle with a radius of 10 centimeters is about 40 cm^2.

   a. Explain why Cesar's estimate is not reasonable.

   b. What is a reasonable estimate for the area of a circle with a radius of 10 centimeters? About 300 cm^2

   c. What is a reasonable estimate for the radius of a circle with an area of 40 cm^2? 3.5 cm to 4 cm

Previously, you learned about the number π and how it is related to the circumference of a circle. You found that if C is the circumference of a circle and d is the diameter, the following is true.

$$\pi = C \div d$$

The number π is also related to the area of a circle. If A is the area of any circle and r is the radius, the following is true.

$$\pi = A \div r^2$$

You can use this fact to develop the formula for the area of a circle.

Area of a Circle
$A = \pi \cdot r^2$
In this formula, A is the area and r is the radius.

9. A circle with a radius of 7.2 cm; Possible explanation: A circle with diameter 12.75 cm has radius 6.375 cm. Since it has the smaller radius, it has less area.

Math Link
Remember to use the $\boxed{\pi}$ key on your calculator to approximate π. If your calculator does not have a $\boxed{\pi}$ key, use 3.14 to approximate π.

1. $A = \pi \cdot r^2$, where A is the area and r is the radius

Real-World Link
There are more than 60,000 pizzerias in the United States, accounting for about 15% of all restaurants.

✓ Develop & Understand: B

For Exercises 7–11, express your answer in terms of π and as a decimal rounded to the nearest hundredths place.

7. What is the area of a circle with a radius of 15 inches?
706.86 in²; 225π in²

8. What is the area of a circle with a radius of 10.15 centimeters?
323.65 cm²; 103π cm²

9. Which has the greater area, a circle with a radius of 7.2 centimeters or a circle with a diameter of 12.75 centimeters? Explain your answer.

★**10.** A pizza parlor makes pizzas in two shapes. The circular pizza has a diameter of 10 inches. The rectangular pizza measures 16 inches by 10 inches. A circular cheese pizza costs $8, and a rectangular cheese pizza costs $14. Which shape gives you more pizza for your money? Explain how you found your answer. See below.

★**11.** This is a diagram of the inner lane of the track at Walker Middle School. The lane is made of two straight segments and two semicircles, or half circles. The area inside the track is covered with grass. What is the area of the grass inside the track? Explain how you found your answer. See margin.

160 yd
120 yd

Share & Summarize

1. Give the formula for the area of a circle. Tell what the letters in the formula represent.

2. How can you calculate the area of a circle if you know only its diameter? See margin.

3. How can you calculate the area of a circle if you know only its circumference? See margin.

10. The rectangular pizza; I divided the area of each pizza by the price to find the amount per dollar. The circular pizza is 78.5 ÷ 8, or about 9.8 in² per dollar. The rectangular pizza is 160 ÷ 14, or about 11.4 in² per dollar.

Lesson 7.2 Calculate Areas **421**

Additional Answers
11. 30,509.7 yd²; The total area is the area of the rectangle plus the area of the two semicircles. Together, the two semicircles form a circle with radius 60 yd. So, the total area is 120 · 160 + π · 60², or about 30,509.7 yd².

Share & Summarize
2. Divide the diameter in half to get the radius. Then use the formula $A = \pi \cdot r^2$.

3. Divide the circumference by π to get the diameter, and divide the diameter in half to get the radius. Then use the formula $A = \pi \cdot r^2$.

✓ Develop & Understand: B

Suggested Grouping: Individuals

In this exercise set, students apply the area formula for a circle.

▶ **Exercise 9** Students should note that they are told the *diameter* of the second circle. They should divide the diameter by 2 to find the radius. Some students may go on to calculate the approximate area of each circle. If they do this correctly, praise their good work, but point out that they could have answered the question in the exercise without the calculations. Be sure they understand how.

▶ **Exercise 10** Some students may get off to a wrong start by trying to compare the perimeters of the pizzas. Help them understand that it makes more sense to use area. Once they know the area of each pizza, dividing price by area will give the cost per square inch.

▶ **Exercise 11** Students should be careful to use the radius rather than the diameter when they calculate the total area of the semicircles.

Share & Summarize
These questions will help you ascertain whether students understand the formula for the area of a circle and how to use it. When you discuss the answers in class, review the meaning of the terms *radius* and *diameter*.

Troubleshooting If students are having trouble keeping the formulas straight, you might help them with memory devices. For example $C = \pi \cdot d$ contains the first letters of the words *circumference* and *diameter*. The area formula $A = \pi \cdot r^2$ contains the first two letters of the word *area*, and r squared is a reminder that area is always given in square units.

On Your Own Exercises
Pages 425–433
Exercises 21–24, 37–41

Areas of Circle Sectors In this investigation, students will find the area of sectors of a circle. Students should already be familiar with finding the area of a circle; explain that they will be learning to divide a circle into equal sections and find the area of each. It is important that students be able to use a protractor and understand that there are 360 degrees in a circle when working the exercises in this investigation.

Teacher Tips Watch to see that students understand the vocabulary. Use additional examples if necessary.

✔ Develop & Understand: A

Suggested Grouping: Individuals

In this exercise set, students identify the central angle of a circle and learn how it applies to finding the corresponding angle of a circle sector.

▶ **Exercise 3** Help students generalize the relationship between the central angle of a circle with the angle of the corresponding circle sector. As them to explain why a central angle of *n*° gives a sector with *n*°.

Investigation ⑤ Areas of Circle Sectors

Vocabulary
- arc
- central angle
- sector

Materials
- protractor
- scissors

Math Link
An *arc* of a circle is a segment of the circle's circumference.

In the previous investigation, you calculated the area of a circle. If someone asked you to find the area of a wedge of a circle with a radius of 2 inches, the shaded region drawn to the right, what strategies would you use?

In answering the question above, you probably first thought about what fraction of the wedge was the circle's area. In mathematics, we refer to a wedge as the **sector** of a circle, or the area enclosed by two radii and the **arc**, which is the part of the circle that connects them.

You may have thought that since the sector was $\frac{1}{4}$ of the area of the whole circle, the area of the sector would be $\frac{1}{4}$ of πr^2, or $\frac{1}{4} \cdot \pi \cdot 2^2 = \pi$ in^2.

Now consider how to find the area of any sector.

Clearly, the area of a sector of a circle depends upon the measure of its **central angle**, which is the angle formed by the two radii.

✔ Develop & Understand: A

1. The central angle of a sector of a circle is 45°. What fraction of the circle's area is the sector's area? $\frac{1}{8}$

2. The central angle of a sector of a circle is 120°. What fraction of the circle's area is the sector's area? $\frac{1}{3}$

3. The central angle of a sector of a circle is *n*°. What fraction of the circle's area is the sector's area? $\frac{n}{360}$

Once you have determined what fraction of the circle's area the sector is, you can determine a general formula for the area of a sector of a circle.

Area of a Circle Sector
$A = \frac{m}{360} \cdot \pi r^2$

In this formula, *A* represents the area of the sector, *m* represents the central angle measured in degrees, and *r* represents the radius.

Reaching *All Learners*

OL **On Level** Have students create their own problems similar to the exercises in this investigation. Instruct them to draw a circle using the protractor, and determine the number of equal pieces they want to find. Then have them trade with a partner and see if they can divide the circle into that number of pieces.

4. $A = \frac{16\pi}{12}$ cm^2
and 4.19 cm^2

5. $A = \frac{49\pi}{96}$ ft^2
and 1.6 ft^2

✅ Develop & Understand: B

4. Find the area of this sector. Express your answer in terms of π and as a decimal rounded to the nearest hundredth of a centimeter.

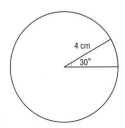

5. A circle has a radius of $3\frac{1}{2}$ feet. The central angle of a sector of this circle is 15°. Find the area of the sector. Express your answer in terms of π and as a decimal rounded to the nearest tenth.

6. The sector of a circle has an area of 6π cm^2 and the radius of the circle is 6 cm. Find the central angle. $m = 60°$

7. The area of a sector of a circle is $\frac{9\pi}{5}$ in^2. Its central angle is 72 degrees. Find the radius of the circle. $r = 3$ in.

✅ Develop & Understand: C

8. $16\pi - 32$ in^2 and 18.27 in^2

8. Find the area of the shaded region. You are given the length of the radius of the circle. Express your answer in terms of π and as a decimal rounded to the nearest hundredth.

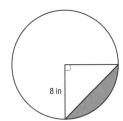

✅ Develop & Understand: B

Suggested Grouping: Individuals

▶ **Exercises 4 and 5** Make sure students know how to substitute for m, the measure of the central angle and for the variable for radius, r in the formula for the area of a circle sector. Demonstrate how to find $\pi \cdot r^2$.

▶ **Exercise 6** Remind students that finding missing information requires them to set up the same problems, only they will solve for different variables. You may want to show students how to work backwards from the area of a circle sector to find the central angle. Demonstrate how to find the angle by showing students how to work with the fractions involved, including reducing the fraction.

▶ **Exercise 7** You may want to show students how to work backwards from the area of a circle sector to find the radius if the central angle is known. Demonstrate how to find radius from the fractions in the equation, and remind them about how to find the square root of 9.

✅ Develop & Understand: C

Suggested Grouping: Small Groups

Remind students that they can use 3.14 on their calculators if their calculators do not have a π button. The answers in this section are calculated using 3.14.

▶ **Exercises 8–11** In these exercises, students will do some critical thinking about how to find the area of a shaded region that may or may not have a direct fit to an area formula. You may want students to work on these exercises in groups. Encourage them to draw the diagrams and label them.

9. Find the area of the shaded region and each white region formed by the square and the circle. Express your answer as a decimal rounded to the nearest hundredth.

Area of shaded region is 3.14 cm². Area of each white region is about 0.21 cm²

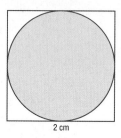

2 cm

10. Find the area of the shaded region and each white region formed by the square with side 4 centimeters.

Area of shaded region is 12.57 cm². Area of each white region is 1.72 cm²

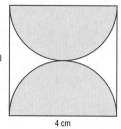

4 cm

11. Suppose a pizza slice is a circle sector with a 24° angle and a radius of 15 inches. If a can of pizza sauce will cover 94 square inches of pizza, how many cans of sauce are needed to cover this slice?
About $\frac{1}{2}$ a can

Share & Summarize

How is the area of a sector of a circle related to the central angle of the sector? See ①.

How is the area of a sector related to the area of a circle? The area of a sector is a fraction of the original circle.

① Sample answer: The central angle determines what fraction of the circle's area the sector's area is. The central angle is some fraction of 360°; the sector's area is that same fraction of the circle's area.

Practice & *Apply*

1. Choose an object in your home with a nonrectangular surface that will fit on a piece of grid paper. A can of soup, your shoe, and an iron are some ideas. Trace the surface onto the grid paper. Estimate its area.   Answers will vary.

2. These parallelograms are drawn on a centimeter grid.

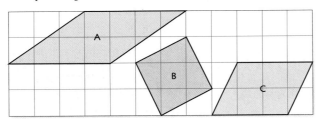

   a. Find the area of each parallelogram.

   b. Sketch a rectangle that has the same area as parallelogram A.

   c. Sketch a rectangle that has the same area as parallelogram C.
   See margin.

2a. Parallelogram A:
8 cm ^{2};
Parallelogram B:
5 cm ^{2};
Parallelogram C:
6 cm ^{2}

2b. Possible rectangle:

3. Find the area of this parallelogram.   60 in^2

4. Yes; the length and width of the rectangle are the base and height.

4. Can you use the area formula for a parallelogram, $A = b \cdot h$, to find the area of a rectangle? If so, where are the base and height on the rectangle? If not, why not?

5. A parallelogram has an area of 42.6 cm^2. The height of the parallelogram is 8 cm. What is the length of the base?   5.325 cm

6. These triangles are drawn on a centimeter grid.   See margin.

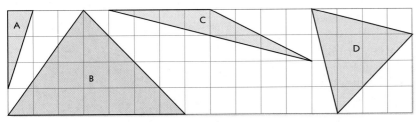

   a. Find the area of each triangle.

   b. For each triangle, sketch a parallelogram with twice the area of the triangle.

6b. Possible parallelograms (They will be drawn on a 1-cm grid.):

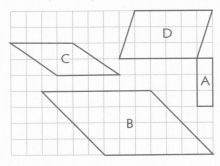

Exercise 2 In **Parts b and c**, there are no restrictions on the base or height except that both are greater than zero and that the rectangle can be sketched.

Exercise 5 Here, as in all exercises of this kind, the word *the* before *base* is not meant to imply that a parallelogram can have only one base.

Exercise 6b Students will probably use two copies of each triangle shown to make their parallelograms. However, the exercise does not require this.

Additional Answers

2c. Possible rectangle:

6a. Triangle A: 1.5 cm^2; Triangle B: 14 cm^2; Triangle C: 4 cm^2; Triangle D: 7.5 cm^2

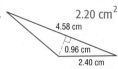

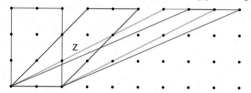

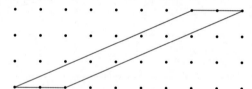

▶ **Exercises 7–9** These exercises give practice in using the area formula for triangles. They will also help assess whether students have a clear understanding of the terms *base* and *height* for triangles.

▶ **Exercise 10** This exercise should remind students of the exercises on page 416. Interested students may think about the possibility of shearing other types of polygons.

Find the area of each triangle. Round your answers to the nearest hundredth.

7.   3.25 cm²
3.29 cm
1.72 cm
3.78 cm

8.   2.20 cm²
4.58 cm
0.96 cm
2.40 cm

9a. 2.17 cm and 3.46 cm; They are a base and height of the triangle.

9. Consider this triangle.

a. Which of the given measurements would you use to find the area of the triangle? Why?

2.17 cm   3.46 cm
4.08 cm

b. What is the triangle's area? Round your answer to the nearest hundredth.   3.75 cm²

10. The green parallelogram was created by shearing parallelogram Z.

Z

a. Create two more parallelograms by shearing parallelogram Z. In each case, "slide" the top of the parallelogram.
See the figure for a possible answer.

10b. No; the base and height remain the same, so the area does not change.

b. Does shearing a parallelogram change its area? Explain.

c. Now shear parallelogram Z to create a parallelogram with the smallest possible perimeter. What does this new parallelogram look like?   It is a rectangle.

10d. No; you can make a longer perimeter by adding more dots to the grid and stretching the top even further to the right.

d. Tessa sheared parallelogram Z to create this figure. She says she has drawn the sheared parallelogram with the greatest possible perimeter. Do you agree with her? Explain.

In Exercises 11–13, express your answer in terms of π and as a decimal rounded to the nearest hundredths place.

11. Calculate the area of a circle with radius 8.5 inches.
226.98 in^2; 72.25π in^2

12. Calculate the area of a circle with diameter 15 feet.
176.71 ft^2; 56.25π ft^2

13. Calculate the area of a circle with radius 9 feet.
254.47 ft^2; 81π ft^2

14. A dog is tied to a 15-foot leash in the center of a yard.

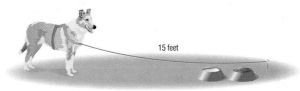

15 feet

a. What is the shape of the area in which the dog can play? A circle

b. To the nearest square foot, what is the area of the space in which the dog can play? 707 ft^2; 225π ft^2

c. Suppose that, instead of being tied in the center of the yard, the dog is tied to the corner of the house. To the nearest square foot, what is the area of the space in which the dog can play? The sides of the house are longer than the leash. 530 ft^2; 168.75π ft^2

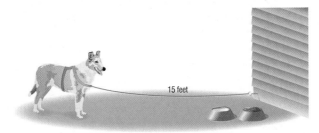

15 feet

▶ **Exercise 12** Students should be careful to use the *radius* of the circle to compute the area.

▶ **Exercise 14c** Students may need to make a sketch to show the shape of the region in which the dog can play. The region will be three quarters of a circle.

Lesson 7.2 Calculate Areas **427**

Exercises 15 and 16 Verify that students can substitute values into the formula for the area of a trapezoid before assigning these exercises.

Exercises 17–20 You may want to verify that students can substitute values into the formula for the area of a trapezoid before assigning these exercises. Check that they can work backward to find the value of other variables in the formula.

Have students list the possible methods for finding area of a trapezoid. Remind them that they may not be able to use the same method for all the problems.

Exercises 21–24 Make sure students remember to use the formula $A = \frac{m}{360} \cdot \pi r^2$. Remind them that they must have the radius length and the central angle measurement to find the area of a sector.

Find the area of each trapezoid.

15.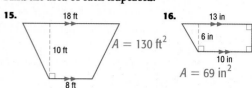

16.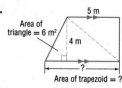

Find the missing lengths and areas for each trapezoid.

18. base = 8 m;
Area of trapezoid = 26 m²

17.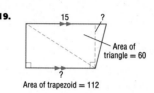
$h = 6$ cm

18.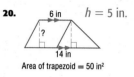

19. base = 13; $h = 8$

19.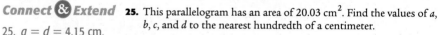

20.

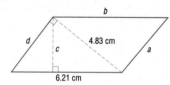

In Exercises 21–24, calculate the area of each circle sector. Use the units given and round to the nearest hundredth of a square unit. Also, express your answer in terms of π.

21. $A = \frac{8\pi}{3}$ and 8.37 cm²

22. $A = \frac{49\pi}{30}$ or 5.13 in²

23. $A = \frac{72\pi}{5}$ or 45.22 in²

24. $A = \frac{25\pi}{9}$ or 8.72 cm²

21. A sector with a central angle of 240° and a radius of 2 cm.

22. A sector with a central angle of 12° and a radius of 7 in.

23. A sector with a central angle of 36° and a radius of 12 in.

24. A sector with a central angle of 40° and a radius of 5 cm.

Connect & Extend

25. $a = d = 4.15$ cm,
$b = 6.21$ cm,
$c = 3.23$ cm

25. This parallelogram has an area of 20.03 cm². Find the values of a, b, c, and d to the nearest hundredth of a centimeter.

26. In this exercise, you will draw parallelograms.

  a. Draw three different parallelograms with base length 15 cm and height 7 cm.   Drawings will vary.

  b. Which of your parallelograms has the least perimeter? Which has the greatest perimeter?   Answers will vary.

  c. Could you draw a parallelogram with the same base and height and an even smaller perimeter? If so, draw it. If not, explain why not.

26c. Answers will vary. The parallelogram with the smallest perimeter is a rectangle with length 15 cm and width 7 cm.

27. A deck of cards has been pushed as shown. Notice that the sides of the deck are shaped like parallelograms.

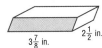

The deck contains 52 cards. Each card is $\frac{1}{48}$ of an inch thick, $3\frac{7}{8}$ inches long, and $2\frac{1}{2}$ inches wide. Find the area of the shaded parallelogram. $4\frac{19}{96}$ in^2, or about 4.2 in^2

28. Below is a floor plan for a museum divided into four parallelograms and a rectangle. Find the area of the floor to the nearest hundredth of a square meter.   50.04 m^2

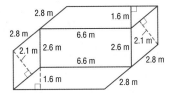

29. The area of this triangle is 782 square centimeters. Find a and b to the nearest tenth of a centimeter. $a = 53.0$ cm, $b = 42.6$ cm

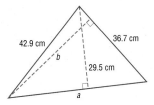

▶ **Exercise 25** Students should carefully note which bases are associated with which heights.

▶ **Exercise 27** Some students may have difficulty visualizing this situation. Tell them not to worry about whether the corners of the cards are curved.

▶ **Exercise 28** For each part of the figure, students should be careful in deciding which lengths correspond to heights and which to bases.

▶ **Exercise 29** If students are uncertain about the segment to which 36.7 refers, tell them that it is the length of the shortest side of the largest triangle.

▶ **Exercise 30** Encourage students to use the make-a-diagram problem solving strategy for this exercise. Point out that it does not matter which side is used to show the base because all sides are congruent for an equilateral triangle.

▶ **Exercise 31c** Some students may prefer to write and simplify mathematical expressions to answer the question.

▶ **Exercise 31e** Students should refer to the diagram as they read the questions posed. This will help them understand exactly what lengths they are being asked to find. It should not be too difficult for students to see that the sides of the surrounding square are twice the height of one of the identical triangles.

Math Link

In a *regular polygon*, all sides are the same length and all angles have the same measure.

31b. $A = \frac{1}{2} \cdot (3 \cdot 6) \cdot 2.6 = 23.4$ cm^2, which is the same area I found in Part a.

31f. He could have found the area of the square and then subtracted the area of the four triangles. The area of the square is 29^2 in^2, or 841 in^2. The area of each triangle is $\frac{1}{2} \cdot 8.5$ in. $\cdot 8.5$ in., or 36.1 in^2, so the area of the octagon is $841 - 4 \cdot 36.1$, or 696.6 in^2, which is very close to my answer from Part c. The difference might be due to rounding.

30. In an *equilateral triangle*, all three sides are the same length. Suppose the area of an equilateral triangle is 27.7 cm^2 and the height is 6.9 cm. How long are each of the triangle's sides?   About 8.0 cm

31. Any regular polygon can be divided into identical triangles. This hexagon is divided into six identical triangles.

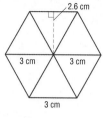

   a. Find the area of each triangle and the area of the hexagon to the nearest tenth of a square centimeter. Explain how you found the areas.   See margin.

   b. This formula can be used to find the area of a regular polygon.

   $$A = \frac{1}{2} \cdot \text{polygon perimeter} \cdot \text{height of one triangle}$$

   Show that this formula gives you the correct area for the hexagon above.

   c. Why do you think the formula works?   See margin.

   d. A stop sign is in the shape of a regular octagon. This sketch of an octagon has been divided into eight identical triangles.

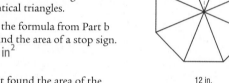

   Use the formula from Part b to find the area of a stop sign. 696 in^2

   e. Brett found the area of the stop sign by surrounding it with a square.

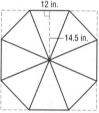

   How long are the sides of the square? How long are the perpendicular sides of the small triangles in the corners of the square?   Square's sides: 29 in.; triangles' sides: 8.5 in.

   f. Explain how Brett might have calculated the area. Show that this method gives the same area that you found in Part d.

Additional Answers

31a. Area of triangle: 3.9 cm^2; Area of hexagon: 23.4 cm^2; Possible explanation: I found the area of a triangle using the formula $A = \frac{1}{2} \cdot b \cdot h$. I found the area of the hexagon by multiplying the area of the triangle by 6.

31c. Possible explanation: Because the perimeter is the sum of the six bases of the triangles. Instead of calculating the area of each triangle individually, the formula groups them all together and multiplies the sum by $\frac{1}{2}$ and the height.

★ indicates multi-step problem

Real-World Link

The world's highest fountain, located in Fountain Hills, Arizona, is capable of sending 8-ton streams of water 560 feet into the air. This is 10 feet higher than the Washington Monument.

★ **32.** The Smallville town council plans to build a circular fountain surrounded by a square concrete walkway. The fountain has a diameter of 4 yards. The walkway has an outer perimeter of 28 yards.

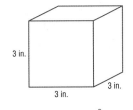

Find the area of the walkway to the nearest tenth of a square yard.
36.4 yd^2

33. Preview The *surface area* of a three-dimensional figure is the sum of the areas of its faces. For example, this cube consists of six faces, each with area 9 in^2. So, its total surface area is 9 • 6, or 54 in^2.

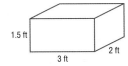

a. Find the surface area of this rectangular box. 27 ft^2

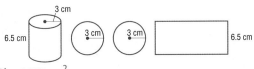

b. To find the surface area of a cylinder, you can imagine it as three separate pieces, the circular top and bottom and the rectangle wrapped around them. Find the surface area of this cylinder. (Hint: You need to figure out what the length of the rectangle is. To do this, think about how this length is related to the circles.)

About 179 cm^2

34. In Your Own Words Explain the similarities and differences among the area formulas you learned in this lesson.
Answers will vary.

▶ **Exercise 33** If students have difficulty visualizing three-dimensional objects, it may help to use a physical model. For **Part a**, a rectangular box for paper clips or a thick book may help. Students need to understand that the information in the diagram actually gives them the lengths of *all* edges of the box, including the edges that cannot be seen in the diagram. Realizing that opposite faces of the box are the same size and shape can save time with the calculations.

For **Part b,** students need to see that the length of the rectangle is equal to the circumference of each of the circular ends. Modeling the curved wall of the can with a piece of paper is easy and convincing. There should be no overlap where the edges meet.

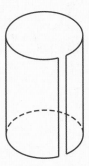

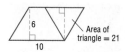

▶ **Exercise 36** Have students work in groups to find the areas of the individual polygons for this exercise on page 433, and then ask the group to find the total area using each student's answer.

▶ **Exercise 37–38** Have students work in groups to find the area of these "composite figures." Ask them to make sure discrepancies in answers are not due to rounding.

36. 89.5 sq units. One way to break down the polygon is: uppermost triangle, $A = 7.5$ sq units; rectangle below it $A = 15$ sq units; leftmost triangle $A = 4$ sq units; trapezoid next to it $A = 24$ sq units; upper right trapezoid $A = 39$ sq units

37a. Semicircle: $A = \frac{144\pi}{2}$ cm^2 = 226.08 cm^2

37b. 2 quarter circles: $A = \frac{100\pi}{4}$ cm^2 + $\frac{100\pi}{4}$ cm^2 = 157 cm^2

37c. Rectangle: $A =$ 24 cm · 10 cm = 240 cm^2

38a. 2 corners + 4 long petals: $A =$ 216π/4 in^2 + $4\left(\frac{64\pi}{8}\right)$ in^2 = 40π or 125.6 in^2

38b. 2 corners + 4 short petals: $A =$ $2\left(\frac{16\pi}{4}\right)$ in^2 + $4\left(\frac{9\pi}{8}\right)$ in^2 = 12.5π or 39.25 in^2

38c. Rectangle – green – grey: $A =$ 28 in · 20 in – 125.6 in^2 – 39.25 in^2 = 395.15 in^2

35. This parallelogram has been divided into a trapezoid and a triangle. Find the area of the trapezoid. 39 sq units

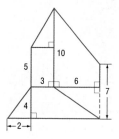

36. Find the total area of this polygon. You will need to add up the areas of the smaller polygons that make up the big one. Show which smaller polygons you used and what each area is.

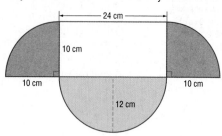

For each mosaic, calculate the area covered by each color.

★ **37.**

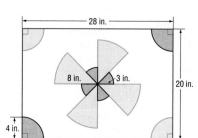

a. Green   **b.** Grey   **c.** White

★ **38.**

a. Green   **b.** Grey   **c.** White

Calculate the area of each circle sector. For Exercises 39–41, express your answers in terms of π and as a decimal rounded to the nearest hundredths place. Use the units given in each picture. Remember, the pictures are not drawn to scale.

39.

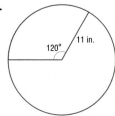

40.

41.

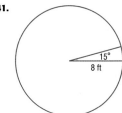

39. $A = \dfrac{121\pi}{3}$ in^2 and 126.65 in^2

40. $A = \dfrac{343\pi}{8}$ cm^2 and 134.63 cm^2

41. $A = \dfrac{64\pi}{24}$ ft^2 and 8.37 ft^2

Mixed Review

Evaluate each expression.

42. 0.25×0.4 0.1   **43.** 0.25×4 1   **44.** 0.25×0.1 0.025

45. 0.04×0.04 0.0016 **46.** 0.02×4 0.08   **47.** 0.2×0.7 0.14

48. Ecology The table lists the number of endangered species for five groups of animals.

48a.

Percentages
42.1%
33.7%
10.9%
10.4%
2.9%

   a. Extend this table showing what the percentage each category is of the total number of species listed. Round to the nearest tenth.

   b. About what percentage of the endangered species in the five groups are mammals or birds?
About 75.8%

Group	Number of Endangered Species
Mammals	316
Birds	253
Fishes	82
Reptiles	78
Snails	22

   c. Write three statements comparing the number of endangered fish species to the number of endangered snail species.

48c. Possible answer: There are about 4 times as many endangered fish species as endangered snail species. There are 60 more endangered fish species than endangered snail species. There is about 1 endangered snail species for every 4 endangered fish species.

Lesson 7.2 Calculate Areas   **433**

Find the area of each figure. Give the exact area in terms of π and the approximate area. Use 3.14 for π.

5.

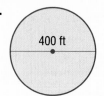

400 ft

40,000 π ft^2; 125,663.7 ft^2

6.

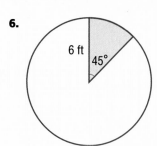

6 ft   45°

4.5 π ft^2; 14.13 ft^2

Lesson 7.2 Calculate Areas   **433**

Quick Check

Informal Assessment Students should be able to:

✔ derive and apply a formula for the areas of parallelograms, triangles, trapezoids, circles, and circle sectors

Quick Quiz

Find the area of each figure to the nearest tenth.

1.

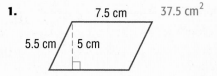

37.5 cm^2

7.5 cm   5.5 cm   5 cm

2.

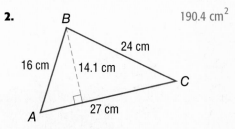

190.4 cm^2

B   24 cm   16 cm   14.1 cm   C   A   27 cm

3.

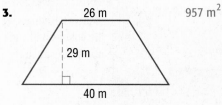

957 m^2

26 m   29 m   40 m

4.

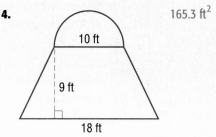

165.3 ft^2

10 ft   9 ft   18 ft

Surface Area and Volume

Objectives

▶ To find the volume of a block structure

▶ To find the surface area of a rectangular prism

▶ To find the volume of a rectangular prism

Overview

In this lesson, students will find the volume of a geometric figure made up of unit blocks. They will learn that the surface area of a rectangular prism is the sum of the areas of the six faces, and the volume of a three-dimensional figure is the amount of space inside of it. They will pay attention to units. Surface area is measured in square units and volume is measured in cubic units.

Advance Preparation

For this lesson, you may want to provide models of block structures and rectangular prisms, along with Lesson 7.3 Masters 1–4.

	Summary	Materials	On Your Own Exercises (pp. 444–448)	Assessment Opportunities
Investigation 1 (p. 435) *Pacing: 2 days*	Students examine and find the volume and surface area of a block structure.	Chapter 7 Master 6, blocks, grid paper or dot paper, Chapter 7 Masters 2, 5 (optional)	Practice & Apply: 1–4, 13 and 14 Connect & Extend: 15 and 16 Mixed Review: 19 and 20	• Share & Summarize (p. 437) • Troubleshooting (p. 437)
Investigation 2 (p. 437) *Pacing: 1 day*	Students find the volume of a rectangular prism.		Practice & Apply: 5–12 Connect & Extend: 17 and 18 Mixed Review: 19 and 20	• Share & Summarize (p. 440) • Troubleshooting (p. 439)
Inquiry Investigation 3 (p. 441) *Pacing: 1 day*	Students construct polyhedra from equilateral triangles.	Lesson 7.3 Masters 1–4, paper polygons, tape	Mixed Review: 19 and 20	• Troubleshooting (p. 442)

Leveled Lesson Resources

 CRM *Available in:* **Chapter 7 Resource Masters**

Also on
TeacherWorks™
Lesson 7.3

Study Guide and Intervention (p. 23) **AL**

Lesson 7.3 Study Guide and Intervention
Surface Area and Volume

The **surface area** of a three-dimensional object is the area of the region covering the object's surface. Surface area is measured in square units. The **volume** of a rectangular prism is the space inside the object measured in cubic units. The volume of a rectangular prism can be found using the formulas below.

$$\text{Volume} = b \cdot (l \cdot w) \qquad \text{or} \qquad \text{Volume} = b \cdot (A)$$

In these formulas, b represents height, l represents length, w represents the width and A represents the area of the base..

Examples   Each cube in a block structure measures one unit on a side.

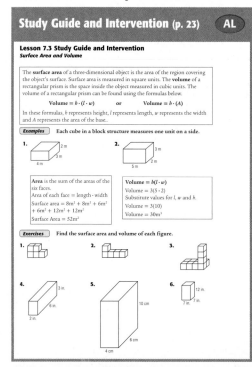

Area is the sum of the areas of the six faces.
Area of each face = length · width
Surface area = $8m^2 + 8m^2 + 6m^2 + 6m^2 + 12m^2 + 12m^2$
Surface Area = $52m^2$

Volume = $b(l \cdot w)$
Volume = $3(5 \cdot 2)$
Substitute values for l, w and b.
Volume = $3(10)$
Volume = $30m^3$

Exercises   Find the surface area and volume of each figure.

Skills Practice (p. 24) **AL** **OL**

Lesson 7.3 Skills Practice
Surface Area and Volume

The view from the top of a prism is shown. Find the volume of the prism with the given height.

1. 3 units high

2. 5 units high

Find the surface area and volume of each figure. Each cube in a block structure measures one unit on a side.

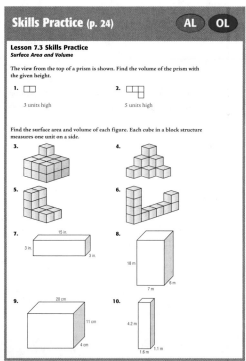

Problem-Solving Practice (p. 25) **AL** **OL**

Lesson 7.3 Problem-Solving Practice
Surface Area and Volume

1. **Fish tank** Amelia's fish tank is a glass rectangular prism. The tank is 36 inches long, 12 inches wide and 18 inches tall. What is the volume of the tank?

2. **Storage unit** Renaldo's storage unit is 4 meters deep, 3 meters wide and 2.5 meters tall. What is the volume of the storage unit?

3. **Pickup truck** The back of Mariah's pickup truck is 8 feet long, 4 feet wide and 2 feet tall. How many cubes with a volume of 2 ft³ will fit in the back of the truck?

4. **Manufacturing** A company makes rectangular boxes for cereal packaging. The dimensions of the box are 80 cm long, 40 cm wide and 100 centimeters high. What is the surface area of the box?

5. **Toy box** Skylar is building an open top box that will hold her son's toys. The dimensions of the box are 4.25 feet wide × 2.5 feet long × 2 feet high What is the volume of the box? How much material is needed to build the box? (Remember the box does not have a top.)

6. **Shipping container** A rectangular shipping container is being repainted before it gets packed for its next delivery. The container is 10 yards long, 2 yards wide and 4 yards high. A can of paint will cover 8 square yards. How many cans of paint are needed for the job? (The bottom will not be painted)

Enrichment (p. 26) **BL**

Lesson 7.3 Enrichment
Surface Area and Volume

Packaging When companies make packing material such as boxes, they need to use the minimum amount of material for a given volume. Since materials are costly, it allows companies to save money on material and increase profits. The goal is to minimize the surface area of the package by using the correct dimensions.

Volume of rectangular prism package = 36 cubic inches

Package A Dimensions: Length = 2 inches, Width = 3 inches, Height = 6 inches Surface Area = 72 square inches

Package B Dimensions: Length = 3 inches, Width = 3 inches, Height = 4 inches Surface Area = 66 square inches

Package B uses less material and has the same volume as Package A.

Find another set of dimensions for a rectangular prism package that uses less material and has the same volume.

1. Package Dimensions: Length = 1 m, Width = 2 m, Height = 4m

2. Package Dimensions: Length = 1 cm, Width = 3 cm, Height = 9 cm

3. Package Dimensions: Length = 2 inches, Width = 8 inches, Height = 4 inches

4. Package Dimensions: Length = 3 cm, Width = 4 cm, Height = 10 cm

5. **Challenge** Explain the best way to minimize the surface area when selecting dimensions for a rectangular prism.

Lesson Quick Quiz (p. 27) **AL** **OL** **BL**

Lesson 7.3 Quick Quiz
Surface Area and Volume

The view from the top of a prism is shown. Find the surface area and volume of the prism with the given height.

1. 2 units high

2. 3 units high

Find the surface area and volume of the rectangular prism.

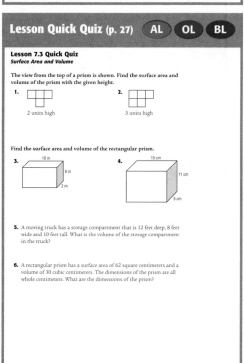

5. A moving truck has a storage compartment that is 12 feet deep, 8 feet wide and 10 feet tall. What is the volume of the storage compartment in the truck?

6. A rectangular prism has a surface area of 62 square centimeters and a volume of 30 cubic centimeters. The dimensions of the prism are all whole centimeters. What are the dimensions of the prism?

Lesson Masters 1–4 (pp. 28–31)

Lesson 7.3 Master 1
Surface Area and Volume

Inquiry Investigation 3

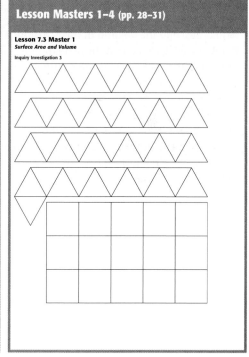

Additional Lesson Resources

Teacher Tech Tools
• TeacherWorks
• ExamView Assessment Suite
• Classroom Presentation Toolkit
• Advance Tracker

Student Tech Tools
• StudentWorks Plus
Math Online ⟩ eGlossary •
Concepts in Motion

Other Print Products
• Investigation Notebook and Reflection Journal
• Quick Review Math Handbook

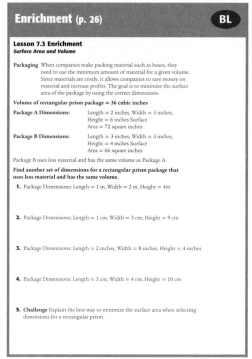

Introduce

Surface Area and Volume In this investigation, students use their knowledge of area to find the surface area or volume of figures. As they learn, monitor to see that they understand that volume is three-dimensional. Point out that when they find volume, they are finding the amount of space inside of a three-dimensional figure.

Teacher Tips Ask students to look at the picture of the irregular shape at the top of the page. Ask them how many dimensions it has. How would they describe the area? Counting the squares and using those squares as the unit of area is appropriate in this situation. Likewise, when they are determining volume, they can simply count the number of cubes in the three-dimensional structure.

Point out that surface area is exactly what its name implies: the area of all the surfaces covering a three-dimensional object.

Discuss volume by asking students to build any block structure. Ask students how they would describe the volume of this structure. Point out to students that they could think of the number of blocks as the volume. Explain that volume is measured in cubic units, and for all the structures they have built, students could simply count the blocks. You may need to return to the blocks to talk about the difference between square units and cubic units, and relate that to specific units of measure such as cm^2 and cm^3.

Think & Discuss

Allow students time to read and solve the exercises before discussing them as a class. Be sure students understand how surface area and volume are found and they know to use the appropriate units.

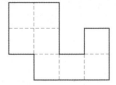

Vocabulary

surface area

volume

Materials

- cubes

- graph paper or dot paper

Math Link

The volume of a one-block structure is 1 cubic unit.

In the previous lesson you discovered that area, the space inside a two-dimensional figure, is measured in *square units*.

You can say that the area of the figure shown here is 8 square units. Or, if you know the size of the squares, you can use it to state the area exactly. For example, these squares have a side length of 1 centimeter, so the area of the figure is 8 cm^2.

The **surface area** of a three-dimensional object is the area of the region covering the object's surface. If you could open up the object and flatten it so you could see all sides at once, the area of the flat figure would be the surface area. Do not forget to count the bottom surface. Surface area is measured in square units.

Volume, the space inside a three-dimensional object, is measured in *cubic units*. If you build a structure with blocks that are each 1 cubic unit, then the volume of a block structure is equal to the number of blocks in the structure. For example, a structure made from eight blocks has a volume of 8 cubic units. If the blocks have an edge length of 1 cm, the structure's volume is 8 cm^3.

In this lesson, when an exercise refers to blocks, the blocks each have an edge length of 1 unit, faces of area 1 square unit, and a volume of 1 cubic unit.

Think & Discuss

What is the surface area of a single block in square units? 6

If the edge lengths of a block are 2 cm, what is the block's surface area? 24 cm^2

What is the volume of the structure at the right in cubic units? 2

What is the surface area of the structure above in square units? Count only the squares on the *outside* of the structure. 10

Investigation 1 Volume

Vocabulary
prism

rectangular prism

Materials
- cubes
- graph paper or dot paper

In the exercises below, you will find the surface area and volume of block structures.

✓ Develop & Understand: A

1. Find the volume and the surface area of each three-block structure.

   a. 3 cubic units, 14 square units
   b. 3 cubic units, 14 square units

2. Find the volume and the surface area of each four-block structure.

   a. 4 cubic units, 18 square units
   b. 4 cubic units, 16 square units
   c. 4 cubic units, 18 square units
   d. 4 cubic units, 18 square units

3. Yes; they are all made of four blocks, so they all have volume 4 cubic units.

3. Do the structures in Exercise 2 all have the same volume? Explain your answer.

4. Structures a, c, and d, have the greatest surface area; structure b has the least.

4. Which of the structures in Exercise 2 have the greatest surface area? Which has the least surface area?

5. Build two block structures with at least six blocks each that have the same volume but different surface areas.

   a. For each structure, draw a view of its top. *Drawings will vary.*

   b. Record the volume and the surface area of each structure. *Answers will vary.*

6a. $8 \times 1 \times 1$: $SA = 34$, $V = 8$; $4 \times 2 \times 1$: $SA = 28$, $V = 8$; $2 \times 2 \times 2$: $SA = 24$, $V = 8$ (Note: Students may include duplicates, such as $2 \times 1 \times 4$.)

If a block structure has a constant height, that is, has the same number of blocks in every column, that structure is a **prism**. If the top view of such a structure is a rectangle, the structure is a **rectangular prism**.

Math Link
The *surface area* of a rectangular prism is the sum of the areas of its six faces. The *volume* of a three-dimensional figure is the amount of space inside it. Surface area is measured in square units, and volume is measured in cubic units.

✓ Develop & Understand: B

By using its dimensions, you can describe a rectangular prism exactly. For example, a prism with edge lengths 3 units, 2 units, and 4 units is a $3 \times 2 \times 4$ prism.

6. Make all the rectangular prisms you can that contain 8 blocks.

   a. Record the dimensions, volume, and surface area of each prism you make.

Lesson 7.3 Surface Area and Volume **435**

Reaching All Learners

OL **On Level** If students are miscalculating the surface areas, they may be forgetting the "bottom" of the structure, the part sitting on the table. Remind students that the bottom is one of the surfaces and thus also part of the surface area. If you have snap cubes available, you might encourage students to build with those. When students can pick up the structure from the table, it is easier for them to remember to count the squares on the bottom face.

Investigation 1

On Your Own Exercises
Pages 444–448
Exercises 1–4, 13 and 14

Volume In this investigation, students are asked to construct different rectangular prisms given a certain number of cubes. These are called *block structures.*

Students then determine which of the structures have the greatest surface areas and which have the least. They also find the volume of a prism.

✓ Develop & Understand: A

Suggested Grouping: Individuals

▶ **Exercises 1–5** Students are asked to calculate the surface area and the volume of each of several 3- and 4-block structures. They are not using formulas for volume and surface area here. Students are asked to think of volume in cubic units and of surface area in square units and to find the volume and surface area by counting cubes and squares. This experience will ground students in the work they do in subsequent lessons in volume and area.

Students should quickly realize that the volume of any 4-block structure is the same regardless of how the cubes are arranged. The surface area, however, differs, and it is important that students think about the relationship here between surface area and volume. The 3-block structures all have the same surface area, but that will be true only for structures of 3 blocks or fewer.

✓ Develop & Understand: B

Suggested Grouping: Pairs

▶ **Exercise 6** For this exercise, students experiment with different numbers of blocks to determine which rectangular prisms have the greatest surface area and which have the least. Students should have blocks to do this exercise, and they will need 20 blocks per pair. You may also wish to have students use Chapter 7 Master 6, 2-Centimeter Dot Paper or Chapter 7 Masters 2 and 5 to help create examples they can use.

Lesson 7.3 Surface Area and Volume **435**

Math Link

Have students explain surface area and volume to a partner. Make sure they can demonstrate the meaning of each concept using objects in the classroom.

▶ **Exercises 7–8** These problems should take a relatively short amount of time to complete, since students will begin to see some patterns as they go through the problems.

✅ *Develop & Understand: C*

Suggested Grouping: Pairs

▶ **Exercises 9 and 10** In these exercises, students begin with a top view and try to construct a prism from this picture. These problems motivate the concept of volume by having students think of layering cubes to produce a three-dimensional structure. As they create these structures, students begin to think of counting the number of layers and multiplying by the number of cubes in each layer—the foundation of the volume formulas. It is important that students build these structures with cubes to reinforce this layering. Each pair will need 35 blocks.

7a. $12 \times 1 \times 1$, *SA* = 50;
$6 \times 2 \times 1$, *SA* = 40;
$4 \times 3 \times 1$, *SA* = 38;
$3 \times 2 \times 2$, *SA* = 32
(Note: Students may include duplicates.)
7b. Yes; 12 cubic units
7c. $12 \times 1 \times 1$
7d. $3 \times 2 \times 2$

Math Link

The length, width, and height are often referred to as *dimensions*.

8a. $20 \times 1 \times 1$, *SA* = 82;
$10 \times 2 \times 1$, *SA* = 64;
$5 \times 4 \times 1$, *SA* = 58;
$5 \times 2 \times 2$, *SA* = 48
(Note: Students may include duplicates.);
$20 \times 1 \times 1$; $5 \times 2 \times 2$
8b. Yes; 20 cubic units
8c. $20 \times 1 \times 1$
8d. $5 \times 2 \times 2$

---

b. Do the rectangular prisms all have the same volume?
Yes, 8 cubic units

c. Which of the rectangular prisms has the greatest surface area? Give its dimensions. $8 \times 1 \times 1$

d. Which of the prisms has the least surface area? $2 \times 2 \times 2$

7. Make all the rectangular prisms you can that have a volume of 12 cubic units. Repeat Parts a, c, and d of Exercise 6 for this prism.

8. Now find all the rectangular prisms that have a volume of 20 cubic units. Try to do it without using your blocks. Repeat Parts a, c, and d of Exercise 6 for this prism.

✅ *Develop & Understand: C*

9. Here is a view of the top of a prism.

a. Build a prism 1 unit high with this top view. What is its volume? 6 cubic units
b. Build a prism 2 units high with this top view. What is its volume? 12 cubic units
c. What would be the volume of a prism 10 units high with this top view? 60 cubic units

d. Write an expression for the volume of a prism with this top view and height *h*. *6h* cubic units

e. What is the area of this top view? 6 square units

10. Here is another top view.

a. Build a prism 1 unit high with this top view. What is its volume? 6 cubic units
b. Build a prism 3 units high with this top view. What is its volume? 18 cubic units

c. Suppose you built a prism 25 units high with this top view. What would be its volume? 150 cubic units

d. Write an expression for the prism's volume, using *h* for height. *6h* cubic units
e. What is the area of this top view? 6 square units

Left page

11c. $\frac{7}{2}$ cubic units, or
3.5 cubic units

1. To build a prism with
the greatest surface
area, place the blocks
in a row, making a
long, skinny prism.
To build a prism with
the least surface area,
build the prism that is
the most like a cube;
its dimensions would
be as close to one
another as possible.

---

11. Here is a third top view.

a. Build a prism 1 unit high with this
top view. What is its volume?
7 cubic units

b. Build a prism 5 units high with
this top view. What is its volume?   35 cubic units

c. Suppose you cut your blocks in half to build
a structure half a unit high with this top view.
What would be its volume?   **Two Half Blocks**

d. Write an expression for the prism's volume, using *h* for height.
7*h* cubic units

e. What is the area of this top view?   7 square units

Share & Summarize

1. If someone gave you some blocks, how could you use all of them
to build a rectangular prism with the greatest surface area? How
could you use all of them to build a rectangular prism with the
least surface area?

2. Suppose the view of the top of a prism contains 8 squares.
What is the volume of a prism that is:

a. 1 unit high?   8 cubic units   **b.** 10 units high?   80 cubic units

c. $\frac{1}{2}$ unit high?   4 cubic units   **d.** *h* units high?   8*h* cubic units

3. Write a general rule for finding the volume of a prism made
from blocks.   area of top view · height in blocks

Investigation ② Volume of a Rectangular Prism

Vocabulary
base of a prism

The identical top and bottom faces of a prism are called the **bases of a
prism**. The other sides of a prism are always rectangles, but as you saw
in Investigation 1, the bases can be any shape. A rectangular prism is a
special kind of prism whose bases are rectangles.

At the end of Investigation 1, you developed a rule for finding the volume
of a rectangular prism. The volume is the area of the base of the prism
multiplied by the height of the prism. This can be stated using a formula.

Volume of a Rectangular Prism
$V = h(A)$
In this formula, *V* represents the volume, *h* represents the height of the prism, and *A* represents the area of the base. There is another formula that is also used to find the volume of a rectangular prism: $V = h(l \times w)$.

Right page

▶ **Exercise 11c** As students begin to think
about fractional parts of a unit height,
students are introduced to the idea that the
height is not necessarily an integer.

Share & Summarize

Exercise 1 addresses concepts from the
exercises on the previous page. The general
conjecture that students should have now is
that the block prism that minimizes surface
area is the one most like a cube. Because
we are working with only whole numbers of
blocks, we cannot always make a cube. If
we could, that would be the best.

For **Exercise 3**, students should have a
general rule that is something like "area of
top view times the height" or "number of
squares in top view times the height."

Troubleshooting It is important that
students understand this general rule before
moving on to the next investigation. If
students are struggling with articulating the
rule, provide additional top views to work
with. Ask the area of the top view, the
volume for a one-cube structure, the
volume for a two-cube structure, and so on.
If the top view has an area of 4 squares,
encourage students to write the volumes as
4 × 1, 4 × 2, and so on.

Investigation ②

On Your Own Exercises
Pages 444–448
Exercises 5–12, 17 and 18

Volume of a Rectangular Prism Students
will learn to find the volume of rectangular
prisms in this investigation. They need to
understand that rectangular prisms have
two rectangular bases. The volume of a
rectangular prism can be found using
formulas that multiply the length, width,
and height. Make sure students understand
the concept of volume and can identify the
bases of a rectangular prism after finishing
this investigation.

Think & Discuss

Discuss with students how volume measures the area of the base of a figure multiplied by the figure's height. Use drawings on the board to show how the area times the height shows the entire amount of space occupied by a figure.

☑ Develop & Understand: A

Suggested Grouping: Groups

▶ **Exercises 1–3** Monitor to see that students correctly multiply the three dimensions of each prism. Make sure they show the units cubed.

▶ **Exercises 4–5** Remind students that they can work in reverse to find missing elements in the volume equation. Have them write out the formula for volume, using a variable for the missing information.

▶ **Exercise 6** This exercise will require students to use trial-and-error until they find the possible dimensions for the prism.

▶ **Exercise 7** Discuss with students why the prisms are the same or different. Have them point out bases and measurements for each prism.

Additional Answers

7b. Sample answer: They are different. Their bases are not congruent, they are different trapezoids, and the height is also different.

7c. Sample answers: All the faces of A and B are rectangles, so no matter how you rotate them, they are still rectangular prisms; you could pick any pair of opposite faces you want and call those the bases; but for C and D, only the trapezoid-shaped faces can be the bases, so if you change around the side lengths, you have changed the whole thing. They are the same situation, in each case, you know what the base is, and it is not the same in A/B, just like it is not the same in C/D.

① Sample answer: The area of the base is the same as the length times the width, so they are really just saying the same thing.

② Sample answer: Yes, $V = h(A)$ should always work because the volume will always be the area of the base (how many cubes in one layer?) multiplied by the height (how many layers are there?).

5b. Sample answers: 8 cm, 8 cm; 16 cm, 4 cm; 32 cm, 2 cm. Fractional answers are also possible.

6. Many answers are possible. Sample answers: $H = 8$ cm, $L = 8$ cm, $W = 5$ cm; $H = 10$ cm, $L = 8$ cm, $W = 4$ cm; $H = 2$ cm, $L = 16$ cm, $W = 10$.

7a. Sample answer: They are the same prism, rotated. But you could say that they are different because by saying which sides were L and W, you defined the base, and the base of A is not the same rectangle as the base of B.

Think & Discuss

Why do these two different formulas both give the same volume? See ①
Could either of these formulas be used to calculate the volume of a prism whose bases are not rectangular? See ②

☑ Develop & Understand: A

In Exercises 1–3, calculate the volume of each rectangular prism. Include the appropriate measurement units in your answer.

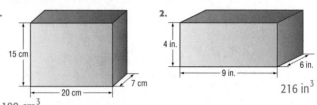

1. 2,100 cm³

2. 216 in³

3. A rectangular prism with height = 2 mm, length = 13 mm, and width = 8 mm   208 mm³

4. A rectangular prism's volume is 96 ft³. The area of its base is 16 ft. What is the height of the prism?   6 ft

5. A rectangular prism's volume is 320 cm³. Its height is 5 cm.

   a. What is the area of the base of the prism?   64 cm²

   b. What could be the length and width of the base? Give two possible length-width pairs.

6. Give the dimensions of two other prisms whose volume is 320 cm³.

7. Consider these four prisms.

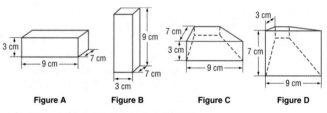

Figure A   **Figure B**   **Figure C**   **Figure D**

   a. Are A and B different prisms? Explain your reasoning.

   b. Are C and D different prisms? Explain your reasoning. See margin.

   c. Explain why your answers to Parts a and b were different or the same.   See margin.

Reaching All Learners

BL Beyond Level Students who quickly grasp the concept of volume for prisms can work in pairs to create a prism from construction paper. Have them determine the shape of the bases, and use rectangles to create the sides for the height. Remind them to measure each dimension and to find the volume of the figure they have created.

9a. H = 6 in., L = 6 in., W = 2 in.

10a. Sample answers:
H = 6 in., L = 6 in., W = 4 in.;
H = 12 in., L = 6 in., W = 2 in.;
H = 6 in., L = 12 in., W = 2 in.;
H = 3 in., L = 12 in., W = 4 in.; more are possible

10c. Sample answers: any of the sample answers from a.

10d. Sample answer: It is the same; no matter how you arrange the little prisms, their volume does not change, and neither does their combined volume.

13c. It is impossible: To make Prism B, you would create a base layer of 2 copies of Prism A by 4 copies (length = 8 mm, width = 4). But then you would need to stack up 2.5 layers like that to get a height of 5 mm. You cannot make a height of 5 mm with cubes

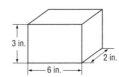

Develop & Understand: B

8. What is the volume of this rectangular prism? 36 in^3

9. Imagine taking two prisms like the one in Exercise 8 and stacking one on top of the other to form a new, larger prism.

  a. What would be the height, length, and width of the new prism?

  b. What would be the prism's volume? 72 in^3

10. Imagine stacking together four of the prisms like the one in Exercise 8 to make a larger rectangular prism.

  a. What would be the height, length, and width of the new prism?

  b. What would be the volume of the new prism? 144 in^3

  c. Give the dimensions of another rectangular prism you could create of the same four prisms.

  d. Is the volume of this prism different from the volume of the prism created in Part a? Explain why or why not.

11. How many of the prisms from Exercise 9 would you need to combine to create a rectangular prism whose volume is 360 in^3? 5

12. What could be the length, width, and height of the prism created in Exercise 11? Sample answers: H = 30 in., L = 6 in.; W = 2 in.; H = 3 in., L = 60 in.; W = 2 in.; H = 3 in., L = 6 in.; W = 20 in.

13. Consider these two rectangular prisms.

	Prism A	Prism B
Height	2 mm	5 mm
Length	2 mm	8 mm
Width	2 mm	4 mm

  a. What is the volume of prism A? Of prism B? 8 mm^3; 160 mm^3

  b. How many copies of prism A would you need to combine to equal the volume of prism B? 20

  c. Can you create prism B by stacking together copies of prism A? Explain how to do it, or why it is impossible.

  d. Prism C has these dimensions: height = 1 mm, length = 2 mm, width = 2 mm. Describe how you would create prism B by stacking together copies of prism C. How many copies of prism C would you need? Sample Answer: Create a base layer of 2 copies of prism C by 4 copies (length = 8 mm, width = 4 mm). It is 1 mm tall, so you need 5 layers like that to get a height of 5. That is 5 · 2 · 4 copies of prism C, 40 copies in all.

Lesson 7.3 Surface Area and Volume **439**

Teacher Tips For the next set of exercises, you may want students to use blocks as models so they understand how to find the dimensions of the prisms.

Develop & Understand: B

Suggested Grouping: Pairs

▶ **Exercises 9–11** Remind students to label each dimension and make new sketches as they try new combinations of the prisms. Point out that using the same number of prisms in a different configuration still provides the same volume.

Troubleshooting

Many students have difficulty understanding how two figures with the same volume might have different dimensions. Provide various figures with dimensions that give the same volume. Have students create a figure using blocks based on the dimensions they were given. Compare the figures and have students explain why they are different.

Develop & Understand: C

Suggested Grouping: Pairs

▶ **Exercise 14** Remind students that volume tells how much an object will hold. Have partners find the object of all the bags and compare their findings to determine which will hold the most.

▶ **Exercises 15 and 16** Make sure students understand that the size restriction means that any bag with dimensions larger than those given are too large to be carried on the plane. Have them compare the dimensions of each bag to those on the sign.

▶ **Exercise 17** Discuss with students how figures with different dimensions can have the same volume, so the airline's rule makes sense. Have students think about the amount of space under their chairs and how a bag that is too tall would not fit, even if it had the same volume as one with a smaller height.

Math Link

Point out that X's are also used in place of "by" when describing dimensions.

Share & Summarize

Have students use blocks or other manipulatives to verify how the volume changes if one or two of the dimensions are doubled.

Additional Answer
Share & Summarize

3. The volume is multiplied by 4; it is like you place two copies of the prism side by side (double the length), and then another copy of the prism on top of each of those two (double the height), making four copies in all.

---

14. Tyra's bag holds the most: its volume is 2744 in^3. Grant's bag's volume is 1750 in^3 and Carla's is 2240 in^3, so Grant's holds the least.

Math Link

The dimensions of a rectangular prism are often written as 15 ft · 23 ft · 4 ft. This notation can be read "15 feet by 23 feet by 4 feet." This notation can also be used for rectangles, for example, 3 cm · 2 cm. (A "two by four" is a piece of wood whose base is a rectangle 2 inches wide and 4 inches long and whose length varies as needed.)

15. All of them; the sum of each bag's dimension is 42 in.

17b. All of them; their bags all have smaller volumes than 2772 in^3.

17c. Sample answer: They restrict the size of bags so they will fit under seats and in compartments. Maybe the compartments are only 10 inches wide, so a bag like Tyra's would not fit into them even if the volume of the bag is not too big.

Develop & Understand: C

Carla, Grant, and Tyra boarded an airplane in Boston bound for San Francisco. Grant found out that each passenger was allowed to bring one piece of carry-on luggage. The rule was that the height, length, and width of the bag must add up to 45 inches or less.

| Carla: | Grant: | Tyra: |
| 20 in. × 14 in. × 8 in. | 25 in. × 10 in. × 7 in. | 14 in. × 14 in. × 14 in. |

14. Whose bag holds the most? The least? Explain your answer.

15. Which bags meet the size restriction?

When they got to the airport, they saw this sign.

16. Which bags will the airline allow onto the plane as carry-on luggage, following the second size restriction? None of them: Each is too long in one dimension.

17. Carla said, "It would be simpler if the rule gave a maximum for a bag's volume, instead of dimensions."

   a. What is the volume of the largest allowable bag? 2772 in^3

   b. Which of the three friends could bring their bags onto the plane if the airline used this volume rule?

   c. Why might the airline not want to use this rule? Explain your reasoning.

Maximum Carry-On Baggage Size

Only one item per person.

Carry-on item must fit within the space below. If it does not fit, please check in your carry-on item at the front desk.

Share & Summarize

1. If you double the height of a rectangular prism, what happens to the volume? The volume doubles.

2. If you double the area of the base of a rectangular prism, what happens to the volume? The volume doubles.

3. What happens to the volume of a rectangular prism if you double two of its dimensions, for example, length and width, or length and height? See margin.

Inquiry
Investigation 3 Polygons to Polyhedra

Materials
- paper polygons
- tape

In this Inquiry investigation, you will continue to explore three-dimensional shapes.

A *polyhedron* is a closed, three-dimensional figure made of polygons. The shapes below are polyhedra. You have probably seen some of these shapes.

Pentagonal Prism   **Square Pyramid**   **Rectangular Prism**   **Cube**

The polygons that make up a polyhedron are called *faces*. The segments where the faces meet are called *edges*. The corners are called *vertices*.

Math Link
A *regular polygon* has sides that are all the same length and angles that are all the same size.

In a *regular polyhedron*, the faces are identical regular polygons. The same number of faces meet at each vertex. The cube shown above is a regular polyhedron. It has identical square faces and three faces meet at each vertex. None of the other shapes above is a regular polyhedron. Can you see why?

There is an infinite number of regular polygons. You can always make one with more sides. However, there is a very small number of regular polyhedra. In this Inquiry investigation, you will find them all.

Construct the Polyhedra

1. Start with the equilateral triangles. Follow these steps.

1.

   Step 1. Tape three triangles together around a vertex as shown.

Vertex

Go on

Inquiry
Investigation 3

Suggested Grouping: Groups of 2 or 3

Materials and Preparation
Each group will need at least one copy of Lesson 7.3 Masters 1–3, which have 45 triangles, 15 squares, 20 pentagons, 5 hexagons, and 5 heptagons. You may also want to use Lesson 7.3 Master 4 to build cubes. In order to complete the investigation in one day, the polygons need to be cut out before class. If you want students to cut out their own sets, have them do so the day before the investigation or include cutting as part of their homework assignment. Explain that they will need to cut carefully, because they will use the shapes to build solids.

Teacher Tips This lab can run long. To keep a good pace, move quickly through the introduction. Discuss the terminology for solids: *faces, edges,* and *vertices.*

Be sure that students understand how a regular polyhedron is different from a regular polygon. This difference is crucial to the investigation. Point out that a regular polyhedron has two properties: its faces are all the same regular polygon, and it has the same number of faces around each vertex. Have students explain why the polyhedra shown are or are not regular. Throughout the investigation, discourage students from using the word *side* when talking about polyhedra, because its meaning might be interpreted as either a face or an edge. Encourage them to use precise terms in their discussions.

Construct the Polyhedra
▶ **Exercise 1** Students will be able to follow the steps and use the illustration to build the polyhedron quickly in this exercise.

Point out that students will be using the make a model problem-solving strategy to find all regular polyhedra that exist.

▶ **Exercise 2** Students may need to be reminded that they can add more than four triangles to their figures as long as the two properties of a regular polyhedron are met.

▶ **Exercises 4, 6, and 8–10** For these exercises, make sure students realize why the polygons cannot make polyhedra. In Exercises 8 and 10, the polygons overlap. In the other questions, the connected polygons lie flat.

Troubleshooting A common error students make when constructing the icosahedron in **Exercise 3** is to create two sets of "five triangles around a vertex" and attach them together. This shape only has 10 faces, not 20 faces as it should. This shape is not a regular polyhedron because it has five triangles around the top and bottom vertices, but only four triangles around each middle vertex. Remind students making this error that, to be a regular polyhedron, this shape must have five triangles around *every* vertex. If they are not sure how to make this happen, encourage them to put five triangles around one vertex and then add more triangles to the "unfilled" vertices.

Math Link

The word *hedron* is Greek for "face," so a *polyhedron* is a figure with "many faces." Polyhedra are named for the number of faces they have. A cube, for example, can also be called a *hexahedron* for "six faces."

2.

3.

7. Yes

8. Four regular pentagons around a vertex overlap. You cannot create a solid unless you make a "dented" (concave) one.

Step 2. Bring the two outside triangles together. Tape them in place to create a three-dimensional shape.

Step 3. Notice that, at one of the vertices, three triangles meet. At the other vertices, only two triangles meet. At a vertex with only two triangles add another triangle, so the vertex now has three triangles around it.

Now see if you can create a closed shape with three triangles at each vertex. If not, continue to add triangles until you can create a closed shape.

2. Repeat the process that you used in Question 1. This time, start with four triangles around a vertex. Add triangles until the figure closes and there are four triangles around each vertex.

3. Repeat the process again, starting with five triangles around a vertex.

4. Repeat the process once again, starting with six triangles around a vertex. What happens? The six triangles lie flat; you cannot create a solid from them.

5. Now start with squares. Create a polyhedron with three squares around each vertex. What polyhedron did you make? A cube

6. Try to create a polyhedron with four squares around each vertex. What happens? The four squares lie flat; you cannot create a solid from them.

7. Now start with pentagons. Try to create a polyhedron with three regular pentagons around each vertex. Can you do it?

8. Try to create a polyhedron with four regular pentagons around each vertex. What happens?

9. Now start with hexagons. Try to create a polyhedron with three regular hexagons around each vertex. What happens? The three regular hexagons lie flat; you cannot create a solid from them.

10. What happens when you try to create a polyhedron from regular heptagons? Three regular heptagons overlap; you cannot create a solid from them.

Reaching *All Learners*

BL Beyond Level *Semiregular polyhedra* are similar to regular polyhedra, but they can have two or three different types of faces. The faces must be regular polygons, and the number of polygons around each vertex must be the same. Have students create a semiregular polyhedron with two different faces. Here is one possibility: 2 triangles and 2 squares.

You have just created all of the regular polyhedra.

| Tetrahedron | Octahedron | Icosahedron | Cube | Dodecahedron |

Math Link
Regular polyhedra are also called *Platonic solids* for the Greek philosopher Plato, who believed they were the building blocks of nature. He thought fire was made from tetrahedra, earth from cubes, air from octahedra, water from icosahedra, and planets and stars from dodecahedra.

An interesting pattern relates the number of faces, edges, and vertices of all polyhedra. Looking at the regular polyhedra that you created can help you find that pattern.

Find a Pattern

11. On each of your polyhedra, find the number of faces, the number of vertices, and the number of edges. Record your results in a table.

Polyhedron	Faces	Vertices	Edges
Tetrahedron	4	4	6
Octahedron	8	6	12
Icosahedron	20	12	30
Cube	6	8	12
Dodecahedron	12	20	30

12. Can you find a way to relate the number of faces and vertices to the number of edges? Possible answer: faces + vertices = edges + 2

What Did You Learn?

13. Use what you learned while building the polyhedra to explain why there are only five regular polyhedra. See margin.

Lesson 7.3 Surface Area and Volume **443**

Find a Pattern

▶ **Exercise 11** You may want to complete this exercise as a class. Create a table like the one shown on this page on the board or an overhead transparency. This is a quick way of making sure all students will be using the same data to look for the relationship in Exercise 12, even if their constructions may have been incorrect.

Counting all of the vertices and edges can get tricky. You may want to ask students to share counting strategies. Some students may use reasoning from the number of faces. For example, with the icosahedron, once they have counted the 20 faces, they can reason that each face has 3 vertices, giving a total of 20 · 3, or 60, vertices. Since each vertex of the icosahedron touches 5 faces, there are 60 ÷ 5, or 12, vertices.

▶ **Exercise 12** Make sure you allow at least 15 minutes for students to answer this exercise. If students need help, you may want to suggest that they add the number of faces and vertices for each polygon and compare it to the number of edges. They should be able to see that the sum is always 2 more than the number of edges.

What Did You Learn?

▶ **Exercise 13** Discuss what the exercise is asking before having students answer it individually or in small groups. The reasoning presented in the sample answer is accessible to students and should not be skipped. If there is not enough time to let students answer the question in class and discuss it, you may assign it as homework or have them answer it the next day.

Math Link
What are the names of some polyhedra? What is common in their names?

Teacher Tips The relationship in Exercise 12 is called Euler's (pronounced *oilers*) formula, although Euler and Descartes independently discovered it. It is true of all polyhedra, not just regular ones.

Additional Answer

13. Possible answer: To make a solid, you need the sum of the angles around a vertex to be less than 360° so you can fold it up to create the solid.

• There are only three regular solids with regular triangular faces (three, four, and five triangles around a vertex). For six or more triangles around a vertex, the angle sum is 360° or more, so no regular solid is possible.

• There is only one regular solid with square faces (three squares around

a vertex). For four or more squares, the angle sum is 360° or more, so no regular solid is possible.

• There is only one regular solid with regular pentagon faces (three pentagons around a vertex). For four or more pentagons, the angle sum is more than 360°, so no regular solid is possible.

• For regular polygons with six sides or more, the angle sum for three (or more) angles is 360° or more, so no regular solid is possible.

Investigation 1
Pages 435–437
Practice & Apply: 1–4, 13 and 14
Connect & Extend: 15 and 16

Investigation 2
Pages 437–440
Practice & Apply: 5–12
Connect & Extend: 17 and 18

Inquiry Investigation 3
Pages 441–443

Assign Anytime
Mixed Review: 19 and 20

▶ **Exercises 1–3** Remind students that they may not be able to use a formula when a figure is not a prism; discuss how they can find the volume of each figure.

Practice & Apply   Determine the volume of each block structure.

1.

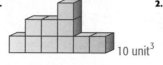

10 unit^3

2.

18 unit^3

3.

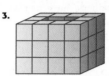

30 unit^3

4.

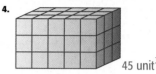

45 unit^3

For Exercises 5–8, calculate the volume of each rectangular prism from its dimensions. Include appropriate measurement units in your answers.

5. Height = 5 cm   Length = 9 cm   Width = 4 cm   180 cm^3

6. Height = 6 ft   Length = 14 ft   Width = 20 ft   1,680 ft^3

7. Height = 2 m   Length = 3 m   Width = 1.5 m   9 m^3

8. Height = $\frac{3}{4}$ in.   Length = 5 in.   Width = $\frac{1}{3}$ in. $\frac{15}{12}$ in^3 = $1\frac{1}{4}$ in^3

9. A prism has a volume of 300 in^3 and a base of 25 in^2. What is the height of the prism?   12 in.

10. A prism has a volume of 140 cm^3, a height of 4 cm, and a length of 5 cm. What is the width?   7 cm

11. Volume = 324 cm^3, Height = 6 cm

a. What is the area of the base?   54 cm^2

b. What could be the length and width?   Sample answer: Length = 9, width = 6

c. Give another length-width pair that would give the prism the same volume.   Sample answer: Length = 27, width = 2. Other answers are possible.

12a. $V = 7500 \text{ ft}^3 + 12500 \text{ ft}^3 = 20000 \text{ ft}^3$

....

Math Link
Volume is measured in cubic units. *Surface area* is measured in square units.

....

14. Sample answer: One structure could have a length of 12 cm, width of 2 cm, and height of 1 cm. The volume would be 24 cm^3 and the surface area would be 76 cm^2. A second structure could be 6 cm in length, 4 cm wide, and have height of 1 cm. The volume would still be 24 cm^3. The surface area would be 68 cm^2. The second figure would require less paint because it has less surface area.

12. This swimming pool is 4 feet deep at the shallow end and 10 feet deep at the deep end. The shallow end is 75 feet long.

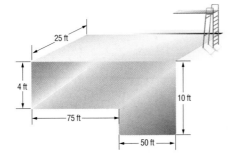

a. What is the total volume of the pool?

b. Another pool has the same length and width as this one but is the same depth everywhere. If the volume is the same as the volume of the first pool, what is the depth?   6.4 feet

13. Consider all the rectangular prisms that can be made with 27 blocks.

a. Give the dimensions of each prism.
$27 \cdot 1 \cdot 1, 9 \cdot 3 \cdot 1, 3 \cdot 3 \cdot 3$

b. Which of your 27-block prisms has the greatest surface area? Which has the least surface area?
Greatest: $27 \cdot 1 \cdot 1$; least: $3 \cdot 3 \cdot 3$

14. In Your Own Words Give two examples of structures with the same volume and different surface areas. Suppose you are making one of these structures for art class, and you want to paint them. Which one will need less paint? Explain.

▶ **Exercise 12** Make sure students understand that having a different depth can change the total amount of water in the pool, so the volume changes.

▶ **Exercise 13** Students are asked to solve this exercise without actually building the different prisms. The real question is whether students processed the fact that when volume is unchanged, the cube has the greatest surface area and a row has the least surface area, or do they need to check all the different prisms?

▶ **Exercise 15** This exercise requires students to predict the shape and volume of the next figure in the sequence. Remind students to look for patterns in the changes from one figure to the next.

▶ **Exercise 16** Finding volume of various figures requires students to use different formulas and methods. Have pairs determine the best method or formula for each exercise.

Additional Answers

15b. Sample answer: The cube structure will be 3 cubes wide, 4 cubes high, and will have 1 cube missing from the center of each level.

15e. Possible answer: One layer is a 3×3 rectangle with the middle block missing. The nth prism is made of n layers. So the volume is n (the height) $\cdot (3 \cdot 3 - 1)$ (length times width, minus the one missing block).

Connect & Extend   **15.**

a. What is the volume of each figure?   8 cubic units, 16 cubic units, 24 cubic units

b. What will the next figure in this sequence look like?   See margin.

c. What will be the volume of that figure?   32 cubic units

d. Write a rule to calculate the volume of the nth figure in the sequence.   Sample answer: $n(3 \cdot 3 - 1)$

e. Explain how you know your rule is correct. Use diagrams if necessary.   See margin.

16.

a. What is the volume of each figure?   16 cubic units, 20 cubic units, 24 cubic units

b. What will the next figure in this sequence look like?
Sample answer: A $6 \cdot 3 \cdot 2$ prism, with the middle 4 blocks missing

c. What will be the volume of that figure?   28 cubic units

d. Write a rule to calculate the volume of the nth figure in the sequence.   Sample answer: $2(3 + 3 + 2n)$

e. Explain how you know your rule is correct. Use diagrams if necessary.

16e. Sample answer: The base always has 3 blocks along one edge and 3 blocks along the other, so I represented that as $3 + 3$. The middle is always 3 blocks wide and n blocks long, which would be $3n$ total. One out of 3 blocks is missing, so it is $2n$. The height of the prism is always 2, so I multiplied everything by 2. That gives me $2(3 + 3 + 2n)$.

17. Each pair of pictures shows a prism seen from the side and from the top.

Prism A

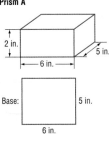

Prism B

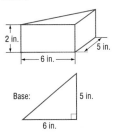

Prism C

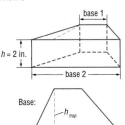

Cylinder D

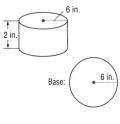

a. What is the volume of prism A?   60 in³

b. What is the volume of prism B?   30 in³

17c. Sample answer:
base *1* = 4 in.,
base *2* = 8 in.,
h_{trap} = 5 in.

c. The base of prism C is a trapezoid. The height of the trapezoid has been labeled h_{trap}, to distinguish it from h, the height of the prism. ($h = 2$.) Find values for base 1 b_1, base 2 b_2, and h_{trap} that will make the volume of prism C equal to the volume of prism A.

17d. Sample answer:
The version of the formula that states
$V = h(A)$ should work for a cylinder. Like the prism, the cylinder is a stack of identical layers with area A, *h* units high.

d. Cylinder D is a cylinder. Like a prism, it has two identical bases, which are parallel to each other. You could imagine making a cylinder by stacking up circles on top of each other. Does the formula for the volume of a rectangular prism also work to find the volume of a cylinder? Explain your reasoning.

e. Which volume is larger: a prism with $h = 4$ cm, $l = 15$ cm, and $w = 5$ cm, or a cylinder with $h = 4$ cm and $r = 5$ cm? Explain your reasoning.   See margin.

▶ **Exercise 17** In this exercise, students will find the volume of various figures by looking at them from the side and from the top. Have pairs determine the best method or formula for each exercise. Then have them check each other's answers.

Additional Answer

17e. Sample answer: The cylinder. They have the same height, so the one with the bigger base area will have the bigger volume. The prism's base area is 15 cm · 5 cm, or 3 · 5 · 5 cm². The cylinder's base is 5 cm · 5 cm · π. π is a little more than 3. So, the area of the circle is a little more than the area of the rectangle, making the volume of the cylinder bigger than the volume of the prism.

Quick Check

Informal Assessment Students should be able to:

✔ find the volume of a block structure

✔ find the surface area of a rectangular prism

✔ find the volume of a rectangular prism

Quick Quiz

The view from the top of a prism is shown. Find the surface area and volume of the prism with the given height.

1.

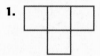

2 units high   28 square units; 8 cubic units

2.

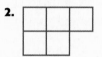

3 units high   40 square units; 15 cubic units

Find the surface area and volume of the rectangular prism.

3. 184 cm^2, 120 cm^3

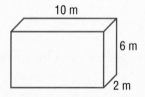

10 m
6 m
2 m

4. 590 cm^2, 825 cm^2

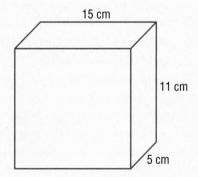

15 cm
11 cm
5 cm

18b. The flat is 30 in. × 48 in. × 36 in. You can stack the cereal boxes 2 high (15 × 15 in.), 4 long (12 × 12 × 12 × 12) and 18 deep (18 × 2). That is 2 × 4 × 18 boxes, or 144 boxes. They will all fit with no extra space.

18c. The arrangement that fills the greatest volume is 4 flats by 2 flats by 2 flats. It

Mixed Review

fills 480 ft^3 and uses 16 flats. There are 6 ways to arrange the flats in the truck (length against length, height against height; length against length, width against height; width against length, height against height; height against length, length against height; height against length, width against height). This was the arrangement that filled the most volume. It leaves a 2 ft × 5 ft × 6 ft volume empty.

18. The FreshStuff grocery store buys cereal boxes with dimensions of 15 in. × 12 in. × 2 in.

a. Cereal boxes arrive at the store in big containers called flats. The volume of a flat is 51,840 in^3. What is the maximum number of cereal boxes that could fit into a flat, judging by volume?   144

b. The dimensions of a flat are 2.5 ft × 4 ft × 3 ft. Can the number of boxes you calculated in Part a actually be arranged so that they will fit into the flat? Explain your reasoning.

c. Cereal is delivered in a truck whose shipping compartment is 18 ft × 5 ft × 6 ft. What is the maximum number of flats that will actually fit in the truck? Assume that all the flats have to be stacked facing in the same direction. Explain how you know.

d. What is the volume of the truck that will be empty if it is packed as in Part c?   The empty volume = 2 ft × 5 ft × 6 ft = 60 ft.

19. Stewart answered 14 out of 18 questions correctly on his math test. What percent did he answer correctly? Round your answer to the nearest whole percent.   78%

20. Statistics The pictograph shows the numbers of new dogs of seven breeds that were registered with the American Kennel Club during 2006.

Dogs Registered During 2006

Scottish Terrier	
Chinese Shar-Pei	
Pug	
Chihuahua	
Poodle	
German Shepherd	
Labrador Retriever	

= 10,000 dogs

Number Registered

Source: www.akc.org/reg/dogreg_stats_206.cfm

a. About how many Labrador Retrievers were registered with the AKC during 2006?   Possible answer: 123,000

b. In 2001, about 35,000 Chihuahuas were registered with the AKC. About how many fewer Chihuahuas were registered in 2006?   Possible answer: 12,000

c. The number of German Shepherds registered is about how many times the number of Chinese Shar-Peis registered?   Possible answer: 9

5. A moving truck has a storage compartment that is 12 feet deep, 8 feet wide and 10 feet tall. What is the volume of the storage compartment in the truck?   960 ft^3

6. A rectangular prism has a surface area of 62 square centimeters and a volume of 30 cubic centimeters. The dimensions of the prism are all whole centimeters. What are the dimensions of the prism?   5 cm, 2 cm, 3 cm

Capacity

- To find the capacity of a container in metric units
- To find the capacity of a container in customary units

Overview

In this lesson, students will use the metric system of measurement and the customary system of measurement to find the capacity of a container. They will learn to convert from one unit to the next within the metric system and investigate the capacity of various types of containers.

Advance Preparation

For this lesson, each group of students will need one or two-liter bottles.

	Summary	Materials	On Your Own Exercises (pp. 457–461)	Assessment Opportunities
Investigation 1 (p. 450) **Pacing:** 1 day	Students measure the capacity of various containers using the metric system.	1-liter or 2-liter bottles, scissors, tape, string, half-gallon milk or juice carton, Chapter 7 Master 6 (optional)	Practice & Apply: 1–6 Connect & Extend: 16, 17 Mixed Review: 21–23	• On the Spot Assessment (p. 453) • Share & Summarize (p. 453) • Troubleshooting (p. 453)
Investigation 2 (p. 454) **Pacing:** 1 day	Students measure the capacity of various containers using the customary system of measurement.	juice or milk cartons, drinking glasses, water bottles (assorted sizes), small and medium container, measuring cups, funnel, water	Practice & Apply: 7–15 Connect & Extend: 18–20 Mixed Review: 21–23	• Share & Summarize (p. 456) • Troubleshooting (p. 455)

Leveled Lesson Resources

Also on
TeacherWorks™
Lesson 7.4

Study Guide and Intervention (p. 32) — AL

Lesson 7.4 Study Guide and Intervention
Capacity

Capacity is the amount of liquid a container can hold. Metric capacity is usually expressed in liters or milliliters (thousandths of a liter).

| 1 liter = 1,000 mL | 1 cm³ = 1 mL |

Example 1 Find the equivalent metric measurement in milliliters.
How many milliliters are in 3.5 liters?

The milliliter measurement can be found using a ratio table.

liters	1	2	3	3.5	4
milliliters	1000	2000	3000	3500	4000

There are 3,500 milliliters in 3.5 liters.

Example 2 Find the capacity of the rectangular prism.

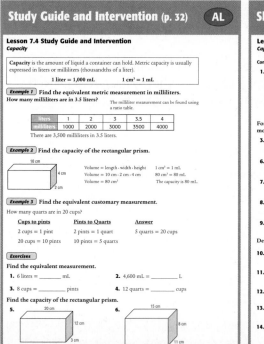

Volume = length · width · height   1 cm³ = 1 mL.
Volume = 10 cm · 2 cm · 4 cm   80 cm³ = 80 mL.
Volume = 80 cm³   The capacity is 80 mL.

Example 3 Find the equivalent customary measurement.

How many quarts are in 20 cups?

Cups to pints	Pints to Quarts	Answer
2 cups = 1 pint	2 pints = 1 quart	5 quarts = 20 cups
20 cups = 10 pints	10 pints = 5 quarts	

Exercises

Find the equivalent measurement.

1. 6 liters = _____ mL   **2.** 4,600 mL = _____ L

3. 8 cups = _____ pints   **4.** 12 quarts = _____ cups

Find the capacity of the rectangular prism.

5.   **6.**

Skills Practice (p. 33) — AL OL

Lesson 7.4 Skills Practice
Capacity

Complete each ratio table.

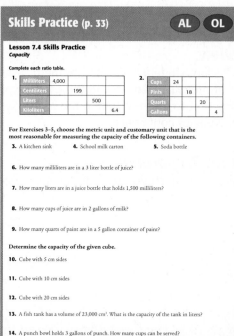

1.
Milliliters	4,000		
Centiliters		199	
Liters			500
Kiloliters			6.4

2.
Cups	24		
Pints		18	
Quarts			20
Gallons			4

For Exercises 3–5, choose the metric unit and customary unit that is the most reasonable for measuring the capacity of the following containers.

3. A kitchen sink   **4.** School milk carton   **5.** Soda bottle

6. How many milliliters are in a 3 liter bottle of juice?

7. How many liters are in a juice bottle that holds 1,500 milliliters?

8. How many cups of juice are in 2 gallons of milk?

9. How many quarts of paint are in a 5 gallon container of paint?

Determine the capacity of the given cube.

10. Cube with 5 cm sides

11. Cube with 10 cm sides

12. Cube with 20 cm sides

13. A fish tank has a volume of 23,000 cm³. What is the capacity of the tank in liters?

14. A punch bowl holds 3 gallons of punch. How many cups can be served?

Problem-Solving Practice (p. 34) — AL OL

Lesson 7.4 Problem-Solving Practice
Capacity

1. Paint A contractor's bucket of green paint is made by using a mixture of yellow and blue paint. One bucket requires 4,560 mL of yellow paint.
a. How many liters of yellow paint are needed in making 1 bucket?
b. How many liters of yellow paint are needed to make 6 buckets?

2. Lotion A skin lotion company uses 6,550 mL of Aloe extract and 450 mL of eucalyptus oil to make 1 batch of lotion.
a. How many liters of each ingredient does each batch contain?
b. How many batches of skin lotion can be made with 3.6 liters of eucalyptus oil?

3. Kiddie pool A kiddie pool is 100 cm long, 100 cm wide and 20 cm deep. Derek's hose fills at a rate of 40 liters a minute.
a. What is the capacity of the pool in liters?
b. How many minutes will it take to fill the pool?

4. Coffee pot The coffee maker at a banquet hall can brew 2 gallons of coffee. Each coffee pot placed on the tables can hold 2 pints of coffee. How many coffee pots can be filled from the coffee maker?

5. Wallpaper Tyson is following a homemade recipe for wallpaper remover. The recipe calls for $2\frac{1}{2}$ cups of vinegar mixed with 3 quarts of warm water. How many cups of vinegar are needed when mixed with $4\frac{1}{2}$ gallons of warm water?

6. Fuel The directions on a fuel injector cleaner suggests that $\frac{1}{4}$ cup of cleaner be added to 4 quarts of unleaded gasoline. A gas tank has a capacity of 16 gallons. How many cups of fuel injector cleaner are needed in a full tank of gas?

Enrichment (p. 35) — BL

Lesson 7.4 Enrichment
Capacity

Converting Between Systems

Products that are made in the United States have the capacity of the item listed in both Customary units and Metric units. This allows for products made in the United States to be sold internationally in countries that use the Metric system. Consumers in those countries are then able to buy products that are measured in the system they know.

Equivalent Measure Between Customary and Metric

| 1 gallon = 3.8 liters |

How many milliliters are in a 1.5 gallon container of laundry detergent?

Change gallons to liters	Sum of liters	Change to mL
1 gallon = 3.8 liters	3.8 L + 1.9 L = 5.7 liters	1L = 1,000 mL
0.5 gallons = 1.9 liters	5.7 L = 5,700 mL	

There are 5,700 mL in a 1.5 gallon container of laundry detergent.

Find the equivalent metric measure for the given customary measurement.

1. A gas tank can hold 10 gallons of gas. How many liters does the gas tank hold?

2. A container holds 2 quarts of milk. How many liters of milk are in the container?

3. The eel tank at the city aquarium can hold 5,000 gallons of water. How many kiloliters of water does the tank hold?

4. A bread recipe calls for 4 cups of flour. Deidre only has a metric measuring cup. How many milliliters of flour are needed for the recipe?

Lesson Quick Quiz (p. 36) — AL OL BL

Lesson 7.4 Quick Quiz
Capacity

Complete each ratio table.

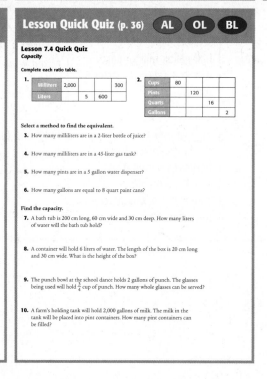

1.
Milliliters	2,000		300
Liters		5	600

2.
Cups	80		
Pints		120	
Quarts			16
Gallons			2

Select a method to find the equivalent.

3. How many milliliters are in a 2-liter bottle of juice?

4. How many milliliters are in a 45-liter gas tank?

5. How many pints are in a 5 gallon water dispenser?

6. How many gallons are equal to 8 quart paint cans?

Find the capacity.

7. A bath tub is 200 cm long, 60 cm wide and 30 cm deep. How many liters of water will the bath tub hold?

8. A container will hold 6 liters of water. The length of the box is 20 cm long and 30 cm wide. What is the height of the box?

9. The punch bowl at the school dance holds 2 gallons of punch. The glasses being used will hold $\frac{3}{4}$ cup of punch. How many whole glasses can be served?

10. A farm's holding tank will hold 2,000 gallons of milk. The milk in the tank will be placed into pint containers. How many pint containers can be filled?

Additional Lesson Resources

Teacher Tech Tools
- TeacherWorks
- ExamView Assessment Suite
- Classroom Presentation Toolkit
- Advance Tracker

Student Tech Tools
- StudentWorks Plus
- Math Online ▷ eGlossary •
- Concepts in Motion

Other Print Products
- Investigation Notebook and Reflection Journal
- Quick Review Math Handbook

LESSON 7.4

Capacity

Vocabulary

capacity

Real-World Link
The world consumes about 500 million gallons, or 1.9 billion liters, of milk a day.

① Answers will vary depending on the containers used and students' personal estimates. Sample answer uses a teaspoon.

In the previous lesson, you studied the concept of volume. **Capacity**, the amount of liquid a container can hold, is closely related to volume. A brick has volume, but no capacity to hold liquid.

Prefix	Meaning
milli-	Base unit ÷ 1000
centi-	Base unit ÷ 100
deci-	Base unit ÷ 10
no prefix	Base unit • 1
deca-	Base unit • 10
hecto-	Base unit • 100
kilo-	Base unit • 1000

The metric system of measurement can be used to measure capacity. Since it was created to be consistent with our decimal number system, the rule for converting from one unit to another is always the same. Ten of a unit equals one of the next larger unit, whether you are measuring length, mass, or capacity.

The metric system always uses the same pattern for naming the units. A *prefix* added to the name of the base unit tells you the size of the unit.

In this activity, you will investigate the capacities of some everyday containers to develop a sense of various metric measurement units.

Explore

Pick a container. Fill it with water. Use a funnel to transfer the water from the container into a 1-liter bottle. Estimate how many times you would have to do this in order to completely fill the 1-liter bottle. Record your estimate in a table. See ①.

Container	teaspoon
How many in 1 liter? (estimate)	100
Capacity in milliliters (measure)	5 milliliters
Capacity in liters	0.005 liters
How many in 1 liter? (calculate)	200
Closest metric unit	1 milliliter or 1 centiliter

How many milliliters do you think your container will hold?

Reaching *All Learners*

BL **Beyond Level** Students who understand capacity and the Metric system can measure water in measuring spoons and/or cups and write down their measurements. Then have them convert the numbers from milliliters to liters or from liters to milliliters. Have them write two sentences explaining their findings.

Capacity

LESSON 7.4

Introduce

Capacity In this investigation, students will explore capacity. They will learn that we use capacity to measure the amount of liquid an object will hold. Students will use the metric system to measure capacity, so they will be using prefixes to indicate base units. It is important to help students develop a firm understanding of the metric system as they learn about capacity and other forms of measurement.

Teacher Tips For the Explore, have different groups use different containers and share their results with the class.

Explore

Suggested Grouping: Small Groups

▶ **Prepare** Make sure there are several different sizes of containers for students to use.

▶ **Play** Have students pour liquid into the containers and do all the measurements. Have them record their estimates in the table and repeat the activity until they understand it.

▶ **Record** As students measure the liquids into the bottle, have them explain to each other why the container they are using has a capacity closer to one milliliter, one centiliter, or one liter. Discuss how they made their choices. Have students share their results with the class.

▶ **Score** Give students credit for doing the activity.

Capacity Point out that the base unit for measuring capacity with the metric system is the *liter*. Use one- or two-liter bottles to introduce the investigation.

✓ Develop & Understand: A

▶ **Exercises 1 and 2** Make sure students understand that the relationship between liters and milliliters is a constant one, as are all the units in the metric system. Every time students find a number of liters, they can know that one thousand times that number tells the number of milliliters.

✓ Develop & Understand: B

Suggested Grouping: Small groups

▶ **Exercise 3** Make sure students see that the answer revolves around converting from milliliters to liters, and not solving for another answer. Remind them to set up a proportion to determine the correct answer.

Teacher Tips Teaching capacity requires a strong understanding of the metric system. Have students look for metric measurements on liquid products when they go home, and write down the measurements and the units. As a class, discuss their findings and convert some of them from milliliters to liters or vice versa.

Fill the container again. This time use the funnel to transfer the water into a graduated cylinder. The graduated cylinder is marked in milliliters. How many milliliters of water did you pour into the cylinder? Record your answer in the table.
Answers will vary.
Express the container's capacity in liters, using decimals as needed.
Answers will vary.
How many times would you need to empty your container into a 1-liter bottle to fill the bottle all the way? Is the capacity of your container closer to 1 milliliter, 1 centiliter, 1 deciliter, or 1 liter?
Answers will vary.
Name something whose capacity it would make most sense to measure in milliliters.   Sample answers: baby food jar, soda can, spoon, pencil sharpener
Name something whose capacity it would make most sense to measure in liters.   Sample answers: large milk carton, backpack, sink, cooking pot

Investigation 1 Metric Units for Capacity

Materials

- 1-liter bottle (for example, a soda bottle)
- one or more different-sized drinking glass
- one or more different-sized eating spoons
- small containers such as an empty aspirin bottle or a dental floss box
- graduated cylinder marked in milliliters
- funnel
- 2 nets to create cubes
- scissors
- tape
- half-gallon milk/orange juice carton (square bottom, straight sides)
- string

The *base unit* for measuring capacity is the liter. A liter has the capacity of about a quart. You are probably familiar with 1-liter or 2-liter drink bottles. When items in the store are labeled with metric units, capacity is usually expressed either in liters or milliliters (thousandths of a liter).

✓ Develop & Understand: A

1. Complete this ratio table showing the relationship between milliliters and liters.

Liters	1	3	45	1.5	7.453	0.5	0.386
Milliliters	1000	3,000	45,000	1500	7,453	500	386

2. Write a ratio to express the relationship between milliliters and liters. Include units so that it is clear what the numbers represent.
1000 milliliters : 1 liter or 1000 milliliters / 1 liter or "1000 milliliters to 1 liter."

✓ Develop & Understand: B

You are the manager of a small factory that manufactures kitchen cleaning products. The active ingredient in your Eco-Fresh Cleaning Liquid is citric acid. One batch of Eco-Fresh requires 2,750 milliliters of citric acid.

3. How many liters of citric acid are required for one batch of Eco-Fresh? For five batches? Write your answer as a decimal.
2.75 liters; 13.75

Reaching *All Learners*

AL Approaching Level Help students fill in the ratio table in Exercise 1. Bring in some empty bottles of products measured in liters, and have students put those numbers in the ratio table as well. Discuss with students how the number of liters and milliliters are related.

4. Your supplier sells citric acid in 1-liter jugs. You do not want to waste any ingredients.

   a. How many batches of Eco-Fresh do you need to make in order to use up all the citric acid you buy?   4

   b. How many jugs of citric acid will you need to do this?   11

One batch of Spring Rinse dish soap contains 3,850 milliliters of coconut oil and 650 milliliters of citric acid. These are the only two ingredients. Use this information to answer Exercises 5–9.

5. How many liters of each ingredient does a batch contain?
   3.85 liters of coconut oil, 0.65 liters of citric acid

6. How many liters of Spring Rinse does one batch make?   4.5 liters

7. How many batches of Spring Rinse can you make with 23.1 liters of coconut oil?   6

8. If you use 11550 milliliters of coconut oil, how many liters of citric acid do you need?   1.95 liters

9. The new and improved formula for Spring Rinse calls for 983 milliliters of coconut oil for each liter.

   a. How many milliliters of citric acid are in one liter of Spring Rinse made according to this formula?   17 milliliters

   b. How many liters is that?   0.017 liters

✓ Develop & Understand: C

How much water does a rectangular baking pan like this one hold?
Student answers will vary.
You already know how to calculate the volume of a rectangular prism. The volume and capacity of a container are related as follows.

28 cm   23 cm   3 cm

> A 1-centimeter cube has a capacity of 1 milliliter.

Real-World Link

A *prefix* is a piece of a word that has its own meaning and can be attached to the front of other words. For example, the prefix "re-" means "again." "Revisit" means "visit again," "reapply" means "apply again."

A *suffix* is just like a prefix, except that it goes at the end of a word instead of the beginning.

▶ **Exercise 4** Remind students to set up proportions for this exercise. Monitor to see that students are solving for the correct information.

▶ **Exercises 5–9** These exercises require students to use the same methods they used in Exercises 3–5, only with a new example. Remind them that it is important to set up the correct proportions in each exercise.

Teacher Tips You may also want students to use nets for Exercises 10–12. Have them use Chapter 7 Master 6 to help them build the nets. A sample net for a cube is shown below.

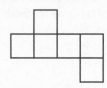

✓ Develop & Understand: C

Suggested Grouping: Pairs

▶ **Exercises 10–12** Students should use their knowledge of units to determine the capacity of each net. Remind them that they can measure each side of a cube to find its volume, and the capacity of one cubic centimeter is one milliliter.

▶ **Exercise 13** Have partners make sketches to determine how to arrange the smaller cube inside the larger cube. Discuss their suggestions. Remind them that there should be no empty space, so the arrangement should use straight lines to keep the cubes flush and tight.

▶ **Exercises 14–16** In these exercises, students see that items can have the same capacity and be shaped differently.

. . . .

Real-World Link

Have students list other words they can think of using the prefix *re-*. Discuss how prefixes and suffixes change the meanings of the words they accompany.

. . . .

12. The second net has sides that are 10 cm long. It is 10 times larger than the first net.

13. Sample answer: 10 cubes fit along each side, so you could cover the bottom with 10 rows of 10 cubes; that layer has 100 cubes. 10 layers stacked on each other would fill the big cube; it is 10 cm high. 10 layers of 100 is 1000 little cubes.

14a. Answers may vary depending on the carton; one standard kind is 9.5 cm on a side.

15. Sample answer: the bottle looks to me like it ought to hold more water because it is taller. But it is thinner than the cube; if the cube were open on top you could stand the bottle in it. Since volume depends on all three dimensions, it makes sense that something tall and thin could hold the same amount of water as something short and fat. In fact, the carton is like the cube, only a little smaller in base area and a little taller to make up for it.

10. Each of these squares is 1 cm on each side. Cut out and assemble a net like this one to make a cube 1 cm on each side. What is the capacity of this cube?   1 milliliter

11. How long should the sides of a cube be so that it will hold 1 liter of water?   Each side should be 10 cm.

12. When you have answered Exercise 11, get a second net from your teacher. Check the length of the sides of the squares and compare them to your answer for Exercise 11. Assemble the new cube.

13. Describe how you could arrange 1,000 copies of the smaller cube inside the larger one.

14. Examine a milk carton with a square bottom.

   a. Measure and record the length in centimeters of the sides of the square.

   b. Calculate the area of the bottom of the carton.
   Answers will vary.

   c. If the carton were the same height as your 1-liter cube, what would be the carton's volume?   Answers will vary.
   902.5 milliliters or 0.9025 liters

   d. Approximately how many centimeters high would the carton have to be for its capacity to be 1 liter? Round your answer to the nearest centimeter.   Answers will vary. 11 cm

   e. Cut the carton down to the height you calculated in Part c.
   See students' work.

15. You now have three different containers with capacities of 1 liter. Compare the carton, cube, and bottle. Do they look as though they all hold the same amount of liquid? Explain how they can all have the same capacity even though they are different shapes.

16. How long should the sides of a cube be, so that it can hold 1 kiloliter of water?   Each side should be 100 cm, or 1 meter.

   a. How many of your 1-liter cubes would fit inside such a cube?   1,000

   b. How many of your 1-milliliter cubes would fit inside the 1-kiloliter cube?   1,000,000

17. Simon bakes with a rectangular baking pan that is 28 cm long, 23 cm, and 3 cm deep.

   a. What is the volume of the pan in cubic centimeters? $1,932 \text{ cm}^3$

   b. What is the capacity of the pan in milliliters?   1,932 milliliters

   c. What is the capacity of the pan in liters?   1.932 liters

18b. Sample answer: It makes most sense to use liters because it is easier to imagine about 40 of something or calculate with that smaller number than to use a huge number like 39,600. Or you could say the capacity is 3.96 decaliters.

19a. 201,600 cm³

18. Simon's kitchen sink is 55 cm long, 40 cm wide, and 18 cm deep.

a. What is the volume of the sink in cubic centimeters? In milliliters? In liters? 39,600 cm³; 39,600 milliliters; 39.6 liters

b. Which metric unit would you choose to describe the capacity of the sink? Explain your reasoning.

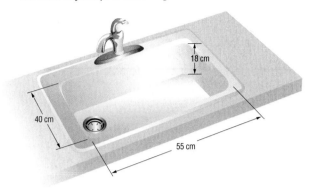

19. Simon's bathtub is 48 cm wide, 140 cm long, and 30 cm deep.

a. What is the volume of the bathtub in cubic centimeters?

b. Simon filled his sink and then transferred all the water into the bathtub. About how many times would he need to do this to fill the bathtub? About 5 times

c. Use your answer from Part b to estimate how many liters of water the bathtub holds. About 200 (5 · 40 L)

d. Use your answer from Part a to calculate the capacity of the bathtub in liters exactly. 201.6 L

e. About how many bathtubs would be needed to hold 1 kiloliter of water? About 5

Share & Summarize

1. How many milliliters are in a liter? How many centiliters are in a liter? How many milliliters are in a centiliter? 1,000; 100; 10

2. What metric units would be reasonable to use for measuring the capacity of a drinking glass? A soup pot? A bathtub? A swimming pool? Deciliters or centiliters; liters; liters or hectoliters; kiloliters

▶ **Exercise 18** Remind students that volume can be converted to milliliters with the formula *1 cubic centimeter = 1 milliliter*.

▶ **Exercise 19** Discuss why students would want to choose to use liters or milliliters to describe the capacity of the sink.

Have students discuss the relative sizes of a sink and of a bathtub. Remind them that the units they use should be chosen based on the size of the amount they are measuring.

Share & Summarize

Review the metric units students have used in this investigation. Discuss how to decide which unit to use in various situations, and have students each name one object or amount and the unit they would use to measure it.

Troubleshooting Many students have difficulty understanding the relationship between capacity and volume. Explain that capacity is used to show liquid measures for products such as milk and water. Have students suggest other products that might have capacity, and compare them to cubes that are used to show only volume unless filled with liquid.

 Assessment

It should be relatively easy to tell if students understand the relationship between units and capacity. If students consistently name items that are much too large when finding items to measure in milliliters, they need assistance in understanding the size of a milliliter. Likewise, if students consistently name items that are much too small when discussing liters, they need some help understanding the size of a liter.

Customary Units for Capacity In this investigation, students will identify and use U.S. Customary units for capacity. They will find relative amounts in cups, pints, quarts, and gallons. Point out to students that in the United States, most people use customary units instead of metric units in everyday situations.

Math Link

Ask students to suggest items they have seen labeled in fluid ounces. Make sure students understand that fluid ounces are often written as *FL. OZ.* on packages.

✅ *Develop & Understand: A*

Suggested Grouping: Small Groups

▶ **Exercises 1 and 2** Students will give estimates concerning the capacity of the containers in these exercises. If their answers are unreasonable, stop and review customary units again.

▶ **Exercises 3–5** In these exercises, students will check the reasonableness of their estimates. Remind them that estimates are not exact, so it is okay if their answers were not exactly the same as what they should have been. If their answers were close, they did well.

Investigation **2** Customary Units for Capacity

Materials

- juice or milk cartons or bottles (gallon, half-gallon, quart, pint, cup)
- drinking glasses and water bottles of assorted sizes
- small and medium-sized saucepans, or other appropriately-sized containers
- measuring cups
- funnel
- water

In Investigation 1, you measured capacity using metric units. In this investigation, you will learn about U.S. customary units for capacity.

The customary units for capacity are *cups*, *pints*, *quarts*, and *gallons*. You have probably seen drinks sold in containers of all these sizes, as well as half-gallons.

✅ *Develop & Understand: A*

1. Find the capacity of each carton on the label.
   a. Arrange the five cartons in order of size. gallon, half-gallon, quart, pint, cup
   b. Estimate how many of the 1-cup cartons it would take to fill the pint carton.
   Answers may vary; it actually takes 2.
2. Estimate:
   a. How many pints it would take to fill a quart container? 2
   b. How many quarts it would take to fill a half-gallon container? 2
   c. How many half-gallons it would take to fill a gallon container? 2

3. Use the cartons as benchmarks to help you to estimate the capacities of other containers. Answers will depend on the containers available.
   a. Which container holds about a cup?
   b. Which holds less than a cup?
   c. Which holds about a pint?
   d. Which holds about a quart?
   e. Which holds more than a gallon?

4. Fill a 1-cup measuring cup with water. Use a funnel to transfer the water into one of the containers. Repeat as many times as you need to fill the container. How much water does the container hold? Was your estimate of its capacity close to the real value? Answers will vary.

Math Link

Fluid ounces are another unit for measuring capacity that you may have seen on labels. Fluid ounces also belong to the U.S. customary system. There are 8 fluid ounces in 1 cup.

5. Now check your estimates for Exercise 2a–c by the same method. Answers will vary.

Reaching All Learners

OL On Level Have students choose a customary unit and a number to go with it. Then have them trade and convert each other's amounts into another customary unit. For example, if one student writes 18 cups, the other student might convert it to 9 pints.

Develop & Understand: B

6. Complete the ratio table showing the conversion ratios among customary units of capacity.

Cups	32	16	12	10	8	4	3	2	1
Pints	16	8	6	5	4	2	$1\frac{1}{2}$	1	$\frac{1}{2}$
Quarts	8	4	3	$2\frac{1}{2}$	2	1	$\frac{3}{4}$	$\frac{1}{2}$	$\frac{1}{4}$
Gallons	2	1	$\frac{3}{4}$	$\frac{5}{8}$	$\frac{1}{2}$	$\frac{1}{4}$	$\frac{3}{16}$	$\frac{1}{8}$	$\frac{1}{16}$

7. Express each relationship as a ratio.

a. Cups : Pints   2:1

b. Pints : Quarts   2:1

c. Quarts : Gallons   4:1

8. How many cups are in one gallon?   16

9. What fraction of a quart is a cup? $\frac{1}{4}$

10. Martina has a soup recipe that measures all the ingredients in cups. If she substitutes pints for cups for each ingredient, how will the final volume of punch compare to the volume the original recipe made?   The volume will be twice the original volume.

Real-World Link

Drinking glasses come in many sizes and shapes, but two common sizes hold 1 cup or $1\frac{1}{2}$ cups. When you buy an individual serving of milk or juice at the store, it often comes in $1\frac{1}{2}$ cup, $1\frac{3}{4}$ cup, or 2-cup portions. Take a look at the drinks in your cafeteria or at the store. How much is in an individual serving?

Develop & Understand: B

Suggested Grouping: Whole Group

▶ **Exercise 6** Work through the ratio table as a class. Discuss each conversion, making sure students understand the relationships between the units.

▶ **Exercises 7–9** Refer students to the ratio table in Exercise 6 when working these exercises. Have them use the relationships they found to create ratios comparing the units.

▶ **Exercise 10** Remind students that the ratios they created apply to situations like the soup recipe. Discuss other situations that might call for such knowledge.

Real-World Link

Discuss how companies often sell individual servings of drinks that contain more than one serving, according to the label. Have students suggest reasons for companies doing this; point out factors like price, calories, etc.

Troubleshooting

A common place for error in using customary units is in remembering the proper number of cups in a pint, pints in a quart, and quarts in a gallon. Students will need to memorize this information to make it useful for them in everyday life. Have a drill and practice game and call out a question for students to answer quickly, such as *How many pints in a quart?*

Suggested Grouping: Pairs

▶ **Exercises 11–14** Remind students to look back at the ratio table they completed earlier and any notes they have taken if they have trouble with the ratios in this problem. Point out that the juice/concentrate ratio is a constant proportion that they can use for each instance.

▶ **Exercise 15** Have students list the information they have for each problem. Point out that the ratio of concentrate to water remains the same, regardless of the amount of juice Ana makes.

. . . .

Math Link
Have students describe times they have used teaspoons, half-cups, etc. Point out that most of the units mentioned are used in cooking.

. . . .

Share & Summarize
Draw a Venn diagram on the board and have students help you compare the metric system to U.S. customary units. Discuss how both systems are used to create constant measures, but each uses different units.

Additional Answer
① Sample answers: The metric units get 10 times bigger from one to the next; the customary units get only 2 times bigger (and unless you count the half-gallon, there is one step of times-four instead of times-two (quarts to gallons). In both systems, the relationship between any two units is proportional; you multiply or divide by a constant to change the units.

Develop & Understand: C

Christopher and Ana mixed juice for a party. They mixed frozen juice concentrate with water. Each can of concentrate is $1\frac{1}{2}$ cups.

11. The instructions on a can of concentrate state that one can makes $\frac{1}{2}$ gallon of juice. How many cups of water do Christopher and Ana need to add to one can of concentrate? $6\frac{1}{2}$ cups

12. How many cups of concentrate should they use if they want to make 3 gallons of juice? 9 cups

13. How many gallons of juice can they make with 9 cups of concentrate? 3 gallons

14. How many cups of concentrate should they use to make 1 quart of juice? $\frac{3}{4}$ cups

15. Ana's drinking glasses each held 1 cup of juice. She knew that there would be 20 guests at the party. She wanted to estimate how much juice to make.

   a. If each guest drinks 2 glasses of juice, how many gallons of juice do Ana and Christopher need to make?

   b. How many cups of concentrate do they need? $7\frac{1}{2}$ cups

   c. How many cups of concentrate do they need if each guest drinks 3 glasses of juice? $11\frac{1}{4}$ cups

   d. Ana decided to make 4 gallons of juice. At the end of the party, 2 quarts of juice were left. How much juice did each guest drink? 3 cups = 3 glasses

15a. $2\frac{8}{16}$ gallons = $2\frac{1}{2}$ gallons

. . . .

Math Link
For measuring capacities smaller than a cup, the U.S. customary system uses either fluid ounces (16 fluid ounces = 1 cup) or teaspoons (8 teaspoons = 1 cup). A tablespoon equals 2 teaspoons.

You can also use fractions of a cup (for example, kitchen measuring cups usually come in 1-cup, half-cup, third-cup, and quarter-cup sizes).

. . . .

Share & Summarize
1. How many cups are in a pint? In a quart? In a gallon? 2; 4; 16
2. What fraction of a gallon is 3 quarts? $\frac{3}{4}$
3. What are some similarities and differences between the metric system for measuring capacity and the customary system? See margin.

Reaching All Learners

AL **Approaching Level** Students who have trouble converting from one unit to the next using customary units may need more help understanding how units can describe the same amount in different ways. Use a large measuring cup that has cups and quart(s) labeled. Demonstrate how pouring liquid to the quart line is the same as 2 pints or 4 cups. Repeat with different amounts.

Practice & Apply

1. Complete each ratio table. Write your answers as decimals.

Milliliters	3,000	1870	2,090,000	746,000	125	9	33,000
Centiliters	300	187	209,000	74,600	12.5	0.9	3,300
Liters	3	1.87	2,090	746	0.125	0.009	33
Kiloliters	0.003	0.00187	2.09	0.746	0.000125	0.000009	0.033

Which metric unit is most reasonable to measure the capacity of the following containers?

2. a coffee mug   Deciliters

3. a refrigerator   Kiloliters

4. a small spoon   Milliliters

5. a cooking pot   Liters

6. The label on a bottle of Rainbow Juice advertises that the drink contains 12% fruit juice.

   a. How many milliliters of fruit juice are in a 2-liter bottle of Rainbow Juice?   240 milliliters

   b. How many milliliters of fruit juice are in a $\frac{1}{2}$ liter bottle?   60 milliliters

   c. What is the ratio of fruit juice to other ingredients in Rainbow Juice? Write your answer as a ratio with the smallest whole numbers possible.   3:22 or $\frac{3}{22}$

   d. How many liters of Rainbow Juice can be made with 12 milliliters of fruit juice?   0.1 liters

   e. What is the proportion of fruit juice in the final mixture? Write your answer as a ratio with the smallest whole numbers possible.   3:25 or $\frac{3}{25}$

   f. How many liters of Rainbow Juice can be made with 600 milliliters of fruit juice?   5 liters

7. Complete each ratio table. Write your answers as fractions or mixed numbers.

Cups	80	28	48	5	$\frac{1}{2}$	15	26
Pints	40	14	24	$2\frac{1}{2}$	$\frac{1}{4}$	$7\frac{1}{2}$	13
Quarts	20	7	12	$1\frac{1}{4}$	$\frac{1}{8}$	$3\frac{3}{4}$	$6\frac{1}{2}$
Gallons	5	$1\frac{3}{4}$	3	$\frac{5}{16}$	$\frac{1}{32}$	$\frac{15}{16}$	$1\frac{5}{8}$

Investigation 1
Pages 450–453
Practice & Apply: 1–6
Connect & Extend: 16, 17

Investigation 2
Pages 454–456
Practice & Apply: 7–15
Connect & Extend: 18–20

Assign Anytime
Mixed Review: 21–23

▶ **Exercise 1** Remind students that the table is based on the metric system, and that all answers for each number should be directly proportional to one another.

▶ **Exercises 2–5** Check students' work to be sure their answers are reasonable.

▶ **Exercise 6** Have students write 12% as a fraction before they solve the problem.

▶ **Exercise 7** Make sure students remember to use the proportions for customary units instead of metric units for this ratio table.

▶ **Exercises 8–11** Check students' work to be sure their answers are reasonable.

▶ **Exercises 12–13** Remind students to keep their answers organized to make it easier to determine the correct amounts of each kind of paint. Encourage them to create a small ratio table if it helps.

▶ **Exercise 14** Make sure students understand that the teapot's labeled capacity is not exactly what it says; solving for a $\frac{3}{4}$ cup teacup will require them to do more work.

Which customary unit is most reasonable to measure the capacity of the following containers?

8. a bathtub   Gallons

9. a drinking glass   Cups

10. a swimming pool   Gallons

11. a cereal bowl   Pints (or cups)

12. Doug and Arleta repainted Doug's bedroom. First, they mixed different colors of paint to make the shade of green Doug wanted. The sample mixture contained 1 cup of white paint, $\frac{1}{2}$ cup of blue paint, and $\frac{3}{4}$ cup of yellow paint. They used the same recipe to make larger quantities of paint for their project.

a. If they use 3 cups of white paint, how much yellow paint do they need? $\frac{9}{4}$ cups $= 2\frac{1}{4}$ cups

b. If they use 1 quart of blue paint, how much white paint do they need?   8 cups $=$ 2 quarts

c. If they use 1 gallon of white paint, how much blue paint do they need? $\frac{1}{2}$ gallon

d. If they use 3 gallons of yellow paint, how much white paint do they need?   4 gallons

e. If they use 2 gallons of blue paint, how much paint will they have when it is all mixed together?   9 gallons

13a.   27 cups $= 6\frac{3}{4}$
quarts $= 1\frac{11}{16}$
gallons

13. Doug and Arleta had 5 pints of blue paint, 1 gallon of yellow paint, and 3 quarts of white paint.

a. How much of the paint mixture from Exercise 12 could they make?

b. How many quarts of each color was left over after they made the mixture?   1 quart of blue, $1\frac{3}{4}$ quarts yellow, no white

14. Teacups often hold $\frac{3}{4}$ cup of tea. The capacity of a teapot is often described in terms of how many teacups it can fill. For example, a 5-cup teapot holds enough tea to fill 5 teacups.

a. What is the capacity, in U.S. customary units, of a teapot that can fill 5 teacups? $3\frac{3}{4}$ cups

b. How many teacups can you fill from a teapot that holds 3 pints of tea?   8 teacups

c. How many quarts of tea do you need to fill 16 teacups?   3 quarts

d. Rachel likes to drink her tea out of a standard coffee mug, which holds $1\frac{1}{2}$ cups. How many times can she fill her mug from a teapot that can fill 5 teacups? $2\frac{1}{2}$ times

e. Rachel wants to buy a teapot that holds enough tea for 5 mugs. So far, she has found a teapot that holds 3 pints, one that holds 2 quarts, one that holds 7 cups, and one that holds enough for 10 teacups. Are any of these pots big enough for Rachel? If so, which?

14e. She needs $7\frac{1}{2}$ cups of capacity, so the 2-quart pot (8 cups) and the 10-teacup ($7\frac{1}{2}$ cups) are big enough, but the others are too small.

15. Adrian paid $2.70 for 3 pints of milk. Mariella bought 2 gallons of milk and paid a total of $9.80. Jerome bought a quart of milk for $1.60. Who got the best deal? Explain your reasoning. See margin.

Connect & Extend

16h. Sample answer: Because to find the volume of a cube, you multiply the side length by itself three times. If you multiplied the length of just one side by 2, the volume would also be multiplied by 2. But you are really multiplying the length of all three sides by 2, so the volume is multiplied by 2 three times. Since capacity is directly proportional to volume, the capacity also gets multiplied by 8 when the volume is multiplied by 8.

16. Remember that a cube whose sides are 1 cm long has a volume of 1 cubic centimeter and a capacity of 1 milliliter. A cube with 10 cm sides has a volume of 1,000 cubic centimeters and a capacity of 1 liter.

a. Complete the table below.

Side length of cube (centimeters)	1	2	3	4	5	6	7	8	9	10
Capacity of cube (milliliters)	1	8	27	64	125	216	343	512	729	1,000 (1 liter)

b. Approximately how long are the sides of a cube whose capacity is $\frac{1}{2}$ liter?   8 cm

c. Approximately how long are the sides of a cube whose capacity is $\frac{1}{4}$ liter?   6 cm

d. What fraction of a liter is the capacity of a cube with 5 cm sides? $\frac{1}{8}$

e. Compare the capacity of a cube with 2 cm sides to the capacity of a cube with 4 cm sides. How many times larger is the capacity of the larger cube?   8 times

f. Now compare the cube with 3 cm sides to the cube with 6 cm sides. How many times larger is the capacity of the larger cube? 8 times

g. What happens to the volume of a cube when you double the length of the sides?   It is multiplied by 8.

h. Why doesn't the capacity of a cube double when you double the length of the sides?

▶ **Exercise 15** Discuss with students how companies might sell different units of a product at different prices per unit, such as the milk in this problem. Have them tell how the people could have used units to find a better deal.

▶ **Exercises 16 and 17** Make sure students correctly complete the ratio table so that they find the correct answers for the other problems.

Additional Answer

15. Sample answer: Adrian's pints cost $0.90 each. Jerome's quart cost $1.60, or $0.80 per pint. Mariella's gallons cost $4.90 each, which means they cost about $1.23 per quart, or about $0.61 per pint. So, Mariella paid the lowest price per pint, which means she got the best deal.

▶ **Exercise 17** Have students use the ratio table from page 459. Have them compare answers for accuracy.

▶ **Exercise 18** Have students solve this exercise with a partner.

Additional Answers

19. Sample answer: I do not know how volume and capacity are related in Customary units, but the relationship must be directly proportional like it is in Metric units, because a 1 in. by 1 in. by 1 in. cube must always hold the same amount of water. So, whatever the conversion between volume and capacity is, twice as many cubic inches must hold twice as many cups. So, the capacity of the big jug must be twice the capacity of the little one, since the volume is doubled. The capacity of the big jug must be 3 pints = 6 cups.

18. Sample answer: The silver bowl holds 1 quart less than 1 gallon, so its capacity is 3 quarts. The red bowl holds as many pints as there are quarts in the silver bowl, so the red bowl's capacity must be 3 pints (or $1\frac{1}{2}$ quarts). The red bowl holds 1 quart more than the yellow bowl, and the red bowl holds $1\frac{1}{2}$ quarts, so the capacity of the yellow bowl must be $\frac{1}{2}$ quart, or 1 pint.

17. Use the table from Exercise 16 to help you solve this exercise.

a. Which of the cubes in the table has a capacity closest to 1 centiliter (10 milliliters)?   The cube with sides 2 cm long

b. Use your calculator to find a closer approximation of the length of the sides of a cube whose capacity is 1 centiliter. Approximate the side length to the closest tenth of a centimeter.   2.2 cm

c. Now approximate the side length to the closest hundredth of a centimeter.   2.15 cm (but 2.16 is very nearly as close)

d. Which of the cubes in the table has capacity closest to 1 deciliter (100 milliliters)?   The cube with sides 5 cm long

e. Use your calculator to approximate the side length of a cube whose capacity is 1 deciliter. Approximate the side length to the nearest hundredth of a centimeter.   4.64 cm

18. Jason has three mixing bowls. Use the following clues to figure out the capacity of each bowl. Explain your reasoning.

Clue 1: The red bowl holds 1 quart more than the yellow bowl.

Clue 2: The silver bowl holds the same number of quarts as the red bowl holds pints.

Clue 3: When Jason poured milk from a gallon jug into the silver bowl, he was able to fill the bowl and had a quart of milk left.

19. The small jug's capacity is $1\frac{1}{2}$ pints. The volume of the big jug is twice the volume of the small jug. What is the capacity of the big jug in cups? Explain your reasoning. See margin.

20. In Your Own Words You are helping Carisa plan for a party at school. You have purchased several different containers to hold the punch. Carisa has called one evening to discuss how much punch the containers will hold. Write your side of the conversation that explains to Carisa what size the containers are and approximately how much punch each will hold.   See margin.

Mixed Review

21a. The pattern is formed by squares and circles. If the outside figure of the nth stage is a white square, the next stage will have an outside figure of a blue circle.

21. Here are the first four stages of a sequence.

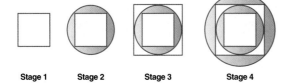

Stage 1   Stage 2   Stage 3   Stage 4

a. Describe the pattern in this sequence.

b. Draw the next stage in the sequence.   See margin.

c. Draw stage 15. Explain how you know you are correct.
     See margin.

22. The number of students in the Science club is 87.5% of the number on the Math team. If there are 21 students in the Science club, how many are on the Math team?   24

23. Of the 21 students in the Science club, 8 are also on the Math team. What percent of the Science club is this?   About 38%

Lesson 7.4   Capacity   **461**

Additional Answers

20. Answers will vary. Students should use vocabulary and estimation skills that they have learned in this chapter. Check that students' estimations and comparisons are reasonable.

21b.

Stage 5

21c. This is correct because every odd stage ends in a square. There are 8 squares and seven circles in this stage.

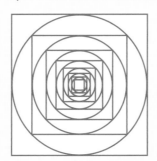

Quick Check

Informal Assessment At the end of the lesson, students should be able to:

✔ find the capacity of a container in metric units

✔ find the capacity of a container in customary units

Quick Quiz

Complete each ratio table.

1.

Milliliters	2,000	5,000	600,000	300
Liters	2	5	600	0.3

2.

Cups	80	240	64	32
Pints	40	120	32	16
Quarts	20	60	16	8
Gallons	5	15	4	2

Select a method to find the equivalent.

3. How many milliliters are in a 2-liter bottle of juice?   2,000 mL

4. How many milliliters are in a 45-liter gas tank?   45,000 mL

5. How many pints are in a 5-gallon water dispenser?   40 pints

6. How many gallons are equal to 8-quart paint cans?   2 gallons

Find the capacity.

7. A bathtub is 200 cm long, 60 cm wide and 30 cm deep. How many liters of water will the bathtub hold?   360 liters

8. A container will hold 6 liters of water. The length of the box is 20 cm long and 30 cm wide. What is the height of the box?   10 cm

9. The punch bowl at the school dance holds 2 gallons of punch. The glasses being used will hold $\frac{3}{4}$ cup of punch. How many whole glasses can be served?   42 glasses

10. A farm's holding tank will hold 2,000 gallons of milk. The milk in the tank will be placed into pint containers. How many pint containers can be filled?   16,000 pint containers

Review & Self-Assessment

Chapter Summary

This summary helps students recall the major topics of the chapter.

Vocabulary

Students should be able to explain each of the terms listed in the vocabulary section.

▶ **Exercises 3–5** You may need to remind students that when they "square a number," they multiply it by itself.

▶ **Exercise 8** You may want to go over this exercise with the class. Have volunteers explain how to find the area of a triangle both with a formula and with finding half of the associated parallelogram.

Vocabulary

arc

area

capacity

central angle

circle sector

parallelogram

perfect square

prism

rectangular prism

surface area

trapezoid

volume

6. No; Possible explanation: Both shapes below have perimeter 8 units. The shape on the left has area 3 unit^2 and the shape on the right has area 4 unit^2.

7. About 6.7 cm^2; Possible answer: First I chose a side to be the base.
   I used my protractor to draw a segment that formed a right angle with the base and extended to the opposite side. I found the length of this segment and the length of the base, and multiplied them to get the area.

Review & Self-Assessment

Chapter Summary

You learned that the area of a shape is the number of square units that fit inside it. You estimated areas of shapes by counting squares, and you learned formulas for calculating areas of rectangles, parallelograms, triangles, trapezoids, and circles.

You were asked to explore the concept of volume by finding the volume and surface area of various block structures. You looked as the simple method of finding the volume and the more complex visual method of finding the surface area. By studying these block structures, you were able to then progress into finding the volume of rectangular prisms using a formula. Both finding the volume when given three measurements and finding a missing measurement when given the volume and other two measurements were applied. Finally, an introduction to polyhedra from polygons was discussed including construction of polyhedra.

Strategies and Applications

The questions in this section will help you review and apply the important ideas and strategies developed in this chapter.

Find the area of each shape.

1. 3 in. 9 in^2
   3 in.

2. 9 cm
   $\frac{1}{3}$ cm 3 cm^2

Square each number.

3. 16.4 268.96   **4.** 12 144   **5.** 0.5 0.25

Finding and estimating areas

6. If two shapes have the same perimeter, must they also have the same area? Use words and drawings to help explain your answer.

7. Find the area of this parallelogram in centimeters. Explain the steps you followed.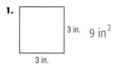

8a. The base is any side of the triangle. The height is the length of the segment from the vertex opposite the base to the base, perpendicular to the base.

8c. Possible answer: The area of a triangle is half the area of the parallelogram formed from two copies of the triangle. The base parallelogram correspond to a base and height of the triangle. Since the area of the parallelogram is the base times the height, the area of the triangle is half the base times the height.

11. Perimeter: 7.2π, or about 22.6 ft; area: 12.96π, or about 40.7 ft^2

13. Perimeter: $15 + \dfrac{5\pi}{2}$ or about 22.9 in.; area: $25 + 3.125\pi$ or about 34.8 in.^{2}

---

8. In this chapter, you learned how to find the area of a triangle.

  a. Describe the base and height of a triangle.

  b. Explain how to find the area of a triangle if you know the lengths of the base and the height. Multiply the base by the height and divide the result by 2.

  c. How is finding the area of a triangle related to finding the area of a parallelogram?

9. A CD has a diameter of about 12 cm. The hole in the center of a CD has a diameter of about 1.5 cm. Find the area of a CD, not including the hole, to the nearest tenth of a square centimeter. Explain how you found your answer.   See margin.

Demonstrating Skills

Find the perimeter and area of each figure.

10.

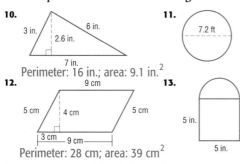

Perimeter: 16 in.; area: 9.1 in.^{2}

11.

7.2 ft

12.

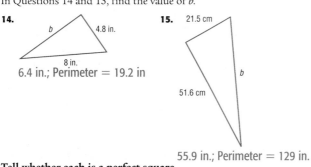

Perimeter: 28 cm; area: 39 cm^2

13.

5 in.

5 in.

In Questions 14 and 15, find the value of *b*.

14.

b   4.8 in.

8 in.

6.4 in.; Perimeter = 19.2 in

15.

21.5 cm

b

51.6 cm

55.9 in.; Perimeter = 129 in.

Tell whether each is a perfect square.

16. 289   Yes   **17.** 72   No   **18.** 1.69   No

19. Elena squared a number and the result was twice the number with which she started. What was her starting number?   2

▶ **Exercise 9** It may help students to make a sketch of a CD and show the given information in the sketch.

▶ **Exercises 10–13** Review how to find the area of polygons using formulas. Have pairs of students compare their solution steps and answers.

▶ **Exercises 14 and 15** Have students work on these exercises in groups. Have them use the Pythagorean theorem to write these equations and then use the guess-check-and-improve problem-solving strategy to find the solution.

Additional Answer

9. About 111.3 cm^2; I found the area of the outside circle and the area of the hole using the formula $A = \pi r^2$. (I had to remember to divide the diameters in half to get the radii.) The area of outside circle is $\pi \cdot 6^2 = 36\pi$, or about 113.1 cm^2. The area of the inside circle is $\pi \cdot 0.75^2 = 0.5625$, or about 1.8 cm^2. The area of the CD is the area of the outer circle minus the area of the hole, which is about $113.1 - 1.8$, or 111.3 cm^2.

▶ **Exercises 20 and 21** Review how to find the area of a trapezoid. Use the parallelogram model if necessary.

▶ **Exercises 23–26** Review how to find the area of a sector as a fraction of the area of a circle. Have volunteers share their solutions.

Find the area of each trapezoid.

20.
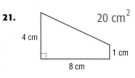
5 in.
4 in.
10 in.
30 in^2

21.
20 cm^2
4 cm
1 cm
8 cm

22. A trapezoid has an area of 240cm^2. Its two bases are 12 cm and 18 cm. What is its height?   16 cm

Calculate the area of each circle sector. Round to the nearest hundredth of a square unit.

23.
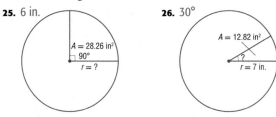
45°
$r = 9$ mm
$\dfrac{81\pi}{8}$ and 31.81 mm^2

24.
120°
$r = 15$ in.
$\dfrac{225\pi}{3}$ and 235.62 in^2

Find the missing information.

25. 6 in.
$A = 28.26$ in^2
90°
$r = ?$

26. 30°
$A = 12.82$ in^2
?
$r = 7$ in.

Calculate the volume of each rectangular prism. Include the appropriate measurement units in your answer.

27.
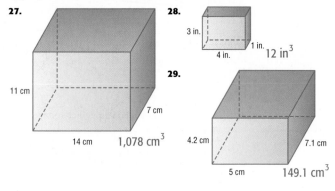
11 cm
7 cm
14 cm
1,078 cm^3

28.
3 in.
1 in.
4 in.
12 in^3

29.
4.2 cm
7.1 cm
5 cm
149.1 cm^3

30. Jenelle's fish tank is 40 cm long, 15 cm wide, and 20 cm high.
She has a bucket with a capacity of 19.8 liters.

a. What is the volume of the fish tank in cubic centimeters?
Cubic meters?   12,000 cm³; 0.012 m³

b. About how many times would she need to fill the bucket and then
transfer all the water to the fish tank in order to fill the tank?
About one time

c. Use your answer from Part b to estimate about how many liters
of water the fish tank holds.   About 12L

▶ **Exercise 30** Review the connection
between the metric capacity of an object
with cubic centimeters. Have students check
their answers in groups.

Test-Taking Practice

SHORT RESPONSE

1 Shana is wrapping a package that has
the shape of a right triangular prism,
as shown to the right.

What is the minimum amount of paper
that would be needed to cover all the
surfaces of the package? The surface
area of a right triangular prism = $wh +
lw + lh + ls$.

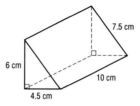

7.5 cm

6 cm

10 cm

4.5 cm

Show your work.

Answer _____

Show your work:
Surface area = $wh + lw + lh + ls$ = $(4.5)(6) + (10)(4.5) + (10)(6) + (10)(7.5)$ = $27 + 45 + 60 + 75 = 207$

Answer: 207 square
centimeters

MULTIPLE CHOICE

2 Which of the following numbers
is not a perfect square?

(A) 156
B 196
C 256
D 324

3 What is the area of the triangle
shown?

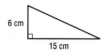

6 cm

15 cm

F 21 square centimeters
(G) 45 square centimeters
H 60 square centimeters
J 90 square centimeters

4 A fish tank is 20 inches long, 10
inches wide, and 12 inches high.
What is the volume of the tank?

A 240 cubic inches
B 1,120 cubic inches
C 1,200 cubic inches
(D) 2,400 cubic inches

5 What is the area of a circle with a
15-cm diameter? Use 3.14 for π.

F 23.55 centimeters
G 47.1 centimeters
(H) 176.6 centimeters
J 706.5 centimeters

CHAPTER 7 Review & Self-Assessment   **465**

Coordinate Plane

Chapter Overview

This chapter develops the concept that representing information graphically is one way to communicate mathematical ideas. Although students have been using graphs throughout their school years, this chapter introduces a more formal way of making and interpreting graphs.

The first lesson focuses on finding the relationship between the two variables for a given point or line. Students learn that graphs can be used to make comparisons and to show stories. They make simple point and line graphs from written descriptions. Graphing coordinates is the focus of the second and third lessons, including coordinates in the four quadrants. Students use ordered pairs to plot and identify points as the first step toward making graphs.

The **Big** Picture

Links to the Past	Chapter **8**	Links to the Future
Grade 5 Interpreting bar graphs and pictographs.	**Lesson 8.1** (p. 468) Interpret Graphs	**Course 2, Chapter 8** Linear Relationships (pp. 366–433) **Course 3, Chapter 1** Linear Relationships (pp. 2–63)
Grade 5 Creating bar graphs and pictographs; plotting points with whole-number coordinates.	**Lesson 8.2** (p. 489) Draw and Label Graphs	**Course 3, Chapter 8** Quadratic and Inverse Relationships (pp. 372–463)
Grade 5 Plotting points with whole-number coordinates.	**Lesson 8.3** (p. 509) Graph in Four Quadrants	**Course 2, Chapter 8** Linear Relationships (pp. 366–433) **Course 3, Chapter 2** Lines and Angles (pp. 64–109)

Mathematical Background

This chapter introduces students to reading, interpreting, and constructing coordinate graphs. Graphing is a powerful mathematical tool that they will use in a myriad of applications of mathematics including algebra, trigonometry, and calculus. While the mathematics of plotting and reading points on a graph is straightforward, interpreting graphs requires some critical thinking.

One of the most common uses of graphs is to provide a visual representation of data and to use the representation to help determine what kinds of relationships between the variables can be inferred. Some line graphs, such as those showing the noise level during a play, are irregular in form. Although these graphs can be understood and interpreted after the fact, they cannot be used to predict the future with any degree of accuracy.

Interpreting Discrete Points Every point on a coordinate graph represents a relationship between the values for the two variables shown in the labels of the axes. Considering the axes as number lines can help in the analysis of the relative relationship between points in a graph, even when there are no scales on the axes, since the values will increase when moving to the right on the horizontal axis and when moving up on the vertical axis.

Making sense of a graph that shows qualitative relationships can take much thought. When a graph has many points, and thus more data to consider, interpretations may be more general.

Constructing Graphs Constructing a point or line graph is a matter of identifying the variables and units, gathering data, determining the horizontal and vertical axes, defining a scale, plotting points, and deciding whether to connect the points. Students may have difficulty defining a scale and determining where to plot the points, especially when the coordinates lie between scale values and grid lines. The simplest graph has each grid line standing for one unit of each variable, and every point with whole-number coordinates can be plotted on an intersection of two grid lines. In practice, graphs are frequently more complex. The available space and the range of the graph determine the scale.

Additional Reading

According to Monk in *Representation in School Mathematics: Learning to Graph and Graphing to Learn,* graphing should be a way to think and communicate information about data. In this chapter, students will analyze graphs as a way to communicate information.

Planning Guide
Lesson Resources

	Lesson 8.1 Pacing: 4 days	**Lesson 8.2** Pacing: 4 days	**Lesson 8.3** Pacing: 6 days
Lesson Title	**Interpret Graphs** (p. 468)	**Draw and Label Graphs** (p. 489)	**Graph in Four Quadrants** (p. 509)
Lesson Objectives	• To interpret points on a qualitative graph • To understand the meaning of *variable* as it relates to graphing with horizontal and vertical axes • To analyze the relationship between the variables on a graph • To understand the difference between line and point graphs	• To create graphs that describe a story relating two variables that change over time • To plot points in the first quadrant of a coordinate grid • To observe any patterns, or trends, in data and use them to make predictions • To determine an appropriate scale for a set of data	• To graph positive and negative numbers on a number line • To identify opposites and find absolute values • To compare and order positive and negative numbers • To create and interpret four-quadrant graphs • To use the distinguishing characteristics of points in the plane to analyze graphs
Materials	Lesson 8.1 Masters 1 and 2, transparency of Lesson 8.1 Master 1	Lesson 8.2 Masters 1–6, transparency of Lesson 8.2 Master 1 or graph paper, Chapter 8 Masters 1 and 2	Lesson 8.3 Masters 1–3, *counters in 2 colors
Quick Review Math Handbook	**Lesson 4.2** Displaying Data	**Lesson 4.2** Displaying Data; **Lesson 5.7** Graphing on the Coordinate Plane	**Lesson 5.7** Graphing on the Coordinate Plane; **Lesson 1.5** Integer Operations
Print Resources	CRM Study Guide and Intervention (p. 5) CRM Skills Practice (p. 6) CRM Problem-Solving Practice (p. 7) CRM Enrichment (p. 8) • Investigation Notebook and Reflection Journal • Differentiation Handbook	CRM Study Guide and Intervention (p. 12) CRM Skills Practice (p. 13) CRM Problem-Solving Practice (p. 14) CRM Enrichment (p. 15) • Investigation Notebook and Reflection Journal • Differentiation Handbook	CRM Study Guide and Intervention (p. 23) CRM Skills Practice (p. 24) CRM Problem-Solving Practice (p. 25) CRM Enrichment (p. 26) • Investigation Notebook and Reflection Journal • Differentiation Handbook
Technology Resources	TeacherWorks Plus Classroom Presentation Toolkit ExamView Assessment Suite StudentWorks Plus Math Online Brain Pops • Concepts in Motion	TeacherWorks Plus Classroom Presentation Toolkit ExamView Assessment Suite StudentWorks Plus Math Online Brain Pops • Concepts in Motion	TeacherWorks Plus Classroom Presentation Toolkit ExamView Assessment Suite StudentWorks Plus Math Online Brain Pops • Concepts in Motion

*Included in Impact Mathematics Manipulative Kit

Assessment Resources

MARS Assessment: Teaching with Purpose

Congruent Triangles

In *Congruent Triangles*, students identify congruent triangles and find the area of a polygon. Using a diagram, students plot the coordinates of the vertices of a square, mark the correct points, and join the given lines to form congruent triangles.

Targeting the Task

- **Diagnostic**—Use Exercises 1–3 in the *Congruent Triangles* assessment to determine students' understanding of how to identify congruent triangles, understand the coordinate plane, and find the area of a polygon. For those students who do not have this understanding, completing this unit is needed.

- **Formative**—Exercises 1–3 can be administered individually according to the lessons.

- **Summative**—Administer the complete *Congruent Triangles* performance-based assessment.

CRM Chapter 8 MARS Assessment
(pp. 50–52)

Chapter 8 MARS Performance-Based Assessment

Congruent Triangles

This problem gives you the chance to:
• identify congruent triangles
• find the area of a polygon

This diagram shows a square *ABCD* drawn on coordinate axes.

1. Write down the coordinates of the vertices of the square.
   A (   )   B (   )   C (   )   D (   )

2. Mark the points *E* (-2, 0), *F* (2, -2), *G* (4, 2), *H* (0, 4) on the diagram.
   Draw the lines *EF, FG, GH, HE*.

3. Write down the names of any triangles that are congruent to triangle *AHE*.
   Explain why they are congruent.

Assessment Planning Guide

Assessments are available for investigations, lessons, and chapters.

 **ExamView®** Assessment Suite — Customize and create multiple versions of tests and quizzes.

	Student Edition	**Teacher Edition**	**Other Resources**
Diagnostic			CRM Chapter 8 Pretest (p. 30) Math Online › Online Chapter Quiz
Formative	Share & Summarize (pp. 472, 476, 481, 490, 494, 499, 500, 502, 512, 514, 518, 521)	Troubleshooting (pp. 470, 472, 476, 481, 499, 502, 512, 518, 521, 522) On the Spot Assessment (pp. 473, 477, 492, 495, 498, 501, 511, 513, 515, 520) Quick Check (pp. 487, 507, 526) Quick Quiz (pp. 488, 508, 527)	
Summative	Review & Self-Assessment (pp. 528–531)		CRM Chapter 8 Test: Forms A and B (pp. 35–44) CRM Standardized Test Practice (p. 48)
Performance-Based	In Your Own Words (pp. 487, 507, 527)		CRM MARS Performance-Based Assessment (p. 50) CRM Chapter Performance Assessment (p. 45)

Differentiated Instruction

Reaching All Learners

Below are suggestions on differentiating the materials presented in this chapter. Additional modifications should be considered.

Approaching Level · AL

Lesson 8.1: Interpreting Graphs For students who have trouble reading and interpreting graphs, create several graphs like the ones on page 486, Exercise 3. Use various labels on both axes, and have students tell about each graph. Have pairs decide what each axis represents and what the points on the graph represent. Ask students to write a sentence describing the graph and its purpose. Read the students' answers to determine what parts of the lessons they have difficulty understanding. Then draw some blank graph outlines, and have pairs create their own descriptions for each axis and point. Have pairs trade and interpret each other's graphs.

Beyond Level · BL

Lesson 8.3: Quadrants Have students draw a coordinate plane and plot several points in all four quadrants. Remind them to label each point with a different letter and to mark the axes so that the center is 0. Point out that it is important to place negative and positive numbers correctly and carefully. Then have them trade with a friend. Have each student call out a quadrant. The partner should call out all the points in that quadrant. Players take turns, calling out quadrants or other rules (e.g., all points with a negative first coordinate). Tell each pair to check each other and themselves; make sure they are choosing the correct points for each category or rule.

On Level · OL

Lesson 8.3: Coordinates Have students create a coordinate plane and randomly plot points in all four quadrants. Remind them to label each axis carefully, with zero in the center and negative and positive numbers placed in appropriate positions. Then have them list the coordinates for each of the points they plotted. Have students trade lists with a partner. Tell partners to plot each other's points and compare graphs to see if they correctly identified the coordinates for each point. If they did, the points on both students' graphs should all be in the same place. If not, they need to check for errors. Remind them that errors commonly occur in reversing the order of coordinates; make sure they wrote the *x*-coordinate first.

English Language Learners · ELL

Lesson 8.1: Interpret Graphs Because word problems cause the most difficulty for students with language barriers, it may help to have English Language Learners read the problems in this lesson with a partner. Have them create a symbol to use each time they see words that appear frequently in the problems, such as using an arrow for *connect* or a question mark for the word *variable*. Tell students to read the problem and find those words, and remind them to draw the symbol they created over its respective word. Then have them read the problem out loud and tell how they would answer it. Encourage them to use the words they labeled in their explanations, so that they can become more comfortable with math terminology.

KEY

 Approaching Level On Level Beyond Level English Language Learners

Intervention Planning Guide

CRM Assess students' prerequisite skills and knowledge using the
Chapter Pretest found in the Chapter 8 Resource Masters, p. 31.

Intensive Intervention two or more years below grade level	Strategic Intervention below grade level	On Level	Beyond Level
If students miss 75% of the exercises: **Then** use *Math Triumphs,* an intensive intervention	**If** students miss 50% of the exercises: **Then** choose a resource:	**If** students miss 25% of the exercises: **Then** choose a resource:	**If** students miss 0%–10% of the exercises: **Then** choose a resource:
Math Triumphs, Grade 6 • Chapter 9: Variables and Expressions	CRM Study Guide and Intervention (pp. 5, 12, 23) • Investigation Notebook and Reflection Journal • Differentiation Handbook Math Online Brain Pops • Concepts in Motion	CRM Skills Practice (pp. 6, 13, 24) CRM Problem-Solving Practice (pp. 7, 14, 25) • Investigation Notebook and Reflection Journal	CRM Enrichment (pp. 8, 15, 26) • Differentiation Handbook

Literature Connections

Recommended Outside Reading for Students

Nonfiction

William P. Berlinghoff and Fernando Q. Gouvea. *Math Through the Ages: A Gentle History for Teachers and Others.* Oxton House, 2002.

This book provides a framework of important people and events that shaped mathematics. The history of negative integers is one of several topics examined.

Fiction

Julie Glass. *The Fly on the Ceiling: A Math Myth.* Bt Bound, 1999.

This humorous tale combines math with history. It is based on the story of Rene Descartes, the French mathematician for whom the Cartesian Coordinate System is named.

McGraw Hill Professional Development

Targeted professional development has been articulated throughout the *IMPACT Mathematics* series. The **McGraw-Hill Professional Development Video Library** provides short videos that support the mathematics standards. Log on to <u>www.glencoe.com</u>.

Model Lessons   Instructional Strategies

Real-Life Math

Let It Snow, Let It Snow, Let It Snow Ask students if they have ever seen a snowstorm. Have them share when and where they have seen the most snow at one time. Have students identify some of the characteristics of the graph about snowstorms in New York City. Depending upon their prior experience, students may identify the title, the labels, and the scales. If they cannot, you may want to point out these characteristics. They will be introduced in greater depth during the first lesson.

Think About It According to the graph, about 30 inches of snow fell in February, 2006 and about 10 inches fell in December, 2005. Therefore, about three times more snow fell in February, 2006 than in December, 2005.

CHAPTER

8 # Coordinate Plane

Real-Life Math

Let It Snow, Let It Snow, Let It Snow Do you remember what you were doing on February 12, 2006? If you lived in New York City, it probably involved snow. The graph below shows the snowfall amounts in New York City for five months during the 2005–2006 season.

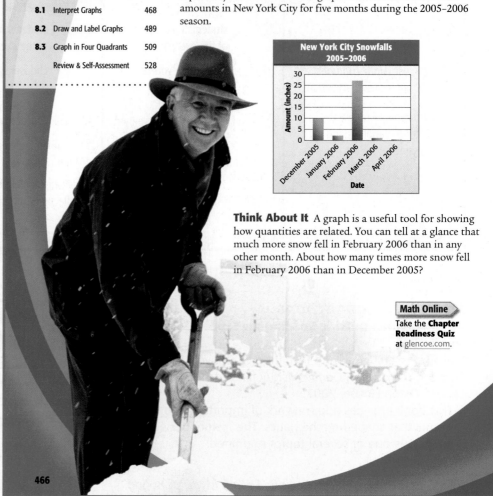

Think About It A graph is a useful tool for showing how quantities are related. You can tell at a glance that much more snow fell in February 2006 than in any other month. About how many times more snow fell in February 2006 than in December 2005?

Math Online
Take the **Chapter Readiness Quiz** at glencoe.com.

Chapter Resources

CRM Chapter 8 Resource Masters

CRM English/Spanish Family Letter (pp. 1 and 2)

CRM Lesson Masters (pp. 3, 4, 10, 11, 17–22, 28–30)

CRM Chapter 8 Pretest (pp. 31–34)

CRM Chapter 8 Tests (pp. 35–47)

Math Online Online Readiness Quiz • eGlossary

Dear Family,

Graphs can be seen everywhere, on the sports page of the newspaper, in advertisements, and in your Science or Social Studies books. Most of these graphs are line graphs, bar graphs, or circle graphs. In this chapter, your student will learn about graphs that use points and lines to show patterns and relationships in data.

Key Concept—Graphs

Here is an example. This graph has a horizontal axis and a vertical axis. It shows the prices of different bags of sugar. From this graph, facts like the following can be determined.

Bags of Sugar

- *D* is the heaviest.

- *B* and *F* are the same weight.

- *C*, *E*, and *D* are heavier than *B*.

- *E* and *F* cost more than *D*.

- *C* would give you a better value for the money than *B* because you get more sugar for only a little more cost.

In this chapter, your student will draw graphs for many types of situations. Some graphs, like the one above, will not have numerical values. Others will have scales, or sequences of numbers, along each axis.

Chapter Vocabulary

absolute value	opposites
axes	ordered pair
coordinates	origin
line graph	positive numbers
negative numbers	quadrants

Home Activities

- Help your student find examples of how graphs are used in everyday life by looking in newspapers and magazines.
- Encourage your student to determine what the graphs show, as well as the values for specific points in the graphs.

Family Letter

Another version of the Family Letter, available in English and Spanish, is found in the Chapter 8 Resource Masters. You may want to send a copy of this letter home with your students.

Key Concept—Use Points and Lines to Show Patterns Introduce students the patterns and relationships in data by asking them to verify the interpretations for the graph. Then ask them where they would plot Bag G of sugar that weighs more than all the rest. Where would they plot Bag H of sugar that costs about half as much as Bag F?

Home Activities

- Each day have your student look at the business pages of a newspaper and cut out graphs they see. What do the graphs represent?

- Have your student collect data for one week about how many hours they study. Then ask them how they might show the data as a graph.

Key Vocabulary

English (Spanish) *Introduce the most important terms from Chapter 8.*

absolute value (valor absoluto) The distance between a number and zero on a number line. (p. 513)

axes (ejes) The horizontal and vertical line that are used to represent variable quantities on a graph. (p. 469)

coordinates (coordenadas) Numbers that represent the location of a point on a graph. For example, if a point is 3 units to the right and 7 units up from the origin, its coordinates are 3 and 7. (p. 491)

line graph (graficá lineal) A graph in which points are connected with line segments. (p. 476)

ordered pair (par ordenade) A pair of numbers that represent the coordinates of a point, with the horizontal coordinate of the point written first. For example, the point with horizontal coordinate 3 and vertical coordinate 7 is represented by (3, 7). (p. 491)

origin (origen) The point where the axes of a graph meet. The *origin* of a graph is usually the 0 point for each axis. (p. 469)

Interpret Graphs

Overview

In this lesson, students interpret points on graphs making use of the use a graph problem-solving strategy. They focus their attention on the relationships among such points, considering the comparative qualities of the variables involved. They also look at how graphs tell stories over time and write possible stories, or explanations, for the data in graphs. Students are asked to observe whether multiple points form a pattern, thereby indicating a relationship between the variables. They describe these relationships in words. Later in the lesson, students explore the issue of whether to connect the points on a graph by looking at discreet versus continuous data, although they do not use this terminology.

Advance Preparation

You may want to provide Lesson 8.1 Masters 1 and 2 to facilitate class discussion while presenting new topics, including looking at patterns in graphs.

Objectives

▶ To interpret points on a qualitative graph

▶ To understand the meaning of *variable* as it relates to graphing with horizontal and vertical axes

▶ To analyze the relationship between the variables on a graph

▶ To understand the difference between line and point graphs

	Summary	Materials	On Your Own Exercises (pp. 482–488)	Assessment Opportunities
Investigation 1 (p. 468) **Pacing:** 2 days	Students look at the relationship between points on graphs without scales.	Lesson 8.1 Master 1, transparency of Lesson 8.1 Master 1 (optional)	Practice & Apply: 1, 2 Mixed Review: 14–37	• Share & Summarize (p. 472) • Troubleshooting (pp. 470, 472)
Investigation 2 (p. 472) **Pacing:** 1 day	Students extend their skills from Investigation 1 and look at patterns shown by multiple points on a graph.		Practice & Apply: 3, 4 Connect & Extend: 8–10 Mixed Review: 14–37	• On the Spot Assessment (p. 473) • Share & Summarize (p. 476) • Troubleshooting (p. 476)
Investigation 3 (p. 476) **Pacing:** 1 day	Students make and interpret line graphs and determine when it is appropriate to connect points on a graph.	Lesson 8.1 Master 2	Practice & Apply: 5–7 Connect & Extend: 11–13 Mixed Review: 14–37	• On the Spot Assessment (p. 477) • Share & Summarize (p. 481) • Troubleshooting (p. 481)

Leveled Lesson Resources

CRM *Available in:* **Chapter 8 Resource Masters**

Study Guide and Intervention (p. 5) — AL

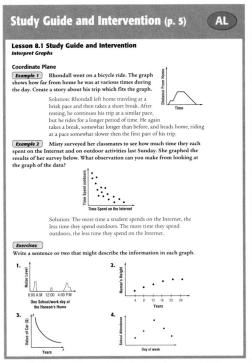

Lesson 8.1 Study Guide and Intervention
Interpret Graphs

Coordinate Plane

Example 1 Rhondall went on a bicycle ride. The graph shows how far from home he was at various times during the day. Create a story about his trip which fits the graph.

Solution: Rhondall left home traveling at a brisk pace and then takes a short break. After resting, he continues his trip at a similar pace, but he rides for a longer period of time. He again takes a break, somewhat longer than before, and heads home, riding at a pace somewhat slower then the first part of his trip.

Example 2 Misty surveyed her classmates to see how much time they each spent on the Internet and on outdoor activities last Sunday. She graphed the results of her survey below. What observation can you make from looking at the graph of the data?

Solution: The more time a student spends on the Internet, the less time they spend outdoors. The more time they spend outdoors, the less time they spend on the Internet.

Exercises

Write a sentence or two that might describe the information in each graph.

Skills Practice (p. 6) — AL OL

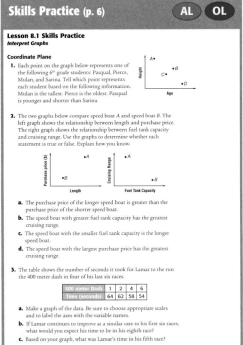

Lesson 8.1 Skills Practice
Interpret Graphs

Coordinate Plane

1. Each point on the graph below represents one of the following 6th grade students: Pasqual, Pierce, Mulan, and Sarina. Tell which point represents each student based on the following information. Mulan is the tallest. Pierce is the oldest. Pasqual is younger and shorter than Sarina.

2. The two graphs below compare speed boat A and speed boat B. The left graph shows the relationship between length and purchase price. The right graph shows the relationship between fuel tank capacity and cruising range. Use the graphs to determine whether each statement is true or false. Explain how you know.

a. The purchase price of the longer speed boat is greater than the purchase price of the shorter speed boat.

b. The speed boat with greater fuel tank capacity has the greatest cruising range.

c. The speed boat with the smaller fuel tank capacity is the longer speed boat.

d. The speed boat with the largest purchase price has the greatest cruising range.

3. The table shows the number of seconds it took for Lamar to the run the 400 meter dash in four of his last six races.

400 meter Dash	1	2	4	6
Time (seconds)	64	62	58	54

a. Make a graph of the data. Be sure to choose appropriate scales and to label the axes with the variable names.

b. If Lamar continues to improve at a similar rate to his first six races, what would you expect his time to be in his eighth race?

c. Based on your graph, what was Lamar's time in his fifth race?

Problem-Solving Practice (p. 7) — AL OL

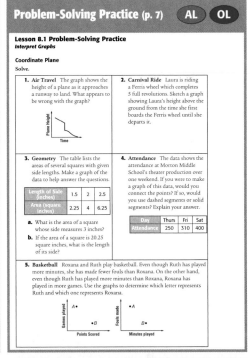

Lesson 8.1 Problem-Solving Practice
Interpret Graphs

Coordinate Plane

Solve.

1. **Air Travel** The graph shows the height of a plane as it approaches a runway to land. What appears to be wrong with the graph?

2. **Carnival Ride** Laura is riding a Ferris wheel which completes 5 full revolutions. Sketch a graph showing Laura's height above the ground from the time she first boards the Ferris wheel until she departs at.

3. **Geometry** The table lists the areas of several squares with given side lengths. Make a graph of the data to help answer the questions.

Length of Side (inches)	1.5	2	2.5
Area (square inches)	2.25	4	6.25

a. What is the area of a square whose side measures 3 inches?

b. If the area of a square is 20.25 square inches, what is the length of its side?

4. **Attendance** The data shows the attendance at Morton Middle School's theater production over one weekend. If you were to make a graph of this data, would you connect the points? If so, would you use dashed segments or solid segments? Explain your answer.

Day	Thurs	Fri	Sat
Attendance	250	310	400

5. **Basketball** Roxana and Ruth play basketball. Even though Ruth has played more minutes, she has made fewer fouls than Roxana. On the other hand, even though Ruth has played more minutes than Roxana, Roxana has played in more games. Use the graphs to determine which letter represents Ruth and which one represents Roxana.

Enrichment (p. 8) — BL

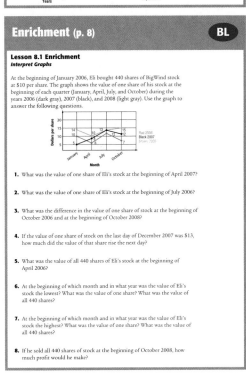

Lesson 8.1 Enrichment
Interpret Graphs

At the beginning of January 2006, Eli bought 440 shares of BigWind stock at $10 per share. The graph shows the value of one share of his stock at the beginning of each quarter (January, April, July, and October) during the years 2006 (dark gray), 2007 (black), and 2008 (light gray). Use the graph to answer the following questions.

1. What was the value of one share of Eli's stock at the beginning of April 2007?

2. What was the value of one share of Eli's stock at the beginning of July 2006?

3. What was the difference in the value of one share of stock at the beginning of October 2006 and at the beginning of October 2008?

4. If the value of one share of stock on the last day of December 2007 was $13, how much did the value of that share rise the next day?

5. What was the value of all 440 shares of Eli's stock at the beginning of April 2006?

6. At the beginning of which month and in what year was the value of Eli's stock the lowest? What was the value of one share? What was the value of all 440 shares?

7. At the beginning of which month and in what year was the value of Eli's stock the highest? What was the value of one share? What was the value of all 440 shares?

8. If he sold all 440 shares of stock at the beginning of October 2008, how much profit would he make?

Lesson Quick Quiz (p. 9) — AL OL BL

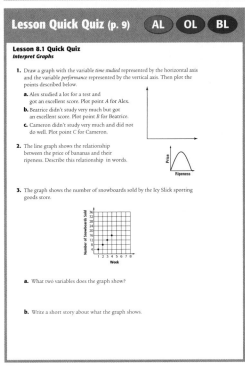

Lesson 8.1 Quick Quiz
Interpret Graphs

1. Draw a graph with the variable *time studied* represented by the horizontal axis and the variable *performance* represented by the vertical axis. Then plot the points described below.

a. Alex studied a lot for a test and got an excellent score. Plot point A for Alex.

b. Beatrice didn't study very much but got an excellent score. Plot point B for Beatrice.

c. Cameron didn't study very much and did not do well. Plot point C for Cameron.

2. The line graph shows the relationship between the price of bananas and their ripeness. Describe this relationship in words.

3. The graph shows the number of snowboards sold by the Icy Slick sporting goods store.

a. What two variables does the graph show?

b. Write a short story about what the graph shows.

Lesson Masters 1 and 2 (pp. 10–11)

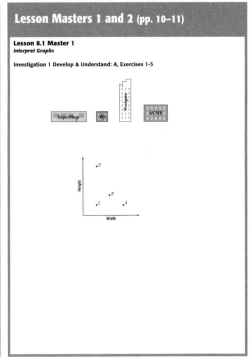

Lesson 8.1 Master 1
Interpret Graphs

Investigation 1 Develop & Understand: A, Exercises 1–5

Additional Lesson Resources

Teacher Tech Tools
- TeacherWorks
- ExamView Assessment Suite
- Classroom Presentation Toolkit
- Advance Tracker

Student Tech Tools
- StudentWorks Plus
- **Math Online** eGlossary •
  Concepts in Motion

Other Print Products
- Investigation Notebook and Reflection Journal
- Quick Review Math Handbook

Introduce

Interpret Graphs Explain to students that they will be using graphs to describe and analyze situations. Ask them the following question to assess their knowledge of, and familiarity with, graphs.

If someone asked you what a graph was, how would you respond? At this point, students should feel comfortable describing graphs as a display of information that can be counted or measured.

Explore

Suggested Grouping: Pairs or Small Groups

This activity has students think about the essential characteristics of a graph as they invent their own situations and describe how the graphs of the situations would look. Students are not asked to make a graph, although some may want to quickly sketch one before describing it. Encourage students to think of quick examples and to give simple explanations of how their graphs look.

Investigation 1

On Your Own Exercises
Pages 482–488
Exercises 1, 2

Understand Graphs Have students compare the views of the four buildings. They should note that the buildings have different heights and widths. Introduce the term *variable* as given here. A more formal definition is inappropriate at this stage. Encouraging the use of the word in describing aspects of relationships is a good idea, however. The many meanings of the term will be developed throughout the program in Courses 1–3. Ask students why they think the height and width of the buildings can be called variables. Point out that the heights and widths of the buildings as a group vary. Without additional construction, the height and width of an individual building cannot vary.

LESSON 8.1 Interpret Graphs

You can find graphs in many places, in your school books, on television, and in magazines and newspapers. Graphs are useful for displaying information so it can be understood at a glance. They are also a wonderful tool for making comparisons.

Explore

Choose a topic in which you are interested, such as cars, dogs, or music. Think about some aspects of your topic that would be interesting to display in a graph. Describe what the graph might look like. Answers will vary.

For example, if you choose cars for your topic, you might graph the number of cars of different sizes sold at a local dealership. You could list the sizes as compact, midsize, and full-size along the bottom and then draw bars to show how many cars of each size are sold in a day.

You have seen graphs that use bars, sections of circles, and pictures to display data. In this lesson, you will focus on graphs that use points and curves to show information.

Investigation 1 Understand Graphs

Vocabulary

axes

origin

Materials

- drawing of the buildings
- graph of the buildings

Here are the front views of four buildings.

SuperShop   Post Office   Westgate   Acme

Some of the buildings are taller than others, and some are wider than others. In other words, the heights and widths of the buildings vary. As you may recall, quantities that vary, or change, are called variables.

Graphs are a convenient way to show information about two variables at the same time. This graph displays information about the heights and widths of the buildings shown on page 468. Each point represents one of the buildings.

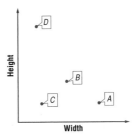

The horizontal line, representing the variable *width*, and the vertical line, representing the variable *height*, are called **axes**. The point where the axes meet is called the **origin**. The origin of a graph is usually the 0 point for each axis.

The arrow on each axis shows the direction in which the values of the variable are increasing. For example, points on the right side of the graph represent wider buildings than points on the left. Points near the top represent taller buildings than points near the bottom.

This graph does not have numbers along the axes, so it does not tell you the actual heights or widths of the buildings. However, it does show you how the heights and widths compare.

Think & Discuss

Which point represents a wider building, *A* or *B*? Explain how you know. Point *A*; it is further to the right.

Which building does Point *A* represent? How do you know? SuperShop; since *A* is further right, it represents the widest building.

Lesson 8.1 Interpret Graphs **469**

Develop & Understand: A

Suggested Grouping: Pairs

▶ **Exercises 1–5** Point out that these exercises focus on the relationship between points on a graph. Providing students with copies of Lesson 8.1 Master 1 will allow them more time to work through the problems since it eliminates the need to copy the graph.

▶ **Exercises 2 and 3** Encourage students to use the graph to answer these exercises, rather than label the building art on their masters with the corresponding point names, and use that illustration to make the comparisons.

Wrap-Up Go over students' responses to the exercises. Because the relationship between points on a graph is critical to graph interpretation, spend enough time discussing this exercise set to make sure that students understand this concept. Have students describe where they added the points in Exercise 4. If you made a transparency of the graph, have volunteers plot the points on that graph so students see that there is more than one correct answer.

Develop & Understand: B

Suggested Grouping: Pairs

▶ **Exercise 6** This exercise may expose a fairly common misconception of sixth graders that a graph is like a photograph, in the sense that if straight lines were drawn from a point to each of the axes, the rectangle formed would approximate the shape of the front view of the building. By switching the variables on the axes, students can see that this interpretation is inaccurate.

Troubleshooting Watch for students who do not look at the axes and confuse the variables when looking at the points, especially in Exercise 1, where height is along the horizontal axis. These kinds of problems force students to think about what the axes and corresponding values mean. You might choose a point on the graph in question and ask, "Is this building taller than the others?"

Develop & Understand: A

1. Identify the buildings represented by points *B*, *C*, and *D* on the graph of the buildings on page 469. Point *B* is Acme; point *C* is the post office; point *D* is Westgate.
2. Which letters represent buildings that are less wide than the building represented by point *B*?   *C* and *D*
3. Which letters represent buildings that are shorter than the building represented by point *B*?   *C* and *A*
4. On a copy of the graph, add two more points, one to represent a skyscraper and the other to represent a doghouse. Explain how you decided where to put the points.   See margin.
5. Now imagine a building with a different height and width from the four in the drawing.
   a. On a copy of the drawing, make a sketch of the building you are imagining.   Answers will vary.
   b. Add a point to the graph to represent your building. Answers will vary.
   c. Show your graph to a partner. Ask him or her to sketch or describe your building.   Answers will vary.

In the graph you used in Exercises 1–5, the variable *width* is represented by the horizontal axis. The variable *height* is represented by the vertical axis. You could instead label the axes the other way.

Develop & Understand: B

6. In this graph, the horizontal axis shows height. The vertical axis shows width.
   a. Plot a point for each of the four buildings on a copy of this set of axes.
   b. How does your graph compare to the graph on the previous page? Possible answer: It is as if the first graph is turned on its side. For example, point *D* was high and to the left on the first graph. In the second graph, it is low and to the right.

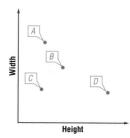

Real-World Link
One of the world's largest hotels is the MGM Grand in Las Vegas, Nevada. The hotel has 5,044 guest rooms and covers 112 acres.

Additional Answer

4. Possible answer: A doghouse would be shorter and less wide than the other buildings, so I put it below and to the left of the other points. A skyscraper would be very tall and not very wide. I put it above all the other points and made it a little wider than the post office.

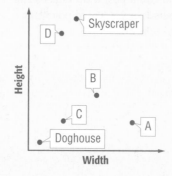

7. The points on the graph below represent the height and weight of the donkey, dog, crocodile, and ostrich shown in the drawing.

a. What are the two variables represented in the graph?
Weight and height

b. Tell which point represents each animal. Explain how you decided.
See margin.

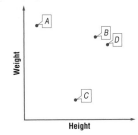

8. The two graphs below compare car A and car B. The left graph shows the relationship between age and value. The right graph shows the relationship between size and maximum speed.

8a. False; since point B is to the right of point A on the first graph, car B is older. It is also above point A on the same graph, so car B is more valuable.

8b. True; since point B is above point A on the second graph, car B is faster. It is also to the right of point A on this graph, so car B is larger.

8c–e. See margin.

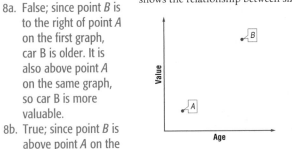
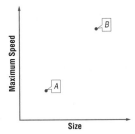

Use the graphs to determine whether each statement is true or false. Explain how you know.

a. The older car is less valuable.　**b.** The faster car is larger.

c. The larger car is older.　**d.** The faster car is older.

e. The more valuable car is slower.

Lesson 8.1 Interpret Graphs　**471**

▶ **Exercise 7** Encourage students to use language such as, "The farther to the right a point is, the taller the animal," when determining which point represents which animal.

▶ **Exercise 8** Students have to use both graphs for **Parts c–e**. For example, in Part e, students can use the first graph to find that Car B is more valuable and the information from the second graph to determine that Car B is faster; combining these facts, the students should see that the statement is false. These problems may be difficult for some students. If you have students work in pairs, encourage them to talk about how they are interpreting the graphs.

Wrap-Up Discuss Exercise 7, and encourage students to talk about where they started in determining how to match an animal with a point. You might ask them which animal was the easiest for them to locate. Many may say that they started with the crocodile since it had the shortest height. Then have students share how they determined their answers in Exercise 8.

Additional Answers

7b. Point A: crocodile; Point B: donkey; Point C: dog; Point D: ostrich; Possible explanation: Point A represents the shortest animal, which is the crocodile. Point D represents the tallest animal, which is the ostrich. The dog is the second shortest, and it looks like the lightest animal, so it must be represented by Point C. The donkey must be Point B.

8c. True; since Point B is to the right of Point A on the second graph, Car B is larger. Since Point B is to the right of Point A on the first graph, Car B is older.

8d. True; Car B is faster, since Point B is above Point A on the second graph, and Car B is older, since Point B is to the right of Point A on the first graph.

8e. False; since Point B is above Point A, Car B is more valuable. Since Point B is above Point A on the second graph, Car B is faster.

Lesson 8.1 Interpret Graphs　**471**

Share & Summarize

Like Exercise 6 on page 470, this exercise addresses the misconception that a graph is a picture of the corresponding situation. You may want to have students work on this question in pairs or small groups, and have the groups present their different drawings to the whole class. You may want to ask clarifying questions such as:

Which chimney is the tallest? Chimney A

Which two chimneys have the greatest difference in width? Chimneys B and D

Troubleshooting If students are having difficulty making comparisons on graphs with multiple points, use one of the graphs in an exercise set and break the questions down into simpler tasks. For example, have students begin by thinking about extreme points: the tallest, the shortest, the heaviest, and so on. Then have them determine where these points would lie on the graph.

Investigation 2

On Your Own Exercises
Pages 482–488
Exercises 3, 4, 8–10

Interpret Points Remind students that they learned about how to determine the relationship between two points on a graph in Investigation 1. Tell them they will practice this skill in this investigation to help them become more confident in their abilities. Point out that the graphs in this investigation have no scales, which means they must focus on the relationship between objects.

Example

Work through this example, especially if the previous investigation proved difficult for students. Encourage students to make other suggestions as to what Y and Z could represent in the graph. If students feel comfortable with this example, they will not have difficulty with the next exercise set.

Share & Summarize

This graph shows the heights and widths of four chimneys. Sketch four chimneys that the points could represent. On your sketch, label each chimney with the correct letter.   See margin.

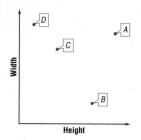

Investigation 2 Interpret Points

It takes practice to become skillful at reading graphs. When you look at a graph, you need to think carefully about what the variables are and where each point is located.

Example

What information does this graph show?
* The two variables are speed and age.
* Y is faster than Z. Z is older than Y.

What might Y and Z represent?
* Y and Z could be computers since a newer computer usually processes information faster than an older computer.
* Y could represent a boy. Z could represent his grandfather. The grandfather is older than the boy. The boy runs faster than the grandfather.

Additional Answer
Share & Summarize:
Possible sketch:

Chimney A

Chimney B

Chimney C

Chimney D

Lesson 8.1 Interpret Graphs **473**

1a. Distance from the ocean and rainfall

1b. *B* is closer to the ocean and has more rainfall than *A*. Possible answer: *A* and *B* could represent cities; *B* could be Seattle and *A* could be Phoenix.

2a. Price and size

2b. *D* is larger than *C*, but *C* and *D* sell for the same price. Possible answer: *C* and *D* could represent pairs of jeans of the same brand but different sizes.

3a. Height and circumference

3b. *E* and *F* have the same circumference, but *F* is taller. Possible answer: *E* and *F* could be trees; *E* could be an oak and *F* could be a redwood.

4a. Rainfall and temperature

4b. *G* has a lower temperature and more rainfall than *H*. Possible answer: *H* could be a desert and *G* could be a forest.

5, 6. See margin.

✓ Develop & Understand: A

Complete Parts a and b for each graph.

  a. Tell what two variables are shown on the graph.

  b. Describe what the graph tells you about the variables represented by the points. Then state what the points could represent.

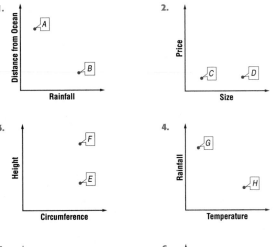

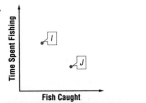

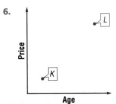

 Spot **Assessment**

Watch for students who do not recognize which variable has the same value for the two points in Exercises 2 and 3. Encourage them to trace the graphs and draw lines from the points to each axis to see which axis has only one line intersecting it. The label for that axis gives the variable that has the same value for both points. Students will still not know the exact values, but they will know which values are the same.

✓ Develop & Understand: A

Suggested Grouping: Pairs

▶ **Exercises 1–6** In this exercise set, students continue to identify variables on axes and describe the relationship shown for points plotted. They also think of situations that the graphs could represent. However, students should use caution when making generalizations from these graphs. For example, the first graph shows the relationship between two places in terms of rainfall and distance from the ocean. It is important to note that it is only a graph about those *two places* and does not suggest any relationship between the *two variables*. In other words, not all places that have more rainfall are closer to the sea. It is important to help students come up with counterexamples as a strategy for dealing with this misconception. For example, you might ask students if they can apply the same reasoning to the graph in Exercise 5. In fact, most students would think that more time spent fishing would mean *more* fish caught, not less. Use that problem to remind students that these graphs are about the particular pieces of data represented and do not support any more general conclusions.

Teacher Tips You may want to suggest that students consider three dimensional, cylindrical objects when thinking about what the points in Exercise 3 could represent.

Wrap-Up You may want to pick one or more of these graphs and ask each pair of students to volunteer what they thought the two points could represent.

Additional Answers

5a. Time spent fishing and the number of fish caught

5b. *I* spent more time fishing but caught fewer fish than *J*. Possible answer: *J* could be someone fishing from a boat and *I* could be someone fishing from a dock.

6a. Price and age

6b. *L* is older and costs more than *K*. Possible answer: *K* could be a new table and *L* could be an antique table.

Real-World Link

Ask students if they can identify common foods that contain sugar. Point out that they would be surprise at the many "unexpected" foods that contain sugar. Challenge them to read labels on the food at home and give a report.

Teacher Tips In this exercise set, students look at the relationship between points on a graph as they compare the weights and prices of bags of sugar. They use information in another graph to write a story that explains what could have happened to result in that graph.

✓ Develop & Understand: B

Suggested Grouping: Pairs

▶ **Exercises 7b and 7c** Encourage students to explain their reasoning. For example, if the bags are the same weight, then the points must be the same distance to the right of the horizontal axis so that they line up vertically.

▶ **Exercise 8** Encourage students to fully develop a story for the graph and give a reason for each change in the number of pens. The stories should have more substance than just, "She had more pens one day than the next."

Wrap-Up Have students share their stories from Exercise 8.

Teacher Tips Point out that the graphs in this lesson have had more points as students have worked through the exercise sets and gained more experience. Introduce the idea that students can also consider the pattern formed by the points in a graph to help them gather information.

Real-World Link

Common white sugar is made from both sugar cane and sugar beets. Although these two sources of sugar look very different, the sugar they produce is identical.

7b. *B* and *F* are the same weight and *C* and *E* are the same weight; *C, E,* and *D* are heavier than *B*.

7c. *A* and *C, E* and *F*

8. Possible answer: On Monday, Gina had about a third of her felt pens. She used her pens for homework that night and forgot to return them to her case. So, on Tuesday, she had no pens in her case. On Wednesday, she found a few of the pens she had left at home and put them in her case. She did not take out any pens on Thursday. On Friday, she found all of the pens she had lost and returned them to her case. She let her little brother use some of her pens over the weekend.

✓ Develop & Understand: B

7. Each point on this graph represents one bag of sugar.

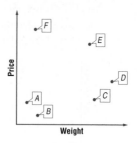

a. Which bag is heaviest? Which bag is lightest? *D, A*

b. Which bags are the same weight? Which bags are heavier than *B*?

c. Which bags are the same price? Which bags cost more than *D*?

d. Which bag is heavier than *B* and costs more than *D*? *E*

e. Assuming all of the bags contain sugar of the same quality, is *D* or *F* a better value? How can you tell?
   D; it has more sugar for less money.

8. Gina is careless with her pens, often losing some and then finding them again. This graph shows how many pens were in her case at noon each day last week. Use the information in the graph to write a story about Gina and her pens over the course of the week.

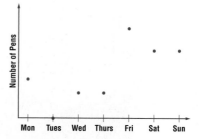

The graphs you have been exploring have had only a few points. Graphs of real data often contain many points. Although looking at individual points gives you information about the data, it is also important to consider the overall *pattern* of points.

✅ Develop & Understand: C

Ms. Dimas surveyed two of her classes to find out how much time each student spent watching television and reading last weekend. She made this graph of her results.

9. Choose one of the four students represented by points A, B, C, and D. Write a sentence or two describing the time that student spent reading and watching television. Do not mention the student's letter in your description.

10. Exchange descriptions with your partner. Try to figure out which student your partner described. **Answers will vary.**

11. Now think about all the points in the graph, not just the four labeled points. Which of these statements best fits the graph?
Statement c

a. There is not much connection between how much time the students spent reading and how much time they spent watching TV.

b. Most students spent about the same amount of time reading as they did watching TV.

c. The more time students spent reading, the less time they spent watching TV.

9. Possible answers:
A: This student spent lots of time reading and very little time watching TV.
B: This student spent about the same amount of time reading as watching TV.
C: This student did not spend much time reading or watching TV.
D: This student spent lots of time watching TV and very little time reading.

Real-World Link

By the time the average American child graduates from high school, he or she will have spent 13,000 hours in school and 18,000 hours watching television.

✅ Develop & Understand: C

Suggested Grouping: Pairs

▶ **Exercises 9–11** In these exercises, students consider a scatter plot of data, although they are not introduced to the term *scatter plot*. They use the scatter plot to generalize about the relationship between time spent reading and time spent watching TV.

▶ **Exercise 11** Offer assistance to poor readers and to other students who are not understanding how the descriptions fit the graph.

Wrap-Up Ask volunteers to share their descriptions from Exercise 9. Try to provide the class with at least one description for each of the four labeled points.

Real-World Link

Take a survey of how many hours students watch television per day and then per week. Extrapolate the information to find the total number of hours spent watching television by age 18.

Reaching All Learners

BL **Beyond Level** Challenge students to construct a graph with many data points that would show the number of seats in an auditorium and the number of tickets sold to a performance. Although there may be other factors that influence the sale of tickets, such as the popularity of the theater and of the performers, the overall pattern would typically be that more tickets are sold when there are more seats available. Have students explain their answers to account for other possibilities.

This activity encourages students to be creative in thinking about what graphs can convey. After students create their own graphs, let the class try to put them in the categories given: telling a story, making comparisons, or showing a relationship.

Teacher Tips In the previous investigations, students looked at graphs that generally had only a few points. In this investigation, students will explore graphs that show more information than a few points can convey, that is, graphs in which the points can be connected with a line or a curve. They also decide when it is appropriate to connect the points on a graph.

The material in the next investigation could be spread over two days, if you so choose. Several of the activities suggest that students create stories or graphs; if you want most students to share their stories with the whole class, the activities will take longer. Alternatively, students can share their stories in small groups, and you can have a whole-group discussion at the end.

Investigation 3

On Your Own Exercises
Pages 482–488
Exercises 5–7, 11–13

Interpret Line and Curves Have students look at the graph. Tell them that a line is made up of a series of points, so they can apply the skills they used to interpret graphs with points to help interpret graphs with lines. Be sure they understand that each point on the line makes up a part of the graph. Then discuss the basic features of the graph, such as the labels and the increments on the time scale. More specific questions about how the noise level changes in Ms. Whitmore's class are addressed in the Think & Discuss on the next page.

① Possible answer: My graph shows the relationship between size and price of beverages at a convenience store. The price increases as the size increases but by less and less each time.

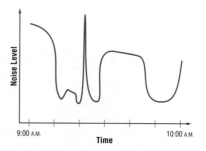

Share & Summarize

You have seen several uses for graphs.

- Graphs can help *tell a story*. For example, the graph on page 474 shows how the number of pens Gina had changed throughout the week.
- Graphs can be used to *make comparisons*. For example, the graph on page 474 shows weights and prices of bags of sugar.
- Graphs can *show an overall relationship*. For example, the graph on page 475 shows how time spent watching TV is related to time spent reading.

Create your own graph. Explain its use.   See ①.

Investigation 3 Interpret Lines and Curves

Vocabulary

line graph

Materials

- Megan's height graph

The graphs you have seen so far have been made up of separate points. When a graph shows a line or a curve, each point on the line or curve is part of the graph. The skills you developed for interpreting graphs with individual points can help you understand information given by a line or a curve.

This graph shows the noise level in Ms. Whitmore's classroom one Tuesday morning between 9 A.M. and 10 A.M.

The variable on the horizontal axis is *time*. If you read this graph from left to right, it tells a story about how the noise level in the classroom changed over time.

Troubleshooting

If students continue to have difficulty interpreting the relationship between points on a graph, you may want to create some simplified versions of the point graphs shown in the exercise sets. For example, you can create a vertical axis labeled *width* and a horizontal axis labeled *height*, and plot two points on the graph. To help students having difficulty interpreting the meaning of the points, ask comparative questions such as which point represents a taller object. Plot a third point, and have students compare the heights.

Real-World Link

Sound levels are measured in decibels (dB). Sound levels above 80 dB for extended periods can be harmful. Here are decibel measures for some common sounds.

whisper	25 dB
conversation	60 dB
lawn mower	90 dB
chain saw	100 dB
rock concert	110 dB

① Possible answer: From just before 9:30 until about 9:47. The graph goes up at around 9:30 and then remains at a fairly constant level until 9:47.

1c. Just after 9:00; the noise level increases very quickly.

Think & *Discuss*

- At about what time did the room first get suddenly quiet? How is this shown on the graph? 9:10; the curve goes down at this time.

- At one point during the hour, the class was interrupted for a very short announcement on the public address system. At about what time did this happen? How do you know? 9:22; the graph suddenly goes to its highest point.

- When were the students the noisiest? Ignore the PA announcement. At the start of class

- During part of the hour, students worked on an exercise in small groups. When do you think this happened? Explain why you think so. See ①.

- Ms. Whitmore stopped the group activity to talk about the next day's homework. When did this happen? Explain how you know. At about 9:47; the graph goes down at that point.

✓ Develop & Understand: A

1. This graph shows the audience noise in a school auditorium on the evening of a school play. The graph shows only the noise made by the audience, not the noise created by the actors on stage.

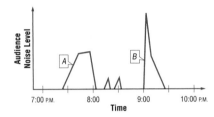

a. At 7:00 P.M., the auditorium was empty. At about what time do you think people started entering the auditorium? Explain why you think so. Just before 7:30; the noise level starts to increase.

b. What time do you think the play started? How is this shown on the graph? At around 8:00; the graph suddenly drops.

c. At the end of the performance, the audience burst into applause. At what time do you think this happened? Why?

d. There are some small "bumps" in the graph between 8:00 P.M. and 9:00 P.M. What might have caused these bumps? See margin.

e. A and B mark sections that show an increase in noise level. In which section does the noise level increase more quickly? How can you tell? See margin.

Think & *Discuss*

These questions require students to use the scale on the horizontal axis as they describe the shape of the graph on page 476. You might want to have students work in pairs before discussing the five sets of questions as a class. If necessary, point out that PA is an abbreviation for public address (system). If your school uses other terminology for a public address system, you may need to provide students with a definition. The third bulleted question refers to noise made by students in the class. Students are told to ignore the PA announcement (the loudest time during the hour) to help make this distinction more obvious.

✓ Develop & Understand: A

Suggested Grouping: Pairs

▶ **Exercise 1** In this exercise, students are guided through a possible story that could describe a noise-and-time graph similar to the one in the Think & Discuss. Then they write a story for a graph showing the change in one person's hunger level over time.

▶ **Exercise 1e** Students must consider, for the first time, how steep a line is. They will need to understand how the steepness shows the speed of the change to work future problems in this investigation. They will be formally introduced to slope in later courses.

Real-World Link

Ask students to research *decibel*. What is a safe level for normal hearing?

Additional Answers

1d. Possible answer: People in the audience might be laughing, talking, or coughing.

1e. Section B; the graph increases over a much shorter period of time than it does in Section A.

On the Spot Assessment

Watch for students who have difficulty estimating values that are located between the labeled times on the scale. For example, they may not be able to give a reasonable time that people started entering the auditorium in Exercise 1a. Suggest that these students trace the graph and draw vertical lines through the times that would show each quarter hour.

► **Exercise 2** There are a variety of possible interpretations that will fit the graph in this exercise. Allow students ample time to think of plausible explanations for the increases and decreases in hunger level. The issue is to help students come up with reasonable explanations based on incomplete data, and to recognize that there are many valid explanations.

Wrap-Up Have volunteers share their stories from Exercise 2.

Teacher Tips Ask students how the three graphs they have studied in the investigation are alike. Students may notice that all three show changes over time. Point out that sometimes information about a variable at given times can be used to estimate what happened between these times. Tell them that they will learn how to make and use these estimates in the next exercise set.

In the next exercise set, students connect points on graphs and estimate values on a line graph to help them develop the concept of continuity of values between points. Students will need copies of the graph, Megan's Growth, for Exercise 4. Lesson 8.1 Master 2 reproduces the graph so that students start with a graph that has the points accurately plotted.

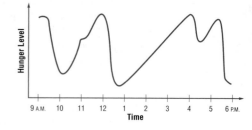

2. Possible answer: Rita ate breakfast at around 9. Between 10 and 11:30, she had soccer practice. By the time practice was over, she was very hungry. At noon, she had lunch at a friend's house. She and her friend went to the mall, and then went to a movie from 3:30 to 5:30. By late afternoon she was very hungry, and she ate a box of popcorn at around 4:30. After the movie, she went home. She had dinner at 6:00.

2. This graph shows how Rita's hunger level changed over one Saturday. Write a story about Rita's day that fits the information in the graph. Your story should account for all the increases and decreases in her hunger level.

The graphs in this investigation have shown how the values of a variable change over a period of time. In some cases, you will have information about a variable only at certain times during a time period. You can often use what information you *do* have to estimate what happens between those times.

✅ *Develop & Understand: B*

As Megan was growing up, her mother measured her height on each of her birthdays. She recorded the results in a graph in the family scrapbook.

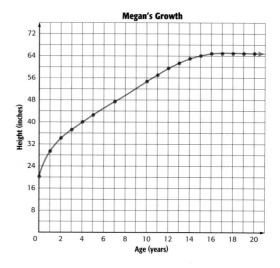

Reaching *All Learners*

ELL English Language Learners Be sure to pair low-level readers with strong readers for these exercises, or read the problems out loud as students work through the exercise set.

Read the introduction, and have students consider Megan's height graph. Point out the two 0s at the origin, noting that each scale begins with 0. You may want to tell students that some graphs use only one 0 to show this situation.

On Megan's sixth birthday, her family was on vacation, and her mother forgot to measure her. Megan's family moved right before her eighth birthday, and the scrapbook was misplaced. A few weeks before Megan turned ten, her mother found the scrapbook and started recording again.

Megan wonders what her height was in the missing years.

3. From the graph, what do you know about Megan's height when she was six years old? Possible answer: It is between her height at age 5 (about 43 in.) and age 7 (about 48 in.).

Megan thought connecting the points might help her estimate her height in the missing years.

4. See the graph. Answers will vary but should be close to the following: age 6: 45 in.; age 8: 50 in.; age 9: 52 in.

4. On a copy of Megan's graph, draw line segments to connect the points in order. Use the segments to estimate Megan's heights at ages 6, 8, and 9.

5. Not necessarily. Megan did not necessarily grow at a steady rate between the years shown on the graph. For example, she might have grown a lot just before she was 8 and only a little between 8 and 9.

5. Do you think the values you found in Exercise 4 give Megan's exact heights at ages 6, 8, and 9? Explain.

6. Estimate how tall Megan was at age $1\frac{1}{2}$. Possible answer: 32 in.

7. At what age did Megan's height begin to level off? At about age 16

Connecting the points in Megan's height graph allowed you to make predictions. It also helped you to see *trends*, or patterns, in the data. Graphs in which points are connected with line segments are called **line graphs**.

▶ **Exercise 3** Students should be able to reason that Megan's height at age 6 has to be somewhere between her heights at ages 5 and 7.

▶ **Exercise 5** Students may not use the word *rate,* although they should be able to get the point across that exactly how quickly Megan grew might not be the same over the years given.

▶ **Exercise 7** This exercise has students interpret a line graph. Some students may disagree on the age at which the graph begins to taper off if they look at the age that *shows* when the graph *slows* its increase instead of the age at which it flattens out. Accept any reasonable answer that students can explain.

Wrap-Up Discuss Exercise 5 and make sure students understand why the values from Exercise 4 are estimates. Exercise 7 provides a good transition to a discussion of how a graph can help us to make predictions and to see trends, or patterns.

Teacher Tips Tell students that graphs with line segments showing data, such as the one students created in this exercise set when they added line segments, are called *line graphs.* Then discuss how graphs can show patterns, or trends.

Teacher Tips Introduce the graph of the fishing trip, and have students describe what it shows: the number of fish caught during fishing trips in each of the years from 1987 to 2007. Then ask students whether it would make sense to connect the points in this graph, and have them explain their reasoning.

If necessary, point out that there are no values that make sense for the times between fishing trips. Therefore, values between the points on the graph would not represent what has happened. Remind students that each part of a line graph represents a value, and it makes sense to connect points when there are values between the plotted points.

Tell students they will make decisions about whether to connect the points on a graph in the next exercise set.

✅ Develop & Understand: C

Suggested Grouping: Pairs

▶ **Exercises 8–11** In this exercise set, students determine whether it is reasonable to connect the points on a graph for four different situations.

Wrap-Up Have students share their answers to each situation in the problem set to help insure that they solidify their understanding. If students are comfortable with the idea that the values represented by the lines, or the points along the lines, are not meaningful in a context like the annual fishing trips, you might want to extend the discussion to bring up the point that sometimes it *might* make sense to draw a line in these contexts. For example, in Exercise 8, if a clear pattern showed, a line might help someone make an estimate or a prediction about what would happen on the next game, or if the data for one game were missing. You might tell students that using a dashed rather than a solid line is a way to communicate that the line does not represent actual data.

In Megan's height graph, it makes sense to connect the points because she continues to grow between birthdays. In other words, there are values between those plotted on the graph.

For some graphs, there are no values between the plotted values. For example, Megan's father keeps a graph of how many fish he catches each year on his annual fishing trip.

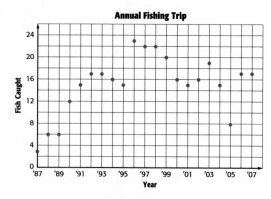

Annual Fishing Trip

Since the number of fish caught does not change between fishing trips, there are no values between the values shown in the graph. In this case, connecting the points does not make sense.

✅ Develop & Understand: C

Tell whether it would make sense to connect the points in each graph described below. Explain why you think so.

8. a graph showing the number of tickets sold for each football game during the season   No, there are no values between games.

9. a graph showing the speed of a race car every ten minutes during a race   Yes; the speed of the car existed between the 10-minute marks.

10. a graph of the sun's perceived height at each hour during the day   Yes; the sun moves between the hours.

11. a graph of Clara's weekly paycheck amount for ten weeks   No; there are no values between paychecks.

Reaching *All Learners*

AL **Approaching Level** Some students may have difficulty deciding whether to draw lines to connect the points in Exercise 8 because some tickets may be sold in advance. Encourage them to sketch a graph showing the situation, with the number of tickets on the vertical axis and each game on the horizontal axis. Question students about the values between the points by focusing on the values to the right of each point. Ask students if it makes sense that on the day after a football game, there were nearly as many tickets sold for the next game as there were for the game just played.

Share & Summarize

These graphs show how something changes over time. For each graph, write a sentence or two describing the change. Then try to think of something that might change in this way.

For example, this graph shows something increasing slowly at first and then more quickly. It could represent the speed of someone running a long-distance race. The runner starts out slowly and then moves faster and faster as she sprints toward the finish line.

1. This graph shows a steady increase. Possible explanation: This could show the change in the distance covered by a car traveling at a constant speed.

2. This graph shows something that is not changing at all. Possible explanation: This could represent how the amount of homework I have completed changes while I am sleeping.

3. This graph shows a steady decrease. Possible explanation: This could represent how my distance from school changes as I walk toward it.

4–6. See margin.

7. Possible answer: The outside temperature measured every hour for a day

1.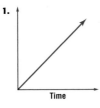

2.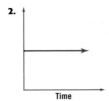

3.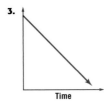

4.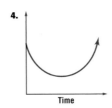

5.

6.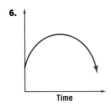

7. Describe a graph involving change over time for which it would make sense to connect the points.

8. Describe a graph involving change over time for which it would not make sense to connect the points. Possible answer: The number of hours I slept each night over a week

Additional Answers

4. This graph shows something that first decreases and then increases. Possible explanation: The graph could show a person's height above the ground during one swing on a swing.

5. This graph shows something decreasing quickly at first and then continuing to decrease, but more and more slowly. Possible explanation: This could show how the amount of food in my lunch changes when I start out very hungry.

6. This graph shows something increasing and then decreasing. Possible explanation: This could represent how my hunger level changes from an hour before I eat lunch until I am done eating lunch.

Share & Summarize

You may want to have students work in pairs since these graphs are slightly different from the others in this lesson. Students are asked to describe what is happening over time in six different line graphs without scales. These graphs are, for the most part, simplified pieces of graphs similar to those students have been working with in this lesson.

▶ **Exercises 1–6** Encourage students to look at how steep the graph is as well as its shape when describing the change in these exercises. Remind them that a steeper graph shows a more rapid change.

▶ **Exercises 7 and 8** As an extension, you could ask students to sketch graphs for the information in these exercises and then discuss the shape of the graphs they drew.

Troubleshooting If students are having difficulty interpreting graphs with many increases and decreases, you could focus on simpler graphs like those in Exercises 1–3 of Share & Summarize, which show only one change over time that is either increasing, decreasing, or staying the same. In these cases, you can ask students what is happening over the given time for that particular interval.

If students are having difficulty interpreting graphs without scales, have them make up a scale and describe the graph in specific terms. Then they can use the specifics to make a generalization of the activity. For example, in Exercise 5 of the Share & Summarize, students could draw lines and say that the "unknown" decreased by, say, three units in the first unit of time and decreased by one unit in the second unit of time, so there was a greater decrease at the beginning, and then it gradually leveled off.

Investigation 1
Pages 468–472
Practice & Apply: 1, 2

Investigation 2
Pages 472–476
Practice & Apply: 3, 4
Connect & Extend: 8–10

Investigation 3
Pages 476–481
Practice & Apply: 5–7
Connect & Extend: 11–13

Assign Anytime
Mixed Review: 14–37

▶ **Exercise 2** You may want to discuss this exercise as a whole class since it deals with a subject that is inherently interesting to students. It is also a good way to assess students' understanding of how to interpret the relationship among the variables for different points.

Practice & Apply

Real-World Link
One of the world's tallest apartment buildings is the John Hancock Center in Chicago, Illinois. The building is 1,127 feet tall and has 100 stories.

. . . .

1b. See graph for possible placement. The garage is taller and wider than the doghouse and shorter and narrower than the school.

1. This drawing shows the front view of several buildings.

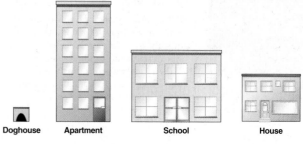

Doghouse   Apartment   School   House

a. Copy this set of axes. Plot a point to represent the height and width of each building.

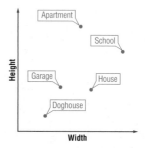

b. Add a new point to your graph. Write a brief description of the building it represents. Describe how the height and width of your building compare to the height and width of at least two of the other buildings.

2. This graph shows the relationship between effort and test results for five students.

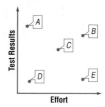

The teacher wrote the following comments on the report cards for these students.

- Allen's poor attendance this term has resulted in an extremely poor test performance.
- Nicola is a very able pupil, as her test mark clearly shows. But her concentration and behavior in class are poor. With more effort, she could do even better.
- Hoang has worked very well and deserves his marvelous test results. Well done!
- Adrienne has worked reasonably well this term. She has achieved a satisfactory test mark.

  a. Match each student's performance to a point on the graph.
  Allen: *D*; Nicola: *A*; Hoang: *B*; Adrienne: *C*
  b. Write a comment about the student represented by the point that you did not mention in Part a.

2b. Possible answer: Jamie (point *E*) has worked extremely hard this term, and this low test mark is a disappointment.

3. Complete Parts a and b for each graph.   See margin.

  a. Tell what two variables the graph shows.

  b. Describe what the graph tells you about the subjects represented by the points. Then try to think of an idea about what the points could represent.

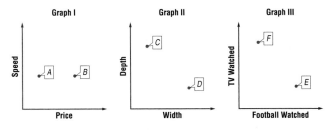

4. Possible answer:
Back: F, E, G, D, H, I
Front: C, A, B

4. The age and height of each person in the photograph are represented by a point on the graph. Going from left to right, match each person to a point.

▶ **Exercise 3** You may want students to discuss their answers to this exercise in groups of three. Have each student do one part of Part 3b and then rotate answers to check each other's work.

Additional Answers
Graph I:
3a. Speed and price

3b. *A* and *B* have the same speed, but *B* is more expensive. Possible answer: They could be cars; *A* could be a compact car and *B* could be a minivan.

Graph II:
3a. Depth and width

3b. *C* is narrower and deeper than *D*. Possible answer: *C* could be a well and *D* could be a swimming pool.

Graph III:
3a. The amount of TV watched and the amount of football watched

3b. *E* watches more football but less TV overall. Possible answer: *E* could be a football fan who does not watch much else. *F* could be a person who watches lots of TV, including some football.

Lesson 8.1 Interpret Graphs   **483**

▶ **Exercise 6b** Students might enjoy reading their stories to the class.

Additional Answer

6b. Possible answer: When Tyson woke up, he was grumpy because he had not had enough sleep, but then he remembered he had a basketball game, and he got more and more excited as the morning wore on. He got to the pregame practice and then played in the game. They lost the game in overtime and he was sad, but there was a big party after the game and he got much happier as the evening wore on. At the end of the evening he had an argument with a friend and that made him very sad.

5. This graph shows the height of a hay crop over a summer.

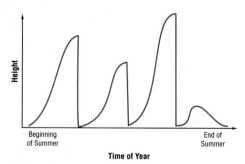

a. How many times was the crop harvested during the summer? How can you know this by looking at the graph? 3; The height suddenly drops to 0 three times.

b. Before which harvest was the hay tallest? The third

c. Describe the change in the hay's height after the third harvest. Why do you think the height changed this way?

5c. Possible answer: The height increases a little and then decreases again. Maybe it was too cold and the crop died.

6. This graph shows Tyson's mood during one Saturday.

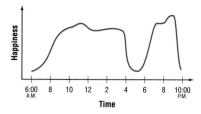

6a. Time of day and level of happiness

a. What two variables does this graph show?

b. Write a short story about what might have happened during Tyson's day. Your story should account for all his mood changes. See margin.

7. Dario's; Mitchell is interpreting the graph as a change in *height* rather than a change in *distance*.

7. The De Marte family went on a picnic last Sunday. This graph shows how far the family was from home at various times of the day.

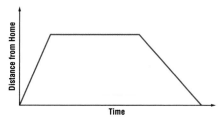

Mitchell and Dario each told a story about the graph. Which story best fits the graph? What is wrong with the other story?

Mitchell: "The family drove up a tall mountain and stayed on a level area for several hours. Then the family came down the mountain on a road that was less steep than the first."

Dario: "The family drove fairly quickly to the picnic spot and stayed there for most of the day. The family drove home more slowly."

Connect & Extend

8. In Exercise 8 on page 471, you used these graphs to compare two cars.

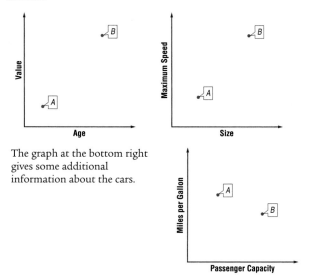

The graph at the bottom right gives some additional information about the cars.

▶ **Exercise 7** Mitchell's explanation involves the standard misconception that a graph is simply a picture or photograph of what happened. It is worth spending some time on this exercise to help students understand this misinterpretation. Some students may be confused because if Mitchell's family lived at the bottom of a mountain, distance from home and altitude might be synonymous. Point out that this explanation still does not mention the criteria described in the labels, and since these facts are not given, students cannot assume that this is what Mitchell meant.

▶ **Exercise 8b** Remind students that they need to use the three preceding graphs to mark and label the points on the graphs.

▶ **Exercise 9** Have students share their descriptions to help others who have language or writing difficulties.

Additional Answers

9. Possible answers:
   Graph I:
   a.

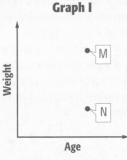

Graph I

b. *M* and *N* are the same age but different weights. Possible answer: *M* and *N* could be dogs of the same age; *M* could be a German shepherd and *N* could be a beagle.

   Graph II:
   a.

Graph II

b. *M* is younger and lighter than *N*. Possible answer: They could represent people; *M* could be a young child and *N* could be her father.

a. *True or false?* The car that holds more passengers gets fewer miles per gallon.   True

b. Copy each set of axes below. Mark and label points to represent car A and car B.

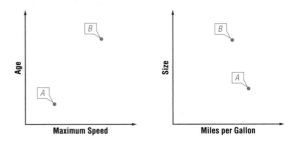

9. Complete Parts a and b for each graph below.   See margin.

   a. Copy the graph. Make up a variable for each axis.

   b. Describe what the graph tells you about the things represented by the points. Then try to think of an idea about what the points could represent.

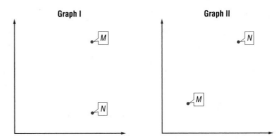

10. **In Your Own Words** Make a graph that shows how something changes over time. Write a story to go with your graph.
    Answers will vary.

11. In an experiment, the heights of 192 mothers and their adult daughters were measured.

Based on this graph, does there appear to be a connection between the heights of the mothers and the heights of their daughters? Explain your answer.

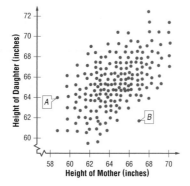

11. Possible answer: Yes; the points tend to go up from left to right. Overall, taller mothers seem to have taller daughters.

12. There is a vertical jump in the graph both up and down. The amount of air in a balloon cannot change instantaneously like this.

12. Science This graph was created to show how the amount of air in a balloon changed as it was blown up and then deflated. What is wrong with this graph?

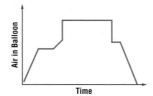

13. A firefighter walked from the fire truck up the stairs to the second floor of the firehouse. Several minutes later, the alarm rang. The firefighter slid down the pole and returned to the fire truck.

Sketch a graph to show the firefighter's height above the ground from the time she left the fire truck to the time she returned to it.

Possible graph:

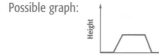

Lesson 8.1 Interpret Graphs **487**

▶ **Exercise 11** This exercise will be a challenge for many students. It can be used to raise the issue of *correlations*, which students will see again in Course 3. Point out that while there is a general trend for tall mothers to have tall daughters, it is possible for short mothers to have tall daughters and for tall mothers to have short daughters.

▶ **Exercise 12 Extension** Challenge students to write a story that "fits" for this exercise. Have them share stories with a partner.

Quick Check
Informal Assessment Students should be able to:

✔ interpret points on a qualitative graph

✔ understand the meaning of *variable* as it relates to graphing with horizontal and vertical axes

✔ analyze the relationship between the variables on a graph

✔ understand the difference between line and point graphs

Quick Quiz

1. Draw a graph with the variable *time studied* represented by the horizontal axis and the variable *performance* represented by the vertical axis. Then plot the points described below.

   a. Alex studied a lot for a test and got an excellent score. Plot Point *A* for Alex.

   b. Beatrice did not study very much but got an excellent score. Plot Point *B* for Beatrice.

   c. Cameron did not study very much and did not do well. Locate Point *C* for Cameron. Possible graph:

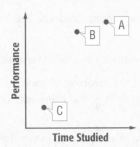

2. The line graph shows the relationship between the price of bananas and their ripeness. Describe this relationship in words. Possible answer: An unripe banana has no value. The price increases as the fruit ripens, with the peak price being when the fruit is ripe. As it becomes overripe, the price starts to fall.

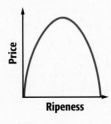

Mixed Review

Economics Tell how much change you would get if you paid for each item with a $5 bill.

14. a small salad for $1.74 $3.26

15. a pack of mints for $.64 $4.36

16. a magazine for $3.98 $1.02

17. a pack of collector cards for $2.23 $2.77

Measurement Express each measurement in meters.

18. 13 mm   0.013 m

19. 123 cm   1.23 m

20. 0.05 cm   0.0005 m

21. 430 mm   0.43 m

Find each sum or difference.

22. $5\frac{6}{7} + 1\frac{5}{14}$ $7\frac{3}{14}$

23. $\frac{11}{12} - \frac{5}{18}$ $\frac{23}{36}$

24. $\frac{5}{9} + \frac{13}{7}$ $2\frac{26}{63}$

25. $3 - 1\frac{31}{72}$ $1\frac{41}{72}$

26. $2\frac{5}{8} - 1\frac{3}{4}$ $\frac{7}{8}$

27. $\frac{7}{8} + \frac{7}{12} + \frac{7}{16}$ $1\frac{43}{48}$

Complete each table.

28.

Fraction	Decimal	Percent
$\frac{1}{2}$	0.5	50%
$\frac{3}{4}$	0.75	75%
$\frac{3}{10}$	0.3	30%
$\frac{1}{4}$	0.25	25%

29.

Fraction	Decimal	Percent
$\frac{1}{2}$	0.5	50%
$\frac{1}{8}$	0.125	12.5%
$\frac{4}{5}$	0.8	80%
$\frac{1}{20}$	0.05	5%

Write each fraction or decimal as a percent. Round to the nearest tenth of a percent.

30. $\frac{1}{3}$ 33.3%

31. 0.06   6%

32. $\frac{1}{2}$ 50%

33. $\frac{3}{10}$ 30%

34. 0.561   56.1%

35. $\frac{2}{3}$ 66.7%

36. 1.25   125%

37. $\frac{11}{10}$ 110%

3. The graph shows the number of snowboards sold by the Icy Slick sporting goods store.

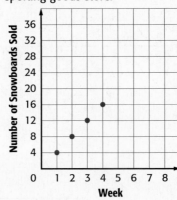

   a. What two variables does the graph show? Week and number of snowboards sold

   b. Write a short story about what the graph shows. Possible answer: The store sold four snowboards more each week.

Draw and Label Graphs

Objectives

▶ To create graphs that describe a story relating two variables that change over time

▶ To plot points in the first quadrant of a coordinate grid

▶ To observe any patterns, or trends, in data and use them to make predictions

▶ To determine an appropriate scale for a set of data

Overview

Students begin this lesson by graphing various situations on labeled graphs without scales. Then they plot data points in first-quadrant graphs, observe and describe patterns, and use patterns to make predictions. They also revisit the issue of whether to connect the points in a graph. The lesson ends with students determining appropriate scales for graphing sets of data. Students will practice these skills throughout this course and in later courses.

Advance Preparation

You may want to provide students with graph paper and Lesson 8.2 Masters 1–5 to facilitate class discussion while presenting new topics, including plotting points and choosing scales.

	Summary	Materials	On Your Own Exercises (pp. 503–508)	Assessment Opportunities
Investigation 1 (p. 490) *Pacing:* 1 day	Students graph various situations that show changes over time on graphs without scales.		Practice & Apply: 1, 2 Connect & Extend: 8, 9 Mixed Review: 16–24	• Share & Summarize (p. 490)
Investigation 2 (p. 491) *Pacing:* 1 day	Students identify and plot points using ordered pairs.	Lesson 8.2 Masters 1–3, transparency of Lesson 8.2 Master 1 or graph paper	Practice & Apply: 3–6 Connect & Extend: 10 Mixed Review: 16–24	• On the Spot Assessment (p. 492) • Share & Summarize (p. 494)
Investigation 3 (p. 495) *Pacing:* 1 day	Students choose appropriate scales for graphs, make graphs, and interpret data from graphs.	Chapter 8 Masters 1 and 2 or graph paper	Connect & Extend: 11–13 Mixed Review: 16–24	• On the Spot Assessment (pp. 495, 498) • Share & Summarize (p. 499) • Troubleshooting (p. 499)
Investigation 4 (p. 500) *Pacing:* 1 day	Students create point graphs. They decide whether to connect the points in their graphs and, if so, whether to use a solid or a dashed line.	Lesson 8.2 Masters 4 and 5	Practice & Apply: 7 Connect & Extend: 14–15 Mixed Review: 16–24	• On the Spot Assessment (p. 501) • Share & Summarize (p. 502) • Troubleshooting (p. 502)

Leveled Lesson Resources

Also on
TeacherWorks™
Lesson 8.2

Study Guide and Intervention (p. 12) — AL

Lesson 8.2 Study Guide and Intervention
Draw and Label Graphs

Coordinate Plane

Example The graph shows a map of Lake Minnow located in High Hills State Park. The distance between the graph lines represents one mile.

The point labeled *A* is the location of the entrance to the park, point *B* is the location of a raft in the lake, point *C* is the location of Max's cabin, point *D* is the location of Trixie's cottage, and point E is location of the park ranger's office.

1. What are the coordinates of the raft? Answer: B(3, 7)

2. What are the coordinates of a point *F* that is 3 miles east and one mile north of Max's cabin? Answer: (5, 11)

3. Trevor wants to build a home halfway between Trixie's cottage and the park ranger's office. What are the coordinates of the location where Trevor wants to build? Answer: (8, 6)

Exercises

The graph shows a map of Normal Park located in Center City. The distance between graph lines represents one city block.

The point labeled *A* is the location of Center City's town hall, points *B, C, D,* and *E* are the locations of the corners of Normal Park, and point *F* is the location of Center City's post office.

1. If you leave the town hall and walk one block east and two blocks north, will you be in the park? Explain your answer.

2. If the citizens of Center City want to place a water fountain in the center of Normal Park, what would be the coordinates of its location?

3. If the park manager wants to plant a tree halfway between the post office and point *D*, what would be the coordinates of the location of the tree?

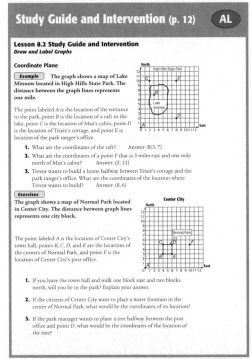

Skills Practice (p. 13) — AL OL

Lesson 8.2 Skills Practice
Draw and Label Graphs

Coordinate Plane

1. Manuel wants to go to the movies with some of his friends. He has $30 to spend and is willing to pay the $4 admission fee for each friend who goes with him.

a. Complete the table to show what the cost of admission is based on the number of friends who go to the movies with him.

Number of Friends	1	2	3	4	5	6
Total Cost ($)	8			20		

b. Plot and label the points for the values from your table.

c. Would it make sense to connect the points on this graph? Explain.

2. Home Cell Phone Company charges $0.05 per minute for minutes used beyond an individual's basic cell phone plan.

a. Complete the table to show the cost of various amounts of minutes beyond the basic cell phone plan.

Time (hours)	1	2	3	4	5	6	7	8
Cost ($)								

b. Graph the data from the table on the 10-by-10 grid. Your horizontal axis should represent time. Label each axis and use appropriate scales.

c. Do the points on your graph make a pattern? If so, describe it.

d. Use your graph to predict the cost for 10 hours of cell phone minutes beyond the basic plan.

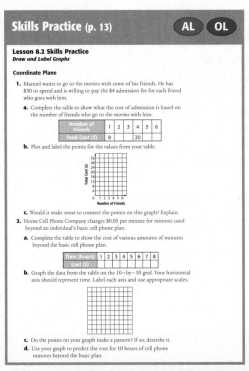

Problem-Solving Practice (p. 14) — AL OL

Lesson 8.2 Problem-Solving Practice
Draw and Label Graphs

Coordinate Plane

Solve.

1. Felix is watching a grasshopper hop across his driveway. Sketch a graph which might represent the height of the grasshopper as it hops across the driveway.

2. It is Maui's birthday. Maui wants each of her guests to get three balloons. Complete the table to show how many balloons she needs based on the number of guests invited.

Number of Guests	1	2	3	4	5
Number of Balloons					

If Maui were to graph the data, should she connect the points? Explain.

3. Describe a problem in which the graph of the data points should be connected and a problem in which the graph of the data points should not be connected.

4. Rio just returned from a leisurely drive. Her average driving speed was 45 miles per hour. Complete the table to show how far she had driven after the indicated number of hours.

Hours	1	2	3	4
Miles				

Use a graph to determine if there is an overall pattern. If a pattern exists, explain the pattern.

5. Harriet and Kyle are playing the game Plot That Point. Kyle is supposed to locate, graph, and label each point based on Harriet's instructions. His starting point is (0, 0). Below are Harriet's instructions to Kyle. Follow them and locate, graph, and label the same points as Kyle did.

A Starting at the point (0, 0), move two units to the right and five units up.

B Starting at this new second point move four units to the right and one unit down.

C Starting at this third point move two units left and four units up.

Enrichment (p. 15) — BL

Lesson 8.2 Enrichment
Draw and Label Graphs

The Honest Oaks Automobile Dealership sells Sports utility vehicles (SUV's). The table below contains data about the number of SUV's sold by the dealership in six consecutive years.

Year	2003	2004	2005	2006	2007	2008
Sales of SUV's (hundreds)	1	1.5	2	2.5	3	3.5

1. Graph the data found in the table. Your horizontal axis should represent the year. Label each axis and use appropriate scales.

2. Does the data graphed have a pattern? If so, describe the pattern.

The graph to the right shows the average sale price of the SUV sold at the Honest Oaks Automobile Dealership in five consecutive years.

3. Does the data graphed have a pattern? If so, describe the pattern.

The owner of Honest Oaks wants to know the revenue generated from the sales of SUV's during the years shown in the table below. Revenue is found by multiplying the number of SUV's sold in a given year by the average selling price in that same year.

4. Complete the table to determine each year's revenue.

Year	2004	2005	2006	2007
Revenue Generated (millions $)				

5. Graph the data from the table. Your horizontal axis should represent the year. Label each axis and use appropriate scales.

6. Does the data graphed have a pattern? If so, describe the pattern.

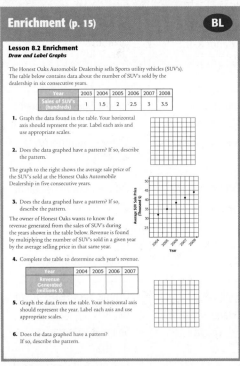

Lesson Quick Quiz (p. 16) — AL OL BL

Lesson 8.2 Quick Quiz
Draw and Label Graphs

1. On Joachin's first day at school, he walked slowly into the cafeteria at lunchtime and stopped to look around for his friends. He didn't see anyone he knew, so he ran out the back door. Sketch a graph that shows his walking speed over this period of time.

2. A shade of green dye is made by mixing three pints of green dye for each pint of water.

a. Fill in the missing values for the table below.

Pints of Water	Pints of Green Dye
1	3
2	
3	
4	
5	

b. Plot the points from the table on a graph, choosing an appropriate scale.

c. Do the points in the graph make a pattern? If so, describe it.

d. Does it make sense to connect the points? Why or why not?

e. Use your graph to predict the number of pints of water needed for 10 pints of green dye.

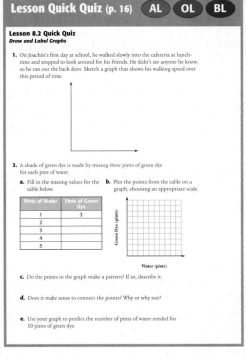

Lesson Masters 1–6 (p. 17–22)

Lesson 8.2 Master 1
Draw and Label Graphs

Investigation 2 Develop & Understand: A, Exercises 6–11

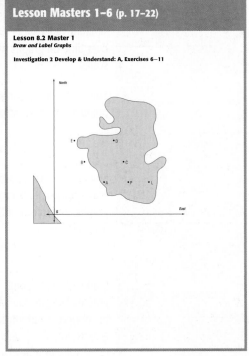

Additional Lesson Resources

Teacher Tech Tools
- TeacherWorks
- ExamView Assessment Suite
- Classroom Presentation Toolkit
- Advance Tracker

Student Tech Tools
- StudentWorks Plus
- **Math Online** eGlossary •
- Concepts in Motion

Other Print Products
- Investigation Notebook and Reflection Journal
- Quick Review Math Handbook

You have already had experience describing the information shown by graphs. In this investigation, you will practice making your own graphs.

Real-World Link
When an Argentinean child has a birthday, it is customary to tug his or her earlobe once for each year of age. In Israel, the birthday child sits in a chair while adults raise and lower it once for each year, plus once for good luck.

Explore

Ella and Chase wanted to make a graph to show how the noise level at a typical birthday party is related to time. Here is the first graph that they drew.

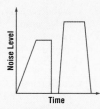

Ella said the graph was not quite right since it is not usually completely quiet at the start of a party. Chase said that most people arrive on time for a party, and the noise level would go up more quickly. They also realized that the party would probably never be completely silent. They drew a new graph.

Think about birthday parties that you have attended. What would you change to improve Ella and Chase's graph?
Possible answer: Add more variation in noise level.
Another pair of variables that might be useful for describing what happens at a birthday party is the amount of food and the time. Draw a graph showing how these variables might be related. Explain what your graph represents.
See ② in margin.

Introduce

Drawing Graphs Explain to students that they will continue their work with graphing in this lesson. You might also point out that part of the process of creating graphs is checking that the graphs accurately show the information and, if not, correcting any errors.

Explore

Suggested Grouping: Pairs

▶ **Prepare** Discuss how the first graph shows the noise level at a typical birthday party. Have students identify the variables *noise level* and *time* used in the graph. Then ask students why the second graph might be an improvement over the first graph. Note that, technically, the first graph is not wrong, but it does have some characteristics that are implausible, such as no noise at all for a certain amount of time and instantaneous changes in the noise level as represented by the nearly vertical lines.

▶ **Play** Ask pairs to answer the questions in the Explore. Encourage them to improve the graphs they draw. Their successive graphs should reflect the reality of this situation.

▶ **Record** Have students evaluate whether their successive graphs are improving. Do they show the relationship between the amount of food and the time?

▶ **Score** Give students credit for doing the Explore activity.

Additional Answer
Explore

② Possible answer: The amount of food is greatest at the beginning of the party. It decreases gradually for a while as people eat snacks and then goes down more rapidly when the cake and ice cream are served.

Investigation 1

On Your Own Exercises
Pages 503–508
Exercises 1, 2, 8, 9

Draw Graphs In this investigation, students sketch graphs that represent a variety of stories. The graphs are drawn without scales so that students focus on the shape of the graph and not on making up and plotting possible data points.

✓ Develop & Understand: A

Suggested Grouping: Pairs

▶ **Exercises 1–6** In this exercise set, more than one possible graph can be drawn for each situation. Encourage students with unique graphs to explain their reasoning. All students' graphs should be labeled, but none should have scales. Remind students to draw arrows at the ends of both axes.

▶ **Exercise 2** The sample graph shows the descent as a curve rather than a straight line because the child gains speed as he slides. If students cannot make this distinction, point out that dashed graph shows where the child's head would be in relation to the ground.

▶ **Exercise 2** Some students may draw a graph that resembles steps, thinking that a per-minute charge is not prorated for partial minutes. In that case, a call lasting 4 minutes 2 seconds would have the same charge as a call lasting 4 minutes 58 seconds.

▶ **Exercise 4** Tell students to consider the entire 24-hour period as the school day, not just the hours that students are in school.

Wrap-Up Ask students to share their graphs.

Share & Summarize

Students should create their own situations and graphs and then trade with a partner. This activity assesses the graphing skills used in the exercise set by having students write and graph a situation that changes over time. They must also interpret graphs that others have drawn.

Investigation 1 Draw Graphs

In this investigation, you will sketch graphs to fit various situations.

✓ Develop & Understand: A   3–6. See margin.

For Exercises 1–6, create your own graph. Then compare and discuss graphs with your partner. Work together to create a final version of your graph. Be sure to label the axes.

1. Possible graph:

2. Possible graph:

Real-World Link
In the summer in Barrow, Alaska, the sun does not set for more than 80 consecutive days. In the winter, the town experiences about 64 days of darkness.

---

1. At a track meet, the home team won a relay race, and the crowd roared with excitement. Make a graph to show how the noise level might have changed from just before the win to a few minutes after the win.

2. A child climbs to the top of a slide, sits down, and then starts to slide, gaining speed as he goes. At the bottom, he gets up quickly, runs around to the ladder, and climbs up again. Make a graph to show how the height of the child's feet above the ground is related to time.

3. At Computer Cafe, customers are charged a fixed price plus a certain amount per minute for using a computer. Create a graph that shows how the amount a customer is charged is related to the time he or she spends using a computer.

4. Smallville is a town surrounded by farms. The number of people in Smallville changes a lot during a typical school day. During the day, many children come to town for school, and adults drive in for business and shopping. In the evenings, people come to town to eat dinner or attend social events. Draw a graph to show how the number of people in town might be related to time on a typical school day.

5. Make a graph showing how the number of hours of daylight is related to the time of year. Assume the time axis starts in January and goes through December.

6. Make a graph showing approximately how the temperature outside has changed over the past three days.

Share & Summarize

Write a description of something that changes over time. Then sketch three graphs, one that matches your description and two that do not. See if your partner can guess which graph is correct. See margin.

Additional Answer
Share & Summarize

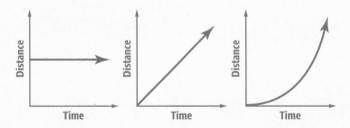

Possible answer: The distance covered by an airplane flying at a steady speed of 500 mph

The second graph is correct.

Additional Answers for Develop & Understand: A Exercises 3–6 are on page 531A.

Investigation (2) Plot Points

Vocabulary
coordinates

ordered pair

Materials
- copy of the map
- copy of the grid
- grid paper

When you made your graphs in the last investigation, you had to think about the overall shape of the graph, not about exact values. To draw a graph that shows exact values, you need to plot points.

This graph shows a map of an island just off the coast of a continent. The point labeled S represents a major city on the coast. The distance between grid lines represents one mile.

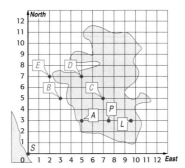

Point A represents a resort that is located five miles east and three miles north of point S. The values 5 and 3 are the **coordinates** of point A. The coordinates can be given as the **ordered pair** (5, 3), where 5 is the horizontal coordinate and 3 is the vertical coordinate.

As you might guess, the *order* of the numbers in an ordered pair is important. The first number is always the horizontal coordinate. The second number is always the vertical coordinate.

Lesson 8.2 Draw and Label Graphs **491**

On Your Own Exercises
Pages 503–508
Exercises 3–6, 10

Plot Points Point out that so far, students have been primarily concerned with interpreting the shapes of graphs rather than finding exact values of points. Remind them that they did look at values when they considered the ages in the graph of Megan's growth in the last lesson. Then explain that they will now learn how to plot points to help them make graphs with exact values.

You may want to make transparencies of Lesson 8.2 Masters 1 and 2 to use when introducing the investigation and with the next exercise set if you elect to work through the problems as a teacher-directed activity. Otherwise, each student or pair of students should have a copy of Lesson 8.2 Master 1 for the exercise set.

Teacher Tips Discuss the characteristics of the island map, and have students identify the labels, the scale, and the origin. Have them locate Point S at the origin of the graph. They should note that the labels are *North* and *East* and that the scale is in intervals of 1 unit for both axes. Point out that a resort is located at Point A, and use that point to explain how *coordinates* and *ordered pairs* can be used to describe the location of a point. You may want to have students count the intervals to find Point A and see that it is 5 miles east and 3 miles north of Point S, which is the origin and represents a major city on the coast.

Emphasize the importance of the order of the coordinates in an ordered pair. The first number is always the horizontal coordinate, and the second number is always the vertical coordinate. This distinction is addressed in the first four problems in the next exercise set.

Teacher Tips In this problem set, students plot points and identify the coordinates of points using the island map from the introduction. Use these problems for diagnostic purposes, or if you elect to make this a teacher-led activity, have volunteers write the points asked for on a transparency of Lesson 8.2 Master 1. If students work on these problems in pairs, they will find copies of the master helpful. Otherwise, they will need to re-create the map on graph paper.

✅ Develop & Understand: A

Suggested Grouping: Pairs

▶ **Exercise 6** Students who subtract to find the distance are taking the first step toward using the Distance Formula. This formula, introduced in Course 2, is used to find the distance between any two points on a graph.

▶ **Exercises 7 and 8** Students may use one of the strategies below to determine the coordinates for points in these exercises. The first strategy is the only one that gives an exact answer.

- Divide the sum of the first coordinates in the ordered pairs by 2 to get the first coordinate of the midpoint. The second coordinate stays the same since the points are on a horizontal line.

- Use the graph to estimate the midpoint, and then estimate the coordinates for that point.

- Count the spaces between the points in the graph, and then estimate the midpoint. For example, in Exercise 7, count one space from both Point *L* and Point *P* to find the midpoint.

▶ **Exercises 9–11** Be sure students understand that they should list coordinates for any points that satisfy the conditions, not just for points that are labeled with letters. Using the wrong interpretation results in an impossible task since there are not three points labeled that fit the parameters for Exercises 9 and 10.

Wrap-Up If the activity was not teacher-led, encourage pairs to share their strategies for solving Exercises 6–8 and for finding the points in Exercises 9–11.

✅ Develop & Understand: A

1. On a copy of the map on page 491, mark the point that is three miles east and five miles north of point *S*. Label it *B*. Is point *B* in the water or on the island? Is point *B* in the same place as point *A*? **See the map. Point *B* is in the water; no.**

2. Mark the point that is seven miles east and five miles north of point *S*. Label it *C*. Then mark the point that is five miles east and seven miles north of point *S*. Label it *D*. Are points *C* and *D* in the same place? Give the coordinates of points *C* and *D*. **See the map. They are not the same place: *C* (7, 5); *D* (5, 7).**

3. Which point is in the water, (2, 7) or (7, 2)? Mark the point on your map. Label it *E*.   **(2, 7); See the map on page 491.**

4. Developers want to build another resort on the island. Which would be the better location, (6, 11) or (11, 6)? Why? **(6, 11); (11, 6) is not on the island.**

5. Give the coordinates of two points on the island that are exactly two miles from point *A*.   **Possible answer: (7, 3) and (5, 5)**

6. Coordinates are not always whole numbers. For example, point *L*, the island lighthouse, has coordinates (9.5, 3). Point *P* represents the swimming pool. What are the coordinates of point *P*? How far is the lighthouse from the pool? **(7.5, 3), 2 miles**

7. Give the coordinates of the point that is halfway between points *L* and *P*. **(8.5, 3)**

8. Give the coordinates of the point that is halfway between points *A* and *P*. **(6.25, 3)**

9. List three points on the island with a first coordinate greater than 8. **Possible answer: (9, 2), (9, 3), (10, 7)**

10. List three points on the island with a second coordinate equal to 8. **Possible answer: (7, 8), (7.3, 8), (8.1, 8)**

11. List three points on the island with a second coordinate less than 4. **Possible answer: (10, 3), (10, 2.4), (9, 3.1)**

In Exercises 12–17, you will use what you know about plotting points to make a graph.

 Assessment

Watch for students who do not know which coordinate should be the first number in an ordered pair in Exercises 1–4. These students may always reverse the coordinates or they may not be consistent in ordering the coordinates, sometimes placing the horizontal value first and sometimes placing the vertical value first. Have students write an ordered pair such as (horizontal, vertical) or (East, North) at the top of their papers to remind them that the value for the horizontal coordinate is written first.

✅ Develop & Understand: B

Roberta wants to use some of the money she earns from her paper route to sponsor a child in a developing country. Sponsors donate money each month to help pay for food, clothing, and education for a child in need.

Roberta learned that sponsoring a child costs $48 a month. This is more than she can afford, so she wants to ask some of her friends to share the cost.

12. If two people divide the monthly sponsorship cost, how much will each person pay? If three people divide the cost, how much will each pay? $24; $16

13. Copy and complete the table to show how much each person would pay if the given number of people split the cost.

Number of People	1	2	3	4	6	8	12	16	24	48
Cost per Person (dollars)	48	24	16	12	8	6	4	3	2	1

14. On a copy of the grid below, plot and label points for the values from your table. For example, for the first entry, plot the point with coordinates (1, 48). Two of the points have been plotted for you.

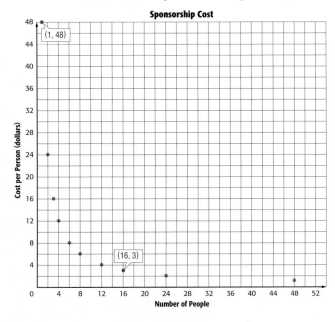

Sponsorship Cost

Teacher Tips In the next exercise set students graph a situation that relates the cost per person for sponsoring a child in a developing country and the number of people who sponsor a child. Students will find copies of Lesson 8.2 Master 3 helpful. Otherwise, they will need to copy the grid onto graph paper.

Have students write the values from tables as ordered pairs before they make their graphs. This reinforces the relationship between the coordinates and the variables represented and helps prevent students from mixing up the coordinates by forgetting which variable they used to represent the first coordinate.

✅ Develop & Understand: B

Suggested Grouping: Pairs

▶ **Exercise 14** Watch for graphs that have a point that does not contribute to the overall pattern. You might ask the students if the point looks odd compared to the others, and have them recalculate the coordinate values for that point.

▶ **Exercise 15** It is important that students are able to recognize that the graph goes downward and that they may need to plot several points to determine whether the graph is curved rather than straight.

▶ **Exercise 17** Some students may resist the notion that the graph will never actually touch the horizontal axis or the vertical axis. Ask them to pose arguments as to why they believe this might be true or false. At this stage, it is fine to leave them with some ambiguity.

Wrap-Up Discuss Exercises 15–17 to make sure students can describe the pattern of the data, tell whether it is appropriate to connect the points, and make predictions based on the graph.

Share & Summarize

These exercises assess students' ability to plot points. Students will need copies of Chapter 8 Master 2 or other graph paper to plot the points.

In **Exercise 1**, suggest that students use scales with intervals of one on the horizontal axis. Some students may find the last two exercises challenging, so you may want to have them work in pairs. Encourage students to graph the points and make a rectangle and then use a picture to help them think about all of the possibilities in **Exercise 4**.

Additional Answer
Share & Summarize

1. and 2. (2, 5)

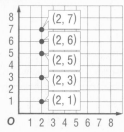

15. Possible answer: The points seem to fall on a curve that decreases quickly at first and then levels off.

16. Lamar is correct. Numbers between the whole numbers do not make sense in this situation.

17a. The points would get closer and closer to the horizontal axis, but no point would ever touch the axis.

17b. No; no matter how many people there are, each will pay some fraction of $48, even if that fraction is less than 1 cent.

15. Describe the overall pattern of points in your graph.

16. Jake wanted to connect the points on his graph with line segments. Lamar said, "That wouldn't make sense. How can $1\frac{1}{2}$ people share the cost?" What do you think?

17. As the number of people increases, the amount each person pays decreases.

  a. If you continued to plot points for more and more people, what would the graph look like?

  b. Could there ever be so many people that each person would pay nothing? Explain.

Share & Summarize

1. Give the coordinates of the point halfway between (2, 7) and (2, 3). Then make a graph showing all three points. Label the points with their coordinates. *See margin.*

2. Give the coordinates of two more points on the same vertical line. Plot and label the points. *Possible answer: (2, 6) and (2, 1); See the answer to Exercise 1 for the graph.*

3. Give the coordinates of two points that, along with (2, 7) and (2, 3), form the vertices of a rectangle. *Possible answer: (4, 7) and (4, 3).*

4. Is your answer for Question 3 the only one possible? Explain. *No; except for the original pair of points, any pair of points with the same horizontal coordinate and with vertical coordinates 7 and 3 will work.*

Mathematical Background

The graph in this exercise set displays asymptotic behavior as the graph gets closer and closer to, but never intersects, the axes. The situation provides a partial explanation for the behavior of the graph. If the graph were to intersect the horizontal axis, the cost per person would be $0. This is impossible, since the cost per person times the number of people must equal $48, and any number multiplied by 0 has a product of 0. Therefore, there is no number of people that can each pay $0 and result in a total of $48. Likewise, if there are no sponsors, the total cannot be $48.

Investigation ③ Choose Scales

Materials

- 10-by-10 grids

① Possible graph:

② Possible answer: In Sara's graph, the values on the horizontal axis are not in order. I would put them in order. In Nina's graph, the values on the horizontal axis are not evenly spaced. I would have each grid line represent 4 batches.

When you created a graph showing the relationship between the number of sponsors and the amount each sponsor would have to pay, you were given a set of axes labeled with *scale values*. Often when you make a graph, you have to choose the scales yourself.

Think & Discuss

Sara and Nina are baking ginger snaps for the school bake sale. They need half a cup of molasses for each batch of cookies.

Sketch a rough graph showing the relationship between the number of batches and the number of cups of molasses. Your graph does not need to show precise points.   See ①.

Sara and Nina made a table to show how much molasses they would need for different numbers of batches.

Batches	Molasses (cups)
1	$\frac{1}{2}$
12	6
20	10
3	$1\frac{1}{2}$
8	4
40	20

They each decided to graph the data. Here are their graphs.

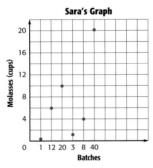
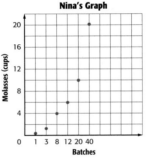

Discuss each graph. Do you think the graph is correct? If not, explain what is incorrect. Tell how you would fix it.   See ②.

Lesson 8.2 Draw and Label Graphs   **495**

On the Spot Assessment

As students study the graphs in the Think & Discuss, stress that graphs must have points plotted in increasing order from left to right on the horizontal axis and from bottom to top on the vertical axis. Likewise, the numbers on each axis should be evenly spaced. You might suggest that students think of each axis as a number line. Students are shown one way to draw a more accurate graph of these data on page 496.

Investigation ③

On Your Own Exercises
Pages 503–508
Exercises 11–13

Choose Scales In this investigation, students explore the scales they might use for different graphs. All graphs have (0, 0) as the intersection of the horizontal and vertical axes. Students determine the values and intervals of the scales on a graph and plot points on those graphs. They also estimate the coordinates for points that do not lie on labeled grid lines and look at patterns in the graphed data to predict other points that will fall on the graph.

To introduce the investigation, remind students about the graph of sponsor data from the exercises on pages 493–494. Have them look at those graphs and point out the numbers along the axes. Ask students to describe how the axes are labeled. They should note that the numbers on the vertical axis go from 0 to 48 in units of 4 and the numbers on the horizontal axis go from 0 to 52 in units of 4.

Think & Discuss

Read the problem situation, and then have students sketch rough graphs without using scales and focus on the shape of the graph rather than precise points. You might have them sketch their own, and then have a volunteer copy his or her graph onto the board or overhead. Next, have students consider the table. You might ask how Sara and Nina might have found the number of cups of molasses shown in the table. Some students may suggest that they divided the number of batches by 2 while others may think that they multiplied the number of batches by $\frac{1}{2}$. Then have students look at the two graphs and, as a class, discuss how useful each graph is. Encourage students to compare the patterns shown by the points in the graphs to the pattern shown in the graph they sketched. The first graph, in which the points on the horizontal axis are plotted out of numerical order, addresses a common error that some students make when creating graphs. The second graph addresses another error, in which the intervals do not have the same width.

Teacher Tips Discuss how to choose the greatest value and scale for each axis of a graph. Point out that the same interval does not have to be used for the scales on both axes. Be sure students understand that the greatest value and the scale for each axis of a graph must be chosen to accommodate the data to be graphed.

Then have students compare the two new graphs of the cookie data. Some characteristics they may notice are that the scale for the vertical axis is the same on both graphs and that the data points fall in a straight line. The intervals on the horizontal axes are different, as are the slants (slopes) of the lines.

You might ask students which graph they prefer, but stress that either graph can be used to show the data.

Then tell students that they will determine scales for the data they will graph in the exercises on page 497.

When you draw a graph, you need to think about the greatest value that you want to show on each axis. For the cookie data, you need to show values up to 40 on the "Batches" axis and up to 20 on the "Molasses (cups)" axis.

You also need to consider the scale to use on each axis. The *scale* is the number of units each equal interval on the grid represents. You want to choose a scale that will make your graph easy to read but will not make it so large that it will not fit on your paper. Here are two possibilities for the cookie data.

- Let each interval represent four batches on the horizontal axis and two cups on the vertical axis. Then the graph would fit on a 10-by-10 grid.

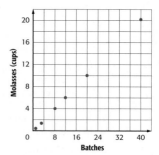

- Let each interval represent two batches on the horizontal axis and two cups on the vertical axis. Then the graph would fit on a 20-by-10 grid.

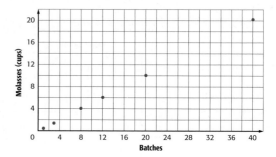

✅ Develop & Understand: A

Pablo wants to buy a birthday present for his sister. He has $10 to spend on the present and the gift wrap.

1. Copy and complete this table to show some of the ways the $10 Pablo has to spend can be distributed between the cost of the present and the cost of the gift wrap.

Cost of Present (dollars)	10	9	8	7	6	5	4	3
Cost of Gift Wrap (dollars)	0	1	2	3	4	5	6	7

2. $10 on the horizontal axis and $7 on the vertical axis

3. Possible answer: On both axes, I would let one grid interval represent $1.

5. The points fall on a straight line that slants down from left to right.

6. See graph in the answer to Exercise 4. The point follows the same pattern.

2. Suppose you want to graph these data with the cost of the present on the horizontal axis and the cost of the gift wrap on the vertical axis. What is the greatest value you need to show on each axis?

3. What scale would you use on each axis? In other words, how many dollars would you let each interval on the grid represent?

4. Make a graph of the data. Be sure to do the following.
   • Label the axes with the names of the variables.
   • Add scale labels to the axes.
   • Plot a point for each pair of values in the table.
   See margin.

5. Describe the pattern of points on your graph.

6. In this situation, either variable could have a value that is not a whole number. For example, Pablo could spend $6.50 on the present and $3.50 on the wrapping. Plot the point (6.5, 3.5) on your graph. Does this point follow the same pattern as the others?

7. Find two more pairs of non-whole-number values that fit this situation. Plot points for these values. Check that the points follow the same pattern as the others.   Answers will vary.

8. You can use your graph to make predictions.
   a. Connect the points with line segments.   See margin.
   b. Choose a point on the graph that is not one of the points that you plotted. Use the coordinates of the point to predict a pair of values for the present cost and the wrapping cost. Then check your prediction by verifying that the values add to $10.
   Answers will vary.

Teacher Tips In this exercise set, students determine suitable scales for graphing data on coordinate axes, label the axes, and plot points for data. They then describe the pattern of the data and use the graph to make predictions. Students work with non-whole-number coordinates so that they begin to think about the kinds of numbers that make sense for the variables given in each exercise. Activities like these can be time-consuming, but they help to make sure that all students get enough practice with the plotting and interpreting skills involved.

Students will need graph paper or copies of Chapter 8 Master 2 to graph the data.

✅ Develop & Understand: A

Suggested Grouping: Pairs

▶ **Exercise 1** Some students may question why the table does not include all possible whole-number values that have a sum of $10. Tell these students that they will find out why as they proceed through the exercise set. (They make predictions of other data values in Exercise 8b.)

▶ **Exercise 7** Remind students that fractions and decimals can be non-whole-number values, if necessary. Point out that the sum of the coordinates in each ordered pair should be $10.

▶ **Exercise 8b** Watch students' interpretations of "a point on the graph." If necessary, tell students that this means a point on the line segments they drew, not any point in the 10 × 10 grid. You may want to point out that a possible answer may not be a reasonable answer. For example, it is possible to spend $9.90 for gift wrap and only $.10 for a present, but this is unlikely.

Wrap-Up Discuss Exercise 3 to see if any students chose intervals other than one. If so, you may want to have them draw their graphs on a transparency and then ask the class to compare the various graphs. Then have students share their answers to Exercises 5, 7, and 8b to reinforce identifying patterns and finding other data points on graphs.

Additional Answers

4. Possible graph:

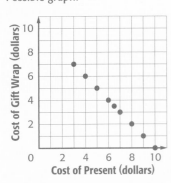

8a.

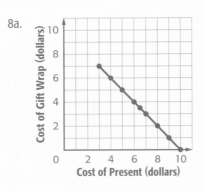

Teacher Tips Remind students that the intervals used in scales can affect how easy it is to plot points and to find patterns in the data.

✓ *Develop & Understand: B*

Suggested Grouping: Pairs

▶ **Exercise 9** In this exercise set, students determine a scale that makes sense for a data set and then graph the data. They must also decide whether to connect the points and then use the graph to make predictions. Students will need graph paper or copies of Chapter 8 Master 1 to make their graphs. For this exercise, students may decide to use a scale with intervals of six for the vertical scale, since that scale will make it easier to plot the points.

▶ **Exercise 9f** It makes sense to consider non-whole numbers for the cost but not for the number of people. Because it does not make sense to connect the points for one variable, it does not make sense to connect the points on this graph.

Additional Answer

9c. Possible answer:

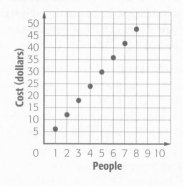

9b. Possible answer: On the horizontal axis, he should let 1 grid square represent 1 person. On the vertical axis, he should let 1 grid square represent $5.

9d. Yes; the points seem to lie on a straight line that slants up from left to right.

· ·

Real-World Link
Americans eat 100 acres of pizza every day!

· ·

When you make the graphs in Exercises 9 and 10, you will need to choose a scale that gives a good view of the overall pattern in the data.

✓ *Develop & Understand: B*

Make each graph on a 10-by-10 grid in Exercises 9 and 10.

9. James is planning a party at a local pizza parlor. The party will cost $6 per person.

   a. Complete the table to show the cost for various numbers of people.

People	1	2	3	4	5	6	7	8
Cost (dollars)	6	12	18	24	30	36	42	48

   b. James wants to graph these data on a 10-by-10 grid with the number of people on the horizontal axis. What scale do you think he should use on each axis?

   c. Graph the values in the table using an appropriate scale. See margin.

   d. Do the points on your graph form a pattern? If so, describe it.

   e. Use your graph to predict the cost of the pizza for nine people. Check that your prediction is correct. $54

   f. Would it make sense to connect the points on this graph? Explain.   No; the number of people must be a whole number.

 Assessment

For Exercise 9b, watch for students who choose scale values before they think about the range of values for the variables. Encourage them to look at their completed tables and think about the range of numbers that need to fit into the given space on the axes before they make decisions about scale.

10. The social committee needs streamers for decorations. Material for the streamers costs 20¢ per yard.

   a. Complete the table to show the cost of various lengths of material.

Length (yards)	1	2	3	4	5	6	7	8	9
Cost (cents)	20	40	60	80	100	120	140	160	180

   b. Suppose you graphed these data with the length on the horizontal axis and the cost on the vertical axis. What would happen if you let each interval on the vertical axis represent 1¢?
   Possible answer: The graph would not fit on a 10-by-10 grid.

   c. What scale would be appropriate for each axis?

   d. Make a graph of the data with length on the horizontal axis. See margin.

   e. Do the points on your graph form a pattern? If so, describe it.
   Yes; they lie on a line that slants up from left to right.

   f. Would it make sense to connect the points on this graph? Explain. See below.

   g. Use your graph to predict the cost for $4\frac{1}{2}$ yards. Check your prediction by multiplying the number of yards by the cost per yard. $0.90

   h. Draw another graph using the same data. But this time, put the cost on the horizontal axis.

   i. Describe how your two graphs are alike and different.

10c. Possible answer: On the horizontal axis, let 1 grid square represent 1 yard. On the vertical axis, let 1 grid square represent 20¢.

10h.

10i. Possible answer: In both graphs, the points fall on a line. In the second graph, the coordinates of the points on the first graph are "flipped." For example, the point (1, 20) is on the first graph while (20, 1) is on the second graph.

Share & Summarize

1. When you make a graph, how do you decide on the scale for each axis?

2. After you have plotted points from a table, how do you decide whether to connect the points?

1. Possible answer: Consider how large the values of each variable get and choose a scale so that the greatest value fits reasonably into a graph.

2. Possible answer: If the values between the plotted points make sense, I connect the points.

10f. Yes; the length does not have to be a whole number of yards, so the in-between points make sense.

Lesson 8.2 Draw and Label Graphs   **499**

▶ **Exercise 10c** Watch for students who neglect to consider the range of values before choosing scales.

Wrap-Up Discuss the scales that students used for each axis, the pattern shown by the data points, and whether it makes sense to connect the points. These are Exercises 9b, 9d, 9f, and 10c, 10e, and 10f. You may also want to discuss Exercises 10h and 10i since they point out the arbitrary nature, in some cases, of choosing a particular variable for a particular axis.

Share & Summarize

Have students answer these exercises on their own so you can assess their understanding of how to create a scale when graphing and how to determine whether to connect the points on a graph. Having them articulate how they make these decisions, either orally or in writing, will help them clarify their own reasoning. Discuss the answers after all students have a chance to write their responses.

Troubleshooting If students are having difficulty determining the intervals to use on a scale, encourage them to look for any multiples in the data that can be used to make plotting the points easier. If students are having difficulty deciding whether to connect points, have them choose an in-between value and see if it makes sense. Have students use these suggestions to evaluate the scales for graphs they have made and those shown in the text and to evaluate whether to connect the points in those graphs.

Additional Answer
10d. Possible graph:

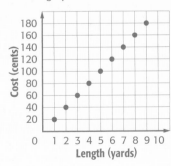

Investigation 4

On Your Own Exercises
Pages 503–508
Exercises 7, 14, 15

Make Predictions from Graphs In this investigation, students plot points to create graphs, and they use the graphs to make predictions about possible data not plotted. They learn that line segments can be used to show that there is a trend, pattern, or rule for the data, but that not all in-between values make sense in terms of the context of the problem, in which case a dashed line is often used. Point out that connecting points on graphs can help students find other values that have the same relationship between the two variables and can help them make predictions.

✓ Develop & Understand: A

Suggested Grouping: Pairs

Provide copies of Lesson 8.2 Master 4 so that the patterns in the graphs can be extended.

▶ **Exercises 1 and 2** These exercises involve reading values from the graph. You may want to quickly discuss these problems as a class before having students work in pairs.

▶ **Exercise 3** Point out that students are not expected to find the costs for decks of cards. They are only expected to determine if it is possible to use the graph to find the costs. However, depending on your class, you may indeed want them to suggest costs for 4 and 10 decks.

Wrap-Up Discuss Exercise 3 with the class and lead into the cartoon, which introduces the use of dashed lines to show related data when the in-between values do not make sense.

Think & Discuss

Discuss these questions. Students should understand that both Hannah and Jahmal are correct, depending upon what the allowable values are for numbers of decks of cards. However, connecting the points when in-between values does not make sense. The use of dashed line segments in the next section addresses this.

Investigation 4 Make Predictions from Graphs

Materials

• graph paper
• copy of the graph

You have seen that when the points in a graph form a pattern, you can use the graph to make predictions. Connecting the points on a graph with line segments can help you find in-between values. Extending the pattern can help you make predictions about values beyond those shown in the graph.

✓ Develop & Understand: A

This graph shows the cost of various numbers of decks of playing cards.

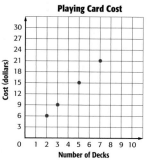

Playing Card Cost

1. How much do five decks of cards cost? **$15**

2. How many decks of cards can you buy for $9? **3**

3. Can you use the graph to find the cost for four decks of cards? For ten decks of cards? Why or why not? **See margin.**

Here is how Hannah thought about Exercise 3.

Think & Discuss

What do you think about Hannah's method? Does it make sense? Is Jahmal correct? **Possible answer: Hannah's method is a good one. Although Jahmal is right that all the in-between points do not make sense, some of them do, and connecting the points made it easy for Hannah to find the answer.**

500 CHAPTER 8 Coordinate Plane

Additional Answer

3. Yes, yes; Possible explanation: Although there are no points for 4 or 10 decks, the pattern in the graph indicates that the price increases by $3 for each deck. So 4 decks would cost $12, and 10 decks would cost $30.

Sometimes connecting the points in a graph can help you find information or to see a pattern, even when all the in-between points do not make sense. In cases like this, people often use dashed segments to connect the points.

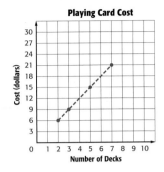

Playing Card Cost

The dashed segments in the graph above make it easy to find information and to see that all the points fall on a straight line. The dashes also indicate that not every point on the line makes sense.

✅ Develop & Understand: B

4. This table shows the cost for different numbers of packs of fruit snacks.

Packs	3	5	8	15
Cost	$1.50	$2.50	$4.00	$7.50

a. Make a graph of the data. Be sure to choose appropriate scales and to label the axes with the variable names.   See margin.

b. Use your graph to find the cost of six packs of fruit snacks and the cost of nine packs of fruit snacks. Explain how you found your answers.

c. Use your graph to find the cost of 19 packs of fruit snacks. Explain how you found your answer.

d. Use your graph to find how many packs of fruit snacks you can buy for $6. Explain how you found your answer.   12; Possible explanation: I found the point on the dashed line with vertical coordinate 6 and then found its horizontal coordinate.

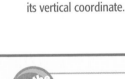

4b. $3.00, $4.50; Possible explanation: I connected the points with dashed segments to form a line. I found the points with horizontal coordinates 6 and 9 on that line and then found their vertical coordinates.

4c. $9.50; Possible explanation: I extended my dashed line, found the point with horizontal coordinate 19 on that line and then found its vertical coordinate.

Teacher Tips In the next exercise set, point out that students graph data and then use their graphs to predict values. They decide whether to connect the data points and, if the points are connected, whether to use solid or dashed line segments.

✅ Develop & Understand: B

Suggested Grouping: Pairs

▶ **Exercise 4** Students need to decide which variable to place on which axis. If you notice that students are choosing different variables for the axes (that is, some are putting cost on the horizontal axis while some are putting it on the vertical axis), you may want to discuss whether one way shows the information more clearly or seems more helpful than the other. In this particular exercise, it does not matter which variable is on which axis, although it may be somewhat easier to determine a rule or pattern if the number of packs is on the horizontal axis.

Additional Answer
4a. Possible graph:

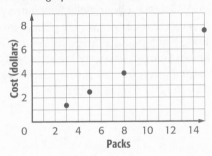

On the Spot Assessment

Watch for students who cannot estimate values for points that lie between two grid lines. This may occur when students use scales with intervals greater than 1 for their graphs in Exercise 4. Encourage students to use a straightedge and pencil to draw a line from the point to the axis to help them read the value associated with that point.

▶ **Exercise 5a** Although reading in-between values on a graph can be inexact, most students should choose a value within one tenth of 6.5 as their answer.

Wrap-Up Discuss whether to connect points for the two graphs, and have students explain their reasoning. Most will say they connected the points in Exercise 4 with a dashed line to help them predict values and to show that there are no values for in between points. If students had difficulty finding or estimating values on graphs, you may want to have them share their answers and explanations for Exercises 4b–4d, 5a, 5c, and 5d.

Share & Summarize

Discuss these questions, which focus on when to connect points on a graph and, when connecting points, whether to use solid or dashed line segments. If there is time, have students graph the data and write a couple of questions (with answers) that would require making a prediction using a line through the points on the first graph. Students might try the same with the second graph but, because it is not linear, they may have more difficulty with it.

Additional Answer

5b. Possible answer: Yes; solid; connecting the points lets you estimate information about pipes that aren't plotted on the graph. For instance, no information is given about the mass of a 175-cm pipe, but by connecting the points and finding the vertical coordinate of the point on that line with horizontal coordinate 175, you can estimate the mass. I would use solid segments, since the lengths and weights do not have to be whole numbers.

Real-World Link
The Statue of Liberty contains 200,000 pounds of copper.

5c. About 11.5 kg; I connected the points to form a line. Then I found the vertical coordinate of the point along that line with horizontal coordinate 180.

① Possible answer: Yes; dashed; I would connect the points because it would allow me to find the prices of other numbers of tickets. I would use dashed segments because not all the in-between points make sense.

Real-World Link
On January 11, 1980, the temperature at Montana's Great Falls International Airport rose 47°, from −32°F to 15°F, in only seven minutes!

5. This graph shows the masses of different lengths of a certain type of copper pipe.

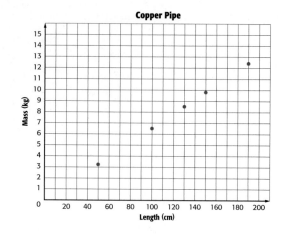

a. What is the mass of 100 centimeters of copper pipe?   6.5 kg

b. Would you connect the points on this graph? If so, would you use dashed or solid segments? Explain your answers.   See margin.

c. Estimate the mass of a copper pipe with length 180 centimeters. Explain how you found your answer.

d. Estimate the length of a copper pipe with a mass of 5 kilograms. Explain how you found your answer.   About 75 cm; I found the horizontal coordinate of the point along my line with vertical coordinate 5.

Share & Summarize

1. If you were to make a graph of these data, would you connect the points? If so, would you use dashed or solid segments? Explain your answers. See ①.

Tickets	Price ($)
1	3
5	15
8	24
15	45
21	63

2. If you were to make a graph of these data, would you connect the points? If so, would you use dashed or solid segments? Explain your answers.
Possible answer: Yes; solid; I would connect the points because it would allow me to estimate the temperature at other times. I would use solid segments because the temperature "exists" at all times between those given.

Time	Temp. (°F)
6 A.M.	17
8 A.M.	20
10 A.M.	25
noon	32
2 P.M.	30
4 P.M.	28
6 P.M.	15

502   CHAPTER 8   Coordinate Plane

Troubleshooting

If students are having difficulty deciding on whether to connect points on a graph, remind them that points are connected only when there is a pattern. If there is a pattern, students must decide whether to use dashed or solid line segments to connect points. Have them choose any fraction, such as $\frac{1}{2}$, and ask if it makes sense to have that number for either of the variables. For example, they could ask themselves if it makes sense to have $\frac{1}{2}$ of a car or $\frac{1}{2}$ of a day of the week. If it does not make sense, that is an indication that the points could be connected by a dashed line or not at all.

Practice & Apply

1. A weight lifter grips a barbell and struggles with it for several seconds. She suddenly lifts it part of the way and then steadily raises it until it is fully above her head. She holds it for a few seconds and then drops it.

   Sketch a graph to show how the height of the barbell changes from the time the weight lifter first grips the barbell until just after she drops it. **1–3. See margin.**

2. Goin' Nuts sells mixed nuts by the pound. Draw a graph that shows how the cost for cashews is related to the number of pounds purchased.

3. For this exercise, use a grid with horizontal and vertical axes from 0 to 14. Plot the points below in order, reading across the rows. Connect the points as you go with straight line segments. The line segments should form a picture.

(7, 3)	(13, 3)	(10, 1)	(2, 1)	(1, 2)	(1, 3)	(7, 3)
(7, 12)	(13, 4)	(7, 4)	(8, 5)	(8, 10)	(7, 12)	(6, 10)
(6, 5)	(7, 4)	(0, 4)	(7, 12)	(5, 13)	(7, 13)	(7, 12)

4. **Geometry** The area of a square is the product of the lengths of two sides.

   a. What is the area of a square with side length 1? What is the area of a square with side length 2?   **1, 4**

   b. Complete the table to show areas of squares with the given side lengths.

Side Length	1	2	3	4	5	6
Area	1	4	9	16	25	36

   c. On a copy of the axes at right, plot and label points for the values from your table. For example, for a square with side length 5, plot the point (5, 25).

   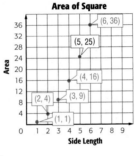

   Area of Square

   d. Describe the overall pattern of points in your graph.

   e. Would it make sense to connect the points on this graph? Explain. **Yes; the side length of a square does not have to be a whole number.**

4d. Possible answer: The points seem to fall on a curve that increases slowly at first and then more quickly.

Lesson 8.2 Draw and Label Graphs   **503**

Investigation 1
Practice & Apply: 1, 2
Connect & Extend: 8, 9

Investigation 2
Practice & Apply: 3–6
Connect & Extend: 10

Investigation 3
Connect & Extend: 11–13

Investigation 4
Practice & Apply: 7
Connect & Extend: 14, 15

Assign Anytime
Mixed Review: 16–23

▶ **Exercise 1** Note how students portray the weight lifter dropping the bar in their graphs. Some students may draw this action as a vertical line, which is more like a picture or photograph of what is happening. Point out that some time does elapse while the bar is being dropped and therefore the line should be a very steep, but not vertical, line drawn down from left to right.

▶ **Exercises 3 and 4** Students will need graph paper or copies of Lesson 8.2 Master 6 to draw their graphs.

▶ **Exercise 4** You may want to remind students that the area of a square is found by multiplying the lengths of two sides.

Additional Answers
1. Possible graph:

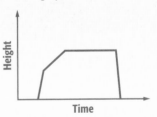

2. Possible graph:

3.

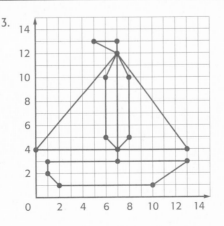

▶ **Exercises 5 and 6** Students will need graph paper or copies of Chapter 8 Master 1 to make their graphs.

▶ **Exercise 6b** Students may have difficulty plotting points with decimal values. Remind them to estimate the positions as closely as possible.

Additional Answers

5a. Possible table:

Violin Time (min)	5	10	15	20	25	30
Study Time (min)	25	20	15	10	5	0

5d. Possible graph:

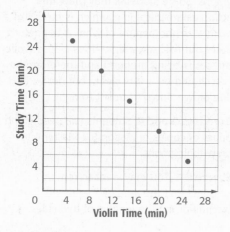

6b. Possible graph:

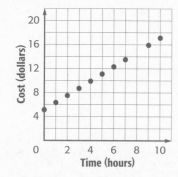

5. Calvin has only 30 minutes to finish his homework, which includes practicing the violin and studying for a history quiz.

  a. Make a table showing at least six ways Calvin can split up the time between the two activities. See margin.

  b. Suppose you want to graph your data with the time spent practicing the violin on the horizontal axis. What is the greatest value you need to show on each axis? Possible answer: 30 min on each axis

  c. What scale would you use on each axis? Possible answer: I would let 1 grid square represent 2 min.

  d. Make a graph of your data. Be sure to add labels and scale values to the axes. See margin.

  e. Describe the general pattern of points on your graph. The points fall on a straight line that slants down from left to right.

  f. Connect the points on your graph with line segments. Then choose a point on the graph that is not one of the points you plotted. Use the coordinates of the point to predict a pair of values for the violin time and the study time. Answers will vary.

6. Economics Sparks Internet Service charges $5 per month plus $0.02 for each minute a customer is online.

Time (hours)	0	1	2	3	4	5	6	7	9	10
Cost (dollars)	5	6.20	7.40	8.60	9.80	11	12.20	13.40	15.80	17

  a. Complete the table to show the cost for various amounts of time online.

  b. Graph the data from the table on a 10-by-10 grid. Show time on the horizontal axis. Use appropriate scales. See margin.

6c. Yes; the points seem to lie on a straight line that slants up from left to right.

  c. Do the points on your graph make a pattern? If so, describe it.

  d. Does it make sense to connect the points on this graph? Explain. Yes; a customer could be on line for a fraction of an hour.

  e. Use your graph to predict the cost for eight hours. Check that your prediction is correct. $14.60

7b. Possible answer: About 12.5 cm; I connected the points, found the point on the connecting segments with horizontal coordinate 4 and then found its vertical coordinate.

Connect & Extend

8a. Possible graph:

8b. Possible graph:

8c. Possible graph:

7. **Geometry** *Circumference* is the distance around a circle. The table lists the approximate circumferences of circles with given diameters.

Diameter (cm)	Circumference (cm)
0.5	1.6
1.5	4.7
2	6.3
3	9.4
3.5	11.0
5	15.7

a. Make a graph of the data. Be sure to choose appropriate scales and to label the axes with the variable names.   See margin.

b. Use your graph to estimate the circumference of a circle with diameter 4 cm. Explain how you found your answer.

c. Use your graph to estimate the diameter of a circle with circumference 8 cm. Explain how you found your answer. See margin.

8. A family is driving to visit some relatives a few hundred miles away. The drive begins at a moderate pace along back roads and moves to several hours on a major highway. When the family gets to the city where the relatives live, travel is slowed by heavy traffic and lights at intersections.

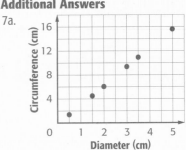

a. Sketch a graph showing the time since the trip began on the horizontal axis and the family's speed on the vertical axis.

b. Sketch a graph showing the time on the horizontal axis and the family's distance from the starting point on the vertical axis.

c. Sketch a graph showing the time on the horizontal axis and the distance from the destination on the vertical axis.

9. Annie said, "When my schoolwork is much too easy, I don't learn very much. But I also don't learn very much when it is much too hard. I learn the most when the difficulty level is somewhere between 'too easy' and 'too hard.'" Draw a graph to illustrate Annie's ideas.   Possible graph:

Lesson 8.2 Draw and Label Graphs   **505**

▶ **Exercise 7** Students will need copies of Chapter 8 Masters 1 and 2 or graph paper to make their graphs.

Additional Answers

7a.

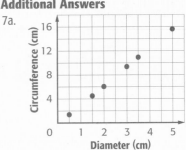

7c. Possible answer: About 2.5 cm; I extended my connecting line, found the point on the line with vertical coordinate 8, and then found its horizontal coordinate.

▶ **Exercise 8** This exercise may be more challenging for students than it first appears. Students may need to clarify what is meant by *distance from the starting point* and *distance from the destination*. After completing the graphs, they may note that the graphs in Exercises 8b and 8c appear to be mirror images of each other, more or less.

▶ **Exercise 9** The graph should not intersect the axis labeled "Difficulty Level" since Althea implies that she does learn something, even when the work is at the extreme levels.

▶ **Exercise 10** Students begin to reason about the relationship between coordinates of points that lie on the same vertical and horizontal lines. These questions will be important in later courses when they develop equations for these lines.

10a. If they have the same vertical coordinate, they are on the same horizontal line.

10b. If they have the same horizontal coordinate, they are on the same vertical line.

10c. Possible answer: For the diagonal line going through (0, 0), (1, 1), and (2, 2), each of the three points has two identical coordinates. For the diagonal line going through (2, 0), (1, 1), and (0, 2), the sum of the coordinates is 2 for all three points.

11b.

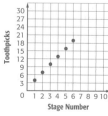

11c. Possible answer: The points fall on a straight line that slants up from left to right.

10. You could play tic-tac-toe on a grid like this. Instead of writing X's and O's in the squares, you would write them at points where the grid lines meet. For example, you could mark (0, 0) or (2, 1).

a. How can you tell from just the coordinates whether three points are on the same horizontal line?

b. How can you tell from just the coordinates whether three points are on the same vertical line?

c. How can you tell from just the coordinates whether three points are on the same diagonal line?

11. Consider the toothpick pattern below.

Stage 1   Stage 2   Stage 3   Stage 4

a. Imagine that this pattern continues. Complete the table to show the number of toothpicks in the first six stages.

Stage	1	2	3	4	5	6
Toothpicks	4	7	10	13	16	19

b. Make a graph with the stage number on the horizontal axis and the number of toothpicks on the vertical axis. Make the horizontal axis from 0 to 10 and the vertical axis from 0 to 30.

c. Describe the pattern of points in your graph.

d. Use the pattern in your graph to predict the number of toothpicks in stages 7 and 8. Check your answers by drawing these stages.   22, 25

e. Would it make sense to connect the points on this graph? Explain.   No; stage numbers must be whole numbers, so in-between points do not make sense.

12a. Possible rule: output = 3 · input −1

12b.

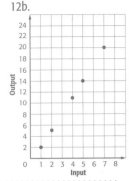

13c. Yes; dashed; although values between months do not make sense, connecting the points can help you estimate the values for the months for which there are no points.

13d. Possible answer: 53°F, 45°F; I connected the points and found the vertical coordinates of the points on the segments corresponding to April and November.

12. Consider this input/output table.

Input	1	2	4	5	7
Output	2	5	11	14	20

a. Describe a rule relating the input and output values.

b. Graph the values from the table. Make the "Input" axis from 0 to 8 and the "Output" axis from 0 to 24.

c. Use your graph to predict the outputs for inputs of 3, 6, and 8. Use your rule to check your predictions.   8, 17, 23

13. Earth Science This table represents the normal monthly temperatures for Washington, D.C.

a. Graph the data with the month on the horizontal axis and the temperature on the vertical axis.   See margin.

b. In which month is the temperature highest? In which month is the temperature lowest?
July, January

c. Would you connect the points on your graph? If so, would you use dashed or solid segments? Explain your answers.

d. Use your graph to estimate the temperatures for April and November. Explain how you made your estimates.

Washington, D.C. Normal Monthly Temperatures

Month	Temperature (°F)
January	31
February	34
March	43
April	
May	62
June	71
July	76
August	74
September	67
October	55
November	
December	35

Source: *World Almanac and Book of Facts 2000.*
Copyright © 1999 Primedia Reference Inc.

14. In Your Own Words Sketch a graph that shows how your height has changed since you were born. Use as much exact information as you can recall or that you can obtain from family members. Extend your sketch to show your prediction for your full adult height and the age when you will reach it. Write an explanation of what your graph represents about your growth.   Answers will vary.

▶ **Exercise 12** Point out that students can graph the data and use the graph to predict outputs even if they have trouble describing the rule.

▶ **Exercise 13** Students will need copies of Chapter 8 Masters 1 and 2 or graph paper to make their graphs.

Additional Answers

13a.

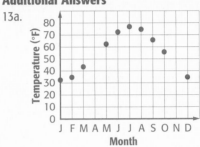

Quick Check

Informal Assessment Students should be able to:

✔ create graphs that describe a story relating two variables that change over time

✔ plot points in the first quadrant of a coordinate grid

✔ observe any patterns, or trends, in data and use them to make predictions

✔ determine an appropriate scale for a set of data

Lesson 8.2 Draw and Label Graphs   **507**

Quick Quiz

1. On Joachín's first day at school, he walked slowly into the cafeteria at lunchtime and stopped to look around for his friends. He did not see anyone he knew, so he ran out the back door. Sketch a graph that shows his walking speed over this period of time. Possible graph:

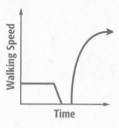

2. A shade of green dye is made by mixing three pints of green dye for each pint of water.

a. Fill in the missing values for the table below.

Pints of Water	Pints of Green Dye
1	3
2	6
3	9
4	12
5	15

b. Plot the points from the table on a graph. Choose an appropriate scale.

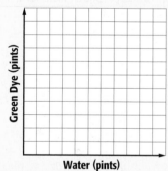

c. Do the points in the graph make a pattern? If so, describe it. Yes; they appear to be on a straight line that slants up from left to right.

d. Does it make sense to connect the points? Why or why not? Yes; there can be fractional parts of water or dye in the mixture.

e. Use your graph to predict the number of pints of water needed for 10 pints of green dye. $3\frac{1}{3}$

15b.

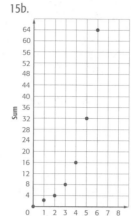

15. Here are the first seven rows of Pascal's triangle.

```
                1                      Row 0
              1   1                    Row 1
            1   2   1                  Row 2
          1   3   3   1                Row 3
        1   4   6   4   1              Row 4
      1   5  10  10   5   1            Row 5
    1   6  15  20  15   6   1          Row 6
```

a. Complete a table to show the sum of the numbers in each row.

Row	0	1	2	3	4	5	6
Sum	1	2	4	8	16	32	64

b. Make a graph of these values. Put the row number on the horizontal axis and the sum on the vertical axis.

c. Describe the pattern of points in your graph. Possible answer: They form a curve that increases from left to right.

Mixed Review

Find each product or quotient.

16. $\frac{4}{5} \cdot \frac{5}{7}$ $\frac{4}{7}$ **17.** $\frac{10}{13} \div \frac{5}{26}$ 4   **18.** $4\frac{2}{3} \div 1\frac{5}{6}$ $2\frac{6}{11}$

Find each sum or difference.

19. $3\frac{1}{2} - 1\frac{5}{8}$ $1\frac{7}{8}$ **20.** $1\frac{7}{12} + 4\frac{2}{3}$ $6\frac{1}{4}$ **21.** $12\frac{6}{7} + 5\frac{5}{6}$ $18\frac{29}{42}$

22. Economics The Book Bin is having a clearance sale.

a. All dictionaries are marked $33\frac{1}{3}$% off. Ramesh bought a French dictionary with a sale price of $18. What was the dictionary's original price? $27

b. Novels are on sale for 20% off. Diana bought a novel with an original price of $11.95. What was the sale price? $9.56

c. Travel books are all marked down by a certain percent. Nestor bought a book about African safaris. The book was originally priced at $27.50, but he paid only $16.50. What percent did Nestor save? 40%

For each square, estimate the percent of the area that is shaded.

23.

25%

24.

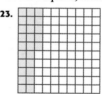

55%

Possible graph for 2b:

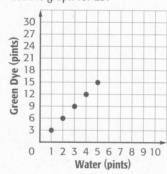

Graph in Four Quadrants

Objectives

▶ To graph positive and negative numbers on a number line

▶ To identify opposites and find absolute values

▶ To compare and order positive and negative numbers

▶ To create and interpret four-quadrant graphs

▶ To use the distinguishing characteristics of points in the plane to analyze graphs

Overview

In this lesson, students are introduced to integers and then examine relationships between quantities that are sometimes negative. The coordinate plane is one important way relationships can be represented. In this lesson, students learn how to plot points and interpret graphs in all four quadrants and then use coordinates to create a picture. They work with the absolute value of numbers and explore how absolute value can be used to understand real-life situations.

Advance Preparation

You may want to provide students Lesson 8.3 Masters 1–3 to facilitate class discussion while presenting new topics, including absolute value and coordinates.

	Summary	Materials	On Your Own Exercises (pp. 524–527)	Assessment Opportunities
Investigation 1 (p. 510) *Pacing: 2 days*	Students graph numbers on number lines. They identify opposites and find absolute values.	Lesson 8.3 Master 1 (optional), counters in 2 colors (optional)	Practice & Apply: 1–8 Connect & Extend: 19–23 Mixed Review: 32–43	• On the Spot Assessment (p. 511) • Share & Summarize (p. 512) • Troubleshooting (p. 512)
Investigation 2 (p. 512) *Pacing: 1 day*	Students find the absolute value of numbers and compare tables of temperature change.		Practice & Apply: 9–15 Connect & Extend: 24–28 Mixed Review: 32–43	• On the Spot Assessment (p. 513) • Share & Summarize (p. 514)
Investigation 3 (p. 515) *Pacing: 1 day*	Students learn how to plot points in four quadrants and get to know the coordinate plane.	Lesson 8.3 Masters 2–3	Practice & Apply: 16–17 Connect & Extend: 29 Mixed Review: 32–43	• On the Spot Assessment (p. 515) • Share & Summarize (p. 518) • Troubleshooting (p. 518)
Investigation 4 (p. 519) *Pacing: 1 day*	Students explore characteristics of points in the coordinate plane.		Practice & Apply: 18 Connect & Extend: 30 Mixed Review: 32–43	• On the Spot Assessment (p. 520) • Share & Summarize (p. 521) • Troubleshooting (p. 521)
Inquiry Investigation 5 (p. 522) *Pacing: 1 day*	Students write the coordinates of points in each of the four quadrants.	Grid paper	Mixed Review: 32–43	• Troubleshooting (p. 522)

Leveled Lesson Resources

Study Guide and Intervention (p. 23) · AL

Lesson 8.3 Study Guide and Intervention
Graph in Four Quadrants

A **coordinate** system is a grid used to locate points. The horizontal number line is the *x*–axis; the vertical number line is the *y*–axis.

The *x*–axis and *y*–axis separate the **coordinate system** into four regions called **quadrants**.

An ordered pair helps you locate any point on the coordinate plane. The first number is the *x*–**coordinate**. The second number is the *y*–**coordinate**.

Example 1 Identify the ordered pair that names point *A*.

Step 1 Move left on the *x*–axis to find the *x*–coordinate of point *A*, which is −3.

Step 2 Move up the *y*–axis to find the *y*–coordinate, which is 4. Point *A* is named by (−3, 4).

Example 2 Graph point *B* at (5, 4).

Use the coordinate plane shown above. Start at 0. The *x*–coordinate is 5, so move 5 units to the right.

Since the *y*–coordinate is 4, move 4 units up.

Draw a dot. Label the dot *B*.

Exercises

Use the coordinate plane at the right. Write the ordered pair that names each point.

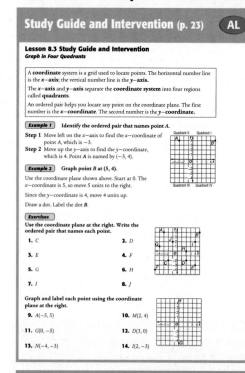

1. *C*
2. *D*
3. *E*
4. *F*
5. *G*
6. *H*
7. *I*
8. *J*

Graph and label each point using the coordinate plane at the right.

9. *A*(−5, 5)
10. *M*(2, 4)
11. *G*(0, −5)
12. *D*(3, 0)
13. *N*(−4, −3)
14. *I*(2, −3)

Skills Practice (p. 24) · AL · OL

Lesson 8.3 Skills Practice
Graph in Four Quadrants

For Exercises 1–8, use the coordinate plane at the right. Identify the point for each ordered pair.

1. (−2, 4)
2. (−2, −3)
3. (4, 4)
4. (3, −5)
5. (3, 5)
6. (4, −1)
7. (−1, 3)
8. (−4, −2)

For Exercises 9–16, use the coordinate plane above. Write the ordered pair that names each point. Then identify the quadrant where each point is located.

9. *K*
10. *L*
11. *M*
12. *N*
13. *O*
14. *P*
15. *Q*
16. *R*

Tell which number is greater.

17. −8 or −9
18. −4$\frac{1}{2}$ or −5$\frac{3}{4}$
19. 10 or −12
20. |−5| or 4
21. |−6| or |−2|
22. −10 or |−1|

Evaluate each expression.

23. |8| + 3
24. |−8| ÷ −2
25. $\frac{1}{2}$ · |−6|
26. |−2| · |10|
27. |−9| −2
28. |−5| + |5|

Problem-Solving Practice (p. 25) · AL · OL

Lesson 8.3 Problem-Solving Practice
Graph in Four Quadrants

Money For Exercises 1–4, use the table and the coordinate plane.

School buttons sell for $2 each. When you have completed the table and the graph, both the table and graph will show the costs of purchasing up to 5 school buttons.

Number of Buttons Sold	Price ($)
1	
2	
3	
4	
5	

1. Now complete the second column of the table by writing the cost of each number of buttons.

2. To prepare to graph the data, make a list of ordered pairs from the table.

3. Graph the ordered pairs. Label each point with its ordered pair. Describe the graph of the points.

4. Describe the coordinate plane that you have completed. How is it different from other systems you have used?

5. **Weather** The table gives the high temperature on each day during the past week. Which day had the highest temperature?

6. **Weather** Using the table from Exercise 5, on which day was the temperature the lowest?

Day	Mon	Tue	Wed	Thurs	Fri
Temp	−4°	−11°	−2°	−9°	−8°

Enrichment (p. 26) · BL

Lesson 8.3 Enrichment
Graph in Four Quadrants

Creative Coordinates

Graph each set of points on the coordinate grid below. Then use line segments to connect the points in order from left to right.

1. (−2, 5); (1, 5); (2, 6); (1, 7)
(0, 7); (−2, 5); (−1, 8); (−1, 9);
(−2, 9); (−3, 8); (−2, 5); (−4, 7);
(−5, 7); (−6, 6); (−5, 5); (−2, 5);
(−5, 4); (−5, 3); (−4, 2); (−3, 2);
(−2, 5); (−1, 2); (0, 2); (1, 3);
(1, 4); (−2, 5); (−2, −3); (0, 0);
(3, 1); (−2, −3); (−1, −5); (−5, −4); (4, 2);
(−7, −5); (−1, −5); (3, −8)

2. (1, 6); (−1, 6); (−2, 8);
(−3, 6); (−4, 5); (−4, 2);
(−4, 7); (−2, 0); (−3, −1); (−4, −3);
(−4, −6); (−2, −8); (7, −8);
(9, −7); (11, −4); (9, −5);
(7, −7); (3, −7); (4, −6);
(4, −3); (3, −1); (2, 0);
(4, 5); (3, 6);
(2, 8); (1, 6)

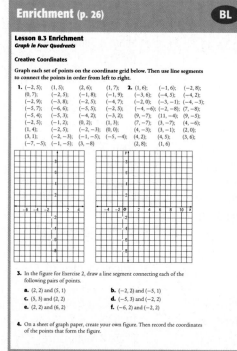

3. In the figure for Exercise 2, draw a line segment connecting each of the following pairs of points.

a. (2, 2) and (5, 1)
b. (−2, 2) and (−5, 1)
c. (5, 3) and (2, 2)
d. (−5, 3) and (−2, 2)
e. (2, 2) and (6, 2)
f. (−6, 2) and (−2, 2)

4. On a sheet of graph paper, create your own figure. Then record the coordinates of the points that form the figure.

Lesson Quick Quiz (p. 27) · AL · OL · BL

Lesson 8.3 Quick Quiz
Graph in Four Quadrants

1. Find the coordinates of points *A* − *D*.

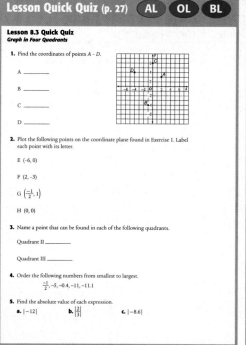

A _____
B _____
C _____
D _____

2. Plot the following points on the coordinate plane found in Exercise 1. Label each point with its letter.

E (−6, 0)
F (2, −3)
G $\left(\frac{-1}{2}, 1\right)$
H (0, 0)

3. Name a point that can be found in each of the following quadrants.

Quadrant II _____
Quadrant III _____

4. Order the following numbers from smallest to largest.
$\frac{-1}{2}$, −5, −0.4, −11, −11.1

5. Find the absolute value of each expression.

a. |−12|
b. $\left|\frac{2}{3}\right|$
c. |−8.6|

Lesson Masters 1–3 (p. 28–30)

Lesson 8.3 Master 1
Graph in Four Quadrants

Investigation 1 Develop & Understand: A, Exercises 1 and 2
On Your Own Exercises 1–3

Investigation 1 Develop & Understand: A, Exercise 3

On Your Own Exercise 4

On Your Own Exercise 20

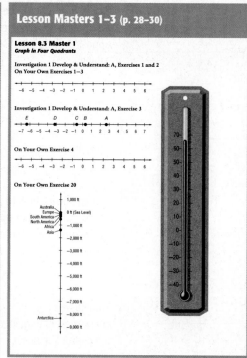

Additional Lesson Resources

Teacher Tech Tools
- TeacherWorks
- ExamView Assessment Suite
- Classroom Presentation Toolkit
- Advance Tracker

Student Tech Tools
- StudentWorks Plus
- **Math Online** ▶ eGlossary •
- Concepts in Motion

Other Print Products
- Investigation Notebook and Reflection Journal
- Quick Review Math Handbook

LESSON 8.3

Graph in Four Quadrants

Vocabulary

negative numbers

positive numbers

① Possible answer: (1, 17) tells me that on the first day of his vacation, Deane could hold his breath for only 17 seconds. (12, 67) tells me that by the end of his vacation, he could hold his breath for over a minute.

② 40 seconds; On the *x*-axis, find day 6. Go up to the point on the graph, and see how high that point is on the *y*-axis.

As you have seen, making a graph is a useful way to represent the relationship between two quantities. For example, during a two-week snorkeling vacation, Deane timed how long he could hold his breath under water. The graph shows his maximum breath-holding time each day.

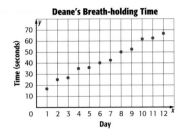

Deane's Breath-holding Time

Think & Discuss

Choose two points on the graph. Give their coordinates. Explain what the coordinates tell you about Deane's breath-holding time.   See ①.

How long could Deane hold his breath at the end of his sixth day of practicing? How did you find your answer from the graph? See ②.

In the graph above, both quantities, day and time, are always positive. What if one or both of the quantities you want to graph are sometimes negative?

You have had a lot of experience working with **positive numbers**, numbers that are greater than 0. You are familiar with positive whole numbers, positive decimals, and positive fractions. You will now turn your attention to **negative numbers**, which are numbers that are less than 0.

Introduce

Graph in Four Quadrants Tell students in this lesson, they will be introduced to integers and then look at signed numbers on a graph. Some students may benefit from a quick review of graphs before working on the Think & Discuss questions. These students may not recall which axis is the *x*-axis and which is the *y*-axis or how to use coordinates to name a point on the graph.

You might have to use the graph on this page to initiate a short discussion with students about how graphs help us understand the relationship between two quantities. Emphasize that the visual nature of graphs often helps us spot patterns more easily.

Think & Discuss

Discuss the questions in this section. Be sure that students can read and interpret the graph. Students will rely on these skills as they expand their graphing abilities to using four-quadrant graphs.

Have students work in pairs on the temperature questions. If students have difficulty using the thermometer on page 510, provide them with copies of Lesson 8.3 Master 1. This master has an enlarged copy of the thermometer and can be used with other exercises as well.

Investigation 1

On Your Own Exercises
Pages 524–527
Exercises 1–8, 19–23

Understand Integers In this investigation, students graph positive and negative numbers on a number line and estimate values for fractional or decimal points on the number line. They also identify opposites and absolute values. The investigation concludes with students comparing and ordering positive and negative numbers.

Be sure students understand that the sign before a negative number is read as *negative*, not as *minus*. For example, they should read −20 as "negative 20," not "minus 20." Stress that *minus* indicates subtraction, which is an operation rather than a type of number.

Point out that positive numbers can be written with or without a positive sign; for positive numbers, the sign can be ignored when reading the number. However, as with negative numbers, the sign is a label, not a symbol for an operation, so when it is read, it is read as *positive*, not *plus*.

Introduce the terms *opposites* and *absolute value*. You may want to ask students to find the opposites of numbers such as 6 and −8, and the absolute value of numbers such as 10 and −15, to make sure that they understand the concepts before they begin work on the exercise set.

Real-World Link
What is the lowest temperature ever recorded in your town? How did you find it?

510 CHAPTER 8 Coordinate Plane

Investigation 1 Understand Integers

Vocabulary
opposites

Below, three students describe the current temperatures in the cities where they live. Use the thermometer to help figure out the temperature in each city.

- Carlita lives in Cincinnati, Ohio. She says, "It's not very cold here. If the temperature rises 5 degrees, it will be 47.5°F." 42.5°F
- Trey lives in Niagara Falls, New York. He says, "You think that's cold? If the temperature rises 30 degrees here, it will be only 30°F!" 0°F
- Jean lives in Juneau, Alaska. She says, "We can top all of you up here! If our temperature went up 30 degrees, it would be only 10°F!" −20°F

Create a temperature puzzle, like those above, for which the answer is negative. Exchange puzzles with your partner. Solve your partner's puzzle.
Answers will vary.

In colder climates, it is not unusual for the temperature to drop to −20°F, meaning 20 degrees *below* 0. There are many other contexts in which the number −20 might be used. For example, if you were standing at a location 20 feet below sea level, your elevation would be −20 feet. If you wrote checks for $20 more than you had in your bank account, your account balance would be −$20.

Here are a few facts about the number −20.

- −20 is read as "negative twenty" or "the opposite of twenty."
- −20 is located 20 units to the left of 0 on a horizontal number line.
- −20 is located 20 units below 0 on a vertical number line or thermometer.
- −20 is located halfway between −21 and −19 on a number line.

Real-World Link
The lowest temperature ever recorded on Earth is −128.6°F. This temperature occurred on July 21, 1983 at Vostok, a Russian station in Antarctica.

The numbers −20 and 20 are *opposites*. Two numbers are **opposites** if they are the same distance from 0 on the number line but on different sides of 0. What is the result when you add two opposites?
They equal 0.

As you know, the number 20 is positive. You will occasionally see 20 written as +20. The notations 20 and +20 have the same meaning. Both can be read as "positive twenty" or just "twenty."

3. Possible answer:

A: $2\frac{3}{4}$, or 2.75

B: $\frac{1}{3}$, or 0.3

C: $-\frac{3}{4}$, or -0.75

D: $-3\frac{1}{8}$, or -3.1

E: $-6\frac{3}{8}$, or -6.4

5. Possible explanation: No; if a number is negative, its opposite is positive.

① The greater number is further to the right.

✓ Develop & Understand: A

1. Copy the number line below. Plot the following points to show the locations of the numbers listed, and label each point with the corresponding number.

$$1.25, -2, -\frac{1}{3}, 3.7, -4\frac{3}{4}, -1\frac{3}{8}$$

2. On your number line from Exercise 1, plot and label points for three more negative mixed numbers. **Answers will vary.**

3. Give a number that describes the approximate location of each labeled point.

4. Find the opposite of each number.

a. 3.2 -3.2 **b.** $-\frac{3}{4}$ $\frac{3}{4}$ **c.** -2 2   **d.** 317 -317

5. Is the *opposite* of a number always negative? Explain.

Think & Discuss

How can you tell which of two numbers is greater by looking at their locations on a horizontal number line?   See ①.

Which is the warmer temperature, $-20°F$ or $-15°F$? How do you know? $-15°F$ because -15 is to the right of -20 on the number line.

✓ Develop & Understand: B

6. The table shows record low temperatures for each continent.

Continent	Location	Temperature
Africa	Ifrane, Morocco	$-11°F$
Antarctica	Vostok Station	$-129°F$
Asia	Oimekon and Verkhoyansk, Russia	$-90°F$
Australia	Charlotte Pass, New South Wales	$-9.4°F$
Europe	Ust'Shchugor, Russia	$-67°F$
North America	Snag, Yukon, Canada	$-81.4°F$
South America	Sarmiento, Argentina	$-27°F$

Source: *World Almanac and Book of Facts 2000.* Copyright © 1999 Primedia Reference Inc.

Lesson 8.3 Graph in Four Quadrants   **511**

On the Spot Assessment

When students graph negative fractions and decimals on a number line, they often forget that negative numbers form a mirror image of their opposites. They may graph fractions and decimals between the correct integers but position them in decreasing, rather than increasing, order. For example, they will put $-4\frac{1}{4}$ closer to -5 than to -4 because when graphing positive numbers, one fourth marks the leftmost section between two numbers. You might have these students draw and label the half and quarter tick marks on a number line to use as a reference.

✓ Develop & Understand: A

Suggested Grouping: Pairs

▶ **Exercises 1–3** Lesson 8.3 Master 1 has copies of the two number lines in this exercise set. Providing students with a copy of this master will insure that they have an accurate number line on which to plot the points in Exercises 1 and 2 and enable struggling students to fold or divide the number line in Exercise 3 to help determine values for each point.

▶ **Exercise 1** If many students are new to negative numbers, you may want to have them plot the points in this exercise and review their number lines as a class before having pairs work through the remaining exercises. If students have difficulty graphing the numbers, you might consider working through the whole exercise set as a class activity.

Wrap-Up Discuss these exercises to make sure students understand opposites and absolute values. If they are having difficulty understanding the connection, you may want to use counters to practice identifying opposites. One color can represent negative numbers while another represents positive numbers. When you form two groups of counters, having the same number of counters but different colors, the two numbers represented are opposites. This can also be done with algebra tiles.

Think & Discuss

Have students discuss the relationship between two numbers on a number line. Point out that number lines show the relative size and order of the numbers. Some students may think that because the absolute value of -20 is greater than the absolute value of 15, it is the greater number. These students may find it helpful to draw, or refer to, a number line so they can look at the positions of the numbers. Depending on your class, you may want to point out that students can use absolute value to help them order negative numbers. Negative numbers with greater absolute values are lesser numbers because they are farther from 0.

Develop & Understand: B

Suggested Grouping: Pairs

▶ **Exercise 6a** Encourage students having difficulty ordering the numbers to draw a number line. This can help them visualize the position of each number in relation to 0. Remind them that negative numbers close to 0 are greater than those farther away.

▶ **Exercise 6b** Explain *frostbite* if necessary. You might point out that it is possible to get frostbite at temperatures much higher than −30°F, depending on the wind and the length of exposure.

▶ **Exercise 6c** Subtraction of negative numbers is previewed in this exercise. Students may use one of these strategies to find the difference in temperature:

- Subtract to find the difference between −9.4 and −129.

- Subtract the absolute values of the two temperatures if the signs of the two numbers are the same.

- Count down or up, possibly using a number line. For example, to count down, students may count the tenths between −9.4 and −10, the tens between −10 and −120, and the ones between −120 and −129, and then add: 0.6 + 110 + 9 = 119.6.

Share & Summarize

Encourage students to give examples of opposites for Exercise 1.

Troubleshooting If students have difficulty solving temperature puzzles, provide them with manipulative thermometers that include negative values, or copies of Lesson 8.3 Master 1, which they can use to shade and count values.

Investigation 2

On Your Own Exercises
Pages 524–527
Exercises 9–15

Absolute Value In this investigation, students measure numbers based on their distance from zero rather than their sign. They learn that absolute value tells the size of a number or change, without considering whether it is positive or negative.

---

a. Order the temperatures from coldest to warmest.
−129°F, −90°F, −81.4°F, −67°F, −27°F, −11°F, −9.4°F

b. When temperatures drop below −30°F, people often experience frostbite. For which locations in the table is the record low temperature below −30°F? See margin.

c. In the table, how many degrees below the warmest temperature is the coldest temperature? 119.6°F

7. Ten students measured the outside temperature at different times on the same winter day. Their results are shown in the table.

7a. −1.80°F, −1.75°F, −1.30°F, −1.00°F, −0.80°F, −0.33°F, 0.33°F, 0.80°F, 1.08°F, 1.30°F

a. List the temperatures in order from coldest to warmest.

b. On the night the students recorded the temperatures, a weather reporter said, "The average temperature today was a chilly 0°F." Which students recorded temperatures that were closest to the average temperature? Gabe and Marco

Student	Temperature
Gabe	−0.33°F
Jill	1.30°F
Fabiana	−0.80°F
Marco	0.33°F
Micheala	−1.30°F
Brad	−1.80°F
Phil	1.08°F
Jasmine	−1.75°F
Kurt	−1.00°F
Sophia	−0.80°F

1. Possible answer: a number that is the same distance from 0 on a number line but on the other side of 0

Share & Summarize

1. Explain what the opposite of a number is.

2. Name three negative numbers between −3 and −2. Possible answer: $-2\frac{1}{2}$, $-2\frac{1}{9}$, −2.75

Investigation 2 Absolute Value

Vocabulary

absolute value

For a Science project, Trina studied how the temperature varies from day to day. She recorded the temperature at noon every day for a week.

Day	Monday	Tuesday	Wednesday	Thursday	Friday	Saturday	Sunday
Temperature	60°F	51°F	61°F	67°F	45°F	50°F	42°F

Develop & Understand: A

Trina calculated the change in temperature between each day and the next. If the temperature rose, she recorded the change as a positive number. If the temperature fell, she recorded the change as a negative number.

Reaching All Learners

AL Approaching Level Students who are having difficulty ordering negative numbers might benefit from classifying the temperatures in Exercise 7 as positive or negative numbers. They can then order the two groups separately, using number lines to help, if necessary.

Additional Answer

6b. Vostak Station, Antarctica; Oimekon and Verkhoyansk, Russia; Snag, Yukon, Canada; Ust'Shchugor, Russia

1. Calculate each temperature change. Complete the table.

Days	Monday–Tuesday	Tuesday–Wednesday	Wednesday–Thursday	Thursday–Friday	Friday–Saturday	Saturday–Sunday
Change in Temperature	−9°F	10°F	6°F	−22°F	5°F	−8°F

2. Between which days did the greatest increase in temperature occur?
   Between Tuesday and Wednesday
3. Between which days did the greatest decrease in temperature occur?
   Between Thursday and Friday

Trina saw that sometimes the temperature changed a lot from one day to the next, and sometimes it changed very little. She wanted to compare the differences in the changes. She made a new table. This time, she listed just the size of each change, without showing whether it was an increase or a decrease.

4. Complete the table.

Days	Monday–Tuesday	Tuesday–Wednesday	Wednesday–Thursday	Thursday–Friday	Friday–Saturday	Saturday–Sunday
Size of Change	9°F	10°F	6°F	22°F	5°F	8°F

5. When was the greatest temperature change?   Thursday to Friday

6. When was the least temperature change?   Friday to Saturday

7. Trina found that during the next week, the temperature change from Monday to Tuesday was 8°. The temperature on Monday was 63°. Give two possible temperatures for Tuesday.   71° or 55°

① No; the first table has all the information that is in the second table, but the second table does not tell you the sign of the change. You cannot tell if the temperature rose or fell.

② Yes, but she would have had to ignore the signs of the numbers and just look at the numbers, in other words, the same thing she did to create the second table.

Think & Discuss

Compare the two tables of temperature change.

Can you get the same information from each of them?   See ①.

Could Trina have used the first table to figure out what the greatest and least changes were?   See ②.

The **absolute value** of a number is its distance from zero on the number line.

On the number line, 5 and −5 are both 5 units away from 0. They both have the same absolute value, 5. *Absolute value* is indicated by vertical bars around a number, $|-5|$ or $|5|$.

Lesson 8.3   Graph in Four Quadrants   **513**

Develop & Understand: A
Suggested Grouping: Pairs

▶ **Exercise 1** Make sure students find the change in temperature, and not the actual temperature. Remind them to show decreases as negative and increases as positive.

▶ **Exercises 2 and 3** Remind students that an increase means that numbers grow larger, and a decrease means the numbers become smaller. Have them look for the greatest changes in the numbers.

▶ **Exercises 4–6** Students may have difficulty understanding that the size of the change is the same, with or without the sign. Explain that it is the distance from one number to the next that is important.

▶ **Exercise 7** This exercise reinforces the idea that absolute value is the distance from a number in either direction.

Think & Discuss

Draw a number line on the board illustrating the comparison of −5 to 5. Have students count off the distance of each number from zero. Then write −5 and 5 in absolute value bars and discuss how they have the same value. Make sure students see that the absolute value bars make negative signs unimportant in determining the value of the number.

Assessment

On the Spot Assessment

Monitor for signs of understanding in students. Draw a number line on chart paper from −10 to 10 and call out a number. Have students use the number line to tell the absolute value of the number. Use their answers to determine who needs further help in understanding the concept.

Use the football example to clarify the concept of absolute value for students.

Develop & Understand: B

Suggested Grouping: Groups

▶ **Exercises 8 and 9** Make sure students are finding the correct numbers on the number line, and that they are not confusing negatives and positives.

▶ **Exercise 10** Make sure students can correctly identify $4\frac{1}{2}$ as 4.5 on the number line. Remind them that, when working with absolute value, it does not matter which form of a number is shown (fraction, decimal, etc.). The value of the number and its distance from zero are still the same.

▶ **Exercise 11** Discuss the possibilities for the number. Remind students that an absolute value has only two possibilities: the positive value of the number and the negative value of the number.

Think & Discuss

This question illustrates an important fact about absolute value: students need to understand that they always work the problem inside the absolute value bars before removing the sign of the answer. Work both problems on the board, and show students both the correct and the incorrect ways to work them. Make sure they see how the answer can be very different if they do not work in the proper order.

Develop & Understand: C

Suggested Grouping: Groups

▶ **Exercises 20–23** Have groups evaluate the expressions. Listen to their conversations to be sure they fully understand absolute value and the importance of working the problem inside the absolute value bars before removing the sign.

Share & Summarize

Have students answer the questions and use their answers to explain absolute value to a partner.

Real-World Link
At the beginning of a football play, the ball starts at the *line of scrimmage*. If the offensive team moves the ball 5 yards towards their goal line, they gain 5 yards (+5 yards). But if the quarterback is tackled 5 yards towards the defensive team's goal line, the offense loses 5 yards (−5 yards). In both cases, the ball is now 5 yards away from the line of scrimmage. Its position has changed by |5| yards.

Develop & Understand: B

$$\xleftarrow{\;\;\;\;}{-5\;-4\;-3\;-2\;-1\;\;0\;\;1\;\;2\;\;3\;\;4\;\;5}\xrightarrow{\;\;\;\;}$$

Find the distance of each number from 0.

8. −4   4   **9.** −3.5   3.5   **10.** $4\frac{1}{2}$ $4\frac{1}{2}$, or 4.5

Which is further from 0?

11. 4 or −3?   4   **12.** −2.5 or −4.5?   −4.5   **13.** $-\frac{1}{2}$ or $-\frac{1}{3}$? $-\frac{1}{2}$

Find the absolute value of each expression.

14. $|-6|$ 6   **15.** $\left|\frac{3}{5}\right|$ $\frac{3}{5}$

16. $|-3^3|$ 27   **17.** $|57.01|$ 57.01

18. Quin wrote down a number whose absolute value is 21.5. What could be Quin's number?   21.5 or −21.5

19. The Bulldogs are playing the Rangers in football. The Bulldogs have 30 yards to go to score a touchdown. On the next play, the Rangers push them back to the 42 yard line. Write an equation to show what happened. How many yards did the Bulldogs lose?
$30 - 42 = -12$; $|-12| = 12$; 12 yards

You can take the absolute value of any expression. $|4 + 2|$, $|-25 \div 3|$, and $|-7 \cdot 40|$ all mean "evaluate the expression between the absolute value bars, and then find the absolute value of the result."

Think & Discuss

Which is greater, $|-5| + |4|$ or $|-5 + 4|$? $|-5| + |4|$ would be $5 + 4 = 9$. $|-5 + 4|$ would be $|-1| = 1$. So, $|-5| + |4|$ is greater.

Develop & Understand: C

Evaluate each expression.

20. $|50 - 25|$ 25   **21.** $|-3| + |-15|$ 18

22. $|-17| - |-17|$ 0   **23.** $\left|\frac{2}{3}\right| - \left|-\frac{1}{5}\right|$ $\frac{7}{15}$

Share & Summarize

What happens to a negative number when you take its absolute value?   It becomes positive.

What happens to a positive number when you take its absolute value?   It stays positive.

What is $|0|$?   The distance of 0 from 0 on the number line is 0, so $|0| = 0$.

Reaching *All Learners*

AL Approaching Level For students who need more practice, have them work in pairs to find absolute value. Tell each student to write down ten numbers, some negative and some positive. Then have them trade and find the absolute value of the numbers on each other's papers. If there is time, have them create a number line and each find the distance of the numbers from zero.

Investigation ③ Plot Points with Negative Coordinates

Materials
- graph paper
- coordinate grids with x-axis and y-axis from −3 to 3

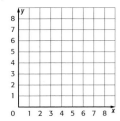

You know how to plot points on a coordinate grid that looks like the one at left. The x-axis of the grid is a horizontal number line. The y-axis is a vertical number line.

In the graphs with which you have previously worked, the number lines included only numbers greater than or equal to 0. But if they are extended to include negative numbers, the coordinate grid will look something like this.

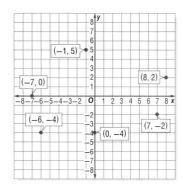

① Possible answer: Move right or left to the value of the first coordinate (right if positive, left if negative), and then move up or down to the value of the second coordinate (up if positive, down if negative).

Using a grid like this, you can plot points with negative coordinates.

Think & Discuss

Rashelle plotted six points on the grid above. See if you can discover the procedure she used to plot the points. See ①.

✓ Develop & Understand: A

1.

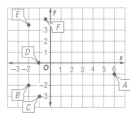

1. Plot points A–F on the same coordinate grid. Label each point with its letter.

Point A: (6, −1)	Point B: (−2, −2)	Point C: (−1, −3)
Point D: (−1, 0)	Point E: (−2, 3.5)	Point F: $\left(-\frac{1}{3}, 4\right)$

Lesson 8.3 Graph in Four Quadrants **515**

On the Spot Assessment

Watch for students who confuse the x- and y-coordinates in Exercise 1. You may want to help these students remember that x-coordinates always come before y-coordinates by thinking of the alphabet and remembering that x comes before y. Remind them that the x-axis is horizontal and the y-axis is vertical.

Investigation ③

On Your Own Exercises
Pages 524–527
Exercises 16–17, 29

Plot Points with Negative Coordinates In this investigation, students learn how to plot points on a coordinate plane. It might help students to think about the x- and y-axes as the intersection of two number lines. You may want to elaborate on this concept in class and ask students to give the coordinates of the intersection. Have students look at the two grids on page 516. Ask them to compare the two grids. Among their observations, students should note that the smaller two-quadrant grid is like the upper right-hand part of the larger four-quadrant grid and that the larger grid includes negative numbers.

Think & Discuss

The rule for plotting points with negative coordinates should be easy for students to understand. You might want to have students share what they think the rule is for plotting points. Make sure that students state how to plot points in any of the four quadrants and on both of the axes.

Once students have correctly identified the rule, they can practice using it in the exercise set. You may want to post the rule on chart paper in your classroom for students to refer to while they are still familiarizing themselves with the coordinate plane.

✓ Develop & Understand: A

Suggested Grouping: Pairs

▶ **Exercise 1** Give students practice plotting and interpreting plots. You may want to have students plot their points for Exercise 1 on Lesson 8.3 Master 2, 10 by 10 Grids, which has an empty grid with darkened axes and unnumbered grid lines.

516   **CHAPTER 8**   Coordinate Plane

► **Exercise 2** Point out that this exercise gives students more practice plotting points.

► **Exercise 3** Point out that this exercise gives students an opportunity to use a higher level thinking skill, interpreting a graph. Data were taken from a Web site containing background information on the Gulkana Glacier basin in Alaska.

Wrap-Up You may want to discuss the graph in Exercise 3. Some students may not understand why all four quadrants of the graph are not shown. They may also need to be reminded of what the broken line between 0 and 9 on the *x*-axis means. Neither of these concerns should affect students' ability to answer the questions unless they cannot read the labels on the graph or move on the graph from the origin to the point to find the coordinates.

2. G (−3, 7);
   H (6, −2);
   I (−5, −6);
   J (−2, 0);
   K (4.4, −7.8);
   L (0, −3$\frac{1}{3}$)

2. Give the coordinates of each point plotted on this grid.

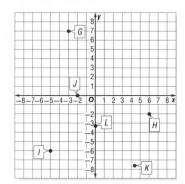

3. The graph shows daily average temperatures at the Gulkana Glacier basin in Alaska from September 9 to September 18 in a recent year.

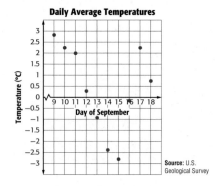

a. What was the lowest of these temperatures?   About −2.8°C
b. On which day was the temperature lowest?   September 15
c. What was the highest of these temperatures?   About 2.8°C
d. On which day was the temperature highest?   September 9

Reaching All Learners

BL **Beyond Level** Have students use the Internet to collect temperature data for the glacier of their choice. Have them choose a way to record the data. Most students will either list the data or make a table. Then have them graph the data on a coordinate grid. You may want to display the graphs so students can compare the temperatures from different times of the year.

The game you will now play will give you practice locating points on a coordinate grid.

✅ Develop & Understand: B

In the *Undersea Search* game, you and your partner will hide items from each other on a coordinate grid. To win the game, you need to find your partner's hidden items before he or she finds yours.

Each player will need two coordinate grids with *x*- and *y*-axes that range from −4 to 4. Think of each grid as a map of part of the ocean floor. During the game, you will be hiding a buried treasure and a coral reef on one of your grids.

The grid below shows one way you could hide the items.

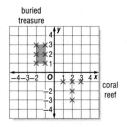

You can bury the items anywhere on the grid, but they must have the shapes shown above.

- The buried treasure must be a rectangle with an area of 2 square units. It must be drawn using two Xs along one side and three along the other.
- The coral reef must be a T-shape made from five Xs.

The Xs must all be placed where grid lines intersect. The buried treasure and the reef cannot overlap, so they cannot share points on your map.

Teacher Tips Most of the time for the next exercise set will be spent playing *Undersea Search*. Playing the game gives students practice plotting points and identifying the coordinates of points on the coordinate plane. It also helps familiarize students with the structure of the coordinate plane.

✅ Develop & Understand: B

Suggested Grouping: Small Groups

In order to save time, use Lesson 8.3 Master 3, Grid for *Undersea Search* Game, which contains two grids whose axes extend from −4 to 4. Make sure that when students bury their treasure, they do not enlarge or shrink the pictures of the coral reef and the buried treasure. Within each picture, each X should be one unit apart on the grid.

Share & Summarize

Here is how you play the game.

- *Hide the buried treasure and the coral reef.* Start with one of your grids. Without showing your partner, use Xs to mark the places you want to hide the buried treasure and the coral reef. Make sure you put all your Xs where grid lines intersect.

- *Search the sea.* You and your partner take turns calling out the coordinates of points, trying to guess where the other has hidden the items.

  If your partner calls out a point where you have hidden something, say "X marks the spot." If your partner calls out any other point, say "Sorry, nothing there."

  Use your blank grid to keep track of your guesses. If you guess a point where your partner has hidden something, put an X on that point. If you guess a point where nothing is hidden, circle the point so you know not to guess it again.

- *Victory at sea.* The first person to guess all the points for both hidden items wins.

Play *Undersea Search* with your partner at least once. Then answer the questions.

4. No; the upside-down L configuration of the points could be part of either item, or they could be points from both items.

5. It could be the coral reef or parts of both items; the points are too far apart to be the buried treasure alone.

6. $(1, -1)$, $(0, -1)$, and $(-1, -1)$; or $(1, -3)$, $(0, -3)$, and $(-1, -3)$

7. Sample answer; I would increase the area of the buried treasure on the grid.

4. Suppose your partner said "X marks the spot" when you guessed the points $(-3, 1)$, $(-3, 2)$, and $(-2, 2)$. Can you tell whether you have found the buried treasure or the coral reef? Why or why not?

5. Suppose your partner said "X marks the spot" when you guessed the points $(-2, -2)$, $(-3, 0)$, and $(-1, 0)$. Can you tell whether you have found the buried treasure or the coral reef? Why or why not?

6. Suppose you have already found the coral reef, and you know that part of the buried treasure is at the points $(1, -2)$, $(0, -2)$, and $(-1, -2)$. What could be the coordinates of the other three points that make up the buried treasure? Name as many possibilities as you can.

7. Suppose you are playing *Undersea Search* with your younger cousin. You want to alter the rules of the game so it will be easier to locate the buried treasure. How could you change the area of the treasure?

Share & Summarize

Write a letter to a student a grade below you explaining how to plot points with negative coordinates on a coordinate grid.
Possible answer: To plot a point, move left or right to the value of the first coordinate. Then move up or down to the value of the second coordinate.

Investigation 4 Parts of the Coordinate Plane

Vocabulary

quadrants

The x- and y-axes divide the coordinate plane into four sections called **quadrants**. The quadrants are numbered with roman numerals as shown below. Points on the axes are not in any of the quadrants.

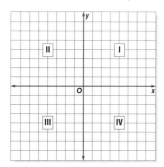

✅ Develop & Understand: A

Points A through R are plotted on the grid.

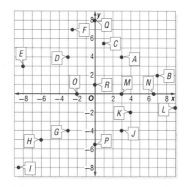

1. Look at the points in Quadrant I.

1a. A (3, 4), B (7, 2), C (1, 5½)

   a. Record the coordinates of each point in Quadrant I.

   b. What do you notice about the signs of the coordinates of each point?   Both are positive.

   c. If someone gives you the coordinates of a point, how can you tell whether it is in Quadrant I without plotting the point?   If both coordinates are positive, the point is in Quadrant I.

Parts of the Coordinate Plane
In this investigation, students practice pattern-seeking and classifying skills while simultaneously reinforcing their understanding of the coordinate plane. They discover distinguishing characteristics of points in each quadrant and on each axis as they analyze and create graphs. Direct students' attention to the coordinate plane on this page. Define *quadrant* and explain the use of Roman numerals to identify quadrants. Be sure students understand that the points on the axes are not in any quadrant.

✅ Develop & Understand: A

Suggested Grouping: Pairs

▶ **Exercise 1** Students look for patterns in the signs of the coordinates in each quadrant and on each axis. They can use patterns to identify the quadrant that a point lies in without plotting the point. Discuss answers with the whole class.

▶ **Exercises 2–6** Students will continue to look for patterns in the signs of the coordinates in each quadrant and on each axis. Watch for students having difficulty discovering the distinguishing characteristics of points in quadrants and on axes. Have them find the coordinates of more points. Repeating the process of naming points in the same region can help students get a sense of what actions stay the same each time they graph a point in a particular region of the graph. Discuss the answers with the whole class.

2a. $D\,(-3, 4)$, $E\,(-8, 3)$, $F\left(-2\frac{1}{2}, 7\right)$

2c. If the *x*-coordinate is negative and the *y*-coordinate is positive, the point is in Quadrant II.

3a. $G\,(-3, -4)$, $H\,(-6, -5)$, $I\left(-8\frac{1}{2}, -8\right)$

4a. $J\,(3, -4)$, $K\,(4, -2)$, $L\left(9, -1\frac{1}{2}\right)$

4c. If the *x*-coordinate is positive and the *y*-coordinate is negative, the point is in Quadrant IV.

5a. $M\,(3, 0)$, $N\left(6\frac{1}{2}, 0\right)$, $O\,(-2, 0)$

6a. $P\left(0, -5\frac{1}{2}\right)$, $Q\,(0, 8)$, $R\,(0, 1)$

2. Look at the points in Quadrant II.
   a. Record the coordinates of each point.
   b. What do you notice about the signs of the coordinates of each point? The *x*-coordinates are negative, and the *y*-coordinates are positive.
   c. If someone gives you the coordinates of a point, how can you tell whether it is in Quadrant II without plotting the point?

3. Look at the points in Quadrant III.
   a. Record the coordinates of each point.
   b. What do you notice about the signs of these coordinates? Both are negative.
   c. If someone gives you the coordinates of a point, how can you tell whether it is in Quadrant III without plotting the point? If both coordinates are negative, the point is in Quadrant III.

4. Look at the points in Quadrant IV.
   a. Record the coordinates of each point.
   b. What do you notice about the signs of these coordinates? The *x*-coordinates are positive, and the *y*-coordinates are negative.
   c. If someone gives you the coordinates of a point, how can you tell whether it is in Quadrant IV without plotting the point?

5. Look at the points on the *x*-axis.
   a. Record the coordinates of each point.
   b. What do these coordinates have in common? The *y*-coordinates are 0.
   c. If someone gives you the coordinates of a point, how can you tell whether it is on the *x*-axis without plotting the point? If the *y*-coordinate is 0, the point is on the *x*-axis.

6. Look at the points on the *y*-axis.
   a. Record the coordinates of each point.
   b. What do these coordinates have in common? The *x*-coordinates are 0.
   c. If someone gives you the coordinates of a point, how can you tell whether it is on the *y*-axis without plotting the point? If the *x*-coordinate is 0, the point is on the *y*-axis.

✅ Develop & Understand: B

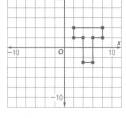

In Chapter 7 you found the area of several figures using formulas. You can also find the area of a figure when placed on a coordinate plane.

7. On a sheet of graph paper, draw a coordinate plane showing the four quadrants. Make the *x*- and *y*-axis range from −10 to 10.
   a. Plot the following ordered pairs. Connect consecutive points with straight lines.

   $(4, -3)$, $(4, 2)$, $(2, 2)$, $(2, 4)$, $(8, 4)$, $(8, 2)$, $(6, 2)$, $(6, -3)$, $(4, -3)$

 Assessment

Ask students who are having difficulty with the quadrants to classify larger regions of the graph. For example, you might ask them what distinguishes all points above the *x*-axis. Then have students tell how the regions are defined. You might ask a question such as this: If the fourth quadrant is below the *x*-axis and to the right of the *y*-axis, what does that say about the coordinates of points in the fourth quadrant? They have positive *x*-coordinates and negative *y*-coordinates.

7d. Area = 22 sq units; I found it by counting the squares inside the polygon.

8a. Answers will vary. Check students' work.

b. What kind of figure did you create?   Polygon that is T-shaped

c. In which Quadrants does this figure lie?   Quadrants I and IV

d. Find the area of this figure. Explain how you found it.

8. On the same sheet of graph paper, plot four points to create a rectangle that lies in all four quadrants.

a. Record the coordinates of each point.

b. What is the area of the rectangle?   Answers will vary.

Share & Summarize

1. Without plotting each point, determine in which quadrant or on which axis or axes it lies.

a. $(-5, -2)$ Quadrant III

b. $(0, 0)$ *x*- and *y*-axes

c. $\left(3, -\frac{2}{7}\right)$ Quadrant IV

d. $(-35, 0)$ *x*-axis

2. In general, if you are given the coordinates of a point, how can you tell which part of the coordinate plane the point is in without plotting it? You might organize your ideas in a chart like the one below.   See margin.

x-coordinate	y-coordinate	Part of Coordinate Plane

Share & Summarize

These exercises give students an opportunity to apply their discoveries from the exercises on pages 519 and 520. In Exercise 1b, watch for students who forget that (0, 0) is on both of the axes. As an extension question, you might ask students whether there are any other points that are on more than one axis. They should recognize that there are none.

Troubleshooting Some students may still be having difficulty understanding the distinguishing characteristics of coordinates of points on the coordinate plane. You might have them work with a large coordinate plane that you set up in the classroom. Ask students what sets of moves they must make to move to each of the four quadrants. For example, if they start at (0, 0) and want to move to the third quadrant, they must move to the left and move down. That corresponds to a negative *x*-coordinate and a negative *y*-coordinate.

Real-World Link
As students to think of other words with the prefix "quad." What do these words mean?

Additional Answer

2.

x-coordinate	y-coordinate	Part of Coordinate Plane
positive	positive	Quadrant I
positive	negative	Quadrant IV
negative	positive	Quadrant II
negative	negative	Quadrant III
0	anything	*y*-axis
0	0	origin
anything	0	*x*-axis

Inquiry

Investigation 5

Suggested Grouping: Individuals

Materials and Preparation
Students will need grid paper for this investigation.

Travel on a Grid
This investigation reinforces the importance of absolute value. Students will see that distance traveled is the same, regardless of direction. Help students put the situation into perspective by discussing family trips. Talk about the costs involved, and how to save money on things like gas and lodging. Remind students that, by helping the family save gas, they can afford to do more fun things on the trip. Draw a sample Cartesian plane on the board to show students what they will be doing.

Try It Out

▶ **Exercise 1** When drawing the Cartesian plane, make sure students correctly label both the *x*-axis and *y*-axis. If the plane is drawn incorrectly, students will not be able to complete the rest of the activity properly.

▶ **Exercise 2** Remind students of the proper way to plot points. Make sure they understand that ordered pairs give directions for the *x*-axis first, then the *y*-axis.

▶ **Exercise 3** Finding the answers to these questions requires students to use trial-and-error to find the best path from one point to the next. Remind students to draw lightly in pencil until they are sure they have the right path, so their Cartesian planes do not get messy and hard to read.

▶ **Exercises 4 and 5** Have students pay attention to the moves it takes to reach a place. Help them see how using fewer moves required less gas, and saved more money for the Robinson family.

Inquiry

Investigation 5 Travel on a Grid

Materials
• grid paper

The Robinson family is planning a weekend trip. During the trip, the family plans to visit a zoo, an amusement park, and a water park. There is a strict gasoline budget for the trip. Destinations must be reached using the shortest distance possible.

There is not a map available, so you will have to help guide the Robinson family. Each line on the grid represents a road, and the Robinsons must stay on the road during the trip. Your directions can have them move only up or down spaces or to the left and right. Remember, they cannot cut *through* spaces.

1.

Try It Out

1. Draw a Cartesian plane. Be sure to include the four quadrants. Give the *x*-axis a scale of −10 to 10. Give the *y*-axis a scale from −10 to 10.

2. The Robinson's house is located at (−2, 4). Plot and label a point representing the Robinson's house. In what quadrant do the Robinsons live? Quadrant II

3. The family plans to visit the zoo, which is located at (−7, −1). There is only enough gas to move 35 spaces. Each line on the grid represents one space.

   a. Can the Robinson family make it to the zoo on that tank of gas?
   Yes
   b. In what quadrant is the zoo located? Quadrant III

   c. Plot and label the point representing the zoo. Trace the lines from the Robinson's house to the zoo to show the route.
   Answers will vary.
   d. How many spaces did the family move to get to the zoo? 10

4. The next destination is the amusement park. It is located in Quadrant I. The family planned 15 moves to get to the park. The amusement park is located nine spaces to the right and up three spaces from the zoo. Draw your route and place a point representing the amusement park. Label the point.

   a. What are the coordinates of this point? (2, 2)

   b. Did the family follow its plan? How do you know?
   Yes, 15 moves were planned. The trip took 12 moves.
5. If you recall, there was enough gas to move 35 spaces for the entire weekend trip. The family has already visited the zoo and the amusement park. How many spaces are left to visit the water park and to return home? 13 more spaces

Troubleshooting

For students who understand the concept of absolute value, but have trouble using the coordinate plane, it may be helpful to practice plotting points. Write ordered pairs on the board, and have pairs work together to plot them. Watch for errors in using the *x*-axis and *y*-axis, and placement of positive and negative numbers.

6a. The *x*-coordinate is a positive number because it is in Quadrant IV.

6b. The *y*-coordinate is a negative number because all Quadrant IV ordered pairs are (+, −).

8. The most direct route is 8 spaces away.

6. From the amusement park, the family is ready to travel to the water park to finish out the weekend trip. The water park is located in Quadrant IV.

   a. Is the *x*-coordinate of the water park a positive or negative number? Explain.

   b. Is the *y*-coordinate of the water park a positive or a negative number? Explain.

7. The family leaves the amusement park and travels vertically three spaces and to the left one space. Name the ordered pair in which the Robinsons have arrived. Place a point on this ordered pair and label it. (1, −1)

8. After a day of swimming, the family is ready to make the trip home. On your graph, trace a route from the water park back to the Robinson's home. How many spaces did it take to go from the water park to the family's home?

9. Was the family able to stay within its allotted gasoline budget of 35 spaces? Explain. Yes, the family only moved 34 spaces. It had planned on 35 spaces.

Try It Again

10. The following weekend, the Robinsons want to visit relatives. For this trip, there is a way that allows the family to "cut" through spaces. The Robinsons travel vertically for 9.5 spaces and horizontally for 6 spaces. The relatives live in Quadrant III. Give the coordinates of the relatives' house. (−8, −5.5)

What Did You Learn?

11. Give the coordinates of the point on your grid that is halfway between the zoo and the water park. (−3, −1)

12. List three coordinates on the grid with the first coordinate greater than 3. Possible answer: (5, 2), (4, 1), (11, 8)

13. List three coordinates on the grid with a second coordinate less than 2. Possible answer: (4, −1), (−2, −7), (−1, 10)

14. List three coordinates in Quadrant IV. Answers will vary.

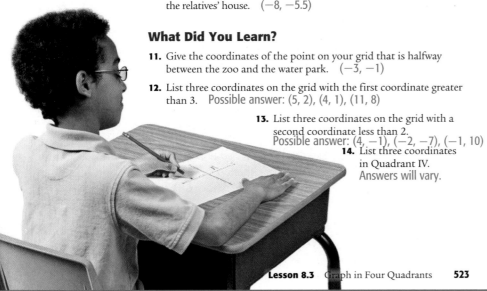

Lesson 8.3   Graph in Four Quadrants   **523**

▶ **Exercise 6** Discuss how the position of numbers in the plane affects their signs. Point out that distances on the plane are not affected by the signs of the coordinates; this is the same as absolute value.

▶ **Exercise 7** Make sure students understand the difference between vertical and horizontal moves. Have them demonstrate the directions with their hands, and then find the appropriate point on the plane.

▶ **Exercise 8** Finding the most direct route may require several different tries. Have pairs try different routes, then compare to see which is the shortest.

▶ **Exercise 9** Make sure students understand the meaning of staying on a budget. Discuss the gasoline allotment the Robinsons had for the trip. Point out that when the Robinsons made their trip using less gasoline than they planned on, they stayed within their budget.

Try It Again

▶ **Exercise 10** Cutting across spaces may confuse students. Make sure they understand how to move 9.5 spaces, and to travel across the space at the right place. Remind them that the coordinates for the last position should show that the point is in the middle of a space by using a half (−5.5).

What Did You Learn?

▶ **Exercises 11–14** When giving the coordinates for a specific spot on the Cartesian plane, make sure students pay attention to the rules in each exercise. Remind them to look at the appropriate quadrant, and to carefully read the exercise to determine which coordinate must fit a certain criteria.

Reaching All Learners

BL **Beyond Level** For students who quickly grasp the concepts of absolute value and using ordered pairs, have partners create a new Cartesian plane. Tell each student to list several coordinates for points on the plane. Then have them trade lists and plot each of the points on their planes.

On Your Own Exercises
Lesson 8.3

Investigation 1
Pages 510–512
Practice & Apply: 1–8

Investigation 2
Pages 512–514
Practice & Apply: 9–15

Investigation 3
Pages 515–518
Practice & Apply: 16–18

Investigation 4
Pages 519–521
Practice & Apply: 19–23
Connect & Extend: 24–28

Investigation 5
Pages 522–523
Connect & Extend: 29–31

Assign Anytime
Mixed Review: 32–43

▶ **Exercises 1–8** You may want to provide students with Lesson 8.3 Master 1 to use as they complete these exercises. The thermometer is an enlargement of the one shown in the student edition. The number line in Exercise 4 is reproduced on the master, so students will have an accurate number line to use.

▶ **Exercises 5–8** Encourage students to use number sense to decide which temperature is warmer and then use the thermometer to verify that their answers are correct.

▶ **Exercises 9 and 10** Remind students to find the absolute value of the numbers inside the absolute value bars before determining which number is greater. Have them rewrite each pair of numbers to compare them after they find the absolute values.

▶ **Exercises 11–15** These exercises require students to use absolute value in solving problems. Remind them to find the absolute values before solving the expressions, and to think carefully about whether each answer should be positive or negative.

▶ **Exercise 16** You may want to encourage students to work on these problems using the empty coordinate grids on Lesson 8.3 Master 2.

Practice & Apply

1. If the temperature rises 10°F, it will be −25°F. What is the temperature now?   −35°F

2. If the temperature goes down 33°F, it will be −10°F. What is the temperature now?   23°F

3. If the temperature goes up $1\frac{1}{4}$°F, it will be 0°F. What is the temperature now? $-1\frac{1}{4}$°F

4. Copy the number line. Plot points to show the locations of the numbers listed. Label each point with the corresponding number.

$$-2.5 \quad -1.75 \quad 2\frac{1}{3} \quad -3 \quad 0.4 \quad 4\frac{1}{2} \quad -0.8$$

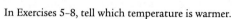

In Exercises 5–8, tell which temperature is warmer.

5. 5°F or −15°F   5°F

6. −35°F or −25°F   −25°F

7. $-5\frac{1}{2}$°F or $-5\frac{3}{4}$°F $-5\frac{1}{2}$°F

8. −100.9°F or −100.5°F   −100.5°F

9. Which is greater, |−5| or |3|? |−5|

10. Which is greater, −8 or |−8|? |−8|

Evaluate each expression.

11. |5.8| 5.8

12. $\frac{1}{3} \cdot |-21|$ 7

13. |−4.5| + |−3.25| 7.75

14. $\left|5\frac{1}{3}\right| - 8$ $-2\frac{2}{3}$

15. If |x| = 7.1, what is x equal to?   7.1 or −7.1

16.

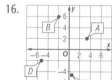

16. Plot these points on a coordinate plane. Label each point with its letter.

   a. $(3\frac{2}{5}, 2)$ **b.** (−2, 6)   **c.** (0.4, −4.4)   **d.** (−5, −2)

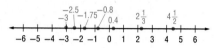

18a. *x*-axis

18b. *y*-axis

18c. Quadrant IV

18d. Quadrant I

18e. Quadrant III

18f. Quadrant II

17. Find the coordinates of points *J* through *O*.

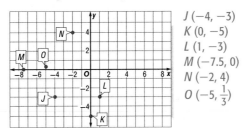

$J\,(-4, -3)$
$K\,(0, -5)$
$L\,(1, -3)$
$M\,(-7.5, 0)$
$N\,(-2, 4)$
$O\,\left(-5, \dfrac{1}{3}\right)$

20.

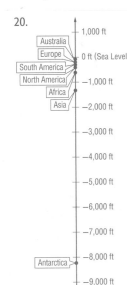

18. Without plotting each point, tell in which quadrant or on which axis it lies.

　a. (2, 0)　　　　**b.** (0, −24)　　　　**c.** (35, −23)

　d. (3, 5)　　　　**e.** (−2, −2)　　　　**f.** (−52, 5)

Earth Science Elevations are measured from sea level, which has an elevation of 0 feet. Elevations above sea level are positive. Elevations below sea level are negative. In Exercises 19–23, use this table, which shows the elevation of the lowest point on each continent.

Continent	Location of Lowest Point	Elevation
North America	Death Valley	−282 ft
South America	Valdes Peninsula	−131 ft
Europe	Caspian Sea	−92 ft
Asia	Dead Sea	−1,312 ft
Africa	Lake Assal	−512 ft
Australia	Lake Eyre	−52 ft
Antarctica	Bentley Subglacial Trench	−8,327 ft

Source: *World Almanac and Book of Facts 2000.* Copyright © 1999 Primedia Reference Inc.

Connect & Extend

19. Order the elevations in the table from lowest to highest.
−8,327 ft; −1,312 ft; −512 ft; −282 ft; −131 ft; −92 ft; −52 ft

20. Draw a number line. Plot each elevation given in the table. Label the point with the name of the continent.

21. How much lower is the Dead Sea than the Caspian Sea?　1,220 feet

22. One of the elevations in the table is significantly lower than the others.

　a. On which continent is this low point located?　Antarctica

　b. How much lower is this point than the next lowest point?
　7,015 ft lower

▶ **Exercise 18** Have student pairs check the quadrants they chose.

▶ **Exercise 20** Lesson 8.3 Master 1 includes a copy of the number line.

▶ **Exercises 22b and 23** These exercises preview addition and subtraction of negative numbers.

▶ **Exercises 24–27** Draw a plane on the board and have students tell where each point should be placed. Have them tell where the point would be if they had not found the absolute values first.

▶ **Exercise 28** Make sure students see that all coordinate pairs will have two positive numbers since they are all absolute values, and that pairs with two positive numbers will always fall in Quadrant 1. Discuss how a negative coordinate would affect the position of each point.

Quick Check

Informal Assessment Students should be able to:

✔ to graph positive and negative numbers on a number line

✔ to identify opposites and find absolute values

✔ to compare and order positive and negative numbers

✔ to create and interpret four-quadrant graphs

24. See graph.
a: y-axis, b: yes
25. See graph.
a: Quadrant I,
b: No, it would
have been in
Quadrant II
26. See graph.
a: Quadrant I,
b: No, it would
have been in
Quadrant III
27. See graph.
a: Quadrant I,
b: No, it would
have been in
Quadrant IV
28. Because all the
absolute values are
positive numbers,
all the points move
to Quadrant I.

23. **Challenge** The highest point in North America is the summit of Denali, a mountain in Alaska with an elevation of 20,320 feet. How many feet higher than Death Valley is the Denali summit? 20,602 ft

Graph each of the following coordinates. Answer Parts a and b for Exercises 24–27.

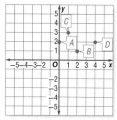

a. In which quadrant did you graph the point?

b. Would the point have been in the same location if you did not take the absolute value?

24. $A: (|0|, |2|)$ 25. $B: (|-2|, |1|)$

26. $C: (|-1|, |-3|)$ 27. $D: (|4|, |-2|)$

28. Is there a pattern to your answers to Exercises 24–27? Explain.

29. **Astronomy** The average surface temperatures of the planets in the solar system are related to their average distances from the Sun. a–d. See margin.

Planets in the Solar System

Planet	Distance from Sun (millions of miles)	Surface Temperature (°F)
Mercury	36	662
Venus	67	860
Earth	93	68
Mars	142	−9
Jupiter	483	−184
Saturn	888	−292
Uranus	1,784	−346
Neptune	2,799	−364

a. Create a graph with distance from the Sun on the x-axis and average surface temperature on the y-axis. Plot the eight points listed in the table.

b. Generally speaking, how does temperature change as you move further from the Sun?

c. Why do you think the relationship you noticed in Part b happens?

d. Which planet or planets do not fit the general pattern? Why might a planet not follow the pattern?

Additional Answers for Exercises 29a, 29b, 29c, and 29d are on page 531A.

30. Quadrants I and II and the origin; x can be any number, and y must be positive or 0.

30. If you plotted all points for which the y-coordinate is the square of the x-coordinate, in which quadrants or on which axes would the points lie? Explain how you know your answer is correct.

31. In Your Own Words Explain how a number line can help you order a set of positive and negative numbers.

Mixed Review

31. Sample answer: I can organize my positive numbers by placing them in order to the right of the zero. I can organize the negative numbers by ordering them to the left of the zero.

Find the value of each expression in simplest form.

32. $\frac{5}{6} + \frac{4}{9}$ $1\frac{5}{18}$

33. $\frac{19}{26} - \frac{17}{39}$ $\frac{23}{78}$

34. $\frac{45}{56} \cdot \frac{32}{35}$ $\frac{36}{49}$

35. $\frac{14}{15} \div \frac{2}{5}$ $2\frac{1}{3}$

36. $11\frac{19}{21} + 6\frac{1}{7}$ $18\frac{1}{21}$

37. $5\frac{1}{4} - 2\frac{5}{12}$ $2\frac{5}{6}$

38. $3\frac{5}{8} \cdot 1\frac{3}{4}$ $6\frac{11}{32}$

39. $9\frac{1}{3} \div \frac{5}{9}$ $16\frac{4}{5}$

40. Mrs. Heflin conducted a survey of students in her class to determine their opinions about the amount of homework they were given in class. Write each fraction as a decimal and a percent. Write each given percent as a decimal and as a fraction.

 a. She found that $\frac{9}{10}$ of the students did their homework every night. 0.9; 90%

 b. She found that $\frac{3}{4}$ of the students would prefer less homework. 0.75; 75%

 c. She learned that 1% would prefer to have no homework. 0.01; $\frac{1}{100}$

41. Which is greater, 0.25 or $\frac{1}{8}$?   0.25

42. Which is greater, 1.2 or 120%?   They are equal.

43. List in order from least to greatest: $\frac{2}{3}$, 60%, 0.66.   60%, 0.66, $\frac{2}{3}$

5. Find the absolute value of each expression.
 a. $|{-12}|$ 12
 b. $\left|\frac{2}{3}\right|$ $\frac{2}{3}$
 c. $|{-8.6}|$ 8.6

1. Find the coordinates of points $A - D$.
 A _____ (2, 3)
 B _____ (−1, −4)
 C _____ (0, 6)
 D _____ (−4, 4)

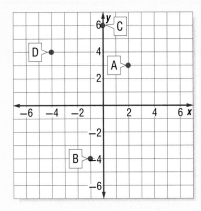

2. Plot the following points on the coordinate plane found in Exercise 1. Label each point with its letter.

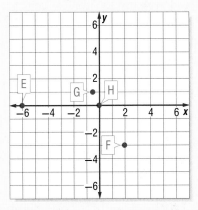

 E (−6, 0)
 F (2, −3)
 G (−$\frac{1}{2}$, 1)
 H (0, 0)

3. Name a point that can be found in each of the following quadrants.
 i. Quadrant II Answers will vary.
 j. Quadrant III Answers will vary.

4. Order the following numbers from smallest to largest.
 $-\frac{1}{2}$, −5, −0.4, −11, −11.1   −11.1, −11, −5, $-\frac{1}{2}$, −0.4

Review & Self-Assessment

Chapter Summary

This summary helps students recall the major topics of the chapter.

Vocabulary

Students should be able to explain each of the terms listed in the vocabulary section.

CHAPTER 8

Vocabulary

- absolute value
- axes
- coordinates
- line graph
- negative numbers
- opposites
- ordered pair
- origin
- positive numbers
- quadrants

Review & Self-Assessment

Chapter Summary

In this chapter, you interpreted and created graphs. You started by looking at graphs with only a few points and discovering what information was revealed by the positions of the points. Then you looked at graphs with lines and curves. You saw that when the variable on the horizontal axis is time, the line or curve tells a story about how the other variable changes.

You then made your own graphs. For some graphs, you drew a line or curve to fit a story or description without worrying about specific values. For other graphs, you made a table of values, chose scales for the axes, and plotted points. You saw that sometimes it makes sense to connect the points on a graph and that connecting points can help you see patterns and make predictions.

You also learned that plotting collected data and looking for trends, or patterns, can help you determine whether the variables are related. When the plotted points do show a pattern, you can make predictions about values not on the graph.

Finally, you can use a graph to show a relationship between quantities. On a single horizontal number line, negative integers are graphed to the left of zero and positive integers are graphed to the right of zero. The distance a number is from zero is called the absolute value. The further a number is to the left, the smaller it is.

On a coordinate grid, the number lines divide the plane into four sections labeled quadrants. Points may either lie in one of the four quadrants or on the x- or y-axis. You learned that a point in Quadrant I will have positive x- and y-coordinates. A point in Quadrant II will have a negative x-coordinate and a positive y-coordinate. A point in Quadrant III will have both negative x- and y-coordinates. A point in Quadrant IV will have a positive x-coordinate and a negative y-coordinate.

Strategies and Applications

The questions in this section will help you review and apply the important ideas and strategies developed in this chapter.

1a. True; on Graph X, Bones' point is farther to the left, indicating he is smaller. It is also lower, indicating he is less playful.

1b. True; on Graph X, Bowser's point is to the right of Bones', so Bowser is larger. On Graph Y, Bowser's point is above Bones', so he is more obedient.

1c. False; on Graph Y, Bones' point is to the right of Bowser's, so he is faster. On Graph X, Bones' point is below Bowser's, so he is less playful.

1d. False; Graph Y shows that Bowser is slower since his point is to the left of Bones'. Graph X shows that Bowser is larger since his point is to the right of Bones'.

Interpreting graphs

1. These graphs give information about Lydia's dogs. Use them to determine whether each statement that follows is true or false. Explain how you decided.

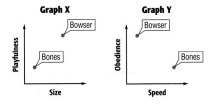

a. The smaller dog is less playful.

b. The larger dog is more obedient.

c. The faster dog is more playful.

d. The slower dog is smaller.

2. This graph shows how Jackie's distance from home changed one Saturday morning. Write a story about Jackie's morning. Your story should account for all the changes in the graph. See margin.

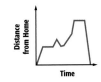

3. This graph shows the percent of the U.S. labor force that was unemployed in even-numbered years from 1980 to 2000.

a. In which year was the unemployment rate highest? In which year was it lowest? 1982, 2000

b. Over which two-year period did the unemployment rate decrease most? By about how much did it decrease? 1982 to 1984, about 2.2%

c. Over which two-year period did the unemployment rate increase most? By about how much did it increase? 1980 to 1982, about 2.6%

d. Over which two-year period did the unemployment rate change least? 1988 to 1990

e. Predict what the unemployment rate was in 1993. Possible answer: about 6.8%

Source: *World Almanac and Book of Facts 2003.* Copyright © 2003 Primedia Reference Inc.

CHAPTER 8 Review & Self-Assessment **529**

Additional Answer

2. Possible answer: Jackie left home Saturday morning and rode her bike to softball practice. After practice, she left the park to go to her piano lesson. She rode for a short distance and then realized she had forgotten her softball glove. She returned to the park, picked up her glove, and started riding again. She was riding fairly slowly at first but then realized she was late. She rode faster. After her piano lesson, she rode straight home.

▶ **Exercise 4** Have student volunteers share their graphs with the class.

▶ **Exercise 5** Have students check their table entries in pairs. You may want to display the table on the board and ask for volunteers to fill in the blanks.

▶ **Exercises 6–13** Display the answers and ask students to ask questions if they disagree. Monitor for accuracy.

4. Possible graph:

5b.

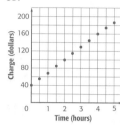

5c. Possible answer: Yes; the plumber could work and charge for fractions of a half hour.

5d. Possible answer: $138; I connected the points and then found the point on the connecting segments with horizontal coordinate 3.25.

Creating graphs

4. Frank went diving to explore a sunken ship. He descended quickly at first and then more slowly. As he was descending, he noticed an interesting fish. Frank ascended a little and stayed at a constant depth for awhile as he watched the fish. Then Frank slowly descended until he reached the sunken ship. He explored the ship for several minutes and then returned to the surface of the water at a slow, steady pace. Draw a graph that shows how Frank's depth changed during his dive.

5. A plumber charges $40 for a house call plus $15 for each half hour he works.

   a. Copy and complete the table to show how much the plumber charges if he works the given numbers of hours.

Time (hours)	0	0.5	1	1.5	2	2.5	3	3.5	4	4.5	5
Charge (dollars)	40	55	70	85	100	115	130	145	160	175	190

   b. Choose an appropriate scale. Graph the data.

   c. Does it make sense to connect the points on your graph? Explain.

   d. Suppose the plumber charges by fractions of a half hour. Use your graph to estimate how much the plumber would charge if he worked 3 hours 15 minutes. Explain how you found your answer.

Find the distance of each number from 0.

6. 3.5   3.5

7. $-1\frac{1}{2}$ $1\frac{1}{2}$

Which is further from 0?

8. 3.5 or -2.5 3.5

9. -4.5 or -3.5 -4.5

Find the value of each expression.

10. $|-4|$ 4

11. $-|-2.5|$ -2.5

12. $-|1.5|$ -1.5

13. $|-2^2|$ 4

The table shows the change in the number of people at the movies for each day of the week.

Day of the Week	Monday	Tuesday	Wednesday	Thursday	Friday	Saturday	Sunday
Size of change	-75	-10	5	10	25	60	-25

14. When was the greatest change in the number of people at the movies?
From Sunday to Monday

15. When was the smallest change in the number of people at the movies?
From Tuesday to Wednesday

Demonstrating Skills

16. Plot each point on one set of axes. Label each point with its coordinates.

16a–f.

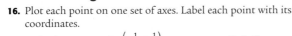

a. $(0, 5)$ **b.** $\left(1\frac{1}{2}, 5\frac{1}{2}\right)$ **c.** $(9.5, 8)$

d. $(7, 7)$ **e.** $(7, 0)$ **f.** $(3.3, 6.5)$

17. Give the coordinates of the point halfway between $(3, 5)$ and $(7, 5)$.

17. $(5, 5)$

18. Plot the points $(1, 4)$ and $(5, 4)$. Plot two more points so that the four points can be connected to form a square. Give their coordinates.

18. Possible answers:
$(1, 0)$ and $(5, 0)$ or
$(1, 8)$ and $(5, 8)$

Identify the quadrant where each point is located.

19. $(-2, 3)$ II   **20.** $(-1.5, -6.5)$ III

21. $(4, 6)$ I   **22.** $\left(3\frac{1}{2}, -7\right)$ IV

23. What is the sign of the x-value of a point in Quadrant II?   Negative

24. What is the sign of the y-value of a point in Quadrant I?   Positive

25. What is the x-value of a point on the y-axis?   0

26. What is the y-value of a point on the x-axis?   0

Order the numbers from least to greatest.

27. $-3, 2, -9, 5, 6, -10, 3, -6$ $-10, -9, -6, -3, 2, 3, 5, 6$

28. $-35, -15, -45, -25, 0, -5, -20, 5, 10, -15$
$-45, -35, -25, -20, -15, -15, -5, 0, 5, 10$

Test-Taking Practice

SHORT RESPONSE

1 Use the data in the graph to describe the pattern or trend of the New York population.

What do you predict the population to be in 2010?

Show your work.

Answer _____

Show your work:
The population
increased more rapidly
from 1990 to 2000. If
this rate continues, the
population in 2010
should be around
19.5 million.

Answer: The population
in general has
increased, with a
decrease from 1970
to 1980; About 19.5
million

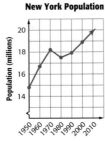

New York Population

MULTIPLE CHOICE

2 Which point lies on the y-axis in the coordinate plane?

A $(0, -4)$

B $(-6, 0)$

C $(-3, 3)$

D $(7, 0)$

3 Which expression is equivalent to $|-16| + |4| + |-8|$?

F $-16 + 4 - 8$

G $-16 + 4 + 8$

H $16 + 4 + 8$

J $16 + 4 - 8$

▶ **Exercises 14 and 15** Have students check their answers with a partner.

▶ **Exercises 16 and 17** You may want to have student volunteers plot these points on an overhead grid. Ask other students to check their graphs.

▶ **Exercises 24 and 25** You may want to go over the answers slowly and carefully. Students may have difficulty with these abstract concepts, so also provide extra examples, if necessary.

Lesson 8.2, Develop & Understand: A (p. 490)

3. Possible graph:

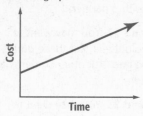

4. Possible graph:

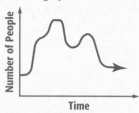

5. Possible graph:

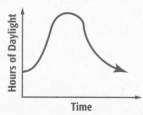

6. Possible graph:

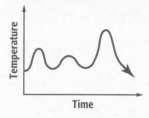

Lesson 8.3, On Your Own Exercises (p. 526)

29a.

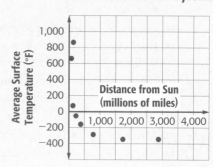

29b. It decreases.

29c. As planets get farther from the sun, less energy from the sun reaches them.

29d. Possible answer: Venus and Mercury don't fit the pattern; the temperature of Venus should be less than 662°F, or Mercury's should be greater than 860°F. Composition of the planet might affect its temperature, and the effect of distance might be more complicated than the pattern in Part b.

Notes

CHAPTER 9

Equations

Chapter Overview

This chapter begins with a look at true and false equations. Students learn that if an equation contains a variable, the values of the variable that make the equation true are called *solutions* of the equation.

Next, students learn about two methods for solving equations. The backtracking method is introduced by means of flowcharts. Students can use this method to find solutions for many equations in which the variable occurs only once. The second method, called the guess-check-and-improve method, allows students to find exact or approximate solutions for an even broader group of equations.

The Big Picture

Links to the Past	Chapter 9	Links to the Future
Grade 5 Reviewing number sentences, open sentences, and variables.	**Lesson 9.1** (p. 534) Understand Equations	**Course 2, Chapter 9** Equations (pp. 434–491)
Course 1, Chapter 3 Using properties of fundamental operations to write expressions in equivalent forms.		**Course 3, Chapter 7** Inequalities and Linear Systems (pp. 310–371)
Grade 5 Solving addition/subtraction number stories by modeling with open sentences.	**Lesson 9.2** (p. 546) Backtracking	**Course 2, Chapter 9** Equations (pp. 434–491)
		Course 3, Chapter 7 Inequalities and Linear Systems (pp. 310–371)
		Course 3, Chapter 9 Solve Quadratic Equations (pp. 464–521)
Grade 5 Solving addition/subtraction number stories by modeling with open sentences.	**Lesson 9.3** (p. 560) Guess-Check-and-Improve	**Course 2, Chapter 9** Equations (pp. 434–491)
		Course 3, Chapter 7 Inequalities and Linear Systems (pp. 310–371)

Mathematical Background

Chapter 9 introduces students to solving equations by the backtracking method and the guess-check-and-improve method. Before they study these methods, students examine true and false equations and inequalities. They learn what is meant by a solution of an equation.

Students will solve various types of equations in this chapter. As they observe the characteristics of the equations they solve, they learn to look for clues that can help them select the most efficient solution method.

Backtracking The backtracking method is developed by the use of flowcharts. A flowchart starts with an input value and uses a sequence of operations that eventually results in an output value. Students call on their experience from Think of a Number games to gain insight into how to construct a flowchart. The numbers for the flowchart are written in ovals. Arrows from one oval to the next indicate what operations are being performed. For instance, think of these instructions for a Think of a Number game:

Think of a number. Add 3. Multiply by 5. Subtract 15 to get the final result. The flowchart would look like this:

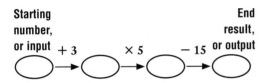

For any number put in the oval on the left, the flowchart tells what operations to perform to get a final result, or output. Students learn how to start with the final result and use inverse operations to work backward to the original input. They learn that many simple, one-variable equations can be represented by flowcharts similar to the one above. Knowing the output lets them solve the equation, or find the value of the variable that will make the equation true.

Guess-Check-and-Improve The guess-check-and-improve method can be applied to a much larger class of equations than the backtracking method. The idea is simple: guess the solution, and then successively refine the guesses to get closer and closer to the solution. In some cases, a guess will turn out to be the exact solution. In many instances, guessing and reasoning can be used together to arrive at the exact solution. Often, however, one is obliged to settle for an approximate solution. In many real-world applications, a sufficiently accurate approximation to the solution is all that is really needed.

The ideas in this chapter lay the groundwork for more extensive work on solving equations in Courses 2 and 3. In particular, this chapter will prepare students for solving equations by transforming them into equivalent equations, using the zero-product property, and using more sophisticated approximation techniques.

Additional Reading

According to Sutherland and Rojano in "A Spreadsheet Approach to Solving Algebra Problems," which appeared in *Journal of Mathematical Behavior*, spreadsheets can be used to help students understand variables and algebraic expressions. Pointing out the similarities between designing a flowchart to solve an equation and a flowchart for a spreadsheet may be helpful for this chapter.

Planning Guide
Lesson Resources

	Pacing: 4 days	Pacing: 4 days	Pacing: 4 days
	Lesson 9.1	**Lesson 9.2**	**Lesson 9.3**
Lesson Title	**Understand Equations** (p. 534)	**Backtracking** (p. 546)	**Guess-Check-and-Improve** (p. 560)
Lesson Objectives	• To decide whether a number sentence is true or false • To use the symbols $=$, $>$, and $<$ to write true number sentences • To use trial-and-error to find solutions of equations	• To construct flowcharts that represent input/output rules and equations • To solve equations by using flowcharts for backtracking (working backward)	• To solve equations systematically by using guess-check-and-improve • To find appropriate solutions to equations, to the nearest tenth or hundredth • To write and solve equations that describe mathematical puzzles or word problems • To decide whether to use backtracking or guess-check-and-improve to solve equations
Materials	*red and blue blocks, *yellow and green counters		
Quick Review Math Handbook	**Lesson 5.4** Equations **Lesson 5.6** Inequalities	**Lesson 5.4** Equations	**Lesson 5.4** Equations
Print Resources	[CRM] Study Guide and Intervention (p. 3) [CRM] Skills Practice (p. 4) [CRM] Problem-Solving Practice (p. 5) [CRM] Enrichment (p. 6) • Investigation Notebook and Reflection Journal • Differentiation Handbook	[CRM] Study Guide and Intervention (p. 9) [CRM] Skills Practice (p. 10) [CRM] Problem-Solving Practice (p. 11) [CRM] Enrichment (p. 12) • Investigation Notebook and Reflection Journal • Differentiation Handbook	[CRM] Study Guide and Intervention (p. 14) [CRM] Skills Practice (p. 15) [CRM] Problem-Solving Practice (p. 16) [CRM] Enrichment (p. 17) • Investigation Notebook and Reflection Journal • Differentiation Handbook
Technology Resources	TeacherWorks Plus Classroom Presentation Toolkit ExamView Assessment Suite StudentWorks Plus [Math Online] Brain Pops • Concepts in Motion	TeacherWorks Plus Classroom Presentation Toolkit ExamView Assessment Suite StudentWorks Plus [Math Online] Brain Pops • Concepts in Motion	TeacherWorks Plus Classroom Presentation Toolkit ExamView Assessment Suite StudentWorks Plus [Math Online] Brain Pops • Concepts in Motion

*Included in the Impact Mathematics Manipulative Kit

Assessment Resources

MARS Assessment: Teaching with Purpose

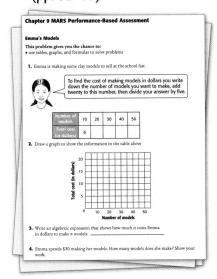

Emma's Models

In *Emma's Models,* students use tables, graphs, and formulas to solve problems. Students complete a table showing the cost to make clay models, plot information on a graph, and write an algebraic expression that shows the cost in dollars to make *n* models.

Targeting the Task

- **Diagnostic**—Use Exercises 1–4 in the *Emma's Models* assessment to determine students' understanding of how to use tables, graphs, and formulas to solve problems. For those students who do not have this understanding, completing this unit is needed.

- **Formative**—Exercises 1–4 can be administered individually according to the lessons.

- **Summative**—Administer the complete *Emma's Models* performance-based assessment.

CRM Chapter 9 MARS Assessment
(pp. 32–35)

Assessment Planning Guide

Assessments are available for investigations, lessons, and chapters.

 Customize and create multiple versions of tests and quizzes.

	Student Edition	Teacher Edition	Other Resources
Diagnostic			CRM Chapter 9 Pretest (p. 19) Math Online Online Chapter Quiz
Formative	Share & Summarize (pp. 536, 538, 549, 552, 554, 563, 565, 573)	Troubleshooting (pp. 554, 563, 565, 573) On the Spot Assessment (pp. 534, 561) Quick Check (pp. 545, 559, 572) Quick Quiz (pp. 545, 559, 572)	
Summative	Review & Self-Assessment (pp. 573–575)		CRM Chapter 9 Test: Forms A and B (pp. 22–27) CRM Standardized Test Practice (p. 30)
Performance-Based	In Your Own Words (pp. 542, 559, 570)		CRM MARS Performance-Based Assessment (p. 32) CRM Chapter Performance Assessment (p. 28)

Differentiated Instruction

Reaching All Learners

Below are suggestions on differentiating the materials presented in this chapter. Additional modifications should be considered.

Approaching Level (AL)

Lesson 9.1: Variables Students who have difficulty understanding and using equations often do not fully grasp the use of variables. Using a variable can make a problem seem more confusing than it really is. Point out to students that a variable is simply a way to say "some number." Teach students to think of the variables in problems as question marks, meaning something they do not know. Write one equation several times, using different letters in the place of the variable each time. Make sure students see that the problem still has the same answer, regardless of the letter used as the variable. Students who are comfortable with variables should have less trouble understanding equations.

Beyond Level (BL)

Lesson 9.2: Flowcharts Students who understand backtracking can work in groups to create a mini-lesson to explain it to those who need more help. Have them create a flowchart as a visual aid. Remind them to label each input and output oval, and to write the steps for the problem clearly. Then have them decide how to teach the process to other students. Make sure they include a step-by-step presentation of the problem and a time for vocabulary instruction. Then, have each group present their lesson to the class. Allow students who have more trouble and who ask for help to work with the students who wrote the lesson. Have them work together to create a flowchart for a new problem.

On Level (OL)

Lesson 9.3: Guess-Check-and-Improve Help students see the reasoning behind using guess-check-and-improve. Give them a problem to solve. Have pairs try to solve it using another method. Then have them work together to solve it using use the guess-check-and-improve method. Assist them if necessary in finding the answer to the problem. Help them draw a table to record their answers. Have students tell why they think the guess-check-and-improve method was better. Tell students to write their thoughts in a sentence. Some possible answers could include: backtracking did not work, guessing and improving got us closer to the right answer faster, and so on.

English Language Learners (ELL)

Lesson 9.2: Backtracking Students new to the English language may need extra help with *backtracking*. Reading the flowcharts for backtracking in Lesson 9.2 can be confusing if students do not have a thorough understanding of working problems forward and using words like *inverse operations* and *undo*. To help English language learners, work a problem forward, using the flowcharts. Have them echo you as you describe the steps. Ask a student to tell what went in the last oval. Copy the number into the first oval of the backtracking problem. Then, have another student point to the next-to-the-last number, and so on. Make sure students see the relationship between both problems.

KEY

 Approaching Level   On Level   Beyond Level   English Language Learners

Intervention Planning Guide

CRM Assess students' prerequisite skills and knowledge using the **Chapter Pretest** found in the Chapter 9 Resource Masters, p. 19.

Intensive Intervention two or more years below grade level	**Strategic Intervention** below grade level	**On Level**	**Beyond Level**
If students miss 75% of the exercises: **Then** use *Math Triumphs,* an intensive intervention	**If** students miss 50% of the exercises: **Then** choose a resource:	**If** students miss 25% of the exercises: **Then** choose a resource:	**If** students miss 0%–10% of the exercises: **Then** choose a resource:
Math Triumphs, Grade 6 • Chapter 9: Variables and Expressions	**CRM** Study Guide and Intervention (pp. 3, 9, 14) • Investigation Notebook and Reflection Journal • Differentiation Handbook **Math Online** Brain Pops • Concepts in Motion	**CRM** Skills Practice (pp. 4, 10, 15) **CRM** Problem-Solving Practice (pp. 5, 11, 16) • Investigation Notebook and Reflection Journal	**CRM** Enrichment (pp. 6, 12, 17) • Differentiation Handbook

Literature Connections

Recommended Outside Reading for Students

Nonfiction

Burns, Marilyn. *The I Hate Mathematics! Book.* Bt. Bound, 1999.

This book is a collection of puzzles, riddles, magic tricks, and brain teasers that are designed to encourage non-math people to give math a chance. It is designed for students to read and work through with or without the help of an adult.

Fiction

Wise, Bill. *Whodunit Math Puzzles.* Sterling Publications, 2001.

A junior detective and mathematical genius solves crimes and puzzles that are math based. The adventures are short and require common problem-solving skills. The clearly presented solutions are in the back of the book.

Professional Development

Targeted professional development has been articulated throughout the *IMPACT Mathematics* series. The **McGraw-Hill Professional Development Video Library** provides short videos that support the mathematics standards. Log on to **www.glencoe.com**.

Model Lessons   Instructional Strategies

Real-Life Math

It's for the Birds The problem on this page illustrates how solving equations can help people find answers to real-world problems.

Point out that Amy can use equations to determine the number of birdhouses she can afford to make, as well as the number she needs to sell in order to achieve her profit goal. Explain that finding the number that will make the expression on the left side of the equation equal in value to the right side is called *solving the equation*. Solving equations will give answers for Amy's questions. Tell students that in this chapter they will study two methods of solving equations.

Think About It
To figure out how many birdhouses Amy needs to sell to earn $120, she can solve $120 = 8n$.

CHAPTER
9

Equations

Real-Life Math

It's for the Birds Amy makes and sells birdhouses at her town's craft fair. It costs $10 to rent a table. Amy spends an average of $5 for supplies to make each birdhouse.

The equation $c = \$10 + \$5n$ represents the total cost of making the birdhouses. In the equation, c represents the total cost, and n represents the number of birdhouses. Suppose Amy has a total of $75 to spend on rent and supplies. The equation $\$75 = \$10 + \$5n$ represents the number of birdhouses that she can make.

Think About It Amy plans to sell her birdhouses for $8 each. The equation $m = \$8n$ represents the amount of money she will earn. In the equation, m represents the amount of money she will earn, and n represents the number of birdhouses. She hopes to earn $120. What equation should she solve?

Contents in Brief

Math Online
Take the **Chapter Readiness Quiz** at glencoe.com.

532

Chapter Resources

- CRM Chapter 9 Resource Masters
- CRM English/Spanish Family Letter (pp. 1 and 2)
- CRM Lesson Masters (p. 8)
- CRM Chapter 9 Pretest (pp. 19–21)
- CRM Chapter 9 Tests (pp. 22–29)

Math Online Online Readiness Quiz • eGlossary

Dear Family,

The next chapter is about solving equations. An equation is a number sentence that includes an equals sign, which means that two expressions have the same value. Here are three examples.

$$9 + 6 = 15 \qquad 9 + 6 = 5 \cdot 3 \qquad 7 + 8 = 18 - 3$$

In this chapter, the class will explore equations with variables, such as $3 \cdot n = 18$.

Key Concept—Backtracking

The class will learn two methods for solving equations: backtracking and guess-check-and-improve. To find the output t for the equation $4 \cdot n + 5 = t$, start with the input n. Multiply the input by 4 and then add 5.

Here is the flowchart for an input of 3.

If given an output of 21, the flowchart could be used to work backward and determine that the input was 4.

Chapter Vocabulary

backtracking	inequality
equation	open sentence
flowchart	solution
guess-check-and-improve	

Home Activities
- Have your student share newly learned strategies for solving equations.
- Take turns writing equations on slips of paper. Then solve one another's equations.

533

Family Letter

Another version of the Family Letter, available in English and Spanish, is found in the Chapter 9 Resource Masters. You may want to send a copy of this letter home with your students.

Key Concept—Backtracking Introduce students to flowcharts by having them diagram an activity, such as making a sandwich. Start with the input of two slices of bread. Then add peanut butter and jelly. The result should be a sandwich.

Draw a horizontal flowchart and then a vertical flowchart to demonstrate different ways to show the process.

Home Activities
- Discuss situations where you need to solve an equation. If you can charge $10 to walk a dog for a week and you need to make $80 in a week, how many dogs must you walk?

- Each morning, have your student write an equation to post on the refrigerator that represents some activity for the day.

Key Vocabulary

English (Spanish) *Introduce the most important terms from Chapter 9.*

backtracking (vueltra atras) The process of using a flowchart to work backward, starting with the output and undoing each operation to find an input. (p. 548)

equation (ecuacion) A mathematical sentence stating that two quantities have the same value. An equal sign, $=$, is used to separate the two quantities. (p. 535)

flowchart (flujograma) A diagram, using ovals and arrows, that shows the steps for going from an input to an output. For example, the diagram below is a *flowchart*. (p. 547)

guess-check-and-improve (conjectura, verifica y mejora) A method for solving an equation that involves first guessing the solution, then checking the guess by substituting into the original equation, and then using the result to improve the guess until the correct solution is found. (p. 560)

inequality (desigualdad) a mathematical sentence stating that two quantities have different values. For example, $5 + 9 > 12$ is an *inequality*. The symbols $\neq$, $<$, and $>$ are used in writing inequalities. (p. 535)

open sentence (enunciado abierto) An equation of inequality that can be true or false depending on the value of the variable. For example, $5 + n = 20$ is an *open sentence*. (p. 536)

solution (solucion) A value of a variable that makes an equation true. For example, 4 is the solution of $3n + 7 = 19$. (p. 536)

Understand Equations

Objectives

▶ To decide whether a number sentence is true or false

▶ To use the symbols =, >, and < to write true number sentences

▶ To use trial-and-error to find solutions of equations

Overview

In this lesson, students learn about the two main kinds of mathematical sentences that describe how two quantities are related: equations and inequalities. *Equations* state that two quantities are equal in value. *Inequalities* state that one quantity is greater than or less than another. Students see that, as with sentences in ordinary language, mathematical sentences may be true or false.

Students learn that equations containing variables are usually true for some values of the variables but false for others. If an equation contains a variable, the values of the variable that make the equation true are called *solutions* of the equation. Students explore trial-and-error methods for finding solutions of equations and also solve equations by backtracking.

Advance Preparation

You may want to make copies of Lesson 9.1 Master 1 to facilitate class discussion while presenting new topics, including writing and solving number sentences and inequalities.

	Summary	Materials	On Your Own Exercises (pp. 541–545)	Assessment Opportunities
Investigation 1 (p. 535) *Pacing: 2 days*	Students learn to use inequality symbols to tell how two unequal numbers are related.		Practice & Apply: 1–9 Connect & Extend: 24–27 Mixed Review: 35–38	• On the Spot Assessment (p. 534) • Share & Summarize (p. 536)
Investigation 2 (p. 536) *Pacing: 1 day*	Students use trial-and-error to find solutions of equations that contain variables.		Practice & Apply: 10–23 Connect & Extend: 28–34 Mixed Review: 35–38	• Share & Summarize (p. 538)
Inquiry Investigation 3 (p. 539) *Pacing: 1 day*	Students use the idea of undoing instructions in preparation for their study of the backtracking method for solving equations.	Lesson 9.1 Master 1, red and blue blocks, yellow and green counters	Mixed Review: 35–38	

Leveled Lesson Resources

CRM *Available in:* **Chapter 9 Resource Masters**

Study Guide and Intervention (p. 3) **AL**

Lesson 9.1 Study Guide and Intervention
Understand Equations

Solving Equations
Finding the values of a variable that make an equation true is called *solving* the equation. The variable that makes the equation true is called a *solution*. The solution of an equation can be found by using a table.

Example 1 Solve $2 \cdot x + 4 = 10$ using a table.

Try several values for x.

x	$2 \cdot x + 4$	Test	Solution?
0	4	$2 \cdot x + 4 < 10$	no
1	6	$2 \cdot x + 4 < 10$	no
2	8	$2 \cdot x + 4 < 10$	no
3	10	$2 \cdot x + 4 = 10$	yes
4	12	$2 \cdot x + 4 > 10$	no
5	14	$2 \cdot x + 4 > 10$	no

A value of 3 for x is the solution to $2 \cdot x + 4 = 10$ since $2 \cdot 3 + 4 = 10$. The values increase as x increases, so 3 is the only solution.

Example 2 Solve $c + 6 = 2c$ using a table.

Try several values for c.

c	$c + 6$	$2c$	Test	Solution?
3	9	6	$c + 6 > 2c$	no
4	10	8	$c + 6 > 2c$	no
5	11	10	$c + 6 > 2c$	no
6	12	12	$c + 6 = 2c$	yes
7	13	14	$c + 6 < 2c$	no
8	14	16	$c + 6 < 2c$	no

A value of 6 for c is the solution to $c + 6 = 2c$ since $6 + 6 = 2 \cdot 6$.

Exercises Solve each equation. Use tables if necessary.

1. $4m + 5 = 9$
2. $3n + 4 = 13$
3. $4x + 8 = 16$
4. $19 = 2s + 11$
5. $c + 10 = 3c$
6. $5 \cdot y + 10 = 25$
7. One more than four times a number is 13. What is the number?
8. Three is seven less than two times a number. What is the number?

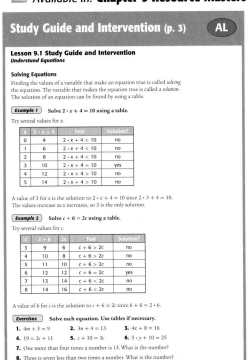

Skills Practice (p. 4) **AL** **OL**

Lesson 9.1 Skills Practice
Understand Equations

Solving Two-Step Equations
Solve each equation. Use tables if necessary.

1. $2a + 4 = 6$
2. $3b + 4 = 10$
3. $7 = 4c - 5$
4. $4x + 6 = 14$
5. $8 = 2g + 3$
6. $x + 4 = 5x$
7. $1 = 2f - 7$
8. $6 + m = 2m$
9. $5z + 1 = 16$
10. $7m - 5 = 9$
11. $1 = 8n - 7$
12. $16 = 4s + 14$
13. $12 = k + 5$
14. $4r = 3r + 2$
15. $6 = 2x - 10$
16. $5x = 3x + 10$
17. $2r - 5 = 3$
18. $5 = 2z - 9$

Tell whether each equation below is always true, sometimes true or never true. Explain how you know.

19. $\dfrac{f}{2} = f$
20. $g + 4 = g + 6$
21. $2 \cdot v = v + 6$

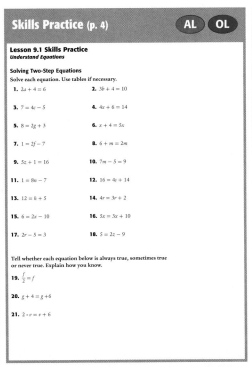

Problem-Solving Practice (p. 5) **AL** **OL**

Lesson 9.1 Problem-Solving Practice
Understand Equations

Solve.

1. **Scale Balance** A scale has x pencils and 6 erasers on one side and 13 pencils on the other. The scale is balanced and is represented by the equation, $x + 6 = 13$. How many pencils are on one side of the balance?

2. **Measurement** At today's check-up, Madelyn was 40 inches tall. She is 6 inches taller than she was at her last check-up. Her height at last the last check-up is represented by the equation $40 = 6 + h$. What was her height at the last check-up?

3. **Exchange Rate** Horatio is exchanging euros from his trip to Europe back to U.S. dollars. The exchange rate is represented by the equation below, where D is the amount in dollars and E is the amount in euros.

   $$D = 1.50 \cdot E$$

   How many dollars will Horatio receive if he exchanges 20 euros?

4. **Driving** The distance that a car traveling 55 miles per hour can be calculated by the equation below, where d represents distance and t represents time in hours.

   $$d = 55 \cdot t$$

   How long does it take the car to travel a distance of 220 miles?

5. **Bike Rental** The price of a bike rental p at Kevin's shop is represented by the equation $p = \$3 + \$2h$, where h is the number of hours a bike is rented. How many hours was a bike rented if the value of p is $11?

6. **Storage Unit** A storage company charges $40 for the first month and $15 for each additional month. The cost of renting a unit c is represented by the equation $c = \$15m + \$40$, where m is the number of each additional months. How many additional months was a unit rented if c equals $130?

7. **Plumber** A plumber charges $50 for material and $30 per hour for labor. The amount of the bill a is represented by the equation $a = \$50 + \$30h$. How many hours did the plumber work if $a = \$110$?

8. **Profit** A kite company's monthly profit p is represented by the equation $p = \$12k - \$50$. The cost of a kite is represented by k. How many kites does the company have to sell to make a profit of $94?

Enrichment (p. 6) **BL**

Lesson 9.1 Enrichment
Understand Equations

Chunking
Have you ever seen an equation like $3(t + 1) = 18$? The expression inside parentheses might make you think that solving this equation is going to be difficult. But, if you can solve $3t = 18$, you probably can solve this equation too. The trick is to think of the expression $(t + 1)$ as a **chunk**. Here's how.

$3(t + 1) = 18$ means the same as $\boxed{(t+1)} \cdot 3 = 18$.

$\boxed{(t + 1)} = 18 \div 3$

$\boxed{(t + 1)} = 6$

You know $5 + 1 = 6$, so $t = 5$.

Solve each equation by chunking.

1. $4(a + 3) = 40$
2. $2(m - 5) = 8$
3. $3(c - 2) = 18$
4. $25 = 5(z + 4)$
5. $14 = 7(k - 4)$
6. $20 = 4(x + 1)$
7. $6(1 + x) = 24$
8. $3(12 - r) = 30$
9. $8(9 + t) = 104$
10. $8 = 8(b - 5)$
11. $2(6 - q) = 0$
12. $0 = 6(10 - a)$
13. $1.3(x + 1) = 6.5$
14. $0.4(j - 9) = 0.8$
15. $1.5(k - 6) = 9$
16. $0.2 = 0.05(y + 2)$
17. $0.24(d - 5) = 2.16$
18. $0.12(e + 2) = 0.36$

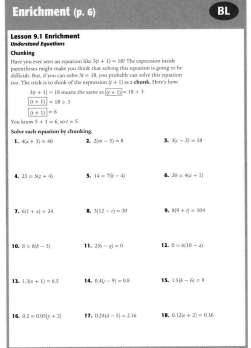

Lesson Quick Quiz (p. 7) **AL** **OL** **BL**

Lesson 9.1 Quick Quiz
Understand Equations

1. Make at least two true equations using the numbers 2, 3, 3, 4, 6, 7, and 9.

2. Tell whether each equation is true or false. If it is false, make it true by replacing the equals sign with < or >.

   a. $13 - 3 \cdot 3 = 30$
   b. $8 + 3^2 = 27 - 10$
   c. $8 \div 4 - 2 = 8 - (5 - 3)$
   d. $5 \cdot 4 + 7 = 56 \div 8$

3. Solve each equation.

   a. $4 \cdot x = 28$
   b. $n + 15 = 20$
   c. $3 \cdot k + 7 = 13$
   d. $8x = x^2 + 15$
   (There are two solutions.)

4. Tell whether each equation is *always true*, *sometimes true*, or *never true*. Explain how you know.

   a. $p + 4 = 7 + p$
   b. $m^2 + 9 = 13$
   c. $7x = 5x + 2x$

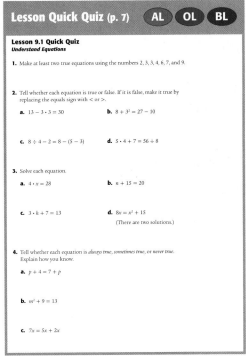

Lesson Master 1 (p. 8)

Lesson 9.1 Master 1
Understand Equations

Inquiry Investigation 3

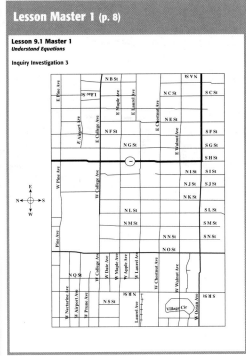

Additional Lesson Resources

Teacher Tech Tools
- TeacherWorks
- ExamView Assessment Suite
- Classroom Presentation Toolkit
- Advance Tracker

Student Tech Tools
- StudentWorks Plus
- **Math Online** eGlossary •
- Concepts in Motion

Other Print Products
- Investigation Notebook and Reflection Journal
- Quick Review Math Handbook

Introduce

Vocabulary Take time to discuss the meaning of the word *equation*. Students have probably already used this word. Make clear that an equation is a mathematical sentence that uses the equal sign (=) to state that two quantities have the same value.

Explore

Suggested Grouping: Groups of 3 or 4

▶ **Prepare** Read through the rules and examine the sample equations with the class. Tell students that the square root operation is allowed. In order to include squaring, the number 2 must be among the numbers that you call out, since students will need to use 2 as an exponent.

▶ **Play** Give students 5 minutes to work individually on creating equations. Then have them compare equations. Ask each group to come up with a list of five equations that they think no one else wrote. These can be equations that students developed individually or new equations from the group.

▶ **Report** Have a reporter from each group share the group's equations with the class. Look for duplication among groups. Discuss any equations that are particularly creative (using parentheses, complex fractions, and so on). Be sure that the quantities joined by the equal sign represent quantities that have the same value.

▶ **Score** If you want to keep score as added motivation, you can give each group one point for an equation that is not on another group's list. The equation must be a true equation that meets all the rules of the game.

Understand Equations

Vocabulary

equation

Math Link

The equals sign was first used by Robert Recorde in his book, *Whetstone of Witte*, published in 1557. Recorde states that he chose parallel line segments of equal length because "no two things can be more equal."

You have been working with equations for many years. An **equation** is a mathematical sentence stating that two quantities have the same value. An equals sign, =, is used to separate the two quantities. Here are three examples of equations.

$$9 + 6 = 15 \qquad 9 + 6 = 5 \cdot 3 \qquad 7 + 5 = 15 - 3$$

Explore

In the game *Equation Challenge*, you will see how many equations you can make using a given set of numbers.

Equation Challenge Rules

• Your teacher will call out seven single-digit numbers. Write the numbers on a sheet of paper. (Note: Your teacher may call the same number more than once. For example, the numbers might be 1, 2, 5, 3, 4, 9, and 3.)

• You have five minutes to write down as many correct equations as you can. Use only the seven numbers, an equals sign, operation symbols, decimal points, and parentheses. Follow these guidelines when writing your equations.

  — Use each of the seven numbers only once in each equation.

  — You do not need to use all the numbers in each equation.

  — You can combine the numbers to make numbers with more than one digit. For example, you could combine 1 and 2 to make 12, 21, 1.2, or $\frac{1}{2}$.

• Check your equations to make sure they are correct.

Here are some sample equations for the numbers 1, 2, 5, 3, 4, 9, and 3.

$$9 + 5 = 14 \qquad \frac{35 + 1}{4} = 9 \qquad 9 \cdot 5 = 3 \cdot 3 \cdot (4 + 1)$$

Play *Equation Challenge*. Be creative when writing your equations.

 Assessment

Some groups may propose equations that seem to fit the rules of the game but do not to work because students have misapplied the order of operations. If that is the case, it would probably be a good idea to conduct a brief review of the order of operations rules.

Investigation 1 Equations and Inequalities

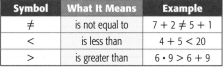

Vocabulary

inequality

An *equation* is a mathematical sentence stating that two quantities have the same value. A mathematical sentence stating that two quantities have *different* values is called an **inequality**. Inequalities use the symbols ≠, <, and >. The table below explains these symbols.

Symbol	What It Means	Example
≠	is not equal to	$7 + 2 \neq 5 + 1$
<	is less than	$4 + 5 < 20$
>	is greater than	$6 \cdot 9 > 6 + 9$

Just as sentences with words can be true or false, so can equations and inequalities. Consider these six sentences.

Stop signs are yellow. $4 = 32 \div 8$

The sun is hot. $5 \cdot 6 > 6 \cdot 5$

Alaska is south of Texas. $5 \cdot 4 = 27 - 3$

Think & Discuss

Which of the sentences above are true? Which are false?
"$4 = 32 \div 8$" and "The sun is hot" are true. The rest are false.
Find a way to make each false sentence true by changing or adding just one word, symbol, or number.   See ①.

✓ Develop & Understand: A 1–10. See margin.

The sentences below are false. Make each sentence true by changing one symbol or number.

1. $17 + 5 < 3^2 + 12$ **2.** $14 + 5 = 12 + 11$

3. $23 - 11 = 22 \div 2$ **4.** $6 \cdot 5 > (4 \cdot 7) + 8$

Tell whether each sentence is true or false. If it is false, make it true by replacing the equals sign with < or >.

5. $5 + 13 = 2 + 4^2 + 3$ **6.** $7 + (2 \cdot 3) = (6 \cdot 2) + 1$

7. $24 \div 5 = 2 + 3$ **8.** $\frac{2}{5} = \frac{1}{2}$

9. $0.25 = \frac{1}{4}$ **10.** $8 + 12 \div 4 = (8 + 12) \div 4$

① Possible answers:
Stop signs are red.
Yield signs are yellow.
Stop signs are not yellow.
$5 \cdot 6 = 6 \cdot 5$.
$5 \cdot 6 > 6 + 5$.
Alaska is north of Texas. Mexico is south of Texas. Alaska is not south of Texas.
$6 \cdot 4 = 27 - 3$.
$5 \cdot 4 = 27 - 7$.
$5 \cdot 4 < 27 - 3$.

Lesson 9.1 Understand Equations   **535**

Additional Answers

1. Possible answers: $17 + 5 > 3^2 + 12$, $17 + 5 > 3^2 + 20$

2. Possible answers: $14 + 5 < 12 + 11$, $14 + 5 = 12 + 7$

3. Possible answers: $23 - 11 \neq 22 \div 2$, $23 - 11 > 22 \div 2$

4. Possible answers: $6 \cdot 5 < (4 \cdot 7) + 8$, $6 \cdot 10 > (4 \cdot 7) + 8$

5. false, $5 + 13 < 2 + 4^2 + 3$

6. true

7. false, $24 \div 5 < 2 + 3$

8. false, $\frac{2}{5} < \frac{1}{2}$

9. true

10. false, $8 + 12 \div 4 > (8 + 12) \div 4$

Investigation 1

On Your Own Exercises
Pages 541–545
Exercises 1–9, 24–27

True or False? In this investigation, students explore the idea that equations and other number sentences can be true or false. This idea can be puzzling to students. Since $7 - 4$ does not give the same number as $8 - 3$, we do not usually write $7 - 4 = 8 - 3$ because it is a false statement.

Help students understand that the mathematical meaning of the word equation is based on the syntax, or form, of the mathematical statement rather than the truth or falsity of the statement. In the example above, $7 - 4 = 8 - 3$ is an equation (two number expressions with the equal sign between them), even though it is a false statement.

Analyze the Table Similar considerations apply to mathematical statements that use symbols of inequality (≠, <, and >).

Think & Discuss

Some students may see that a false equation can easily be made into a true statement by replacing the = symbol with the ≠ symbol.

Point out that another way to change a false equation into a true equation is to change one or both of the number expressions.

✓ Develop & Understand: A

Suggested Grouping: Individuals

▶ **Exercises 1–4** Make sure students change only one number or symbol.

▶ **Exercise 5** Watch for students who incorrectly evaluate $2 + 4^2 + 3$. Some students may compute 4^2 as 8 rather than 16.

▶ **Exercise 10** Students who say that the equation is true have probably misapplied the order of operations rules in evaluating $8 + 12 \div 4$. You may need to remind them that the division should be done before the addition.

Lesson 9.1 Understand Equations   **535**

Use these questions to see whether students understand that the *form* of the number sentence that determines whether the sentence is an equation or an inequality. For **Exercise 1**, look for students who say that an inequality is a false equation.

For **Exercise 2**, the example and explanation are important. Students sometimes conclude that a false equation can be made into a true sentence by replacing the equal sign with any one of the inequality symbols. The symbol ≠ will always work, and one of the < and > symbols will work if the equal sign is the only item changed in the original sentence.

Investigation ②

On Your Own Exercises
Pages 541–545
Exercises 10–23, 28–34

Variables In this investigation, students learn that equations or inequalities that contain variables are called open sentences. Replacing the variable in an open equation with a specific value leads to an equation that contains only numbers. The truth or falsity of this new equation can be decided. The values of the variable that result in a true equation are the solutions of the equation.

Think & Discuss

The key idea for students to understand is that an open sentence is not true or false. However you may be able to change it into a true sentence by replacing the variable with the right number. Discuss that only one number will make each of these open sentences true.

Additional Answer for Share & Summarize

1. An equation states that two quantities have the same value. An equation uses an equal sign between the two quantities. For example, $8 + 8 = 4^2$ is an equation since both sides have a value of 16. An inequality is a mathematical sentence that uses ≠, <, or > to state that two quantities are not equal. For example, $7 + 8 < 7 \cdot 8$ is an inequality.

Share & Summarize

1. Explain the difference between an equation and an inequality. Give an example of each. See margin.

2. Give an example of an equation or an inequality that is false. Then explain how you could change the sentence to make it true.
   Possible answer: $4 \cdot 3 = 6 + 5$ is false because the left side has a value of 12 and the right side has a value of 11. You could make the sentence true by replacing = with >.

Investigation ② Equations with Variables

Vocabulary

open sentence
solution

You can determine whether the equations in Investigation 1 are true by finding the value of each side. But what if an equation contains a variable? For example, consider this equation.

$$3 \cdot n = 18$$

You cannot tell whether this equation is true or false unless you know the value of n. An equation or inequality that can be true or false depending on the value of the variable is called an **open sentence**.

Think & Discuss

For each open sentence, find a value of n that makes it true. Then find a value of n that makes it false.

$3 \cdot n = 18$ $n \div 2 = 2.5$ $n + 5 = 25$
6, any other value   5, any other value   20, any other value

Finding the values of the variable or variables that make an equation true is called *solving* the equation. A value that makes an equation true is a **solution** of the equation. Consider this equation.

$$6 \cdot n - 1 = 29$$

Finding a solution of $6 \cdot n - 1 = 29$ is the same as answering the following question.

For what value of n is $6 \cdot n - 1$ equal to 29?

Math Link
These are three ways to write "6 times."

$6 \times n$ $6 \cdot n$ $6n$

Mathematical Background

Open sentences in mathematics always contain one or more variables. It is sometimes helpful to think of variables as being analogous to indefinite pronouns in English. Compare the following:

He loves her.
$x = y + 4$

The English sentence is neither true nor false, but it will become so if you replace the pronouns with the names of specific individuals. Likewise, the equation is neither true nor false, but it will become so if you "close" the sentence by replacing x and y with specific numbers.

Jing tried several values for n. Here is what she found:

n	$6 \cdot n - 1$	Test	Solution?
3	17	$6 \cdot n - 1 < 29$	no
4	23	$6 \cdot n - 1 < 29$	no
5	29	$6 \cdot n - 1 = 29$	yes
6	35	$6 \cdot n - 1 > 29$	no
7	41	$6 \cdot n - 1 > 29$	no
8	47	$6 \cdot n - 1 > 29$	no

Jing found that 5 is a solution of $6 \cdot n - 1 = 29$ since $6 \cdot 5 - 1 = 29$. The results kept increasing as n increased, so she concluded that 5 must be the only solution.

✓ Develop & Understand: A

Each of these equations has one solution. Solve each equation.

1. $6 \cdot n - 1 = 41$ 7

2. $6 \cdot n - 1 = 11$ 2

3. $2p + 7 = 19$ 6

4. $4 + 4 \cdot b = 20$ 4

5. $\frac{5}{4} = \frac{25}{d}$ 20

6. $m + 3 = 2m$ 3

7. Try the numbers 1, 2, 3, 4 in the equation $2 \cdot d + 3 = 15 - 2 \cdot d$ to test whether any of them is a solution.   3 is a solution.

8. Write three equations with a solution of 13. Check that your equations are correct by substituting 13 for the variable.
Possible answer: $t + 1 = 14$, $t \cdot 2 = 30 - 4$, $26 \div t = 2$

All of the equations you have seen so far have one solution. It is possible for an equation to have more than one solution or to have no solution at all.

For some equations, every number is a solution. Such equations are always true, no matter what the values of the variables are.

Math Link
Equations with squared variables, for example, $m^2 - 3m = 0$, are called *quadratic equations*. They can be used to describe the path in which a projectile travels.

Think & Discuss

Equations that include a squared variable often have two solutions. Find two solutions for the equation $m^2 - 3m = 0$.   0 and 3

Explain why each equation below is always true.

$$n + 3 = 3 + n \qquad a \cdot 5 = a + a + a + a + a$$

Changing the order in which two numbers are added does not change the sum.

Multiplying a number by 5 is the same as adding the number 5 times.

Lesson 9.1   Understand Equations   **537**

Reaching All Learners

OL **On Level** If students are confused about why m, n, and a must have the same value on both sides of the equation, explain that these equations could also be written using empty shapes instead of letter variables. This would give the following equations:

$$\square^2 - 3\,\square = 0$$

$$0 + 3 = 3 + 0$$

$$\triangle \cdot 5 = \triangle + \triangle + \triangle + \triangle + \triangle$$

Analyze the Table Discuss the table at the top of the page to help students understand why Jing was convinced that $6 \cdot n - 1 = 29$ has one and only one solution.

✓ Develop & Understand: A

Suggested Grouping: Pairs

▶ **Exercises 1–6** Students are told that each equation has only one solution. Call on volunteers for each problem. Trial-and-error is a perfectly acceptable approach. Some student may have used reasoning. Ask students how they know their solutions work. They should understand that replacing the variable with the solution must give a true equation. In Exercise 1, for example, a proof that 7 is a solution might proceed as follows. Replace n with 7 in $6 \cdot n - 1 = 41$. The resulting equation is $6 \cdot 7 - 1 = 41$. Since $6 \cdot 7 - 1 = 42 - 1$ and $42 - 1 = 41$, the open sentence $6 \cdot n - 1 = 41$ is true when $n = 7$.

▶ **Exercise 7** Students replace d with each of the trial numbers. Try 1 in place of d. ($5 = 13$ False) Try 2 in place of d. ($7 = 11$ False) Try 3 in place of d. ($9 = 9$ True) Try 4 in place of d. ($11 = 7$ False)

The trial shows that only 3 is a solution of $2 \cdot d + 3 = 15 - 2 \cdot d$.

Think & Discuss
Suggested Grouping: Pairs

Ask students to think about these questions with a partner before discussing them as a class. In all of these examples, it is important that students realize that if a variable appears in an equation more than once, it must have the same value in each location. Thus, if students try the value 4 for m in the first equation, they must replace m with 4 in both places where m occurs. The same is true for n and a in the second and third equations.

Math Link

Students may need to see how the path of a projectile looks. Have students draw possible paths on the board and discuss them.

▶ **Exercises 9–15** Point out that there are open equations that are true for only a few values of the variable or for no values of the variable.

▶ **Exercise 9** Students will probably try each of the values of t given in the exercise. You may want to ask students if they think there are values other than 2 and 4 that are solutions. Making a table of values for $t^2 + 8$ and for $6 \cdot t$ is a good way to think about this question. A table of values will probably convince students that if there are any other solutions, they are not greater than 4, because the value of $t^2 + 8$ appears to be increasing more rapidly than the value of $6 \cdot t$ when t is greater than 4.

▶ **Exercises 10–15** Encourage students to think about what each equation means. For example, in Exercise 10, students might ask, "Is there some number I could subtract from it to get 0?" A moment's thought should lead them to answer, "Sure, that works for every number. So the equation is always true."

▶ **Exercise 14** A table of values for $n \cdot 2$ and $n + 1$ can make it clear that when the value of n is greater than one, doubling will give a greater number than adding one. You may want to ask students if they can use reasoning to see why this is so.

▶ **Exercise 15** Point out the use of the distributive property.

Share & Summarize

Use these exercises to assess how well students understand the concept of the solution of an open equation. You may want to call on volunteers to read their answers to each question. Use a class discussion of the answers to focus on the main ideas of the investigation.

Additional Answers

13. Always true; finding $\frac{1}{7}$ of a number is the same as dividing the number by 7.

14. Sometimes true; the equation is true when n is 1 but not when n is 2 (or any other value).

---

10. Always true; when you subtract a number from itself, the result is 0.

11. Sometimes true; the equation is true when r is 0 but not when r is 1 or any other value.

12. Never true; if you add 7 to a number, you always get a greater result than when you subtract 7 from the number.

13–15. See margin.

Real-World Link

In *meteorology*, the science of weather, an equals sign represents fog.

. . . .

1. 2; Possible explanation: I tried $p = 1$ and saw that the left side was less than 11. So, I tried $p = 2$ and it worked.

---

9. Try the values 1, 2, 3, and 4 to test whether any are solutions of this equation. 2 and 4 are solutions.

$$t^2 + 8 = 6 \cdot t$$

Tell whether each equation below is always true, sometimes true, or never true. Explain how you know.

10. $m - m = 0$

11. $\frac{r}{3} = r$

12. $q + 7 = q - 7$

13. $p \div 7 = \frac{1}{7} \cdot p$

14. $n \cdot 2 = n + 1$

15. $(a + 3) \cdot 2 = 2a + 6$

16. Which number is a solution to the equation below? d

$$5n + 7 = 27$$

　a. 1　　　b. 2　　　c. 3　　　d. 4

17. Which number is a solution to the equation below? c

$$t^2 + 3 = 12$$

　a. 1　　　b. 2　　　c. 3　　　d. 4

18. Which equation does **not** have at least one solution? c

　a. $4x + 3 = 16$　　　b. $5m - 2 = 28$

　c. $3y - 1 = 3y + 1$　　d. $n^2 - 2 = 23$

19. Which equation is true for all values of d? d

　a. $5d - 2 = 8$　　　b. $5d + 2 = 20$

　c. $5d \div 4 = 5d \cdot 2$　　d. $5d + 1 = 5d + 1$

20. **Challenge** Tell whether each equation has a whole-number solution. Explain how you know. See margin.

　a. $2 \cdot n - 1 = 37$　　b. $2n + 1 = 18$

　c. $3 \cdot n + 5 = n + 7$　　d. $n^2 + 2 = 1$

Share & Summarize

1. Solve the equation $3p + 5 = 11$. Explain how you found the solution.

2. Give an example of an equation that is always true and an example of an equation that is never true. Possible answer: $\frac{1}{2} \cdot x = x \div 2$ is always true. $x + 10 < x$ is never true.

---

15. Always true; $(a + 3) \cdot 2$ is the same as $(a + 3) + (a + 3)$, which is the same as $a + a + 3 + 3$, or $2a + 6$.

20a. Yes; this has a whole-number solution of 19.

20b. no; Possible explanation: If n is a whole number, then $2n$ must be an even number and $2n + 1$ must be an odd number. So, $2n + 1$ can never equal 18.

20c. Yes; this has a whole-number solution of 1.

20d. no; Possible explanation: If n is a whole number, then n^2 must be greater than or equal to 0, so $n^2 + 2$ must be greater than or equal to 2.

Inquiry

Investigation ③ Instructions and Directions

Materials

- 1 red block and 1 blue block
- 1 yellow counter and 1 green counter
- Lompoc, California, street map

In this investigation, you will practice "undoing" sets of instructions. In Lesson 9.2, you will see how the strategies used in this investigation can help you solve equations.

Undoing Instructions

Starting with a blank sheet of paper, follow these instructions.

- Draw a small X (in pencil) in the center of the paper.
- Put the red block on the X.
- Put the yellow counter on the red block.
- Put the blue block on the yellow counter.
- Put the green counter on the blue block.

1. Write a list of steps that you think would undo these instructions, leaving you with a blank sheet of paper. Do not touch any of the items on the paper until you have finished writing your instructions.

2. Follow your steps from Question 1. Did your steps undo the above instructions? If not, rewrite them until they do.   Answers will vary.

3. How do your steps compare with the original set of steps?

Reversing Directions

Madeline lives in Lompoc, California, on the corner of Nectarine Avenue and R Street. Today, she met her friend T.J. at the town pool. T.J. had given her these directions to get to the pool.

- Start at the corner of Nectarine Avenue and R Street.
- Walk 2 blocks east along Nectarine Avenue.
- Turn right from Nectarine Avenue onto O Street.
- Walk 4 blocks south on O Street.
- Turn left from O Street onto Maple Avenue.
- Walk 5 blocks east on Maple Avenue.
- Turn right from Maple Avenue onto J Street.
- Walk 4 blocks south on J Street.
- Turn left from J Street onto Ocean Avenue.
- Walk 7 blocks east on Ocean Avenue.
- The pool is at the corner of Ocean Avenue and C Street.

1. • Remove the green counter.
   • Remove the blue block.
   • Remove the yellow counter.
   • Remove the red block.
   • Erase the X.

3. Possible answer: In my steps, the items are removed. In the original steps, the items are placed on the other items. The order in which items are removed is the reverse of the order in which they were added.

Go on ▶

Lesson 9.1 Understand Equations   **539**

Inquiry

Investigation ③

Suggested Grouping: Pairs

Materials and Preparation

Each pair of students will need one red block, one blue block, one yellow counter, and one green counter. They will also need a copy of Lesson 9.1 Master 1.

Undoing Instructions

Students should follow the instructions in this first part of the investigation. Exercise 1 is intended to make students think about how to undo the instructions before they actually attempt the steps. They can refer to the printed instructions they used to stack the blocks and counters. Most students will probably prefer to simply look at the stack and imagine disassembling it from the top down.

For Exercise 3, students should observe that there should be five steps in the "undoing" procedure, just as there were in the original instructions.

Reversing Directions

Each student should have a copy of the map on Lesson 9.1 Master 1. Point out that streets running east-west have names preceded by E or W (for example W Chestnut Ave and E Chestnut Ave) while streets running north-south have names preceded by N or S (for example, N K St and S K St). If necessary, point out how students can tell from the map which direction to move to go east, west, north, or south.

Instructions that say turn left or turn right may be troublesome for some students. You may want to point out that the very next instruction will help them know that they turned the correct way, because it tells them whether they are then headed north, south, east, or west.

Have students follow the directions on this page to confirm that the directions will indeed get them from the starting point to the pool.

Lesson 9.1 Understand Equations   **539**

▶ **Exercise 4** Students may find it helpful to check the directions on page 539 and imagine how to reverse each step. They will need to keep in mind that an instruction such as "walk 7 blocks west" is the opposite of "walk 7 blocks east."

▶ **Exercise 6** Students need to understand that a "turn left" or "turn right" instruction is best followed by a statement telling which direction you are headed after the turn. In many real-life situations, it can be difficult operating without a map, but with a map of a city that contains east-west and north-south streets, knowing the compass direction makes it easier.

What Did You Learn?

▶ **Exercise 9** This exercise gives students an opportunity to think about how to undo instructions. You may want to have a class discussion of what students have learned.

Real-World Link

The science of making maps is called "cartography."

Additional Answers

4. • Start at the corner of Ocean Avenue and C Street.
   • Walk 7 blocks west on Ocean Avenue.
   • Turn right from Ocean Avenue onto J Street.
   • Walk 4 blocks north on J Street.
   • Turn left from J Street onto Maple Avenue.
   • Walk 5 blocks west on Maple Avenue.
   • Turn right from Maple Avenue onto O Street.
   • Walk 4 blocks north on O Street.
   • Turn left from O Street onto Nectarine Avenue.
   • Walk 2 blocks west along Nectarine Avenue.
   • Your house is at the corner of Nectarine Avenue and R Street.

Real-World Link

It is believed that humans have been making maps since prehistoric times. Archaeologists have discovered systems of lines drawn on cave walls and bone tablets that may be maps of hunting trails made by prehistoric peoples.

Now Madeline must reverse the directions to get home.

4. Without looking at the map, write a set of directions Madeline could follow to get home from the pool.   See margin.

5. On the street map, carefully follow the directions that you wrote in Question 4. Do you end up at the corner of Nectarine Avenue and R Street? If not, make changes to your directions until they work.   Answers will vary.

6. Write a set of directions to get from one place on the map to another. Word your steps like those on page 539.
   • When you describe a turn, mention the street where you start, whether you turn left or right, and the street where you end.
   • When you describe a walk along a street, mention the number of blocks, the direction, and the street name in which you walked.

When you are finished, try your directions to make sure they are accurate.   Directions will vary.

7. Exchange directions with your partner. Without looking at the map, write the steps that reverse your partner's directions. Then use the street map to test your directions.   Answers will vary.

8. Describe some general strategies that you find useful when reversing a set of directions.   See margin.

What Did You Learn?

9. In this investigation, you undid two types of instructions.
   • Steps for stacking blocks and counters
   • Directions for getting from one place to another

Describe how the methods that you used to undo the instructions in each case were similar.   Possible answer: In each case, you undo the actions in the reverse order.

8. Possible answer: Start with the last step in the original directions and work toward the first step. Change east to west, west to east, north to south, and south to north. Change left turns to right turns and right turns to left turns, and change the order of the streets. For example, change a left turn from 1st Street onto 2nd Street into a right turn from 2nd Street onto 1st Street.

Practice & Apply

1. Possible answer:
$5 + 5 + 2 = 12$,
$5 \div 2 = 2.5$, $\frac{1}{2} = \frac{2}{4}$,
$5 + 4 - 2 = 9 - 2$,
$(9 - 5) \div 4 = 2 \div 2$

3. Possible answers:
$8 \cdot 5 = 17 + 16 + 7$,
$8 \cdot 4 \neq 17 + 16 + 7$

5. false, $(3 \cdot 5) + 4 >$
$4 + 5 + 1$

Real-World Link
The solution to the equation in Exercise 10, $x \cdot 12 = 48$, is the number of 12-egg cartons needed to hold four dozen eggs.

16. Always true; both sides are equal to $5 \cdot m$ since $\frac{25 \cdot m}{5}$ $= \frac{25}{5} \cdot m = 5 \cdot m$.

17. Sometimes true; the equation is true for $s = 5$ but not for $s = 25$ or any other value of s.

Explore In a round of the game *Equation Challenge,* the numbers 1, 2, 2, 4, 5, 5, and 9 were called.

1. Make at least four equations using these numbers.

In Exercises 2 and 3, the sentence is not true. Change or add one number or symbol to make it true.

2. $5 + 16 = 3 \cdot 8$ **3.** $8 \cdot 5 \neq 17 + 16 + 7$

2. Possible answers: $5 + 16 < 3 \cdot 8$, $5 + 16 = 3 \cdot 7$

In Exercises 4–9, tell whether the sentence is true or false. If it is false, make it true by replacing the equals sign with < or >.

4. $3 \cdot 11 = 42 - 9$ true   **5.** $(3 \cdot 5) + 4 = 4 + 5 + 1$

6. $\frac{1}{3} + \frac{4}{6} = \frac{3}{7} + \frac{16}{28}$ true   **7.** $0.95 = \frac{9}{10}$ false, $0.95 > \frac{9}{10}$

8. $3 \cdot 13 = 54 - 16$ **9.** $16 - 8 \div 4 = (16 - 8) \div 4$
false, $3 \cdot 13 > 54 - 16$ false, $16 - 8 \div 4 > (16 - 8) \div 4$

Solve each equation.

10. $x \cdot 12 = 48$ 4   **11.** $56 + m = 100$ 44

12. $6p + 10 = 28$ 3   **13.** $50 - 4 \cdot z = 30$ 5

14. Consider the equations $s + 13 = 20$ and $p + 13 = 20$.

  a. Solve each equation.   7, 7

  b. How do the solutions to the two equations compare? Explain why this makes sense.   See margin.

15. Test the values 0, 1, 3, 4, and 6 to see whether any are solutions of $7m - m^2 + 10 = 16$.   1, 6

Tell whether each equation is always true, sometimes true, or never true. Explain how you know.

16. $5 \cdot m = \frac{25 \cdot m}{5}$ **17.** $5s = 25$

18. $t - 1 = t + 1$ **19.** $p^2 = p \cdot p$

20. $n + 6 = 7 \div n$ **21.** $7p = p \div 7$

22. Write three equations with a solution of 3.5.

18. Never true; the result of subtracting 1 from a number is always less than the result of adding 1 to the number.

19. Always true; a number squared is equal to the number times itself.

20. Sometimes true; the equation is true for $n = 1$ but not for $n = 7$ or any other value of n.

21–22. See margin.

Investigation 1
Pages 535–536
Practice & Apply: 1–9
Connect & Extend 24–27

Investigation 2
Pages 536–538
Practice & Apply: 10–23
Connect & Extend: 28–34

Assign Anytime
Mixed Review: 35–38

▶ **Exercise 11** Students can try several values of m until they find the one that works, or they can use the related subtraction equation $m = 100 - 56$.

▶ **Exercise 16** To explain why the equation is always true, students may find it helpful to rewrite the fraction $\frac{25 \cdot m}{5}$ as $\frac{25}{5} \cdot m$. Since $\frac{25}{5} = 5$, the expression $\frac{25 \cdot m}{5}$ becomes $5 \cdot m$.

Additional Answers

14b. The solutions are the same because, except for the letter used to represent the variable, the equations are identical. The letter used to represent a variable does not affect the solution.

21. Sometimes true; the equation is true for $p = 0$ but not for $p = 7$ (or any other value of p).

22. Possible answer: $2t = 7$, $7 - t = 3.5$, $14 \div t = 4$.

▶ **Exercise 23c** Students are often inclined to test only whole numbers when they look for solutions. You may need to remind them that the solution might be a fraction.

▶ **Exercise 24** Students can connect the questions in this exercise with their work on solving equations by substituting each output for the variable *o* and then solving for *i*.

23. Of these three equations, one has no solution, one has one solution, and one has two solutions. Decide which is which, and find the solutions.

a. $p^2 + 6 = 5 \cdot p$ Two solutions, 2 and 3

b. $3p + 5 = 3p - 5$ No solutions

c. $4 \cdot p + 5 = 7$ One solution, $\frac{1}{2}$

Connect & Extend   **24. What's My Rule?** Isabela and Jada were playing a game of *What's My Rule*. Here is Isabela's secret rule.

$o = 37 - 4 \cdot i$, where *o* is the output and *i* is the input

a. What input value gives an output of 17? Check your answer by substituting it into the rule.   5

b. What input value gives an output of 5? Check your answer.   8

c. What input value gives an output of 0? Check your answer. $\frac{37}{4}$

25. Pretend you are playing a game of *What's My Rule*. Make up a secret rule for calculating an output value from an input value. Your rule should use one or two operations.   Answers will vary.

a. Write your rule in symbols.

b. Find the input value for which your rule gives an output of 25.

c. Find the input value for which your rule gives an output of 11.

26. Paul and Katarina were playing a game of *What's My Rule*. Here is Katarina's secret rule.

$m = \frac{n}{10}$, where *n* is the input and *m* is the output

a. Write an equation to find the input value that gives an output of 1.5. $\frac{n}{10} = 1.5$

b. Solve your equation from Part a to find the input value *n*.   15

c. Write an equation to find the input value that gives an output of 20. $\frac{n}{10} = 20$

d. Solve your equation from Part c to find the input value *n*.   200

27. In Your Own Words Explain the meaning of equation, inequality, open sentence, and solution.   Answers will vary.

Balancing Equations You can think of an equation as a balanced scale. The scale at right represents the equation $3 \cdot 5 = 9 + 6$. The scale is balanced because both sides have the same value.

The second scale represents the equation $4 + n = 10$. To solve this equation, you need to find the value of n that will make the scale balance.

In Exercises 28–32, you will solve puzzles involving scales. Thinking about these puzzles may give you some ideas for solving equations.

28. This scale is balancing bags of peanuts and boxes of popcorn.

a. How many bags of peanuts will balance one box of popcorn?   2

b. If a bag of peanuts weighs 5 ounces, how much does a box of popcorn weigh?   10 oz

29. Consider this scale.

a. Write the equation this scale represents.
$n + n = 10$, or $2n = 10$
b. What number will balance one n?   5

▶ **Exercise 28** In **Part a**, students should see that removing one bag of peanuts and two boxes of popcorn from each side of the scale would leave the scale in balance.

Students can use their answer from Part a to find the answer to **Part b**.

Lesson 9.1 Understand Equations   **543**

▶ **Exercise 31** In **Part a**, students can imagine removing half the contents of each pan of the second scale to discover that two jacks balance one marble. Therefore, the marble in the left pan of the first scale can be replaced with two jacks. This shows that three jacks balance one block. In the course of getting the answer for Part a, the students will also get the answer for **Part b**.

▶ **Exercise 32** In **Part a**, one can combine the contents of the left pans of the scales on the left side of the first scale and then combine the contents of the right pans on the right side of the first scale. Remove two blocks and one spring from each side of the first scale to find that four marbles balance one spring.

For **Part b**, use the result from Part a. On the first scale, replace the two springs with eight marbles. Then remove three marbles from each side to find that one block balances five marbles.

Some students may see how to write and manipulate equations to answer both parts.

In Exercises 30–32, refer to the information on page 543.

30. Consider this scale.

30a. $b + 7 = b + b$, or $b + 7 = 2b$

  a. Write the equation this scale represents.
  b. What number will balance one b?   7

31. These two scales hold jacks, marbles, and a block.

  a. How many jacks will balance the block?   3
  b. How many jacks will balance one marble?   2
  c. If the block weighs 15 grams, how much does a jack weigh? How much does a marble weigh?   5 g, 10 g

32. Challenge These scales hold blocks, springs, and marbles.

  a. How many marbles will balance one spring?   4

  b. If a marble weighs 1 ounce, how much does a spring weigh? How much does a block weigh?   4 oz, 5 oz

Real-World Link

There are no negative temperatures on the Kelvin scale. The term "absolute zero" is equivalent to 0 Kelvin. It is thought to be the temperature at which all movement, including the motion of molecules and atoms, completely stops.

Mixed Review

33c. Mercury; Possible explanation: The mean temperature on Mercury is much greater than the maximum temperature on Mars.

35a. Mean: $15.\overline{4}$; median: 17; mode: 20

33. Science You are familiar with the Fahrenheit and Celsius temperature scales. The Kelvin scale is a temperature scale that is used frequently in science. This equation shows how Kelvin temperatures K are related to Celsius temperatures C.

$$K = C + 273$$

a. The mean surface temperature on Mercury is about 180°C. Express this temperature in Kelvins.   453 K

b. The maximum surface temperature on Mars is about 290 Kelvin. Express this temperature in degrees Celsius.   17°C

c. Which planet is hotter, Mercury or Mars? Explain your answer.

34. Economics The unit of currency in South Africa is the rand. In November 2007, one U.S. dollar was worth about 6.48 rand. This relationship can be expressed as an equation, where R stands for the number of rand and D stands for the number of dollars.

$$6.48 \cdot D = R$$

a. On that day, Jacob exchanged $75 for rand. How many rand did he receive?   486

b. Jacob wanted to buy a small statue that cost 20 rand. He thought this was about $3.08. His sister thought it was about $129.60. Who was correct? Explain your answer.   Jacob; Possible explanation: 6.48 · 3.08 is about 19.96, so $3.08 is about 20 rand.

35. Statistics Jaleesa received the following scores on her 20-point spelling quizzes.

| 20 | 15 | 18 | 19 | 20 | 0 | 14 | 17 | 16 |

a. Find the mean, median, and mode of her scores.

b. Which measure of center do you think best represents Jaleesa's typical quiz score? Give reasons for your choice.   See margin.

c. Jaleesa's teacher has agreed to drop each student's lowest score. Drop the lowest score. Compute the new mean, median, and mode of Jaleesa's scores.   See margin.

Find the indicated percentage.

36. 50% of 12   6

37. 25% of 12   3

38. 75% of 12   9

Lesson 9.1 Understand Equations   **545**

Additional Answers

35b. Possible answer: The median; the mode is the highest score, and it does not reflect the lower scores. The mean seems a little low; it was influenced by the score of 0. The median seems like the best average. Except for the 0, most of the scores are close to 17.

35c. Mean: 17.375; median: 17.5; mode: 20

Quick Check

Informal Assessment Students should be able to:

✔ decide whether a number sentence is true or false

✔ use the symbols =, >, and > to write true number sentences

✔ use trial-and-error to find solutions of equations

Quick Quiz

1. Make at least two true equations using the numbers 2, 3, 3, 4, 6, 7, and 9.
   Possible answers: $6 - 2 = 9 - 4 + 3 + 3 - 7$, $(3 \cdot 3) \div 9 + 2 = 4 - (7 - 6)$, $3^2 + (4 - 3) = 9 + 7 - 6$

2. Tell whether each equation is true or false. If it is false, make it true by replacing the equal sign with < or >.
   a. 13 - 3 · 3 = 30 False; $13 - 3 \cdot 3 < 30$
   b. $8 + 3^2 = 27 - 10$ True
   c. $8 \div 4 - 2 = 8 - (5 - 3)$ False; $8 \div 4 - 2 < 8 - (5 - 3)$
   d. $5 \cdot 4 + 7 = 56 \div 8$ False; $5 \cdot 4 + 7 > 56 \div 8$

3. Solve each equation.
   a. $4 \cdot x = 28$ 7
   b. $n + 15 = 20$ 5
   c. $3 \cdot k + 7 = 13$ 2
   d. $8x = x^2 + 15$ (There are two solutions.) 3, 5

4. Tell whether each equation is *always true*, *sometimes true*, or *never true*. Explain how you know.
   a. $p + 4 = 7 + p$ Never true; 7 is greater than 4, so the sum of 7 and p is always greater than the sum of p and 4.
   b. $m^2 + 9 = 13$ Sometimes true; the equation is true for $m = 2$, but it is not true for $m = 1$.
   c. $7x = 5x + 2x$ Always true; $5x + 2x = (x + x + x + x + x) + (x + x)$, and the sum of seven x's can be written as $7 \cdot x$, or $7x$.

Lesson 9.1 Understand Equations   **545**

Backtracking

Overview

In this lesson, students learn to solve equations by working backward, a technique called *backtracking*. First, they learn to make flowcharts to represent rules and equations.

Then, they use these flowcharts to help them see how to backtrack. They apply their new skills to solve many types of equations in which the variable appears only once. Ultimately, they write and solve equations for real-life situations.

Advance Preparation

No advance preparation is needed for this lesson.

	Summary	Materials	On Your Own Exercises (pp. 555–559)	Assessment Opportunities
Investigation 1 (p. 547) **Pacing:** 2 days	Students make and use flowcharts to represent rules, to find the output for a given input, and to find the input for a given output.		Practice & Apply: 1–6 Connect & Extend: 18 Mixed Review: 26–35	• Share & Summarize (p. 549) • Troubleshooting (p. 549)
Investigation 2 (p. 550) **Pacing:** 1 day	Students make and use flowcharts to solve equations by backtracking.		Practice & Apply: 7–13 Connect & Extend: 19, 20 Mixed Review: 26–35	• Share & Summarize (p. 552)
Investigation 3 (p. 552) **Pacing:** 1 day	Students write equations for real-life situations and use backtracking to solve the equations.		Practice & Apply: 14–17 Connect & Extend: 21–25 Mixed Review: 26–35	• Share & Summarize (p. 554) • Troubleshooting (p. 554)

Leveled Lesson Resources

Also on
TeacherWorks™
Lesson 9.2

CRM *Available in:* **Chapter 9 Resource Masters**

Study Guide and Intervention (p. 9) — AL

Lesson 9.2 Study Guide and Intervention
Backtracking

A process called backtracking can used to solve equations. In backtracking, an output is given and flowcharts are used to undo each operation to find the input.

Example 1 Use backtracking to find the input.

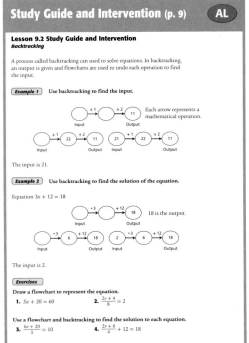

The input is 21.

Example 2 Use backtracking to find the solution of the equation.

Equation $3x + 12 = 18$

The input is 2.

Exercises

Draw a flowchart to represent the equation.

1. $5x + 20 = 60$
2. $\frac{2v + 4}{8} = 2$

Use a flowchart and backtracking to find the solution to each equation.

3. $\frac{6v + 20}{5} = 10$
4. $\frac{2v + 6}{4} + 12 = 18$

Skills Practice (p. 10) — AL OL

Lesson 9.2 Skills Practice
Backtracking

For each flowchart, write the equation that is being solved. Backtrack to find the solution. Be sure to check your solution.

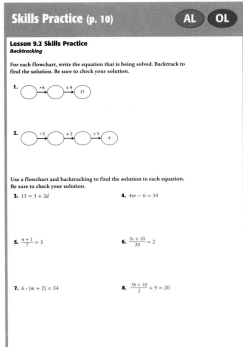

Use a flowchart and backtracking to find the solution to each equation. Be sure to check your solution.

3. $13 = 3 + 2d$
4. $4m - 6 = 34$

5. $\frac{n + 1}{7} = 3$
6. $\frac{5c + 10}{20} = 2$

7. $6 \cdot (m + 2) = 54$
8. $\frac{3b + 10}{2} + 9 = 20$

Problem-Solving Practice (p. 11) — AL OL

Lesson 9.2 Problem-Solving Practice
Backtracking

Solve.

1. **Dragons** The luck dragons that live in the enchanted forest weigh four times as much as their age in *x* years. Write an equation that could be used to find the age of a 24-pound luck dragon. Use backtracking to solve your equation. What is the age of the luck dragon?

2. **Roller coaster** Twelve people are able to ride the Serpent of Fire roller coaster at one time. Write an equation that could be used to find the number of rides *n* if 60 people have been on the roller coaster. Use backtracking to solve your equation. How many rides have there been?

3. **Car rental** A car rental company charges $25 a day plus $0.05 a mile. Write an equation that could be used to find the number of miles traveled *m* if the total cost is $27. Use backtracking to solve your equation. How many miles were traveled?

4. **School fair** The admission to the school fair is $2 and $0.25 for every game ticket. Samson spent $6.50 at the fair. Write an equation to determine the number of tickets *n* Samson bought. Use backtracking to solve your equation. How many tickets did Samson buy?

5. **Phone plan** A phone company charges $10 a month for a connection fee and $0.03 a minute for long-distance calls. Write an equation that could be used to find the number of long-distance minutes *m* used if last month's phone bill was $10.90. Use backtracking to solve your equation. How many long-distance minutes were used?

6. **Sailboat** At Saratoga Lake, you can rent a sailboat for $4 plus $2.50 an hour. Kyle and Sophia paid $16.50 for the rental. Write an equation that could be used to calculate the number of hours *n* that Kyle and Sophia rented the sailboat. Use backtracking to solve your equation. How many hours did they rent the sailboat?

Enrichment (p. 12) — BL

Lesson 9.2 Enrichment
Backtracking
Dot Patterns

Equations are often used to describe geometric patterns. In the pattern at the right, for example, do you see this relationship?

1st figure: $3 \cdot 1 = 3$ dots
2nd figure: $3 \cdot 2 = 6$ dots
3rd figure: $3 \cdot 3 = 9$ dots
4th figure: $3 \cdot 4 = 12$ dots

So the "*n*th" figure in this pattern would have $3 \cdot n$, or $3n$, dots. The number of *d* dots can be found by the equation, $d = 3n$. Backtracking can be used to find the number in the pattern given a certain number of dots.

Write an equation that could be used to find the number of dots *d* in the *n*th figure.

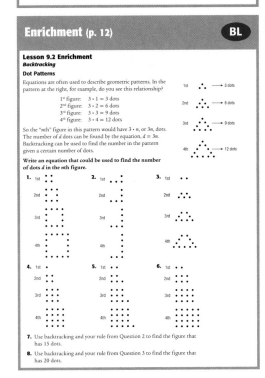

7. Use backtracking and your rule from Question 2 to find the figure that has 15 dots.

8. Use backtracking and your rule from Question 3 to find the figure that has 20 dots.

Lesson Quick Quiz (p. 13) — AL OL BL

Lesson 9.2 Quick Quiz
Backtracking

1. Write an equation for each flowchart. Use backtracking to solve the equation.

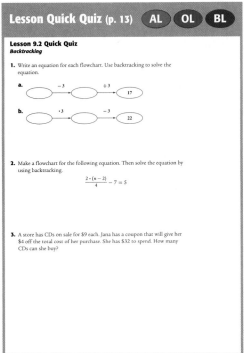

2. Make a flowchart for the following equation. Then solve the equation by using backtracking.

$$\frac{2 \cdot (n - 2)}{4} - 7 = 5$$

3. A store has CDs on sale for $9 each. Jana has a coupon that will give her $4 off the total cost of her purchase. She has $32 to spend. How many CDs can she buy?

Additional Lesson Resources

Teacher Tech Tools
- TeacherWorks
- ExamView Assessment Suite
- Classroom Presentation Toolkit
- Advance Tracker

Student Tech Tools
- StudentWorks Plus
- Math Online eGlossary •
- Concepts in Motion

Other Print Products
- Investigation Notebook and Reflection Journal
- Quick Review Math Handbook

Introduce

Backtracking In this lesson, students learn to solve equations by working backward, a technique called *backtracking*. First, they learn to make flowcharts to represent rules and equations. Then, they use these flowcharts to help them see how to backtrack. They apply their new skills to solve many types of equations in which the variable appears only once. Ultimately, they write and solve equations for real-life situations.

Have students read the introductory cartoon. Then have them work on the Think & Discuss.

Think & Discuss

In this Think & Discuss, students use the method illustrated in the cartoon to solve the equation $3n + 7 = 40$. This equation is like the one for the cartoon, except the output number is now 40 instead of 43. Discuss the fact that the method used in the cartoon works well with this new output.

Solving equations by working backward is an approach that many students find easy and intuitively natural. You may want to work through some additional examples, each time changing the output in Jay's equation. Any output greater than or equal to seven will do.

To wrap up your discussion of the Think & Discuss, point out that the technique used in the cartoon is called backtracking.

LESSON 9.2

Backtracking

Jay was playing *What's My Rule* with his friend Marla. He figured out that this was the rule.

To find the output, multiply the input by 3 and then add 7.

He wrote the rule in symbols, using n to represent the input and t to represent the output.

$$t = 3n + 7$$

Jay wanted to find the input that would give an output of 43. This is the same as solving the equation $3n + 7 = 43$.

Think & Discuss

Using Jay's rule, what input gives an output of 40?   11

Explain the reasoning you used to find the input. Check your answer by substituting it into the equation $3n + 7 = 40$. See ①.

Jay's method of solving $3n + 7 = 43$ involves working backward from the output value to find the input value. In this lesson, you will learn a technique for working backward called *backtracking*.

① Possible explanation: 3 times the input, plus 7, equals 40.
   So, there must have been 33 before 7 was added.
   That means 3 times the input equals 33.
   The input must be 11.

Investigation 1 Learn to Backtrack

Vocabulary
backtracking
flowchart

Real-World Link
Computer programmers and engineers use complex flowcharts to represent the steps in computer programs, manufacturing operations, construction projects, and other procedures.

Hannah's class was playing *What's My Rule*. Hannah found that the rule was $t = 4n + 5$, where n is the input and t is the output.

To find an output with this rule, you do the following.

Start with an input.
Multiply it by 4.
Add 5.

Hannah drew a diagram called a **flowchart** to show these steps.

The oval at the left side of the flowchart represents the input. Each arrow represents a *mathematical operation*. The oval to the right of an arrow shows the result of a mathematical operation. The oval at the far right represents the output.

Here is Hannah's flowchart for the input value 3.

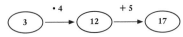

In Exercises 1–4, you will practice working with flowcharts.

✓ Develop & Understand: A

Copy each flowchart. Fill in the ovals.

1.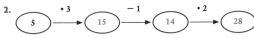

2.

3. In the rule $j = 7m - 2$, you can think of m as the input and j as the output.

   a. Create a flowchart for the rule but do not fill in the ovals. See margin.
   b. Use your flowchart to find the value of j when the value of m is $\frac{5}{3}$.

3b. $\frac{29}{3}$, or $9\frac{2}{3}$

4. In the rule $d = 3.2 + a \div 10$, you can think of a as the input and d as the output.

   a. Create a flowchart for this rule but do not fill in the ovals. Be sure to think about order of operations. See margin.

   b. Use your flowchart to find the value of d when the value of a is 111.
   14.3

Lesson 9.2 Backtracking **547**

Additional Answers
3a.
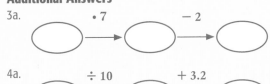
4a.

Use Flowcharts In this investigation, students use flowcharts to work forward from an input to the output. Then they use flowcharts to work backward from an output to the input.

Draw Hannah's flowchart on the board, starting with the input, n, and adding the operations, · 4 and + 5, one at a time.

Then draw another copy of the flowchart, but leave the ovals blank. Have students choose a starting number. Write this number in the first oval. Then have students find the numbers that should go in the two remaining ovals.

✓ Develop & Understand: A

Suggested Grouping: Individuals

▶ **Exercise 3** If students have trouble constructing the flowchart, ask them what happens to the input first, and then what happens to each subsequent result.

▶ **Exercise 4** For the equation in this exercise, the division must be done before the addition.

Since the order of the addends does not affect the result, students will need to use a closely related, equivalent rule to create the flowchart: $d = a \div 10 + 3.2$. The flowchart for this equivalent rule gives the correct outputs:

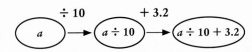

Without the ovals filled in, the flowchart is as follows:

Lesson 9.2 Backtracking **547**

Wrap-Up Discuss Exercises 1 and 2 on page 547 with the class. Then ask students if they can write an equation for the rule exhibited by each flowchart.

For Exercise 1, students can start with the variable *n* in the first oval and then fill in the remaining ovals:

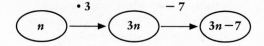

If *p* is the output, then the rule is $p = 3n - 7$.

For Exercise 2, the flowchart will look like this:

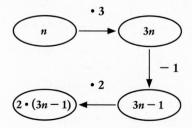

If *k* is the output, then the rule is $k = 2 \cdot (3n - 1)$.

Example

Carefully go through the Example with the class. By making a flowchart, students are using the draw a diagram problem-solving strategy. Be sure students understand that as they work their way back from output to input, they are using inverse operations to go from an oval on the right to the preceding oval on the left.

Math Link

Use an example to help understand how inverse operations work. For example, if they add $10 to their savings account and then subtract $10, they did inverse operations.

Math Link

Operations that undo each other are called *inverse operations*. To undo the division, Hannah used the inverse operation, multiplication. To undo the addition, she used the inverse operation, subtraction.

In Exercises 1–4, you used flowcharts to *work forward*, starting with the input and applying each operation to find the output. You can also use flowcharts to *work backward*, starting with the output and undoing each operation to find the input. This process is called **backtracking**. It is useful for solving equations.

Example

When playing the *What's My Rule* game, Hannah figured out that the secret rule was

$$t = \frac{n + 1}{2}.$$

Hannah wanted to find the input that gives an output of 33. That is, she wanted to solve this equation.

$$\frac{n + 1}{2} = 33$$

To find the solution, she first made a flowchart.

Then she found the input by backtracking.

"Since 33 is the output, I'll put it in the last oval."

"Since the number in the second oval was divided by 2 to get 33, it must be 66."

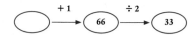

"One was added to the input to get 66, so the input must be 65."

Hannah checked her solution, 65, by substituting it into the original equation.

$$\frac{65 + 1}{1} = \frac{66}{2} = 33$$

Reaching *All Learners*

ELL **English Language Learners** For some students, you may need to point out that the word *backtrack* is made up of the two words *back* and *track*. Tell students that backtracking means following one's own tracks backward to return to the starting place. A phrase with a similar meaning is *retracing your steps*.

5. 105; The number in the second oval was divided by 2 to get 53, so it must be 106. To get 106, 1 was added to the input, so the input must be 105.

9b. $(k \cdot 5 - 1) \cdot 2 = 40$ and $2 \cdot (5k - 1) = 40$; You need to subtract 1 before you multiply by 2, so you need parentheses around the $5k - 1$. It does not matter whether the multiplication by 2 comes before or after the parentheses. Order does not matter in multiplication. In $5 \cdot k - 1 \cdot 2 = 40$ and $5k - 1 \cdot 2 = 40$, the multiplication is done before the subtraction, which does not fit the flowchart.

✓ Develop & Understand: B

5. Marcus used Hannah's rule, $t = \dfrac{n+1}{2}$, and got the output 53.

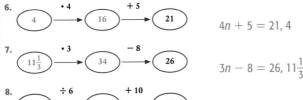

Use backtracking to find Marcus' input. Explain each step in your solution.

Backtracking Terry solved three equations by backtracking. Below are the flowcharts with which he started. For each flowchart, write the equation he was trying to solve. Use any letter you would like to represent the input variable. Then backtrack to find the solution. Check your solutions.

6. 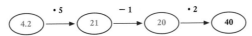 $4n + 5 = 21$, 4

7. 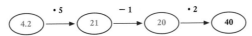 $3n - 8 = 26$, $11\frac{1}{3}$

8. $\dfrac{n}{6} + 10 = 97$, 522

9. Tyrone drew this flowchart.

  a. Copy Tyrone's flowchart. Fill in the ovals.

  b. Which of these equations can be represented by Tyrone's flowchart? Explain how you know.

  $5 \cdot k - 1 \cdot 2 = 40$ $(k \cdot 5 - 1) \cdot 2 = 40$

  $2 \cdot (5k - 1) = 40$ $5k - 1 \cdot 2 = 40$

Share & Summarize

1. Explain what a flowchart is. Demonstrate by making a flowchart for the rule $t = 5n - 3$.   See margin.

2. Use this flowchart to find the output for input $\dfrac{7}{10}$. $\dfrac{1}{2}$

3. Explain what backtracking is. Demonstrate how backtracking can be used to solve $5n - 3 = 45$. Check your solution. See margin.

✓ Develop & Understand: B

Suggested Grouping: Pairs

▶ **Exercise 6** If students have difficulty writing the equation, have them copy the flowchart and leave all the ovals blank, as shown below.

Next, have them select a variable, say *n*, to represent the input. Have them write it in the first oval.

Then have students fill in the remaining ovals, using appropriate expressions involving *n*.

To write the equation Terry used, students can use the output expression $4n + 5$ and the value for that expression, 21, given in the problem. The equation is $4n + 5 = 21$.

▶ **Exercise 9b** Encourage students to copy the flowchart, leaving the ovals blank, and then put *k* in the oval for the input and fill in the remaining ovals.

Share & Summarize

Ask students to do these exercises individually before you discuss them with the class. This will help you determine whether all students understand how to create flowcharts and use them for backtracking.

Troubleshooting
If students could not complete Share & Summarize exercises correctly, work through some additional problems with them before they go on to the next investigation. It is important that they understand the basics of creating a flowchart and backtracking before going on to do more complex problems.

Additional Answers for Share & Summarize 1 and 3 are on page 575A.

Reaching All Learners

OL **On Level** If students are having difficulty working backward, they may not have caught on to the role of inverse operations. Use the flowchart in Exercise 6 to provide some help. Draw the flowchart on the board. Below each arrow, draw an arrow that goes in the opposite direction and label it with the corresponding inverse operation:

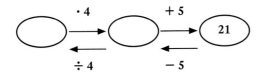

Students can use these arrows to help them work from right to left, from output to input.

Practice Backtracking In this investigation, students use flowcharts and backtracking to solve more complex equations, including those that require parentheses.

✓ Develop & Understand: A

Suggested Grouping: Individuals

▶ **Exercise 1a** Some students may wonder where the variable *P* belongs in the flowcharts. Emphasize that *P* is the output. It may help to show this by writing labels for the first and last ovals of the flowcharts, as shown below.

Miguel's rule:

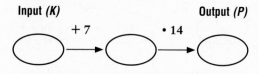

Althea's rule:

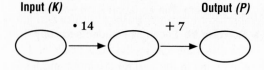

Each flowchart shows how to compute *P* if you know *k*, and how to compute *k* (by backtracking) if you know *P*.

▶ **Exercise 2b** Point out that students need to use parentheses around $3f - 6$. If students write the equation $3f - 6 \cdot 5 = 60$, remind them of the order of operations rules to help them understand that $3f - 6 \cdot 5$ does not mean the same as $(3f - 6) \cdot 5$.

Teacher Tips Review the order of operations rules.

Investigation ② Practice Backtracking

1c. No; Possible explanation: In Miguel's rule, 7 is added to the input and the result is multiplied by 14. In Althea's rule, the input is multiplied by 14 and then 7 is added. The fact that the rules give different inputs for the same output also shows that the rules are not equivalent.

In this investigation, you will practice backtracking so you can use it to solve equations quickly and easily.

✓ Develop & Understand: A

1. A group of students was playing *What's My Rule* Miguel and Althea thought they knew what the rule was. Both students used *K* to represent the input and *P* to represent the output.

   Miguel's rule: $P = 14 \cdot (K + 7)$

   Althea's rule: $P = 14 \cdot K + 7$

   a. Make a flowchart for each rule. Do not fill in the ovals. See margin.
   b. For each rule, use backtracking to find the input that gives the output 105.   Miguel's rule: 0.5; Althea's rule: 7
   c. Are these two rules equivalent? Explain why or why not.

2. Gabriela and Erin were playing a game called *Think of a Number*.

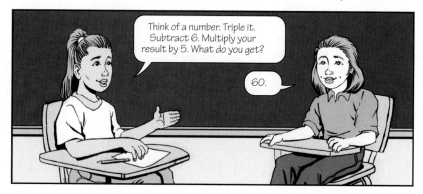

Think of a number. Triple it. Subtract 6. Multiply your result by 5. What do you get?

60.

Gabriela must figure out Erin's starting number.

   a. Draw a flowchart to represent this game.   See below.
   b. What equation does your flowchart represent? $(3f - 6) \cdot 5 = 60$
   c. Use backtracking to solve your equation. Check your solution by following Gabriela's steps.   6

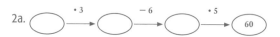

2a.

Additional Answer

1a. Flowchart for Miguel's rule:

Flowchart for Althea's rule:

Luke wanted to solve this equation by backtracking.

$$\frac{2 \cdot (n + 1)}{3} - 1 = 5$$

He made this flowchart.

Does Luke's flowchart correctly represent the equation? Why or why not?   See ①.

Solve the equation. Explain how you found the solution.   See ②.

The equation in Think & Discuss involves several operations. You can often solve equations like this by backtracking, but you need to pay close attention to order of operations as you draw the flowchart.

✅ *Develop & Understand: B*

3. Conor, Althea, and Miguel each made a flowchart to represent this equation.

$$\frac{1 + n \cdot 3}{4} - 11 = 10$$

Tell whose flowchart is correct. Explain the mistakes that the other students made.

Conor's flowchart

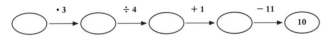

Althea's flowchart

Miguel's flowchart

Miguel's flowchart is correct.
In Conor's, the addition should come before the division.
In Althea's, the multiplication should come before the addition.

① No; the flowchart multiplies by 2 first and then adds 1. It should add 1 first and then multiply by 2.

② 8; Possible explanation: I fixed Luke's flowchart by reversing the · 2 and + 1 steps, and then I used backtracking.

Think **&** *Discuss*

This Think & Discuss introduces an incorrect flowchart as a way of getting students to focus on the order of operations in an equation and in a flowchart. If students do not volunteer the answer given, ask them which operation is used with *n* first. They should see that *n* + 1 is the first calculation. Help them recognize that the arrow labeled "+ 1" should have come first in the flowchart.

✅ *Develop & Understand: B*

Suggested Grouping: Pairs

This exercise set provides practice using flowcharts for relatively complex equations. Students can first work on each problem individually, and then compare results with their partners. If they get different results, they can work together until their answers agree.

▶ **Exercise 3** Students may find this exercise difficult because the first and last flowcharts both start with multiplying *n* by 3, but then they differ in the next two steps. If students have difficulty understanding the correct order of operations, you may wish to point out that the original equation can be rewritten as follows:

$$(1 + n \cdot 3) \div 4 - 11 = 10$$

▶ **Exercise 4** If students have difficulty making the flowchart, ask them to think of the expression in relation to a Think of a Number game. The game would go as follows: Think of a number (n). Subtract 13 (this gives $n - 13$). Divide the result by 6 (this gives $\frac{n-13}{6}$). Finally, add 6 (this gives $\frac{n-13}{6} + 6$). The other player announces a result of 15, so the equation is $\frac{(n-13)}{6} + 6 = 15$. The instructions correspond to the following flowchart:

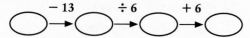

When the second player announces 15 as the number for the last oval, the person who called out the instructions uses backtracking to discover the value of n.

▶ **Exercise 5** Suggest that students use the same approach as Exercise 4.

Share & *Summarize*

Ask students to write down their best answer to the exercise, and then ask volunteers to read their answers. Use a class discussion to see which explanations the class understands and agrees with.

Investigation ③

On Your Own Exercises
Pages 555–559
Exercises 14–17, 21–25

Use Backtracking to Solve Problems
Have students examine the toothpick "ladders" in the diagrams. Then have them work on the Think & Discuss.

Think & *Discuss*

Ask volunteers to explain why they think the rule $n = 3r + 2$ works. The answer given in the margin is one approach. Another is to note that there are five toothpicks in the first ladder. Thereafter, there are 3 toothpicks added for each new rung. So when $r - 1$ new rungs have been added, there are a total of $5 + 3(r - 1)$ toothpicks. This simplifies to $3r + 2$.

4, 5. See margin.

In Exercises 4 and 5, draw a flowchart to represent the equation. Then use backtracking to find the solution. Be sure to check your solution.

4. $\frac{n-13}{2} + 6 = 15$

5. $7\left(\frac{n+4}{7} + 1\right) = 84$

Solve each equation. Be sure to check your solutions.

6. $\frac{7z + 2}{15} = 2$ 4

7. $(n \cdot 12 + 8) \cdot 100 = 2{,}100$ $1\frac{1}{12}$

8. $\frac{q - 36}{6} + 16 = 83$ 438

9. $4 \cdot \left(\frac{b}{2} - 3\right) + 1 = 97$ 54

Share & *Summarize*   See margin.

Give an example to demonstrate why it is important to pay close attention to order of operations when you make a flowchart.

Investigation ③ **Use Backtracking to Solve Problems**

These "ladders" are made from toothpicks.

① Possible explanation: For each rung, 3 toothpicks are added. A "ladder" with no rungs would be made from 2 toothpicks.

② A ladder with 36 rungs; the answer is the solution of the equation $3r + 2 = 110$. I can set up a flowchart and use it to solve this equation.

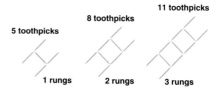

The rule for the number of toothpicks n in a ladder with r rungs is $n = 3r + 2$.

Think & *Discuss*

Can you explain why the rule for the number of toothpicks n in a ladder with r rungs is $n = 3r + 2$?   See ①.

Suppose you have 110 toothpicks. What size ladder can you make? How can you use backtracking to help you find the answer?   See ②.

Additional Answers

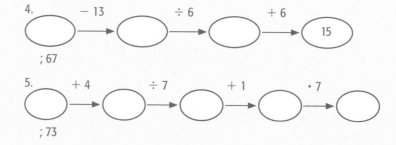

4.   − 13   ÷ 6   + 6   15
; 67

5.   + 4   ÷ 7   + 1   · 7
; 73

Additional Answer for Share & Summarize is on page 575A.

Develop & Understand: A

1. Write and solve an equation to find the number of rungs on a toothpick ladder made with 53 toothpicks. $3r + 2 = 53, 17$

2. Look at this pattern of toothpick shapes.

1 trapezoid   **2 trapezoids**   **3 trapezoids**

   a. Write a rule for finding the number of toothpicks n you would need to make a shape with t trapezoids. $n = 4t + 1$

   b. Write and solve an equation to find the number of trapezoids in a shape with 125 toothpicks. $4t + 1 = 125, 31$

3. Look at the pattern in this table.

n	0	3	6	9	12
y	19	20	21	22	23

   a. Write a rule that relates n and y. $y = n \div 3 + 19$

   b. Write and solve an equation to find the value of n when y is 55. $n \div 3 + 19 = 55, 108$

In Exercises 4–7, you will see that backtracking can also be used to solve everyday situations.

Develop & Understand: B

4. Leong makes candy apples to sell at the farmer's market on Saturday. He makes a profit of 35¢ per apple.

   a. Write a rule Leong could use to calculate his profit if he knows how many candy apples he sold. Tell what each letter in your rule represents.

   b. Leong wants to earn $8 so he can see a movie Saturday night. Write an equation Leong could solve to find the number of candy apples he must sell to earn $8. $8 = 0.35A$

   c. Use backtracking to solve your equation. How many candy apples does Leong need to sell? The solution is about 22.86, so Leong must sell at least 23 candy apples to earn $8.

4a. $P = 0.35A$, where P stands for the profit and A stands for the number of candy apples sold

---

Teacher Tips

Problem-solving strategies in the next exercise set are:

- looking for a pattern;

- writing an equation;

- working backward.

Develop & Understand: A

Suggested Grouping: Individuals

▶ **Exercise 1** Point out that this exercise uses the rule from Think & Discuss on page 552.

▶ **Exercise 2a** Students can think of starting with one toothpick. To get one trapezoid, 4 more toothpicks must be added. To get the next trapezoid, another four toothpicks must be added, and so on.

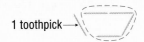

1 toothpick→

**1 group of
4 toothpicks**

1 toothpick→

**2 groups of
4 toothpicks**

▶ **Exercise 3a** Tell students that the numbers in the top row of the table are multiples of three.

Develop & Understand: B

Suggested Grouping: Pairs

▶ **Exercise 4** Point out that the profit per apple is given in cents and that the amount Leong wants to earn is given in dollars. They should also understand that the amount he earns from an apple is the profit he makes from the sale of the apple, not what he charges for the apple.

► **Exercise 6a** Students may prefer to write an equation that uses a variable for the distance traveled in miles.

Share & Summarize

This is a multistep problem. First, students need to find a rule connecting the term to the number of toothpicks used. They will then need to backtrack to solve the equation. Problem solving strategies used are:

• write an equation;

• work backward.

Troubleshooting If students have trouble writing equations and solving them using backtracking, you may want to have them work with partners on additional examples.

Additional Examples For each toothpick pattern, write a rule for finding the number of toothpicks n in Term t. Then write and solve an equation to find the numbers of the term that contains 46 toothpicks.

1.

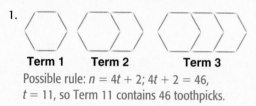

Term 1   Term 2   Term 3

Possible rule: $n = 4t + 2$; $4t + 2 = 46$, $t = 11$, so Term 11 contains 46 toothpicks.

2.

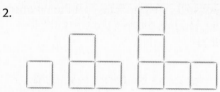

Term 1   Term 2   Term 3

Possible rule: $n = 6t - 2$; $6t - 2 = 46$, $t = 8$, so Term 8 contains 46 toothpicks.

6a. $20 = 2 + 0.75d$, where d stands for the distance in quarter miles

7a. $4.5 + 0.09s = 30$, where s is the length of the string in yards

5. The plumbers at DripStoppers charge $45 for a house call plus $40 for each hour of work.

  a. Write a rule for the cost of having a DripStoppers plumber come to your home and do n hours of work. $c = 45 + 40n$

  b. DripStoppers sent Mr. Valdez a plumbing bill for $105. Write and solve an equation to find the number of hours the plumber worked at Mr. Valdez's home. Check your solution.
  $45 + 40n = 105$, 1.5 hours

6. When you hire a taxi, you are usually charged a fixed amount of money when the ride starts plus an amount that depends on how far you travel. Suppose a taxi charges $2 plus $0.75 for every quarter mile.

  a. Write an equation to find out how far you can travel for $20.

  b. Solve your equation. How far could you travel for $20? Check your answer.   24 quarter miles, or 6 miles

7. Caroline and Althea are making a kite. The materials for the main part of the kite cost $4.50. The string costs 9¢ per yard.

  a. Write an equation to find how long the string could be if the friends have $30 to spend on their project.

  b. Solve your equation to find how long the string could be.
  About 283 yd

Share & Summarize

Jing used toothpicks to create this pattern.

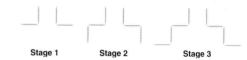

Stage 1   Stage 2   Stage 3

For one of the stages, she needed 112 toothpicks. Which stage was it? Explain how you found your answer. 55; Possible explanation: I wrote a rule for finding the number of toothpicks t in stage n: $t = 2 + 2n$. To find the number of the stage with 112 toothpicks, I needed to solve $2 + 2n = 112$. I used backtracking to find the solution.

Practice & Apply Copy each flowchart. Fill in the ovals.

1.

2.
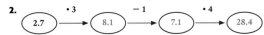

Backtracking Hannah solved three equations by backtracking. Below are the flowcharts with which she started. For each flowchart, write the equation she was trying to solve. Then backtrack to find the solution. Check your solutions.

3.
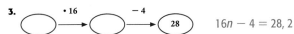

$16n - 4 = 28, 2$

4.

$\frac{n}{3} + 11 = 41, 90$

5. **Challenge** $(n + 1) \cdot 4 - 5 = 15, 4$

6. In a game of *What's My Rule*, Rosita wrote the rule $b = 3a \div 4$, where a is the input and b is the output.

   a. Make a flowchart for Rosita's rule. See below.

   b. Use your flowchart to find the output when the input is 18. $13\frac{1}{2}$

   c. Backtrack to solve the equation $3a \div 4 = 101$. $134\frac{2}{3}$

Flowcharts Make a flowchart to represent each equation. Then use backtracking to solve the equation. Be sure to check your solutions.

7. $4k + 11 = 91$

8. $4 \cdot (m - 2) = 38$

6a.

Investigation 1
Pages 547–549
Practice & Apply: 1–6
Connect & Extend: 18

Investigation 2
Pages 550–551
Practice & Apply: 7–13
Connect & Extend: 19, 20

Investigation 3
Pages 552–554
Practice & Apply: 14–17
Connect & Extend: 21–25

Assign Anytime
Mixed Review: 26–35

▶ **Exercise 5** Watch for students who say that the equation is $n + 1 \cdot 4 - 5 = 15$.

9a.

9. Neva and Jay were playing *Think of a Number*. Neva said,

Think of a number. Subtract 1 from your number. Multiply the result by 2. Then add 6.

Jay said he got 10. Neva must figure out Jay's starting number.

a. Draw a flowchart to represent this game.   See above.

9b. $(n - 1) \cdot 2 + 6 = 10$ **b.** What equation does your flowchart represent?

c. Use backtracking to find the number with which Jay started. Check your solution by following Neva's steps.   3

10. For a round of the *What's My Rule* game, Mia and Desmond wrote the rule $y = 9(2x + 1) + 1$, where x is the input and y is the output.

a. Draw a flowchart for Mia and Desmond's rule.   See margin.

b. Use your flowchart to solve the equation $9(2x + 1) + 1 = 46$.   2

Draw a flowchart to represent each equation. Then use backtracking to find the solution. Be sure to check your solutions.   See margin.

11. $\dfrac{3 \cdot m \cdot 2}{6} - 2 = 1$ **12.** $\dfrac{8p + 2}{5} - 5 = 19$ **13.** $3\left(\dfrac{5 + n}{3} - 4\right) = 15$

14. Look below at the toothpick sequence. The rule for the number of toothpicks t needed to make stage n is $t = 2n + 3$.

Stage 1   Stage 2   Stage 3

a. Explain why this rule works for every stage.   See margin.

15b. $100 + 0.5x =$
197.5; 195

16a. Possible rule:
$C = 5 + 6.5h$

b. Write and solve an equation to find the number of the stage that requires 99 toothpicks. $2n + 3 = 99$, 48

15. Look at the pattern in this table.

x	0	5	10	15	20
y	100	102.5	105	107.5	110

a. Write a rule that relates x and y. $y = 100 + 0.5x$

b. Write and solve an equation to find the value of x when y is 197.5.

16. **Economics** At Marshall Park, you can rent a canoe for $5 plus $6.50 per hour.

a. Write a rule for calculating the cost C of renting a canoe for h hours.

b. Conor, Jing, and Miguel paid $27.75 to rent a canoe. Write and solve an equation to find the number of hours the friends used the canoe. Check your solution. $5 + 6.5h = 27.75$, 3.5 hours

Real-World Link
The earliest canoes had frames made from wood or whale bone and were covered with bark or animal skin.
. . . .

▶ **Exercise 11** Some students may draw flowcharts that show multiplication by 2 followed by multiplication by 3. That order is also acceptable since multiplication is a commutative operation.

▶ **Exercise 14a** There are several ways to select three toothpicks in the first term and then add 2 toothpicks at a time to get the subsequent terms of the sequence.

▶ **Exercise 15** Students should note that each time the value of x increases by 5, the value of y increases by 2.5.

Additional Answers

10a.   · 2   + 1   · 9   + 1
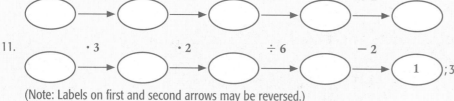

11.   · 3   · 2   ÷ 6   − 2
1   ;3
(Note: Labels on first and second arrows may be reversed.)

12.   · 8   + 2   ÷ 5   − 5
19
14.75

13.   + 5   ÷ 3   − 4   · 3
15
22

14a. There are 3 toothpicks in the beginning of each stage:

For each stage, an additional 2 toothpicks are added in the shape of the letter V:

So, the number of toothpicks in Stage n is $2n + 3$.

17. Economics Avocados cost $1.89 each. Hannah plans to make a large batch of guacamole for a party. She wants to buy as many avocados as possible. She has $14.59 to spend.

a. Write an equation to find how many avocados Hannah can buy for $14.59. $1.89a = 14.59$, where a is the number of avocados

b. Solve your equation. How many avocados can Hannah buy? See margin.

Connect & Extend

18. Evita wants to make a fence out of wooden poles. She drew a diagram to help her figure out how many poles she would need.

1 section   2 sections   3 sections

4 poles   7 poles   10 poles

a. Write a rule connecting the number of poles p to the number of sections s. $p = 1 + 3s$

b. The lumber yard has 100 poles in stock. Write an equation to find the number of fence sections Evita can build with 100 poles. $1 + 3s = 100$

c. Solve your equation. How many fence sections can Evita build? 33

d. If each pole is 2 yards long, how long will a 100-pole fence be? 66 yd

19. Physics A bus is traveling at an average speed of 65 miles per hour.

a. Copy and complete the table to show the distance the bus would travel in the given numbers of hours.

Time (hours), t	1	2	3	4	5
Distance (miles), d	65	130	195	260	325

b. On a grid like the one below, plot the points from your table. If it makes sense to do so, connect the points with line segments.

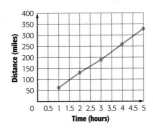

c. Use your graph to estimate how long it would take the bus to travel 220 miles. About 3.5 h

Lesson 9.2 Backtracking **557**

▶ **Exercise 18** Watch for students who think that 4 poles are added for every new section of fence. The correct rule starts with one pole and adds 3 poles for each new section.

▶ **Exercise 19c** If a student's estimate is not reasonably close to 3.5 h, ask the student to explain to you how he or she estimated the time to travel 220 miles.

Additional Answer

17b. The solution is about 7.72, so Hannah can buy 7 avocados.

▶ **Exercise 20a** Some students may prefer to write the equation by using a fraction: $\frac{n^2 + 3}{10} = 8.4$.

d. Write a rule that relates the time traveled t, in hours, to the distance traveled d, in miles. $d = 65t$

19e. $65t = 220$; It would take about 3.38 h, or about 3 h 23 min. This is slightly less than my estimate.

★**e.** Write and solve an equation to find how long it would take the bus to travel 220 miles. How does the solution compare to your estimate from Part c?

20. Julie and Noah were playing *Think of a Number.* Noah said,

Think of a number. Square it. Add 3. Divide your result by 10. What number do you get?

Julie said she got 8.4. Noah must figure out Julie's starting number. He drew this flowchart to represent the game.

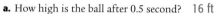

a. What equation does Noah need to solve to find Julie's starting number? $(n^2 + 3) \div 10 = 8.4$

b. Use backtracking to solve your equation. Check your solution by following Noah's steps.   9

22c. Possible answer: About 0.75 second; 20 ft is halfway between 16 ft and 24 ft, so I think the ball would reach this height halfway between 0.5 s and 1 s.

21. Economics Althea wants to buy a jacket at Donovan's department store. The store is having a "20% off" sale. In addition, Althea has a coupon for $5 off any item in the store.

a. Write a rule Althea could use to calculate the price P she would pay for a jacket with an original price of d dollars. (Note: The $5 is subtracted *after* the 20% discount is calculated.) $P = 0.8d - 5$

b. Althea pays $37.80 for a jacket. Write and solve an equation to find the original price of the jacket. $0.8d - 5 = 37.8$, $53.50

22. Preview This equation gives the height h of a baseball, in feet, t seconds after it is thrown straight up from ground level.

$$h = 40 \cdot t - 16 \cdot t^2$$

a. How high is the ball after 0.5 second?   16 ft

b. How high is the ball after 1 second?   24 ft

c. Based on what you learned in Parts a and b, estimate how long it would take the ball to reach a height of 20 feet. Explain your estimate.

d. Substitute your estimate for t in the equation to find out how high the ball would be after that number of seconds. Were you close? Was your estimate too high or too low?   21 ft; Possible answer: too high

23. Sports Lana is making fishing lures. Each lure requires 2¢ worth of fishing line. Lana uses feathers and weights to make the lures. The feathers cost 17¢ apiece. The weights cost 7¢ apiece.

a. Write a rule for the cost C of a lure made with f feathers and w weights. $C = 0.17f + 0.07w + 0.02$

23b. $0.65 = 0.17 \cdot f + 0.14 + 0.02$, or $0.65 = 0.17 \cdot f + 0.16$

b. Lana does not want to spend more than 65¢ on each lure. Write an equation you could solve to find how many feathers she could use on a lure made with two weights.

c. Solve your equation to find how many feathers Lana can use on a lure with two weights. $f \approx 2.88$, 2 feathers

24. In Your Own Words In this lesson, you used flowcharts to help solve equations. Explain how to make a flowchart for this equation.

$$\left(\frac{d}{3} - 5\right) \cdot 2 + 4 = 30$$

Also, show how you would use your flowchart to find the value of d. See below.

25. Economics Jordan has a part-time job as a telemarketer. He earns $14.00 per hour plus 50¢ for every customer he calls.

a. Write a rule for computing how much Jordan will earn on a three-hour shift if he calls c customers. $D = 42 + 0.50c$

b. Jordan would like to earn $100 on his 3-hour shift. How many customers must he call?   116

Mixed Review

Change each fraction or decimal to a percent.

26. $\frac{2}{5}$ 40%   **27.** 0.78   78%   **28.** $\frac{1}{3}$ $33\frac{1}{3}$%

29. 0.7   70%   **30.** $\frac{112}{70}$ 160%   **31.** 3.06   306%

Geometry Find the area of each figure in Exercises 32–35.

24. Possible answer: You would make a flowchart to help you work backward, start with the output and undo each operation to find the input.

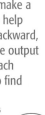

32.
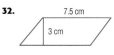
22.5 cm^2

33.

6.25 π ft^2, or about 19.6 ft^2

34.
2 cm, 4 cm, 2 cm, 1 cm, 2 cm, 5 cm
22 cm^2

35.
4 in., 4 in.
16 + 2 π in.^{2}, or about 22.3 in.^{2}

▶ **Exercise 23** In **Part a**, students might write an equation that expresses the cost of a lure in cents: $C = 17f + 7w + 2$. If so, the equation to solve in **Part b** is $65 = 17f + 16$.

Quick Check

Informal Assessment Students should be able to:

✔ construct flowcharts that represent input/output rules and equations

✔ solve equations by using flowcharts for backtracking (working backward)

Quick Quiz

1. Write an equation for each flowchart. Use backtracking to solve the equation.

a.
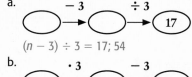
$(n - 3) \div 3 = 17$; 54

b.
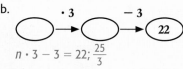
$n \cdot 3 - 3 = 22$; $\frac{25}{3}$

2. Make a flowchart for the following equation. Then solve the equation by using backtracking.

$$\frac{2 \cdot (n - 2)}{4} - 7 = 5$$

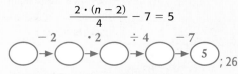
; 26

3. A store has CDs on sale for $9 each. Jana has a coupon that will give her $4 off the total cost of her purchase. She has $32 to spend. How many CDs can she buy?   4 CDs

Guess-Check-and-Improve

Objectives

▶ To solve equations systematically by using guess-check-and improve

▶ To find approximate solutions to equations, to the nearest tenth or hundredth

▶ To write and solve equations that describe mathematical puzzles or word problems

▶ To decide whether to use backtracking or guess-check-and improve to solve equations

Overview

In this lesson, students examine several types of equations and learn to identify those that cannot be solved by backtracking. They learn to use the guess-check-and-improve method, which can be used to find exact and approximate solutions for a wide variety of equations.

Advance Preparation

No advance preparation is needed for this lesson.

	Summary	Materials	On Your Own Exercises (pp. 568–572)	Assessment Opportunities
Investigation 1 (p. 560) *Pacing: 2 days*	Students learn to use the guess-check-and-improve method to solve equations that are not suitable for backtracking.		Practice & Apply: 1–4 Connect & Extend: 21–23 Mixed Review: 31–39	• On the Spot Assessment (p. 561) • Share & Summarize (p. 563) • Troubleshooting (p. 563)
Investigation 2 (p. 563) *Pacing: 1 day*	Students write equations for number puzzles and real life situations, and then solve the equations by using the guess-check-and-improve method.		Practice & Apply: 5–10 Connect & Extend: 24, 25 Mixed Review: 31–39	• Share & Summarize (p. 565) • Troubleshooting (p. 565)
Investigation 3 (p. 566) *Pacing: 1 day*	Students examine given equations and use the more appropriate method (backtracking or guess-check and-improve) to solve each equation.		Practice & Apply: 11–19 Connect & Extend: 20, 26–30 Mixed Review: 31–39	• Share & Summarize (p. 567) • Troubleshooting (p. 573)

Leveled Lesson Resources

Study Guide and Intervention (p. 14) — AL

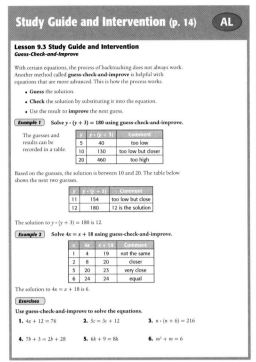

Lesson 9.3 Study Guide and Intervention
Guess-Check-and-Improve

With certain equations, the process of backtracking does not always work. Another method called **guess-check-and-improve** is helpful with equations that are more advanced. This is how the process works.

- **Guess** the solution.
- **Check** the solution by substituting it into the equation.
- Use the result to **improve** the next guess.

Example 1 Solve $y \cdot (y + 3) = 180$ using guess-check-and-improve.

The guesses and results can be recorded in a table.

y	y · (y + 3)	Comment
5	40	too low
10	130	too low but closer
20	460	too high

Based on the guesses, the solution is between 10 and 20. The table below shows the next two guesses.

y	y · (y + 3)	Comment
11	154	too low but close
12	180	12 is the solution

The solution to $y \cdot (y + 3) = 180$ is 12.

Example 2 Solve $4x = x + 18$ using guess-check-and-improve.

x	4x	x + 18	Comment
1	4	19	not the same
2	8	20	closer
5	20	23	very close
6	24	24	equal

The solution to $4x = x + 18$ is 6.

Exercises

Use guess-check-and-improve to solve the equations.

1. $4x + 12 = 76$ 2. $5c = 3c + 12$ 3. $n \cdot (n + 6) = 216$

4. $7b + 3 = 2b + 28$ 5. $6k + 9 = 8k$ 6. $m^2 + m = 6$

Skills Practice (p. 15) — AL OL

Lesson 9.3 Skills Practice
Guess-Check-and-Improve

Use guess-check-and-improve to solve the equations.

1. $m + 2 = 3m$ 2. $n + 10 = 2n + 7$

3. $7 + 3b = 1 + 5b$ 4. $4 \cdot (n + 1) = 32$

5. $w \cdot (w + 4) = 60$ 6. $9x - 7 = 3x + 35$

7. $x^2 + 3x = 40$ 8. $k \cdot (k + 2) = 5k$

9. $8n = 3n + 45$ 10. $\frac{n + 56}{2} = 4n$

Problem-Solving Practice (p. 16) — AL OL

Lesson 9.3 Problem-Solving Practice
Guess-Check-and-Improve

Solve.

1. **Number puzzle** Six more than twice a number is equal to five less than three times the number. Write an equation and use guess-check-and-improve to solve.

2. **Number puzzle** Nine times a number is equal to eighteen more than six times the number. Write an equation and use guess-check-and-improve to solve.

3. **Manufacturing** The surface area of a cube is calculated by the using the formula, Surface Area = $6s^2$, where s represents the length of the cube's edge. What is the edge length of the cube if the manufacturer uses 150 square inches of cardboard?

4. **Basketball** Darius wants to calculate the diameter of a basketball. He has measured the circumference of the ball to be 30 inches.

   a. Write an equation he could use to find the diameter of the basketball.

   b. Use guess-check-and-improve to find the diameter of the ball to the nearest tenth of an inch.

5. **Salary** Naomi and Cheyanne both worked yesterday at the same restaurant. Naomi worked eight hours at a rate of k dollars an hour. Cheyanne worked four hours at a rate of k dollars an hour and also received $36 in tips. They both made the same amount of money at work yesterday.

   a. Write an expression to represent the amount of money that Naomi made.

   b. Write an expression to represent the amount of money that Cheyanne made.

   c. Using your two expressions, write an equation that states that Naomi and Cheyanne made the same amount of money.

   d. Solve the equation to find how much money they earn in an hour.

Enrichment (p. 17) — BL

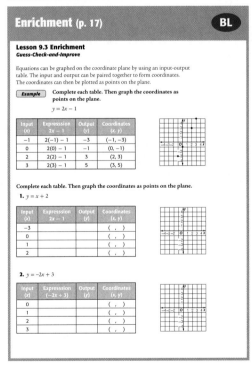

Lesson 9.3 Enrichment
Guess-Check-and-Improve

Equations can be graphed on the coordinate plane by using an input-output table. The input and output can be paired together to form coordinates. The coordinates can then be plotted as points on the plane.

Example Complete each table. Then graph the coordinates as points on the plane.

$y = 2x - 1$

Input (x)	Expression 2x − 1	Output (y)	Coordinates (x, y)
−1	2(−1) − 1	−3	(−1, −3)
0	2(0) − 1	−1	(0, −1)
2	2(2) − 1	3	(2, 3)
3	2(3) − 1	5	(3, 5)

Complete each table. Then graph the coordinates as points on the plane.

1. $y = x + 2$

Input (x)	Expression 2x − 1	Output (y)	Coordinates (x, y)
−3			(,)
0			(,)
1			(,)
2			(,)

2. $y = -2x + 3$

Input (x)	Expression (−2x + 3)	Output (y)	Coordinates (x, y)
0			(,)
1			(,)
2			(,)
3			(,)

Lesson Quick Quiz (p. 18) — AL OL BL

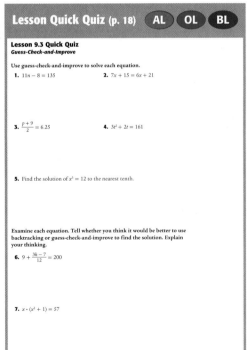

Lesson 9.3 Quick Quiz
Guess-Check-and-Improve

Use guess-check-and-improve to solve each equation.

1. $11n - 8 = 135$ 2. $7x + 15 = 6x + 21$

3. $\frac{p + 9}{2} = 6.25$ 4. $3t^2 + 2t = 161$

5. Find the solution of $x^3 = 12$ to the nearest tenth.

Examine each equation. Tell whether you think it would be better to use backtracking or guess-check-and-improve to find the solution. Explain your thinking.

6. $9 + \frac{3k - 7}{12} = 200$

7. $x \cdot (x^2 + 1) = 57$

Additional Lesson Resources

Teacher Tech Tools
- TeacherWorks
- ExamView Assessment Suite
- Classroom Presentation Toolkit
- Advance Tracker

Student Tech Tools
- StudentWorks Plus
- **Math Online** eGlossary •
  Concepts in Motion

Other Print Products
- Investigation Notebook and Reflection Journal
- Quick Review Math Handbook

Introduce

What's My Rule? Read through the information at the top of the page with the class. Have students work with you to verify that for the given inputs, the equation $n = m \cdot (m + 1)$ gives the outputs shown in the table. Then have students work individually on the Think & Discuss.

Think & Discuss

Discuss these questions with the class. Help students see how the following flowchart can be used to find the outputs shown in the table:

Then write 552 in the oval on the far right. Point out that the input variable *m* occurs above one of the operation arrows. To backtrack from the output 552 to the input, students would have to divide by the value of *m*. But there is no way to find the value of *m* until they are back to the first oval. Thus, backtracking will not work for this equation.

Discuss the fact that this difficulty will occur any time the input variable is used above an operation arrow.

Investigation 1

On Your Own Exercises
Pages 568–572
Exercises 1–4, 21–23

Guess-Check-and-Improve Tell students that they are going to take a close look at a method they have used on some other occasions to solve mathematical problems. Explain that this method can be used to find exact or approximate solutions for many kinds of equations, including equations for which backtracking does not work.

Backtracking is useful for solving many types of equations. However, as you will see in this lesson, some equations are difficult or impossible to solve by backtracking.

Johanna and Rosita were playing *What's My Rule*. Johanna made this table to keep track of her guesses.

From her table, Johanna figured out that Rosita's secret rule was

Input	Output
10	110
20	420
30	930
40	1,640

$$n = m \cdot (m + 1)$$

where *m* is the input and *n* is the output.

① No; Possible explanation: I made the flowchart below. When I tried to backtrack, I found that I had to divide 552 by *m*. I did not know what *m* was. That is what I was trying to find. I could not go any further.

Now the two friends want to figure out what input gives an output of 552. That is, they want to solve the equation $m \cdot (m + 1) = 552$.

Think & Discuss

Rosita suggests they solve the equation by backtracking. Try to solve the equation this way. Are you able to find the solution? Why or why not?   See ① and ②.

What advice would you give Rosita and Johanna to help them solve the equation?   Possible answer: Guess numbers for *m* until you find a solution. The solution is probably between 20 and 30, since 20 gives an output that is too low and 30 gives an output that is too high.

Investigation 1 Use Guess-Check-and-Improve

Vocabulary

guess-check-and-improve

As you have seen, backtracking does not work for every equation. In this lesson, you will learn another solution method. This method is called **guess-check-and-improve** because that is exactly what you do.

The following example shows how Rosita and Johanna used guess-check-and-improve to solve the equation $m \cdot (m + 1) = 552$.

Mathematical Background

Some of the problems in this investigation require solving quadratic equations, or equations in which the variable is squared in one term of the equation. Students will study this type of equation more fully in Course 3. Quadratic equations are used since they typically have more than one solution. For these equations, students will be looking only for positive solutions.

Example

From the table Johanna had made during the game, she could see that the output for $m = 20$ was too low, and the output for $m = 30$ was too high.

Input	Output
10	110
20	420
30	930
40	1,640

Using this information, the friends decided to try 25, the number halfway between 20 and 30. They checked their guess by substituting it for m in the expression $m \cdot (m + 1)$.

$$m \cdot (m + 1) = 25 \cdot (25 + 1)$$
$$= 25 \cdot 26$$
$$= 650$$

The output 650 is too high. Johanna recorded the guesses and the results in the table.

m	$m \cdot (m + 1)$	Comment
20	420	too low
30	930	too high
25	650	too high but closer

The friends now decided the solution must be between 20 and 25. The table below shows their next two guesses.

m	$m \cdot (m + 1)$	Comment
20	420	too low
30	930	too high
25	650	too high but closer
22	506	too low but close
23	552	23 is the solution

A solution to $m \cdot (m + 1) = 552$ is 23.

Review the process that Johanna and Rosita used.
- They *guessed* the solution.
- They *checked* their solution by substituting it into the equation.
- They used the result to *improve* their guess.

Now it is your turn to try guess-check-and-improve.

 Example

This example illustrates the kind of thinking typically used when applying the guess-check-and-improve method. Discuss the example carefully with the class. Have students evaluate $m \cdot (m + 1)$ for each of the inputs in the table to confirm that the products given are correct. This can be thought of as a *check* step. Students can do the calculations using pencil and paper or a calculator. Pay special attention to the reasoning students use to decide what number to try next. This is an *improve* step.

Students will see that the guess-check-and-improve method may require several steps, since one must continue to guess, continue to check, and continue to improve the guess until one has the exact solution or an approximate solution that is close enough to the exact solution to meet the requirements of the problem. All this is summarized in the paragraph that follows the example.

Analyze the Table Watch for students who do not understand how to derive the values in the middle column of the table. Point out that the value of m in the left column is substituted twice in the expression $m \cdot (m + 1)$ and then the expression is evaluated.

Teacher Tips Review the process of guessing, checking, improving the guess, and rechecking with students.

 **Assessment**

If students have difficulty understanding how to find the output values for the tables on this page, point out that the correct order of operations is to add 1 to m first, then multiply the value by m. Have them verify the values in the table at the top of the page.

Develop & Understand: A

Suggested Grouping: Pairs or Individuals

▶ **Exercise 1b** Ask students how they decided what number to use for their first guess. Students might reason that 100 is a good place to start. (The product is large, so the value of *d* should be large.) The product 100 · (100 + 3) is 10,300, which is too large. A good second guess is 90, which turns out to be too small. But the results indicate a solution between 90 and 100. After that, students may pick a number halfway between 90 and 100.

▶ **Exercise 1d** Whole-number solutions are easily ruled out. Students may reason that since the product of *d* and *d* + 3 must be a two-place decimal, the solution might be a one-place decimal.

▶ **Exercise 3** This exercise may be difficult for students. Some students are likely to use decimals for their guesses. Others may try simple fractions. Students who use fractions may arrive at the solution quickly. There is no simple way to know whether one approach is better than the other is.

▶ **Exercise 5** This exercise focuses on the reasoning process. If students' answers to **Parts a and b** show sound thinking, ask for the solution of Miguel's equation. Observant students will see that the equation can be solved by guess-check-and-improve or backtracking.

Wrap-Up Ask students to share their strategies for making their first guess for each of the problems in this set. After getting one student's approach, ask if anyone made a different first guess, and ask for the reasoning behind the guess. It is important for students to understand why a first guess is good and how to decide how much larger or smaller to make the second guess.

1b. 91 (Note: −94 is also a solution, but students are not expected to find it.)

4. 3.5 (Note: −5.5 is also a solution, but students are not expected to find it.)

Math Link

Imagine that a garage contains two tricycles and several bicycles and that there are 20 bicycle wheels in all. You can solve the equation in Exercise 2 to find the number of bicycles in the garage.

....

5a. 3 · *d* is being subtracted from 25. As the value of *d* increases, the value of 3 · *d* also increases, so the value of 25 − 3 · *d* gets smaller.

Develop & Understand: A

1. Conor, Marcus, and Jing are playing *What's My Rule*. Below is Jing's secret rule.

$$d \cdot (d + 3) = J, \text{ where } d \text{ is the input and } J \text{ is the output}$$

a. Conor gave Jing an input. Jing calculated the output as 8,554. Write an equation to find Conor's input. $d \cdot (d + 3) = 8{,}554$

b. Find a solution of your equation using guess-check-and-improve.

c. Marcus gave Jing an input. Jing calculated the output as 32.56. Write an equation to find Marcus' input. $d \cdot (d + 3) = 32.56$

d. Find a solution of your equation from Part c using guess-check-and-improve. 4.4 (Note: −7.4 is also a solution, but students are not expected to find it.)

For each equation, use guess-check-and-improve to find a solution.

2. $2n + 6 = 20$ 7   3. $19 = \frac{4}{q} + 3$ 0.25   4. $s^2 + 2s = 19.25$

5. Miguel is trying to solve this equation using guess-check-and-improve.

$$25 - 3 \cdot d = 17.8$$

The table below shows his first two guesses. Miguel asked, "Why was the output for 8 lower than the output for 7? Shouldn't a greater input give a greater output?"

d	$25 - 3 \cdot d$	Comment
7	4	too low
8	1	still too low

a. Answer Miguel's questions.

b. What input do you think Miguel should try next? Explain. See below.

6. Hannah and Luke were trying to solve $7.25t - t^2 = 12.75$. They made the table below using guess-check-and-improve.

t	$7.25t - t^2$	Comment
5	11.25	too low
6	7.5	too low
4	13	too high
2	10.5	too low

5b. Possible answer: 2; He should try something smaller than 7. Since the output for 7 is not close to 17.8, he should try something much smaller than 7.

Hannah thinks the solution must be between 2 and 4. Luke thinks it must be between 4 and 5.

a. Is there a solution between 2 and 4? If so, find it. If not, explain why not.   Yes, 3

b. Is there a solution between 4 and 5? If so, find it. If not, explain why not.   Yes, 4.25

Share & Summarize

Describe any strategies you have discovered for finding a solution efficiently by using guess-check-and-improve.   Answers will vary.

Investigation 2 Solve Problems Using Guess-Check-and-Improve

In this investigation, you will solve exercises by writing equations and then using guess-check-and-improve. As you work, you will find that you cannot always give an exact decimal value for a solution. In such cases, you can approximate the solution.

✅ **Develop & Understand: A**

1. The floor of Mr. Cruz's basement is shaped like a rectangle. The length of the floor is 2 meters greater than the width.

a. Write a rule to show the connection between the floor's area A and the width w. $A = w \cdot (w + 2)$

b. The area of the basement floor is 85 square meters. Write an equation to find the floor's width. $w \cdot (w + 2) = 85$

c. Use guess-check-and-improve to find an approximate solution of your equation. Give the solution to the nearest tenth.   8.3

d. What are the dimensions of the basement floor?
About 8.3 m by 10.3 m

Lesson 9.3 Guess-Check-and-Improve   **563**

Share & Summarize

This Share & Summarize focuses on the reasoning involved in making guesses based on the information in the equation and the data from previous guesses. Encourage students to estimate two numbers that might have a solution between them.

Troubleshooting If students have had difficulty making reasonable initial guesses, review the exercises on page 562. Ask students to make an initial guess and to justify it with an estimate. Once they have made two guesses, ask them to justify their next guess based on their observations of the results from the first two guesses.

Investigation 2

On Your Own Exercises
Pages 568–572
Exercises 5–10, 24, 25

Solve Problems In this investigation, students write equations to describe various situations. They use guess-check-and-improve to find exact or approximate solutions of their equations.

✅ **Develop & Understand: A**

Suggested Grouping: Pairs

▶ **Exercise 1c** Students will probably find it easy to determine that the width w must be between 8 and 9 meters. It will also be easy to see that the value of w is closer to 8 than to 9. A table that shows values of w and $w \cdot (w + 2)$ from $w = 8.0$ to $w = 8.5$ would make it clear that w is about 8.3 meters, rounded to the nearest tenth.

Additional Answer
Share & Summarize Possible answer: If I find an input that gives an output that is too high and an input that gives an output that is too low, I know there is a solution between those two inputs. I look to see which of the two inputs gives an output closer to the output I want, and I make my next guess closer to that input.

For example, for $m \cdot (m + 1) = 40$, an input of 5 gives an output of 30, which is too low. An input of 6 gives an output of 42, which is too high. I know that the solution must be between 5 and 6, and since 42 is closer to 40 than to 30, I would make my next guess closer to 6 than to 5. I also look at the equation or at the pattern in the table to see if greater inputs give greater or lesser outputs. This helps me to decide whether my next input should be greater than or less than the previous input.

Lesson 9.3 Guess-Check-and-Improve   **563**

▶ **Exercise 2d** Students can use the guesses 4 and 5 to reason that since $6 \cdot 4^2 = 96$ and $6 \cdot 5^2 = 150$, the solution is between 4 and 5, and is very close to 4. The number 4.1 is only one-tenth more than 4, and since $6 \cdot 4.1^2 = 100.86$, and 100.86 is closer to 100 than is 96, the solution is 4.1, accurate to the nearest tenth. You may want to ask students how they would use a calculator with a square root key to check this result.

(Example) ·

This example uses an equation that has the variable on both sides. Discuss the example with the class. Be sure that students understand that the table is useful for showing how close the values of $m + 12$ and $3m$ are for various values of m.

Some students may point out that $m + 12 = 3m$ can be solved by first rewriting the equation as $12 = 3m - m$, or $2m = 12$. It is now easy to see that the solution is 6. Use this observation to emphasize that even when there are other ways to solve an equation, guess-check-and-improve will also work.

Analyze the Table Explain that the table in the example shows how close the values of $m + 12$ and $3m$ are for different values of m.

· ·

Real-World Link
Ask students to research the cubist painters. Do they like their art?

· ·

Real-World Link
Cubism is an art style that was developed in the early 1900s. Cubism today emphasizes flat, two-dimensional surfaces rather than three-dimensional perspective. Cubist paintings show many sides of an object at once. This painting is by Juan Aris and is called *Pedestal Table before the Window.*

· ·

2. A *cube* is a three-dimensional shape with six identical square faces.

The *surface area* of a cube is the sum of the areas of its six faces.

This cube has edges of length L.

a. What is the area of one face of this cube? L^2

b. Write a rule for finding the surface area S of the cube. $S = 6 \cdot L^2$

c. Suppose the cube has a surface area of 100 square centimeters. Write an equation to find the cube's edge length. $6 \cdot L^2 = 100$

d. Use guess-check-and-improve to find the edge length of the cube to the nearest 0.1 centimeter. 4.1 cm

In all of the equations you have solved so far, the variable appears on only one side of the equation. You can also use guess-check-and-improve to solve equations in which the variable appears on both sides.

┌ Example

Solve this number puzzle.
12 more than a number is equal to 3 times the number. What is the number?

If you let m stand for the number, you can write the puzzle as an equation.

$$m + 12 = 3m$$

To solve the equation, substitute values for m until the two sides of the equation are equal.

m	$m + 12$	$3m$	Comment
1	13	3	not the same
2	14	6	a bit closer
5	17	15	very close
6	18	18	Got it!

So, 6 is the solution of the equation $m + 12 = 3m$.

Check that 6 is the solution of the original puzzle. Twelve more than 6 is 18, which is equal to 3 times 6.

In Exercises 3–9, you will practice solving equations in which the variable appears on both sides.

Reaching *All Learners*

BL **Beyond Level** As you go through the example, ask students if they think it is possible there are values between those given for m in the table that are *between* the other values that also may be used to guess-check-and-improve. Point out that values like 5.5 can be used with this strategy, and that students who are good with decimals may try them as input values.

Develop & Understand: B

In Exercises 3–5, write an equation to represent the number puzzle. Then find the solution using guess-check-and-improve.

3. Five added to a number is the same as 1 subtracted from twice the number. What is the number? $5 + x = 2x - 1$, 6

4. Four times a number plus 1 is equal to 4 added to twice the number. What is the number? $4x + 1 = 4 + 2x$, 1.5

5. Two added to the square of a number is equal to 5 times the number minus 4. What is the number? There are two solutions. Try to find them both. $2 + x^2 = 5x - 4$, 2 or 3

6. Consider the equation $2m = 5m - 18$.

   a. Make up a number puzzle that matches the equation.

   b. Solve the equation. Check that the solution is also the answer to your puzzle.   6

6a. 2 times a number is equal to 18 less than 5 times the number. What is the number?

7. Peta and Ali went to the pet store to buy fish for their tanks. Peta bought three black mollies for b dollars each and one peacock eel for $12. Ali bought seven black mollies for b dollars each and an Australian rainbow fish for $2. Peta and Ali spent the same amount of money.

   a. How much money did Peta spend? Your answer should be an expression containing the variable b. $3b + 12$

   b. How much money did Ali spend? Your answer should be an expression containing the variable b. $7b + 2$

   c. Using your two expressions, write an equation that states that Peta and Ali spent the same amount of money. $3b + 12 = 7b + 2$

   d. Solve your equation to find the value of b. How much did each black molly cost? $2.50

   e. How much did each friend spend? $19.50

Use guess-check-and-improve to find a solution of each equation.

8. $3n = 9 - 2n$ 1.8

9. $p + 1 = 5(p - 4)$ 5.25

Share & Summarize

Make up a number puzzle like those with which you have worked in this investigation. Exchange puzzles with your partner. Solve your partner's puzzle.   Puzzles will vary.

Teacher Tips Point out that using tables can be helpful for doing the exercises on this page. Ask students to refer to the example on page 564.

Develop & Understand: B

Suggested Grouping: Pairs

▶ **Exercise 4** If some students used guesses that were fractions and some used guesses that were decimals, you may want to discuss whether one approach was easier than the other was.

▶ **Exercise 5** Students will probably guess both solutions, since both are small whole numbers. Show students that backtracking will not work for this equation, even if the equation is written in an equivalent form.

▶ **Exercise 7** Point out that this exercise requires students to write and solve an equation to solve a problem. **Parts a–c** walk students through setting up the equation.

Share & Summarize

Have students work in pairs on this activity. Ask volunteers to present their number puzzles to the class. Use a class discussion to solve the puzzles, and discuss any features that made certain puzzles especially challenging.

Troubleshooting If students have difficulty translating number puzzles presented in words into equations, you may want to consider more of the puzzles that students wrote for Share & Summarize exercise. Discussing how to translate the puzzles into equations can be helpful for all students.

Lesson 9.3 Guess-Check-and-Improve   **565**

Choose a Method In this investigation, students compare solution methods for a variety of equations. They look for characteristics that will help them decide in advance whether backtracking or guess-check-and-improve will be the more efficient approach for solving a given equation.

Read through the cartoon with the class. Then have students answer Think & Discuss questions on the next page.

The equation shown in this last frame of the cartoon is a quadratic equation, which has two integer solutions, 6 and −16. Students are not expected to find negative solutions in this course.

Teacher Tips The problem-solving strategies used are:

• work backward;

• guess-check-and-improve.

As students read the cartoon, ask them to record their observations so that they can be used to help compare the two problem-solving strategies.

Investigation ③ Choose a Method

Now you have two methods for solving equations, *backtracking* and *guess-check-and-improve*. The exercises in this investigation will help you decide which solution method is more efficient for a particular type of equation.

In the cartoon, Marcus and Rosita are trying to solve some equations. Marcus uses backtracking. Rosita uses guess-check-and-improve.

① $2.4 \cdot n + 4 = 10.36$;
Marcus was able to
solve the equation
faster than Rosita.
Rosita had to make a
lot of guesses because
the answer had two
decimal places.

② $n \cdot (10 + n) = 96$;
Marcus was not able
to solve the equation
using backtracking
because the variable
is in both parts of the
product.

1b. Possible answer:
Both methods work.
Backtracking seems
more efficient.

2b. Possible answer:
Both methods work.
Backtracking seems
more efficient.

3b. Backtracking does
not work.

4a. 8 (Note: −6 is also a
solution, but students
are not expected to
find it.)

4b. Backtracking does
not work.

5. 3.5; I used guess-
check-and-improve.
Backtracking does
not work when
the variable is on
both sides.

6. 4; I used backtracking
because there are many
operations. If I used
guess-check-and-
improve, it would
be tedious to check
each guess.

For which equation in the cartoon is backtracking a better method
than guess-check-and-improve? Why? See ①.

For which equation is guess-check-and-improve a better method
than backtracking? Why? See ②.

For which equation do both methods seem to work well?
$3n + 7 = 19$

Develop & Understand: A

In Exercises 1–4, do Parts a and b.

    a. Find a solution of the equation using one method while your
partner finds a solution using the other. Switch methods for
each equation so you have a chance to practice both.

    b. Discuss your work with your partner. Indicate whether both
methods work. Tell which method seems more efficient.

1. $3p − 8 = 25$ 11   **2.** $1.6r + 3.96 = 11$ 4.4

3. $k + 4 = 6k$ 0.8   **4.** $(j − 2) \cdot j = 48$

**Solve each equation. Tell which solution method you used. Explain
why you chose that method.** See below.

5. $4w + 1 = 2w + 8$ **6.** $5 \cdot \dfrac{2k + 4}{6} = 10$

7. Luke says, "When the variable appears only once in an equation, I
use backtracking. If it occurs more than once, I use guess-check-and-
improve." Discuss Luke's strategy with your partner. Would it be
effective for the equations in Exercises 1–6? Explain.
See margin.

Share **&** *Summarize*

Tell which solution method you would use to find a solution of each
equation. Explain your choice. Possible answers given.

1. $n^2 + n = 30$ **2.** $4 + (v − 3) = 8$

3. $3g = 6g − 7$ **4.** $2e − 7 = 4$

  1. Guess-check-and-improve because the variable appears twice
  2. Guess-check-and-improve because this is fairly easy to do in
     my head
  3. Guess-check-and-improve because the variable appears twice
  4. Backtracking because the variable appears only once

Lesson 9.3 Guess-Check-and-Improve   **567**

Additional Answer

7. Possible answer: Yes; we found that we
could not use backtracking to solve the
equations in Exercises 3, 4, and 5. In
each of these, the variable occurs more
than once.

Think **&** *Discuss*

Call on volunteers to read their answers to
the class. Discuss their answers, and use the
discussion to elicit any further observations
that might be helpful in comparing the two
methods of solving equations.

Some students may point out that Marcus
could have made flowcharts for the first two
equations. For the second equation, Rosita
had to make a table. Discuss what she had
to do to get the numbers for the second
column of her table. Students will quickly
see that Rosita had to do much
multiplication.

Develop & Understand: A

Suggested Grouping: Pairs

▶ **Exercise 2** Students may notice that
multiplication might be necessary if
guess-check-and-improve is used.

▶ **Exercise 3** Some students may observe
that backtracking will not work if the
equation is left in the given form. However,
backtracking will work if the equation is
rewritten in the form $4 = 5k$ or $5k = 4$.

▶ **Exercise 7** Luke's statement is fine for the
equations in Exercises 1–6. However,
backtracking will not work for an equation
such as $\dfrac{1}{n−1} = 5$, even though the variable
occurs only once.

Share **&** *Summarize*

Call on volunteers to read their answers to
the class. The discussion of the answers can
serve as a good wrap-up for all the main
ideas of this lesson.

Troubleshooting If students had trouble
deciding which method to use, write a few
more equations on the board and discuss
the advantages and disadvantages of each
method with the class.

Investigation 1
Pages 560–563
Practice & Apply: 1–4
Connect & Extend: 21–23

Investigation 2
Pages 563–565
Practice & Apply: 5–10
Connect & Extend: 24, 25

Investigation 3
Pages 566–567
Practice & Apply: 11–19
Connect & Extend: 20, 26–30

Assign Anytime
Mixed Review: 31–39

▶ **Exercise 5** You may want to allow the use of calculators for this exercise. If students are using pencil and paper, suggest that they use 3.14 as an approximate value for π.

Math Link
Approximations for π are 3.14 and $\frac{22}{7}$ if the answer can be rounded.

Practice & Apply

1a. $3 \cdot p + p^2 = 24.79$
1b. 3.7 (Note: -6.7 is also a solution, but students are not expected to find it.)
1c. $3 \cdot p + p^2 = 154$
1d. 11 (Note: -14 is also a solution, but students are not expected to find it.)

Math Link
The area of a circle is given by the formula $A = \pi \cdot r^2$, where r is the radius of the circle.

Real-World Link
Tomatoes are the world's most popular fruit, in terms of tons produced each year.

1. Hannah, Althea, and Jahmal are playing *What's My Rule*. Here is Althea's secret rule.

   $3 \cdot p + p^2 = q$, where p is the input and q is the output

   a. Hannah gives Althea an input. Althea calculates the output as 24.79. Write an equation you could solve to find Hannah's input.

   b. Find a solution of your equation using guess-check-and-improve.

   c. Jahmal gives Althea an input. Althea calculates the output as 154. Write an equation you could solve to find Jahmal's input.

   d. Find a solution of your equation in Part c using guess-check-and-improve.

For each equation, use guess-check-and-improve to find a solution.

2. $16 - 5k = 2$ 2.8

3. $h \cdot (5 + h) = 26.24$ 3.2 (Note: -8.2 is also a solution, but students are not expected to find it.)

4. $y^2 + 72 = 17y$ There are two solutions. Try to find them both.   8, 9

5. **Geometry** Reina is planning her summer garden.

   a. Reina wants to plant strawberries in a circular plot covering an area of 15 square meters. Write an equation to find the radius Reina should use to lay out the plot. $\pi \cdot r^2 = 15$

   b. Use guess-check-and-improve to find the strawberry plot's radius to the nearest tenth of a meter.   2.2 m

   c. Reina also wants to plant tomatoes in five identical circular plots with a total area of 25 square meters. Write an equation to find the radius of one of the tomato plots. $5 \cdot \pi \cdot r^2 = 25$

   d. What should be the radius of each tomato plot, to the nearest tenth of a meter?   1.3 m

9a. $2 \cdot m - 21.75 =$
$\frac{1}{2} \cdot m$

10a. 3 times a number, minus 11, is equal to the number plus 3.

Real-World Link

The macaw is a long-tailed parrot. In the rain forest, macaws have an average life span of 25 to 30 years. In captivity, they can reach ages of 70 years or more.

....

14. 2 (−1 is also a solution, but students are not expected to find it.)

16. 12 (−12 is also a solution, but students are not expected to find it.)

In Exercises 6–8, write an equation to represent the number puzzle. Then find the solution using guess-check-and-improve.

6. Three times a number plus 5 is equal to 5 times the number. What is the number? $3s + 5 = 5s$, 2.5

7. Ten plus the square of a number is equal to 6 times the number plus 2. What is the number? (This puzzle has two solutions. Find them both.) $10 + M^2 = 6M + 2$, 4 or 2

8. Three times a number plus 1 is equal to 9 plus the number. What is the number? $3n + 1 = 9 + n$, 4

9. Marjorie said, "If you double my macaw's age and then subtract 21.75, your answer will be half my macaw's age."

  a. Write an equation to find how old Marjorie's macaw is.

  b. Use guess-check-and-improve to find the macaw's age. Check your answer in Marjorie's original statement. $14\frac{1}{2}$

10. Consider the equation $3m - 11 = m + 3$.

  a. Make up a number puzzle that matches the equation.

  b. Solve the equation. Check that the solution is also the answer to your puzzle.   7

Find a solution of each equation.

11. $3.3h - 7 = 2.801$ 2.97

12. $2l = 4l - 20$ 10

13. $j \cdot (3 - 2j) = 1$ 1 or 0.5

14. $2 = m^2 - m$

15. $9 \cdot \dfrac{g \div 2 + 1}{5} = 12$ $11\frac{1}{3}$

16. $143 = (q + 1) \cdot (q - 1)$

In Exercises 17–19, tell whether you would use backtracking or guess-check-and-improve to find a solution. Explain your choice.

17. $n^2 + n = 30$

18. $47(2v - 3.3) = 85$

19. $s = 17.5s - 0.5$

17. Possible answer: guess-check-and-improve because the variable appears twice

18. Possible answer: backtracking because the variable appears only once

19. Possible answer: guess-check-and-improve because the variable appears twice

▶ **Exercises 11–16** You may want to ask students to draw a flowchart for any equation they solved by backtracking.

▶ **Exercise 15** You may want to go over with the class how to draw a flowchart for this equation because it requires care in following the order of operations.

▶ **Exercise 18** You may want to ask students to find the solution of this equation by backtracking. The exact solution is $2\frac{521}{940}$.

Students will probably realize that finding the exact solution by guess-check-and-improve would be extremely tedious.

▶ **Exercise 23c** Students will probably find it helpful to make a table showing their guesses and the value of $4.9 \cdot t^2$ for each value of t.

Connect & Extend

20. It is important to be able to solve equations in more than one way because sometimes one method may not work or it may take a long time.

21a. $n \cdot (n - 1) = 272$, where n is the number

21b. 17 (−16 is also a solution, but students are not expected to find it.)

22a. $s^2 = 6$, where s is the length of a side

20. **In Your Own Words** You have learned how to solve equations using two methods: backtracking and guess-check-and-improve. Compare these two methods, and explain why it is important to be able to solve equations in more than one way.

21. Aisha and Terrell were playing *Think of a Number*. Terrell said,

    Think of a number. Multiply the number by 1 less than itself. What number do you get?

    Aisha got 272. Terrell must figure out Aisha's starting number.

    a. What equation does Terrell need to solve to find Aisha's number?

    b. Use guess-check-and-improve to find Aisha's number. Check your answer by following the steps to verify that you get 272.

22. **Geometry** The elevator in Rafael's apartment building has a square floor with an area of 6 square meters.

    a. Write an equation to find the dimensions of the elevator floor.

    b. Use guess-check-and-improve to find the dimensions of the elevator floor to the nearest tenth of a meter.   2.4 m by 2.4 m

23. **Physical Science** When an object is dropped, the relationship between the distance it has fallen and the amount of time it has been falling is given by the rule

$$d = 4.9 \cdot t^2$$

where d is the distance in meters and t is the time in seconds.

a. Jing dropped a ball from a pier. It took the ball 1.1 seconds to hit the water. How many meters did the ball travel?   About 5.9 m

b. A bolt falls 300 meters down a mine shaft. Write an equation to find how long it took the bolt to fall. $4.9 \cdot t^2 = 300$

c. Find how long it took the bolt to fall, to the nearest tenth of a second.   7.8 s

★ **24. Nutrition** Three blueberry muffins and a plain bagel have the same number of calories as two blueberry muffins and one bagel with cream cheese. A bagel has 150 calories, and cream cheese adds 170 calories. How many calories are in a blueberry muffin?   170

25. Number Sense This formula can be used to find the sum S of the whole numbers from 1 to n.

$$S = \frac{n \cdot (n + 1)}{2}$$

For example, you can use the formula to find the sum of the whole numbers from 1 to 100.

$$S = \frac{n \cdot (n + 1)}{2}$$
$$= \frac{100 \cdot (100 + 1)}{2}$$
$$= \frac{100 \cdot 101}{2}$$
$$= \frac{10,100}{2}$$
$$= 5,050$$

a. Use the formula to find the sum of the whole numbers from 1 to 9. Calculate $1 + 2 + 3 + 4 + 5 + 6 + 7 + 8 + 9$ to check your answer.   45

b. If the sum of the numbers from 1 to n is 6,670, what must n be?   115

c. If the sum of the numbers from 1 to n is 3,003, what must n be?   77

For each equation, use guess-check-and-improve to find a solution.

26. $x^3 + x = 130$ 5

27. $4n^4 = 48$ About 1.86

28. $2a^4 - 4a^2 = 16$

29. $c^4 = \frac{1}{100}$

28. 2; −2 is also a solution, but students are not expected to find it.
29. 0.32; −0.32 is also a solution, but students are not expected to find it.

▶ **Exercise 27** Students will find it helpful to make a table of values for n and $4n^4$. You may want to allow the use of a calculator for this exercise and point out that students can enter a number and press $\boxed{x^2}$ twice to find the fourth power of the number. Discuss the fact that this works because $(n^2)^2 = n^2 \cdot n^2 = n \cdot n \cdot n \cdot n = n^4$.

▶ **Exercise 29** You may want to suggest that students rewrite the equation using a decimal: $c^4 = 0.01$. You can also adapt the suggestions for Exercise 27 for this exercise.

Quick Check

Informal Assessment Students should be able to:

✔ solve equations systematically by using guess-check-and-improve

✔ find approximate solutions to equations, to the nearest tenth or hundredth

✔ write and solve equations that describe mathematical puzzles or word problems

✔ decide whether to use backtracking or guess-check-and-improve to solve equations

Quick Quiz

1. $11n - 8 = 135$ 13

2. $7x + 15 = 6x + 21$ 6

3. $\dfrac{p + 9}{2} = 6.25$ 3.5

4. $3t^2 + 2t = 161$ 7

5. Find the solution of $x^3 = 12$ to the nearest tenth. 2.3

Examine each equation. Tell whether you think it would be better to use backtracking or guess-check-and-improve to find the solution. Explain your thinking.

6. $9 + \dfrac{3k - 7}{12} = 200$ Backtracking; Possible explanation: The variable occurs only once, and it is easy to make a flowchart for the equation.

7. $x \cdot (x^2 + 1) = 57$ Guess-check-and-improve; Possible explanation: The variable is in two factors, one of which is a sum of a variable and the number 1. It is not possible to make a flowchart for the equation.

30a. 20π cubic centimeters, or about 62.8 cubic centimeters

30. Geometry The *volume* of a three-dimensional shape is the amount of space inside of it. Volume is measured in cubic units, such as cubic centimeters and cubic inches. You can calculate the volume V of a cylinder with radius r and height h using this formula: $V = \pi \cdot r^2 \cdot h$.

a. Calculate the volume of a cylinder with radius 2 centimeters and height 5 centimeters.

b. A can of fruit has a volume of 350 cubic centimeters and a height of 15 centimeters. Write an equation you could solve to find its radius. $\pi \cdot r^2 \cdot 15 = 350$

c. Solve your equation to find the can's radius to the nearest tenth of a centimeter. 2.7 cm

Mixed Review

31. Geometry A rectangle has an area of 48 square feet and a perimeter of 32 feet. What are the dimensions of the rectangle? 12 ft by 4 ft

32. Which has the greater area, a circle with diameter 11 meters or a square with side length 10 meters? The square

33. Sports In a track-and-field competition, ten women participated in the 100-meter run. Here are their times in seconds.

12.2   11.3   13.5   11.5   11.7   12.6   15.5   11.8   13.4   11.5

a. Find the mean and the median time. Mean: 12.5 s; median: 12 s

Fill in the blanks.

34. 25% of __56__ = 14

35. __$33\frac{1}{3}$__ % of 75 = 25

36. 80% of 200 = __160__

37. 125% of __240__ = 300

38. __85__ % of 280 = 238

39. 1% of 30 = __0.3__

Review & Self-Assessment

Chapter Summary

You started this chapter by looking at numeric equations and inequalities. Then you turned your attention to equations containing variables. You learned that a value of a variable that makes an equation true is called a *solution* of the equation. You saw that while many equations have only one or two solutions, some have every number as a solution. Others have no solution at all.

You then created flowcharts to represent rules. You also saw how *backtracking*, working backward from an output using a flowchart, can be used to solve some equations. You were then faced with equations that could not be solved by backtracking, and you learned how to use *guess-check-and-improve* to solve them. Finally, you learned some strategies for determining which solution method to use for a given equation.

Strategies and Applications

The questions in this section will help you review and apply the important ideas and strategies developed in this chapter.

Understanding equations and inequalities

1. Explain what the symbols =, >, <, and ≠ mean. For each symbol, write a true mathematical sentence using that symbol.

2. Give an example of an open sentence. Provide a value of the variable that makes your sentence true.   Possible answer: $5 \cdot x = 45$, 9

3. Explain why the sentence $P + 5 = P$ is never true.

4. Explain why the sentence $2 \cdot (x + 3) = 2 \cdot x + 2 \cdot 3$ is always true.

Solving equations by backtracking

5. Solve this equation by creating a flowchart and backtracking.

$$10 \cdot \frac{4 + 9x}{7} - 25 = 45$$

Explain each step in your solution.   See margin.

6. Admission to the town carnival is $4.50 per person. Tickets for rides cost 75¢ each. Russ has $10 to spend at the carnival, and he wants to go on as many rides as possible.

a. Write an equation you could solve to find the number of tickets *t* Russ can buy. $4.5 + 0.75t = 10$

b. Solve your equation by backtracking. How many tickets can Russ buy? $7.\overline{3}$; Russ can buy 7 tickets.

Vocabulary
- backtracking
- equation
- flowchart
- guess-check-and-improve
- inequality
- open sentence
- solution

1. = means is equal to. Possible example: $7 + 3 = 2 \cdot 5$. > means is greater than. Possible example: $7 \cdot 8 > 7 + 8$. < means is less than. Possible example: $7 - 7 < 7 + 7$. ≠ means is not equal to. Possible example: $6 + 2 \neq 6 \div 2$.

3. When you add 5 to a number, the result is always greater than the number.

4. Possible explanation: $2 \cdot (x + 3) = (x + 3) + (x + 3) = x + x + 3 + 3 = 2 \cdot x + 2 \cdot 3$

Review & Self-Assessment

Chapter Summary
This summary helps students recall the major topics of the chapter.

Vocabulary
Students should be able to explain each of the terms listed in the vocabulary section.

▶ **Exercise 1** Check students' examples to be sure they can correctly distinguish = from ≠, and < from >.

▶ **Exercises 3 and 4** Provide a sentence frame for students to use when starting an explanation, such as, "$P + 5 = P$ can never be true because _____." Sentence frames like this help students form their ideas around the main thought they are explaining.

▶ **Exercise 5** Have students read the problem out loud forward. Then tell them to say the reverse steps out loud as they fill in the flowchart. Remind them that the only change they can make to the steps is to reverse them if they want to find the correct answer.

▶ **Exercises 6 and 7** Tell students to take notes or draw illustrations as they read each problem. Remind them that they can refer back to their notes in each step, so they should pay close attention to the problem and try to make their notes/drawings as accurate as possible.

Additional Answer
Review & Self-Assessment

5. Possible answer: First, I made a flowchart. The output is 45.

Then I worked backward from the output to find the input. 25 was subtracted from the number in the fifth oval to get 45, so that number must be 70. The number in the fourth oval was multiplied by 10 to get 70, so it must be 7. The number in the third oval was divided by 7 to get 7, so it must be 49. 4 was added to the number in the second oval to get 49, so it must be 45.

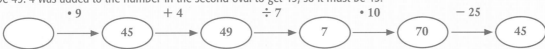

The number in the first oval was multiplied by 9 to get 45, so it must be 5. The solution is 5.

▶ **Exercises 9 and 10** Have students make a list of the possible solution methods they have learned. Tell them to make quick notes that tell which types of problems can be solved with each method. Students can refer to the list as they solve these exercises.

▶ **Exercises 11–14** Students have to simplify both sides of each equation. It may be necessary to provide some extra time and/or assistance when students are determining what number or symbol needs to be changed to make a false equation true.

▶ **Exercises 15–20** Tell students that these problems check their understanding of many concepts they have learned. Remind them to think about what seems right or wrong about each problem, and tell them to substitute in a number if the variables make the problems too confusing.

▶ **Exercise 21** If students have difficulty with this problem, remind them to think of possible solution methods, such as backtracking.

▶ **Exercise 22** Students who have difficulty using variables may need help solving these problems. Explain that solving for a variable means using the operations in the problem to make it easier to find the value of the variable. Solve one problem on the board for students to use as a reference while working.

Additional Answers

7b. 4.2 m; Possible table:

x	$15 \cdot x^2$	Comment
6	540	too high
4	240	too low
5	375	too high
4.4	290.4	still too high
4.2	264.6	solution

7a. $15 \cdot x^2 = 264.6$

10. Possible answer: I would use backtracking. Since the numbers are all decimals, the solution is probably a decimal, too. It might take lots of guesses to find it. Since one side of the equation is a number and the variable appears only once on the other side, this equation would be fairly easy to solve by backtracking.

15. Always true; the exponent of 3 means that c is multiplied together 3 times.

16. Never true; Possible explanation: If you subtract 5 from any number, the result is always smaller than when you add 1 to that number.

17. Sometimes true: Possible explanation: The equation is true when $x = 9$ but not when $x = 10$ (or any other number).

Solving equations using guess-check-and-improve

7. The Smallville community garden is made up of 15 identical square plots with a total area of 264.6 m².

   a. Write an equation to find the side length of each plot.

   b. Solve your equation using guess-check-and-improve. Make a table to record your guesses and the results. What is the side length of each plot? See margin.

8. A number multiplied by 2 more than the number is 9 times the number, plus 8.

   a. Write an equation to represent the number puzzle.
   $x \cdot (x + 2) = 9 \cdot x + 8$

   b. Solve your equation using guess-check-and-improve. 8; −1 is also a solution, but students are not expected to find it.

Choosing a solution method for an equation

9. Explain why you could not use backtracking to solve the equation $(n + 3.5) \cdot n = 92$. See margin.

10. Tell which solution method you would use to solve the equation $6.34 + 10.97 \cdot y = 208.188$. Give reasons for your choice.

Demonstrating Skills

Tell whether each sentence is *true* or *false*. If it is false, make it true by changing one number or symbol.

11. $(4 + 5) \cdot 6 = 24 + 30$ True

12. $4^2 = 4 \cdot 2$ False; Possible answer: $4^2 > 4 \cdot 2$

13. $30 \div (3 + 2) = 30 \div 3 + 30 \div 2$ False; $30 \div (3 + 2) \neq 30 \div 3 + 30 \div 2$

14. $7 + 4 - 1 > 5 + 6$ False; $9 + 4 - 1 > 5 + 6$

Tell whether each equation is *always true, sometimes true,* or *never true.* Explain how you know.

15. $c^3 = c \cdot c \cdot c$ 16. $n - 5 = n + 1$

17. $x - 9 = 0$ 18. $2m - 2m = 0$ See margin.

Find a solution of each equation.

19. $4.7x + 12.3 = 42.85$ 6.5   20. $m \cdot (m + 5) = 336$ See margin.

21. $5n + 7 = 14$ 1.4   22. $\frac{5(x - 1)}{3} = 7.5$ 5.5

9. Possible answer: You could try to make a flowchart like this.

But when you tried to backtrack, the first step would be to find the number that was multiplied by *n* to get 92. Since you do not know what *n* is, this is impossible.

18. Always true; when you subtract a number from itself, you always get 0.

20. 16; −21 is also a solution, but students are not expected to find it.

23. Sarah lives near the library. In the summer, she likes to walk to the library. The following directions describe how to get from Sarah's house to the library.

- Start at the corner of Winfree Drive and Dempsey Road.
- Walk two blocks west on Dempsey.
- Turn right from Dempsey to Hempstead Road.
- Walk 3 blocks north on Hempstead Road.
- Turn left on Schrock Road.
- Walk 2 blocks west on Schrock Road.
- Turn right on Otterbein Road.
- Walk 4 blocks north on Otterbein Road.
- Turn left on Walnut Street.
- Walk 5 blocks west on Walnut Street.
- The library is on the corner of Walnut Street and State Street.

Write a set of directions that Sarah could follow to get home from the library.   See margin.

Test-Taking Practice

SHORT RESPONSE

1 Tell whether the sentence is true or false. If it is false, make it true by changing one number or symbol.

$$13 + 26 = (3 + 4) \cdot 7$$

Show your work.

Answer _____

MULTIPLE CHOICE

2 Which is a solution to the equation $7x = 63$?
(A) 9
B 56
C 70
D 441

3 Which operation can be used to solve the equation $\frac{h}{3} = 6$?
F add 3 to both sides of the equation
G subtract 3 from both sides of the equation
H divide both sides of the equation by 3
(J) multiply both sides of the equation by 3

4 Solve the following equation.
$$6m + 11 = 35$$
(A) 4
B 6
C 7
D 8

5 You buy 3 pens for $4.50. The equation that can be used to find the cost of each pen is $3p = 4.5$. How much does each pen cost?
F $1.00
G $1.25
(H) $1.50
J $1.75

Show your work:
$13 + 26 = (3 + 4) \cdot 7$
$39 = 7 \cdot 7$
$39 = 49$
The sentence is false. To make the sentence true, 13 could be changed to 23. Then $23 + 26 = 49$, and $49 = 49$.

Answer: False; sample answer: change 13 to 23

▶ **Exercise 23** Have students who have difficulty with this problem tell you how to get to their houses from the school. Then have them tell you how to get to the school from their houses. Explain that this exercise is asking for the same changes as the ones in their own directions.

Additional Answer

23. • Start at the corner of Walnut Street and State Street.
- Walk 5 blocks east on Walnut Street.
- Turn right on Otterbein Road.
- Walk 4 blocks south on Otterbein Road.
- Turn left on Schrock Road.
- Walk 2 blocks east on Schrock Road.
- Turn right on Hempstead Road.
- Walk 3 blocks south on Hempstead Road.
- Turn left on Dempsey Road.
- Walk 2 blocks east on Dempsey Road.
- Arrive at the corner of Dempsey Road and Winfree Drive.

Lesson 9.2, Share & Summarize (p. 549)

1. Possible answer: A flowchart is a diagram that traces the steps you follow to evaluate a rule. In the rule $t = 5n - 3$, you find the output t in two steps: multiply the input n by 5, and then subtract 3. This is shown below. The arrows represent the steps, or the operations, and the results of the steps go in the ovals.

3. Possible answer: Backtracking is a method for finding the input that gives a certain output by working backward using a flowchart. In the equation $5n - 3 = 45$, you can think of 45 as the output. To solve the equation, find the value of the input n. Start by writing the output, 45, in the last oval:

Since 3 was subtracted from the number in the second oval to get 45, that number must be 48:

Since the input was multiplied by 5 to get 48, it must be equal to $\frac{48}{5}$, or 9.6.

Lesson 9.2, Share & Summarize (p. 552)

Possible answer: Suppose you want to use backtracking to solve the equations $6 + n \cdot 3 = 21$. If you don't pay attention to order of operations, you might make a flowchart that does the addition before the multiplication:

If you backtrack using this flowchart, you get 1, which is not the solution since $6 + 1 \cdot 3$ is equal to 9, not to 21.

Notes

CHAPTER 10

Data and Probability

Chapter Overview

In this chapter students work with mathematical tools for analyzing data to help them uncover and understand the story behind the data. In some investigations, students role-play as analysts in a data-consulting group named Data Inc. to use their developing knowledge about data to solve problems for clients.

The first lesson builds on many of the ideas about graphing from Chapter 8. Students work with familiar line graphs and bar graphs and are introduced to a new visual display, histograms. They consider the shape of the graph to help them describe data. Students then go on to collect and analyze data and then to make predictions and choose a graph.

In the last lessons, students study basic concepts of probability. They use data in situations involving equally likely outcomes to compute experimental probabilities. They then compare experimental and theoretical probabilities. Students see how probability can help them decide whether a game is fair, and they use probability to devise strategies for scoring points in some simple games of chance. Finally, students compare and contrast situations involving independent and dependent events.

The **Big** Picture

Links to the Past	Chapter 10	Links to the Future
Grade 5 Creating and interpreting bar graphs.	**Lesson 10.1** (p. 578) Data Displays	**Course 2, Chapter 6** Data and Probability (pp. 260–317) **Course 3, Chapter 11** Data and Probability (pp. 576–625)
Grade 5 Understanding number lines; creating and interpreting pictographs; choosing the appropriate operation to solve a problem.	**Lesson 10.2** (p. 601) Collect and Analyze Data	**Course 2, Chapter 6** Data and Probability (pp. 260–317) **Course 3, Chapter 11** Data and Probability (pp. 576–625)
Grade 5 Exploring probability; collecting and recording data from an experiment; collecting and analyzing data samples to determine whether a game is fair.	**Lesson 10.3** (p. 617) The Language of Chance	**Course 2, Chapter 6** Data and Probability (pp. 260–317)
Grade 5 Finding probabilities in equally likely situations.	**Lesson 10.4** (p. 638) Make Matches	**Course 2, Chapter 6** Data and Probability (pp. 260–317)

Mathematical Background

Chapter 10 gives students an opportunity to explore basic concepts of probability. They learn how data about a situation can be used to find an experimental probability for an event. They learn to calculate theoretical probabilities in situations that involve equally likely outcomes. They also explore geometric probability. Finally, they use probability to analyze some situations in which one outcome can affect subsequent outcomes.

Experimental vs. Theoretical Probability The probability of an event is a number that tells how likely the event is to occur. In the first lesson of this chapter, students examine two ways of gauging probability. *Experimental probability* is based on data about a situation. The fraction that compares the number of times a particular event actually occurred to the total number of times it might have occurred is called the experimental probability of the event.

Theoretical probability is based on reasoning. When you roll a die, there are only six numbers that can be outcomes. Each number on the die has the same chance of coming up as any other number. If you are interested in the chances of rolling a multiple of three, you can simply write a fraction comparing the number of outcomes that represent successfully rolling a multiple of three to the total number of possible outcomes. The way experimental and theoretical probabilities are defined ensures that they will be numbers from zero to one. It is important to note that experimental probabilities can change if you acquire more data about a situation. Theoretical probabilities, on the other hand, are fixed quantities that do not vary.

Equally Likely Outcomes Situations in which the individual outcomes are equally likely to occur are especially simple and easy to study. Examples of such situations are rolling a die, flipping a coin, spinning a spinner that is divided into equal-sized sections, and drawing a card of a particular suit from a standard deck. Students learn to think about all the possible outcomes in such situations and to calculate the probabilities of various events that might occur.

Games of Chance Students then focus on how probability can be used to analyze games of chance. Some of the games use specially labeled number cubes, and others use standard dice. Tables can be used to examine all the possible outcomes and hence to calculate theoretical probabilities. One of the games that are examined theoretically involves an infinite number of possible outcomes. This final game uses a rectangular game board. Students drop a grain of rice on the board and collect data about the shapes in which the rice lands. They discover that the likelihood of the rice landing in a particular shape is the fraction of the total area of the game board occupied by that shape.

Additional Reading

Guidelines by the American Statistical Association and the Mathematical Association of America emphasize statistical thinking, data, concepts, and active learning. The exercises in these lessons should help emphasize these areas.

Planning Guide
Lesson Resources

	Pacing: 5 days **Lesson 10.1**	Pacing: 5 days **Lesson 10.2**	Pacing: 5 days **Lesson 10.3**	Pacing: 3 days **Lesson 10.4**
Lesson Title	**Data Displays** (p. 578)	**Collect and Analyze Data** (p. 601)	**The Language of Chance** (p. 617)	**Make Matches** (p. 638)
Lesson Objectives	• To interpret and compare line graphs • To use bar graphs and histograms to display data • To create bar graphs and histograms from sets of data • To decide whether to use a bar graph or a histogram to display a given set of data	• To prepare and follow a plan that includes selecting the appropriate statistical measures • To estimate large quantities based on sample size • To choose an appropriate graph to display data	• To associate a number from 0 to 1 with the likelihood that an event will occur • To find the experimental probability of an event • To find the theoretical probability of an event	• To make tree diagrams to show outcomes for situations that involve independent or dependent choices • To count the number of possibilities using the counting principle
Materials	Lesson 10.1 Masters 1–9	Lesson 10.2 Masters 1–4, bags of beans, Chapter 10 Master 1, ruler, protractor, compass	Lesson 10.3 Masters 1–2, Chapter 10 Masters 1–2, paper cups, coins, dice, scissors, tape counters, inch rulers	*counters, *blocks, buckets or paper bags
Quick Review Math Handbook	**Lesson 4.2** Displaying Data	**Lesson 4.1** Collecting Data	**Lesson 4.4** Probability	**Lesson 4.4** Probability
Print Resources	CRM Study Guide and Intervention (p. 6) CRM Skills Practice (p. 7) CRM Problem-Solving Practice (p. 8) CRM Enrichment (p. 9) • Investigation Notebook and Reflection Journal • Differentiation Handbook	CRM Study Guide and Intervention (p. 20) CRM Skills Practice (p. 21) CRM Problem-Solving Practice (p. 22) CRM Enrichment (p. 23) • Investigation Notebook and Reflection Journal • Differentiation Handbook	CRM Study Guide and Intervention (p. 29) CRM Skills Practice (p. 30) CRM Problem-Solving Practice (p. 31) CRM Enrichment (p. 32) • Investigation Notebook and Reflection Journal • Differentiation Handbook	CRM Study Guide and Intervention (p. 36) CRM Skills Practice (p. 37) CRM Problem-Solving Practice (p. 38) CRM Enrichment (p. 39) • Investigation Notebook and Reflection Journal • Differentiation Handbook
Technology Resources	TeacherWorks Plus Classroom Presentation Toolkit ExamView Assessment Suite StudentWorks Plus Math Online ▸ Brain Pops • Concepts in Motion	TeacherWorks Plus Classroom Presentation Toolkit ExamView Assessment Suite StudentWorks Plus Math Online ▸ Brain Pops • Concepts in Motion	TeacherWorks Plus Classroom Presentation Toolkit ExamView Assessment Suite StudentWorks Plus Math Online ▸ Brain Pops • Concepts in Motion	TeacherWorks Plus Classroom Presentation Toolkit ExamView Assessment Suite StudentWorks Plus Math Online ▸ Brain Pops • Concepts in Motion

*Included in the Impact Mathematics Manipulative Kit

Assessment Resources

MARS Assessment: Teaching with Purpose

Travel To School

In *Travel To School,* students complete and interpret a data table and a bar graph that show how students travel to school. Students also find the percentage of students who use the different modes of transportation.

Targeting the Task

- **Diagnostic**—Use Exercises 1–2 in the *Travel To School* assessment to determine students' understanding of how to complete and interpret a data table and a bar graph. Students also use percents. For those students who do not have this understanding, completing this unit is needed.

- **Formative**—Exercises 1–2 can be administered individually according to the lessons.

- **Summative**—Administer the complete *Travel To School* performance-based assessment.

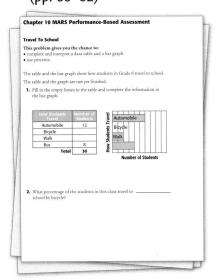

CRM Chapter 10 MARS Assessment (pp. 60–62)

Assessment Planning Guide

Assessments are available for investigations, lessons, and chapters.

ExamView® Assessment Suite Customize and create multiple versions of tests and quizzes.

	Student Edition	Teacher Edition	Other Resources
Diagnostic			CRM Chapter 10 Pretest (p. 41) **Math Online** Online Chapter Quiz
Formative	Share & Summarize (pp. 580, 584, 587, 591, 604, 606, 608, 610, 620, 625, 632, 642, 644, 647)	Troubleshooting (pp. 587, 604, 606, 608, 620, 625, 632, 642, 646) On the Spot Assessment (pp. 581, 589, 604, 619, 631, 640) Quick Check (pp. 599, 616, 637, 653) Quick Quiz (pp. 600, 616, 637, 653)	
Summative	Review & Self-Assessment (pp. 654–657)		CRM Chapter 10 Test: Forms A and B (pp. 45-54) CRM Standardized Test Practice (p. 58) CRM Semester Test: Forms A and B (pp. 63–74)
Performance-Based	In Your Own Words (pp. 599, 613, 636)		CRM MARS Performance-Based Assessment (p. 60) CRM Chapter Performance Assessment (p. 55)

Differentiated Instruction

Reaching All Learners

Below are suggestions on differentiating the materials presented in this chapter. Additional modifications should be considered.

Approaching Level (AL)

Lesson 10.1: Data Displays For students who have difficulty creating histograms, have a timed class event, such as writing all the letters of the alphabet backward and forward. Have each student raise a hand when finished so you can mark his or her times. Record the finishing times in the chart (excluding names) and have students help you determine the number in each appropriate bracket of time. Discuss the numbers that should be on the axes of the bar graph. Then have pairs work together to create a bar graph showing the information from the chart. Under their graphs, have students write a short description of the graph and the information it displays. You can also use the same data to create a histogram.

Beyond Level (BL)

Lesson 10.2: Choose a Graph Have students work in small groups to create a survey for the class. Suggest topics such as favorite music, number of pets, and so on. Remind students that they will be making a graph from their findings, so it is important to take accurate notes during the survey. Instruct groups to decide how the information they gathered should be displayed. Have them choose a line graph, a histogram, or a bar graph; then provide poster paper for them to use in making the graph. Allow groups to share their posters with the class. Then discuss why the graphs the groups chose were the best choice. Point out that the information in each graph is most easily understood when displayed correctly.

On Level (OL)

Lesson 10.3: Probability Have pairs design a probability experiment. Tell them to use small objects in the classroom, such as pencils or erasers. Remind students that a probability experiment involves seeing what happens, so they must set up an experiment that has different possible results. Have them write a list of predictions, using *likely*, *unlikely*, *probably*, and *certain*. Then have them conduct their experiments and record the results. Make sure they compare their results to their predictions to see if they were right. Then have students create proportions to show how the results for each possibility compared to the total number of tries in the experiment. Encourage them to share their results with the class and discuss their findings.

English Language Learners (ELL)

Data Displays The many types of data displays in this chapter can be confusing. Use index cards to create an example of each type the students use in the chapter. On one side, create the example; on the other, write the type of example and a short description of its uses. Review the cards with the students, and discuss each display's purpose. Read the descriptions aloud and ask students to point out important details about each example. Have pairs quiz each other. One student holds up a card with the example showing, and the other student names the kind of display and its uses. Or, one student reads the description and then spreads out the examples from which the other student chooses. Allow students to use the cards as a study guide for this chapter.

KEY

(AL) Approaching Level   (OL) On Level   (BL) Beyond Level   (ELL) English Language Learners

Intervention Planning Guide

CRM Assess students' prerequisite skills and knowledge using the
Chapter Pretest found in the Chapter 10 Resource Masters, p. 41.

Intensive Intervention two or more years below grade level	Strategic Intervention below grade level	On Level	Beyond Level
If ▶ students miss 75% of the exercises: **Then** ▶ use *Math Triumphs,* an intensive intervention	**If** ▶ students miss 50% of the exercises: **Then** ▶ choose a resource:	**If** ▶ students miss 25% of the exercises: **Then** ▶ choose a resource:	**If** ▶ students miss 0%–10% of the exercises: **Then** ▶ choose a resource:
Math Triumphs, Grade 6 • Chapter 7: Ratios, Rates, and Unit Rates	**CRM** Study Guide and Intervention (pp. 6, 20, 29, 36) • Investigation Notebook and Reflection Journal • Differentiation Handbook **Math Online** ▶ Brain Pops • Concepts in Motion	**CRM** Skills Practice (pp. 7, 21, 30, 37) **CRM** Problem-Solving Practice (pp. 8, 22, 31, 38) • Investigation Notebook and Reflection Journal	**CRM** Enrichment (pp. 9, 23, 32, 39) • Differentiation Handbook

Literature Connections

Recommended Outside Reading for Students

Nonfiction

Bamberger, Honi and Patricia Hughes. *Super Graphs, Venns & Glyphs.* Scholastic Trade, 1999.

> Geared toward a young audience, this book presents fun opportunites for data collection in one's own home. Packed with ideas and designed to spark creativity, it supplements the graphing lessons in this chapter.

Moscovish, Ivan, and Brion, David. *Probability Game.* Workman Publishing Company, Inc., 2000.

> This illustrated book covers prediction, luck, and random chance in a variety of games. Readers experience the challenge of solving problems and new ways of viewing things.

Fiction

Cole, Joanna. *The Magic School Bus on the Ocean Floor.* Scholastic Trade, 1994. Use with *A Guide for Using The Magic School Bus on the Ocean Floor*® in the Classroom. Teacher Created Materials, 1996.

> In this book from the famous series, teacher Ms. Frizzle takes her class on a lively tour of the ocean. The companion book includes student activities collecting, analyzing, and graphing of data related to the ocean.

McGraw Hill Professional Development

Targeted professional development has been articulated throughout the *IMPACT Mathematics* series. The **McGraw-Hill Professional Development Video Library** provides short videos that support the mathematics standards. Log on to **www.glencoe.com**.

Model Lessons   Instructional Strategies

Real-Life Math

Fat Chance! The facts on this page give students some idea of the broad variety of situations in which chance and probability play a role. Students have most likely heard about people winning fabulous lottery prizes, but they may not have realized how remote the chances are of picking the winning numbers. Tell students that in this chapter they will see how probability can help them analyze situations like those on this page. They will also see how probability can be used to study games and determine whether a game is fair.

Think About It Students will need to locate the local weather report in the newspaper, on television, or on the Internet. Discuss the probability of rain tomorrow, which is usually given as a percent. Students may wish to write the percent as a fraction and as a decimal to more easily compare it to the other probabilities.

Data and Probability

Real-Life Math

Fat Chance! A probability is a number between 0 and 1 that tells you the chance that an event will occur. The closer a probability is to 0, the less likely the event is to happen.

Just how likely is it that some everyday events happen?

- If you toss a coin to determine the answers of a 10-question true-false test, the probability you will get all the answers correct is $\frac{1}{1,024}$, or about 0.001.
- If you randomly dial a three-number combination on a dial lock with numbers from 0 to 29, the probability you will open the lock is $\frac{1}{27,000}$, or about 0.00004.

Contents in Brief

Think About It To better understand how unlikely these events are, compare these probabilities to the probability that it will rain tomorrow in your community.

Math Online
Take the **Chapter Readiness Quiz** at glencoe.com.

576

Chapter Resources

- CRM Chapter 10 Resource Masters
- CRM English/Spanish Family Letter (pp. 1 and 2)
- CRM Lesson Masters (pp. 3–5, 11–19, 25–28, 34, 35)
- CRM Chapter 10 Pretest (pp. 41–44)
- CRM Chapter 10 Tests (pp. 45–57)
- **Math Online** Online Readiness Quiz • eGlossary

Dear Family,

The class will close its exciting year of mathematics by exploring probability and analyzing data with graphs. Probability tells you that it is very unlikely for you to win the grand prize in a state lottery. Suppose you have to pick six different numbers from 1 to 54. To win the grand prize, all six numbers must match those selected in a random drawing. The probability that you will win is only 1 in 25,827,165, or 0.00000004.

Along with analyzing data, numbers, facts, or other measurable information, it is important to display your findings. Graphs can make it easier to see patterns and draw conclusions.

Key Concept–Probability

The probability that some event will happen can be described by a number between 0 and 1.
- A probability of 0 means that the event has no chance of happening. So, the probability of winning a state lottery is very close to 0.
- A probability of 1 means that the event is certain to happen.
- A probability of $\frac{1}{2}$, or 50%, means that the event is just as likely to happen as not to happen.

For example, if a weather forecaster states that the probability of rain tomorrow is 90%, it's probably a good idea to take your umbrella, although it might not rain after all. If the probability of rain is 10%, it is unlikely that it will rain.

In this chapter, the class will use mathematical reasoning to calculate probabilities in simple situations like tossing coins or drawing names from a hat. Students will also do some experiments in which they actually toss coins or draw names and then compare the results with the calculated probabilities.

Chapter Vocabulary

distribution	Fundamental Counting Principle	simulation
equally likely		theoretical probability
experimental probability	histogram	
	probability	Venn diagram

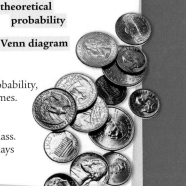

Home Activities
- Look for situations in everyday life that involve probability, such as the chance of rain or the odds in sports games.
- Encourage your student's exploration by playing games of chance together.
- Have your student teach you the games we play in class. Ask him or her to describe what part probability plays in each game.

577

Family Letter

Another version of the Family Letter, available in English and Spanish, is found in the Chapter 10 Resource Masters. You may want to send a copy of this letter home with your students.

Key Concept–Probability Introduce students to probability by describing how weather forecasters give the probability of rain or other weather events as a percent, or number that is between zero and one. Ask students to interpret the forecast. Does a 10% chance of rain mean that rain is likely?

Home Activities
- Each day have your students keep a log of the chance of rain either for your town or for another town. Ask them to use newspapers or the Internet to find these percents.

- Have your students plan a simulated vacation to a location far from home. How will they know what to pack? Do they need rain gear?

Key Vocabulary

English (Spanish) *Introduce the most important terms from Chapter 10.*

equally likely (equiprobables) Outcomes of a situation or experiment that have the same probability of occurring. For example, if one coin is tossed, coming up heads and coming up tails are *equally likely* outcomes. (p. 621)

experimental probability (probabilidad experimental) A probability based on experimental data. An *experimental probability* is always an estimate and can vary depending on the particular set of data that is used. (p. 619)

probability (probabilidad) The chance that an event will happen, described as a number between 0 and 1. For example, the probability of tossing a coin and getting heads is $\frac{1}{2}$ or 50%. A probability of 0 or 0% means the event has no chance of happening, and a probability of 1 or 100% means the event is certain to happen. (p. 618)

simulation (simulacro) An experiment in which you use different items to represent the items in a real situation. For example, to simulate choosing markers and looking at their colors, you can write the color of each number on a slip of paper and put all the slips into a bag. You can simulate choosing markers by drawing slips from the bag. Mathematically, the situations are identical. (p. 639)

theoretical probability (probabilidad teórica) Probability calculated by reasoning about the situation. Since *theoretical probabilities* do not depend on experiments, they are always the same for a particular event. (p. 621)

Data Displays

Objectives

▶ To interpret and compare line graphs

▶ To use bar graphs and histograms to display data

▶ To create bar graphs and histograms from sets of data

▶ To decide whether to use a bar graph or a histogram to display a given set of data

Overview

In this lesson, students use tables, line graphs, bar graphs, histograms, and Venn diagrams to analyze data. Double bar graphs are reviewed in the On Your Own Exercises. This lesson provides an introduction to data analysis. Students not only engage with real data and experience the power of graphical representations of data, but also think about and try to understand what stories the data tell in each situation.

Advance Preparation

You may want to provide Lesson 10.1 Masters 1-9 to facilitate class discussion while presenting new topics, including using graphs to display data.

	Summary	Materials	On Your Own Exercises (pp. 592–600)	Assessment Opportunities
Investigation 1 (p. 579) *Pacing: 2 days*	Students use unlabeled line graphs and other clues to solve a mystery.	Lesson 10.1 Masters 1 and 2 or transparencies of them	Practice & Apply: 1 Connect & Extend: 9, 10 Mixed Review: 16–28	• Share & Summarize (p. 580)
Investigation 2 (p. 581) *Pacing: 1 day*	Students use information from multiple bar graphs to analyze trends in vehicle emissions.	Lesson 10.1 Masters 3 and 4	Practice & Apply: 2 Connect & Extend: 11–13 Mixed Review: 16–28	• On the Spot Assessment (p. 581) • Share & Summarize (p. 584)
Investigation 3 (p. 585) *Pacing: 1 day*	Students make histograms to display and interpret frequency data.	Lesson 10.1 Master 5 Transparency of Lesson 10.1 Master 5 (optional), Lesson 10.1 Masters 6–9 (optional)	Practice & Apply: 3, 8 Mixed Review: 16–28	• Share & Summarize (p. 587) • Troubleshooting (p. 587)
Investigation 4 (p. 588) *Pacing: 1 day*	Students use Venn diagrams to organize and display data.		Practice & Apply: 4–7 Connect & Extend: 14, 15 Mixed Review: 16–28	• On the Spot Assessment (p. 589) • Share & Summarize (p. 591)

Leveled Lesson Resources

Also on
TeacherWorks™
Lesson 10.1

CRM *Available in:* **Chapter 10 Resource Masters**

Study Guide and Intervention (p. 6) | AL

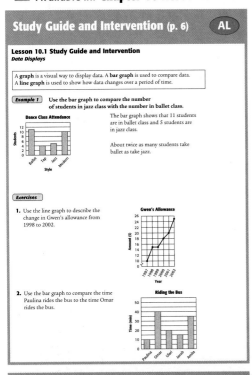

Lesson 10.1 Study Guide and Intervention
Data Displays

A **graph** is a visual way to display data. A **bar graph** is used to compare data. A **line graph** is used to show how data changes over a period of time.

Example 1 Use the bar graph to compare the number of students in jazz class with the number in ballet class.

The bar graph shows that 11 students are in ballet class and 5 students are in jazz class.

About twice as many students take ballet as take jazz.

Exercises

1. Use the line graph to describe the change in Gwen's allowance from 1998 to 2002.

2. Use the bar graph to compare the time Paulina rides the bus to the time Omar rides the bus.

Skills Practice (p. 7) | AL | OL

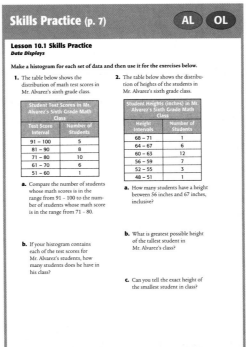

Lesson 10.1 Skills Practice
Data Displays

Make a histogram for each set of data and then use it for the exercises below.

1. The table below shows the distribution of math test scores in Mr. Alvarez's sixth grade class.

Test Score Interval	Number of Students
91 – 100	5
81 – 90	8
71 – 80	10
61 – 70	6
51 – 60	1

a. Compare the number of students whose math scores is in the range from 91 – 100 to the number of students whose math score is in the range from 71 – 80.

b. If your histogram contains each of the test scores for Mr. Alvarez's students, how many students does he have in his class?

2. The table below shows the distribution of heights of the students in Mr. Alvarez's sixth grade class.

Height Intervals	Number of Students
68 – 71	1
64 – 67	6
60 – 63	12
56 – 59	7
52 – 55	3
48 – 51	1

a. How many students have a height between 56 inches and 67 inches, inclusive?

b. What is greatest possible height of the tallest student in Mr. Alvarez's class?

c. Can you tell the exact height of the smallest student in class?

Problem-Solving Practice (p. 8) | AL | OL

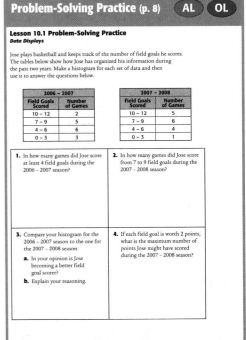

Lesson 10.1 Problem-Solving Practice
Data Displays

Jose plays basketball and keeps track of the number of field goals he scores. The tables below show how Jose has organized his information during the past two years. Make a histogram for each set of data and then use it to answer the questions below.

2006 – 2007	
Field Goals Scored	Number of Games
10 – 12	2
7 – 9	5
4 – 6	6
0 – 3	3

2007 – 2008	
Field Goals Scored	Number of Games
10 – 12	5
7 – 9	6
4 – 6	4
0 – 3	1

1. In how many games did Jose score at least 4 field goals during the 2006 – 2007 season?

2. In how many games did Jose score from 7 to 9 field goals during the 2007 – 2008 season?

3. Compare your histogram for the 2006 – 2007 season to the one for the 2007 – 2008 season.
   a. In your opinion is Jose becoming a better field goal scorer?
   b. Explain your reasoning.

4. If each field goal is worth 2 points, what is the maximum number of points Jose might have scored during the 2007 – 2008 season?

Enrichment (p. 9) | BL

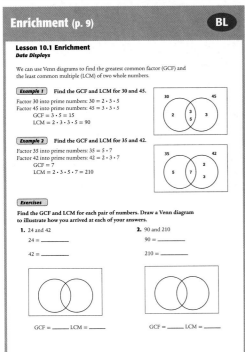

Lesson 10.1 Enrichment
Data Displays

We can use Venn diagrams to find the greatest common factor (GCF) and the least common multiple (LCM) of two whole numbers.

Example 1 Find the GCF and LCM for 30 and 45.

Factor 30 into prime numbers: $30 = 2 \cdot 3 \cdot 5$
Factor 45 into prime numbers: $45 = 3 \cdot 3 \cdot 5$
GCF $= 3 \cdot 5 = 15$
LCM $= 2 \cdot 3 \cdot 3 \cdot 5 = 90$

Example 2 Find the GCF and LCM for 35 and 42.

Factor 35 into prime numbers: $35 = 5 \cdot 7$
Factor 42 into prime numbers: $42 = 2 \cdot 3 \cdot 7$
GCF $= 7$
LCM $= 2 \cdot 3 \cdot 5 \cdot 7 = 210$

Exercises

Find the GCF and LCM for each pair of numbers. Draw a Venn diagram to illustrate how you arrived at each of your answers.

1. 24 and 42
   24 = _____
   42 = _____

2. 90 and 210
   90 = _____
   210 = _____

GCF = _____ LCM = _____   GCF = _____ LCM = _____

Lesson Quick Quiz (p. 10) | AL | OL | BL

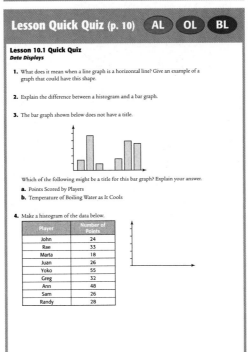

Lesson 10.1 Quick Quiz
Data Displays

1. What does it mean when a line graph is a horizontal line? Give an example of a graph that could have this shape.

2. Explain the difference between a histogram and a bar graph.

3. The bar graph shown below does not have a title.

Which of the following might be a title for this bar graph? Explain your answer.
   a. Points Scored by Players
   b. Temperature of Boiling Water as It Cools

4. Make a histogram of the data below.

Player	Number of Points
John	24
Rae	33
Marta	18
Juan	26
Yoko	55
Greg	32
Ann	48
Sam	26
Randy	28

Lesson Masters 1–9 (p. 11–19)

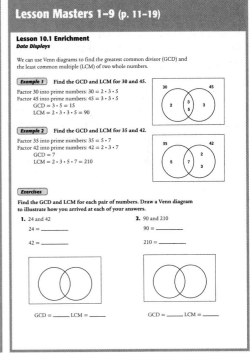

Lesson 10.1 Enrichment
Data Displays

We can use Venn diagrams to find the greatest common divisor (GCD) and the least common multiple (LCM) of two whole numbers.

Example 1 Find the GCD and LCM for 30 and 45.

Factor 30 into prime numbers: $30 = 2 \cdot 3 \cdot 5$
Factor 45 into prime numbers: $45 = 3 \cdot 3 \cdot 5$
GCD $= 3 \cdot 5 = 15$
LCM $= 2 \cdot 3 \cdot 3 \cdot 5 = 90$

Example 2 Find the GCD and LCM for 35 and 42.

Factor 35 into prime numbers: $35 = 5 \cdot 7$
Factor 42 into prime numbers: $42 = 2 \cdot 3 \cdot 7$
GCD $= 7$
LCM $= 2 \cdot 3 \cdot 5 \cdot 7 = 210$

Exercises

Find the GCD and LCM for each pair of numbers. Draw a Venn diagram to illustrate how you arrived at each of your answers.

1. 24 and 42
   24 = _____
   42 = _____

2. 90 and 210
   90 = _____
   210 = _____

GCD = _____ LCM = _____   GCD = _____ LCM = _____

Additional Lesson Resources

Teacher Tech Tools
- TeacherWorks
- ExamView Assessment Suite
- Classroom Presentation Toolkit
- Advance Tracker

Student Tech Tools
- StudentWorks Plus
- **Math Online** ▸ eGlossary •
  Concepts in Motion

Other Print Products
- Investigation Notebook
  and Reflection Journal
- Quick Review Math Handbook

Introduce

Data Displays Ask students what kinds of tasks they think a data analyst performs. Continue the discussion to include the tools analysts might use and the skills they might need to complete their work. Inform students that they will use some of these tools as they take on the roles of data analysts for a company called Data, Inc.

Remind students that in Chapter 8 they made predictions from graphs. Point out that they can also find patterns and compare data found in tables and other types of graphs to help them make decisions.

Explore

Suggested Grouping: Pairs

▶ **Prepare** Ask students to identify the two types of graphs shown. They should be familiar with both the line graph and the bar graph.

▶ **Play** Have groups or pairs of students work through the Explore, and make sure they understand that there are multiple parts to consider for each situation. For example, when one graph could describe the situation, students must also decide what each axis would represent and what the graph reveals about the situation. When neither graph describes the situation, students must draw and label a graph for that situation.

▶ **Record** Have groups share their answers. Point out that there may be more than one reasonable answer for each situation. For example, the bar graph may not be a good display for the fifth situation, the number of school days remaining, if the school is on a year-round schedule.

▶ **Score** Give groups credit for doing the activity.

Data Displays

Math Link

The word *data* is plural and means "bits of countable or measurable information." The singular form of data is *datum.* When you talk about data, you should use the plural forms of verbs, for example *are, were,* or *show.*

People in many professions use data to help make decisions. When data are first collected, they are often just lists of numbers and other information. Before they can be understood, data must be organized and analyzed. In this chapter, you will investigate several tools for understanding data.

In many activities in this chapter, your class will play the role of a company called Data, Inc., a consulting group that specializes in organizing and analyzing data. Various people and organizations will come to Data, Inc. for advice and suggestions.

In Chapter 8, you saw how graphs can help you discover patterns and trends. In this lesson, you will look at several types of graphs and compare the kinds of information each tells you about a set of data.

Explore

These graphs have no labels or scale values. Tell whether one of these graphs could describe each situation below. If it could, tell what the axes would represent and what the graph would reveal about the situation. If neither graph could describe the situation, describe or sketch a graph that could.

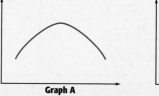
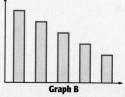

Graph A   Graph B

- the number of visitors to a zoo over the past year   See ①.
- the weight of a young hippo from birth to age one   See ②.
- the distance from a ball to the ground after the ball is dropped   See ③.
- the number of minutes of daylight each day during a year   See ④.
- the number of school days remaining on the first of each month, from February through June   See ⑤.
- the number of children born each month in one year in Canada   See ⑥.

①–⑥ See margin.

Additional Answers

① Possible answer: Graph A: The horizontal axis would show days from January 1 through December 31, and the vertical axis would show the number of visitors. The graph shows that there are more visitors during the summer.

② Possible answer: Neither; this situation could be described by a line graph that increases from left to right.

③ Possible answer: Neither; this situation could be described by a line graph that decreases from left to right.

④ Possible answer: Graph A; the horizontal axis would show days from January 1 through December 31, and the vertical axis would show minutes of daylight. The graph shows there are more minutes of daylight during the summer.

⑤ Possible answer: Graph B; the bars could represent the months, with the height of each bar representing the number of school days left.
The graph shows that the number of school days remaining decreases each month.

⑥ Possible answer: Neither; a bar graph with 12 bars would be most appropriate. Graph B has only 5 bars.

Investigation 1 Line Graphs

Materials
• copies of the "clues"

The Smallville police department is investigating the disappearance of a man named Gerald Orkney. Here is what they know so far.

• Mr. Orkney lives alone with his pet iguana, Agnes.

• Mr. Orkney did not show up for work on December 15. When his friends came to check on him, he and Agnes were gone.

• An atlas and the graphs below, which have no scales or labels, were found in Mr. Orkney's apartment.

The police department has asked Data, Inc. to help the investigators figure out what happened to Gerald Orkney.

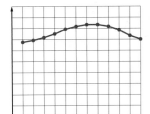 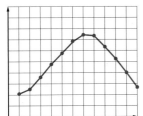 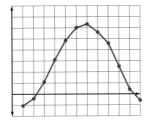

① Possible answer: All three graphs have 12 divisions of the horizontal axis. The third graph has points that are below the horizontal axis. All three graphs go up and then come down again. The first graph is the "flattest" of the three. The third graph has the most dramatic increase and decrease.

③ Possible answers: He might have gone on a trip or moved somewhere. If the graphs show change over 12 months, he might have gone somewhere for a long time, rather than just a few days.

Think & Discuss

Look carefully at the three graphs found by police. Think about the shape of each graph and about the axes. How are the graphs alike? How are they different? **See ①.**

Since the graphs do not have labels, it is impossible to know exactly what they represent or how they are related to Gerald Orkney's disappearance. However, you may be able to make a *hypothesis*, or an educated guess, based on the information you do have. **See ② in margin.**
Try to think of some ideas about what the graphs might show. Consider both what the graphs look like and how they might be related to the other information found by police.

Using the graphs and the other information given, try to create at least one hypothesis about what might have happened to Gerald Orkney. **See ③.**

Lesson 10.1 Data Displays **579**

Additional Answer for Think & Discuss
② Possible answer: Since the horizontal axis has 12 intervals, the graphs might show some sort of change over 12 months—such as change in temperature, rainfall, or hours of daylight. Since an atlas was found by the graphs, they might have to do with different places.

Investigation 1

On Your Own Exercises
Pages 592–600
Exercises 1, 9, 10

Line Graphs In this investigation, students act as analysts employed by Data, Inc. to solve the mystery of the disappearance of Gerald Orkney and his pet iguana. Students make hypotheses about what the unlabeled graphs might represent to help them determine Gerald's whereabouts. During the investigation, more information is revealed so that students can check and revise their hypotheses. Introduce the mystery situation by having students read the clues. Then have them look at the three graphs.

Although students analyze the graphs in more detail in Think & Discuss on this page, you might want to discuss the two-quadrant graph at the bottom of the page since one of its scales includes negative values.

Ask students what the coordinates of the point closest to the vertical axis would be if both scales were in intervals of 1 and the origin was (0, 0). $(1, -1)$ After this brief review of axes with negative numbers, proceed to the Think & Discuss.

Think & Discuss

Suggested Grouping: Small Groups

Have students compare the graphs as part of a class discussion. Encourage them to look for patterns and consider how high and how low the graphs are when they describe the shape. Discuss the definition of *hypothesis* as an educated guess. Then have students work in small groups to think about what the graphs might show and to develop their hypotheses of what happened to Gerald Orkney and his iguana.

Teacher Tips In the next exercise set, students are gradually given more information about Gerald Orkney's disappearance and asked to refine their hypotheses. As part of this refinement process, students should see the importance of labels and titles on graphs. You will need either to make transparencies of Lesson 10.1 Masters 1 and 2 or provide students with copies of these masters. These masters contain versions of the graphs that are more detailed and provide additional clues to help students determine Gerald Orkney's location. They should be distributed as students work through the exercise set. Each problem parallels many of the steps in the Think & Discuss as students make observations and offer hypotheses for the situation.

✓ Develop & Understand: A

Suggested Grouping: Small Groups

▶ **Exercise 1** Students will need the information from Lesson 10.1 Master 1 to work through this exercise. Remind students to use the data at the top of page 579 along with the detailed graphs to make their hypotheses in **Exercise 1c**. Ask them to present and explain how they derived their hypotheses.

▶ **Exercise 2** After providing students with the list of cities and the veterinarian's letter, given on Lesson 10.1 Master 2, have them work in their groups to complete this exercise.

Wrap-Up As students share their hypotheses from **Exercise 2c**, have each group tell what facts support the hypotheses. Students will summarize their investigation in written form in Share & Summarize.

Share & Summarize

You may want to briefly discuss or show a sample of a business letter, pointing out the various parts of the letter, such as the business address and salutation. Suggest that students give explanations to support any hypotheses that they state in the letter. Students could practice their word processing skills by composing the letter on a computer.

1a. Possible answer: The horizontal axis represents months, so the graphs probably show how something changes over a year. The highest part of each graph is in the summer months and the lowest parts are in the winter months. The first graph has points with vertical-axis values from about 65 to 85, the second has values from about 20 to 75, and the third has values from about -10 to 65. These could be temperatures. The graphs could show monthly temperatures of different places.

1b. Answers will vary.

1c. Possible answers: If the graphs show monthly temperatures of different places, Orkney may have been trying to figure out where to go. Since he left in December, maybe he went to a place with a warm climate in the winter (or all year long).

✓ Develop & Understand: A

1. During a search of Gerald Orkney's office, the police found more detailed versions of the graphs. Your teacher will give you copies of the new graphs. Look at them closely.

   a. What new information do the graphs reveal? Does this information fit any of the ideas your class had in Think & Discuss? Now what do you think the graphs might show?

   b. Does the new information support any of the hypotheses your class made about what happened to Gerald Orkney? Explain.

   c. Make a new hypothesis, or make changes to an earlier hypothesis, to fit all the information you have so far.

2. The police department has discovered more clues, consisting of a list and a note. Your teacher will give you a copy of this new information.

   a. What might the list have to do with the graphs? Do you have new ideas about what each graph might show? If so, add appropriate titles and axis labels to the graphs. See margin.

   b. Does this new information support your hypothesis about what happened to Gerald Orkney? Explain.   Answers will vary.

   c. Now what do you think happened to Gerald Orkney? Make a new hypothesis, or make changes to an earlier hypothesis, to fit this new information.   See below.

Share & Summarize

Write a letter to the Smallville police department summarizing your group's investigation and presenting your hypothesis about what happened to Gerald Orkney. See ① in margin.

2c. Possible answer: He went to Florida because the vet said that Agnes needed a warmer climate, and the note included a flight number.

Additional Answer

2a. Possible answer: The list could be the three cities whose temperatures the graphs show. Graph 1 might show temperatures for Miami because the temperatures are fairly high for all the months. Graph 3 might show temperatures for Fairbanks because the temperatures are very low in some months and never get very high. Graph 2 might show temperatures for Chicago because the temperatures are more moderate.

Additional Answers for Develop & Understand: A Exercise 2a and Share & Summarize ① are on page 657A.

Investigation 2 — Bar Graphs

The environmental group Citizens for Safe Air has asked Data, Inc. to analyze some data about *hydrocarbons*. These compounds are part of the emissions from cars and other vehicles that pollute the air. The group wants to know how the total amount of hydrocarbon emitted by vehicles has changed over the past several decades and how it might change in the future.

Real-World Link
Hydrocarbons react with nitrogen oxides and sunlight to form ozone, a major component of smog. Ozone causes choking, coughing, and stinging eyes. It also damages lung tissue.

The table shows estimates of the typical amount of hydrocarbon emitted per vehicle for each mile driven in the United States for years from 1960 to 2015. The values from 2000 to 2015 are predictions.

Average Per-Vehicle Emissions

Year	Grams of Hydrocarbon per Mile
1960	17
1965	15.5
1970	13
1975	10.5
1980	7.5
1985	5.5
1990	3
1995	1.5
2000	1
2005	0.75
2010	0.5
2015	0.5

Source: "Automobiles and Ozone," Fact Sheet OMS-4 of the Office of Mobile Sources, the U.S. Environmental Protection Agency.

Develop & Understand: A

1. For which five-year period is the decrease in per-vehicle emissions greatest? For which five-year period is it least?
   1975–1980, 2010–2015

2. On a set of axes like this one, draw a bar graph showing the typical per-vehicle emissions for each year given in the table.

Average Per-Vehicle Emissions

On Your Own Exercises
Pages 592–600
Exercises 2, 11–13

Bar Graphs Introduce the investigation by reminding students that even though cars make many people's lives easier, this comfort comes at a cost to the environment. Ask students how cars contribute to pollution. Their responses may include the facts that exhaust from tailpipe emissions pollutes the air, oil or gas leaks pollute the ground and water, and waste from gasoline production can pollute air, ground, and water. Then ask students how air pollution caused by cars could be reduced. Answers may include driving less, improving engines so they emit fewer pollutants, finding better fuels that cause less pollution, and improving public transportation systems.

Teacher Tips In the exercise set, students make bar graphs of the average per vehicle emissions data from the table in the introduction to this investigation. They analyze the data and compare the table and graph. Some students may need a brief review of the different components of a bar graph before completing the graph in this exercise.

Develop & Understand: A

Suggested Grouping: Pairs

▶ **Exercise 2** Connect the importance of a title on the graph and labels on the axes to students' experiences in Investigation 1. You may want to distribute Lesson 10.1 Master 3 to help students create their graphs in this exercise set and the next.

Review the guidelines for making bar graphs and have students use the graph on page 581 as a model when making their graphs. Some students may find it easier to use the master since the axes are already labeled.

On the Spot Assessment

Watch for students who incorrectly draw the bars when making bar graphs in Exercise 2. Besides drawing the bars with incorrect heights, students may make bars with unequal or varying widths. These errors can distort the meaning of the graphs.

▶ **Exercise 3** You may want to go over this exercise as a class to make sure students have found all the patterns in the graphs.

Wrap-Up Have students share answers to Exercise 3. Students should understand that the emissions from individual vehicles have tapered off over time. When discussing Exercise 4, make sure that students mention that a bar graph makes it easier to see patterns and draw conclusions about trends while a table makes it easier to find exact values.

Teacher Tips Read and discuss together the paragraphs and tables that present additional information needed to determine how the *total* hydrocarbon emissions have changed over the past several decades. The data in the exercise set on page 581 showed a decrease in the emissions each vehicle emits per mile traveled. These new data present the number of miles driven in the U.S. during the same time period.

3. Possible answer: The graph indicates that per-vehicle emissions have decreased over the years and are expected to level off in the future. The graph is at its highest point in 1960 and then the height of the bars decreases each year until 2010, when the bar height levels off. The greatest change occurs from 1975 to 1980. There is no change from 2010 to 2015.

4. Possible answer: It is easier to use the graph because the differences in emissions are clearly shown.

3. Describe what your graph indicates about the change in per-vehicle emissions over the years. Discuss high and low points, periods of greatest and least change, and any other patterns you see.

4. To determine when the greatest decrease in per-vehicle emissions occurred, is it easier to use the table or the graph? Explain.

You have seen that the amount of hydrocarbon *each vehicle* emits *per mile* has decreased over the years. But this is not enough information to conclude that the *total amount* of hydrocarbon emitted by *all vehicles* is decreasing. You also need to consider the total number of miles driven by all vehicles.

This table shows estimates of the number of miles driven, or expected to be driven, by all vehicles in the United States for various years between 1960 and 2015.

Miles Driven in U.S.

Year	Miles in Billions
1960	750
1965	950
1970	1,150
1975	1,250
1980	1,500
1985	1,500
1990	2,000
1995	2,300
2000	2,600
2005	2,850
2010	3,150
2015	3,400

Source: "Automobiles and Ozone," Fact Sheet OMS-4 of the Office of Mobile Sources, the U.S. Environmental Protection Agency, Jan. 1993.

582   **CHAPTER 10**   Data and Probability

5. Look at the table on page 582. During which five-year period does the number of miles driven increase most? During which five-year period does it increase least? **1985–1990, 1980–1985**

6. On a set of axes like the one below, draw a bar graph showing the billions of vehicle miles traveled for each year given.

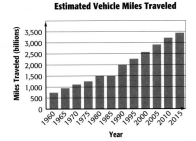

Estimated Vehicle Miles Traveled

7. Possible answer: The graph indicates that the total number of miles driven has increased over the years and will continue to increase. The graph is at its lowest point in 1960. The bar heights increase each year shown in the graph, increasing more slowly at first and then by greater amounts. The graph does not level off as the previous graph did.

7. Describe what your graph indicates about the change in the total number of miles over the years. Discuss high and low points, periods of greatest and least change, and any other patterns you see.

You now know that, over time, the typical amount of hydrocarbon emitted per vehicle has decreased. You also know that more miles are driven each year. In Exercises 8–10, you will combine this information to answer this question.

> Is the *total amount* of hydrocarbon emitted from vehicles increasing or decreasing?

Think & Discuss

How could you use the data in the two previous tables to calculate estimates of the total amount of hydrocarbon emitted by all vehicles each year? Multiply the emissions per mile driven by the number of miles driven.

✓ Develop & Understand: B

Suggested Grouping: Small Groups

Exercises 5–7 In these exercises, students make and interpret bar graphs about the total number of miles driven in the U.S. Lesson 10.1 Master 3 reproduces the data and axes for this problem set.

Wrap-Up Briefly discuss Exercise 7. Encourage students to share any patterns they found. Be sure they conclude that the number of miles driven has increased dramatically since 1960 and that the increase is *projected* through 2015, the last year given on the graph.

Teacher Tips Recap the data previously given: the average per-vehicle emissions and the total miles traveled in the U.S. for the same years. Remind students that the objective is for Data, Inc. to look at the change in *total* hydrocarbon emissions. They will look for ways to accomplish this goal in the Think & Discuss.

Think & Discuss

Be sure that all students have a reasonable way to use the tables shown for the exercise sets on pages 581–582 to find the total amount of hydrocarbon emitted from all vehicles each year. They will use their method to complete Exercise 8 on page 584.

Reaching All Learners

BL Beyond Level Ask students to find the percents of increase in the total number of miles driven in 1960 and the total number of miles expected to be driven in 2015. The answer can be found as follows:

$$\frac{3400 - 750}{750} = 353\%$$

⊘ *Develop & Understand:* C

Suggested Grouping: Small Groups

▶ **Exercises 8–10** In these exercises, students apply the method from Think & Discuss to create a table and a bar graph showing the estimated total emissions. Then they analyze the bar graph. You may want to distribute Lesson 10.1 Master 4, which reproduces the table and includes axes for constructing the graph.

Wrap-Up Discuss Exercise 10, and ask students to relate their new knowledge to what they have already learned about hydrocarbon emissions. Students may note that the average per-vehicle emissions have decreased since 1960, which might indicate that air quality has improved. During the same time period, the number of miles driven has increased. The increasing number of miles driven only partially offsets the decreasing rate of emissions, so total emissions have declined.

Share & *Summarize*

Students are asked to prepare a brief report organizing the data they have displayed and analyzed during this investigation, specifically the trends discovered in the exercises on this page. Encourage them to include explanations of how they used the data to reach their conclusions, essentially summarizing the findings from Exercise 10 in the exercise set. Although Data, Inc. is asked only to present the results of the analysis, you may also want students to provide possible ways to reduce emissions.

Additional Answer

9.

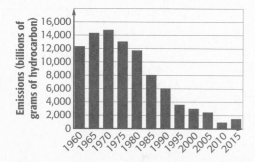

Total Emissions

Additional Answer for Share & Summarize is on page 657A.

⊘ *Develop & Understand:* C

8. Copy and complete the table to show the total amount of hydrocarbon emitted by U.S. vehicles each year.

Estimated Total Emissions

Year	Billions of Grams of Hydrocarbon
1960	12,750
1965	14,725
1970	14,950
1975	13,125
1980	11,250
1985	8,250
1990	6,000
1995	3,450
2000	2,600
2005	2,137.5
2010	1,575
2015	1,700

10. Possible answer: The graph indicates that, although the total emissions have decreased since 1970, they may level off or begin to increase again in the future. The graph goes up for the first three bars and then goes down, slowly at first, then more quickly, and then more slowly again. In 2015, it rises slightly. The greatest increase is between 1960 and 1965. The greatest decrease is between 1980 and 1985.

9. Make a bar graph of the data in the table. See margin.

10. Describe what your graph indicates about the change in the total hydrocarbon emissions over the years. Discuss high and low points, periods of greatest and least change, and any other patterns you see.

Share & *Summarize*

Write a letter to Citizens for Safe Air. Describe Data, Inc.'s investigation of hydrocarbon emissions, summarizing your findings about how total emissions have changed over the past few decades and how they might change in the future. See margin.

Reaching All Learners

AL **Approaching Level** To help students more easily make their calculations in Exercise 8 suggest that they use the make an organized list problem-solving strategy by inserting two columns in their tables: one showing the average per-vehicle emissions (from the table on page 581) and the other showing the miles driven in the U.S. (from the table on page 582).

Vocabulary

distribution

histogram

There are many types of graphs. The graph that is best for a given situation depends on the data you have and the information you want to convey.

✓ Develop & Understand: A

This bar graph shows the times of some of the participants in the women's team sprint cross-country skiing event at the 2006 Winter Olympics.

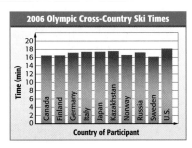

2006 Olympic Cross-Country Ski Times

Real-World Link
The oldest known skis are 4,000 to 5,000 years old. In the tenth century, Viking soldiers used skis for transportation. From the 15th to the 17th centuries, several northern European armies had companies of ski troops.

1. How many countries are represented?   10

2. From which country was the gold medalist? What was her time?
   Sweden; About 16.3

3. How many participants completed the race with a time between 17 minutes and 18 minutes?   5

4. The bars in the graph are arranged alphabetically by country. Think of another way the bars could be ordered. What kinds of questions would be easier to answer if they were ordered that way?
   See margin.

It probably took you some time to figure out the answer to Exercise 3 above. Although it is easy to use the bar graph to find the time for each participant, it is not as easy to find the number of skiers who finished within a particular time interval.

You will now use a *histogram* to display the ski times. In a **histogram**, data are divided into equal intervals with a bar for each interval. The height of each bar shows the number of data values in that interval. There are no gaps between intervals.

Lesson 10.1 Data Displays   **585**

Reaching All Learners

OL **On Level** In Exercise 3, it may be difficult for students to determine which skiers have times that fall in the desired range. Suggest that they estimate where the values for 16 minutes and 17 minutes 59 seconds are on the vertical scale, and then use a straightedge to form horizontal lines for these values to help them find the relevant data.

Additional Answer

4. Possible answer: From least to greatest (or greatest to least) time. It would be easier to answer questions about how the skiers placed and about who finished within a particular period of time.

Investigation 3

On Your Own Exercises
Pages 592–600
Exercises 3, 8

Histograms This investigation introduces histograms. Histograms, like bar graphs, use bars to show categorical data. Unlike bar graphs, the data on the horizontal axis represent ranges of data, and the heights of the bars show the frequency of data. In this investigation, students are given a bar graph that shows the times of participants in the women's team sprint cross-country skiing event at the 2006 Winter Olympics. Students create frequency tables to sort the items into ranges and then make histograms to display the data. Introduce the investigation by having students name some of the types of graphs they have studied. Encourage them to describe some situations that can best be shown by each type of graph.

Teacher Tips You may want to provide students with copies of Lesson 10.1 Master 5, which reproduces the bar graph, frequency table, and partially constructed histogram shown in the exercise sets on pages 585 and 586.

The exercise set on this page asks students to interpret a bar graph showing Olympic skiing data. They analyze the data in terms of ranges. This time-consuming task previews the idea of ranges that will be explored through histograms in the next two exercise sets.

✓ Develop & Understand: A

Suggested Grouping: Pairs

▶ **Exercise 3** It is likely that students will have different answers for this exercise. If this occurs, you can either challenge the students to suggest a way to reconcile the differences or simply make a list on the board of the countries that students find. Then look for omissions or disagreements. You might point out that the bars allow readers to estimate the times for each skier. Since the times are recorded to the nearest hundredth and the graph shows intervals of two minutes, it is difficult to read the precise values on the graph.

Teacher Tips Before students begin
working through the next exercise set, you
may want to introduce the term *frequency*.
Point out that the table in Exercise 5 is
called a frequency table since it shows the
number of skiers (frequency) that had times
in a given interval. Have students complete
their histograms on transparencies of
Lesson 10.1 Master 5 so that they can
display their graphs for the class. This
can facilitate discussion, help students
internalize the characteristics of a histogram,
and distinguish the similarities and
differences of histograms and bar graphs.

Develop & Understand: B

Suggested Grouping: Pairs

▶ **Exercises 5–8** In this exercise set, students
use data from the bar graph on page 585 to
create a frequency table and a histogram. It
may take some time for students to
correlate the data accurately. You may want
to make a transparency of Lesson 10.1
Master 5 to show the histogram when
discussing Exercise 6.

▶ **Exercises 5 and 6** If you did not discuss
the characteristics of a histogram earlier, or
if you want the class to graph the same
data, you may want to bring the class
together to discuss these exercises. The
crucial step is connecting the ranges in the
chart to the ranges on the horizontal axis of
the histogram. Point out that the horizontal
scale is in intervals of one and the vertical
scale is in intervals of one. Students may
note that the bars are over the "spaces"
between numbers on the horizontal scale.

Wrap-Up Have students share their
histograms from Exercise 6. Then discuss
their answers to Exercises 7 and 8. Be sure
students understand that the *distribution* of
data means how the data are spread out
over the axes.

***
Math Link
Sometimes relative frequency is given as a
percent. Ask students why.
***

Develop & Understand: B

In Exercises 5–8, you will make a table of frequencies. *Frequencies* are
counts of the number of data values in various intervals. You will use
your frequency table to create a histogram.

5. Copy this table. Use the bar graph on page 585 to count the number
   of participants who finished in each time interval. Record this
   information in the "Frequency" column.

Time (minutes:seconds)	Frequency
15:00–15:59	0
16:00–16:59	4
17:00–17:59	5
18:00–18:59	1
19:00–19:59	0

6. Copy the axes below. Create a histogram by drawing bars showing
   the number of participants who finished in each time interval.
   The bar for the interval 17:00–17:59 has been drawn for you.

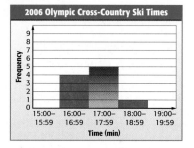

7. In which one-minute interval did the greatest number of
   skiers finish?   17:00–17:59

8. The shape of a histogram reveals the **distribution** of the data
   values. In other words, it shows how the data are spread out, where
   there are gaps, where there are many values, and where there are only
   a few values. What can you say about the distribution of times for
   this event?   Most women finished within 17 to 18 minutes.

***
Math Link
Relative frequency is the
ratio of the number of data
in an interval to the total
number of data in all intervals.
For example, the relative
frequency of the data in the
17:00–17:59 interval is $\frac{5}{10}$,
or 0.50.
***

✅ Develop & Understand: C

Rather than showing the *number* of values in each interval, some histograms show the *percent* of values in each interval. For example, this histogram shows how the test scores for Mr. Wilson's Math exam were distributed. The maximum possible score was 75 points.

9. Describe the shape of the histogram. Tell what the shape indicates about the distribution of test scores. **See margin.**

10. Which interval includes the greatest percent of test scores? About what percent of scores are in this interval? **61–65, 24%**

11. Which interval includes the least percent of test scores? About what percent of scores are in this interval? **36–40, 6%**

12. Suppose 64 students took Mr. Wilson's test. How many of them received a score from 66 to 70? **About 9**

13. If you were to add the percents for all the bars, what should be the total? Why? **100%; the graph shows how all the scores (100%) are distributed among the various intervals.**

Exam Scores

Vertical axis: Percent of Students (0, 2, 4, 6, 8, 10, 12, 14, 16, 18, 20, 22, 24)
Horizontal axis: Test Score (36–40, 41–45, 46–50, 51–55, 56–60, 61–65, 66–70, 71–75)

Math Link

Cumulative frequency is the total number of all data values less than the upper limit of a certain interval. This is found by adding together the frequencies of the interval and all other intervals that come before it. For example, the cumulative frequency of the data less than 50 is $6 + 8 + 10$, or 24.

Cumulative relative frequency is the ratio of the cumulative frequency for an interval to the total number of data in all intervals. For example, the cumulative relative frequency of the 46–50 interval is $\frac{24}{100}$, or 0.24.

Share & Summarize

1. What type of information does a histogram display? Give an example of a situation for which it would make sense to display data in a histogram. **See ① in margin.**

2. In this investigation, you looked at a bar graph and a histogram of Olympic ski data. What are some things the bar graph shows better than the histogram? What are some things the histogram shows better than the bar graph? **See ② in margin.**

Additional Answer

9. Possible answer: Moving from left to right, the bar height increases, reaching its maximum height in the 61–65 interval, and then decreases again. The shape indicates that there are a few very low scores and a small number of very high scores, with most of the scores somewhere in between and the greatest number in the 61–65 interval.

Additional Answers for Share & Summarize Exercises ① and ② are on page 657A.

Teacher Tips Have students look at the histogram for the Exam Scores. Ask them how this histogram differs from those they made for the cross-country skiing times. Point out that the label for the vertical axis of the "Exam Scores" graph shows the *percent* of the class achieving the scores. Discuss how to read the graph, especially if you did not show a sample histogram when introducing histograms. Make sure students understand that the test scores for each bar include the left-hand value in the range but not the right-hand value.

✅ Develop & Understand: C

Suggested Grouping: Pairs

▶ **Exercise 12** In this exercise set, students interpret a histogram with percents on the vertical axis. For Exercise 12, students must use the histogram to find the percent of students that received a specific range of scores and use that percentage to determine how many students in a class of 64 earned those scores. Since 14% of 64 is 8.96, students must round to find the number of students.

Share & Summarize

Students are asked to compare bar graphs and histograms to determine which would be the most appropriate way for displaying given data. Be sure students understand that histograms show frequency and ranges of data and are useful when looking at the distribution of data. Bar graphs show individual items of data and are best in situations when it is necessary to know specific values.

Troubleshooting If students have difficulty deciding when to make a bar graph and when to make a histogram, ask them to choose some context, such as football or rock music, and then think of two kinds of related questions. The first questions should ask how many members of a data set reached different levels of something; the second should focus on comparing different individuals or groups.

On Your Own Exercises
Pages 592–600
Exercises 4–7, 14, 15

Venn Diagrams In this investigation, students learn to sort information in bar graphs. They will use the information to create Venn diagrams, which show areas of overlap in data. To help make students proficient in interpreting data, the scenarios in this lesson are based on relevant situations. Solving the problems will help students develop strong data interpretation skills.

Think & Discuss

Demonstrate that the two given numbers add up to more than 100 with an addition problem on the board. Refer to the graph. Have pairs think of ways to show the information more clearly. List their suggestions on the board, and discuss how well each might work.

Teacher Tips When teaching students to create and use Venn diagrams, make sure they draw the diagrams correctly. Have each student draw a Venn diagram on a piece of paper. Then have them write words in each section. Point out that if they cannot get words in any section, they need to adjust the proportions of their diagrams. Understanding how to draw a Venn diagram quickly and correctly will make this lesson much easier for students.

Investigation 4 — Venn Diagrams

Vocabulary

Venn diagram

The principal of Smallville High School has asked Data, Inc. to help him prepare his annual report to the school board.

At Smallville High School, all 100 freshmen are required to take a Science class, either Biology or Computer Science. The principal of Smallville High made this bar graph showing the number of freshmen enrolled in each Science class.

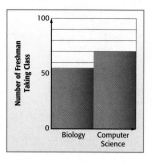

① Sample answer: Maybe some students are in both classes, and they were counted twice. Or, maybe there are some students in the science classes who are not freshmen. So, the total number of students in the class is more than all the students in freshman class.

② Sample answer: If it is the case that some students are in both classes, he could have a bar for "both." Then at least the three bars would add up to 100 students and it would be clear that some students were in both classes.

Think & Discuss

Does the number of students in the graph add up to 100?
No; they add up to 125
Assuming the principal did not make a mistake, what might explain the way the graph looks? See ①.

How could the principal change his bar graph to represent the situation more clearly? See ②.

When you have data about how things are sorted into groups, one useful way to display it is with a **Venn diagram**. A Venn diagram is especially useful for illustrating how groups overlap. This Venn diagram shows the number of freshmen at Smallville High in the different Science classes. You can see that 25 students are taking two Science classes.

Freshmen in Science Class

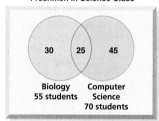

In a Venn diagram, each circle represents a group. The data that is in the circle belongs to that group, and the data that is outside the circle does not belong to the group. If an item belongs to two groups, it goes in the space where the two circles overlap. That is, it is in both circles at the same time.

588   CHAPTER 10 Data and Probability

Reaching All Learners

AL Approaching Level To help students determine the amounts for each section of the Venn diagram, list the steps on chart paper for them to use as a reference. Make sure to have students find the amount over 100 percent and subtract that amount from each amount on the bar graph. Explain to students that the amount they subtracted should be in the overlap area of the diagram.

3.

Chinese   Spanish

4. Answers may vary. Sample answer: since those students should not be in either of the circles, I put the 25% outside the circles. Students may also choose to leave that 25% off of their diagrams, but this makes the diagram difficult to read.

✅ Develop & Understand: A

The juniors at Smallville High all have to take at least one History class. They can take American History, Ancient Civilizations, or both. According to the principal's data, 65% of juniors take American History and 50% take Ancient Civilizations.

1. Complete this Venn diagram showing which History classes the juniors take.

2. What percentage of juniors are enrolled in both History classes?   15%

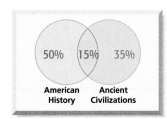

American History   Ancient Civilizations

The juniors can also choose between two foreign languages, Chinese and Spanish. Some students take both languages, while some students do not study a foreign language at all. Here is a bar graph showing the enrollment data for foreign language classes.

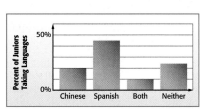

3. Draw a Venn diagram to represent this data.

4. How does your diagram represent the students who are not in a foreign language class?

5. What percentage of juniors study Chinese?   30%

6. What percentage of juniors study Spanish?   55%

You can use Venn diagrams to sort individual items, categories of things, or numerical data like the class enrollment data you have seen.

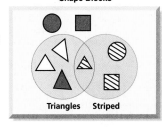

Shape Blocks

Triangles   Striped

Animal Traits

barks canine / fur mammals domestic pet four legs / meows feline

Dog   Cat

✅ Develop & Understand: A

Suggested Grouping: Pairs

▶ **Exercises 1 and 2** Have students add the two percents to determine the amount by which they exceed 100 percent. Remind them that that amount will be the overlap in the Venn diagram.

▶ **Exercises 3 and 4** Make sure students correctly read the bar graph as they create their Venn diagrams. Have them suggest ways to show "neither" in the Venn diagram; discuss which methods would be easiest to understand.

On the Spot Assessment

Monitor students as they create Venn diagrams to be sure they are correctly interpreting the given data. Students who do not sort the information for each category correctly may need more practice interpreting bar graphs and other data. Students who incorrectly adjust the numbers for the diagrams may need help understanding how "both" categories affect the percents.

Develop & Understand: B

Suggested Grouping: Pairs

▶ **Exercise 7** Remind students to check their work by making sure that the numbers in their Venn diagrams add up to correctly match the numbers in the exercise.

▶ **Exercises 8–10** When determining the necessary additional data, tell students to prepare a Venn diagram and see what they are not able to complete without more information.

Develop & Understand: C

Suggested Grouping: Pairs

▶ **Exercises 11–14** Make sure students are correctly interpreting the Venn diagram. Have them point to each colored area as they find what it represents.

- -

Math Link

Have students try to draw a Venn diagram with three or four circles. Discuss how it becomes more difficult to create the diagram with each added circle.

- -

Additional Answer

10. Sample answer: I cannot tell if any of the students do not take a foreign language (in fact, since the numbers are smaller in this exercise than in Exercises 8 and 9, some of the freshmen must not be taking a language class.) I need to know how many students are in the *Both* and *Neither* groups in order to draw the diagram.

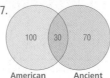

American History   Ancient Civilizations

8. Sample answer: I need to know how many (if any) students take both math classes, or I need to know how many total freshmen there are, which would let me figure out how many take both classes. I also need to be sure that these are the only two possible math classes freshman can take.

- -

Math Link

In theory, a Venn diagram could have four or more circles, but it gets very difficult to draw. When all the categories are circles, you cannot get more than three to overlap in a way that makes an area for each possible combination of categories.

- -

9. Sample answer: I need the same information as in Exercise 8, except now I need to know the total number of freshmen, so I can figure out what percentage of them each of these enrollment numbers represents.

Numerical data can be represented in different ways. For example, the student enrollment data could be represented as numbers of students, instead of percentages.

Develop & Understand: B

7. There are 200 juniors at Smallville High. Seventy students are in Ancient Civilizations and thirty students take both American History and Ancient Civilizations. Make a new Venn diagram that shows the number of students in each History class.

   The principal reports that all the freshmen study Math; 105 of them take Algebra 1 and 85 take Geometry. Use this information for Exercises 8 and 9.

8. What additional data do you need from the principal in order to display the freshmen Math enrollment numbers in a Venn diagram?

9. What additional data do you need if you want to display the enrollment data as percentages in a Venn diagram?

10. The principal also reports that 75 freshmen study Chinese and 80 study Spanish. What additional data do you need in order to display this information in a Venn diagram?   See margin.

Develop & Understand: C

This Venn diagram shows the number of seniors who take Chemistry, Spanish, and Chorus classes. There are 200 seniors attending Smallville High.

Senior Courses

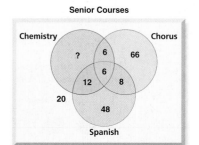

11. What does the gray-shaded area of the diagram represent?
    Students who take both Chemistry and Spanish

12. What does the green-shaded area represent?
    Students who take all three classes

13. How many students in the senior class take Chemistry but not Chorus or Spanish?   34

14. How many students in the senior class are in Chorus?   86

15c. Sample answer: Physics and Trigonometry can meet at the same time because there are no students enrolled in both classes. The overlapping circles are empty. Computer Science cannot meet at the same time as either of the other classes, it has overlap with both.

15. This Venn diagram shows how many seniors are enrolled in Trigonometry, Computer Science, and Physics.

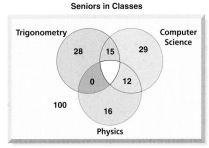

Seniors in Classes

a. How many students are enrolled in two of these three classes? 27

b. What percentage of the senior class takes at least one of these three classes? 50%

c. The principal needs to schedule these three classes so that there are no schedule conflicts. Can any of the three classes be scheduled at the same time? Explain your reasoning.

16. The principal gave this table to Data, Inc.

Class	Latin	World History	Drama	Latin and World History	Latin and Drama	World History and Drama	All Three Classes	None
Seniors in the Class	24	103	23	6	10	4	2	50

Display this data in a Venn diagram. Fill in all the areas of the diagram, including the area outside the circles. Indicate empty areas with zeros.   See margin.

① Sample answer: Each circle represents a category; the areas where the circles overlap represent combinations of categories; the area outside the circles is for things that do not belong in any of the categories represented.

② Sample answer: All of the students in the sample take either Geometry or Algebra 1. No one takes both classes. 42% take Geometry and 58% take Algebra 1.

Share & Summarize

What do the different areas in a Venn diagram represent?   See ①.

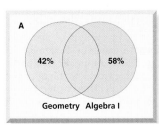

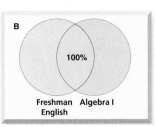

What can you say about the data in Venn diagram A?   See ②.

What can you say about the data in Venn diagram B?
All of the students in the sample take both Freshman English and Algebra 1.

▶ **Exercise 15** Have students point to each overlapping area on the diagram and tell what it represents. Then have them determine how many areas each overlap contains.

▶ **Exercise 16** Draw a three-circle Venn diagram on the board. Have students help you fill in each area. Discuss how to determine which numbers to use for each.

Share & Summarize

Allow students to look at a Venn diagram they have created to answer the question. Have them tell how many categories each area represents. Discuss ways each part of the Venn diagram helps clarify information.

Additional Answer

16.   **Seniors in Classes**

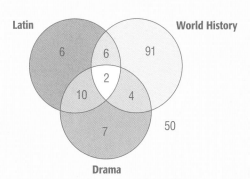

Investigation 1
Pages 579–580
Practice & Apply: 1
Connect & Extend: 9, 10

Investigation 2
Pages 581–584
Practice & Apply: 2
Connect & Extend: 11–13

Investigation 3
Pages 585–587
Practice & Apply: 3, 8

Investigation 4
Pages 588–591
Practice & Apply: 4–7
Connect & Extend: 14, 15

Assign Anytime
Mixed Review: 16–28

▶ **Exercise 1** Encourage students to provide an explanation for the graph they chose in each situation.

▶ **Exercise 2a Extension** Have students give the greatest and the least changes in terms of the number of people. The change from 1997 to 1998 is an increase of 4,600 people and from 1999 to 2000 is a decrease of 1,000 people.

▶ **Exercise 2b** Students may need graph paper or copies of Chapter 10 Master 2 or Chapter 10 Master 3 to make their bar graphs.

Practice & Apply

1. In Parts a–d, tell which graph could represent the situation.

i.   ii.

iii.   iv.

a. a child's activity level from before a nap until after a nap   iv

b. the populations of six cities   ii

c. the change in water level from high tide to low tide   i

d. the change in the weight of a cat from birth until age two   iii

2. This table shows the number of people who visited Milo's Restaurant in the years from 1996 to 2007.

a. The change in the number of customers is greatest from 2006 to 2007. Between which two years is the change in the number of customers least?   1999 to 2000

b. Make a bar graph showing the number of customers during the years shown in the table.
See margin.

c. Describe what your graph indicates about the change in the number of customers during the time period. Discuss high and low points, periods of greatest and least change, and any other patterns you see.

2c. The number of customers increased from 1996 to 1998, decreased from 1998 to 2001, increased again from 2001 to 2003, droppped slightly between 2003 and 2004, increased steadily from 2004 to 2006, then dropped dramatically from 2006 to 2007. The greatest change occurs from 2006 to 2007, and the least change occurs from 1999 to 2000.

Customers at Milo's Restaurant

Year	Visitors (thousands)
1996	39.4
1997	42.7
1998	47.3
1999	45.8
2000	44.8
2001	43.3
2002	46.5
2003	47.8
2004	46.4
2005	48.5
2006	50.9
2007	45.5

Additional Answer

2b.   **Customers at Milo's Restaurant**

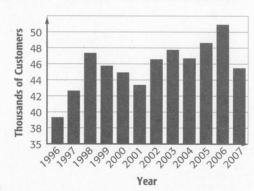

3. Think about the multiplication facts from 0 · 0 to 12 · 12. You can group the products into intervals of 10. For example, a product can be between 0 and 9, between 10 and 19, between 20 and 29, and so on.

a. Would you predict that the products are evenly distributed among the intervals of 10, or do you think some intervals contain more products than others?   Answers will vary.

b. Copy and complete this multiplication table.

×	0	1	2	3	4	5	6	7	8	9	10	11	12
0	0	0	0	0	0	0	0	0	0	0	0	0	0
1	0	1	2	3	4	5	6	7	8	9	10	11	12
2	0	2	4	6	8	10	12	14	16	18	20	22	24
3	0	3	6	9	12	15	18	21	24	27	30	33	36
4	0	4	8	12	16	20	24	28	32	36	40	44	48
5	0	5	10	15	20	25	30	35	40	45	50	55	60
6	0	6	12	18	24	30	36	42	48	54	60	66	72
7	0	7	14	21	28	35	42	49	56	63	70	77	84
8	0	8	16	24	32	40	48	56	64	72	80	88	96
9	0	9	18	27	36	45	54	63	72	81	90	99	108
10	0	10	20	30	40	50	60	70	80	90	100	110	120
11	0	11	22	33	44	55	66	77	88	99	110	121	132
12	0	12	24	36	48	60	72	84	96	108	120	132	144

c. Make a table, like that on the right, showing the number of products that fall in each interval of 10.

d. Make a histogram that shows the number of products in each interval of 10. Be sure to include axes labels and scale values. See margin.

e. What does the shape of your histogram reveal about the distribution of the products?

f. Now make another histogram showing the number of products that fall into intervals of 20, that is, 0–19, 20–39, 40–59, and so on. See margin.

g. Describe the similarities and differences in the two histograms. See margin.

Product	Frequency
0–9	48
10–19	23
20–29	19
30–39	15
40–49	15
50–59	8
60–69	9
70–79	8
80–89	7
90–99	6
100–109	3
110–119	2
120–129	3
130–139	2
140–149	1

3e. The first interval has by far the most products, and the number of products in each interval decreases from left to right, with an occasional "bump."

Lesson 10.1 Data Displays   **593**

▶ **Exercise 3** You may want to provide students with copies of Lesson 10.1 Masters 6 and 7. As an alternative, they could use graph paper or Chapter 10 Masters 2 or 3 to make their histograms but would not have the preprinted table.

For **Part c**, some students may find it easier to organize their data if they add a column for tallies to the table. Others may prefer to shade products in each range a different color and then count the number of products shaded in each color.

Additional Answers

3d.
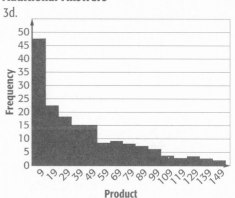

3f.
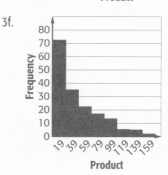

3g. Possible answer: In both graphs, the bar for the first interval is much higher than the others, indicating that most products fall in the first interval (0–9 in the first graph and 10–19 in the second). In the second histogram, the height of the bar decreases with each interval. In the first histogram, the heights fluctuate a bit. For example, the bar for 50–59 is shorter than the bar for 60–69.

▶ **Exercise 4** Make sure students remember that numbers outside the Venn diagram represent the percent of students not involved in any of the listed clubs.

▶ **Exercise 5** Have pairs work together to interpret the bar graphs and data given in this exercise. Instruct them to discuss the information before writing in the Venn diagrams. Then have each pair present one part of the exercise to the class.

Have pairs check their interpretations of the Venn diagrams. Ask them to explain to each other why Diagram B is not accurate.

4. This Venn diagram displays data about after-school clubs at Smallville High.

a. What number of students at Smallville High are in the Drama club? 27

b. What number of students are in both the Drama club and the Quiz Bowl club? 6

c. What number of students do not participate in any of these three clubs? 48

d. What number of students are in only one club? 36

e. Based on this diagram, which two clubs might meet at the same time? Why? Drama and Debate; No one is in both clubs.

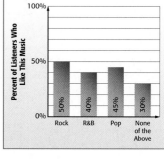

5. Sample answer: Diagram A could represent the same data: the percentages for Rock, R & B, Pop, and None of the Above are the same, and it all adds up to 100%. In Diagram B, the percentages match the bar graph, but the diagram does not make sense. The percentages add up to 115%. So, Diagram B cannot be an accurate representation of the data.

5. A local radio station sent a survey to its listeners asking what kinds of music they enjoyed. This bar graph summarizes the responses to the survey. The percentages are percentages of all the listeners who answered the survey.

Which of these Venn diagrams might represent the same data as the bar graph? Explain your reasoning.

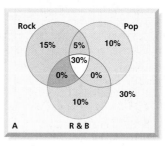

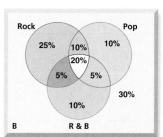

6. Use the data in this table to answer the following questions.

Sport	Soccer (total)	Basketball (total)	Track (total)	Soccer & Basketball	Soccer & Track	Basketball & Track	All Three Sports	None or Other
Number of Students who Participate	21%	34%	30%	2%	6%	9%	?	36%

6a.

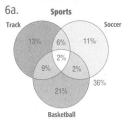

a. Display the data in a Venn diagram.

b. What percentage of students play all three sports?   2%

c. What percentage of students only play soccer?   11%

d. There are 900 students at Smallville High. Make a copy of your Venn diagram, displaying the data as numbers of students.

6d.

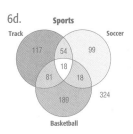

7. Use the Venn diagram to answer Parts a–e.

a. All mammals nurse their babies, and everything that nurses its babies is a mammal. Shade the areas of the Venn diagram that cannot have any animals in them.

Mammal Characteristics

b. The duck-billed platypus and echidna are examples of a kind of mammal called monotremes. Monotremes nurse their babies, like all mammals, but their babies hatch out of eggs. Write Monotremes in the appropriate area of the Venn diagram. See diagram.

c. Placentals are mammals that bear live babies, like cats and squirrels. Marsupials, like opossums and kangaroos, are mammals that carry their babies in a pouch until the babies are big enough to be on their own. Place placentals and marsupials in the appropriate areas of the Venn diagram.   See diagram.

7a. See shading in diagram. The parts of "Nurses Babies" and "Mammals" circles that do not overlap must be shaded.

d. Birds are a separate class from mammals. All birds lay eggs. Place birds in the appropriate area of the Venn diagram. See diagram.

e. Fish are also a separate class. Some fish lay eggs, and others bear live babies. How do fish fit into this Venn diagram? Explain your reasoning.   Sample answer: Fish definitely do not go into the Mammal or Nurses Babies circles because they are not mammals. But you cannot just put all fish into the Lays Eggs circle, or outside of it, because some fish belong in the circle and others do not. So unless you are talking about specific kinds of fish, you cannot put them into this diagram.

Lesson 10.1 Data Displays   **595**

▶ **Exercise 6** Remind students that they need to organize the information they put in the Venn diagram. Have them lightly mark each amount in the diagram, and then check their numbers against the data in the table before completing the diagram.

▶ **Exercise 7** Remind students to organize the information they put in the Venn diagram. Have them lightly mark each amount in the diagram, and then check their numbers against the statements in the exercises before completing the diagram.

▶ **Exercise 8** You may want to provide students with copies of Lesson 10.1 Master 8 to complete the table and histogram. As an alternative, students could use graph paper or copies of Chapter 10 Masters 2 or 3 to make their histograms.

▶ **Exercise 9** Students will need graph paper or copies of Chapter 10 Masters 2 or 3 to make their graphs. You may want to point out that while Europe is a continent, not a country, the name also describes a group of countries.

Additional Answer

8b. The heights of the bars increase, reaching their highest point for the "9 and 10" age group, and then decrease again, reaching their lowest point for the "17 and 18" age group. The shape indicates that most of the girls who play soccer are in the middle of the age range shown on the graph.

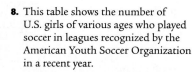

Real-World Link

The U.S. women's soccer team won the 1999 World Cup competition, defeating China 5–4. The game was tied after two overtime periods and had to be decided on penalty kicks.

9a.

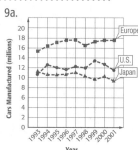

Connect & Extend

Math Link

To make a line graph, plot the data points and connect them with line segments.

8. This table shows the number of U.S. girls of various ages who played soccer in leagues recognized by the American Youth Soccer Organization in a recent year.

   a. Create a histogram showing these data. The first bar, which includes five- and six-year-old girls, has been drawn for you.

   b. Describe the shape of the histogram. Tell what the shape indicates about the distribution of ages.   See margin.

Soccer Players

Ages	Girls
5 and 6	23,805
7 and 8	45,181
9 and 10	46,758
11 and 12	39,939
13 and 14	26,147
15 and 16	11,518
17 and 18	4,430

Source: American Youth Soccer Organization

9. **Economics** Here are data about the number of motor vehicles manufactured in the United States, Europe, and Japan from 1993 to 2001.

   a. On the same set of axes, make a line graph of the data for each group. Use a different point shape or line color for each group.

Motor Vehicles Manufactured (millions)

Year	U.S.	Europe	Japan
1993	10.9	15.2	11.2
1994	12.3	16.2	10.6
1995	12.0	17.0	10.2
1996	11.8	17.6	10.3
1997	12.1	17.8	11.0
1998	12.0	16.3	10.1
1999	13.1	17.6	9.9
2000	12.8	17.7	10.1
2001	11.5	17.7	9.8

Source: *World Almanac and Book of Facts 2003.*
Copyright © 2003 Primedia Reference Inc.

   b. Is there one group that consistently produces more motor vehicles than the others? If so, which group is it?   Yes, Europe

c. Write two or three sentences comparing the number of vehicles manufactured in the United States to the number manufactured in Japan for the years from 1993 to 2001.

d. Given the trends in these data, which group do you think produced the most motor vehicles in 2002? Which group do you think produced the fewest? Give reasons for your answers. See margin.

10. **Earth Science** The *latitude* of a location indicates how far it is from the equator, which has latitude 0°. The further from the equator a place is, the greater its latitude. The latitude measure for a location includes the letter N or S to indicate whether it is north or south of the equator.

This table gives the lowest average monthly temperature and the latitude of nine cities.

Jackson Square, New Orleans

City	Latitude	Lowest Average Monthly Temp. (°F)
Albuquerque, New Mexico, U.S.A.	35° N	34
Georgetown, Guyana	7° N	79
New Orleans, Louisiana, U.S.A.	30° N	51
Portland, Maine, U.S.A.	44° N	22
Porto Alegre, Brazil	30° S	58
Recife, Brazil	8° S	75
San Juan, Puerto Rico	18° N	72
St. John's, Newfoundland, Canada	48° N	23
Stanley, Falkland Islands	52° S	36

Source: www.worldclimate.com

9c. Possible answer: Japan initially produced more vehicles. But from 1994 on, the United States produced more. 1999 shows the greatest difference between the number of vehicles produced in the two countries.

10b. Possible answer: In general, as latitude increases, lowest average monthly temperature decreases.

a. Make a line graph of the latitude and temperature data. When you graph the latitude values, ignore the N and S, graphing only the numbers. This way, you will be graphing each city's distance from the equator. See margin.

b. Does there appear to be an overall relationship between the latitude of a city and its lowest average monthly temperature? If so, describe the relationship.

c. The island of Nassau in the Bahamas has a latitude of about 25° N. Predict Nassau's lowest average monthly temperature. Explain how you made your prediction. See margin.

Lesson 10.1 Data Displays **597**

▶ **Exercise 9d** You may want to point out that the conclusions for Parts b and c are facts while the prediction in Part d is a hypothesis.

▶ **Exercise 10** Students will need graph paper or copies of Chapter 10 Masters 2 or 3 to make their graphs. You may want to suggest that students graph latitude on the horizontal axis and temperature on the vertical axis.

Additional Answers

9d. Possible answer: I would expect that Europe produced the most because they produced the most for all the years shown. I would guess that Japan produced the fewest in 2002, because they produced between 10,000 and 11,000 for each of the previous 5 years while the United States produced about 12,000 in each of the previous 5 years.

10a.

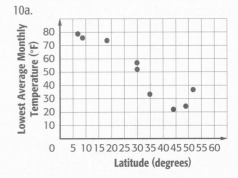

10c. Possible answer: About 63°F. I looked at the pattern in the graph. There are points on the graph for cities with latitudes 18° and 30°. The latitude for Nassau is between these, so I predicted that its temperature would be between the temperatures for those two cities (72°F and 54.5°F, the average of 51°F and 58°F). (Note: Nassau's actual lowest monthly temperature is 69°F.)

▶ **Exercise 11** This exercise introduces students to double bar graphs. You may want to briefly discuss the partial graphs, pointing out that the bars showing the time boys spend and the time girls spend are adjacent to one another but in different colors. Be sure students understand that they should use two adjacent bars, and that all the bars for boys should be the same color and all the bars for girls should be the same color.

You may want to provide students with copies of Lesson 10.1 Master 9, which reproduces the data set and the partially constructed graph. Alternatively, students could use graph paper or copies of Chapter 10 Masters 2 or 3 to make their graphs.

11. Preview Middle school students were asked in a survey how much time they spend with their parents or guardians on a typical weekend. Here are the results.

Time Spent with Parents	Boys (percent)	Girls (percent)
Almost all	39.6	49.6
One full day	18.6	21.8
Half a day	17.5	17.1
A few hours	24.3	11.5

If you wanted to compare the boys' responses with the girls' responses, you could display these data in two circle graphs.

Time Spent with Parents

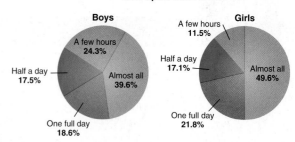

a. You could also show the data in a *double bar graph*. For each time category, the graph will have two bars, one showing the percent of boys in that category and the other showing the percent of girls. Copy and complete the graph below.

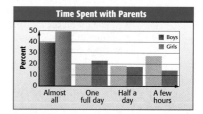

b. Which display do you think makes it easier to compare the two categories of data? Give reasons for your choice.   Possible answer: The double bar graph; it lets you see the percent of boys and girls in each category side by side.

12b. The scale on the vertical axis starts at 7 rather than 0. Each grid line on the vertical axis represents only 0.5. But because the space between grid lines is so great, an improvement of 1 point looks very large.

12c. Possible graph:

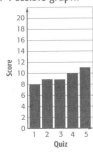

12. Drake's mother told him he could not play video games after school until his performance in math class improved significantly. Drake's math teacher gives a 20-point quiz each week. Drake made this bar graph to show his mother how much his scores had improved over the past five weeks.

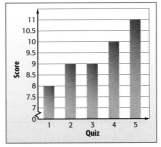

a. The bar for Quiz 5 is three times the height of the bar for Quiz 1. Is Drake's score on Quiz 5 three times his score on Quiz 1?   No

b. Drake's mother says his graph is misleading because it makes his improvement look more dramatic than it really is. What features of the graph make it misleading?

c. Make a new bar graph that you feel gives a more accurate view of Drake's performance on the weekly quizzes.

13. In Your Own Words Describe two types of graphs you have used to display data. For each type of graph, give an example of a set of data you might display with that type of graph.   Answers will vary.

14. Use the following clues to help you complete this Venn diagram.

a. There are no numbers outside of the circles.

b. The sum of the numbers in the three overlapping areas equals the number in the center area.

c. The total of the numbers in circle C is 10.

d. The total of the numbers in circle A is twice the total of the numbers in circle B.

e. The total of the numbers in all the areas of the diagram is 31.

Number Puzzle

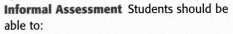

▶ **Exercise 12** This exercise has students consider some aspects that make a bar graph misleading. Since this may be a new idea for many students, you may want to work through the exercise as a class activity or, if assigned as independent study, have students share their answers. Students may want to use graph paper or Chapter 10 Masters 2 or 3 to make their graphs in Part c.

▶ **Exercises 14 and 15** Remind students that when solving exercises like these, it is often necessary to use trial and error. Point out that it may take several tries to get all the numbers in the diagram to fit the given rules.

Quick Check
Informal Assessment Students should be able to:

✔ interpret and compare line graphs

✔ use bar graphs and histograms to display data

✔ create bar graphs and histograms from sets of data

✔ decide whether to use a bar graph or a histogram to display a given set of data

Quick Quiz

1. What does it mean when a line graph is a horizontal line? Give an example of a graph that could have this shape.
Possible answer: That the values do not change; a car's speed when it is on cruise control

2. Explain the difference between a histogram and a bar graph. Possible answer: A bar graph often shows categorical data for individual items in a data set. A histogram shows the frequencies for categorical data given in ranges of values.

3. The bar graph shown does not have a title. Which of the following might be a title for this bar graph?
Explain your answer.
a. Points Scored by Players.
b. Temperature of Boiling Water as It Cools

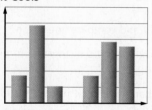

a. Points Scored by Players. Temperature would probably be shown as a line graph. If it were shown as a bar graph, the bars would have a decreasing pattern.

4. Make a histogram of the data below.

Player	Number of Points
John	24
Rae	33
Marta	18
Juan	26
Yoko	55
Greg	32
Ann	48
Sam	26
Randy	28

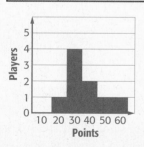

15. Draw a different Venn diagram that fits all the clues from Exercise 8.   Sample answer given.

Mixed Review

15. **Number Puzzle**

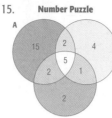

22. $\frac{1}{5}$; 0.2

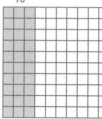

23. $\frac{3}{10}$; 0.3

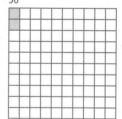

Solve each equation.

16. $5n - 3 = 17$ 4
17. $x + 5 = 12$ 7
18. $2 + 3a = 14$ 4
19. $\frac{x}{10} = \frac{25}{50}$ 5
20. $5a - 5 = 15$ 4
21. $4d + 3 = 19$ 4

Shade the given percent of a 100-grid. Then express the part of the area that is shaded as a fraction and as a decimal.

22. 20%   **23.** 30%
24. 2%   **25.** 25%
26. 120%   See margin.   **27.** 75%   See margin.

28. A group of girls is selling cookies. Miss Susanne wants the girls to sell the same number of boxes. Last year, 20 girls sold 80 boxes of cookies.

a. Complete this ratio table based on last year's information.

Girls	5	10	15	20	25	30
Boxes of cookies	20	40	60	80	100	120

b. How many girls will sell 20 boxes?   5

c. There are 25 girls selling cookies. How many cookies will they sell?   100

24. $\frac{1}{50}$; 0.02   25. $\frac{1}{4}$; 0.25

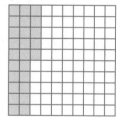

Additional Answers for Mixed Review are on page 657A.

Collect and Analyze Data

Objectives

▶ To prepare a plan that includes selecting the appropriate statistical measures

▶ To estimate large quantities based on sample size

▶ To choose an appropriate graph to display data

Overview

In this lesson, students apply data analysis tools to complete a project about activities that middle school students participate in outside of school. The first investigation focuses on planning as students consider what information they need to help them answer six questions. They decide which statistical measures, mathematical calculations, and data displays they would use when reporting their findings. They also complete a form and collect data. Students implement their plans in Investigation 2.

Students will make predictions about sampled data in Investigation 3 and then analyze the information content of various data displays so they can choose an appropriate graph in Investigation 4.

Advance Preparation

You may want to provide students with Lesson 10.2 Masters 1–4 to facilitate class discussion while presenting new topics, including collecting and analyzing data.

	Summary	Materials	On Your Own Exercises (pp. 611–616)	Assessment Opportunities
Investigation 1 (p. 602) *Pacing: 2 days*	Students plan how they will collect, analyze, and present data for a research project.	Lesson 10.2 Masters 1-3 (optional), transparencies of Lesson 10.2 Master 1 (optional)	Practice & Apply: 1 Connect & Extend: 10 Mixed Review: 16–26	• On the Spot Assessment (p. 604) • Share & Summarize (p. 604) • Troubleshooting (p. 604)
Investigation 2 (p. 605) *Pacing: 1 day*	Students analyze data and present their findings.	Lesson 10.2 Master 4 (optional)	Practice & Apply: 2 Connect & Extend: 14 Mixed Review: 16–26	• Share & Summarize (p. 606) • Troubleshooting (p. 606)
Investigation 3 (p. 607) *Pacing: 1 day*	Students estimate large quantities based on smaller groups, using the capture-tag-recapture method.	Bags of beans	Practice & Apply: 3 Connect & Extend: 11–13 Mixed Review: 16–26	• Share & Summarize (p. 608) • Troubleshooting (p. 608)
Investigation 4 (p. 609) *Pacing: 1 day*	Students analyze the information content of various displays of a given set of data and select appropriate graphs to fit the data.	Chapter 10 Master 1 or graph paper, ruler, protractor, compass	Practice & Apply: 4–9 Connect & Extend: 10, 15 Mixed Review: 16–26	• Share & Summarize (p. 610)

Leveled Lesson Resources

Study Guide and Intervention (p. 20) — AL

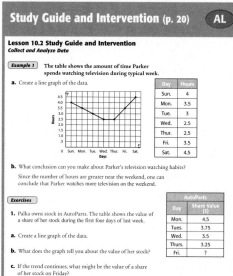

Lesson 10.2 Study Guide and Intervention
Collect and Analyze Data

Example 1 The table shows the amount of time Parker spends watching television during typical week.

a. Create a line graph of the data.

Day	Hours
Sun.	4
Mon.	3.5
Tue.	3
Wed.	2.5
Thur.	2.5
Fri.	3.5
Sat.	4.5

b. What conclusion can you make about Parker's television watching habits?

Since the number of hours are greater near the weekend, one can conclude that Parker watches more television on the weekend.

Exercises

1. Palka owns stock in AutoParts. The table shows the value of a share of her stock during the first four days of last week.

AutoParts	
Day	Share Value ($)
Mon.	4.5
Tues.	3.75
Wed.	3.5
Thurs.	3.25
Fri.	?

a. Create a line graph of the data.

b. What does the graph tell you about the value of her stock?

c. If the trend continues, what might be the value of a share of her stock on Friday?

Skills Practice (p. 21) — AL OL

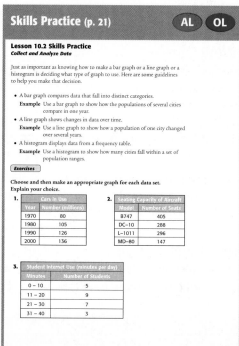

Lesson 10.2 Skills Practice
Collect and Analyze Data

Just as important as knowing how to make a bar graph or a line graph or a histogram is deciding what type of graph to use. Here are some guidelines to help you make that decision.

- A bar graph compares data that fall into distinct categories.
  Example Use a bar graph to show how the populations of several cities compare in one year.
- A line graph shows changes in data over time.
  Example Use a line graph to show how a population of one city changed over several years.
- A histogram displays data from a frequency table.
  Example Use a histogram to show how many cities fall within a set of population ranges.

Exercises

Choose and then make an appropriate graph for each data set. Explain your choice.

1.
Cars in Use	
Year	Number (millions)
1970	80
1980	105
1990	126
2000	136

2.
Seating Capacity of Aircraft	
Model	Number of Seats
B747	405
DC–10	288
L–1011	296
MD–80	147

3.
Student Internet Use (minutes per day)	
Minutes	Number of Students
0 – 10	5
11 – 20	9
21 – 30	7
31 – 40	3

Problem-Solving Practice (p. 22) — AL OL

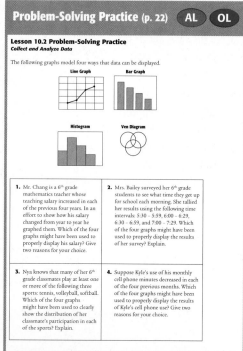

Lesson 10.2 Problem-Solving Practice
Collect and Analyze Data

The following graphs model four ways that data can be displayed.

Line Graph   Bar Graph

Histogram   Ven Diagram

1. Mr. Chang is a 6th grade mathematics teacher whose teaching salary increased in each of the previous four years. In an effort to show how his salary changed from year to year he graphed them. Which of the four graphs might have been used to properly display his salary? Give two reasons for your choice.

2. Mrs. Bailey surveyed her 6th grade students to see what time they get up for school each morning. She rallied her results using the following time intervals: 5:30 – 5:59, 6:00 – 6:29, 6:30 – 6:59, and 7:00 – 7:29. Which of the four graphs might have been used to properly display the results of her survey? Explain.

3. Nya knows that many of her 6th grade classmates play at least one or more of the following three sports: tennis, volleyball, softball. Which of the four graphs might have been used to clearly show the distribution of her classmate's participation in each of the sports? Explain.

4. Suppose Kyle's use of his monthly cell phone minutes decreased in each of the four previous months. Which of the four graphs might have been used to properly display the results of Kyle's cell phone use? Give two reasons for your choice.

Enrichment (p. 23) — BL

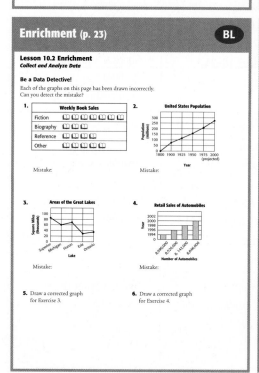

Lesson 10.2 Enrichment
Collect and Analyze Data

Be a Data Detective!

Each of the graphs on this page has been drawn incorrectly. Can you detect the mistakes?

1. Weekly Book Sales
Fiction
Biography
Reference
Other

Mistake:

2. United States Population

Mistake:

3. Areas of the Great Lakes

Mistake:

4. Retail Sales of Automobiles

Mistake:

5. Draw a corrected graph for Exercise 3.

6. Draw a corrected graph for Exercise 4.

Lesson Quick Quiz (p. 24) — AL OL BL

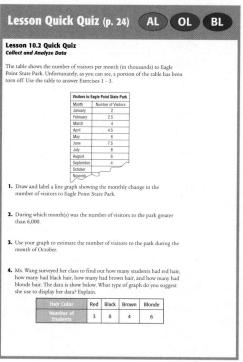

Lesson 10.2 Quick Quiz
Collect and Analyze Data

The table shows the number of visitors per month (in thousands) to Eagle Point State Park. Unfortunately, as you can see, a portion of the table has been torn off. Use the table to answer Exercises 1 – 3.

Visitors to Eagle Point State Park	
Month	Number of Visitors
January	2
February	2.5
March	4
April	4.5
May	6
June	7.5
July	8
August	6
September	4
October	
Novemb	

1. Draw and label a line graph showing the monthly change in the number of visitors to Eagle Point State Park.

2. During which month(s) was the number of visitors to the park greater than 6,000.

3. Use your graph to estimate the number of visitors to the park during the month of October.

4. Ms. Wang surveyed her class to find out how many students had red hair, how many had black hair, how many had brown hair, and how many had blonde hair. The data is show below. What type of graph do you suggest she use to display her data? Explain.

Hair Color	Red	Black	Brown	Blonde
Number of Students	3	8	4	6

Lesson Masters 1–4 (pp. 25–28)

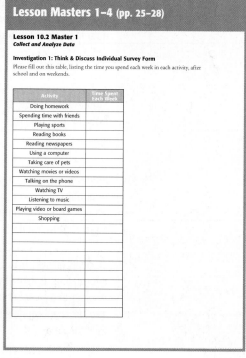

Lesson 10.2 Master 1
Collect and Analyze Data

Investigation 1: Think & Discuss Individual Survey Form

Please fill out this table, listing the time you spend each week in each activity, after school and on weekends.

Activity	Time Spent Each Week
Doing homework	
Spending time with friends	
Playing sports	
Reading books	
Reading newspapers	
Using a computer	
Taking care of pets	
Watching movies or videos	
Talking on the phone	
Watching TV	
Listening to music	
Playing video or board games	
Shopping	

Additional Lesson Resources

Teacher Tech Tools
- TeacherWorks
- ExamView Assessment Suite
- Classroom Presentation Toolkit
- Advance Tracker

Student Tech Tools
- StudentWorks Plus
- **Math Online** eGlossary •
  Concepts in Motion

Other Print Products
- Investigation Notebook and Reflection Journal
- Quick Review Math Handbook

LESSON 10.2

Collect and Analyze Data

The editors of *All about Kids!* magazine are researching an article about the activities in which middle school students participate. They would like the article to address these questions.

- In what activities do middle school students participate after school and on weekends?
- What percent of students participate in each activity?
- How many hours a week do students typically spend on each activity?
- What are students' favorite activities?
- Do boys and girls like different activities?
- Do students tend to spend the most time on the activities they like best?

The editors have hired Data, Inc. to help with the article. They would like you to answer the above questions for the students in your class.

They have suggested using the form below to collect your class data.

Materials
- survey form

Are you male or female?

Please fill out this table, listing the time you spend each week in each activity, after school and on weekends.

What is your favorite activity?

Activity	Time Spent Each Week
Doing homework	
Spending time with friends	
Playing sports	
Reading books	
Reading newspapers	
Using a computer	
Taking care of pets	
Watching movies or videos	
Talking on the phone	
Watching TV	
Listening to music	
Playing video or board games	
Shopping	

Introduce

Collect and Analyze Data Introduce the lesson by asking students to name some of the ways they have learned to analyze data. They may mention measures of central tendency and various types of graphs. Then introduce the context of this lesson, pointing out that students will use some of the methods they mentioned to collect and analyze data for a magazine article about activities that middle school students participate in and enjoy.

Remind students that data must be collected before they can be analyzed. Have them read the six questions that the magazine editors would like to have answered. Point out the form supplied by the magazine editors that is printed at the bottom of the page. Students will discuss this form in more detail in Think & Discuss on page 602.

Students determine whether the activities in the table provide sufficient information to answer the six questions presented by the magazine editors. They may think of other questions that the magazine article should address. Be aware that additional questions are the focus of Share & Summarize for this investigation. There are several ways to approach this whole-class exercise. You could provide students with copies of Lesson 10.2 Master 1 so they can revise the form during the class discussion. You could also record students' suggestions for any revisions on a transparency of the master and combine the data onto Lesson 10.2 Masters 2 and 3.

Investigation ①

On Your Own Exercises
Pages 611–616
Exercises 1, 10

Plan Your Analysis This investigation is the planning step in a larger project of collecting and analyzing data. Organize students into small groups to work together for the duration of these two investigations.

✅ Develop & Understand: A

Suggested Grouping: Small Groups

▶ **Exercise 1a** In this exercise set, groups determine how to use the collected data and determine which mathematical calculations and statistical measures, if any, will be most useful in answering each of the six questions. In this exercise, point out that students may think that they *must* describe a procedure as part of the answer and not recognize that additional computations are unnecessary.

▶ **Exercise 6** The answer suggested for this exercise includes finding percents. Students may be focusing on the statistical measures taught in this chapter and overlook this calculation. You may want to use this exercise to remind them that they can also use other mathematical computations to analyze data.

Wrap-Up Discuss each exercise. Have groups present their answers to a problem and then have others add their own ideas.

1a. Possible answer: I will need the list of activities in which students participate.

1b. Possible answer: I will not need to do any computations. I need to list all the activities for which one or more students recorded a time.

2a. Possible answer: For each activity, I will need a count of how many students participate in it.

2b. Possible answer: For each activity, I will need to divide the number of students who participate in it by the total number of students surveyed and convert the answer to a percent.

Answers will vary.
Look over the list of activities. Decide with your class whether to add or delete any activities.

Consider each question the editors want answered. Think about whether the survey form will collect the information needed to answer it. Decide as a class whether anything should be added to the form.

Each student in your class should fill out a survey form. All the data from the class will be combined later.

Investigation ① Plan Your Analysis

In this investigation, you will think about what types of statistics and graphs might be useful for reporting the results of the survey. You will not do your analysis until the next investigation, but carefully planning your strategy now will make your analysis much easier.

✅ Develop & Understand: A

Exercises 1–6 list the six questions asked by the magazine editors. For each question, complete Parts a and b.

   a. Tell which collected data you will need to answer the question.

   b. Describe a procedure you could use to answer the question. Be sure to indicate any statistical measures (like mean, median, mode, or range) that you will need to find or computations you will need to do.

1. In what activities do middle school students participate after school and on weekends?

2. What percent of students participate in each activity?

3. How many hours a week do students typically spend on each activity?   See margin.

4. What are students' favorite activities?   See margin.

5. Do boys and girls like different activities?   See margin.

6. Do students tend to spend the most time on the activities they like best?   See margin.

Save your answers from these exercises for Investigation 2.

Additional Answers

3. Possible answer:
   a. For each activity, I will need data about the number of hours each student spends each week.
   b. I will find the range, mean, and median number of hours for each activity.

4. Possible answer:
   a. I will need the list of activities students listed as their favorites.
   b. I will find the mode activity (or maybe the top two or three most popular activities).

5. Possible answer:
   a. I will need the list of activities boys said were their favorites and the list girls said were their favorites.
   b. I will find the top two or three activities for boys and the top two or three activities for girls.

6. Possible answer:
   a. For each student, I will need the favorite activity and the list of times that each student spent on each activity.
   b. I will see whether each student spends the most time on the activity he or she likes best. I will calculate the percent of students who spend the most time on their favorite activity.

Magazine articles often use graphs to present data. In Exercises 7–12, you will think about what types of graphs might be useful to include in the magazine article.

You are familiar with several types of graphs, such as line graphs, bar graphs, histograms, pictographs, and circle graphs. You might also consider one of the special types of bar graphs described in the example below.

Math Link

A *pictograph* uses symbols or pictures to represent data.

Example

A *double bar graph* compares data for two groups. For example, this double bar graph compares the favorite primary colors of boys and girls in one middle school class.

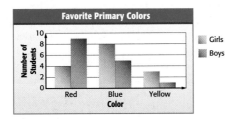

A *stacked bar graph* shows how the data represented by each bar is divided into two or more groups. This graph shows how the number of children who chose each color is divided between boys and girls.

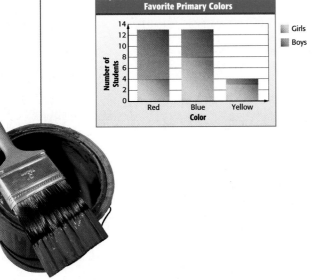

Teacher Tips Point out that some magazine articles use graphs to relay information. Ask students to think about the types of graphs that might appear in a magazine article. Inform students that there are variations of some of these graphs. If you assigned On Your Own Exercise 11 in Lesson 6.1, remind students that they made a double bar graph to show the data. Then discuss the characteristics of the double bar graph and the stacked bar graph in the Example.

Math Link

Ask students to recall any pictographs they may have seen. Remind them that special characters may be used in pictographs. For example, a pictograph about baseball may use pictures of baseballs as representing data.

Example

Have students compare each graph with a traditional bar graph. Most students will identify the differences, which include the use of a key, a different arrangement of bars, and displaying two sets of data on the same graph. To be sure students understand and can use these graphs, ask questions similar to these:

How many students chose red as their favorite color? 13

How many boys chose blue as their favorite color? 5

Discuss which graph students used to answer each question. Encourage them to use the other graph to check that their answer is correct.

Suggested Grouping: Pairs

▶ **Exercises 7–12** In this exercise set, students consider how graphs could be used to support their conclusions and convey information to the reader. As with the exercises on page 602, they just plan the report. Any graphs will be drawn when students implement their plans in Investigation 2.

Wrap-Up Have students share their opinions about the type of graph they would make for each question. Remind them to save their answers to use in Investigation 2.

Share & Summarize

Have students continue working in their small groups. They may have suggested other questions during the planning stages of the investigation. If so, allow them to describe the data they would collect and the mathematical calculations and graph they would use to answer one of those questions.

Troubleshooting If students are having difficulty deciding which, if any, mathematical calculations to use to answer a question, encourage them to use the solve a simpler problem strategy. Have students make up a data set with five values and see how they can describe the data set. For a small number of data, students may find it easier to see which measures or calculations can describe the data. Likewise, they could use a graph problem-solving strategy by sketching simple graphs to see which is appropriate for their small data set.

Additional Answers for Share & Summarize

Possible answer: What are students' least favorite activities? I would need each student to specify the activity he or she likes least. I would compute the mode of these activities. I might make a circle graph showing the percent of students who chose each activity as their least favorite.

---

8. Possible answer: I could include a bar graph with a bar for each activity. The height of each bar would represent the percent of students who participate in that activity.

9. Possible answer: I could make a bar graph with a bar for each activity and the height of the bar indicating the average (mean, median, or mode) number of hours spent by students in the activity. For some activities, I might include a histogram. The histogram would show time intervals on the horizontal axis, and the height of each bar would indicate the number of students who spend that amount of time doing the activity.

10. Possible answer: I would make a bar graph in which each bar represents an activity and the height shows the number of students who chose that activity as their favorite.

Develop & Understand: B

For each question, decide whether it would be useful to include a graph with the answer to the question. If so, describe the graph you would use. Include at least one double bar graph or stacked bar graph.

7. In what activities do middle school students participate after school and on weekends? Possible answer: I do not think I need a graph for this question.

8. What percent of students participate in each activity?

9. How many hours a week do students typically spend on each activity?

10. What are students' favorite activities?

11. Do boys and girls like different activities? See below.

12. Do students tend to spend the most time on the activities they like best? Possible answer: I would not use a graph for this question.

Save your answers from these exercises for Investigation 2.

Share & Summarize

Think of at least one more question you think would be interesting to address in the magazine article, such as training horses. Describe the data you would need to collect to answer the question. Tell what statistics and graphs you would include in your answer. See margin.

11. Possible answer: I would make a double bar graph with separate bars for boys and girls. Each bar would show the number of boys or girls who chose that activity as their favorite.

604 **CHAPTER 10** Data and Probability

 Assessment

Watch for students who want to make a graph for Exercises 7 or 12. Ask them what information would be in the graph. Help them realize that all graphs use numbers; either on a scale, on a label, or through a key. Point out that while each of these exercises has categories of data, they contain no numerical information that can readily be shown in a graph.

Investigation ② Carry Out Your Analysis

- results of class survey
- answers for Investigation 1

You have collected data about the activities in which the students in your class participate. Now you will analyze the class data and use your results to answer the questions posed by the magazine editors.

✅ Develop & Understand: A

The editors' six questions appear in Exercises 1–6. Work with your group to analyze the data and answer each question. Include the following information for each exercise.

- the results of your computations and the measures you found
- a few sentences answering the question, including statistical measures that support your answers
- a graph, if appropriate, to help illustrate your answer

You can use your answers from Exercises 7–12 in Investigation 1 as a guide, but you may change your mind about what statistics and graphs to include.

As you work, you may want to create tables to organize your data and calculations. Here is an example you might find useful.

Activity	Number Who Participate			Percent Who Participate			Mean Time Spent			Median Time Spent		
	Boys	Girls	All	Boys	Girls	All	Boys	Girls	All	Boys	Girls	All
Doing homework												
Spending time with friends												
Playing sports												
Reading books												
Reading newspapers												
Using a computer												
Taking care of pets												
Watching movies or videos												
Talking on the phone												
Watching TV												
Listening to music												
Playing video or board games												
Shopping												

Investigation ②

On Your Own Exercises
Pages 611–616
Exercises 2, 14

Carry Out Your Analysis In this investigation, students will implement the plans they made in the previous problem sets. They will analyze the data to address each of the six questions proposed by the magazine editors. They should work in their small groups from Investigation 1.

Students may want to organize the data into a table to help them compute the statistical measures they have chosen to use and to reflect on the appropriateness of the results.

Remind students that in the last class, they planned how they would analyze data for the magazine article. Tell them that they will carry out those plans in today's class.

✅ Develop & Understand: A

Suggested Grouping: Small Groups

▶ **Exercises 1–6** Students will now implement their plans from Investigation 1. You may want to discuss the directions and table before students begin working. Be sure students understand that the responses to each exercise should contain references to the bulleted items. Some students may think that the only appropriate graph is one that is necessary, and since the answer can be stated in words, they do not need to make any graphs. Point out that an *appropriate* graph is any graph that helps support the answer. Stress that the table is optional and students are welcome to organize the data in any way they choose.

Teacher Tips You can provide students with copies of Lesson 10.2 Master 4 if they would like to use the table to assist with their analysis. Have students retrieve their copies of the combined class data and their answers to the exercises on pages 602 and 604.

Wrap-Up Depending on the available time and class interest, you can either have students discuss the answers to the questions as a class or have groups prepare and write answers to the questions.

Share & Summarize

Exercise 1 reinforces how to work in groups and organize data by focusing on the *process* rather than the end result.

Exercise 2 previews determining the validity of a sample. For example, students in different areas of the country, with different cultural backgrounds, or with different economic situations may participate in different activities. Ultimately, students' answers will be based on how much they believe their interests are like other students in the country.

Troubleshooting This is a complex project, and it is important that students think about the data, statistical measures, and graphs that are needed to answer the questions. If students had difficulty answering the questions, guide them through the process using one of the additional questions that students suggested in Share & Summarize for Investigation 1 (page 604).

The importance of this project is that students have had opportunities to think about which statistical measures are most appropriate in specific instances and that they have used data to answer questions.

1–6. Answers will vary.

1. In what activities do middle school students participate after school and on weekends?

2. What percent of students participate in each activity?

3. How many hours a week do students typically spend on each activity?

4. What are students' favorite activities?

5. Do boys and girls like different activities?

6. Do students tend to spend the most time on the activities they like best?

Share & Summarize Answers will vary.

1. Write a few sentences summarizing your group's work on Exercises 1–6. Discuss how you divided the work among group members and how you organized the data to make it easier to answer the questions.

2. Do you think a nationwide survey of middle school students would give results similar to your class results? Explain why or why not.

Investigation 3 Make Predictions

Materials
- bag of beans

People sometimes want to estimate large quantities that are difficult or impossible to count, such as the number of animals or plants of a particular endangered species or the number of people affected by a flu epidemic. If you had to count each individual member of these populations, it would be costly, time-consuming, and probably impossible to get exactly right.

In this investigation, you will learn how proportions can help you to estimate such numbers without actually counting every member.

✓ Develop & Understand: A

Each student in your group should take five beans from your bag and mark them. Put all the marked beans back into the bag with the other beans. Mix them carefully.

Without looking in the bag, take out 20 beans. Record the number of marked beans.

1. What is the number of marked beans? **Answers will vary.**

2. Estimate the total number of beans in the bag. How did you make your estimate? **See margin.**

3. What did you need to assume to estimate the total number of beans?

4. Do you think your estimate would be better, worse, or the same if your bag contained thousands of beans? Why? How might you modify the method you used to make the estimate more accurate? **See margin.**

To estimate the numbers of different animals in the wilderness, scientists use a method called *capture-tag-recapture*. This method is similar to the process you used to estimate the number of beans in your bag.

Using this method, scientists capture a certain number of animals and mark them using collars, rings, or other tags. They then release the animals. Some time later, they capture another group of animals and count how many in that group are tagged. They can then solve a proportion to estimate the total number of animals.

3. The ratio of marked beans to all beans in our sample is the same as the ratio of marked beans to all beans in the bag.

Real-World Link
Bird banding is a helpful way to study wild birds. Scientists attach a small, numbered metal or plastic ring to the birds' legs or wings. Scientists can track the migration, longevity, and feeding habits of a bird with this type of identification.

Lesson 10.2 Collect and Analyze Data **607**

Additional Answers
2. Answers will vary. If the group marked 15 beans in all and the number of marked beans in Exercise 1 is 2, students may set up this proportion:

15 marked beans/*y* beans in all = 2 marked beans/20 beans

4. Possible answer: If the bag contained thousands of beans, it is likely that none of the relatively small number of marked beans would be chosen in a group of 20 beans–meaning the estimate of marked beans would be zero. Either more beans must be marked, or more and larger groups must be taken.

Investigation 3

On Your Own Exercises
Pages 611–616
Exercises 3, 11–13

Make Predictions Introduce the lesson by asking students to think about how they would estimate the number of people who caught the flu during one epidemic. Then tell students that they can gather data and use that data and proportions to estimate the size of a larger group. They will learn these techniques in the next exercise set where groups of students will need bags of beans and markers to complete the problems.

✓ Develop & Understand: A

Suggested Grouping: Small Groups

▶ **Exercises 1–4** Students explore sampling and proportions as they estimate the number of beans in a bag. Some groups might get a sample that does not contain any marked beans. Let them take another sample; some groups might want to take the no-show attempt into account. If the situation arises, you might want to discuss probability briefly.

▶ **Exercise 2** Discuss how students made their estimates. Point out how proportions can be used to make these estimates.

▶ **Exercise 4** This exercise hints at the fact that this method becomes less and less reliable as the number of tagged items is smaller and the total population is larger and larger.

Teacher Tips Point out that the bean experiment is an example of a widely used technique in biology for estimating population sizes in the wild, called *capture-tag-recapture*. Underlying the sampling is the basic assumption that your sample is somehow typical of the population. In the bean experiment of this exercise set, you could point out that, if you laid all the marked beans on the top, didn't shake the container to distribute them evenly, and then scooped your sample off the top again, you will get a biased count. Another factor is the size of the sample. Clearly, if you have a sample of one, it will not be a good predictor of the population as a whole.

Lesson 10.2 Collect and Analyze Data **607**

Develop & Understand: B

Suggested Grouping: Pairs

▶ **Exercises 5 and 6** Point out that students can solve these exercises informally using ratio tables, or they can backtrack by undoing dividing by 45.

▶ **Exercises 5–7** The three problems here give students an opportunity to estimate three animal populations using the capture-tag-recapture method. Tell students that surveys are another way to estimate large populations.

Develop & Understand: C

Suggested Grouping: Pairs

▶ **Exercises 8–10** In this exercise set, samples are used to extrapolate from a sample of 1,000 to the whole population of Massachusetts. Have students work individually on these exercises and with a partner on Exercise 11.

Wrap-Up Discuss the assumptions students used in Exercise 11. You might also point out that the science of statistics has been developed to describe exactly how sample size relates to reliability. Tell your students that this unit is just an introduction to this important subject.

Share & Summarize

Have students share their ideas. The sample answer on the opposite page is an example of how police and others actually estimate crowds at events. Consider getting a map of Times Square and ask students how to estimate its area. Again, it is important to look at whether or not the sample data is typical. You have to pick an area that is typical and not particularly more or less crowded than the average density of people. Similar techniques are used in labs to count white/red blood cells to determine whether people are anemic.

Students might enjoy working on a sampling project. For example, they might estimate the attendance at an after-school sporting event.

---

5. 225; Solve the proportion $\frac{x}{45} = \frac{75}{15}$.

11. Possible answer: Proportions can be used to solve the exercises. The assumption we made is that the whole population of Massachusetts has the same ratio of the number of TVs as these 1,000 people have.

Develop & Understand: B

5. Suppose biologists tagged 45 blue whales in the Antarctic waters. The next year, they caught 75 blue whales and found that 15 of them had tags. Estimate the total number of whales in the area. Explain your method.

6. Red wolves have been classified as extinct in the wild, but some still live in captivity. Some efforts have been made to restore red wolves to forests in North Carolina and Tennessee.

   Suppose biologists caught 20 wolves from those forests, tagged them, and then freed them. Later, they caught 15 wolves and found that five had tags. Estimate the number of red wolves in the forests. Explain your method. 60; Solve the proportion $\frac{x}{20} = \frac{15}{5}$

7. Suppose ornithologists tagged and released 240 bald eagles from across the United States. A couple of months later, they caught 100 birds and found that three of them had tags. Estimate the number of bald eagles in the United States. 8,000

Surveys do not use the capture-tag-recapture method, but they do use proportions to make estimates of large populations of people.

Develop & Understand: C

The population of Massachusetts is about 6.4 million people. A survey questioned 1,000 people across the country. It found that approximately 300 people had two televisions in their homes. About 400 people had three or more televisions. The survey also found that about 700 people had cable television service.

8. Estimate how many households in Massachusetts have two televisions. Assume the proportions for Massachusetts are the same as for the sample. About 2 million

9. Estimate how many households have three or more televisions. About 2.6 million

10. Estimate how many households in Massachusetts receive cable television. About 4.5 million

11. Discuss with your partner the methods you used to solve Exercises 8–10. What assumptions did you make and why?

Share & Summarize

What method would you use to estimate the number of people in a large crowd, such as the large gathering at Times Square in New York City on New Year's Eve? Possible answer: Count the number of people in a small area, say a 3 m by 3 m square, and scale that number up to the area of Times Square.

Troubleshooting

You may want to continue talking about sampling even if this material seems difficult for them at this time. The concept of sampling is complex, and this investigation is meant to give students a brief introduction to the application of ratio in a meaningful context.

Investigation 4 — Choose a Graph

When you have a choice of graph for organizing and displaying data, what do you do? The "best" graph for a situation is the one that most clearly shows the data for the purpose you need.

These are some of the types of graphs that you have learned and from which you can choose.

- line graphs
- histograms
- bar graphs

For example, the data below, which show the average monthly temperatures for Knoxville, Tennessee, in degrees Fahrenheit, were used to create the three graphs.

Jan	Feb	Mar	Apr	May	Jun	Jul	Aug	Sep	Oct	Nov	Dec
36	40	49	58	65	73	77	76	70	58	49	40

Reprinted with permission from *The World Almanac and Book of Facts.*

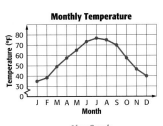
Line Graph

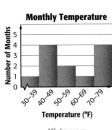
Histogram

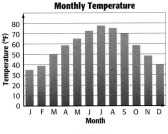
Bar Graph

Develop & Understand: A

Math Link

Math Link
In a histogram, the height of a bar tells how many data values are in a particular range of values. In a bar graph, the height of a bar gives a particular data value.

1. Which graphs give a sense of the temperature changes over the year? Line graph, bar graph

2. From the graphs you named in Exercise 1, describe the average monthly temperatures in Knoxville. See margin.

3. Which graphs seem most useful for displaying the temperature data? Explain. The bar graph and the line graph; They give the most information, including the trend over the year.

4. Are the other graphs useless for displaying the data? Explain. Possible answer: Not necessarily; For example, a histogram could be used to show temperature data.

Lesson 10.2 Collect and Analyze Data **609**

Additional Answer

2. Possible answer: The temperature rises from the 30s in January to the 70s from about June to September and then drops to the 40s by December.

Investigation 4

On Your Own Exercises
Pages 611–616
Exercises 4–9, 10, 15

Choose a Graph This investigation deals with all of the fundamental issues relating to visual displays of quantitative information. In the first exercise set, students are asked to focus information provided by multiple displays of the same information; in the second, they are asked to select displays for different data sets. There will be differences of opinion about choosing a display. As you discuss the choices, concentrate as much on the nature of the information that is lost by picking a display as on the information provided.

Teacher Tips You may want to have copies of Chapter 10 Master 1, Quarter-Inch Graph Paper, or other graph paper, as well as rulers, protractors, and compasses available for students to use when making graphs in class and at home. Be sure students are familiar with the three types of graphs named and shown on this page. Some students may need a quick review of these types of displays.

Develop & Understand: A

Suggested Grouping: Pairs

▶ **Exercises 1 and 2** Students compare different data displays for a set of temperature data. You will probably find that students are most comfortable with the line and bar graph displays of this data because they show temperature changes over the passage of time. These are the displays that students use most often.

Math Link
Point out that a histogram tells how many data values fall into a range, not the actual data itself.

Develop & Understand: B

Suggested Grouping: Small Groups

▶ **Exercises 5 and 6** These exercises can be used for assessment. Keep in mind that answers to these questions cannot be incorrect provided that the student can actually construct the display. However, one display can provide more relevant information than another.

Wrap-Up Be sure students understand that all of the graphs display the same set of data but that some displays relay specific data more effectively. You may want to have students share their graphs for each set of data. If students chose different data displays, they can compare the various representations of the same data.

Teacher Tips You may want to have tools, such as Chapter 10 Master 1, Quarter-Inch Graph Paper, or graph paper, as well as rulers, protractors, and compasses for students to use when making their graphs in Exercise 6.

Share & Summarize

Work through the exercises with the class. Have volunteers share their responses with the class.

---

5. Possible answer: Most popular pets; use bar graph, do not use line graph. Tropical fish; use histogram, do not use line graph. Cost per week; use histogram, do not use line graph. Life expectancy; use histogram, do not use bar graph. Explanations will vary.

1. Data with an independent and dependent variable, especially data measured over time

2. When you want to know how often values in particular ranges appear

3. Data that fall into categories, including time units like months and years

---

Develop & Understand: B

Kyung and Isandro gathered some data on pets for a school project.

Most Popular Pets
Kyung surveyed the 27 students in his class about their favorite pets. Here are his findings.

Dogs	Cats	Birds	Fish	Mice
8	9	5	4	1

Tropical Fish
Isandro found ten students who kept tropical fish. He asked how many fish they each had in their tanks. The responses were as follows.

4 9 11 13 15 16 16 16 18 20

Cost per Week
Kyung and Isandro gathered information on how much it costs students to care for their pets each week, on average. Here are their results.

- under $5: 23%
- between $5 and $10: 48%
- over $10: 29%

Life Expectancy of Dogs
Isandro researched the following data for how long pet dogs live on average.

Years	0 to 4	5 to 8	9 to 12	13 to 16	over 16
Percentage	17%	8%	26%	37%	12%

5. The boys wanted to use graphs to effectively display their data. For each of the four types of data they collected, choose one of the following graph types that you think would be useful and one that would be inappropriate. Explain your choices.
   - line graphs
   - histograms
   - bar graphs

6. For each data set, choose an appropriate graph type. Make a graph to display the data.   Graphs will vary.

Share & Summarize

For each type of graph, describe the kind of data or situation that it would be best for displaying.

1. line graph
2. histogram
3. bar graph

Reaching *All Learners*

OL **On Level** Note that many students will not be able to interpret these graphs without assistance. Ask students to discuss and interpret these graphs in pairs.

Practice & Apply

Real-World Link
Americans aged 13 to 18 spend more than 72 hours a week using electronic media, such as the Internet, cell phones, television, music, and video games.

In Exercises 1 and 2, use this information.

The editors of *All about Kids!* would like to publish an article about teenage Internet users. Here are the questions they would like to answer.

Question 1. How much time do teen Internet users typically spend on the Internet each week?

Question 2. How much time do they typically spend on various Internet activities?

Question 3. What are these teenagers' favorite Internet activities?

The magazine editors have collected data from 15 students who are regular Internet users. The green entries indicate the students' favorite activities.

Weekly Time Spent on the Net (minutes)

Student Initials	Chatting in a Chat Room	Playing Games	Doing Homework	Surfing the Web	E-mail
AB	90	75	80	90	12
BT	75	150	0	150	15
CP	0	75	60	150	5
CT	0	240	0	0	0
GO	120	90	90	60	3
KQ	135	60	40	80	15
LM	75	160	30	45	6
MC	15	0	35	60	15
MH	80	180	30	90	6
NM	90	90	45	90	15
PD	100	150	60	90	0
RL	100	90	45	90	0
SK	90	135	60	240	10
SM	60	135	40	60	22
YS	120	30	60	45	15

1. Complete Parts a and b for Questions 1, 2, and 3 above. See margin.

a. Describe any statistical measures you will need to find or computations you will need to do to answer the question.

b. Describe a graph that would be appropriate to include with the answer to the question.

Investigation 1
Pages 602–604
Practice & Apply: 1
Connect & Extend: 10

Investigation 2
Pages 605–606
Practice & Apply: 2
Connect & Extend: 14

Investigation 3
Pages 607–608
Practice & Apply: 3
Connect & Extend: 11–13

Investigation 4
Pages 609–610
Practice & Apply: 4–9
Connect & Extend: 10, 15

Assign Anytime
Mixed Review: 16–26

▶ **Exercises 1 and 2** In Exercise 1, students perform an analysis similar to that done in Investigation 1—deciding which data, which statistical measures, and which mathematical calculations will be needed to answer specific questions. Remind students that they are not asked to perform any calculations, but they may do so if it helps them create plans. You may want to plan class time to discuss students' responses. Have them keep their plans to help them when they complete the analysis in Exercise 2 on page 612.

Real-World Link
Do a survey of the class and find out how many hours a day the average sixth-grader spends using electronic media per day.

Additional Answers

1a. Possible answers:

Question 1: For each student, I will need to add the times for all the activities to find the total time spent on the Internet. Then I will need to find the mean, median, and mode of the totals.

Question 2: I will find the mean, median, and mode time for each activity.

Question 3: I will list the favorite activities and find the mode.

1b. Possible answers:

Question 1: A histogram showing time intervals on the horizontal axis and the number of students who use the Internet for that amount of time on the vertical axis

Question 2: A bar graph with a bar for each activity and the height of each bar representing the mean, median, or mode time spent on that activity

Question 3: A circle graph with each section representing the percent of students who chose a particular activity as their favorite

Additional Answers

2. Possible answers:

Question 1:

a. The total times for the 15 students are 347, 390, 290, 240, 363, 330, 316, 125, 386, 330, 400, 325, 535, 317, and 270. The median and mode are both 330, and the mean is about 331.

b. The typical total time is about 330 min, or $5\frac{1}{2}$ h. The mean, median, and mode are all close to this time.

c.

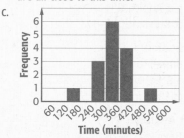

Question 2:

a. This table gives the mode, median, and mean (rounded to the nearest whole number) time for each activity:

Activity	Mode	Median	Mean
Chatting	90	90	77
Playing games	90	90	111
Doing homework	60	45	45
Surfing the Web	90	90	89
Using e-mail	15	10	9

b. The typical times students spend in each activity are as follows: chatting, about 90 min; playing games, about 90 min; doing homework, about 45 min; surfing the Web, about 90 min; using e-mail, about 10 min.

c.

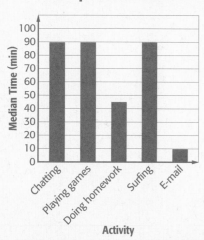

Real-World Link

The manatee, an endangered marine mammal, may grow to 2,000 pounds and eat up to 9% of its body weight in plants everyday. Water pollution, habitat destruction, and run-ins with boat propellers make life extremely difficult for these gentle creatures.

2. Refer to the information on the previous page. Analyze the given data. Use your results to answer the three questions posed by the magazine editors. Provide the following information for each question.   See margin.

a. the results of your computations and the measures you found

b. one or more sentences answering the question

c. a graph to help illustrate your answer

3. **Biology** Marine biologists estimated the number of manatees living in the waters off the coast of Florida. They caught and tagged 120 manatees and then let them go. Of the 150 manatees they caught the next year, nine were marked. Estimate the number of manatees living in these waters.   2,000

4. A farmer recorded the temperature every two hours during daylight.

Time	6 A.M.	8 A.M.	10 A.M.	12 noon	2 P.M.	4 P.M.	6 P.M.	8 P.M.
Temp (°F)	45	50	60	65	80	75	60	50

a. Draw a graph showing the change in the temperature during the day.   See margin.

b. Use your graph to estimate the temperature at 11 A.M.
Possible answer: 62°F

c. During which hours of the day was the temperature above 60°F?
Between 10 A.M. and 6 P.M.

d. It is recommended that crops get irrigated when the temperature is between 50°F and 60°F. From these data, at what times should the farmer irrigate the crops?   8 A.M. to 10 A.M., or 6 P.M. to 8 P.M.

5. Alexis lives on a farm. For a Math project, she measured the growth of several chicks in their first week of life. The table shows the averages for her chicks. What type of graph would you use to display these data? Explain.   Possible answer: Line graph; Explanations will vary.

Day	0	1	2	3	4	5	6	7
Mass (grams)	25	28	31	34	38	43	48	54

6. Kirk counted the colors in a package of candy. What type of graph do you suggest he use to display his data? Explain. Possible answer: Bar graph; Explanations will vary.

Color	Red	Green	Yellow	Brown	Blue	Orange
Number	8	3	10	18	5	13

Question 3:

a. The favorite activity among the 15 students is playing games, with 7 of the 15 students choosing it as their favorite. None of the students listed doing homework as their favorite activity.

b. The mode favorite activity is playing games, followed by chatting, surfing the web, and using e-mail.

c.

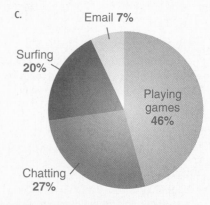

Additional Answer for Exercise 4 is on p. 657B.

7. Ms. Estefan polled her class about their birthday months. What type of graph might she use to display these data? Explain. Possible answer: Line graph, histogram, or bar graph; Explanations will

Month	Jan	Feb	Mar	Apr	May	Jun	Jul	Aug	Sep	Oct	Nov	Dec
Students	5	3	2	3	3	2	0	6	3	2	2	1

8. Mr. Malone polled his class on the kinds of exercise they prefer. Of 24 students, 10 said running, 5 said walking, 4 said swimming, and 3 said biking. The other 2 said they never exercise. What kind of graph do you suggest he use to display these data? Explain. Possible answer: Bar graph; Explanations will vary.

9. Social Studies This double bar graph shows the number of licensed drivers per 1,000 people and the number of registered vehicles per 1,000 people in seven states.

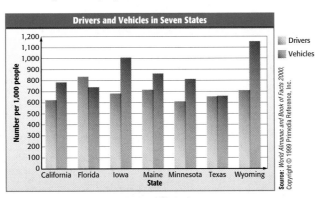

a. Which state has the greatest difference between the number of registered vehicles and the number of licensed drivers? Wyoming

b. Which state has about one registered vehicle per licensed driver? Texas

c. Which state has less than one registered vehicle per licensed driver? Florida

d. Which two states have about the same number of registered vehicles? Maine and Minnesota

10. In Your Own Words Think of a question you could answer by collecting data from a particular group of people. Describe the group you would survey and the type of information you would collect. Then tell what statistical measures and graphs might be useful for summarizing the data. Answers will vary.

Real-World Link
Automobiles were commercially available in the United States beginning in 1896. In 1903, Missouri and Massachusetts adopted the first driver's license laws. In 1908, Rhode Island became the first state to require a driver's test.

▶ **Exercises 7 and 8 Extension** Have students choose a data set and then graph the data after choosing an appropriate graph.

▶ **Exercise 9** Students interpret a double bar graph. Gaining this familiarity will help students when them make graphs in Investigation 2.

Real-World Link
Ask students to tell what they know about driver's license laws in your state.

▶ **Exercise 11** The stacked bar graph is used in this exercise. You might want to have students discuss how they found their answers.

11. **Social Studies** This stacked bar graph shows the number of bachelor's degrees awarded to men and women in the United States in various years.

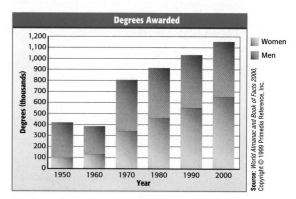

Degrees Awarded

Source: *World Almanac and Book of Facts 2000,* Copyright © 1999 Primedia Reference, Inc.

a. Describe how the total number of bachelor's degrees awarded changed over the years shown in the graph.

b. Describe how the total number of bachelor's degrees awarded to women has changed over the years shown in the graph.

c. In 1970, about how many bachelor's degrees were received by men? About how many were received by women?
About 450,000; about 340,000

d. In 1950, about what fraction of bachelor's degrees were received by women? In 2000, about what fraction were received by women?
About $\frac{1}{4}$, about $\frac{1}{2}$

11a. Possible answer: The number of degrees decreased from 1950 to 1960 but then increased dramatically between 1960 and 1970. Since 1970, the increase in the number of degrees has increased steadily.

11b. Possible answer: The number of degrees awarded to women has increased over the years, with the most dramatic increase between 1960 and 1970.

12. **Social Studies** When a political group holds a rally to show support for a cause or to protest, the police will usually estimate the number of people attending. The estimates are often made by counting the number of people in a particular location. That number and the area of the selected location can be used to set up a proportion for estimating the total attendance.

The organizers of such rallies will often make their own estimates. Usually, their estimates are much higher.

Suppose the organizers of an event want their estimate to be as high as possible to show that many people support their cause. How might they choose the location where they will count people attending? Explain.   Choosing a place that is particularly crowded will make the estimate higher.

13. Life Science A sample of blood was diluted 100,000 times. The drawing represents a microscopic photograph of the red blood cells in 20 cubic millimeters of the diluted blood. Each dot represents one cell.

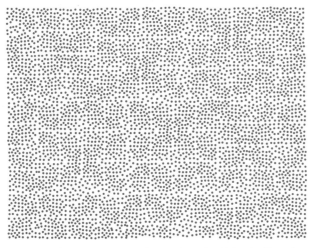

13a. Possible answer: Count the dots in a small area of the drawing, calculate what part of the whole picture the area of the small part is, and then use a proportion to estimate the total number of dots.

a. Think of a way to estimate the number of red blood cells in the drawing without counting all of them. Explain your method.

b. Use your method to estimate how many red blood cells are in 20 mm^3 of the sample of diluted blood.   About 1,000

c. About how many red blood cells were in 1 mm^3 of this blood sample before it was diluted?   About 5 million

14. Geography The table shows population and land area for four states.

14b. Alaska: 1.1 California: 217.2 Illinois: 223.4 Vermont: 65.8; Illinois is the most crowded.

Population and Area in the U.S.

State	2000 Population	Land Area (mi^2)
Alaska	626,932	570,374
California	33,871,648	155,973
Illinois	12,419,293	55,593
Vermont	608,827	9,249

Reprinted with permission from *The World Almanac and Book of Facts.*

a. Estimate how many people live in a particular 15 mi^2 area in California and in a particular 15 mi^2 area in Vermont.
California: 3,257; Vermont: 987

b. Calculate the population density, the number of people per square mile, for each state. Which state is most crowded?

▶ **Exercise 14b** Students need to note that the population density gives only an average density for the state and tells little about the population density in any particular small area. You might notes that this is a property of averages. For example, if a river has an average depth of 5 ft, and you are 6 feet tall, you should not conclude that it is safe for you to wade across it!

Lesson 10.2   Collect and Analyze Data   **615**

▶ **Exercise 15** This exercise provides practice with the graphing topics in this chapter.

Quick Check

Informal Assessment Students should be able to:

✔ prepare a plan that includes selecting the appropriate statistical measures

✔ estimate large quantities based on sample size

✔ choose an appropriate graph to display data

Quick Quiz

The table shows the number of visitors per month (in thousands) to Eagle Point State Park. Unfortunately, as you can see, a portion of the table has been torn off. Use the table to answer Exercises 1–3.

Visitors to Eagle Point State Park	
Month	Number of Visitors (in thousands)
January	2
February	2.5
March	4
April	4.5
May	6
June	7.5
July	8
August	6
September	4
October	?
November	?

1. Draw and label a line graph showing the monthly change in the number visitors to Eagle Point State Park.

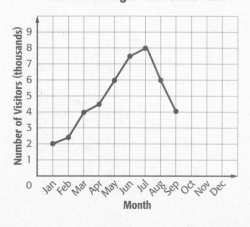

Visitors to Eagle Point State Park

15. Earth Science The maximum distances between the planets in the solar system and the Sun are given to the right.

Planet	Distance from Sun (millions of miles)
Mercury	43.4
Venus	67.7
Earth	94.5
Mars	154.8
Jupiter	507.0
Saturn	936.0
Uranus	1,867.0
Neptune	2,818.0

Reprinted with permission from *The World Almanac and Book of Facts 1999.* Copyright © 1998 Primedia Reference Inc. All rights reserved.

a. Display these data using any kind of graph you like. Explain your choice of graph.
Graphs will vary.

b. Write a few sentences describing any observations you can make about the planets from your graph.
Explanations will vary.

Mixed Review

16. $\frac{2}{3} + \frac{9}{8}$ $1\frac{19}{24}$ **17.** $\frac{6}{10} \div \frac{1}{4}$ $2\frac{2}{5}$

18. $\frac{9}{11} \cdot \frac{4}{12}$ $\frac{3}{11}$ **19.** $\frac{1}{2} - \frac{3}{10}$ $\frac{1}{5}$

For each square, estimate the percent of the area that is shaded.

20. 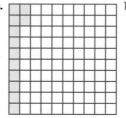 12% **21.** 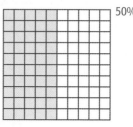 50%

22. Libby is having several friends over to plan their act for the talent show. She wants to serve them bananas for a snack. The farmer's market is selling five bananas for $2.50. The grocery store sells three bananas for $1.80. Where will Libby get the most for her money?
The farmer's market; $0.50 each

Tell whether each given rate is a unit rate or a non-unit rate.

23. 65 mph   Unit   **24.** 500 pages in four hours
                                       Non-unit

25. 65 beats per minute   Unit   **26.** 400 miles in eight hours
                                             Non-unit

2. During which month(s) was the number of visitors to the park greater than 6,000?
June, July

3. Use your graph to estimate the number of visitors to the park during the month of October. Approximately 3,000 visitors

4. Ms. Wang surveyed her class to find out how many students had red hair, how many had black hair, how many had brown hair, and how many had blonde hair. The data is show below. What type of graph do you suggest she use to display her data? Explain.

Hair Color	Red	Black	Brown	Blonde
Number of Students	3	8	4	6

Bar graph; Possible answer: A bar graph compares data that fall into distinct categories.

The Language of Chance

Overview

In this lesson, students make intuitive judgments about the likelihood that various events will occur. They grade the likelihoods on a scale from zero to one. They consider how data about a situation can be used to find the experimental probability that a particular event will occur. Next, students consider situations in which all the outcomes are equally likely. They find the theoretical probability of each outcome and the theoretical probability of events that can be described in terms of the outcomes. They consider simple experiments that allow them to compare experimental probabilities with theoretical probabilities.

They see that with increasingly many trials, experimental probabilities tend to come closer and closer to theoretical probabilities.

Advance Preparation

You may want to provide counters, paper cups, coins and dice, along with Lesson 10.3 Masters 1 and 2 to facilitate class discussion while presenting new topics, including finding probabilities.

	Summary	Materials	On Your Own Exercises (pp. 633–637)	Assessment Opportunities
Investigation 1 (p. 618) *Pacing: 2 days*	Students use intuition to plot the likelihood of certain events on a number line from zero to one. They also use data about simple situations to find experimental probabilities for given events.	paper cups	Practice & Apply: 1–4 Connect & Extend: 10, 11 Mixed Review: 19–35	• On the Spot Assessment (p. 620) • Share & Summarize (p. 620)
Investigation 2 (p. 621) *Pacing: 1 day*	Students learn to recognize situations in which individual outcomes are equally likely. They find the probability of simple events in such situations.	coins, dice	Practice & Apply: 5–7 Connect & Extend: 12–16 Mixed Review: 19–35	• Share & Summarize (p. 625) • Troubleshooting (p. 625)
Inquiry Investigation 3 (p. 626) *Pacing: 1 day*	Students play a game of chance and use ideas about experimental and theoretical probability to analyze the game.	Lesson 10.3 Master 1, scissors, tape, Chapter 10 Masters 1 and 2, counters	Mixed Review: 19–35	
Investigation 4 (p. 628) *Pacing: 1 day*	Students explore geometric probability.	grains of uncooked rice, Lesson 10.3 Master 2, inch rulers	Practice & Apply: 8, 9 Connect & Extend: 17, 18 Mixed Review: 19–35	• On the Spot Assessment (p. 631) • Share & Summarize (p. 632) • Troubleshooting (p. 632)

Leveled Lesson Resources

CRM Available in: **Chapter 10 Resource Masters**

Also on
TeacherWorks™
Lesson 10.3

Study Guide and Intervention (p. 29) AL

Lesson 10.3 Study Guide and Intervention
The Language of Chance

The probability that an event will happen can be described by a number greater than or equal to 0 but less than or equal to 1. A probability of 0, or 0%, means the event can not happen, a probability of $\frac{1}{2}$, or 50%, means the even is just as likely to happen as to not happen, and a probability of 1, or 100%, means the event is certain to happen. In a situation where all outcomes have the same probability, the **theoretical probability** of an event happening is the ratio of the number favorable outcomes divided by the number of possible outcomes.

Example 1 Suppose a number cube is tossed. What is the probability of obtaining an even number?

There are 6 outcomes 1, 2, 3, 4, 5, and 6. Only 2, 4, and 6 are even. The probability of obtaining an even number is the ratio of the number of favorable outcomes, 3, and the total number of outcomes, 6.

$\frac{\text{number of favorable outcomes}}{\text{total number of outcomes}} \quad \frac{3}{6} = \frac{1}{2} = 50\%$

Example 2 Suppose Annie, Abdullah, Ora, and Abagail each want to pass back yesterday's homework assignment. If one person is chosen, what is the probability that

a. The person's name starts with the letter *A*? $\frac{3}{4} = 75\%$
b. The person's name does not start with the letter *A*? $\frac{1}{4} = 25\%$

Exercises

Find the probability for each. Write each answer as a fraction and as a percent.

1. In your dresser drawer you have a red, white, and black pair of socks. It you reach into your drawer and remove one pair of socks, what is the probability that you get the black pair?

2. A jar contains 3 green jelly beans, 3 black jelly beans, 3 yellow jelly beans, and 3 red jelly beans. What is the probability of getting a red jelly bean if you reach into the bag and take one out?

3. The diagonals of a square dart board divide the square up into four congruent triangles. These triangles are numbered 1, 2, 3, and 4. If you toss a dart, what is the probability that your dart lands on a triangle with a number smaller than 4?

Skills Practice (p. 30) AL OL

Lesson 10.3 Skills Practice
The Language of Chance

Find the probability for each. Write each answer as a fraction and as a percent.

1. A whole number is chosen at random from the numbers 1–10.
   a. What is the probability that the number is odd?
   b. What is the probability that the number is less than 8?
   c. What is the probability that the number is 1, 4, or 9?
   d. What is the probability that the number is greater than 10?

2. Maggie is going shopping with her mother. Mom tells Maggie she can bring only one of the following friends: Tekeysia, Chica, Memdi, or Eliza. Suppose she chooses one friend at random.
   a. What is the probability that she chooses Chica?
   b. What is the probability that she doesn't choose Chica?
   c. What is the probability that she chooses Tekeysia or Eliza.

3. Jordon is playing Rice Drop using the game board shown below. He earns one point if he lands on a square labeled with an even number and two points if he lands on a square with an odd number. Note: All squares are of equal size.

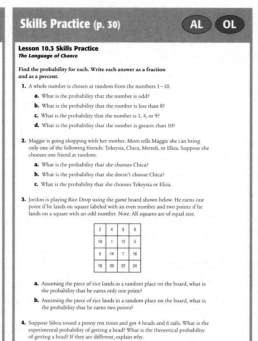

   a. Assuming the piece of rice lands in a random place on the board, what is the probability that he earns only one point?
   b. Assuming the piece of rice lands in a random place on the board, what is the probability that he earns two points?

4. Suppose Silvia tossed a penny ten times and got 4 heads and 6 tails. What is the experimental probability of getting a head? What is the theoretical probability of getting a head? If they are different, explain why.

Problem-Solving Practice (p. 31) AL OL

Lesson 10.3 Problem-Solving Practice
The Language of Chance

For each problem express your answer(s) as a fraction and as a percent.

1. Lola and her friends order 6 one-topping slices of pizza. One slice is just cheese, one has mushroom, one has pepperoni, one has sausage, one has peppers, and one has onions. If she randomly selects a slice of pizza, what is the probability that she gets the piece with mushrooms?

2. Mrs. Rodriquez teaches 6th grade English. She has selected 5 different short stories for her students to read. Each student will select a story at random. What is the probability of a student selecting one of the five stories?

3. La-Ron has a spinner divided into eight equal-sized sections as shown. If he spins the arrow one time, what is the probability that it stops on a number divisible by 3?

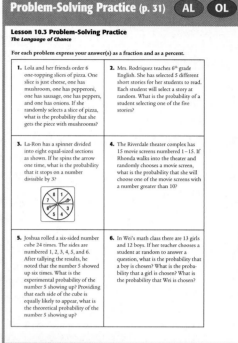

4. The Riverdale theater complex has 15 movie screens numbered 1–15. If Rhonda walks into the theater and randomly chooses a movie screen, what is the probability that she will choose one of the movie screens with a number greater than 10?

5. Joshua rolled a six-sided number cube 24 times. The sides are numbered 1, 2, 3, 4, 5, and 6. After tallying the results, he noted that the number 5 showed up six times. What is the experimental probability of the number 5 showing up? Providing that each side of the cube is equally likely to appear, what is the theoretical probability of the number 5 showing up?

6. In Wei's math class there are 13 girls and 12 boys. If her teacher chooses a student at random to answer a question, what is the probability that a boy is chosen? What is the probability that a girl is chosen? What is the probability that Wei is chosen?

Enrichment (p. 32) BL

Lesson 10.3 Enrichment
The Language of Chance

Spinners and More Spinners

When you spin a spinner, it is not necessarily true that all outcomes are equally likely. With the spinner shown at the right, for example, you can see it is most likely that the pointer will stop in region A. To find probabilities on a spinner like this, you need to consider what fraction of a complete turn of the pointer is associated with each region. In the spinner at the right, region A involves about $\frac{1}{2}$ of a complete turn, so the probability of the spinner landing on region A, written as $P(A)$ and read as "the probability of the event A taking place" is about $\frac{1}{2}$. Using the same reasoning, $P(B)$ or "the probability of the event B taking place" is $\frac{1}{4}$, $P(C)$ or "the probability of the event C taking place" is $\frac{1}{8}$, and $P(D)$ or "the probability of the event D taking place" is $\frac{1}{8}$.

Estimate each probability.

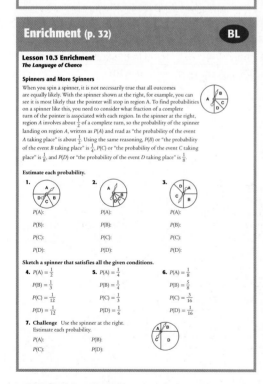

1. $P(A)$:
    $P(B)$:
    $P(C)$:
    $P(D)$:

2. $P(A)$:
    $P(B)$:
    $P(C)$:
    $P(D)$:

3. $P(A)$:
    $P(B)$:
    $P(C)$:
    $P(D)$:

Sketch a spinner that satisfies all the given conditions.

4. $P(A) = \frac{1}{2}$
   $P(B) = \frac{1}{3}$
   $P(C) = \frac{1}{12}$
   $P(D) = \frac{1}{12}$

5. $P(A) = \frac{1}{4}$
   $P(B) = \frac{1}{4}$
   $P(C) = \frac{1}{3}$
   $P(D) = \frac{1}{6}$

6. $P(A) = \frac{1}{8}$
   $P(B) = \frac{5}{8}$
   $P(C) = \frac{3}{16}$
   $P(D) = \frac{1}{16}$

7. **Challenge** Use the spinner at the right. Estimate each probability.
   $P(A)$: $P(B)$:
   $P(C)$: $P(D)$:

Lesson Quick Quiz (p. 33) AL OL BL

Lesson 10.3 Quick Quiz
The Language of Chance

1. The spinner below has 7 equal-sized sections numbered 1 to 7.

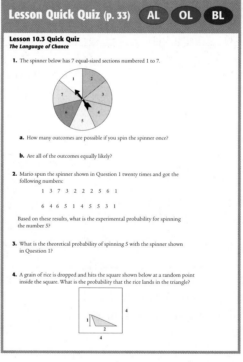

   a. How many outcomes are possible if you spin the spinner once?
   b. Are all of the outcomes equally likely?

2. Mario spun the spinner shown in Question 1 twenty times and got the following numbers:

   1 3 7 3 2 2 2 5 6 1

   6 4 6 5 1 4 5 5 3 1

   Based on these results, what is the experimental probability for spinning the number 5?

3. What is the theoretical probability of spinning 5 with the spinner shown in Question 1?

4. A grain of rice is dropped and hits the square shown below at a random point inside the square. What is the probability that the rice lands in the triangle?

Lesson Masters 1–2 (p. 34 and 35)

Lesson 10.3 Master 1
The Language of Chance

Inquiry Investigation 3: The Spinning Top Game

To construct a four-cornered top, cut out the body and the handle. Cut out the small circle in the top of the body. Fold the body along the dashed lines, and tape it together to form the top. Tightly roll the rectangular piece to form the handle, and insert it into the hole in the top of the body.

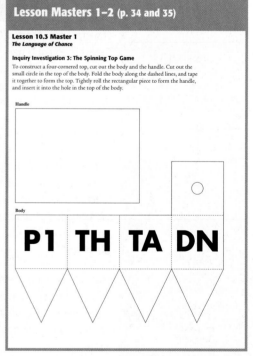

Additional Lesson Resources

Teacher Tech Tools
- TeacherWorks
- ExamView Assessment Suite
- Classroom Presentation Toolkit
- Advance Tracker

Student Tech Tools
- StudentWorks Plus
- Math Online eGlossary •
- Concepts in Motion

Other Print Products
- Investigation Notebook and Reflection Journal
- Quick Review Math Handbook

LESSON 10.3

The Language of Chance

People often make comments like the following.

- "It probably won't rain tomorrow."
- "I expect to have a lot of homework this week."
- "Our team has a good chance of winning the game."
- "It's not likely she will eat that entire cake!"
- "The chances are 50/50 that we'll go to the movies tonight."
- "There's a 40% chance of rain tomorrow."

The words *probably*, *expect*, *chance*, and *likely* are used when someone is making a prediction.

Think & Discuss

What are some other words or phrases people use when predicting the chances of something happening? See ① in margin.

Listed below are six events. How likely do you think each event is? Talk about them with your class. Come to an agreement about whether each event has the given chance of happening.

- has no chance of happening
- could happen but is unlikely
- is just as likely to happen as not to happen
- is likely to happen
- is certain to happen

Event 1: Our class will have homework tonight.
Answer depends on the class.
Event 2: It will snow tomorrow.
Answer depends on climate and time of year.
Event 3: If I toss a penny in the air, it will land heads up.
Just as likely to happen as not to happen
Event 4: A gorilla will eat lunch with us today.
No chance of happening
Event 5: You choose a name from a hat containing the names of all the students in your class, and you get a girl's name.
Answer depends on the class.
Event 6: You draw a number from a hat containing the numbers from 1 to 5, and you get 8.   No chance of happening

Real-World Link
Some gorillas have been taught to communicate with humans by using sign language. One such gorilla, Koko, has a vocabulary of over 1,000 words.

Reaching All Learners

ELL English Language Learners
Words and phrases used to express the likelihood of events are often idiomatic and may not be clear to all students, especially students who are learning the English language. It may be helpful to list such words and phrases on the board and comment briefly on the meaning of each.

The Language of Chance   LESSON 10.3

Introduce

The Language of Chance Read the introduction to the lesson with the class. Ask students to give examples of predictions that they, or people they know, have made. Ask why they think people make predictions. They probably realize that many predictions are made in the hope of affecting future events. People also make predictions to help them set plans for the future. Call attention to the italicized words (*probably, expect, chance,* and *likely*) at the end of the opening paragraph.

Think & Discuss

Use these questions for a class discussion. When you discuss other words and phrases people use to talk about chance, ask students to relate their examples to the five bulleted items in the second paragraph. For example, if someone says, "There's a 50-50 chance I'll stay at home on the weekend," this means that the person is just as likely to stay at home as not to stay at home. The expression "No way!" means that the event has no chance of happening. "You can bet on it" usually means that the person thinks the event is certain to happen. When you discuss the likelihood of the six events listed in Think & Discuss, ask students to explain why they ranked the events the way they did.

Real-World Link
Ask students if any of them know how to use sign language.

Additional Answer
① Possible answers: certain, maybe, unlikely, improbable, possible, impossible, odds, and one in a million, frequent, rare

Probability in Everyday Life In this investigation, students move from informal descriptions of probability to more formal, mathematical descriptions. They learn that collecting data about a situation often makes it possible to calculate *experimental probabilities* for events. They conduct a simple experiment to gather data about how a paper cup lands when it is tossed into the air. They use their data to calculate the experimental probability of the cup landing in a particular way.

Discuss the word *probability* with the class. Point out that in mathematics, the probability of an event is a number that tells how likely it is that the event will happen. The probability that an event will happen can be stated using a number from zero to one. Remind students that numbers can be expressed as percents. So, saying that a probability is a number from zero to one means that probabilities can also be expressed as percents from 0% to 100%.

✅ Develop & Understand: A

Suggested Grouping: Pairs

▶ **Exercise 1** In this exercise set, students think about how to rank events in terms of their likelihood. For this exercise, finding examples of impossible events and certain events will probably be easiest for students, though their examples will likely vary. Allow time for pairs of students to share their responses for all parts of the exercise with the class, but do not have them debate exactly how probable any one event is.

Math Link

Point out that for probability, the percent can never be higher than 100% since probability is the ratio of favorable outcomes to the total number of outcomes.

Investigation ① Probability in Everyday Life

Vocabulary

experimental probability

probability

Materials

• paper cup

Math Link

The probability *P* of an event *E* is the ratio that compares the number of favorable outcomes *f* to the number of possible outcomes *n*. $P(E) = \frac{f}{n}$

The **probability**, or chance, that an event will happen can be described by a number between 0 and 1.

• A probability of 0, or 0%, means the event has no chance of happening.
• A probability of $\frac{1}{2}$, or 50%, means the event is just as likely to happen as not to happen.
• A probability of 1, or 100%, means the event is certain to happen.

For example, the probability of a coin landing heads up is $\frac{1}{2}$, or 50%. This means you would expect a coin to land heads up $\frac{1}{2}$, or 50%, of the time.

The more likely an event is to occur, the greater its probability. If a weather forecaster says the probability of rain is 90%, it is a good idea to take your umbrella when you go outside. Of course, it *might* not rain after all. On the other hand, if the forecaster says the probability of rain is 10%, you might want to leave your umbrella at home. Still, you *might* get wet.

You can represent the probability of an event by marking it on a number line like this one.

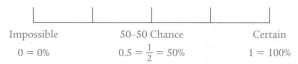

Impossible	50–50 Chance	Certain
0 = 0%	$0.5 = \frac{1}{2} = 50\%$	1 = 100%

For example, the next number line shows the probabilities of tossing a coin and getting heads, of a goldfish walking across a room, and of Alaska getting snow this winter.

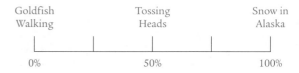

Goldfish Walking	Tossing Heads	Snow in Alaska
0%	50%	100%

✅ Develop & Understand: A

1. Describe an event you think has the given chance of happening.
   Answers will vary.
   a. The event has no chance of happening.
   b. The event could happen but is unlikely.
   c. The event is just as likely to happen as not to happen.
   d. The event is likely to happen.
   e. The event is certain to happen.

2. Copy this number line. Label the number line with your events from Exercise 1. You can use the letters of the events for the labels.

a   b   c   d   e

0%   50%   100%

See the number line. Note: Placement of b and d may vary.

In Exercises 1 and 2, you used your experience to estimate the chances that certain events would occur. For example, you know from experience that when you toss a coin, it lands tails up about half the time. In some situations, you can use data to help estimate probabilities.

✓ Develop & Understand: B

On Saturday, Carolina's baseball team, the Rockets, is playing Marlon's team, the Lions. Carolina decided to look at the scores from the last six times their teams played each other.

Lions	3	8	6	4	4	5
Rockets	5	2	4	5	7	6

3. How many times did the Rockets win?   4

4. Which team do you think is more likely to win the next game?
The Rockets

5. Carolina can estimate the probability that her team will win by dividing the number of times the Rockets won by the number of games played. What probability estimate would she get based on the results of the six games? Give your answer as a fraction and as a percent.   Possible answer: $\frac{2}{3}$, or $66\frac{2}{3}$%

6. Suppose Carolina knew the results of only the first three games. What would be her probability estimate? If she knew the results of only the last three games, what would be her probability estimate?

7. These two teams have played six games against each other. Suppose they had played eight games, and each team had won one more game. What probability estimate would you give for the Rockets winning the next game? $\frac{5}{8}$, or 62.5%

The probabilities you found in Exercises 3–7 are examples of experimental probabilities. An **experimental probability** is always an estimate. It can vary depending on the particular set of data you use.

If you want to find an experimental probability when you have no data available, you might perform *experiments* to create some data.

Real-World Link

Little League baseball was started in 1939 in Williamsport, Pennsylvania, with three teams and 45 players. Today, more than 2.5 million children worldwide play Little League baseball.

. . . .

6. $\frac{1}{3}$, or $33\frac{1}{3}$%; 1, or 100%

On the Spot Assessment

Watch for students who do not understand how probability estimates can be made. After reviewing the problems in the exercise sets discuss the term *experimental probability* with the class. Experimental probabilities are based on data about a set of trials. The number of trials is limited, and the experimental probability can change if more trials are used. It is in this sense that experimental probabilities are estimates.

▶ **Exercise 2** Students do not have to locate the events for Parts b and d of Exercise 1 at the exact points marked b and d in the sample diagram. Unlikely events should fall somewhere in the interval from a to c, and likely events should fall somewhere in the interval from c to e.

✓ Develop & Understand: B

Suggested Grouping: Pairs

▶ **Exercise 5** In this exercise set, students use win-loss data for two baseball teams to estimate the likelihood that one particular team will be the winner of the next game they play together.

Be sure students read the exercise carefully. Students should compare the number of games won to the total number of games played. Some students may read too fast and compare the number of games won to the number of games lost. This gives the *odds* of the Rockets winning, which is not the same as the *probability* of the Rockets winning.

▶ **Exercise 6** Students need to understand that the probability estimates are to be based on only the data about the first three games and then the last three games. Some students may want to argue that the probability estimate based on the first three games should be higher. They may argue that in fact we know the results for all six games and that the Rockets appear to be the better team. Help students understand that they are being asked to put themselves in the shoes of someone with a more limited knowledge of the scoring record.

▶ **Exercise 7** This exercise should help students understand that in real-life situations, probabilities based on data may change as additional data become available.

. . . .

Real-World Link

Take a survey of how many students play Little League baseball. Turn the result into a probability statement.

. . . .

✍ *Develop & Understand: C*

Suggested Grouping: Groups of 2 or 3

▶ **Exercise 8** Students toss their paper cups and tally the results. To keep track of the tosses, it will help to not only make a table and record how the cup lands each time, but also to keep a separate tally of the total number of tosses so that students will know when they have reached the goal of 30 tosses.

▶ **Exercise 11** Ask student to decide whether to use fractions or percents.

▶ **Exercise 12** Students should use fractions if they used a fraction for Exercise 11. They should use percents if they used a percent for Exercise 11.

▶ **Exercise 13** It can be instructive to take a little time to combine the results of all the groups to get a class experimental probability for each way the cup might land. Express the probabilities as percents, and discuss why doing so is helpful when you have a large number of trials. Students will have little trouble seeing that percents are much easier to comprehend and compare than complicated fractions.

Ask questions to help students compare the combined results with those of their individual groups.

• What similarities or differences do you notice? Answers will vary.

• If there are any large differences, what might have caused them? Size and weight of the cups, methods used to toss them

Wrap-Up Have groups compare the probabilities they found with other groups and discuss any similarities and differences. Then ask groups to compare their results for Exercises 11 and 12 to the class results found in Exercise 13. Students can use calculators if necessary to express the group results as percents. Ask students whether their group results or the class experimental probabilities provide a better picture of how the cup is likely to land.

Share & Summarize

Use these questions to assess how well students grasp the meaning of probability, and how to calculate an experimental probability by using data about a situation.

✍ *Develop & Understand: C*

Much like a science experiment, a probability experiment involves trying something to see what happens. You may have some idea of what will occur, but the actual results can be surprising.

8. Toss a paper cup so that it spins in the air. Record how it lands. Does it land right side up, upside down, or on its side? This is one *trial* of the experiment.

Right Side Up   Upside Down   On Its Side

Toss the cup 29 more times, for a total of 30 tosses. Record the landing position each time. You may want to use tally marks as shown below.   Answers will vary.

Right Side Up	Upside Down	On Its Side
‖			‖‖

9. How many trials did you perform in your experiment?   30

10. How many times did the cup land right side up? Upside down? On its side?   Answers will vary.

11. Find the portion of the trials for which the cup landed right side up, stating your answer as a fraction or a percent. Your answer is an experimental probability that the cup lands right side up when tossed.   Answers will vary.

12. Now find an experimental probability that the cup lands upside down and an experimental probability that it lands on its side.   Answers will vary.

13. Possible answers: Combine the number of trials resulting in that position; divide by the total number of trials (30 · number of groups). *Or,* average the probabilities. The two methods will yield the same probability.

13. Share your results with the class. Consider the results found by your classmates. Suggest at least one way you might use them to find a class experimental probability for the cup landing right side up.

Share & Summarize

1. What does it mean to say that the probability of an event is 1?   The event is certain to happen.

2. Rey is in a basketball league. He was practicing free throws one afternoon, and he made 32 out of 50 shots. Estimate the probability that he makes a free throw, expressing it as a fraction and a percent. $\frac{16}{25}$, 64%

3. Suppose you conducted y trials of an experiment, and a particular event happened x times. Find an experimental probability that the event will occur. $\frac{x}{y}$

Troubleshooting

Watch for students who try to calculate experimental probabilities by dividing the number of times the event occurs by the number of times it does not occur. Emphasize that they should always divide by the total number of trials. You can use the situation in the exercises on this page to help explain why this is important.

Investigation 2 Theoretical Probability

Vocabulary

equally likely

theoretical
  probability

Materials

• coin

• die

In some situations, all of the possibilities for a situation, called the *outcomes*, have the same probability of occurring. For example, a coin toss has two possible outcomes, heads or tails. If the coin is fair, about half of the tosses will come up heads and half will come up tails. In situations like these, the outcomes are **equally likely**.

When outcomes are equally likely, you can calculate probabilities by reasoning about the situation. A **theoretical probability** does not depend on an experiment. Therefore, it is always the same for a particular event.

Real-World Link

In 2006, the most popular names for girls born in the U.S. were Emily, Emma, Madison, Abigail, Olivia, Isabella, Hannah, Samantha, Ava, and Ashley.

Example

In a class competition, five students, Althea, Conor, Hannah, Luke, and Rosita, are tied for first place. To break the tie, they will write their names on slips of paper and place them in a bowl. A judge will choose one slip without looking. The student whose name is on that slip will receive first prize. What is the probability that the name chosen has three syllables?

Althea   Conor   Hannah   Luke   Rosita

There are five names. The judge chooses a name *at random,* that is, in a way that all five names have the same chance of being selected. *Althea* and *Rosita* are the only names with three syllables.

Since there are five equally likely outcomes and two of them are three-syllable names, you would expect a three-syllable name to be selected $\frac{2}{5}$ of the time. So, the probability of choosing a name with three syllables is $\frac{2}{5}$, or 40%.

✓ Develop & Understand: A

Think about the situation described in the example. Decide how likely each of the following events is, and determine its theoretical probability. Explain your answers.

1. The name chosen does not begin with *R.*

2. The name chosen begins with *J.*
  0, or 0%; none of the names begin with *J.*

3. The name chosen has four letters or more.
  1, or 100%; all the names have at least four letters.

4. The name chosen has exactly four letters.
  $\frac{1}{5}$, or 20%; of the five names, only one has exactly four letters.

1. $\frac{4}{5}$, or 80%; four of the five names do not begin with *R.*

Mathematical Background

It is important to keep in mind that the concept in the example and the concept of theoretical probability are mathematical concepts. One must be careful not to assume that real-world situations mirror mathematical situations perfectly. For example, you might assume that if you randomly pick a newborn child from a randomly selected location in the United States, then the chances that it is a boy are just the same as the chances that it is a girl. Birth statistics show, however, that this that there is a slightly better chance that the baby will be a boy. In this situation, experimental probabilities make more sense than theoretical probabilities.

Investigation 2

On Your Own Exercises
Pages 633–637
Exercises 5–7, 12–16

Theoretical Probability In this investigation, students are introduced to the concepts of equally likely outcomes and theoretical probability. In the context of a coin-tossing experiment, they compare theoretical and experimental probabilities. Begin by discussing the new vocabulary with the class.

Explain that the outcomes for an action are all the possible things that could happen for that particular action. For example, tossing a coin has two possible outcomes: heads or tails. The outcomes for the situation are equally likely. None of the outcomes has a better chance of happening than any other outcome for that particular situation.

Explain that when a probability can be found without trying out the action, but by simply thinking about the different possibilities, it is called the *theoretical probability* of the event.

(Example)

Discuss this example carefully with the class. Ask students for any ideas they have about how to make the drawing of a name as fair as possible. They may mention such things as: make sure all the slips of paper are the same size and shape, mix the slips after putting them into the bowl, and have the judge draw a slip without looking. The idea is to eliminate anything that would make it more likely for one name to be drawn than another would.

✓ Develop & Understand: A

Suggested Grouping: Pairs

▶ **Exercises 1–4** For this exercise set, students should keep in mind that each name is as likely to be drawn as another name. So, to find the theoretical probability of drawing a name that fits a particular description, divide the number of names that fit that description by 5, which is the total number of names. Students can show their answers as a fraction or percent.

▶ **Exercise 7** Students should have no difficulty seeing that any name drawn either ends with *A* or does not end with *A*. When an event is certain to occur, its probability is 1, or 100%.

Think **&** *Discuss*

Discuss the cartoon with the class to be sure students understand why Conor's statement is incorrect. Conor is making the assumption that the behavior of the coin on one toss can affect the behavior on the next toss. Everyday experience clearly contradicts that assumption. Each toss is completely independent of the others.

. . . .

Real-World Link

Take and informal survey of the names in class. What are the most popular names? What is the probability that a student has that name?

. . . .

7. 1, or 100%; Possible explanation: The three names that were not included for Exercise 5 are the names for Exercise 6. Since all five names are covered by the two exercises, the probabilities must add to 1.

5. The name chosen ends with *A*. $\frac{2}{5}$, or 40%; two of the five names end with *A*.
6. The name chosen does *not* end with *A*. $\frac{3}{5}$, or 60%; three of the five names do not end with *A*.
7. Add the probabilities you found in Exercises 5 and 6. Why does this sum make sense?

When people talk about probabilities involved in games, rolling dice, or tossing coins, they usually mean *theoretical* rather than experimental probabilities. In the rest of this investigation, you will consider the relationship between these two types of probability.

Think **&** *Discuss*

Discuss what the students are saying. Who do you think is correct?
Answers will varv. Jing, Rosita, and Miguel are correct.

. . . .

Real-World Link

In 2006, the most popular names for boys born in the U.S. were Jacob, Michael, Joshua, Matthew, Ethan, Andrew, Daniel, Anthony, Christopher, and Joseph.

. . . .

Mathematical Background

When a coin is tossed, the probability of getting heads is $\frac{1}{2}$ and the probability of getting tails is $\frac{1}{2}$. These are *theoretical* probabilities. Saying that each of these probabilities is $\frac{1}{2}$ is not the same as saying that for several tosses of a coin, half the outcomes must be heads and half must be tails. Tossing a coin an odd number of times could not give a half-and-half result. Conor's statement suggests that he is confusing theoretical probability with experimental probability.

Real-World Link
The United States produced
half-cent coins from 1793
to 1857.

13. If the number
of tosses was
reasonably large, the
result is probably
close to (but not
exactly) half of the
total tosses.

Real-World Link
Abraham Lincoln is the only
U.S. president on a coin who
faces to the right.

✓ *Develop & Understand: B*

8. If you toss a coin 12 times, how many times would you expect to get heads? Explain. 6; you would expect to get heads $\frac{1}{2}$ of the 12 times, which is 6 out of 12.

9. Conduct an experiment to find an experimental probability of getting heads. Toss a coin 12 times. Record the results, writing H for each head and T for each tail.

   a. How many heads did you get?   Answers will vary.

   b. Use your results to find an experimental probability of getting heads when you toss a coin.   Answers will vary.

10. Compare the theoretical results with your experimental results.

   a. Is your result in Part a of Exercise 9 the same as the answer you computed in Exercise 8? Answers will vary. Most students will find they are not exactly the same.

   b. Is your experimental probability the same as the theoretical probability?   Answers will vary.

11. Now combine your experimental results with those of other students. Make a table like this one, showing how many times out of 12 each student's coin came up heads.   Tables will vary.

Student	Number of Heads
James	7
Ali	5

12. Calculate the total number of tosses your class made. How many heads would you expect for that number of tosses? Totals will vary. About half of the tosses would be expected to result in heads.

13. Now add the entries in the "Number of Heads" column. How closely does the result agree with your expectations?

14. What percent of the total number of coin tosses came up heads? In other words, what is the experimental probability of getting heads based on the data for your entire class?   Answers will vary.

15. Which experimental probability is closer to the theoretical probability, the one you calculated for Part b of Exercise 9 or the one you calculated for Exercise 14? Answers will vary, but Exercise 14's result should be closer for most students.

It is normal for experimental probabilities to be different from theoretical probabilities. In fact, when you repeat an experiment a small number of times, the experimental and theoretical probabilities may not be close at all.

✓ *Develop & Understand: B*

Suggested Grouping: Individuals

▶ **Exercise 9b** The purpose of this exercise set is to clarify the relationship between experimental and theoretical probability. For this exercise, you may want to have students express the answer as a fraction and as a percent.

▶ **Exercise 11** Display the class results on the board. Discuss the results to ensure students understand experimental probability.

▶ **Exercise 15** The percent form will be useful when students answer this exercise. You will probably want to put the class results on the board.

Real-World Link
Ask students if they know any other facts about coins.

Teacher Tips If students make errors when expressing the probabilities as percents, you may need to review how to change a fraction to a percent. You may also need to review the concept of rounding to the nearest percent.

Reaching All Learners

BL **Beyond Level** You might have some students try this exercise, which will show the effect of increasing the number of times an experiment is performed. Have students add a third column to their completed table from Exercise 11. For each row, have them calculate the experimental probability for the data up to that point. When they are finished, the table will likely demonstrate an important idea: with an increasingly large number of tosses of a coin, the experimental probability of getting heads approaches the theoretical probability, which is $\frac{1}{2}$.

▶ **Exercises 16–21** In this exercise set, students roll a die 12 times and compute the experimental probability of rolling the number 3. They then combine their results with the results of other students. Finally, they compare the experimental probability based on the class results with the theoretical probability of rolling 3.

▶ **Exercise 19** Make a table on the board to show the results for each student in the class. Add a third column that shows the experimental probability as a percent, rounded to the nearest percent. You might use a calculator to help you do this.

▶ **Exercise 20c** Ask a volunteer to explain how to predict the number of 3s that will be obtained for a given number of rolls.

Wrap-Up To be sure students understand the implications of having equally likely outcomes when rolling a die, ask for the theoretical probability of rolling 4; of rolling 5; of rolling 1. $\frac{1}{6}, \frac{1}{6}, \frac{1}{6}$

Then ask how many times they would expect to get 5 if they rolled a die 120 times. 20 times

---

However, when you repeat an experiment a large number of times, for example, by combining all the coin tosses of everyone in your class or by performing more tosses, the experimental probability will usually grow closer to the theoretical probability.

The theoretical probability tells what is likely to happen *in the long run*, that is, if you try something a large number of times. It does not reveal exactly what will happen each time.

✅ **Develop & Understand: C**

A standard die has six faces, each indicating a different number from 1 to 6. When you roll a die, the *outcome* is the number facing up.

16. Roll a die 12 times. Record each number you roll. How many 3s did you get?   Results will vary.

17. Use your results to find an experimental probability of rolling 3.   Results will vary.

18. Collect results from others in your class. Make a table with these columns.   Tables will vary.

Student	Number of 3s

19. Find the total number of rolls and the total number of 3s for all the students in your class. Then compute an experimental probability of rolling 3. Answers will vary but should be close to $\frac{1}{6}$.

20. Now think about the *theoretical* probability of rolling 3.

    a. How many possible outcomes are there for a single roll? Are they all equally likely?   6; yes

    b. On each roll of a die, what is the probability that you will roll 3? $\frac{1}{6}$

    c. If you roll a die 12 times, how many 3s would you expect?   2

21. Compare your theoretical results from Exercise 20 with your own experimental results from Exercise 17 and to your class experimental results from Exercise 19. Which experimental result is closer to the theoretical result?   Answers will vary. Most students will find that the class result is closer to the theoretical result.

1b. $\frac{7}{10}$; Possible explanation: Since the probability that the number was one of the sisters is $\frac{3}{10}$, the probability that it was not must be be $1 - \frac{3}{10}$, or $\frac{7}{10}$.

2b. No; The probability does not tell exactly what will happen each time.

Share & Summarize

1. At Jewel's birthday party, her mother assigned each of the ten partygoers, including Jewel and her two sisters, a number from 1 to 10.

   To see who would play *Pin the Tail on the Donkey* first, Jewel's father pulled one of ten balls, numbered 1 to 10, from a box. The person whose number was selected would play first.

   a. What is the probability that the number chosen was Jewel's or one of her sisters? $\frac{3}{10}$

   b. What is the probability that the number chosen was *not* Jewel's or one of her sisters? That is, what is the probability that the number belonged to one of the seven guests? Explain how you found your answer.

2. Dalila has a spinner divided into five same-sized sections, numbered from 1 to 5. She spun the arrow 100 times, recording the result each time.

   a. How many times would you expect the arrow to land on section 4?   20

   b. If the actual number of fours Dalila recorded was different from the number you answered in Part a, does that mean your calculation was incorrect? Explain.

3. Suppose you perform an experiment 20 times and a friend performs the same experiment 200 times. You both use your results to calculate an experimental probability.

   Whose experimental probability would you expect to be closer to the theoretical probability? Explain.   My friend's; A theoretical probability predicts what will happen over many trials, and my friend performed many more trails than I did.

Share & Summarize

Have students work on these exercises individually. Then call on volunteers to present their answers and explain their thinking to the class.

When you discuss **Exercise 2**, ask students whether the outcomes are equally likely and why. Students should be able to see that the outcomes are equally likely because the sections of the spinner are all the same size.

Troubleshooting Some students may have trouble calculating the number of times an event can be expected to occur when they know the probability of the event and the number of trials. They can find this number by multiplying the number of trials by the probability. In addition, check to make sure they understand that the product they find should be rounded to the nearest whole number.

Inquiry
Investigation ③

Suggested Grouping: Groups of 3 or 4

Materials and Preparation
Each group of four will need 40 counters. They will also need a four-cornered top, or a copy of Lesson 10.3 Master 1 to construct a four-cornered top, and Chapter 10 Masters 2 or 3 (optional). You may wish to assign construction of the top as homework. Alternatively, you might prefer to ask early finishers to construct enough tops for all the groups before students work on the lab investigation.

Teacher Tips You can replace the 4-cornered top with a 4-section spinner.

Play the Game
Read the rules with the class to ensure that students understand how the game is played. You should probably check the top that each group is using to ensure that it is properly constructed.

▶ **Exercise 1** You may want to suggest that each group selects a player to keep the tally of the symbols the players spin. Students will need to use the data they collect to answer subsequent questions.

▶ **Exercise 3** Students can use the lines on a sheet of notebook paper to help them draw the bars of their graph accurately. Alternatively, you may want to hand out copies of Chapter 10 Masters 2 or 3.

Inquiry
Investigation ③   The Spinning Top Game

Materials
- 4-cornered top with sides marked DN, TA, TH, and P1.
- counters

The *Spinning Top* game is played with a four-cornered top that contains four symbols. There are many variations of this game.

In this investigation, you will look at the probabilities for one of the most common versions of the *Spinning Top* game.

Play the Game

You will play this game in a group of four. Here are the rules.

- Each player begins with ten counters.
- Each player puts a counter in the center of a table.
- Players take turns spinning the top. One of these four symbols will land face up.

DN   TA   TH   P1

The letter facing up tells the player what to do.

DN   Do nothing.

TA   Take all the counters in the center.

TH   Take half of the counters in the center. Round down. For example, if the number of counters is five, take two.

P1   Pay one by placing counter in the center.

- Before each turn, each player puts another counter in the center. A player with no counters left is out of the game.
- The game continues until only one player has counters left or your teacher says time is up. The player with the most counters wins.

2. Answers will vary. If the number of turns is reasonably large, each symbol is likely to have appeared approximately the same number of times.

1. Play the game with your group, keeping a tally of the symbols the players spin.   Tables will vary.

DN	TA	TH	P1
‖		│	

2. How many times did each symbol land face up in the whole game?

3. Draw a bar graph showing the number of times each symbol landed face up.   Graphs will vary.

Calculate Probabilities

Now that you have some experience playing the *Spinning Top* game, you can calculate the probabilities of certain outcomes.

4. Begin by calculating an experimental probability that each letter lands face up, based on the results of your game. Answers will vary.

Assume each symbol is equally likely to land face up.

5. $\frac{1}{4}$ for each

6–10. See margin.

5. Calculate the theoretical probability of each symbol landing face up.

6. How do the theoretical probabilities you calculated in Question 5 compare to your experimental probabilities from Question 4?

7. What is the theoretical probability of winning counters in a turn? Explain.

8. What is the probability of losing a counter in a turn? Explain.

9. Jahmal said the first player has a better chance to win all the counters in the center than the other three players do. Do you agree with Jahmal? Explain your answer.

11. There are two ways to win counters but only one way to lose counters.

12. Answers will vary. Any change so that two of the symbols require the player to put in counters and one requires the player to take out counters will work.

10. Suppose the first player wins all the counters on his or her turn. What is the probability that the second player will also win all the counters? Explain your answer.

What Have You Learned?

11. If you are equally likely to get each of the four sides of the top, why are you not equally likely to win counters as to lose counters?

12. Change the rules of the *Spinning Top* game so that the probability of winning counters on each turn is $\frac{1}{4}$ and the probability of losing counters is $\frac{1}{2}$.

Calculate Probabilities

▶ **Exercise 4** Students will need to find the total number of spins of the top. The experimental probabilities can be expressed as fractions or percents. Percents can facilitate comparison of results. You may want to remind students that the sum of the probabilities should be one or 100%.

▶ **Exercise 8** The probability is the theoretical probability of losing a counter.

What Have You Learned?

▶ **Exercises 11 and 12** You may want to discuss the answers for these questions with the class after asking volunteers to read their answers. If time permits, you might want to combine the results the groups obtained for Exercise 2 and compute the experimental probabilities for Exercise 4 for the entire class.

Additional Answers

6. Answers will vary.

7. $\frac{1}{2}$, or 50%; of the four possible letters, two (TA and TH) win counters for the player.

8. $\frac{1}{4}$, or 25%; of the four letters, one (P1) loses a counter for the player.

9. No; the top does not change, so the chances are the same with each spin.

10. $\frac{1}{4}$; each player has one chance in four to win all the counters. This is not changed by what the previous player did.

Lesson 10.3   The Language of Chance   **627**

Geometric Probability In this investigation, students drop a grain of rice onto a game board on which is drawn closed, two-dimensional figures of various shapes and sizes. Students find experimental and theoretical probabilities that the grain of rice will land on a particular shape.

Teacher Tips Read the game rules on page 628 with the class, and hand out a copy of Lesson 10.3 Master 2 to each group. When students are confident that they understand the rules, they can work on the exercises on page 629.

Real-World Link
Ask students if they like rice. How often do they eat it?

Investigation 4   Geometric Probability

Materials

- *Rice Drop* game board
- grain of uncooked rice
- inch ruler

Real-World Link
Rice is the staple food for about 60% of the world's population providing more than one-third of a person's caloric intake.

To calculate theoretical probabilities for the situations with which you have worked so far, you divided the number of outcomes that mean an event occurred by the total number of outcomes. In this investigation, you will look at a situation where you need to use a different strategy.

✅ Develop & Understand: A

Rice Drop is a game of chance. To play, a larger version of the game board at right should be placed on a hard, flat surface such as a table or desk. The game board is the area inside the outer border, not the entire page.

Here are the game rules.

- On a player's turn, he or she holds a grain of rice about one foot above the game board, near the center.
- The player drops the grain of rice and watches where it lands. If it bounces outside the outer border, the drop does not count. The player must try again.
- If the grain of rice lands in the square, circle, triangle, or parallelogram, the player scores one point. A grain that lands on the edge of a figure should be counted as inside the figure if half or more of the grain is inside.
- Each player gets ten chances to score. Remember, if the grain of rice bounces off the board, the drop does not count. The player with the greatest score wins.

1. Play the game with your group. On your turn, record the results of your drops by making tally marks in a chart like this one.
Answers will vary.

Circle	Square	Triangle	Nonsquare Parallelogram	No Figure

2. Use the results of your ten drops to estimate the chances that the grain of rice will land in one of the following areas. Answers will vary.

   a. the circle

   b. the square

   c. the triangle

   d. the nonsquare parallelogram

   e. no figure

   f. any figure

3. Now combine the results of your group. Calculate new estimates for the probabilities in Exercise 2.   Answers will vary.

4. Which set of probabilities do you think are more reliable, those from Exercise 2 or Exercise 3? Explain.

4. Exercise 3; Since there were more drops with which to work, the experimental probabilities are probably closer to the theoretical probabilities.

Think & Discuss

Do you think a grain of rice is as likely to land on the circle as it is to land outside any of the figures?   Answers will vary.

Can you think of a way you might calculate the theoretical probability of scoring a point on a single drop? Possible answer: Calculate the fraction of the game board covered by the figures.

For the rest of this investigation, assume that the rice lands in a completely random spot on the game board. That is, assume the rice is just as likely to land in one spot on the game board as in another.

5. Suppose you use a game board divided into four equal rectangles, like this one. What is the probability that the rice lands on the shaded rectangle? $\frac{1}{4}$

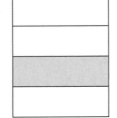

✓ Develop & Understand: A

Suggested Grouping: Groups of 3 or 4

▶ **Exercises 1–4** In this exercise set, students play the *Rice Drop* game and record their results. Individual students keep a record of their results and calculate experimental probabilities that the grain of rice will land on different parts of the board. The students in each group then combine their results and compute a set of group experimental probabilities.

▶ **Exercise 1** Before students begin the game, discuss the chart. Emphasize that each student should keep his or her own chart. The completed chart should have a total of 10 tally marks. Take this opportunity to remind students that if the grain of rice bounces outside the outer border, that trial does not count, and no tally mark is made in the table.

▶ **Exercise 2f** Students need to understand that "any figure" means any of the shaded figures. In other words, the number of outcomes for the event *landed in a shaded area* is the total number of tally marks in the first four columns of the chart.

▶ **Exercise 3** You may want to ask students to express the experimental probabilities both as fractions and as percents. Using percents will make it easier to compare and discuss results with other groups.

Think & Discuss

Ask volunteers to share their answers to these questions with the class.

You might extend the second question in the following manner.

• How can you calculate the fraction of the game board covered by the figures?
Divide the sum of the areas of all the figures by the total area of the game board.

• How can you find the areas of the figures?
Use the area formulas for the square ($A = s^2$), rectangle ($A = lw$), circle ($A = \pi r^2$), and parallelogram ($A = bh$) after taking the appropriate measurements of the figures.

This is a preview of what students will investigate in the exercises on page 631.

....

Real-World Link

The average Cambodian eats more than 350 pounds of rice each year.

The average American eats about 20 pounds of rice each year.

....

7. Less than; Possible explanation: In Exercise 6, if the rice had landed on the removed square, it would have been in the figure, but here it would not be. There are fewer places for the rice to land and be in the figure now.

8. The same; Possible explanation: If the rice has the same chance of landing on the spot where the square used to be as it does of landing where the square is now, the probability is the same.

6. The game board below is also divided into four equal sections. What is the probability that the rice lands on the shaded rectangle?

$\dfrac{1}{4}$

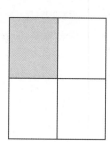

7. To create this game board, a square was removed from the shaded rectangle of the game board in Exercise 6. Is the probability that the rice lands in the shaded figure *less than, greater than,* or *the same as* your answer to Exercise 6? Explain your reasoning.

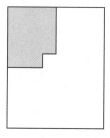

8. Now the square that was removed from the rectangle in Exercise 6 has been returned but in a different place. Is the probability that the rice lands in a shaded figure on this board *less than, greater than,* or *the same as* your answer to Exercise 6? Explain your reasoning.

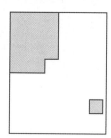

Real-World Link

It takes approximately 300 to 600 gallons of water to produce one pound of rice.

Develop & Understand: B

Rebeca thought she could find the theoretical probabilities for the original *Rice Drop* game board using the areas of the figures and the area of the board.

9. Find the area of the game board and the area of the square.
   Board: 59.5 in²; square: 9 in²

10. Use your answer to Exercise 9 to find the probability that the rice lands in the square. Express your answer as a percent. About 15.1%

11. Find the probability that the rice lands in each of the remaining figures. Express your answers as percents. About 15.1% for the triangle and parallelogram; about 16.2% for the circle

12. About 61.5%, Possible explanations: I added the areas of all the figures and divided by the area of the board. *Or,* I added the probabilities for the four figures.

12. What is the probability that a player will score on a single drop? Explain how you found your answer.

13. **Challenge** The theoretical probabilities that you found in Exercise 9–12 assume that the rice lands randomly. Compare the theoretical probabilities that you found in Exercises 9–12 to the experimental probabilities that you found in Exercises 1–4.

   a. Do you think the rice lands in a completely random spot, or are some spots more likely than others? Explain why you think so. Answers will vary.

   b. What could you do to test whether your answer to Part a is correct? Possible answer: Conduct another experiment with many more trials.

Develop & Understand: B

Suggested Grouping: Pairs

▶ **Exercise 9** In this exercise set, students calculate the theoretical probability that a grain of rice will land in a given shape on the *Rice Drop* game board. For this exercise, students need to measure the length and width of the outer border of the game board and the square in inches. Encourage students to measure as accurately as they can. They will need to multiply the dimensions of each figure to find the area.

▶ **Exercise 10** Students should divide the area of the square by the area of the game board to find what part of the game board is taken up by the square.

▶ **Exercise 11** Students need to take measurements to find the areas of the circle, parallelogram, and triangle. You might refer them to Chapter 7 if they have difficulty recalling how to find the area of any of these figures. You may need to remind students that they can use 3.14 as an approximate value of π. After making the necessary measurements and calculating the area of each figure, they will need to divide the area of each figure by the area of the game board and express the quotient as a percent.

▶ **Exercise 12** Students can divide the total area of the shapes by the area of the game board. Alternatively, they can add the probabilities for the individual shapes. These procedures are valid because the shapes do not overlap.

▶ **Exercise 13a** Some students may say that if the grain of rice is dropped from a point above the center of the board, then spots closer to the center of the board are more likely. This is a plausible conjecture. You might want to ask students if they have any ideas for testing the conjecture.

On the Spot Assessment

Students who have difficulty with Exercise 11 may have forgotten how to calculate the areas of some of the figures. Ask them what measurements they will need to calculate area. Then ask them what formula they will use for each figure.

Share & Summarize

This Share & Summarize is an excellent opportunity to bring together the key ideas of the investigation. After students have had an appropriate amount of time to work on these questions, call on volunteers to present their answers and explain their thinking.

Troubleshooting If students need more practice calculating geometrical probabilities, you might have them work in pairs to create new *Rice Drop* game boards. They can calculate the probability of scoring a point on a single drop with their own board and with their partner's board, and then check answers and compare calculations with their partner.

Share & Summarize

★ **1.** Suppose this was the game board for a game of *Rice Drop*. The measurements are given in inches.

Assuming that the rice lands in a completely random place, what is the probability of scoring a point on a single drop?
About 0.452, or 45.2%

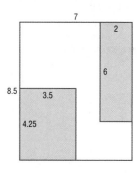

2. $\frac{1}{2}$; Half the squares are purple, half the squares are white, and the squares are all the same size, so the rice should land on purple half the time.

2. Martino and Larisa were playing *Rice Drop* using a checkerboard. They decided that a drop scored a point if the rice landed on a purple square. A drop that does not land on the board does not count.

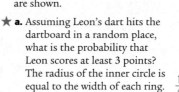

Assuming that the rice lands in a completely random place, what is the probability that a drop scores a point? Explain how you found your answer.

3. Leon likes playing darts. He throws a dart at the dartboard shown here.

The points earned for each ring are shown.

★ **a.** Assuming Leon's dart hits the dartboard in a random place, what is the probability that Leon scores at least 3 points? The radius of the inner circle is equal to the width of each ring. $\frac{1}{4}$

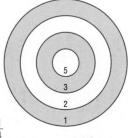

b. Do you think the assumption in Part a is reasonable? Explain.
No; Darts is a game of skill, not chance. If Leon plays a lot, he would be able to get close to the center more often.

Practice & Apply

1. Copy this number line. In Parts a–d, add a label to your number line indicating how likely you think the event is. Answers will vary.

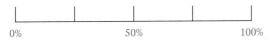

0%   50%   100%

   a. I will listen to the radio tonight.

   b. I will go to a movie sometime this week.

   c. Everyone in my Math class will get a perfect score on the next test.

   d. I will wake up before 7:00 A.M. tomorrow.

2. Estimate the probability of each event. Explain your reasoning.

   a. The school lunch will taste good tomorrow.

   b. Everyone in our class will come to school next Monday.

   c. A giraffe will come to school next Monday. Possible answer: 0; They do not let giraffes in school.

2a. Possible answer: 0; The only school lunch that tastes good is pizza. Pizza day is Friday, but tomorrow is only Wednesday.

2b. Possible answer: $\frac{1}{4}$; We usually have a person absent each week, and Monday seems to be the most likely day for someone to be absent.

3. LaBron is practicing his archery skills. He hit the bulls-eye with 3 of the first 12 arrows he shot. Use these results to find an experimental probability that LaBron will hit the bulls-eye on his next shot. $\frac{1}{4}$

4. Get a plastic spoon and conduct this experiment.

   For each trial, drop the spoon and record how it lands, right side up so it would hold water or upside down. Conduct 30 trials for your experiment. Use your results to find an experimental probability that the spoon will land right side up.
   Answers will vary.

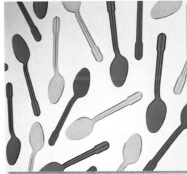

5. A word is chosen at random from *book*, *paper*, *pencil*, and *eraser*.

   a. What is the probability that the word has only one syllable? $\frac{1}{4}$

   b. What is the probability that the word begins with *P*? $\frac{1}{2}$

   c. What is the probability that the word ends with *P*? 0

Investigation 1
Pages 618–620
Practice & Apply: 1–4
Connect & Extend: 10, 11

Investigation 2
Pages 620–625
Practice & Apply: 5–7
Connect & Extend: 12–16

Inquiry Investigation 3
Pages 626–627

Investigation 4
Pages 628–632
Practice & Apply: 8–9
Connect & Extend: 17, 18

Assign Anytime
Mixed Review: 19–35

▶ **Exercise 5** The probabilities in this question are theoretical probabilities. Be sure students recall what is meant by the words *at random*.

▶ **Exercise 8** All the probabilities in this exercise are theoretical. The probability of the rice landing in any one of the shaded figures is the area of that figure divided by the area of the 8-by-10 rectangle.

In **Part a**, students can add the areas of the triangles and divide the result by 80 square units. Another approach is to add the probabilities for the individual triangles.

Similar methods apply for **Parts b and c**.

For **Part d**, the answer can be found by subtracting the answer for Part c from 100%.

Additional Answer

6e. Possible answer: The experimental probability is the percent of tosses that were heads. Ruby made many more tosses than Lupe, so each toss accounts for a much smaller percent of the total tosses. Lupe's results were only 1 head different from what you would expect, but that 1 head is 10% of his total tosses. Ruby's results were 30 heads different from what you would expect, but those 30 heads are only 3% of her total tosses.

Real-World Link

The United States minted silver three-cent pieces from 1851 to 1873 and nickel three-cent pieces from 1865 to 1889.

Math Link

A *prime number* is a whole number greater than 1 with only two factors, itself and 1.

6. Lupe tossed a coin ten times and got six heads. Ruby tossed a coin 1,000 times and got 530 heads.

   a. Based on Lupe's results, what is an experimental probability of getting heads? Express your answer as a percent.   60%

   b. Using theoretical probabilities, how many heads would you expect to get in ten coin tosses? How far was Lupe's result from that number?   5, 1

   c. Based on Ruby's results, what is an experimental probability of getting heads? Express your answer as a percent.   53%

   d. Using theoretical probabilities, how many heads would you expect to get in 1,000 coin tosses? How far was Ruby's result from that number?   500, 30

   e. Challenge The difference between the actual number of heads and the expected number of heads is much greater for Ruby than for Lupe. How is it possible that Ruby's experimental probability is closer to the theoretical probability?   See margin.

7. Claudia has a spinner divided into ten equal sections, numbered from 1 to 10. Think about a single spin of the arrow.

   a. What is the probability that the arrow will point to section 1? $\frac{1}{10}$

   b. What is the probability that the arrow will point to an odd number? $\frac{5}{10}$, or $\frac{1}{2}$

   c. What is the probability that the arrow will point to an even number? $\frac{5}{10}$, or $\frac{1}{2}$

   d. What is the probability that the arrow will point to a prime number? $\frac{4}{10}$, or $\frac{2}{5}$

8. Garrett and Neela were playing *Rice Drop* using this rectangular game board. The dimensions are in inches. Assume the rice will land on a completely random spot.

   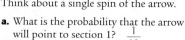
   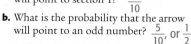

   a. Find the probability that the rice lands in a triangle.   13.75%

   b. Find the probability that the rice lands in a shaded quadrilateral.   16.25%

   c. Find the probability that the rice lands in a shaded figure.   30%

   d. Find the probability that the rice does not land in a shaded figure.   70%

★ indicates multi-step problem

9. About 0.0013 or 0.13%

10a. Possible answer: No; The weather service did not state it would not rain.

Connect & Extend

★ **9.** A small area created by buildings built close together is often called a *courtyard*. Suppose a group of six friends are standing in a square courtyard like the one shown here when it starts to rain.

What is the probability that the first raindrop hits one of the friends? Assume each person occupies a circle about 50 cm in diameter.

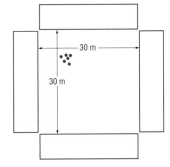

10. Earth Science Irena and a group of her friends planned a beach outing for a certain day. The local weather service reported a 20% chance of rain on that day. When the day came, it rained. The trip was canceled.

Irena said the weather service had been wrong when they gave the 20% rain prediction. They said it was not going to rain, but it did.

a. Do you agree with Irena? Why or why not?

b. If the weather service prediction did not mean that it would not rain, what do you think it meant? Possible answer: It meant there was a one-in-five chance it would rain.

★**11.** Elan's radio alarm clock goes off at 6:37 every morning. He complained that, almost every morning, he wakes up to commercials rather than music. Describe an experiment he could conduct to estimate the probability that he will wake up to a commercial. Explain how you would use the result to find an experimental probability. See margin.

12. Describe a situation for which the probability that something will occur is $\frac{1}{6}$. Possible answer: Rolling a die and getting 1

13. A whole number is chosen at random from the numbers 1 to 10.

a. What is the probability that the number is odd? $\frac{5}{10}$, or $\frac{1}{2}$

b. What is the probability that the number is prime? $\frac{4}{10}$, or $\frac{2}{5}$

c. What is the probability that the number is a perfect square? $\frac{3}{10}$

d. What is the probability that the number is a factor of 36? $\frac{6}{10}$, or $\frac{3}{5}$

14. A whole number is chosen at random from the numbers 10 to 20.

a. What is the probability that the number is odd? $\frac{5}{11}$

b. What is the probability that the number is prime? $\frac{4}{11}$

c. What is the probability that the number is a perfect square? $\frac{1}{11}$

d. What is the probability that the number is a factor of 36? $\frac{2}{11}$

Lesson 10.3 The Language of Chance **635**

▶ **Exercise 9** The areas that students use should be expressed in the same units, either square centimeters or square meters. Students should also note that the exercise gives the *diameter* occupied by each person. To find the area of the circle, they first need to divide by 2 to find the radius.

▶ **Exercise 10** You may want to ask students what it means to say that there is a 20% chance of rain. Ask students how they could find an experimental probability of having rain at the beach.

▶ **Exercise 12** Discuss all the situations that students propose. Some of the responses may require careful analysis to be sure the probability is indeed $\frac{1}{6}$.

Additional Answer

11. Possible answer: For a certain number of days, Elan could keep count of how many days he wakes up to a commercial. To find an experimental probability, he would divide the number of days he woke up to a commercial by the total number of days.

▶ **Exercise 15** Suggest that students make an organized list that shows all the possible arrangements. The example in the opening paragraph indicates that no attempt is being made to distinguish between the two sixth graders or between the two seventh graders.

▶ **Exercise 17** Most students are likely to find this exercise challenging. In **Part b**, students should divide the area covered by Belinda's car by the area of the region within which the acorns might fall. Note that this latter area does *not* include the ground space taken up by the base of the tree trunk.

In **Part d**, students need to divide the area of the moon roof by the ground space covered by the car.

Real-World Link
Ask students to name the state tree in your state.

15a. Two sixth graders playing each other, two seventh graders playing each other, and a sixth grader playing black and a seventh grader playing red

Real-World Link
The white oak tree is the state tree of Illinois. White oaks can live up to 400 years.

16. Rolling dice is an example of a theoretical probability because the outcomes are always equally likely to happen. Predicting the outcome of a sporting event is an example of experimental probability because they are always estimates. The data can vary.

17a. About 1,178 ft^2

15. Two sixth graders and two seventh graders are having a checkers tournament. They decide to randomly choose who the first two players will be and who will use which color. Consider the possible arrangements. For example, the first game might be a seventh grader playing black and a sixth grader playing red.

  a. What other possible arrangements are there?

  Assume each of the arrangements is equally likely to occur.

  b. What is the probability that the seventh graders will play each other in the first game? $\frac{1}{4}$

  c. What is the probability that at least one seventh grader will play in the first game? $\frac{3}{4}$

  d. What is the probability that exactly one sixth grader will play in the first game? $\frac{1}{2}$

16. In Your Own Words Give an example to illustrate the difference between an experimental probability and a theoretical probability.

17. While visiting a friend, Belinda parked her car under a large oak tree. She left open her moon roof. (A *moon roof* is a small window in the roof.)

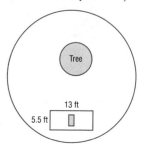

The tree drops acorns in a circular area around its trunk, as shown in the diagram. Assume the acorns fall randomly within the circle, which has a radius of 20 feet. No acorns fall where the trunk is. The trunk has a radius of 5 feet.

  a. Find the area of the region in which an acorn might fall.

  b. While Belinda was at her friend's house, an acorn fell from the tree. Find the probability that the acorn hit Belinda's car, including the moon roof.   About 6.1%

  c. The dimensions of the moon roof are 32 inches by 16 inches. Find the probability that the acorn fell through the moon roof.   About 0.3%

  d. Challenge Suppose the acorn hit Belinda's car. Find the probability that it fell through the moon roof. (Hint: Should this probability be *more than* or *the same as* the probability you answered in Part c?)   About 5%

★ indicates multi-step problem

★**18.** Owen videotaped all six episodes of his favorite hour-long television show. His friend missed an episode, and Owen said he would loan her the tape. The number line illustrates where on the tape the show had been recorded.

Owen often rewinds the tape and watches different parts of previous episodes. He does not remember where on the tape he last stopped watching the show. Before giving the tape to his friend, Owen put it in his VCR and pushed the play button. What is the probability that the tape started somewhere within the show his friend wanted to see? $\frac{1}{6}$

Mixed Review

19. Albert conducted a survey of his class to determine what animals students liked. Write each fraction as a decimal and a percent. Write each given percent as a decimal and as a fraction.

  a. He found that 25% liked cats. $\frac{1}{4}$; 0.25

  b. He found that $\frac{4}{5}$ liked dogs.   0.8; 80%

  c. He found that only $\frac{1}{20}$ liked lizards.   0.05; 5%

20. Which is greater, 0.3 or $\frac{1}{3}$? $\frac{1}{3}$

21. Which is greater, 0.11 or $\frac{1}{9}$? $\frac{1}{9}$

22. List in order from least to greatest: $\frac{3}{8}$, 25%, $\frac{1}{3}$.   25%, $\frac{1}{3}$, $\frac{3}{8}$

Write each fraction or decimal as a percent. Round to the nearest tenth of a percent.

23. $\frac{3}{5}$ 60%   **24.** 0.02 2%   **25.** $\frac{1}{9}$ 11.1%

26. $\frac{1}{2}$ 50%   **27.** 0.125 12.5%   **28.** $\frac{1}{3}$ 33.3%

29. 2.6 260%   **30.** $\frac{5}{4}$ 125%   **31.** 0.002 0.2%

Find the unit rate for each non-unit rate given.

32. 100 pages per hour   **32.** 600 pages in six hours
33. 40 miles per hour   **33.** 200 miles in five hours
34. 70 beats per minute **34.** 140 beats in two minutes
35. $\frac{1}{2}$ pizza per camper   **35.** 12 pizzas for 24 campers

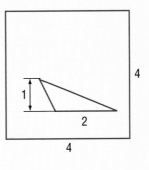

▶ **Exercise 18** This exercise involves geometric probability. Here, however, one uses length rather than area.

Quick Check

Informal Assessment Students should be able to:

✔ associate a number from 0 to 1 with the likelihood that an event will occur

✔ find the experimental probability of an event

✔ find the theoretical probability of an event

Quick Quiz

1. The spinner below has 7 equal-sized sections numbered 1 to 7.

  a. How many outcomes are possible if you spin the spinner once? 7
  b. Are all of the outcomes equally likely? Yes

2. Mario spun the spinner shown in Question 1 twenty times and got the following numbers:

  1 3 7 3 2 2 2 5 6 1
  6 4 6 5 1 4 5 5 3 1

  Based on these results, what is the experimental probability for spinning the number 5? $\frac{1}{5}$ or 20%

3. What is the theoretical probability of spinning 5 with the spinner shown in Question 1? $\frac{1}{7}$

4. A grain of rice is dropped and hits the square shown below at a random point inside the square. What is the probability that the rice lands in the triangle? $\frac{1}{16}$

Lesson 10.3 The Language of Chance   **637**

Make Matches

Objectives

▶ To make tree diagrams to show outcomes for situations involving independent or dependent choices

▶ To count the number of possibilities using the counting principle

Overview

In other lessons of this chapter, students have considered probability for situations in which the events that occur are independent. This means that the occurrence of one event does not affect the occurrence of another. In this lesson, students explore situations in which one event can affect subsequent events. The situations studied here are comparatively simple. Students will explore dependent events in more detail in Courses 2 and 3.

Advance Preparation

For Investigation 1, each pair of students will need counters, blocks, or slips of paper (two in each of two colors) and a bucket or paper bag.

	Summary	Materials	On Your Own Exercises (pp. 648–653)	Assessment Opportunities
Investigation 1 (p. 639) Pacing: 1 day	Students use simple simulations and tree diagrams to investigate probability situations in which the occurrence of one event can affect subsequent events.	counters, blocks, or slips of paper, buckets or paper bags	Practice & Apply: 1–3, 15, 16 Mixed Review: 18–41	• On the Spot Assessment (p. 640) • Share & Summarize (p. 642) • Troubleshooting (p. 642)
Investigation 2 (p. 642) Pacing: 1 day	Students examine how the principles studied in Investigation 1 can be extended to situations that involve matching cards from a standard deck.	playing cards (optional)	Practice & Apply: 4, 5 Mixed Review: 18–41	• Share & Summarize (p. 644)
Investigation 3 (p. 644) Pacing: 1 day	Students count the total number of outcomes of an event using the fundamental counting principle.		Practice & Apply: 6–14 Connect & Extend: 17 Mixed Review: 18–41	• Share & Summarize (p. 647) • Troubleshooting (p. 646)

Leveled Lesson Resources

CRM *Available in:* **Chapter 10 Resource Masters**

Study Guide and Intervention (p. 36) **AL**

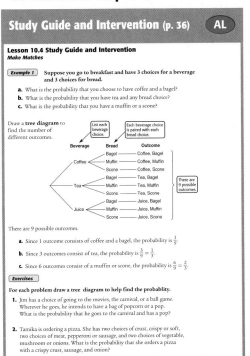

Skills Practice (p. 37) **AL** **OL**

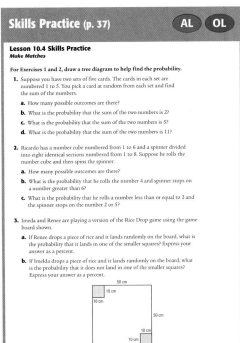

Problem-Solving Practice (p. 38) **AL** **OL**

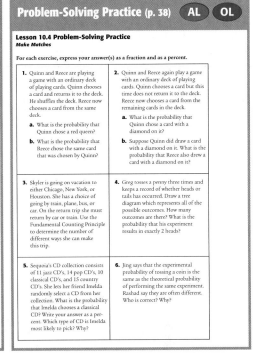

Enrichment (p. 39) **BL**

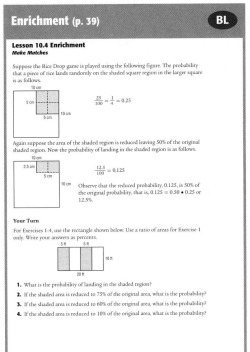

Lesson Quick Quiz (p. 40) **AL** **OL** **BL**

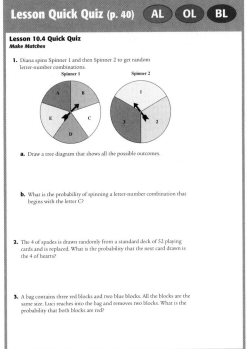

Additional Lesson Resources

Teacher Tech Tools
- TeacherWorks
- ExamView Assessment Suite
- Classroom Presentation Toolkit
- Advance Tracker

Student Tech Tools
- StudentWorks Plus
- **Math Online** eGlossary •
  Concepts in Motion

Other Print Products
- Investigation Notebook
  and Reflection Journal
- Quick Review Math Handbook

Introduce

Make Matches Remind students that when they flip a coin, what happens on one flip does not affect what happens on the next flip. The same is true for rolling a die or spinning a spinner. Tell students that in this lesson, they will consider situations in which the occurrence of one event can affect what happens in the next event.

Think & Discuss

Discuss Think & Discuss questions with the class. The important thing for students to understand is that in the case of rolling a die, the probability of rolling a particular number does not change from one roll to the next since the number of possible outcomes is unchanged from one roll to the next. In the case of drawing markers without looking at them, the probabilities do not stay the same from one stage to the next since choosing a marker at one stage reduces the number of possible outcomes for the next stage.

Make Matches

In the probability games you have considered so far, the result of one round or trial does not affect the result of another. For example, if you toss a coin and get heads, your chances of getting heads when you flip the coin again are still 50%. These are called *independent events*.

In this lesson, you will work with situations called *dependent events*. That is, what happens in one case *does* affect what can happen in the next.

Think & Discuss

Suppose you roll a die several times.

* What is the probability of getting 6 on the first roll? What is the probability of getting 4? $\frac{1}{6}$, $\frac{1}{6}$

* Suppose the first time you roll the die, you get 6. You roll a second time. What is the probability of getting 6 on the second roll? What is the probability of getting 4? $\frac{1}{6}$, $\frac{1}{6}$

① Possible answer: When the die is rolled the second time, it still has the same six sides and they are still equally likely. When the second person takes a marker, the first marker chosen is gone, leaving only five equally likely possibilities.

Now imagine that you and some friends are making a poster for a school party. Your teacher gives you six markers in six different colors. Each of you chooses one without looking. Two of the colors are red and green.

* If you choose first, what is the probability that you will get the red marker? What is the probability that you will get the green marker? $\frac{1}{6}$, $\frac{1}{6}$

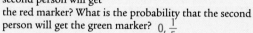

* Suppose you chose first and got the red marker. What is the probability that the second person will get the red marker? What is the probability that the second person will get the green marker? 0, $\frac{1}{5}$

* Why are the probabilities for the dice situation different from those for the marker situation? See ①.

Investigation ① Match Colors

Vocabulary

simulation

Materials

- counters or blocks
  (2 in each of 2 colors)
  or slips of paper
- bucket or bag

A **simulation** is an experiment in which you use different items to represent the items in a real situation. For example, to simulate choosing markers and looking at their colors, you can write the color of each marker on a slip of paper and put all the slips into a bag. You can simulate choosing markers by drawing slips from the bag. Mathematically, the situations are identical.

Using a simulation can help with some of the exercises in this investigation.

✅ Develop & Understand: A

Ken woke up early and found that a storm had knocked out the power in his neighborhood. He has to dress in the dark. Ken has four socks in his drawer, two black and two brown. Color is the only difference between them. As long as both socks are the same color, Ken does not care which he wears. He takes two socks out of the drawer.

1. Simulate this situation, using counters, blocks, or slips of paper with colors written on them. If you use counters or blocks, you may have to let other colors stand for the sock colors. For example, a red block might represent a brown sock, and a blue block might represent a black sock. Use a bucket or bag to represent Ken's sock drawer.

   a. Without looking, pick two "socks," one at a time, from the "drawer." Record whether the socks match. Then put back the socks, mix them up, and try again. Repeat this process 16 times. Record the results. Answers will vary.

   b. Use your results to find an experimental probability that Ken will choose matching socks. Answers will vary.

2. If the first sock Ken picks is brown, what is the theoretical probability that the second sock will also be brown? Explain.

3. If the first sock is black, what is the theoretical probability that the second sock will also be black? $\frac{1}{3}$

4. Ken says that since he has two colors of socks, he has a 50% chance of getting a matching pair. Do you think he is correct? If not, what do you think the actual probability is? Explain. No; Possible explanation: No matter which sock Ken chooses first, he will have a one-in-three chance of getting a matching sock. So, the probability is $\frac{1}{3}$, not $\frac{1}{2}$.

Real-World Link

On August 14, 2003, a massive power failure caused the largest blackout in U.S. history. The blackout affected over 50 million people in eight states and parts of Canada.

2. $\frac{1}{3}$; of the three socks left in the drawer, two are black and one is brown.

Reaching All Learners

OL **On Level** If students have difficulty understanding the reasoning for Exercise 4, it may help to make a table of all the possibilities. Use "First Sock," "Second Sock," "Match?" for column headings and the numbers 1 and 2 to distinguish between the two socks of the same color, as shown in the partial sample below. There are 12 possibilities, and 4 should result in a yes in the last column. Therefore, the probability of a match is $\frac{4}{12}$, or $\frac{1}{3}$.

First Sock	Second Sock	Match?
Brown 1	Black 1	no
Brown 1	Black 2	no

Investigation ①

On Your Own Exercises
Pages 648–653
Exercises 1–3, 15, 16

Match Colors In this investigation, students use a straightforward simulation to examine experimental probabilities for a situation in which choices at one stage can affect choices at the next stage. They learn to make and use tree diagrams to find theoretical probabilities in such situations.

Read the first paragraph on this page with the class and discuss what is meant by *simulation*. Students should have little difficulty seeing that selecting colored markers and selecting colored slips of paper are quite similar. The total number of markers and their colors match the total number of slips of paper. In both cases, objects are selected at random.

✅ Develop & Understand: A

Suggested Grouping: Pairs

▶ **Exercise 1** Students should not look as they draw items from the bucket or paper bag. If they look, their selection will not be completely random. In **Part a**, students can tally matches and nonmatches, checking from time to time to see if they have conducted the required number of trials. A slightly simpler approach is to write the numbers from 1 through 16 in a column to represent the trial numbers. They can circle the trial numbers for which the "socks" matched and draw a line through the trial numbers for which the "socks" did not match.

▶ **Exercise 4** Students need to understand that getting a matching pair depends entirely on the *second* sock drawn. At the stage when the second sock is drawn, there are three socks left. Two of these have the same color, and the third has the same color as the sock that was drawn first. So, there is a $\frac{2}{3}$ chance that the next sock drawn will *not* match the first and only a $\frac{1}{3}$ chance that it will match the first.

Wrap-Up Have students share their answers to Exercise 4.

Teacher Tips When you discuss this page, you might observe that it was difficult in the exercises on page 639 to keep track of all the possibilities when the socks were being drawn. Tell students that a *tree diagram* can make the job a little easier. Discuss the diagrams on page 640 to help students understand the basic idea of constructing a tree diagram. Then go to page 641 to show how the tree diagram allows one to read off the outcomes for tossing two coins.

✓ Develop & Understand: B

Suggested Grouping: Pairs

▶ **Exercise 5** Students should understand that there should be six branches for the first choice. You may want to suggest that students use the first letter of each color name (*R* for red, *O* for orange, and so on) instead of writing the full name of each color.

Teacher Tips After finishing the discussion of how to create the tree diagram for the coin tosses, have students make tree diagrams for situations that involve two successive choices. Then use the tree diagrams to help them find theoretical probabilities related to each situation.

In Lesson 10.3, you saw how you could use a table to keep track of the possible outcomes for two coin tosses. You can also draw a *tree diagram* to show all the possibilities. The possible results for the first coin can be shown like this.

First Coin
Start — H
Start — T

The possibilities for the second coin can be shown as branches from each of the first two branches.

First Coin   Second Coin
Start
H — H
H — T
T — H
T — T

You can read off the possible outcomes by following the branches, beginning with Start. For example, following the top set of branches gives the outcome HH.

First Coin   Second Coin   Outcome
Start
H — H   HH
H — T   HT
T — H   TH
T — T   TT

✓ Develop & Understand: B

5. Suppose you choose one of six markers from a bag in red, orange, yellow, green, blue, or purple. Draw a tree diagram showing the possible colors for the marker.   See the answer to Exercise 6c.

On the Spot Assessment

Watch students to see if they have trouble understanding that the ending branches of the tree are the outcomes, not the other parts of the tree.

6. Now consider what happens when you choose a second marker.

   a. Suppose the first marker you chose was red. What are the possible choices for the second marker? **Orange, yellow, green, blue, and purple**

   b. Add a new set of branches to the "red" branch of your tree diagram for Exercise 5, showing the possibilities for your second choice. **See the answer to Exercise 6c.**

   c. Complete your tree diagram by adding branches that show the possibilities when each of the other colors are picked first. **See margin.**

   d. What is the probability that, if you choose the two colors at random, you will get red and green, chosen in either order? $\frac{1}{15}$

7. Draw a tree diagram to show the possible choices of sock colors for Ken if he chooses two socks from a drawer containing two brown and two black socks. Since there are two socks of each color, label the socks as brown 1, brown 2, black 1, and black 2. **See margin.**

8. How many possible sock pairs are there? How many of them have matching colors? **12, 4**

9. What is the probability that Ken will choose a matching pair? $\frac{1}{3}$

Develop & Understand: C

After choosing socks, Ken has to choose pants and a shirt. His school requires uniforms of blue, tan, or green. He has two pairs of pants, one blue and one tan. He has two shirts, also one blue and one tan. Now he takes one shirt and one pair of pants.

10. Suppose the shirt is blue. What is the probability that the pants will also be blue? Explain how you found your answer.

11. Draw a tree diagram showing the possible choices of shirts and pants.

12. Ken says the probability that he will choose matching shirt and pants is 50%. Is he right? How do you know?

13. Suppose Ken has a third shirt and a third pair of pants, both green. Now what is the probability that he will choose a shirt and pants of the same color? Explain.

14. Suppose Ken has one tan shirt and two blue shirts and one tan pair of pants and two blue pairs of pants. Find the probability that the shirt and pants will match. Show how you found your answer. $\frac{5}{9}$; Possible explanation: There are nine possible combinations of shirts and pants. Of these, four consist of a blue shirt and blue pants, and one consists of a tan shirt and tan pants. So, in five of the nine combinations, the shirt and pants match.

Lesson 10.4 Make Matches **641**

Real-World Link
The knitting machine was invented in 1589 by William Lee of England. Queen Elizabeth I refused to give Lee a patent for his machine because she felt the stockings it produced were too coarse. It may also be that she did not want to put people who knit by hand out of business.

10. $\frac{1}{2}$; There are two pairs of pants, one tan and one blue, so the probability of getting blue pants is $\frac{1}{2}$.

11.
```
               blue
        blue <
Shirt Pants    tan
Start <        blue
        tan <
               tan
```

12. Yes; Possible explanation: There are four possible combinations. In two of them, the shirt and pants match.

13. $\frac{1}{3}$; Possible explanation: Whatever shirt he chooses, one of the three pairs of pants is the same color.

Additional Answers for Develop & Understand: B Exercises 6c and 7 are on page 657B.

▶ **Exercise 6d** Students should see that when the first branch is for red, there is only one second branch that corresponds to green. Likewise, when the first branch is green, only one second branch corresponds to red. The second branches are in six groups of five branches each, for a total of 6 · 5, or 30 second branches. Therefore, there are 30 possible two-color combinations, of which only two are red-green. This means that the probability of choosing red and green (in either order) is $\frac{2}{30}$, or $\frac{1}{15}$.

▶ **Exercise 9** Students should see that the answer can be found by using the answer for Exercise 8.

Develop & Understand: C

Suggested Grouping: Pairs

▶ **Exercise 13** Students can use the following tree diagram for this exercise.

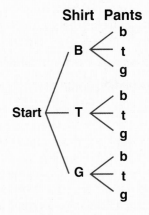

▶ **Exercise 14** Students can use the following tree diagram. Note that B1 and B2 are used to distinguish the two blue shirts, and b1 and b2 are used to distinguish the two pairs of blue pants.

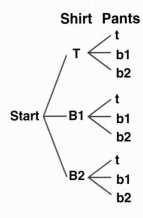

Lesson 10.4 Make Matches **641**

Ask volunteers to share their answers to these exercises to the class. Discuss the answers and correct any mistakes.

Investigation 2

On Your Own Exercises
Pages 648–653
Exercises 4, 5

Match Cards In this investigation, students extend the ideas of Investigation 1 to situations that involve more numerous possibilities for the choices. They analyze card games that involve choosing cards from a standard deck (without actually playing the games). There can often be many possibilities in such situations, and students will see that using logical reasoning is often advantageous in solving probability problems about such situations.

✓ Develop & Understand: A

Suggested Grouping: Pairs

▶ **Exercises 1–5** In this exercise set, students analyze a game in which players score a point depending on whether they draw cards from the same or different suits of a standard deck of cards. You may want to read the rules with the class to be sure all students understand how the game is played.

▶ **Exercise 2** Students need to understand the importance of replacing the card after the first draw. Point out that the probability would be $\frac{12}{51}$ or $\frac{4}{17}$ if Player 1 had not replaced his or her card after the first draw.

Wrap-Up Ask students how they got their answers for Exercise 4. The main point for them to understand is that Player 2 has three times the chance of scoring as Player 1 has. You may also want to have students explain the thinking that led them to their answers for Exercise 5.

Real-World Link

Ask students why cards may have different suits.

---

1. Yes; Whatever color the first sock is, there are fewer socks of that color left in the drawer, so that color has a smaller chance of being chosen second.

2. $\frac{1}{4}$; Since Player 1 put the card back, the deck has the same cards it had before, and Player 2 has the same chance as Player 1 to get a heart.

3. $\frac{1}{4}$; Whatever suit Player 1 chose, there are 13 cards of that suit out of a total of 52 for Player 2 to choose from.

Share & Summarize

1. When Ken is choosing socks in the dark, does the color of the first sock affect the chance of choosing a particular color next? Why or why not?

2. When Ken is choosing shirts and pants in the dark, does the color of the shirt chosen affect the chance of choosing pants of a particular color? Why or why not?   No; When he chooses a shirt, the collection of pants is unchanged.

Investigation 2 Match Cards

Real-World Link
The cards described here are English playing cards. In other countries, different suits are used. Traditional German playing cards use the suits hearts, leaves, bells, and acorns. Spanish playing cards use the suits coins, cups, swords, and clubs.

In an ordinary deck of playing cards, there are four suits.

 Clubs   Diamonds   Spades   Hearts

There are 13 cards in each suit, one to represent each of the numbers from 1 to 10, and three *face cards,* consisting of jack, queen, and king. Clubs and spades are black, while diamonds and hearts are red.

Many kinds of games, involving various combinations of chance and skill, are played with decks of cards. In this investigation, you will work with some simple games of chance that involve choosing cards from a deck.

✓ Develop & Understand: A

In the first game, a deck of cards is shuffled and placed on a table face down. For one round of the game, players do the following.

- Player 1 chooses a card from the deck without looking and writes down its suit of spades, hearts, diamonds, or clubs.
- Player 1 puts the card back and shuffles the deck.
- Player 2 chooses a card without looking. If it has the same suit as the first card, Player 1 scores a point. Otherwise, Player 2 scores a point.
- Player 2 returns the card and shuffles the deck.

The winner is the player with more points at the end of 20 rounds.

1. What is the probability that Player 1 will choose a heart? $\frac{1}{4}$

2. If Player 1 chooses a heart, what is the probability that Player 2 will also choose a heart? Explain.

3. What is the probability that Player 2 chooses a card of the same suit as Player 1's card, no matter what that suit was? How do you know?

4. What would you expect the score to be after 20 rounds?
   Player 1: 5 points; Player 2: 15 points

5. Think of a way to change the scoring rules to give both players the same chance of winning. Possible answer: Player 1 earns 3 points each time the suits match, and Player 2 earns 1 point each time they do not match.

Troubleshooting

If students have difficulty understanding when one choice affects another, you may wish to use simple simulations to show the effect (or lack of effect) that a first choice can have on a second choice.

You can use simulation procedures similar to those in the exercises on page 639 and vary the situations by referring to the exercises on pages 641 and 642.

7b. Yes; Since Player 1 does not return the card, the deck is not the same as it was. There are 51 cards left, and 12 of these are hearts.

9. Less fair; In this game, Player 1 has only a $\frac{12}{51}$ chance of scoring a point, which is less than the $\frac{1}{4}$ chance in the first game.

13.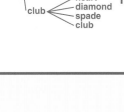

First Card   Second Card

Start
- heart
  - heart
  - diamond
  - spade
  - club
- diamond
  - heart
  - diamond
  - spade
  - club
- spade
  - heart
  - diamond
  - spade
  - club
- club
  - heart
  - diamond
  - spade
  - club

 Develop & Understand: B

The second card game is similar to the first. The only difference is that Player 1 does not put the card back before Player 2 chooses. After both players have chosen, the cards are returned to the deck. Player 1 scores a point if the two cards have the same suit. Player 2 scores a point if they have different suits.

6. What is the probability that Player 1 will choose a heart? $\frac{1}{4}$

7. Suppose Player 1 chooses a heart.

   a. What is the probability that Player 2 also chooses a heart? $\frac{12}{51}$

   b. Is your answer to Part a different from your answer to Exercise 2? Why or why not?

8. What is the probability that Player 2 chooses a card of the same suit as Player 1, no matter what suit Player 1 chooses? $\frac{12}{51}$

9. Is this game *more fair*, *less fair*, or *just as fair* as the game in Exercises 1–5? Explain.

Develop & Understand: C

Suppose you want to draw a tree diagram to show the possible choices for the first card game in which Player 1 replaces the card before Player 2 chooses.

10. How many branches would you need to show the possibilities for the first card? **52**

11. How many branches would you have to add to show the possibilities for the second card? **52**

12. How many total branches would your tree diagram have?
    52 · 52, or 2,704

Since the game concerns only the suits of the cards, and since the four suits are equally likely for each draw, you can draw a simplified tree diagram showing the four possible suits for each draw.

For example, suppose the first card chosen is a heart. Here is the part of the tree diagram showing the possible suits for the second card.

13. Draw a tree diagram showing all the possible suit combinations for the first game.

First Card   Second Card

Heart
- heart
- diamond
- spade
- club

14. Hearts and diamonds are red while clubs and spades are black. What is the probability that the two cards have the same color? $\frac{1}{2}$

15. Can you use a simplified tree diagram for the second game, in which Player 1 keeps the card instead of returning it to the deck before Player 2 chooses? Explain. No; For the second card, the four suits are not equally likely.

Lesson 10.4 Make Matches **643**

 Develop & Understand: B

Suggested Grouping: Pairs

▶ **Exercises 6–9** In this exercise set, students study a second game in which the players draw a card and name the suit of the card. In this game, however, Player 1 does not replace his or her card before Player 2 draws.

Wrap-Up You may want to briefly review the answers before having students continue to the next exercise set.

 Develop & Understand: C

Suggested Grouping: Pairs

Exercises 10–12 In this exercise set, students think about the total number of outcomes for the game in the exercises on page 642. They also consider what is involved in drawing tree diagrams for the first and second card games.

The tree diagram for these exercises is assumed to have enough branches to account for the identities of the individual cards, not just the suits of the cards.

Have students work on these questions in groups. Provide them with cards, if necessary, and ask them to discuss their answers.

Investigation ③

On Your Own Exercises
Pages 648–653
Exercises 6–14, 17

The Fundamental Counting Principle In this investigation, students will use the Fundamental Counting Principle to build on what they have already learned about tree diagrams. Students will add to existing data tables to find patterns in outcomes. The concepts in this investigation will help students interpret and use data.

Think & Discuss

Review the heads/tails tree diagram with students. Point out that HT and TH are different outcomes. Discuss how the number of possible outcomes increases when you add coins.

1a. No
1b. Yes; When one king is removed from a deck, there are fewer kings left.
1c. No
2. Possible answer: Pulling a numbered slip out of a hat and getting an even number, and then pulling out another slip and getting an even number

① 2; They were repeated in this section of the tree diagram making four branches, but there were only two possibilities for the second coin, heads or tails.

Share & Summarize

In some probability situations, one event can affect the probability of another.

1. For each pair of events, decide whether the first event affects the probability of the second. If your answer is "yes," explain why.

First Event	**Second Event**
a. getting heads on the flip of a coin	getting heads on the second flip of the coin
b. getting a king when choosing a card from a deck	getting a king when choosing a second card without returning the first
c. drawing a certain name from names written on slips of paper and chosen at random from a hat	drawing a second name if the first slip is returned to the hat before the second choice

2. Create your own sequence of two events for which the first event affects the probability of the second.

3. Now create your own sequence of two events for which the first event *does not* affect the probability of the second.
   Possible answer: rolling a die and getting an even number, and then rolling the die again and getting an even number

---

Investigation ③ The Fundamental Counting Principle

Vocabulary

Fundamental
Counting Principle

In the previous lessons, you used tree diagrams to show the possible outcomes in probability situations. In this investigation, you will analyze patterns in the tree diagrams to find a more efficient way to determine the number of possible outcomes for a situation.

Think & Discuss

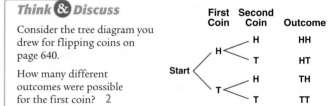

Consider the tree diagram you drew for flipping coins on page 640.

How many different outcomes were possible for the first coin?   2

How many outcomes were possible for the second coin?   See ①.

How many total outcomes, were possible for the situation of flipping two coins, considering HT and TH as different outcomes?   4

644   CHAPTER 10   Data and Probability

Reaching All Learners

BL Beyond Level Students who fully understand the concepts in this investigation can move forward by creating their own data tables. Have them create a table to show possibilities for an event, such as rolling a die or drawing a card. Then have them trade with a partner and create a tree diagram for each other's tables and write a sentence describing patterns in the outcomes.

Develop & Understand: A

1. Copy the table below, which includes the data from Think & Discuss. Include four additional rows to record information from Exercises 2–4.

Type of Event	Number of Possibilities for First Event	Number of Possibilities for Second Event	Total Possible Outcomes
Flipping two coins	2	2	4
Choosing Markers	6	5	30
Shirts and Pants	2	2	4
3 Shirts and 3 Pants	3	3	9
Card Game (first)	4	4	16

2. Look at the tree diagram you drew for choosing among six markers in Exercises 5–9 on pages 640 and 641.

   a. How many choices were there for choosing the first marker? 6

   b. How many choices were there for choosing the second marker? 5

   c. How many ways were there to choose the markers with red, green and green, red as different outcomes? In other words, how many branches did the tree diagram have in the last column? 30 Record this information in the table from Exercise 1. See table.

3. Look at the tree diagram you drew for choosing pants and shirts for Ken to wear in Exercises 10–12 on page 641. Fill in the table for the number of options for his shirts, the number of options for pants, and the number of total outfits. Then add a row to the table for the situation in Exercise 13 where he had three shirts and three pants. See table.

4. Look at the tree diagram you drew for the first card game in Exercises 1–5 on page 642. Fill in the number of options for the suit of the first card, the number of options for the suit of the second card, and the number of total ways to draw the suits for two cards. See table.

5. Total Possible Outcomes is the product of the possibilities for the first event and the possibilities for the second event.

5. What patterns do you see in the table? Is there any relationship between the possibilities for the first and second events and the total possible outcomes?

The **Fundamental Counting Principle** states that if there are M possibilities for one event, and N possibilities for another event, then there are $M \cdot N$ ways for both events to occur. For example, the total outcomes for flipping two coins is 4 because two possibilities for the first coin times two possibilities for the second coin equals four total possible outcomes.

Besides the tree diagram, you can also organize probability outcomes using a chart. This may make it easier to see why the Fundamental Counting Principle is true.

Develop & Understand: A

Suggested Grouping: Small Groups

▶ **Exercise 1** Explain to students that this table will be used to record answers for Exercises 2–5.

▶ **Exercise 2** Make sure students can correctly find the number of choices for an event. Use small pieces of paper to simulate choosing the markers for this exercise. Have students tell the amount of choices as you demonstrate.

▶ **Exercises 3–4** Have students find the information from the earlier diagrams and transfer it to the table in Exercise 1. Remind them that they are still working with the same information, but it is recorded in a different format.

▶ **Exercise 5** Work problems on the board to show students the relationship between the possible outcomes for the first and second events and the total possible outcomes. Have students tell how to get four from two and two, and thirty from six and five, etc. Discuss how each row uses the same operation to find total outcomes.

Teacher Tips You may want to discuss the Fundamental Counting Principle with the whole class. Use the examples below to help them understand the principle.

Additional Examples

1. You have 3 red shirts and 2 pairs of blue jeans. How many ways can you pick a shirt and a pair of jeans? $3 \times 2 = 6$

2. At the ice cream shop, there are 12 flavors of ice cream, 8 toppings, and a choice of 2 cones. How many ways can you choose one flavor, one topping, and one cone to make your ice cream cone? $12 \times 8 \times 2 = 192$

Make sure students understand that the blank spaces in the chart on page 645 are blank because the marker colors in those squares would have been a pair of the same color. Explain how dependent events are portrayed in the chart, and discuss how the Fundamental Counting Principle still applies.

✓ Develop & Understand: B

Suggested Grouping: Pairs

▶ **Exercises 6a and b** Explain to students that by replacing the first drawn block, they still have the full set of blocks to draw from the second time.

▶ **Exercise 6c** Discuss how not replacing the first drawn block decreases the number of possibilities for the second draw. Make sure students understand how that leads to the blank spaces in the chart.

. . . .

Additional Answers

6a.

	R	R	Y	G	B
R	RR	RR	YR	GR	BR
R	RR	RR	YR	GR	BR
Y	RY	RY	YY	GY	BY
G	RG	RG	YG	GG	BG
B	RB	RB	YB	GB	BB

6c.

	R	R	Y	G	B
R		RR	YR	GR	BR
R	RR		YR	GR	BR
Y	RY	RY		GY	BY
G	RG	RG	YG		BG
B	RB	RB	YB	GB	

The information from the tree diagram for flipping two coins would look like this.

	H	T
H	HH	HT
T	TH	TT

However, for a situation like the markers where you found that the events were *dependent*, the chart would be different.

	RED	ORN	PUR	BLU	GRE	YEL
RED		ORN RED	PUR RED	BLU RED	GRE RED	YEL RED
ORN	RED ORN		PUR ORN	BLU ORN	GRE ORN	YEL ORN
PUR	RED PUR	ORN PUR		BLU PUR	GRE PUR	YEL PUR
BLU	RED BLU	ORN BLU	PUR BLU		GRE BLU	YEL BLU
GRE	RED GRE	ORN GRE	PUR GRE	BLU GRE		YEL GRE
YEL	RED YEL	ORN YEL	PUR YEL	BLU YEL	GRE YEL	

① According to the Fundamental Counting Principle, the number of outcomes for choosing markers would be 6 · 5. The chart shows (6 · 6) − (1 · 6), with the six excluded being where a marker color would have been pair with itself.

6b. There are five blocks to draw the first time and five blocks to draw the second time. 5 · 5 = 25, which is the number of outcomes the chart shows.

6d. There are five blocks to draw the first time and four blocks to draw the second time, and 5 · 4 = 20, which is the number of outcomes the chart shows. The chart actually shows (5 · 5) − (1 · 5).

Think & Discuss

Why are some of the squares in the above chart blank? How many squares are blank? How does this chart help explain why the Fundamental Counting Principle works for dependent events? See ①.

✓ Develop & Understand: B

6. Alyssa and Tucker are testing the Fundamental Counting Principle with a new activity. They have placed five blocks in a paper bag. There are two red, one yellow, one green, and one blue blocks.

a. Create a chart to show the possibilities if one block is drawn from the bag and replaced, and then another block is drawn. See margin.

b. How many possible outcomes are there for drawing two blocks? How does this relate to the Fundamental Counting Principle?

c. Recreate the chart to show the possibilities for the blocks if the first block is not returned to the bag. See margin.

d. How many possible outcomes are there for drawing two blocks when the first block is not returned? How does this relate to the Fundamental Counting Principle? How is this shown in the chart?

Troubleshooting

For students who have trouble creating the chart, review the example. Point to a square and have students tell what it is represented by the letters in it. For students who understand the chart but have trouble with blank spaces, demonstrate Exercise 6c using blocks or pieces of colored paper. Make sure students see that keeping the first drawn object out of the bag means one less possibility for the second draw.

Real-World Link

There are 241,000,000 cars registered in the United States. This is 0.006% of the number of cars registered in the world.

....

7a. Digits 0–9 means 10 digits and 26 letters, so the calculation would be 10 · 10 · 10 · 26 · 26 · 26 = 17,576,000 possible license plates.

7b. The calculation would be 10 · 10 · 10 · 10 · 26 · 26 · 26 = 175,760,000 possible license plates, or 10 times as many.

7c. No, the tree diagram would not be helpful because it would be very large. The chart also only allows you to show two events.

7. In 1982, New York changed its license plate format because it ran out of distinct number/letter combinations.

a. The format *before* the change was *number-number-number-letter-letter-letter* where repeated numbers were allowed, repeated letters were allowed, and all digits and letters were allowed. Use the Fundamental Counting Principle to find out how many different license plates were possible with this format. Show your work.

b. The format *after* the change was *number-number-number-number-letter-letter-letter*. How many different license plates were possible with this format? Show your work.

c. Would a chart or tree diagram be helpful in this situation? Explain your thinking.

d. How many different license plates are possible if zero was not used? 115,316,136

Share & Summarize

The cafeteria serves choices for the main dish, side item, fruit item, and dessert. Each student gets one item from each section of the menu. The menu for today is as follows.

Main Dish	Side Item	Fruit	Dessert
Enchilada	Salad	Apple	Brownie
Hamburger	Carrots	Peaches	Ice Cream
Grilled Chicken			Popsicle

1. Which of the methods you learned could you use to find the number of possible meals? Explain.

2. How many meals are possible?

3. How do the total possible outcomes change if there are two drink options? 36 · 2 = 72 possible meals

1. You could use the tree diagram but it would be a long process. The chart would not be possible because there are more than two events. The Fundamental Counting Principle would be the easiest.
2. The total outcomes are found by 3 · 2 · 2 · 3 = 36 different possible meals.

▶ **Exercise 7a** Have groups work together to determine the number of possibilities for each position in the format. Remind them that the Fundamental Counting Principle uses multiplication of possible outcomes to determine the total number of possibilities.

▶ **Exercise 7b** Have students write a sentence explaining how changing the format made more possibilities. Then have them share their sentences with the class.

▶ **Exercise 7c** Have students suggest reasons why a chart or tree diagram would or would not be helpful. List the reasons on the board, and discuss each one.

....

Real-World Link
Discuss how difficult it might be to provide a unique letter/number combination for every license plate when there are so many issued.

....

Share & Summarize

Discuss why a tree diagram would be time-consuming and is not the best way to determine the number of possible meals. Point out that the Fundamental Counting Principle saves time and energy. Remind students to count the number of choices in each column and exclude the blank spaces when finding the number of possible outcomes.

Reaching *All Learners*

OL On Level Make sure students understand that the Fundamental Counting Principle makes finding the number of possible outcomes much faster and easier. Then have pairs think of other times when they might use letter/number combinations, such as account numbers or confirmation numbers. Discuss how one would find the number of possibilities for these combinations.

Investigation 1
Pages 639–642
Practice & Apply: 1–3, 15, 16

Investigation 2
Pages 642–644
Practice & Apply: 4, 5

Investigation 3
Pages 644–647
Practice & Apply: 6–14
Connect & Extend: 17

Assign Anytime
Mixed Review: 18–41

▶ **Exercise 3b** The tree diagram shows not only which marbles can be selected but also the order in which they can be selected. You may wish to see whether students can explain how reasoning can be used to predict the total number of possible outcomes independently of the tree diagram. Some students may see that there are six possibilities for the first choice and that, for each of these, there are five possibilities for the second choice. The total number of possibilities is therefore 6 · 5, or 30.

Practice & Apply

1b. $\frac{1}{2}$; from Part a, the probability is $\frac{1}{2}$ that the first card is a 2. If it is, the second card must be a 1.

2a. 123, 132, 213, 231, 312, 321; There are 3 possibilities for the first card, 2 possibilities for the second card, and 1 possibility for the third card. So, 3 · 2 · 1 = 6 outcomes, which is how many three-digit numbers found.

2d. $\frac{2}{6}$, or $\frac{1}{3}$

1. Suppose there are two cards, numbered 1 and 2. The cards are mixed and placed face down.

   a. You arrange the cards in a row and then turn them over. What is the probability that the first card will be a 2? $\frac{1}{2}$

   b. What is the probability that the cards will form the number 21? Explain.

2. Suppose you have three cards, numbered 1, 2, and 3. The cards are shuffled and placed face down in a row.

   a. List all the three-digit numbers that can be created from these three cards. Does the counting principle verify the number of outcomes you found? Explain.

   b. What is the probability that the cards will form the number 213 when they are turned over? $\frac{1}{6}$

   c. What is the probability that the cards will form a number between 200 and 300? $\frac{2}{6}$, or $\frac{1}{3}$

   d. What is the probability that the cards will form an even number?

   e. What is the probability that the cards will form a number less than 300? $\frac{4}{6}$, or $\frac{2}{3}$

3. Manuel and Hally are splitting a box of marbles. The box contains three red, two green, and one orange marble. Each friend chooses a marble at random.

   a. If Hally chooses first and gets a red marble, what is the probability that Manuel's marble will also be red? $\frac{2}{5}$

   b. Draw a tree diagram showing all the possible combinations when each friend chooses one marble. Label the red marbles R1, R2, and R3. Label the green marbles G1 and G2. Label the orange marble O. Does the counting principle verify the number of outcomes you found? Explain.

   c. What is the probability that the two marbles will be the same color? $\frac{8}{30}$, or $\frac{4}{15}$

Additional Answer

3b. There are 6 marbles, so there are 6 possibilities for the first marble, and 5 possibilities for the second marble, so 6 · 5 = 30 outcomes, as shown in the tree diagram.

Marble Outcomes

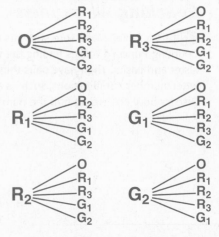

4. Gabriel and Dana are playing a game with an ordinary deck of playing cards. For each turn, Dana chooses a card and returns it to the deck. She shuffles the deck. Then Gabriel chooses a card.

   a. If Dana picks the five of clubs, what is the probability that Gabriel will pick the five of clubs? $\frac{1}{52}$

   b. If Dana picks a black card in either a spade or a club, what is the probability that Gabriel will pick a red card in either a heart or a diamond? How do you know? $\frac{1}{2}$; half the cards are red.

   c. If Dana picks the six of spades, what is the probability that Gabriel will pick a king? $\frac{1}{13}$

   d. If Dana picks a red queen, what is the probability that Gabriel will pick a red queen? $\frac{1}{26}$

5. Gabriel and Dana are playing a game with an ordinary deck of playing cards. For each turn, the deck is shuffled, and the cards are spread out face down. At the same time, Dana and Gabriel each choose a card.

   a. If Dana picks the five of clubs, what is the probability that Gabriel also picks the five of clubs?   0

   b. If Dana picks a black card in either a spade or a club, what is the probability that Gabriel picks a red card in either a heart or a diamond? How do you know?

   c. If Dana picks the six of spades, what is the probability that Gabriel picks a king? $\frac{4}{51}$

   d. If Dana picks a red queen, what is the probability that Gabriel picks a red queen? $\frac{1}{51}$

5b. $\frac{26}{51}$; If one black card is removed, there are 26 red cards out of 51.

For each situation below, use the Fundamental Counting Principle to determine the number of possible outcomes. Verify each using either a chart or a tree diagram.

6. $6 \cdot 2 = 12$ outcomes (can use a chart or tree diagram)

7. $3 \cdot 3 = 9$ outcomes (can use a chart or tree diagram)

8. $2 \cdot 2 \cdot 2 = 8$ outcomes (use a tree diagram)

9. $2 \cdot 26 = 52$ outcomes (can use chart or tree diagram)

6. roll one die and flip one coin

7. playing *Rock, Paper, Scissors*

8. flipping three coins

9. pair a digit 1 or 2 with a letter A–Z

10. form a two-digit number: select a digit 1 to 4, select a digit from those remaining $4 \cdot 3 = 12$ outcomes (can use a chart or tree diagram)

▶ **Exercise 4b** Explain to students that it is important to know that after Dana chooses a card that it is returned to the deck. Otherwise, more than half of the remaining cards would be red. (There would only be 51 cards, 26 of which are red.)

▶ **Exercise 5c** Ask students how they arrived at the answer for this part of the exercise.

▶ **Exercises 6–10** Have pairs work together to create the tree diagrams and/or charts to verify each of the answers they found using the Fundamental Counting Principle. Then have them share their charts/diagrams with the class.

▶ **Exercise 7** If students need a hint to get started, you might ask them how this exercise is similar to Exercise 6.

▶ **Exercise 9** If possible, demonstrate some possible outcomes by using letters *A – Z* written on slips of paper. Have them make a chart of the letters that also includes the digits. Make sure students understand how the chart represents all the possible combinations you might have.

▶ **Exercises 11–13** Have students create the tree diagrams and/or charts to verify each of the answers they found using the Fundamental Counting Principle. Then have them share their charts/diagrams with the class.

For each situation below, use the Fundamental Counting Principle to determine the number of possible outcomes.

11. selecting a card from a stack of face cards with aces and a card from a stack of number cards (ordinary card deck)
16 (face cards and Aces) · 36 (number cards) = 576 outcomes

12. making outfits with 6 shirts, 3 pants, 2 jackets and 2 shoes
6 · 3 · 2 · 2 = 72 outfits (outcomes)

13. selecting two students out of a class with 25 students
25 · 24 = 600 outcomes

14. Kristen has created a game using these six cards.

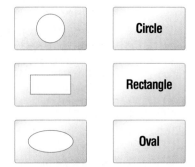

The three shape cards are placed face up. The three word cards are shuffled. One word card is placed face down next to each shape card. A player scores one point for each word card that matches a shape card.

a. Write all the possible arrangements of the three word cards. Use C to stand for the circle card, R to stand for the rectangle card, and O to stand for the oval card. How many possibilities are there?
CRO, COR, OCR, ORC, RCO, ROC; 6

b. What is the probability that a player will match all three word cards correctly? $\frac{1}{6}$

c. What is the probability that a player will match at least one word card correctly? $\frac{4}{6}$, or $\frac{2}{3}$

15. Cheyenne has written letters to four friends. They are Caroline, Raul, Jing, and Ernest. She has four envelopes, each with the name and address of one of the friends. Cheyenne's little brother wants to help, so he puts one letter in each envelope. Since he cannot read yet, he puts the letters in the envelopes at random.

a. How many ways can the letters and envelopes be paired?   24

b. What is the probability that everyone receives the correct letter? $\frac{1}{24}$

16. Life Science *Genes* determine many things about a person, including how he or she looks. For example, a person has two genes that determine eye color. The gene for blue eyes is *recessive*. The gene for brown eyes is *dominant*. This means that if a person has one blue-eye gene and one brown-eye gene, he or she has brown eyes. A person with two brown-eye genes also has brown eyes. To have blue eyes, both genes must be blue.

A child gets one eye-color gene from each parent. Assume the chances of passing either gene to a child are equal. For example, a father with one blue-eye gene and one brown-eye gene has a 50% chance of passing the blue-eye gene to his child.

a. Suppose two people are having a child. One has a blue-eye gene and a brown-eye gene. The other has two brown-eye genes. What is the probability that the child will have blue eyes? (Hint: You can find the possible gene combinations for the child by making a table or a tree diagram.)   0

b. Suppose the two parents both have one blue-eye gene and one brown-eye gene. What is the probability that the child will have blue eyes? $\frac{1}{4}$

c. Now suppose one of the parents has two blue-eye genes and the other has one blue-eye gene and one brown-eye gene. What is the probability that the child will have blue eyes? $\frac{1}{2}$

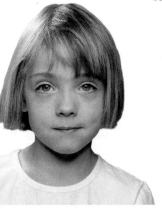

Real-World Link
Eye color is a genetic trait and is determined by the amount and type of pigment in the eye's iris.

▶ **Exercise 15** When you discuss Part a as a class, ask for a volunteer to go to the board to show how a table or tree diagram for this situation would look.

You might also ask students how a table or tree diagram can help in answers **Parts b** and **c**.

▶ **Exercise 16** Ask students to make a table similar to the answer for Exercise 6a on page 646.

▶ **Exercise 17** You may want students to verify how the entries are found for the table in Part a. Then have student pairs share their answers for Parts b–e.

Connect & Extend

17a.

	1	2	3	4	5	6	
	1,1	2,1	3,1	4,1	5,1	6,1	1
	1,2	2,2	3,2	4,2	5,2	6,2	2
	1,3	2,3	3,3	4,3	5,3	6,3	3
	1,4	2,4	3,4	4,4	5,4	6,4	4
	1,5	2,5	3,5	4,5	5,5	6,5	5
	1,6	2,6	3,6	4,6	5,6	6,6	6

17. Tavio is going to play a game where he needs to roll two dice. He wants to examine how many different ways the dice can land before he plays the game. He selects one red die and one green die so he can tell them apart as he collects his information.

a. Create a chart to show what the possibilities are as he rolls the two dice.   See margin.

b. How many possible outcomes are there for rolling two dice? Is this verified by the Fundamental Counting Principle?

c. What is the probability that Tavio will roll a 1 on at least one of the die?   11 outcomes have a 1, so $\frac{11}{36}$

d. In the chart, you found that one possible outcome is rolling a 1 on the red die and a 6 on the green die, or (1, 6). Another outcome is rolling a 6 on the red die and a 1 on the green die, or (6, 1). If your goal is to roll a sum of 7, then both of these outcomes are *favorable* outcomes. List all of the outcomes that result in a sum of 7 on the two dice.

e. What is the probability of rolling a sum of 7 when rolling two dice?   6 outcomes have a sum of 7, so $\frac{6}{36}$ or $\frac{1}{6}$.

Mixed Review

17b. There are 36 possible outcomes, which is verified by there being 6 possibilities for the first die and 6 possibilities for the second die, and $6 \cdot 6 = 36$.

17d. There are 6 ways to roll a sum of 7: (1,6), (2,5), (3,4), (4,3), (5,2), (6,1)

Find the area of each square, rectangle, parallelogram, and triangle.

18. 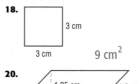   9 cm^2

19. 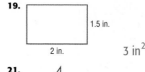   3 in^2

20. 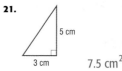   5 cm^2

21.   7.5 cm^2

Find the area of a square with the given side length.

22. 2 in.   4 in^2

23. $\frac{1}{2}$ cm $\frac{1}{4}$ cm^2

24. 12 in.   144 in^2

25. 10 in.   100 in^2

26. What is the area of a circle with a radius of 3.6 in.? Give your answer to the nearest hundredth square inch.   40.69 in^2

Find the volume of each rectangular prism given its dimensions.

27. $l = 2$ in.; $w = 5$ in.; $h = 6$ in.   60 in^3

28. $l = 2.5$ cm; $w = 8$ cm; $h = 3$ cm   60 cm^3

Which customary unit is most reasonable to measure the capacity of the following containers?

29. a pond   Gallons

30. a coffee cup   Cups

31. a child's bucket   Cups or pints

32. a baby pool   Gallons

Find the opposite of each number.

33. 2.4   −2.4

34. −5   5

35. −5.7   5.7

Find the absolute value of each expression.

36. |−3| 3

37. |2.1| 2.1

38. |−2.6| 2.6

Evaluate each expression.

39. |30 − 15| 15

40. |20 − 30| 10

41. |−16| − |16| 0

Give the coordinates of each point plotted on this grid.
$A(5, 6)$; $B(0, 3)$; $C(−2, 4)$; $D(−5, −3)$; $E(3, −7)$

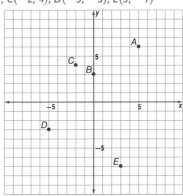

3. A bag contains three red blocks and two blue blocks. All the blocks are the same size. Luci reaches into the bag and removes two blocks. What is the probability that both blocks are red? $\frac{3}{10}$

Quick Check

Informal Assessment At the end of the lesson, students should be able to:

✔ make tree diagrams to show outcomes for situations involving independent or dependent choices

✔ count the number of possibilities using the counting principle

Quick Quiz

1. Diana spins Spinner 1 and then Spinner 2 to get random letter-number combinations.

a. Draw a tree diagram that shows all the possible outcomes.

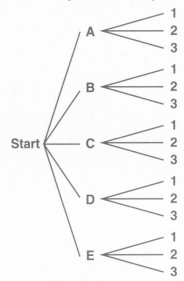

b. What is the probability of spinning a letter-number combination that begins with the letter C? $\frac{1}{5}$

2. The 4 of spades is drawn randomly from a standard deck of 52 playing cards and is replaced. What is the probability that the next card drawn is the 4 of hearts? $\frac{1}{52}$

Review & Self-Assessment

Chapter Summary
This summary helps students recall the major topics of the chapter.

Vocabulary
Students should be able to explain each of the terms listed in the vocabulary section.

▶ **Exercise 2c** Leah calculated the experimental probability correctly. However, Aretha's theoretical probability is more accurate in the sense that the theoretical probability is better than the experimental probability for making predictions.

Review & Self-Assessment

Chapter Summary

Probability is useful in many areas of life, from playing games to making plans based on weather predictions. In this chapter, you learned how to find *experimental* and *theoretical probabilities* for events in which the possible outcomes are *equally likely*.

You examined probabilities in several types of situations, including some in which the possible outcomes were not easy to determine. For certain games of chance, you came up with strategies for play based on your knowledge of probabilities. You also used *simulation* and tree diagrams to examine situations in which the number of possible outcomes were affected by what had previously happened.

Strategies and Applications

The questions in this section will help you review and apply the important ideas and strategies developed in this chapter.

Understanding probability

Aretha took the king of hearts and the king of clubs from a standard deck of cards, leaving only 50 cards. She told Leah that the probability of selecting a queen was now 8%. But she did not tell her how many or what cards she had removed.

1. What does it mean that the probability was 8%?

2. Leah selected a card from Aretha's deck, looked at it, and then put it back. Aretha shuffled the cards. They repeated this process until Leah had chosen a card 100 times.

   a. How many times would you expect Leah to have picked a queen? 8

   b. Leah chose a queen 7 times. She said that this means Aretha was wrong and that the actual probability is 7%. Aretha and Leah both calculated the probabilities they gave. Is either incorrect in her calculation? Explain.

   c. Whose is the more accurate probability, Leah's or Aretha's? Aretha's

   d. Leah kept selecting cards until she had 1,000 trials. She chose a queen 88 times. Aretha said, "The difference between the 88 queens you selected and the 80 you should have expected was 8. But the difference was only 1 when you drew 100 cards. Your experimental probability will be less accurate for the 1,000 draws than it was for the 100 draws."

   Is Aretha correct? Explain. See margin.

Vocabulary

distribution

equally likely

experimental
probability

Fundamental
Counting
Principle

histogram

probability

simulation

theoretical
probability

Venn diagram

1. Possible answers: 8% of the possible draws are queens; if you select a card several times, replacing the chosen card each time, you would expect to get a queen about 8% of the time.

2b. No; Aretha gave a theoretical probability based on what she knew were the possible outcomes. Leah gave an experimental probability based on the actual outcome of several trials.

Additional Answer

2d. No; Possible explanation: The experimental probability for the 1,000 draws is 8.8%, which is closer to 8% than 7% is. Although 8 is greater than 1, 8 is a smaller portion of 1,000 than 1 is of 100.

3. Possible answer:
Creating a table
and making a
tree diagram

First Spin

		B	W	G
Second Spin	B	BB	BW	BG
	W	WB	WW	WG
	G	GB	GW	GG

First   Second
Spin   Spin

Start
— B < B / W / G
— W < B / W / G
— G < B / W / G

6. No; Possible
explanation: The
dice do not
"remember" what
happened on
previous rolls.
Kenna's chances are
the same for the
next roll as they
were for the
previous rolls, $\frac{1}{6}$.

Identifying outcomes

3. Name two strategies for identifying the
outcomes of a probability situation. Illustrate
each strategy by using them to find the number
of outcomes for turning this spinner twice.

Finding probabilities of events

4. Josh said, "Suppose you roll a standard die. To calculate the
probability of getting a prime number, you have to divide 3
by 6, giving 0.5."   4a–c. See margin.

  a. Why did Josh choose 6 for the divisor?

  b. Why did Josh choose 3 for the dividend?

  c. Consider this *Rice Drop* game board. Explain why
the procedure for calculating the probability that
the rice lands in a shaded square is the same as
the one Josh used for getting a prime number on
a die roll.

Using probabilities to analyze games

5. A bag contains five slips of paper numbered 1 to 5. In the game *Find
the Difference*, each player chooses one of the cards below. Players take
turns drawing two numbers from the bag. If the difference of the
numbers is on the player's card, the player covers that difference. The
numbers are returned to the bag after each turn. The first player to
cover all his numbers wins.

Card A	
1	2
3	4

Card B	
1	2
2	1

Card C	
3	4
4	3

Which card gives a player the best chance of winning? Explain.
See margin.

Working with situations in which the probabilities depend on previous results

6. King and Kenna were playing a board game in which they rolled
two dice. Rolling the same number on both dice, lets you take an
extra turn. Kenna rolled two 3s and then two 5s. As she was getting
ready to take another extra turn, King said, "The chances of you
getting doubles again are next to nothing!" Is King correct? Explain
your answer.

Additional Answers

4a. Because there are six equally likely
possible outcomes. They are 1, 2, 3, 4,
5, and 6.

4b. Because three of the outcomes are
prime. They are 2, 3, and 5.

4c. There are six squares. Assuming the
rice is equally likely to land in each,
there are six equally likely outcomes,
just as in Josh's die roll. Since three of
the squares are shaded, there are
three possibilities that make the event
"the rice lands in a shaded square"
happen. Josh had three possibilities
that make the event "getting a prime
number" happen.

5. Possible answer: This list shows
the possible pairs and the
difference for each pair.

Difference	Pair
1	(1,2), (2,3), (3,4), (4,5), (2,1), (3,2), (4,3), (5,4)
2	(1,3), (2,4), (3,5), (3,1), (4,2), (5,3)
3	(1,4), (2,5), (4,1), (5,2)
4	(1,5), (5,1)

Here is the probability of
each difference. Probability of 1 is $\frac{8}{20}$.

Probability of 2 is $\frac{6}{20}$.

Probability of 3 is $\frac{4}{20}$.

Probability of 4 is $\frac{2}{20}$.

Since 1 and 2 are the most likely
differences, Card B is the best choice.

▶ **Exercise 8b** You may want to ask students whether the arrangement of the spaces on the wheel has any effect on the probability of winning a particular prize. Ask them how they know their answer is correct.

▶ **Exercises 9 and 10** You may need to remind students that the legs of a right triangle are the sides that form the right angle. You might also remind them that they can use 3.14 as an approximate value for π.

7. Describe a probability experiment in which the result of one trial changes the probabilities for the next trial's result. You might want to use dice, cards, spinners, or slips of paper drawn from a bag in your experiment.   Answers will vary.

Demonstrating Skills

8. At a fundraising carnival, Mario operated a game in which each player spun a wheel. The section on which the wheel stopped would indicate what prize, if any, the player won.

The table shows how many equal-sized spaces listed each type of prize as well as how many people won each prize by the end of the day.

	Key Chain	Troll Doll	Baseball Cap	Stuffed Animal	Beach Ball	No Prize
Number of Spaces	5	4	3	2	1	45
Number of Winners	14	16	13	6	3	148

a. Find an experimental probability of winning each prize.

b. Find the theoretical probability of winning each prize.

8a. Key chain: $\frac{14}{200}$, or 0.07; troll doll: $\frac{16}{200}$, or 0.08; baseball cap: $\frac{13}{200}$, or 0.065; stuffed animal: $\frac{6}{200}$, or 0.03; beach ball: $\frac{3}{200}$, or 0.015.

8b. Key chain: $\frac{5}{60}$, or about 0.083; troll doll: $\frac{4}{60}$, or about 0.067; baseball cap: $\frac{3}{60}$, or 0.05; stuffed animal: $\frac{2}{60}$, or about 0.033; beach ball: $\frac{1}{60}$, or about 0.017

9b. About 0.039

9c. Rose: about 0.114; Cari: about 0.102

Use the information below for Questions 9 and 10.

At the beginning of a computer game called *Geometry Bug*, players take turns choosing circles, squares, and triangles on the screen. After all the shapes have been chosen, a small "bug" appears and flies over the shapes. The bug lands on a random place on the screen. If it lands on one of the players' shapes, that player scores a point. The winner is the player with the most points after 50 landings.

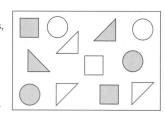

Rosa and Cari were playing with this screen. Rosa's shapes are purple, and Cari's shapes are white. The screen is eight inches wide and five inches high. The circles have a radius of $\frac{1}{2}$ inch. The squares have a side length of one inch. The triangles are right triangles with legs one inch long.

9. Consider probabilities for a single bug landing. Write your answers as decimals to the nearest thousandth.

a. What is the probability that the bug lands in Cari's square? 0.025

b. What is the probability that the bug lands in one of Rosa's circles?

c. Find each player's probability of scoring on a single bug landing.

Review & Self-Assessment
Chapter 10

10. The girls decide to play with an optional rule. When the bug lands on a shape, the shape is removed from the board. For example, if the bug lands on Cari's square, Cari scores a point but the square disappears.

a. Find the probability that the bug lands on one of Cari's triangles. 0.0375

b. Suppose the first shape the bug landed on was Cari's triangle in the bottom right. Now what is the probability that the bug lands on any of Cari's shapes? About 0.089

Test-Taking Practice

SHORT RESPONSE

1 Amber rolled a number cube 20 times. Her results are recorded in the table below. What was the experimental probability of Amber rolling a 6? What is the theoretical probability of rolling a 6?

Number on Number Cube	Number of Times Rolled
1	3
2	5
3	1
4	6
5	1
6	4

Show your work: Experimental probability of rolling a 6: $\frac{4}{20} = \frac{1}{5}$; the theoretical probability of rolling a 6: $\frac{1}{6}$

Answer: $\frac{1}{5}$; $\frac{1}{6}$

Show your work.

Answer ____________________

MULTIPLE CHOICE

2 A bag holds 4 blue marbles, 5 yellow marbles, and 3 green marbles. If a yellow marble is drawn on the first draw and not returned to the bag, what is the probability that the second marble drawn will be yellow?

A $\frac{1}{6}$

B $\frac{1}{3}$

(C) $\frac{4}{11}$

D $\frac{5}{12}$

3 What is the theoretical probability that a card drawn from a standard deck of 52 cards will be of the clubs suit?

F $\frac{1}{52}$

G $\frac{1}{13}$

(H) $\frac{1}{4}$

J $\frac{1}{2}$

Chapter 10 Review & Self-Assessment 657

Lesson 10.1, Develop & Understand: A (p. 580)

2a. (continued)

Miami Temperatures

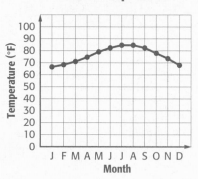

Chicago Temperatures

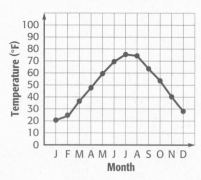

Fairbanks Temperatures

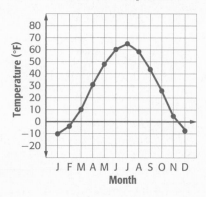

Lesson 10.1, Share & Summarize (p. 580)

① Possible letter:

Dear Smallville Police,

We think that Mr. Orkney and Agnes are in Miami, Florida. At first we didn't have much information, but since an atlas was found near the graphs, we thought maybe they had to do with population or temperatures or rainfall in different places. When we saw the scale labels, we were pretty confident that the graphs show temperatures over different months. We thought that maybe each graph represented a different place. When we saw the list and the note, we were able to match the cities with the graphs. The note indicated that Agnes needed a warmer climate. That information, and the fact that the note included a flight number, led us to the conclusion that Gerald Orkney flew to Miami to help Agnes. We hope you find this information useful.

Sincerely,

Data, Inc.

Lesson 10.1, Share & Summarize (p. 584)

Possible letter:

Dear Citizens for Safe Air:

We have analyzed information about hydrocarbon emissions in the United States from cars for the past several decades. We found that even though cars have been improved and now produce fewer hydrocarbons than in the 1960s and 1970s, cars are driven more. When you look at total hydrocarbon emissions, you can see an increase in the estimate from 2010 to 2015. We think the problem with hydrocarbons from cars may not be over. The United States needs to keep finding ways to reduce hydrocarbons from each car or to reduce the number of miles that people drive.

Sincerely,

Data, Inc.

Lesson 10.1, Share & Summarize (p. 587)

① Possible answer: A histogram shows the frequency or percent of data values in a particular interval. You could use a histogram to show the number of CDs at a music store that fall in various price ranges or to show the number of phone calls a help line receives at different times of the day.

② Possible answer: The bar graph shows the country each skier was from and the time for each individual skier. The bar graph allows you to easily compare times of individual skiers. The histogram does not show individual times or the countries the skiers were from, but it does show the number of times in each interval and gives a picture of how the data values are distributed.

Lesson 10.1, Mixed Review (p. 600)

26. $\frac{6}{5}$; 1.2

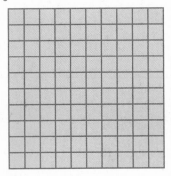 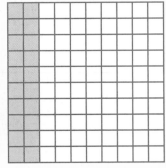

27. $\frac{3}{4}$; 0.75

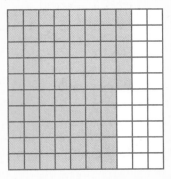

Lesson 10.2, On Your Own Exercises (p. 612)

4a. **Daylight Temperatures**

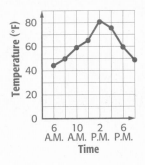

Lesson 10.4, Develop & Understand: B (p. 641)

6c.

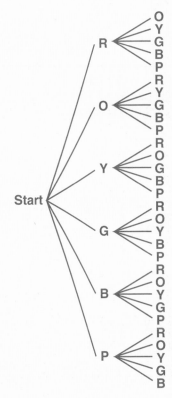

7.

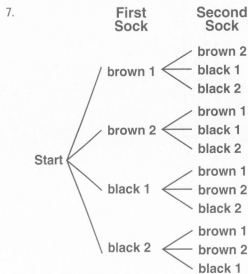

Glossary/Glosario

Cómo usar el glosario en español:

1. Busca el término en inglés que desees encontrar.
2. El término en español, junto con la definición, se encuentran en la columna de la derecha.

English

Español

A

absolute value (p. 513) The absolute value of a number is its distance from 0 on the number line, and is indicated by drawing a bar on each side of the number. For example, $|-20|$ means "the absolute value of -20." Since -20 and 20 are each 20 units from 0 on the number line, $|20| = 20$ and $|-20| = 20$.

valor absoluto (pág. 5) El valor absoluto de un número es su distancia desde 0 en la recta numérica, lo cual se indica trazando una barra en cada lado del número. Por ejemplo, $|-20|$ significa "el valor absoluto de -20." Como -20 y 20 se encuentran a 20 unidades de 0 en la recta numérica, $|20| = 20$ y $|-20| = 20$.

acute angle (p. 27) An angle that measures less than 90°. Each of the angles shown below is an acute angle.

ángulo agudo (pág. 27) Ángulo que mide menos de 90°. Cada uno de los siguientes es un ángulo agudo.

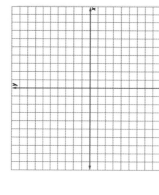

additive identity (p. 185) The sum of any number and 0 is the number. For any number a, $a + 0 = 0 + a = a$. Example: $6 + 0 = 0 + 6 = 6$

identidad aditiva (pág. 185) La suma de cualquier número más 0 es igual al número. Para cualquier número a, $a + 0 = 0 + a = a$. Ejemplo: $6 + 0 = 0 + 6 = 6$

additive inverse (p. 186) A number that when added to a given number results in a sum of zero. Example: The *additive inverse* of 4 is -4 because $4 + (-4) = 0$.

inverso aditivo (pág. 186) Número que sumado a otro da como resultado cero. Ejemplo: El *inverso aditivo* de 4 es -4 porque $4 + (-4) = 0$.

algebraic expression (p. 145) A rule written with numbers and symbols. Examples: $n + n + n + 2$, $3n + 2$.

expresión algebraica (pág. 145) Regla escrita con números y símbolos. Ejemplos: $n + n + n + 2$, $3n + 2$.

angle (p. 9) Two rays with the same endpoint. For example, the figure below is an angle.

ángulo (pág. 9) Dos rayos que parten del mismo punto. Por ejemplo, la siguiente figura muestra un ángulo.

Rayo 2
Rayo 1

area (p. 398) The amount of space inside a two-dimensional shape.

área (pág. 398) La cantidad de espacio dentro de una figura bidimensional.

associative property (p. 178) The way in which three numbers are grouped when they are added or multiplied does not change their sum or product. For any numbers a, b, and c, $(a + b) + c = a + (b + c)$, and $(ab)c = a(bc)$. Example: $(2 + 3) + 4 = 2 + (3 + 4)$ or $(2 \cdot 3) \cdot 5 = 2 \cdot (3 \cdot 5)$.

propiedad asociativa (pág. 178) La forma en que se agrupan tres números cuando se suman o multiplican no altera el resultado. Sean cuales fueren los números a, b, y c, $(a + b) + c = a + (b + c)$, y $(ab)c = a(bc)$. Ejemplo: $(2 + 3) + 4 = 2 + (3 + 4)$ ó $(2 \cdot 3) \cdot 5 = 2 \cdot (3 \cdot 5)$.

axes (p. 469) The horizontal line and vertical line that are used to represent the variable quantities on a graph. For example, in the graph below, the horizontal axis represents width and the vertical axis represents length.

ejes (pág. 469) La recta horizontal y la recta vertical que se usan para representar las cantidades variables en una gráfica. Por ejemplo, en la siguiente gráfica el eje horizontal representa longitud.

B

backtracking (p. 548) The process of using a flowchart to work backward, starting with the output and undoing each operation to find the input.

vuelta atrás (pág. 548) El proceso de usar un flujograma para trabajar en sentido inverso, comenzando con la salida y anulando cada operación hasta llegar a la entrada.

base of a parallelogram (p. 410) Any of the sides of a parallelogram. The base of a parallelogram is used in computing its area.

base de un paralelogramo (pág. 410) Cualquiera de los lados de un triángulo. La base de un paralelogramo se usa para calcular su área.

base of a prism (p. 437) The parallel faces of a prism.

base de un prisma (pág. 437) Las caras paralelas de un prisma.

base of a triangle (p. 413) Any of the sides of a triangle. The base of a triangle is used in computing its area.

base de un triángulo (pág. 413) Cualquiera de los lados de un triángulo. La base de un triángulo se usa para calcular su área.

Glossary/Glosario

C

chord (p. 44) A segment connecting two points on a circle. (See the figure in the glossary entry for radius. This figure shows a chord of a circle.)

circumference (p. 44) The perimeter of a circle (distance around a circle).

commutative property (p. 176) The order in which two numbers are added or multiplied does not change their sum or product. For any numbers a and b, $a + b = b + a$ and $ab = ba$. Example: $2 + 3 = 3 + 2$ or $2 \cdot 3 = 3 \cdot 2$.

concave polygon (p. 12) A polygon that looks like it is "collapsed" or has a "dent" on one or more sides. Any polygon with an angle measuring more than 180° is concave. The figures below are concave polygons.

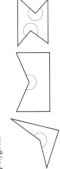

congruent (p. 321) Having the same size and the same shape.

coordinates (p. 491) Numbers that represent the location of a point on a graph. For example, if a point is 3 units to the right and 7 units up from the origin, its coordinates are 3 and 7.

corresponding angles (p. 328) Angles of two similar figures that are located in the same place in each figure. For example, in the figure, angle *B* and angle *E* are corresponding angles.

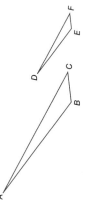

---

corresponding sides (p. 328) Sides of two similar figures that are located in the same place in each figure. For example, in the figure in the glossary entry for corresponding angles, sides *AB* and *DE* are corresponding sides.

counterexample (p. 324) In testing a conjecture, an example for which the conjecture is not true.

D

diameter (p. 44) A chord that passes through the center of a circle. Diameter also refers to the distance across a circle through its center. (See the figure in the glossary entry for radius. This figure shows a diameter of a circle.)

distribution (p. 586) The distribution of a data set shows how the data are spread out, where there are gaps, where there are lots of values, and where there are only a few values.

distributive property (p. 181) To multiply a sum by a number, multiply each addend of the sum by the number outside the parentheses. For any numbers a, b, and c, $a(b + c) = ab + ac$ and $a(b - c) = ab - ac$. Example: $2(5 + 3) = (2 \cdot 5) + (2 \cdot 3)$ and $2(5 - 3) = (2 \cdot 5) - (2 \cdot 3)$.

E

equally likely (p. 621) Outcomes of a situation or experiment that have the same probability of occurring. For example, if one coin is tossed, coming up heads and coming up tails are equally likely outcomes.

equation (p. 534) A mathematical sentence stating that two quantities have the same value. An equal sign, =, is used to separate the two quantities. For example, $5 + 8 - 3 = 10$ is an equation.

equivalent fractions (p. 62) Fractions that describe the same portion of a whole, or name the same number. For example, $\frac{3}{4}$, $\frac{9}{12}$, and $\frac{30}{40}$ are equivalent fractions.

C

cuerda (pág. 44) Segmento que conecta dos puntos en un círculo. (Ver la figura en el inciso del glosario para radio. Dicha figura muestra una cuerda de un círculo.)

circunferencia (pág. 44) El perímetro de un círculo (distancia alrededor del círculo).

propiedad conmutativa (pág. 176) El orden en que se suman o multiplican dos números no altera el resultado. Sean cuales fueren los números a y b, $a + b = b + a$ y $ab = ba$. Ejemplo: $2 + 3 = 3 + 2$ ó $2 \cdot 3 = 3 \cdot 2$.

polígono cóncavo (pág. 12) Polígono que parece que se hubiera "hundido" o que tiene una hendidura en uno o más de sus lados. Cualquier polígono con un ángulo mayor que 180° es cóncavo. Las siguientes figuras son polígonos cóncavos.

congruente (pág. 321) Que tiene el mismo tamaño y la misma forma.

coordenadas (pág. 491) Números que representan la posición de un punto en una gráfica. Por ejemplo, si un punto se encuentra a 3 unidades a la derecha y 7 unidades hacia arriba del origen, sus coordenadas son 3 y 7.

ángulos correspondientes (pág. 328) Ángulos de dos figuras semejantes ubicadas en el mismo lugar en cada figura. Por ejemplo: En la figura, el ángulo *B* y el ángulo *E* son ángulos correspondientes.

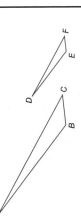

---

lados correspondientes (pág. 328) Lados de dos figuras semejantes ubicados en el mismo lugar en cada figura. Por ejemplo, en la figura de la definición de ángulos correspondientes del glosario, los lados *AB* y *DE* son lados correspondientes.

contraejemplo (pág. 324) Al probar una conjetura, un ejemplo para el cual la conjetura no es verdadera.

D

diámetro (pág. 44) Cuerda que pasa por el centro de un círculo. El diámetro también se refiere a la distancia a través de un círculo, pasando por su centro. (Ver las figuras en el inciso del glosario para radio. Dicha figura muestra un diámetro de un círculo.)

distribución (pág. 586) La distribución de un conjunto de datos muestra la extensión de los datos, las brechas entre los datos, los lugares donde hay muchos valores y donde hay pocos valores.

propiedad distributiva (pág. 181) Para multiplicar una suma por un número, multiplíquese cada sumando de la suma por el número que está fuera del paréntesis. Sean cuales fueren los números a, b y c, $a(b + c) = ab + ac$ y $a(b - c) = ab - ac$. Ejemplo: $2(5 + 3) = (2 \cdot 5) + (2 \cdot 3)$ y $2(5 - 3) = (2 \cdot 5) - (2 \cdot 3)$.

E

equiprobables (pág. 621) Resultados de una situación o experimento que tienen la misma posibilidad de ocurrir. Por ejemplo, si se lanza una moneda, es equiprobable que la moneda caiga mostrando cara o escudo.

ecuación (pág. 534) Enunciado matemático que establece que dos cantidades tienen el mismo valor. Se usa un signo de igualdad, =, para comparar las dos cantidades. Por ejemplo, $5 + 8 - 3 = 10$ es una ecuación.

fracciones equivalents (pág. 62) Fracciones que describen la misma parte de un todo o que representan el mismo número. Por ejemplo, $\frac{3}{4}$, $\frac{9}{12}$, y $\frac{30}{40}$ son fracciones equivalentes.

equivalent ratios (p. 327) Two different ratios that represent the same relationship. For example, 1:3 and 4:12 are equivalent ratios.

experimental probability (p. 619) A probability based on experimental data. An experimental probability is always an estimate and can vary depending on the particular set of data that is used.

exponent (p. 114) A small, raised number that tells how many times a factor is multiplied. For example, in 10^3, the exponent 3 tells you to multiply 3 factors of 10: $10 \cdot 10 \cdot 10 = 1,000$.

F

factor (p. 114) A factor of a whole number is another whole number that divides into it without a remainder. For example, 1, 2, 3, 4, 6, 8, 12, and 24 are factors of 24.

flowchart (p. 547) A diagram, using ovals and arrows, that shows the steps for going from an input to an output. For example, the diagram below is a flowchart.

formula (p. 42) An algebraic "recipe" that shows how to calculate a particular quantity. For example, $F = \frac{9}{5}C + 32$ is the formula for converting Celsius temperatures to Fahrenheit temperatures.

fundamental counting principle (p. 645) If an event M can occur in m ways and is followed by an event N that can occur in n ways, then event M followed by event N can occur in $m \times n$ ways.

razones equivalents (pág. 327) Dos razones diferentes que representan la misma relación. Por ejemplo: 1:3 y 4:12 son razones equivalentes.

probabilidad experimental (pág. 619) Probabilidad que se basa en datos experimentales. Una probabilidad experimental es siempre una estimación y puede variar según el conjunto de datos en particular que se usen.

exponente (pág. 114) Número pequeño y elevado que indica cuántas veces se multiplica un factor. Por ejemplo, en 10^3, el exponente 3 te indica que multipliques 3 factores de 10: $10 \cdot 10 \cdot 10 = 1,000$.

factor (pág. 114) Un factor de un número entero es otro número entero que lo divide sin que quede un residuo. Por ejemplo, 1, 2, 3, 4, 6, 8, 12 y 24 son factores de 24.

flujograma (pág. 547) Diagrama que usa óvalos y flechas para mostrar los pasos a seguir desde un dato de entrada hasta uno de salida. Por ejemplo, el siguiente diagrama es un flujograma.

formula (pág. 42) Una "receta" algebraica que muestra cómo calcular una cantidad dada. Por ejemplo: $F = \frac{9}{5}C + 32$ es la formula para convertir temperaturas Celsius en temperaturas Fahrenheit.

principio fundamental de conteo (pág. 645) Si un suceso M puede darse en m formas y es seguido por un suceso N que puede darse en n formas, entonces el suceso M seguido por el suceso N puede darse en $m \times n$ formas.

G

guess-check-and-improve (p. 560) A method for solving an equation that involves first guessing the solution, then checking the guess by substituting into the original equation, and then using the result to improve the guess until the correct solution is found.

H

height of a parallelogram (p. 410) The distance from the side opposite the base of a parallelogram to the base. The height of a parallelogram is always measured along a segment perpendicular to the base (or to the line containing the base). The figures below show a base and the corresponding height for three parallelograms.

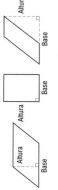

height of a triangle (p. 413) The distance from the base of a triangle to the vertex opposite the base. The height of a triangle is always measured along a segment perpendicular to the base (or the line containing the base). The figures below show a base and the corresponding height for three triangles.

histogram (p. 585) A bar graph in which data are divided into equal intervals, with a bar for each interval. The height of each bar shows the number of data values in that interval.

conjetura, verifica y mejora (pág. 560) Método para resolver una ecuación que implica primero hacer una conjetura, verificar la conjetura y sustituirla en la ecuación original y luego usar el resultado para mejorar la conjetura hasta hallar la solución correcta.

altura de un paralelogramo (pág. 410) La distancia desde el lado opuesto a la base de un paralelogramo, hasta la base. La altura de un paralelogramo se mide siempre a lo largo de un segmento perpendicular a la base (o a la recta que contiene la base). Las siguientes figuras muestran una base y la altura correspondiente de tres paralelogramos.

altura de un triángulo (pág. 413) La distancia desde la base de un triángulo hasta el vértice opuesto a la base. La altura de un triángulo se mide siempre a lo largo de un segmento perpendicular a la base (o de la recta que contiene la base). Las siguientes figuras muestran una base y la altura correspondiente de tres triángulos.

histograma (pág. 585) Gráfica de barras en la cual los datos se dividen en intervalos iguales, con una barra para cada intervalo. La altura de cada barra muestra el número de valores de los datos en ese intervalo.

Glossary/Glosario

I

improper fraction (p. 60) A fraction that has a numerator that is greater than or equal to the denominator. Examples: $\frac{21}{4}, \frac{2}{1}$.

identity element (p. 176) An addend of zero or a factor of one in the real number system. When a number is added to zero or multiplied by one, the result is the original number.

identity property of multiplication (p. 185) The product of a factor and one is the factor. Example: $5 \cdot 1 = 5$

inequality (p. 535) A mathematical sentence stating that two quantities have different values. For example, $5 + 9 > 12$ is an inequality. The symbols $<$, $>$, and $\neq$ are used in writing inequalities.

input (p. 113) The value that is substituted into an expression. In a flowchart, it is represented by the oval on the left side.

intersecting lines (p. 30) Lines that are coplanar and have exactly one point in common.

inverse element (p. 176) The opposite of a number for addition and the reciprocal of the number for multiplication. For any nonzero number n, $-n$ is the additive inverse and $\frac{1}{n}$ is the multiplicative inverse.

L

line graph (p. 479) A graph in which points are connected with line segments.

line plot (p. 266) A number line with X's indicating the number of times each data value occurs.

---

fracción impropia (pág. 60) Fracción que tiene un numerador que es mayor o igual al denominador. Ejemplos: $\frac{21}{4}, \frac{2}{1}$.

elemento identidad (pág. 176) Sumando de cero o un factor de uno en un sistema de números reales. Cuando a cero se le suma un número o cuando cero se multiplica por uno, el resultado es el número original.

propiedad de identidad de la multiplicación (pág. 185) El producto de un factor y uno es igual al factor. Ejemplo: $5 \cdot 1 = 5$

desigualdad (pág. 535) Enunciado matemático que establece que dos cantidades tienen distintos valores. Por ejemplo, $5 + 9 > 12$ es una desigualdad. Los símbolos $<$, $>$, y $\neq$ se usan para escribir desigualdades.

entrada (pág. 113) Valor que se reemplaza en una expresión. En un flujograma, se representa por el óvalo en el lado izquierdo.

rectas secantes (pág. 30) Rectas que son coplanares y tienen exactamente un punto en común.

elemento inverso (pág. 176) El opuesto de un número para la adición y el recíproco del número para la multiplicación. Para cualquier número no nulo n, $-n$ es el inverso aditivo y $\frac{1}{n}$ es el inverso multiplicativo.

gráfica lineal (pág. 479) Gráfica en la cual los puntos se conectan con segmentos de recta.

esquema lineal (pág. 266) Recta numérica que contiene equis que indican el número de veces que ocurre cada valor de los datos.

---

line symmetry (p. 12) A polygon has line symmetry (or reflection symmetry) if you can fold it in half along a line so that the two halves match exactly. The polygons below have line symmetry. The lines of symmetry are shown as dashed lines.

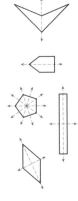

lowest terms (p. 62) A fraction is in lowest terms if its numerator and denominator are relatively prime. For example, $\frac{5}{6}$ is in lowest terms because the only common factor of 5 and 6 is 1.

M

mean (p. 270) The number you get by distributing the total of the values in a data set among the members of the data set. You can compute the mean by adding the values and dividing the total by the number of values. For example, for the data 5, 6, 6, 8, 8, 8, 9, 10, 12, the total of the values is 72 and there are 9 values, so the mean is $72 \div 9 = 8$.

median (p. 266) The middle value when all the values in a data set are ordered from least to greatest. For example, for the data set 4.5, 6, 7, 7, 8.5, 10.5, 12, 12, 14.5, the median is 8.5.

mixed number (p. 60) A whole number and a fraction. For example, $12\frac{3}{4}$ is a mixed number.

mode (p. 266) The value in a data set that occurs most often. For example, for the data set 4.5, 6, 7, 7, 7, 8.5, 10.5, 12, 12, the mode is 7.

---

simetría lineal (pág. 12) Un polígono tiene simetría lineal (o simetría de reflexión) si se puede doblar por la mitad a lo largo de una línea de modo que las dos mitades coincidan exactamente. Los siguientes polígonos tienen simetría lineal. Los ejes de simetría se muestran como líneas punteadas.

en términos reducidos o reducida (pág. 62) Una fracción está en términos reducidos o reducida si su numerador y denominador son primos relativos. Por ejemplo, $\frac{5}{6}$ está reducida dado que el único factor común de 5 y 6 es 1.

media (pág. 270) El número que se obtiene al distribuir el total de los valores en un conjunto de datos entre los miembros del conjunto de datos. Se puede calcular la media sumando los valores y luego dividiendo el total entre el número de valores. Por ejemplo, para los datos 5, 6, 6, 8, 8, 8, 9, 10, 12, el total de los valores es 72 y hay 9 valores, de modo que la media es $72 \div 9 = 8$.

mediana (pág. 266) El valor central cuando todos los valores en un conjunto de datos se ordenan de menor a mayor. Por ejemplo, para el conjunto de datos 4.5, 6, 7, 7, 8.5, 10.5, 12, 12, 14.5, la mediana es 8.5.

número mixto (pág. 60) Un número entero y una fracción. Por ejemplo, $12\frac{3}{4}$ es un número mixto.

moda (pág. 266) El valor en un conjunto de datos que ocurre con más frecuencia. Por ejemplo, para el conjunto de datos 4.5, 6, 7, 7, 7, 8.5, 10.5, 12, 12, la moda es 7.

N

negative number (p. 509) A number that is less than 0. For example, −18 (read "negative eighteen") is a negative number.

número negativo (pág. 509) Un número menor que 0. Por ejemplo, −18 (que se lee "dieciocho negativo") es un número negativo.

O

obtuse angle (p. 27) An angle that measures more than 90° and less than 180°. Each of the angles shown below is an obtuse angle.

ángulo obtuso (pág. 27) Ángulo que mide más de 90° y menos de 180°. Cada uno de los siguientes ángulos es un ángulo obtuso.

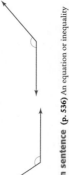

open sentence (p. 536) An equation or inequality that can be true or false depending on the value of the variable. For example, $5 + n = 20$ is an open sentence.

enunciado abierto (pág. 536) Ecuación de desigualdad que puede ser verdadera o falsa dependiendo del valor de la variable. Por ejemplo, $5 + n = 20$ es un enunciado abierto.

opposites (p. 510) Two numbers that are the same distance from 0 on the number line, but on different sides of 0. For example, 35 and −35 are opposites.

opuestos (pág. 510) Dos números equidistantes de 0 en la recta numérica, pero en lados opuestos de 0. Por ejemplo, 35 y −35 son opuestos.

order of operations (p. 126) A convention for reading and evaluating expressions. The order of operations says that expressions should be evaluated in this order:
- Evaluate any expressions inside parentheses and above and below fraction bars.
- Evaluate all exponents, including squares.
- Do multiplications and divisions from left to right.
- Do additions and subtractions from left to right.

For example, to evaluate $5 + 3 \times 7$, you multiply first and then add: $5 + 3 \times 7 = 5 + 21 = 26$. To evaluate $10^2 - 6 \div 3$, you evaluate the exponent first, then divide, then subtract: $10^2 - 6 \div 3 = 100 - 2 = 98$.

orden de las operaciones (pág. 126) Una convención para leer y evaluar expresiones. El orden de las operaciones indica que las expresiones se deben evaluar en el siguiente orden:
- Evalúa cualquier expresión entre paréntesis y sobre y debajo de barras de fracciones.
- Evalúa todos los exponentes, incluyendo los cuadrados.
- Efectúa las multiplicaciones y las divisiones de izquierda a derecha.
- Efectúa las sumas y las restas de izquierda a derecha.

Por ejemplo, para evaluar $5 + 3 \times 7$, multiplica primero y luego suma. $5 + 3 \times 7 = 5 + 21 = 26$. Para evaluar $10^2 - 6 \div 3$, evalúa primero el exponente, luego divide y por último resta. $10^2 - 6 \div 3 = 100 - 2 = 98$.

ordered pair (p. 491) A pair of numbers that represent the coordinates of a point, with the horizontal coordinate of the point written first. For example, the point with horizontal coordinate 3 and vertical coordinate 7 is represented by the ordered pair (3, 7).

par ordenado (pág. 491) Un par de números que representa las coordenadas de un punto, en el cual la coordenada horizontal del punto se escribe primero. Por ejemplo, el punto con la coordenada horizontal 3 y coordenada vertical 7 se representa con el par ordenado (3, 7).

origin (p. 469) The point where the axes of a graph meet. The origin of a graph is usually the 0 point for each axis.

origen (pág. 469) El lugar donde se encuentran los ejes de una gráfica. El origen de una gráfica es por lo general el punto 0 de cada eje.

outlier (p. 274) A value that is much greater than or much less than most of the other values in a data set. For example, for the data set 6, 8.2, 9.5, 11.6, 14, 30, the value 30 is an outlier.

valor atípico (pág. 274) Un valor que es mucho mayor o mucho menor que la mayoría de los otros valores en un conjunto de datos. Por ejemplo, para el conjunto de datos 6, 8.2, 9.5, 11.6, 14, 30, el valor 30 es un valor atípico.

output (p. 113) The result of a mathematical action or series of actions. In a flowchart, it is represented by the oval on the right side.

salida (pág. 113) Resultado de una acción o serie de acciones matemáticas. En un flujograma, se representa por el óvalo en el lado derecho.

P

parallelogram (p. 410) A quadrilateral with opposite sides that are the same length. The opposite sides of a parallelogram are parallel. Each of the figures shown below is a parallelogram.

paralelogramo (pág. 410) Cuadrilátero cuyos lados opuestos tienen la misma longitud. Los lados opuestos de un paralelogramo son paralelos. Cada una de las siguientes figuras es un paralelogramo.

percent (p. 349) Percent means "out of 100." A percent represents a number as a part out of 100 and is written with a percent sign. For example, 39% means 39 out of 100, or $\frac{39}{100}$ or 0.39.

por ciento, porcentaje (pág. 349) Por ciento significa "de cada 100". Un por ciento representa un número como una parte de 100 y se escribe con un signo de porcentaje. Por ejemplo, 39% significa 39 de cada 100 ó $\frac{39}{100}$ ó 0.39.

perfect square (p. 404) A number that is equal to a whole number multiplied by itself. In other words, a perfect square is the result of squaring a whole number. For example, 1, 4, 9, 16, and 25 are perfect squares since these are the results of squaring 1, 2, 3, 4, and 5, in that order.

cuadrado perfecto (pág. 404) Número que es igual a un número entero multiplicado por sí mismo. Es decir, un cuadrado perfecto es el resultado de elevar al cuadrado un número entero. Por ejemplo, 1, 4, 9, 16 y 25 son cuadrados perfectos, dado que son el resultado de elevar al cuadrado 1, 2, 3, 4 y 5, en ese orden.

perimeter (p. 40) The distance around a two-dimensional shape.

perímetro (pág. 40) La distancia alrededor de una figura bidimensional.

Glossary/Glosario

perpendicular (p. 27) Two lines or segments that form a right angle area are said to be perpendicular. For example, see the figures below.

Perpendicular Lines   Perpendicular Segments

polygon (p. 4) A flat (two-dimensional) geometric figure that has these characteristics:
- It is made of straight line segments.
- Each segment touches exactly two other segments, one at each of its endpoints.

The shapes below are polygons.

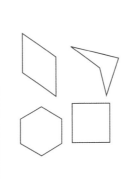

positive number (p. 509) A number that is greater than 0. For example, 28 is a positive number.

prism (p. 435) A figure that has two identical, parallel faces that are polygons, and other faces that are parallelograms.

perpendicular (pág. 27) Se dice que dos rectas o segmentos que forman un ángulo recto son perpendiculares. Por ejemplo, observa las siguientes figuras.

Rectas Perpendiculares   Segmento Perpendiculares

polígono (pág. 4) Figura geométrica plana (bidimensional) que posee las siguientes tres características:
- Está compuesta de segmentos de recta.
- Cada segmento interseca exactamente otros dos segmentos, uno en cada uno de sus extremos.

Las siguientes figuras son polígonos.

número positivo (pág. 509) Número mayor que 0. Por ejemplo, 28 es un número positivo.

prisma (pág. 435) Figura con dos caras paralelas idénticas, las cuales son polígonos, y otras dos caras que son paralelogramos.

---

probability (p. 618) The chance that an event will happen, described as a number between 0 and 1. For example, the probability of tossing a coin and getting heads is $\frac{1}{2}$ or 50%. A probability of 0 or 0% means the event has no chance of happening, and a probability of 1 or 100% means the event is certain to happen.

property (p. 174) A statement that is true for any number or variables.

protractor (p. 25) An instrument used to measure angles.

quadrants (p. 519) One of the four sections created by the axes on the coordinate plane.

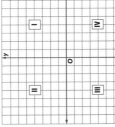

radius (plural: radii) (p. 44) A segment from the center of a circle to a point on a circle. Radius also refers to the distance from the center to a point on a circle. The figure below shows a chord, a diameter, and a radius of a circle.

Chord   Radius   Diameter

probabilidad (pág. 618) La oportunidad de que un evento ocurra, descrita como un número entre 0 y 1. Por ejemplo, la probabilidad de lanzar una moneda y que ésta caiga mostrando cara es de $\frac{1}{2}$ ó 50%. Una probabilidad de 0 ó 0% significa que el evento no tiene oportunidad de ocurrir y una probabilidad de 1 ó 100% significa que el evento ocurrirá con seguridad.

propiedad (pág. 174) Enunciado verdadero para números o variables.

transportador (pág. 25) Instrumento que se usa para medir ángulos.

cuadrante (pág. 519) Una de las cuatro secciones creadas por los ejes en el plano de coordenadas.

radio (pág. 44) Un segmento desde el centro del círculo hasta un punto del mismo. Radio también se refiere a la distancia desde el centro hasta un punto del círculo. La siguiente figura muestra una cuerda, un diámetro y un radio de un círculo.

Cuerda   Radio   Diámetro

range (p. 266) The difference between the minimum and maximum values of a data set. For example, for the data set 4.5, 6, 7, 7, 7, 8.5, 10.5, 12, 12, the range is 12 − 4.5 = 7.5.

rango (pág. 266) La diferencia entre los valores mínimo y máximo en un conjunto de datos. Por ejemplo, para el conjunto de datos 4.5, 6, 7, 7, 7, 8.5, 10.5, 12, 12, el rango es 12 − 4.5 = 7.5.

ratio (p. 291) A way to compare two numbers. For example, when one segment is twice as long as another, the ratio of the length of the longer segment to the length of the shorter segment is 2 to 1, or 2 : 1.

razón (pág. 291) Una manera de comparar dos números. Por ejemplo: cuando un segmento es el doble de largo que otro segmento, la razón de la longitud del segmento más largo al segmento más corto es 2 a 1 ó 2 : 1.

rational numbers (p. 358) Numbers that can be written as ratios of two integers. In decimal form, *rational numbers* are terminating or repeating. For example, 5, −0.274, and $0.\overline{3}$ are rational numbers.

números racionales (pág. 358) Números que se pueden escribir como razones de dos enteros. En forma decimal, *los números racionales* son números terminales o periódicos. Por ejemplo: 5, −0.274 y $0.\overline{3}$ son números racionales.

reciprocal (p. 231) Two numbers are reciprocals if their product is 1. For example, the reciprocal of $\frac{5}{7}$ is $\frac{7}{5}$.

recíproco (pág. 231) Dos números son recíprocos si su producto es 1. Por ejemplo, el recíproco de $\frac{5}{7}$ es $\frac{7}{5}$.

rectangular prism (p. 435) A solid figure that has two pairs of parallel opposite faces and congruent bases that are all rectangles.

prisma rectangular (pág. 435) Figura sólida que tiene dos pares de caras opuestas paralelas y bases congruentes que son rectángulos.

reference line (p. 25) The line that goes through 0° on a protractor.

línea de referencia (pág. 25) Línea que pasa por 0° en un transportador.

regular polygon (p. 12) A polygon with sides that are all the same length and angles that are all the same size. The shapes below are regular polygons.

polígono regular (pág. 12) Polígono cuyos lados son todos de la misma longitud y cuyos ángulos tienen la misma medida. Las siguientes figuras son polígonos regulares.

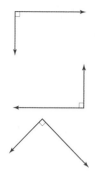

repeating decimal (p. 95) A decimal with a pattern of digits that repeat without stopping. For example, 0.232323 ... is a repeating decimal. Repeating decimals are usually written with a bar over the repeating digits, so 0.232323 ... can be written as $0.\overline{23}$.

decimal periódico (pág. 95) Decimal con un patrón de dígitos que se repiten indefinidamente. Por ejemplo, 0.232323 ... es un decimal periódico. Los decimales periódicos por lo general se escriben con una barra sobre los dígitos que se repiten, de este modo, 0.232323 ... se puede escribir como $0.\overline{23}$.

right angle (p. 27) An angle that measures exactly 90°. Right angles are often marked with a small square at the vertex. Each angle shown below is a right angle.

ángulo recto (pág. 27) Ángulo que mide exactamente 90°. Los ángulos rectos por lo regular se marcan con un cuadrado en el vértice. Cada ángulo siguiente es un ángulo recto.

S

sector (p. 422) A region of a circle bounded by a central angle and its corresponding arc.

sector (pág. 27) Región de un círculo limitada por un ángulo central y su arco correspondiente.

sequence (p. 122) An ordered list. For example, 2, 5, 8, 11, 14, 17 is a sequence.

sucesión (pág. 122) Lista ordenada. Por ejemplo, 2, 5, 8, 11, 14, 17 es una sucesión.

similar (p. 321) Having the same shape but possibly different sizes.

semejante (pág. 321) Que tiene la misma forma, pero posiblemente tamaños diferentes.

simulation (p. 639) An experiment in which you use different items to represent the items in a real situation. For example, to simulate choosing markers and looking at their colors, you can write the color of each marker on a slip of paper and put all the slips into a bag. You can simulate choosing markers by drawing slips from the bag. Mathematically, the situations are identical.

simulacro (pág. 639) Un experimento que usa diferentes artículos para representar una situación real. Por ejemplo, en un simulacro para elegir marcadores y verificar sus colores, puedes escribir el color de cada marcador en tiras de papel y colocar las tiras en una bolsa. Saca tiras de la bolsa para llevar a cabo el experimento de escoger marcadores. Matemáticamente, las situaciones son idénticas.

solution (p. 536) A value of a variable that makes an equation true. For example, 4 is the solution of the equation 3n + 7 = 19.

solución (pág. 536) Un valor de una variable que hace verdadera una ecuación. Por ejemplo, 4 es la solución de la ecuación 3n + 7 = 19.

surface area (p. 434) The area of the exterior surface of an object, measured in square units.

área de superficie (pág. 434) El área de las superficies exteriores de un cuerpo, medida en unidades cuadradas.

Glossary/Glosario

T

terminating decimals (p. 92) A decimal whose digits end. Example: 0.2, −1.345

decimales finitos (pág. 434) Decimal que tiene fin, es decir, cuyos dígitos no se repiten. Ejemplo: 0.2, −1.345

term (p. 122) An item in a sequence. For example, 8 is a term in the sequence 2, 5, 8, 11, 14, 17.

término (pág. 122) Un artículo en una sucesión. Por ejemplo, 8 es un término de la sucesión 2, 5, 8, 11, 14, 17.

theoretical probability (p. 621) Probability calculated by reasoning about the situation. Since theoretical probabilities do not depend on experiments, they are always the same for a particular event.

probabilidad teórica (pág. 621) Probabilidad que se calcula mediante el razonamiento de la situación. Dado que las probabilidades teóricas no dependen de experimentos, son siempre idénticas para un evento en particular.

trapezoid (p. 416) A quadrilateral with exactly one pair of parallel opposite sides.

trapezoide (pág. 416) Cuadrilátero con exactamente un par de lados paralelos opuestos.

U

unit rate (p. 300) Term used when one of two quantities being compared is given in terms of one unit. Example: 65 miles per hour or $1.99 per pound.

tasa unitary (pág. 300) Término que se usa cuando una de dos cantidades bajo comparación se da en términos de una unidad. Ejemplo: 65 millas por hora o $1.99 por libra.

V

variables (p. 144) A quantity that varies, or changes. For example, in a problem about the sizes of buildings, the height and width of the buildings would be variables.

variable (pág. 144) Cantidad que varía o cambia. Por ejemplo, en un problema sobre el tamaño de edificios, la altura y el ancho de los edificios serían variables.

vertex (plural: vertices) (p. 6) A corner of a polygon, where two sides meet. Vertices are usually labeled with capital letters, such as A, B, and C for the vertices of a triangle.

vértice (pág. 6) La esquina de un polígono, donde se encuentran dos de sus lados. Por lo general, los vértices se designan con letras mayúsculas, como por ejemplo, A, B y C para los vértices de un triángulo.

vertical angles (p. 30) Opposite angles formed by the intersection of two lines. In the figure, the *vertical angles* are ∠1 and ∠3, and ∠2 and ∠4.

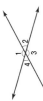

ángulos verticales (pág. 30) Ángulos opuestos formados por la intersección de dos rectas. En la figura, los *ángulos verticales* son ∠1 y ∠3, y ∠2 y ∠4.

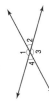

volume (p. 434) The space inside a three-dimensional object, measured in cubic units.

volumen (pág. 434) El espacio dentro de un cuerpo tridimensional, medido en unidades cúbicas.

Index

Index

Index

Photo Credits

While every effort has been made to secure permission for reproduction of copyright material, there may have been cases where we are unable to trace the copyright holder. Upon written notification, the publisher will gladly correct this in future printings.

Student Edition Photo Credits

viii Adrian Sherratt/Alamy; **ix** RubberBall/Alamy; **x** Thomas Fricke/Corbis; **xi** Klaus Tiedge; **xii** Hughes Martin/Corbis; **xiii** George Doyle & Ciaran Griffin; **xiv** Jose-Manuel Colomo/Alamy; **xv** Digital Vision/PunchStock; **xvi** Corbis; **xvii** Jack Hollingsworth; **2** Adrian Sherratt/Alamy; **3** Paul Bricknell/DRK/Getty Images; **5** Digital Vision/Alamy; **7** Veer Jim Barber/Photonica/Getty Images; **8** (tl)Photo and Co/Getty Images, (tr)Nikreates/Alamy, (cl)artpartner-images.com/Alamy, (cr)Robert Harding Picture Library Ltd/Alamy, (bl)Spencer Jones/PictureArts/Corbis, (br)Jupiter Images/Brand X/Alamy; **9** Robert Michael/Corbis; **11** Image Source Pink/Alamy; **13** Peter Arnold, Inc./Alamy; **17** Mazer Creative Services; **19** Photographer's Choice RF/Getty Images; **22** Image100/Corbis; **25** Photodisc/Getty Images; **27** ArkReligion.com/Alamy; **29** Steven May/Alamy; **33** Tatsuhiko Sawada/Getty Images; **41** Dag Sundberg/Getty Images; **42** Alex Cao/Digital Vision/Getty Images; **47** JSC Digital Image Collection; **49** Jurgen Vogt/Stone/Getty Images; **56** Image Source/Corbis; **57** Photodisc/Alamy; **60** Corbis Premium RF/Alamy; **61** Foodfolio/Alamy; **63** C Squared Studios/Getty Images; **67** Stockbyte/Alamy; **68** Ingram Publishing/Alamy; **69** D. Hurst/Alamy; **71** Francesco Ruggeri; **72** Asia Images Group/Alamy; **75** D. Hurst/Alamy; **76** ClassicStock/Alamy; **80** Image Source Pink/Alamy; **81** (l to r, t to b 8)Ingram Publishing/Alamy, (2)Mode Images Limited/Alamy, (3)Siede Preis/Getty Images, (4)Alex Cao, (5)Getty Images, (6)Photostock-Dieter Heinemann/Alamy, (7)D. Hurst/Alamy, (9)Tony Latham/Corbis, (10)Photodisc/Getty Images; **83** Mazer Creative Services; **84** Royalty-Free/Corbis; **85** RubberBall/Alamy; **86** (t)courtesy of D. Carr & H. Craighead/Cornell University, (b)John Foxx; **93** C Squared Studios/Getty Images; **98** Harvey Lloyd; **99** EPA/Corbis; **101** Glen Allison/Getty Images; **108** Thomas Fricke/Corbis; **109** ImageState/Alamy; **112** Radlund & Associates/Getty Images; **118** Royalty-Free/Corbis; **119** Brand X; **123** The Garden Picture Library/Alamy; **125,128** Siede Preis/Getty Images; **131** Pictorial Press Ltd/Alamy; **135** The McGraw-Hill Companies, Inc./Jacques Cornell photographer; **136** North Wind Picture Archives/Alamy; **138** IT Stock Free/Alamy; **154** Goodshoot/Corbis; **155** Comstock/PunchStock; **157** Mazer Creative Services; **160** Laurence Mouton; **164** Digital Archive Japan/Alamy; **165** Design Pics Inc./Alamy; **170** Richard Levine/Alamy; **172** Powered by Light/Alan Spencer/Alamy; **173** Brian North/Alamy; **174** Interfoto Pressebildagentur/Alamy; **176** David Young-Wolff; **183** Robert Harding Picture Library Ltd/Alamy; **184** Helene Rogers/Alamy; **186** Ingram Publishing/Alamy; **187** Digital Vision/Getty Images; **188** Jupiter Images/Brand X/Alamy; **198** Mira/Alamy; **204** D. Hurst/Alamy; **207** Studiohio; **208** Dorling Kindersley; **211** Mazer Creative Services/Texas Instruments; **214** Chuck Choi/Arcaid/Corbis; **216** Ryan McVay; **218** The Garden Picture Library/Alamy; **219** Michael & Patricia Fogden; **220** WR Publishing/Alamy; **223** DK Limited/Corbis; **225** Klaus Tiedge; **227** Luna; **228** D. Hurst/Alamy; **232** Wilfried Krecichwost; **235** graficart.net/Alamy; **238** Ingram Publishing (Superstock Limited)/Alamy; **239** Image Source Black/Alamy; **241** D. Hurst/Alamy; **245** GK Hart/Vikki Hart; **246** Mazer Creative Services/Texas Instruments; **248** Paul Springett/Alamy; **250** George Shelley/Corbis; **251** Hal Lott/Corbis; **252** Judith Collins/Alamy; **254** Robert Clare; **255** Rob Walls/Alamy; **257** ImageState/Alamy; **258** Transtock/Corbis; **260** Lawrence Manning/Corbis; **261** Norman Pogson/Alamy; **262** PhotoLink; **264** WidStock/Alamy; **265** Peter Adams/Corbis; **267** TongRo Image Stock/Alamy; **268** Stockbyte; **288** Hughes Martin/Corbis; **290** Tony Cordoza/Alamy; **298** David Buffington/Getty Images; **299** Judith Collins/Alamy; **301** Photodisc/Getty Images; **302** Robert Glusic/Getty Images; **305** Detail Photography/Alamy, (b)Brand X Pictures/PunchStock; **313** (t)ImageSource/Age Fotostock, (b)Corbis; **314** Image Source/Corbis; **315** Mazer Creative Services; **320** Corbis; **325** Comstock/Jupiter Images; **329** Corbis; **333** Nikreates/Alamy; **337** Phil Degginger/Alamy; **339** Travelshots.com/Alamy; **346** George Doyle & Ciaran Griffin; **347** David Cook/www.blueshiftstudios.co.uk/Alamy; **348** Ingram Publishing/Alamy; **351** Corbis Premium RF/Alamy; **353** Moodboard/Corbis; **354** Image Source Black; **355** Corbis; **360** Huw Jones/Alamy; **361** Mazer Creative Services; **363** (t)David Arky/Corbis, (b)Martin Moos; **365** Antonio M. Rosario; **366** GoGo Images Corporation/Alamy; **368** Don Farrall; **371** (t)Profimedia International S.R.O./Alamy, (b)Lew Robertson; **373** Comstock/Corbis; **375** Thomas Northcut; **377** Jeff Harris Photography; **378** Stockbyte/Getty Images; **379 through 381** Photodisc; **383** Archive Holdings Inc.; **385** Amy Neunsinger; **387** Foodfolio/Alamy; **389** Mazer Creative Services; **391** Peter Christopher/Masterfile; **395** (Siede Preis) Getty Images; **396** Jose-Manuel Colomo/Alamy; **397** Alex MacLean/JupiterImages; **398** magebroker/Alamy; **401** Old Paper Studios/Alamy; **403** Photodisc/Getty Images; **406** MM Productions/Corbis; **407** PhotoLink/Getty Images; **409** Thomas Northcut; **414** Image100/Corbis; **421** (tc)Ingram Publishing/Alamy, (tr) Burke/Triolo Productions/Jupiter Images, (bl)Jose Luis Pelaez Inc; **425** Stockdisc/Getty Images; **430** Comstock Images/Alamy; **432** Ron Niebrugge/Alamy; **440** Jeff Greenberg/Alamy; **444** Studiohio; **445** Mazer Creative Services; **455** Dave Lidwell/Alamy; **457** Ingram Publishing/AGE Fotostock; **460** Envision/Corbis; **466** Steve Smith; **469** Photodisc/Gettty Images; **470** Elvele Images/Alamy; **471** Grand Tour/Corbis; **473** Digital Vision/PunchStock; **475** David W. Hamilton/Alamy; **477** Stockdisc/PunchStock; **478** Photodisc/PunchStock; **479** Dana Menussi; **481** Mylife Photos/Alamy; **482** Robert Harding Picture Library Ltd/Alamy; **483** Tim Dolan Photography; **486** Sean Justice/Corbis; **489** Stockdisc/PunchStock; **492** Ilene MacDonald/Alamy; **494** Floresco Productions/Corbis; **495** D. Hurst/Alamy; **498** Brand X Pictures/Alamy; **499** Heide Benser/zefa/Corbis; **502** Eyewire (Photodisc)/PunchStock; **504** Photodisc Collection/Getty Images; **514** PhotoLink/Getty Images; **517** Stockbyte/PunchStock; **521** Corbis; **523** Mazer Creative Services; **538** Corbis; **539** Cyril Laubscher/Getty Images; **541** Photodisc/Getty Images; **543** C Squared Studios/Getty Images; **544** Ed Pritchard/Getty Images; **545** Dorling Kindersley; **546** Walter Meayers Edwards/NGS/Getty images; **546** Mazer Creative Services; **547** Lars Klove/Getty Images; **555** Mark Lewis/Getty Images; **559** Burke/Triolo Productions/Brand X/Corbis; **560** Nick Dolding/Getty Images; **562** AlaskaStock; **568** Stockdisc/PunchStock; **570** The Art Archive/Thyssen-Bornemisza Collection Madrid/Gianni Dagli Orti; **571** Blickwinkel/Alamy; **574** Marielle/Photocuisine/Corbis; **575** Wolfgang Kaehler/Alamy; **577** Stan Sholik/Alamy; **576** Steve Sant/Alamy; **577, 579** Brand X Pictures/PunchStock; **580** David Hiller/Getty Images; **582** Getty Images/Steve Allen; **584** Hisham F. Ibrahim/Getty Images; **586** Creatas/PunchStock; **587** Andersen Ross; **589** Creatas/PunchStock; **596** Brand X Pictures/PunchStock; **597** C. Borland/PhotoLink/Getty Images; **602** Jack Hollingsworth;

603 Comstock/Jupiter Images; **604** Steve Mason; **606** SW Productions/Getty Images; **607** Iimagebroker/Alamy; **608** Nature Picture Library/Alamy; **613** Ingram Publishing/Alamy; **617** Brand X Pictures/PunchStock; **618** Photodisc Collection/Getty Images; **619** William Manning/Corbis; **621** Travis VanDenBerg/Alamy; **622** Amos Morgan/Getty Images; **623** (t)Heritage Auction Galleries, Dallas, TX, (b)Photodisc/Getty Images; **624** (t) C Squared Studios/Getty Images; **625** Emanuele Taroni/Getty Images; **627** Mazer Creative Services; **628** Food Alan King/Alamy; **631** Getty Images; **632** C Squared Studios/Getty Images; **633** Jupiter Images/Creatas/Alamy; **635** Nancy Brown; **639** PhotoLink/Getty Images; **640** Brand X Pictures/PunchStock; **642** D. Hurst/Alamy.

Teacher Guide Photo Credits

viii Adrian Sherratt/Alamy; **ix** RubberBall/Alamy; **x** Thomas Fricke/Corbis; **xi** Klaus Tiedge; **xii** Mazer Creative Services; **xiii** George Doyle & Ciaran Griffin; **xiv** Jose-Manuel Colomo/Alamy; **xv** Digital Vision/PunchStock; **xvi** Corbis; **1** Jack Hollingsworth